Scott Foresman - Addison Wesley

Grade 4

AUTHORS

Randall I. Charles

Carne S. Barnett   **Diane J. Briars**   **Warren D. Crown**
Martin L. Johnson   **Steven J. Leinwand**   **John Van de Walle**
Charles R. Allan • Dwight A. Cooley • Portia C. Elliott • Pearl Ling
Alma B. Ramírez • Freddie Lee Renfro • Mary Thompson

Teacher's Edition
Volume 1
Chapters 1–6

Scott Foresman
Addison Wesley

Editorial Offices: Menlo Park, California • Glenview, Illinois
Sales Offices: Reading, Massachusetts • Atlanta, Georgia • Glenview, Illinois
Carrollton, Texas • Menlo Park, California

http://www.sf.aw.com

510
S42
H./T
Curr. Coll.

Math
that Makes Sense...

Student Re

The Student's Perspective

"When I see how real kids like me use math, it makes more sense."

Printed in the United States of America

ISBN 0-201-36425-5

2 3 4 5 6 7 8 9 10–VH–02 01 00 99 98

gift

Teacher

The Teacher's Perspective

"My primary concern in teaching is to help **all** my students succeed."

from EVERY Perspective

What kind of a math program are you looking for? What about your students? And how about mathematics education research? Can one program really satisfy all points of view? Through its content, features, and format, *Scott Foresman - Addison Wesley MATH* recognizes the real-life needs and concerns specific to the intermediate grades—supported by research but grounded in real classroom experience.

Welcome to a math program that excels from every perspective—especially yours!

The Research Perspective

"If we are to reach all children, we must strive for meaningful, challenging, and relevant learning in the classroom."

search

MATH THAT CONNECTS TO THE STUDENT'S WORLD!

Students in the intermediate grades have a perspective all their own. Although active learners, students at this age have increased abilities to think and reason in the abstract. They learn best in an atmosphere that recognizes their interests and encourages their growing independence and maturity.

"I want to know when I'll use this."

Real data, real kids

Students don't have to wait to grow up to use this math! Students' interests—like sports, music, and earning money—provide the data. And *real* kids serve up *real* math problems.

Great themes like *Bugs and Bug Eaters* and *Cool Collections*

Placing math in the context of themes such as these captures and holds students' attention.

Multiple approaches

In many lessons, classroom conversations present two approaches to solving one problem, requiring students to analyze, compare and contrast, and make decisions.

Interactive CD-ROM lessons

An interactive lesson for every chapter provides an exciting environment for learning. Lesson format and content are right in tune with today's technology-savvy generation.

MathSURF Internet site

MathSURF's up and so is student interest! Kids can go online to explore the text content of every chapter in safe and exciting destinations around the world.

MATH THAT PROMOTES TEACHING SUCCESS

Helping *all* your students succeed is a big responsibility! You need a program with rich content, approaches for meeting the needs of students who learn in different ways, PLUS practical strategies for problem solving and test taking—a program that meets not only NCTM Standards but, more importantly, *your* standards!

Performance

"My students need a solid foundation in mathematical understanding. And let's face it, how they perform is a reflection of how *I* perform!"

Number sense focus
Meaningful section organization focuses first on establishing a number-sense foundation for skills, which are then taught, extended, and applied.

Focused instruction
For those skills that are more challenging for students—such as adding three-digit numbers at grade 3 or multiplying decimals at grade 5—specially focused lessons provide the extra time needed for students to learn and practice.

Test prep strategies
The next step in strategies! Every lesson builds confidence and provides support for success with standardized tests. Students learn practical test-taking strategies, which are then integrated throughout the text. These strategies enhance the variety of assessment options in the program.

A new standard in problem solving!
Strategies and more! Special problem-solving lessons do more than teach strategies—they focus on analyzing specific strategies so students learn how and when to use them. In addition, students develop skills in reading, understanding, and solving word problems.

A PROGRAM THAT PROMOTES TEACHING SUCCESS

To make sure math instruction makes sense from *your* perspective, you can choose from help with problem solving, assessment, school-home connections, daily routines—plus outstanding technology, and more!

Student Edition
Colorful lessons, grouped to build key understandings, provide developmentally sequenced instruction.

Teacher's Edition
(with Teacher's Resource Planner CD-ROM and Transparencies)
Two spiralbound volumes, packaged with a CD-ROM Planner and full-color Teaching Transparencies. Time-saving help to meet your every challenge.

Teacher's Resource Package

Practice Masters
Exercises reinforce content of every lesson. Also available as a workbook.

Another Look (Reteaching Masters)
Masters for every lesson offer another look at skills and concepts.

Extend Your Thinking (Enrichment Masters)
Masters for every lesson enhance thinking skills and creativity.

Problem-Solving Masters
Masters provide varied problem-solving opportunities to complement each lesson, including applications, interdisciplinary connections, decision making, and guided problem solving.

Assessment Sourcebook
Includes tests and assessment forms to profile students as learners. Test formats include free response, multiple choice, performance, and mixed response.

Home and Community Connections
Make math a family affair! Booklet with letters in English and Spanish, plus classroom tips, community projects, and more.

Teacher's Toolkit
Saves time with a variety of Management Resources, plus Teaching Tool Transparencies and Teaching Tool Masters.

Technology Masters
Computer and calculator activities energize lessons with the power of technology.

Manipulative Kits

Classroom Manipulative Kit
Packaged for easy manageability, items give young children a concrete handle for grasping math concepts.

Teacher's Overhead Manipulative Kit
Makes demonstrating concepts from an overhead projector easy and convenient.

Resources to Customize Instruction

Print Materials

Overhead Transparency Package
Daily Transparencies (for Review, and Quick Check) and full-color Lesson Enhancement Transparencies help clarify and enliven class presentations.

Math-a-pedia
A handy, fun-to-use reference book of math terms for students.

Multilingual Handbook
Enhanced math glossary in multiple languages provides a valuable resource for teaching, especially ESL students.

Class Charts and Kits

Calendar Time Kit and Teaching Guide
Explore time, money, and other concepts that take time to learn with this exciting kit! Includes calendar posters, number line cards, teaching cards, clock faces, graphs, money charts, thermometer, weather map, and more.

Reading Strategies for Math: Flipchart and Blackline Masters
Large write-on, wipe-off pages connect reading, writing, and language skills with math.

Problem of the Day Flipchart and Teaching Guide
For every lesson. Colorful, oversized pages with a variety of problems.

Technology

Teacher's Resource Planner CD-ROM
The entire Teacher's Resource Package on CD-ROM! Includes an electronic planning guide which allows you to set specific criteria when preparing lessons, customize worksheets, correlate your curriculum to national, state, and district objectives, and more.

Performance Math CD-ROM
Disc develops fluency of basic facts through ground-breaking research. One disc for addition and subtraction and another for multiplication and division.

Interactive CD-ROM
Interactive, multimedia lessons for each chapter help students explore concepts in enjoyable and involving ways. Built-in math tools, for graphing, geometry, and more, extend learning opportunities.

MathSURF Internet Site (for Students)
Math on the Web! A fun and safe place for students to explore and extend their learning.

MathSURF Internet Site (for Parents)
This Web site offers a variety of practical tips for parents.

MathSURF Internet Site (for Teachers)
Site provides exciting opportunities for in-service ideas and sharing.

TestWorks: Test and Practice Software
CD-ROM saves hours of test-prep time by generating and customizing tests and worksheets.

DataWonder!
This fun-to-use data analysis software tool helps students organize and summarize information.

AUTHORS WITH DIVERSE EXPERTISE!

Math that makes sense from every perspective—it's a commitment we've kept in all aspects of this program, including our outstanding authors who are shown here with highlights of their many accomplishments. Specialty teams of these program authors worked on grade levels matching their specific areas of expertise. They bring to the program extensive knowledge of how children learn math and how best to teach them.

←

Dinah Chancellor

Coordinator, Pre K–12 Mathematics & Science
Grapevine-Colleyville ISD
Grapevine, Texas

Reviewer, NCTM Arithmetic Teacher

Treasurer, Membership Chair, and President, The Texas Association of Supervisors of Mathematics

Randall I. Charles

Professor, Department of Mathematics and Computer Science
San Jose State University
San Jose, California

Past Vice-President, National Council of Supervisors of Mathematics

Co-author of two NCTM publications on teaching and evaluating progress in problem solving

"The profile of the learner is unique at each stage of development."

←

Lalie Harcourt

Mathematics Consultant
Toronto, Ontario, Canada

NCTM Presenter and Workshop Leader

←

Martin L. Johnson

Professor of Mathematics Education
University of Maryland
College Park, Maryland

Board Member, School Science and Mathematics Association

Chair, Editorial Panel, Journal for Research in Mathematics Education

Member, Research Advisory Committee

Steven J. Leinwand

Mathematics Consultant
Connecticut Department
of Education
Hartford, Connecticut

Member, NCTM Board of Directors

*Past President, National Council
of Supervisors of Mathematics*

Carne S. Barnett

Senior Research Associate WestEd
San Francisco, California

*Member, NCTM Assessment
Addenda Task Force*

→

"Students learn and perform better when they are taught in ways that match their own strengths."

Jane F. Schielack

Associate Professor of Mathematics
Texas A & M University
College Station, Texas

Writer, Professional Standards for
Teaching Mathematics

Diane J. Briars

Mathematics Curriculum Consultant
Pittsburgh Public Schools
Pittsburgh, Pennsylvania

Member, NCTM Board of Directors

Writer, Assessment Standards for
School Mathematics

Writer, Curriculum and Evaluation
Standards for School Mathematics

John Van de Walle

Professor of Education
Virginia Commonwealth University
Richmond, Virginia

Frequent NCTM presenter

Author, Elementary and Middle
School Mathematics: Teaching
Developmentally

Debbie Moore

Title 1 Math Demonstration Teacher
Lubbock Independent School System
Lubbock, Texas

*Frequent presenter for NCTM and
CAMT, Texas*

Expertise

Turn the page for more authors!

MORE EXPERTISE...

More

Ricki Wortzman

Mathematics Consultant
Toronto, Ontario, Canada

*Teacher Training In-service
Workshop Leader*

← **Dwight A. Cooley**

Assistant Principal
Mary Louise Phillips
Elementary School
Fort Worth, Texas

*Member, NCTM Board
of Directors*

← **Linda Bailey**

Mathematics Coordinator
Putnam City Schools
Oklahoma City, Oklahoma

*Oklahoma State Department
Mathematics Supervisor*

*Trainer, Phi Delta Kappa-endorsed
Hands-on Equations program*

"A program that asks real-life questions provides rich possibilities for students."

Portia C. Elliott

Professor of Mathematics Education
University of Massachusetts
Amherst, Massachusetts

*Member and Chairman, Editorial
Panel, NCTM Arithmetic Teacher*

Editor, 1996 NCTM Yearbook

*Member, Commission on the
Future of NCTM Standards*

*Coordinator of Assessment
Standards Outreach*

→

Charles R. Allan

Mathematics Education Consultant
Michigan Department of Education
Lansing, Michigan

*Director, Michigan State
Curriculum Framework Project*

*Michigan State Mathematics
Supervisor*

Shauna Lund

Davis District Mathematics
Specialist
Davis School District
Farmington, Utah

*Presidential Award Winner, Utah
Elementary Mathematics, 1993*

*Summer Math Institute District
Coordinator*

*Utah Language Writing Institute,
Integrated Workshop Leader*

Mary Thompson

Mathematics Instructional
Specialist, New Orleans Public
Schools: Urban Systemic Initiative
New Orleans Public Schools
New Orleans, Louisiana

Reviewer, NCTM Arithmetic Teacher

Alma B. Ramírez

Bilingual Mathematics and
Science Teacher
Oakland Charter Academy
Oakland, California

*Presenter, NCTM, AERA, and
California Mathematics Council*

*Participant, Equals & Family
Mathematics Association at the
University of California at
Berkeley*

Pearl Ling

Mathematics Curriculum
Consultant
Ling & Associates
Shaker Heights, Ohio

**"Students construct new learning from a
basis of prior knowledge and experience."**

Warren D. Crown

Professor of Mathematics Education
Rutgers, The State University of
New Jersey
New Brunswick, New Jersey

Frequent NCTM presenter

Freddie Lee Renfro

Coordinator of Mathematics
Fort Bend Independent School
District
Sugarland, Texas

*Member, National Council
of Supervisors of Mathematics
Board of Directors*

*Trainer for Texas Mathematics
Staff Development Modules*

REVIEWERS FROM ACROSS THE COUNTRY!

A Nationwide Perspective

Educators from across the country helped shape this program with valuable input about local needs and concerns.

Content Reviewers

Peggy Barfuss
Roy, UT

Arlene Berman
Paramus, NJ

Ada L. Bloom
Champaign, IL

Nyla Bristow
Evans, CO

Mary Burke
San Lorenzo, CA

Ann E. Carlson
Westerville, OH

Linda Catanzaro
Walnut, CA

Carol Chervenak
Henrico County, VA

Nancy J. Davis
Baldwin, NY

Sandra Fluck
Bethlehem, PA

Bettye Forte
Fort Worth, TX

Rosemary A. Garmann
Cincinnati, OH

Pat Hickman
Miami, FL

Susan Holt
Irving, TX

Patty Hulnik
Stillwater, OK

Bethena Hunt
Plano, TX

Roberta Irwin
South San Francisco, CA

Lois Kelley
San Bruno, CA

Lisa Karpenske
Plant City, FL

Linda Kolnowski
Detroit, MI

Pat Kramer
Diamond Bar, CA

Kathleen Schutter Krinock
Georgetown, KY

Linda A. Hall
Tulsa, OK

Beverly Millican
Richardson, TX

Robert J. Nagle
Pittsford, NY

Barbara Pollack
Jamaica, NY

Chris Ruda
Miami, FL

Judy Schnarr
Alpharetta, GA

Joan Shapiro
Greenwich, CT

Linda Smith
Tampa, FL

Robin Catania Weber
Lake George, NY

Lynn B. Weeks
Winter Haven, FL

Judy E. Williams
Batavia, IL

Alma Wright
Dorchester, MA

Karol L. Yeatts
Miami, FL

Iris Zackheim
North Tonawanda, NY

ESL Reviewers

Anna Uhl Chamot
Washington, DC

Jim Cummins
Toronto, Ontario, Canada

Valerie Fernandez-Pardo
Bay Shore, NY

Clemens L. Hallman
Gainesville, FL

Maritza Pérez
Elgin, IL

Teresa Walter
San Diego, CA

Phyllis Ziegler
New York, NY

Inclusion Reviewers

Cheryl Baker
Garland, TX

Janet Bell
South Barrington, IL

Marc Fanaroff
Yonkers, NY

Janet Gawler
Potomac, MD

Ellie Giles
Gaithersburg, MD

Raymond Johnson
Purchase, NY

Lillian P. Jones
Dayton, OH

Linda L. Loar
Pittsburgh, PA

Alma Ramírez
San Francisco, CA

Christopher Woodlin
Manchester, MA

Reading Specialist Reviewers

Jenny Anderson
St. Paul, MN

Camille L. Z. Blachowicz
Evanston, IL

Karen Lange
Vernon Hills, IL

Janet Levitt
Oak Park, IL

Karen Mead
San Bruno, CA

Ramón Nieto
Colorado Springs, CO

Cross-curricular Reviewers

Raymond Johnson
Purchase, NY

Lillian P. Jones
Dayton, OH

Luis A. Martínez-Pérez
Miami, FL

Audie M. Nero
New Orleans, LA

Multicultural Reviewers

Linda Barnett
Oklahoma City, OK

Joan E. Best
Bay Shore, NY

Carol Bradley
Indianapolis, IN

Carol Cherry
Malverne, Long Island, NY

Robin Garrett Farnum
Hempstead, NY

Clemens L. Hallman
Gainesville, FL

James E. Hopkins
Auburn, WA

Luis A. Martínez-Pérez
Miami, FL

Irene Miura
San Jose, CA

Audie M. Nero
New Orleans, LA

Ramón Nieto
Colorado Springs, CO

Marie Ramírez Pérez
Brawley, CA

Bonnie S. Reeves
New Orleans, LA

Pamela K. Spearman
Indianapolis, IN

Brenda Spriggs-Bowles
Little Rock, AR

Valerie Taylor
St. Louis, MO

Debra J. Willmon
Quinton, OK

Wanda R. Wilson
New Orleans, LA

Melinda Wong
Burlingame, CA

Technology Reviewer

Bonnie S. Reeves
New Orleans, LA

Table of Contents

Teacher's Edition

From the Authors

Dear Colleague,

We have developed a unique math program that focuses on helping students make sense of mathematics in meaningful ways. Real kids using mathematics in everyday activities appear throughout the program to generate interest and show relevance.

Number sense is a driving force of the program. Number sense includes estimation, mental math, and much more. We believe that students who develop strong number sense will become more proficient with computation and more powerful as problem solvers.

Manipulatives and pictorial models play an important role in helping students make sense of mathematics. Throughout the grades, work with numbers is connected to physical representations to enhance understanding of key concepts and skills. Reasoning and critical thinking permeate the program to deepen that understanding.

Problem-solving strategies are analyzed in specific lessons, as well as thoroughly developed and practiced throughout. Students become proficient problem solvers as they learn to apply their reading skills and the process of reasoning to solving problems.

All students can make sense of mathematics when it's developed in meaningful and interesting ways. This program builds the confidence and mathematical power all children need to succeed in mathematics in the real world now and in the future.

Randall I. Charles

Carne S. Barnett   Charles R. Allan
Diane J. Briars   Dwight A. Cooley
Warren D. Crown   Portia C. Elliott
Martin L. Johnson   Pearl Ling
Steven Leinwand   Alma B. Ramírez
John Van de Walle   Freddie Lee Renfro
                               Mary Thompson

Chapter 1
Data, Graphs, and Facts Review

Every lesson has four or six pages of notes.
Chapter 1 also has these additional pages.

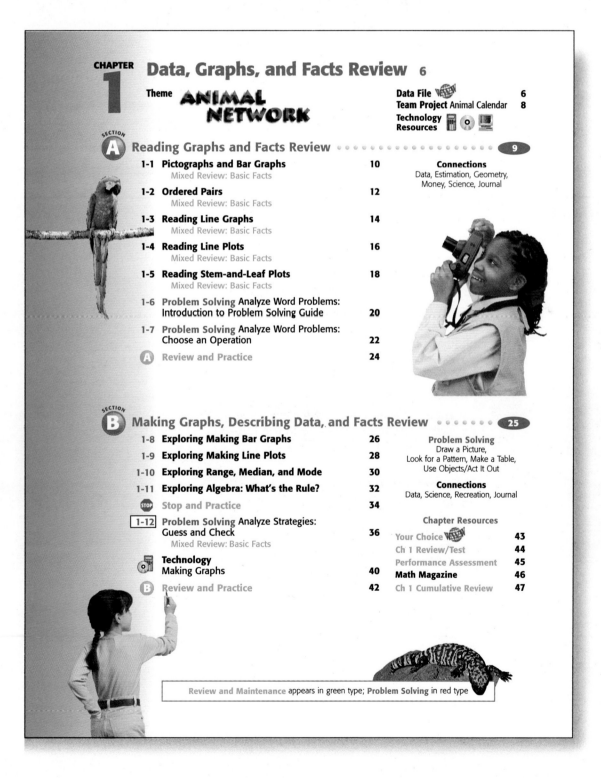

Review and Maintenance appears in green type; **Problem Solving** in red type

Chapter 2
Place Value and Time

Every lesson has four or six pages of notes.
Chapter 2 also has these additional pages.

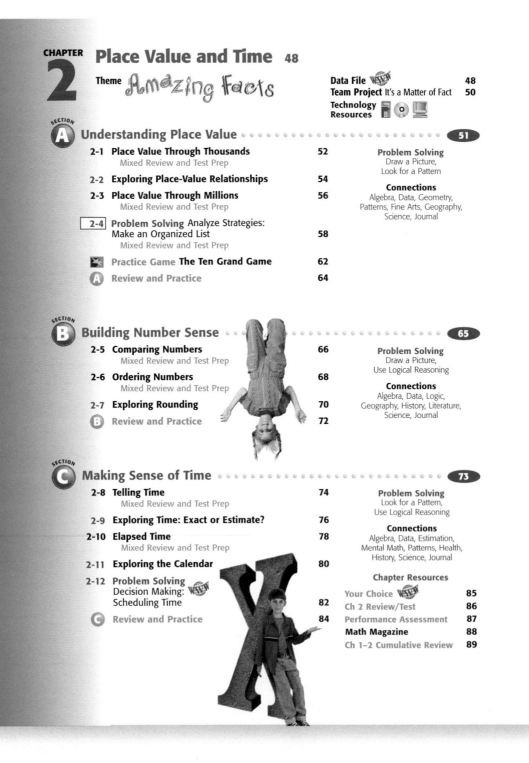

Chapter 3
Adding and Subtracting Whole Numbers and Money

Every lesson has four or six pages of notes.
Chapter 3 also has these additional pages.

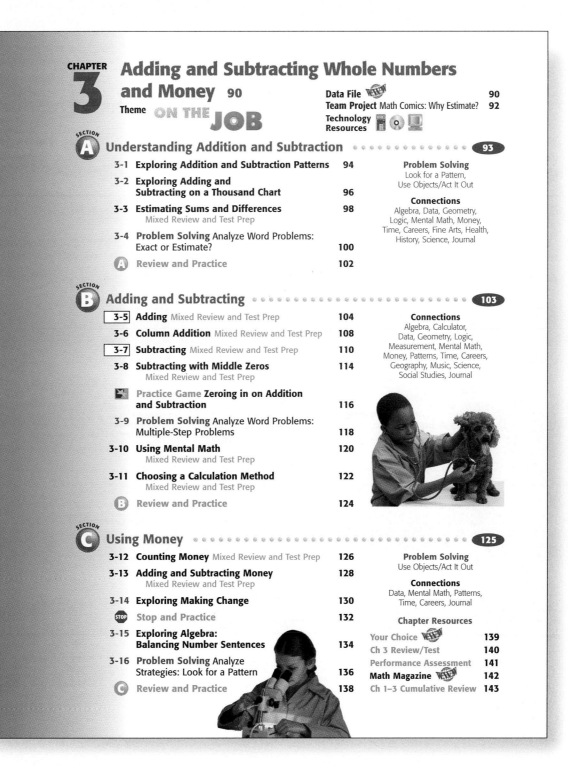

CHAPTER 3

Adding and Subtracting Whole Numbers and Money 90

Theme ON THE JOB

Data File 90
Team Project Math Comics: Why Estimate? 92
Technology Resources

Chapter 4
Multiplication and Division Concepts and Facts

**Every lesson has four or six pages of notes.
Chapter 4 also has these additional pages.**

CHAPTER 4

Multiplication and Division Concepts and Facts 144

Theme **KEEPING FIT**

Chapter 5
Multiplying by 1-Digit Factors

Every lesson has four or six pages of notes.
Chapter 5 also has these additional pages.

CHAPTER 5

Multiplying by 1-Digit Factors   196

Theme **TIME OUT** *School* **FROM**

Chapter 6
Multiplying by 2-Digit Factors

Every lesson has four or six pages of notes.
Chapter 6 also has these additional pages.

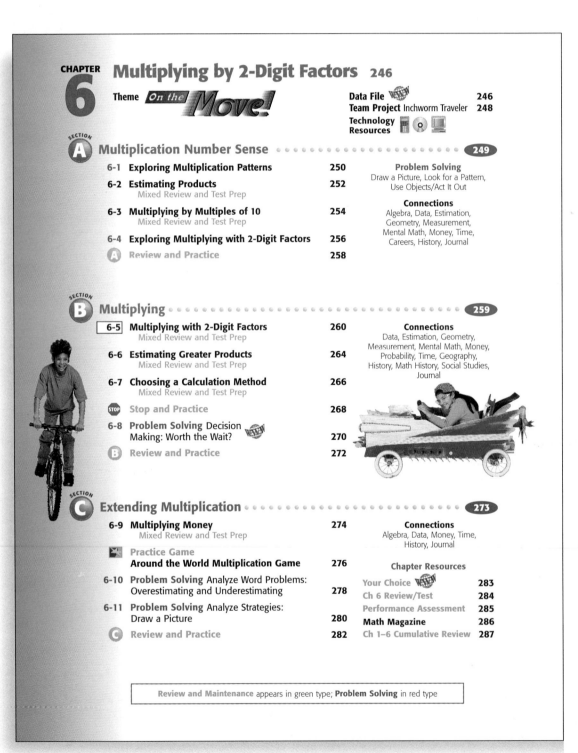

CHAPTER 6

Multiplying by 2-Digit Factors 246

Theme *On the* **Move!**

Data File 246
Team Project *Inchworm Traveler* 248
Technology Resources

Review and Maintenance appears in green type; **Problem Solving** in red type

Chapter 7
Dividing by 1-Digit Divisors

Every lesson has four or six pages of notes.
Chapter 7 also has these additional pages.

Chapter 8
Using Geometry

**Every lesson has four or six pages of notes.
Chapter 8 also has these additional pages.**

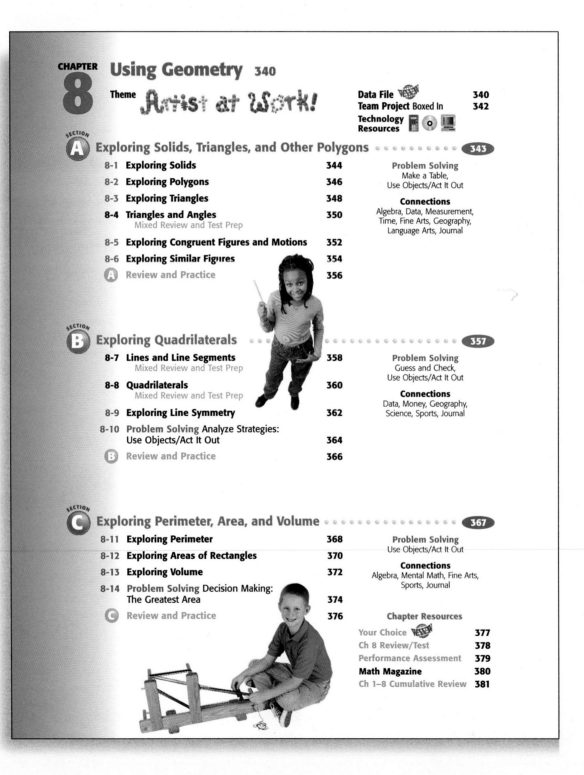

CHAPTER 8

Using Geometry 340

Theme **Artist at Work!**

Data File **340**
Team Project Boxed In **342**
Technology Resources

Chapter 9
Fractions and Customary Linear Measurement

Every lesson has four or six pages of notes.
Chapter 9 also has these additional pages.

CHAPTER
9

Fractions and Customary Linear Measurement 382

Theme Getting Involved

Data File **382**
Team Project We Want You! **384**
Technology Resources

Chapter 10
Fraction Operations and Customary Measurement

Every lesson has four or six pages of notes.
Chapter 10 also has these additional pages.

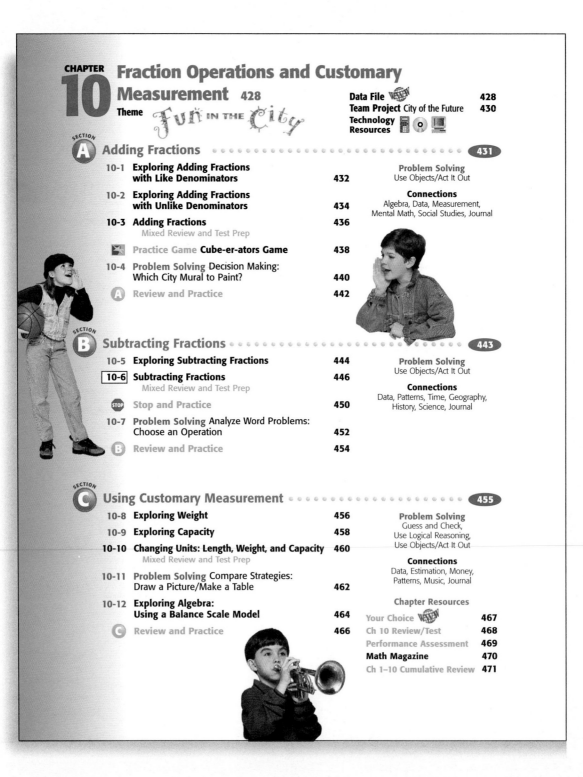

CHAPTER 10 — **Fraction Operations and Customary Measurement** 428
Theme *Fun in the City*

Data File **428**
Team Project City of the Future **430**
Technology Resources

SECTION A   **Adding Fractions**   **431**

10-1   **Exploring Adding Fractions with Like Denominators**   **432**

10-2   **Exploring Adding Fractions with Unlike Denominators**   **434**

10-3   **Adding Fractions**   **436**
    Mixed Review and Test Prep

   Practice Game **Cube-er-ators Game**   **438**

10-4   **Problem Solving** Decision Making: Which City Mural to Paint?   **440**

Ⓐ   Review and Practice   **442**

Problem Solving
Use Objects/Act It Out

Connections
Algebra, Data, Measurement, Mental Math, Social Studies, Journal

SECTION B   **Subtracting Fractions**   **443**

10-5   **Exploring Subtracting Fractions**   **444**

10-6   **Subtracting Fractions**   **446**
    Mixed Review and Test Prep

(STOP)   **Stop and Practice**   **450**

10-7   **Problem Solving** Analyze Word Problems: Choose an Operation   **452**

Ⓑ   Review and Practice   **454**

Problem Solving
Use Objects/Act It Out

Connections
Data, Patterns, Time, Geography, History, Science, Journal

SECTION C   **Using Customary Measurement**   **455**

10-8   **Exploring Weight**   **456**

10-9   **Exploring Capacity**   **458**

10-10   **Changing Units: Length, Weight, and Capacity**   **460**
    Mixed Review and Test Prep

10-11   **Problem Solving** Compare Strategies: Draw a Picture/Make a Table   **462**

10-12   **Exploring Algebra: Using a Balance Scale Model**   **464**

Ⓒ   Review and Practice   **466**

Problem Solving
Guess and Check,
Use Logical Reasoning,
Use Objects/Act It Out

Connections
Data, Estimation, Money, Patterns, Music, Journal

Chapter Resources

Your Choice   **467**
Ch 10 Review/Test   **468**
Performance Assessment   **469**
Math Magazine   **470**
Ch 1–10 Cumulative Review   **471**

Chapter 11
Decimals and Metric Measurement

Every lesson has four or six pages of notes.
Chapter 11 also has these additional pages.

Chapter 12
Dividing by 2-Digit Divisors and Probability

Every lesson has four or six pages of notes.
Chapter 12 also has these additional pages.

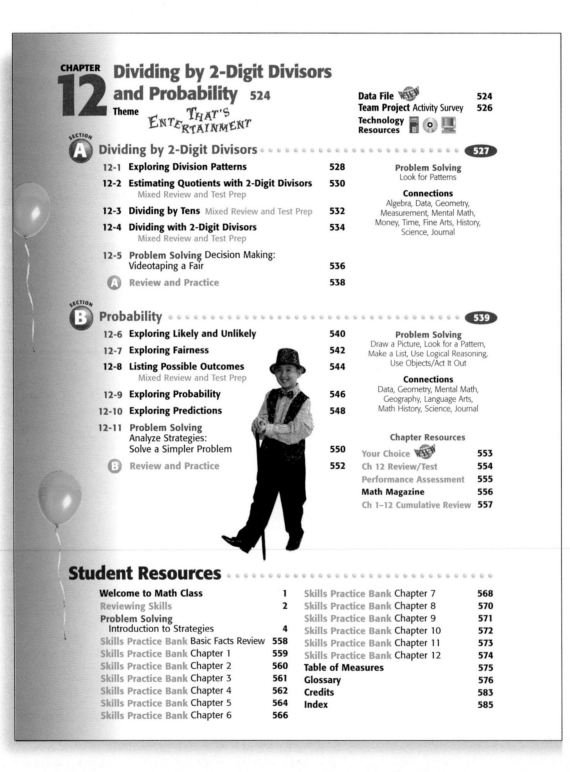

CHAPTER 12

Dividing by 2-Digit Divisors and Probability 524

Theme *THAT'S ENTERTAINMENT*

Data File 524
Team Project Activity Survey 526
Technology Resources

Problem Solving
Look for Patterns

Connections
Algebra, Data, Geometry,
Measurement, Mental Math,
Money, Time, Fine Arts, History,
Science, Journal

Problem Solving
Draw a Picture, Look for a Pattern,
Make a List, Use Logical Reasoning,
Use Objects/Act It Out

Connections
Data, Geometry, Mental Math,
Geography, Language Arts,
Math History, Science, Journal

Student Resources

Pacing Guide

The pacing suggested in the chart at the right assumes one day for most lessons and one day for end-of-chapter assessment. You may need to adjust pacing to meet the needs of your students and your district curriculum.

	Chapter	Pages	Number of Days
1	Data, Graphs, and Facts Review	6-47	13
2	Place Value and Time	48-89	13
3	Adding and Subtracting Whole Numbers, and Money	90-143	17
4	Multiplication and Division Concepts and Facts	144-195	17
5	Multiplying by 1-Digit Factors	196-245	14
6	Multiplying by 2-Digit Factors	246-287	12
7	Dividing by 1-Digit Divisors	288-339	15
8	Using Geometry	340-381	15
9	Fractions and Customary Linear Measurement	382-427	15
10	Fractions Operations and Customary Measurement	428-471	12
11	Decimals and Metric Measurement	472-523	16
12	Dividing by 2-Digit Divisors and Probability	524-557	11
	Total Days		**170**

Materials List

	Chapters											
	1	2	3	4	5	6	7	8	9	10	11	12
2-Color Counters			■	■			■		■			
Color Cubes								■				
Place-Value Blocks		■			■	■	■					
Blank Number Cubes with Stickers										■		■
Money			■				■					■
Measuring Tapes								■		■		
Fraction Strips									■	■		
Spinners										■		
Geoboard								■	■			
Power Polygons								■				
Power Solids								■				
Clock		■										
Rulers		■				■	■	■				■
Balance Scale										■	■	

■ **Student Manipulative Kit**   ■ **Teacher's Overhead Manipulative Kit**   ■ **Transparencies in Teacher's Toolkit or Teacher's Edition**

Welcome to Grade 4

A Guide to Starting the Year

Introducing Manipulatives as Math Tools

To emphasize the value of manipulatives, show different ways 2-color counters can be used as math tools.

- Number tool: Estimate the number of counters in a jar.
- Multiplication tool: Make an array to show 8 x 4 = 32.
- Pattern tool: Make a pattern. Have a partner continue it.
- Measurement tool: Estimate the width of a book in counters and then line up counters to check.
- Geometry tool: Arrange 6 counters to fit into different shapes: a rectangle, a triangle, a circle.
- Data generating tool: Toss 2 counters; record the colors. Predict the results of 24 tosses; then do the tosses.

Finding Out What Students Already Know

You might want to do some informal pre-assessment of students to find out what math they learned last year, what they think math is, and how they feel about math. Consider one or more of the following activities. Ask students to:

- Show 3 things they learned in math last year.
- Explain what math is to someone from another planet.
- Do pages 2–5. These pages check students' understanding of addition and subtraction basic facts and pattern recognition. They also get students started using a math journal.
- Take the Inventory Test in the Assessment Sourcebook or on the TestWorks: Test and Practice Software.

Introducing the Zoombinis

Making Zoombinis

The Zoombinis' Role Zoombinis appear in the Logical Journey of the Zoombinis CD-ROM from Broderbund Software, Inc. There the Zoombini attributes (hair, eyes, nose, and feet) are used in problems to develop logic and reasoning. Zoombinis appear in lessons in the Student Book as math mascots to give helpful comments (see page 1).

Directions for Making Zoombinis

- Have students draw a blank Zoombini (a simple oval) and sketch in a style of hair, eyes, and feet, and color of nose. The 5 possibilities for each attribute as seen on the CD-ROM are shown at the right.
- Have students sort the completed Zoombinis and discuss attributes. Are two of the Zoombinis similar? In what ways? How many different Zoombinis could be made if there were just 2 choices for each attribute? 2 x 2 x 2 x 2 = 16 You might pose the question and wait until Chapter 2, Lesson 4 where students might use the problem solving strategy "Make a List" to find the answer.

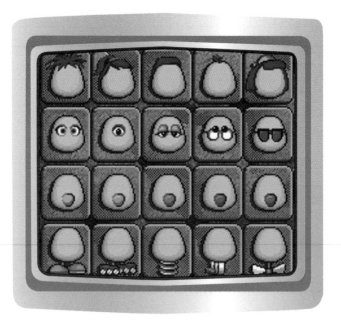

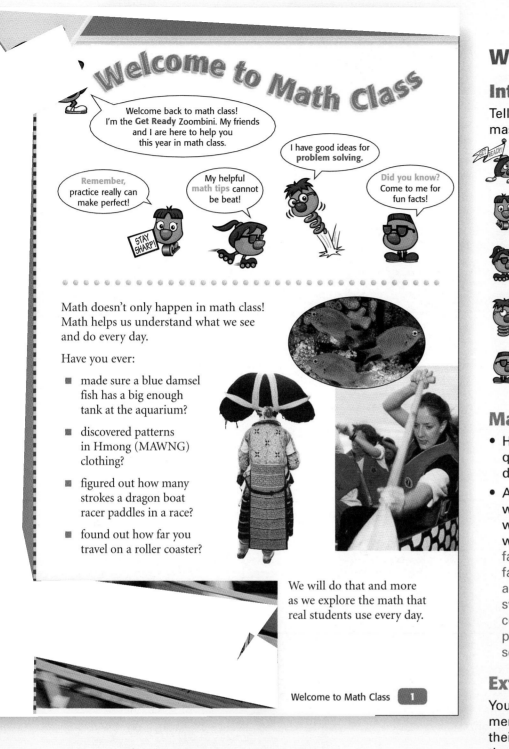

Math doesn't only happen in math class! Math helps us understand what we see and do every day.

Have you ever:

- made sure a blue damsel fish has a big enough tank at the aquarium?

- discovered patterns in Hmong (MAWNG) clothing?

- figured out how many strokes a dragon boat racer paddles in a race?

- found out how far you travel on a roller coaster?

We will do that and more as we explore the math that real students use every day.

Welcome to Math Class

Introduce the Zoombinis

Tell students the purpose of the Zoombini mascots.

Get Ready The Get Ready mascot provides problems that review a skill that will be extended in the section.

Remember The Remember mascot helps students connect prior knowledge to the lesson or problem.

Math Tip The Math Tip mascot provides hints, tips, and situations to watch for when doing math.

Problem Solving The Problem Solving mascot provides useful hints or strategies to solve problems.

Did You Know? The Did You Know? mascot presents numerical data related to the lesson's context.

Math Around Us

- Have students read the statement and questions aloud. Encourage a brief discussion of each question.

- Ask students to brainstorm other areas in which math is used every day and in which math helps us understand the world. Possible answers: Finding food facts such as the number of calories, total fat, sugars, or protein; Finding the amount of water needed to fill a swimming pool; Doubling a recipe for cookies; Comparing costs to get the best price; Reading bus, train, or plane schedules; Understanding elapsed time

Extension

You may wish to have students ask a family member or a friend how they use math in their everyday lives and make a report to the class.

Reviewing Skills

Skills: Addition and Subtraction Basic Facts, Skip Counting, Patterns

Reviewing Skills may be used to review or assess students' knowledge and understanding of addition and subtraction basic facts, skip counting, and pattern recognition skills developed previously.

Review

Exercises 1–50 Review the use of a number line with students. Also ask questions such as the following:

- What addition strategies can you use?
  Possible answer: Count on. Use turnaround facts. Use doubles. Use doubles plus 1. Make 10.

- What subtraction strategies can you use?
  Possible answers: Count back. Use doubles. Think addition to subtract. Use families of facts.

Reviewing Skills

You Will Meet real people like these who use math skills in their everyday lives

On page 539, meet Reginald who plays video games. He also enjoys reading and sports.

Liesl is a member of the International Wheelchair Aviators. She flies airplanes. See her on page 259.

You already know lots of math! Let's review some basic facts.

Review addition facts. Find each sum. You may use the number line to help.

1. 2 + 4 6	**2.** 3 + 7 10	**3.** 5 + 6 11	**4.** 8 + 8 16	**5.** 6 + 2 8
6. 9 + 7 16	**7.** 4 + 3 7	**8.** 7 + 7 14	**9.** 1 + 9 10	**10.** 5 + 3 8
11. 8 + 4 12	**12.** 6 + 7 13	**13.** 5 + 5 10	**14.** 9 + 3 12	**15.** 6 + 6 12
16. 5 + 8 13	**17.** 4 + 6 10	**18.** 7 + 2 9	**19.** 6 + 1 7	**20.** 4 + 9 13
21. 4 + 4 8	**22.** 5 + 7 12	**23.** 6 + 9 15	**24.** 4 + 7 11	**25.** 9 + 9 18

Review subtraction facts. Find each difference. You may use the number line to help.

26. 7 − 2 5	**27.** 6 − 4 2	**28.** 8 − 7 1	**29.** 11 − 3 8	**30.** 10 − 5 5
31. 13 − 6 7	**32.** 10 − 7 3	**33.** 14 − 7 7	**34.** 15 − 9 6	**35.** 13 − 8 5
36. 10 − 2 8	**37.** 17 − 8 9	**38.** 16 − 9 7	**39.** 15 − 7 8	**40.** 9 − 9 0
41. 7 − 6 1	**42.** 14 − 5 9	**43.** 18 − 9 9	**44.** 12 − 4 8	**45.** 13 − 5 8
46. 11 − 8 3	**47.** 12 − 6 6	**48.** 14 − 8 6	**49.** 11 − 4 7	**50.** 16 − 8 8

Review skip counting. Copy and complete each pattern.

51. 6, 8, 10, ▓, ▓ 12, 14

52. 40, 50, 60, ▓, ▓ 70, 80

53. 35, 40, 45, ▓, ▓ 50, 55

54. 18, 15, 12, ▓, ▓ 9, 6

Complete the pattern.

55.  __ __
apple, apple

56. __ __
triangle, square

Add and subtract to solve the riddle. Match each letter to its answer in the blank below. Some of the letters are not used.

What is a giraffe's favorite kind of math?

57. 3 + 2 [S] 5	**58.** 12 − 5 [A] 7	**59.** 5 + 4 [C] 9
60. 10 − 8 [L] 2	**61.** 9 + 9 [O] 18	**62.** 15 − 5 [D] 10
63. 5 + 9 [O] 14	**64.** 16 − 7 [R] 9	**65.** 7 + 8 [N] 15
66. 7 + 5 [V] 12	**67.** 3 + 8 [N] 11	**68.** 10 − 9 [I] 1
69. 3 + 3 [I] 6	**70.** 9 − 6 [I] 3	**71.** 9 + 8 [G] 17

🐭	🐭	🐭	🐭		🐭	🐭	🐭	🐭	🐭	🐭	🐭	🐭
2	14	11	17		10	3	12	6	5	1	18	15
L	O	N	G		D	I	V	I	S	I	O	N

Skills Practice Bank, page 558, Set 1   Reviewing Skills   **3**

PRACTICE AND APPLY

Exercises 51–54 If students have difficulty skip counting, provide them with a number line, have them circle the numbers in the list, then continue the pattern.

Exercises 55 and 56 Some students may benefit from hearing the pattern aloud. Have volunteers represent each type of fruit/figure by saying its name aloud in the sequence shown.

Riddle Have students read the directions for solving the riddle. Ask a volunteer to explain the process in his or her own words.

Extension

Suggest that students create a class riddle book. Throughout the year, students will be asked to solve and/or write more riddles which they can add to the book.

Resources

TestWorks: Test and Practice Software

Performance Math™

Student Edition: Skills Practice Bank, p. 558

Introduction to Strategies

Introduction to Strategies may be used to review or to assess students' knowledge and understanding of the problem solving strategies taught in this program.

Guiding the Activity

Have students read the list of strategies and identify and explain any that they have used. Ask them also to tell about choosing a tool, for example, when they might use objects to solve a problem, when they might use mental math, when they might use a calculator, and so on. Possible answers: Objects are a good tool when the problem is hard to picture in your mind. Using objects to represent the problem can help you understand and solve it. Mental math works well when the numbers are multiples of 10 or 100. A calculator is a good tool when it is hard to solve the problem mentally or when there are lots of steps in the paper-and-pencil method.

You may wish to have students solve the problem on their own before they discuss Ann's and Victor's strategies.

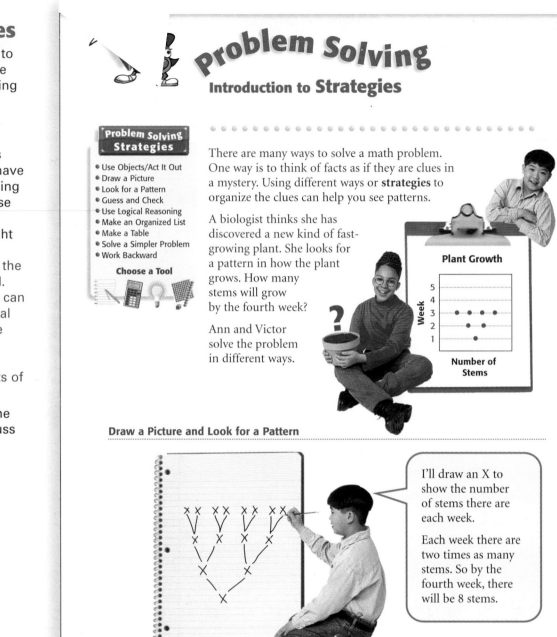

Problem Solving
Introduction to Strategies

Problem Solving Strategies
- Use Objects/Act It Out
- Draw a Picture
- Look for a Pattern
- Guess and Check
- Use Logical Reasoning
- Make an Organized List
- Make a Table
- Solve a Simpler Problem
- Work Backward

Choose a Tool

There are many ways to solve a math problem. One way is to think of facts as if they are clues in a mystery. Using different ways or **strategies** to organize the clues can help you see patterns.

A biologist thinks she has discovered a new kind of fast-growing plant. She looks for a pattern in how the plant grows. How many stems will grow by the fourth week?

Ann and Victor solve the problem in different ways.

Plant Growth

Draw a Picture and Look for a Pattern

I'll draw an X to show the number of stems there are each week.

Each week there are two times as many stems. So by the fourth week, there will be 8 stems.

Make a Table and Look for a Pattern

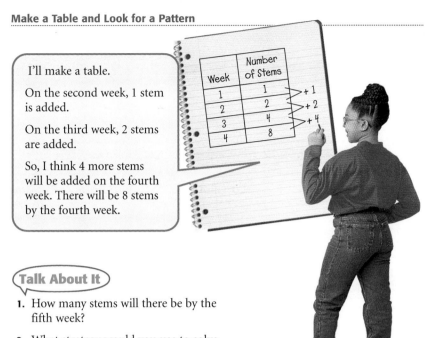

I'll make a table.

On the second week, 1 stem is added.

On the third week, 2 stems are added.

So, I think 4 more stems will be added on the fourth week. There will be 8 stems by the fourth week.

Week	Number of Stems	
1	1	+ 1
2	2	+ 2
3	4	+ 4
4	8	

Talk About It

1. How many stems will there be by the fifth week?

2. What strategy would you use to solve this problem? Why?

Try These

Use any strategy to solve.

1. The library charges 1 cent for the first day a book is late. It charges 3 cents the second day, 6 cents the third day, 9 cents the fourth day, and so on. How much will Sarah have to pay if she returns her book 5 days late? **12¢**

2. Sam likes collecting. Every time he collects 10 insect stickers, he can send in for a spider sticker. If Sam has 6 spider stickers already, how many insect stickers has he sent in? **60 insect stickers**

3. **Journal** Have you ever kept a journal about what you do every day? You can also keep a journal about math. Start by writing about your favorite kinds of math problems. Or, write about what you would like to learn this year. Remember to check your journal throughout the year to see your progress!

Talk About It

Listen for students finding patterns in the number of stems each week. Remind students that there is often more than one way to solve a math problem.

Answers for Talk About It

1 16 stems

2 Accept all reasonable explanations.

***Reading Assist* Find the Main Idea**

Make sure students understand what they are asked to do. Have them tell in their own words what they think their task is. You can rephrase and elaborate on their ideas without correcting them.

Try These

Accept all reasonable strategies for Exercises 1–3.

Exercise 1 Encourage students to try making a table for the data.

Exercise 3 Suggest that students keep a separate notebook for their journals as they will be writing in them almost daily.

Extensions

You may wish to extend this lesson by having students determine how many stems there will be by the sixth and seventh weeks. **32, 64**

Section	Pacing		Lessons		Your Test	Materials	
	Day	Lesson/Page	Objective		Correlation	Student Book	Another Way to Learn
A **Reading Graphs and Facts Review** Students review basic addition and subtraction facts, and read pictographs, bar graphs, line graphs, and line plots. *Problem Solving Skill* *Introduction to Problem Solving* *Choose an Operation*	Day 1	**1-1**	10–11	Read pictographs and bar graphs.			
	Day 2	**1-2**	12–13	Read points as ordered pairs on a coordinate grid.			Centimeter Grid Paper
	Day 3	**1-3**	14–15	Read line graphs.			Transparency of sample line graph
	Day 4	**1-4**	16–17	Read line plots.			Color cubes, index cards
	Day 5	**1-5**	18–19	Read stem-and-leaf plots.			Overhead place-value blocks
	Day 6	**1-6**	20–21	**Problem Solving** Solve problems by using a guide.			Place-value blocks
	Day 7	**1-7**	22–23	**Problem Solving** Solve problems by choosing an operation.			Counters
B **Making Graphs, Describing Data, and Facts Review** Students make bar graphs and line plots, and find range, median, and mode. *Problem Solving Connection* *Make a Table* *Draw a Picture* *Use Objects/Act It Out* *Look for a Pattern* *Problem Solving Strategy* *Guess and Check*	Day 8	**1-8**	26–27	Make bar graphs.		Ruler, Centimeter Grid Paper	
	Day 9	**1-9**	28–29	Make line plots.		Centimeter Grid Paper (optional)	
	Day 10	**1-10**	30–31	Find range, median, and mode.		Scissors, crayons	
	Day 11	**1-11**	32–33	Explore algebra by looking for a pattern to find the rule.		Index cards, envelopes	
	Day 12	**1-12**	36–39	**Problem Solving** Solve problems by using guessing and checking.			Two-color counters
Chapter Assessment	Day 13		44–45	Assess student understanding and skills for Chapter 1.			

Also in this Chapter Data File, pp. 6–7, **Projects/Extensions,** pp. 8, 46

Looking Back
Grade 3 Reading and making pictographs, bar graphs, and line graphs was introduced.

Chapter 1
Key Math Idea

Graphs are pictorial representations of information based on collected data for the purposes of comparing data and predicting trends.

Looking Ahead
Grade 5 Analyzing and making graphs extends to choosing an appropriate scale.

Connections		Section Resources	
Strand	**Subject**	**Technology**	**Review and Assessment**
Using Data	Science, Language	**Performance Math™: Addition and Subtraction** 💿 **World Wide Web** 🌐 www.mathsurf.com/4/ch1 Chapter Opener, p. 7 **Logical Journey of the Zoombinis™** 💿 Ordered Pairs, p. 12A	**Review** Section A Opener, p. 9 Mixed Review: Basic Facts, pp. 11, 13, 15, 17, 19 Section A Review and Practice, p. 24 Skills Practice Bank, p. 559 **Ongoing Assessment** *Teacher's Edition,* all lessons *Assessment Sourcebook,* Quiz Chapter 1 Section A
Geometry Readiness, Using Data	Science, Culture, Reading		
Estimation, Using Data	Science, Social Studies, Language		
Using Data	Science, Language		
	Science, Language, Reading		
Using Data	Science, Geography, Reading, Language		
Money	Science, Literature, Reading		
	Science	**Performance Math™: Addition and Subtraction** 💿 **Interactive CD-ROM Lesson 1** 💿 Exploring Making Line Plots, p. 28 **Interactive CD-ROM** 💿 **Spreadsheet/Grapher Tool** Exploring Making Line Plots, p. 28 **Logical Journey of the Zoombinis™** 💿 Exploring Algebra, p. 32A Analyze Strategies, p. 36A **Interactive CD-ROM Journal** 💿 Analyze Strategies, p. 38 **DataWonder!** 💾 Technology, pp. 40–41 **World Wide Web** 🌐 www.mathsurf.com/4/ch1 Your Choice, p. 43	**Review** Section B Opener, p. 25 Mixed Review: Basic Facts, p. 39 Stop and Practice, pp. 34-35 Section B Review and Practice, p. 42 Your Choice, p. 43 Skills Practice Bank, p. 559 **Ongoing Assessment** *Teacher's Edition,* all lessons *Assessment Sourcebook,* Quiz Chapter 1 Section B
Using Data	Science, Literature, Reading		
Using Data	Careers, Science, Geography, Language		
	Economics, Language		
	Science		
		TestWorks 💿	Chapter Review/Test, p. 44 Performance Assessment, p. 45 Cumulative Review, p. 47

Manipulatives

Using the Manipulatives

Color Cubes Students use color cubes in Another Way to Learn in Lesson 1-4 to model a line plot with the cubes representing the Xs on a 2-dimensional graph.

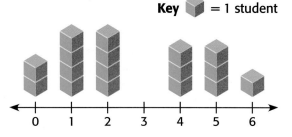

Key = 1 student

Place-Value Blocks (Base 10 Blocks) Place-value blocks are used in Another Way to Learn in Lesson 1-6 to represent the data shown in a line graph.

Suggested Materials	Alternatives
Centimeter Grid Paper	———
Color cubes	Counters, buttons, beans, beads, coins
Place-value blocks	Graph paper
Counters	Buttons, beans, beads, coins
Two-color counters	Buttons, beans, beads, coins

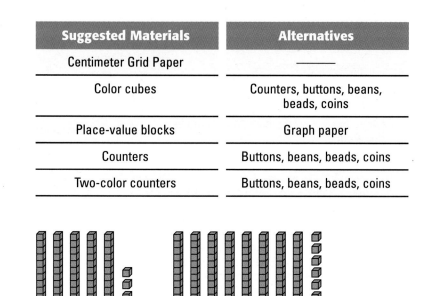

53 in 1992   86 in 1993

Literature

Sideways Stories from Wayside School

Louis Sachar. New York: Camelot, 1985.

Use with Lesson 1-7 Dana claims that she cannot do arithmetic in class because she is covered in mosquito bites. The teacher replies that her bites will stop itching if she counts them.

Any Number Can Play

George Sullivan. New York: HarperCollins Children's Books, 1990.

Use with Lesson 1-9 This book gives the name and jersey numbers of record-setting home-run hitters.

Additional Resources

Investigations in Number, Data, and Space®: The Shape of Data (Statistics), Susan Jo Russell, et al; **Investigations in Number, Data, and Space®: Changes Over Time (Graphs),** Cornelia Tierney, et al.; **Investigations in Number, Data, and Space®: Three Out of Four Like Spaghetti (Data and Fractions),** Maryn Berle-Carman, et al. Menlo Park, CA: Dale Seymour Publications.

Quest 2000: Exploring Mathematics, Grade 4, Randall Charles, et al. Menlo Park, CA: Addison-Wesley Publishing Company. *Unit 1.*

Today's Sports, Today's Math, Don Fraser. Menlo Park, CA: Dale Seymour Publications.

Creative Graphing, Marji Freeman. White Plains, NY: Cuisenaire Company of America.

Developing Skills With Tables and Graphs, Book A, Elaine C. Murphy. Menlo Park, CA: Dale Seymour Publications.

For the Teacher

 Teacher's Resource Planner CD-ROM

The Teacher's Resource Planner CD-ROM allows you to create customized lesson plans tailored to your own class's needs. It also allows you to preview any supplement page, edit if you wish, and print it.

 **World Wide Web**

Visit **www.teacher.mathsurf.com** for additional activities, links to lesson plans from teachers and other professionals, NCTM information, and other useful sites.

 TestWorks Test and Practice Software

A database of questions allows you to generate personalized practice worksheets and tests.

For the Student

 **Interactive CD-ROM**

Use with Lesson 1-9 The Line Plot Tool can be used to generate a line plot based on a set of data. The mean, median, mode, and range are all marked with symbols that are automatically updated when the data set is changed.

World Wide Web

Use with Chapter Opener and Your Choice Have students go online at **www.mathsurf.com/4/ch1** to find out about students' favorite animals and to learn about how explorers are able to find treasure in sunken ships and at archaeological sites.

DataWonder!

Use with Technology: Making Graphs Students use the spreadsheet and reporting tools to record, analyze, and report the monthly egg production of sandhill cranes.

 **Performance Math™**

Use daily throughout Chapter 1 Students can practice daily to increase their familiarity with basic addition and subtraction facts.

Logical Journey of the Zoombinis™

Use with Lessons 1-2, 1-11, and 1-12 Students use their problem solving skills to win at the *Mudball Wall* along the The Deep, Dark Forest Trail, to solve the puzzles at the *Allergic Cliffs, Stone Cold Caves,* and *Pizza Pass,* along The Big, the Bad, and the Hungry Trail, and as they play the puzzle games along the Who's Bayou Trail.

 Calendar Time Kit

Weather

One of the concepts in this chapter is making and reading graphs. You may use the Calendar Time Kit to reinforce this concept with the following activity:

Record the weather in a bar graph and line graph.

- At a consistent time each day, have students record the weather in a horizontal bar graph on the weather chart. Make sure students label each addition to the graph with the date.

- At the same time each day, have students record the temperature on a line graph.

- Each day, ask questions such as **How many days has it been sunny? Cloudy? How many days has the temperature been above 60 degrees?**

- On a day near the end of the chapter, compare the bar graph and the line graph. **Describe what each graph shows. What information is easy to see on the line graph? The bar graph?**

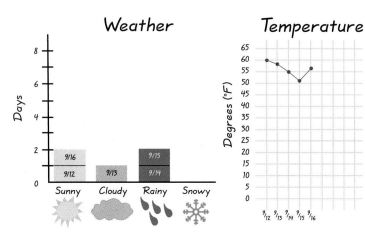

Technology Centers

Research on the World Wide Web

Use the World Wide Web to get information for your classroom.

- Find out what's available for yourself by accessing the Scott Foresman • Addison Wesley Web site at **www.teacher.mathsurf.com.** This site offers additional information and resources; it also directs you to other interesting sites on the World Wide Web. Be sure to bookmark useful sites for easy reference, and don't forget to share them with colleagues.

- Each chapter provides students with opportunities to use the World Wide Web as a research tool. Students can access our Web site at **www.mathsurf.com** or by using the Interactive CD-ROM. In Chapter 1, students can learn about other students' choices for favorite animals and post their own choice to be added to the data. They can also learn about treasures found at archaeological digs and on sunken ships.

Bulletin Board

Objective Show bird-watching data by constructing a bar graph.

Materials Photographs of local birds, construction paper, marker

- Show students photographs of birds common to your area.

- List the names of four or five species on the bulletin board for a class bar graph. Have students determine the scale they will use.

- Have students keep a bird-watching log. Choose a volunteer each day to be the bird spotter. Each day, tally the number of birds spotted. The student can add the appropriate amount to each bar.

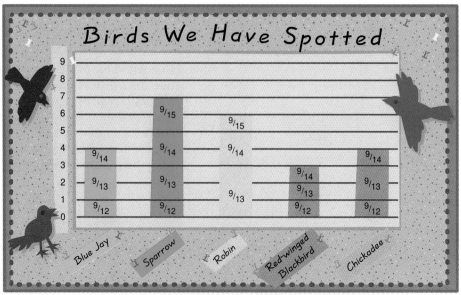

Traditional Assessment	
Review and Practice	Student Edition: pages 24, 42
Cumulative Review	Student Edition: page 47; Assessment Sourcebook: Form F
Section Quizzes	Assessment Sourcebook: Section Quizzes A, B

Chapter Tests
  Free Response
  Multiple Choice
  Mixed Response
	Student Edition: page 44; Assessment Sourcebook: Forms A and B
	Assessment Sourcebook: Form C
	Assessment Sourcebook: Form E

Alternative Assessment	
Ongoing Assessment	Teacher's Edition: every core lesson; Assessment Sourcebook: pages 11–13, 16–19, 21
Portfolio	Teacher's Edition: page 13; Assessment Sourcebook: pages 9, 13, 14, 16, 23
Interview and Observation	Teacher's Edition: page 15; Assessment Sourcebook: pages 18, 20
Journal	Student Edition: pages 15, 21, 23, 24, 27, 29, 31, 33, 39, 42; Teacher's Edition: pages 11, 17, 19; Assessment Sourcebook: pages 8–11, 15
Performance Assessment	Student Edition: page 45; Teacher's Edition: pages: 27, 29, 31, 33; Assessment Sourcebook: Form D

NCTM Assessment Standards

Focus on Mathematics

Interviews Assessment should reflect the important mathematics developed in the instruction. A one-to-one interview lets teachers probe a student's understanding of mathematical skills and concepts in depth. In Chapter 1, an interview opportunity occurs on page 15.

Test Prep

- The Test Prep Strategy **Make Smart Choices: Look for Patterns** is introduced and practiced in the Cumulative Review on page 47.
- Mixed Review: Basic Facts occurs throughout the chapter.

TestWorks

TestWorks can create personalized multiple-choice tests, free-response tests, and practice worksheets.

Standardized-Test Correlation		ITBS	CTBS	CAT	SAT	MAT
Lesson/Objective		**Form M**	**4th Ed.**	**5th Ed.**	**9th Ed.**	**7th Ed.**
1-1	Read pictographs and bar graphs.	●	●	●	●	●
1-2	Read points as ordered pairs on a coordinate grid.		●		●	
1-3	Read line graphs.					
1-4	Read line plots.					
1-5	Read stem-and-leaf plots.					
1-6	Solve problems by using a guide.					
1-7	Solve problems by choosing an operation.	●	●	●	●	●
1-8	Make bar graphs.					
1-9	Make line plots.					
1-10	Find range, median, and mode.					
1-11	Explore algebra by looking for a pattern to find the rule.	●	●	●	●	●
1-12	Solve problems by using guessing and checking.	●	●	●	●	●

Key   **ITBS** Iowa Test of Basic Skills   **CTBS** Comprehensive Test of Basic Skills   **CAT** California Achievement Test
      SAT Stanford Achievement Test   **MAT** Metropolitan Achievement Test

Data, Graphs, and Facts Review

Theme: Animal Network

Teacher Materials *Optional*
Lesson Enhancement Transparency 1

Introduce the Chapter

Animals offer contexts in which students can read, interpret, and display data. Students read and interpret data visually presented in graphs, then learn to make different types of graphs. They are introduced to the Problem Solving Guide and use it along with the choose an operation and guess and check strategies to solve problems.

Activate Prior Knowledge

Discuss as a class students' experiences with animals, including topics such as pet ownership, observations of animals in the wild, and visits to farms or zoos.

Use the Data File

You may wish to use Lesson Enhancement Transparency 1 along with the following questions to discuss the Data File.

- How is the data represented? Pictograph, tally chart
- Use the pictograph to decide which animal the least number of people would like to hold. Rosy boa
- Decide how many people would like to hold the Gila monster. 20 people
- Use the data on kangaroo jumps to see how many kangaroos jumped 39 feet. 8 kangaroos

Chapter 1
Data, Graphs, and Facts Review

ANIMAL NETWORK

SECTION A

9

Reading Graphs and Facts Review

Which animal would the least number of people like to hold? How many people would like to hold the Gila monster?

Animals People Would Like to Hold	
Koala	
Gila monster	
Monkey	
Rosy boa	
Macaw	
Banana slug	

= 5 votes

Extensions

World Wide Web

Go to **www.mathsurf.com/4/ch1** for links to sites where students can find out about their favorite animals. Ask each student to find out information such as:

- the animal's average height, weight, and size
- places where these animals live
- what the animal eats

Performance Math: Addition and Subtraction

Have students use *Performance Math* to assess their knowledge of basic addition and subtraction facts. This pre-test will allow *Performance Math* to create a customized learning program for each student. For students who need to build up their knowledge, follow this pre-test with 10 minutes a day of practice with *Performance Math* throughout the chapter.

Making Graphs, Describing Data, and Facts Review

25

Each tally mark stands for one kangaroo.
How many kangaroos jumped 39 feet?

Surfing the World Wide Web!
Choose your favorite animal from the list at **www.mathsurf.com/4/ch1** Compare your choice with other students' choices. Make a graph of the data.

Preview the Sections

A **Reading Graphs and Facts Review**

Students will read and interpret pictographs, bar graphs, ordered pairs, line graphs, line plots, and stem-and-leaf plots.

B **Making Graphs, Describing Data, and Facts Review**

Students will make bar graphs and line plots and find the range, median, and mode of data presented in tables, pictures, and graphs.

Math in the Community

School-Community Connection

Bird Watching Have students make a list of several birds commonly seen in your community. Group students to research each of the birds and share information with the class.

Have students watch for each of the birds on the class list for one week. Students can use a tally table and graphs to report their observations.

Community Project The Chapter 1 community project is available in *Home and Community Connections.*

Home-School Connection

Graph Hunt Have students scan Chapter 1 to see a variety of graphs. Then have students find other examples of graphs at school and at home, in resources such as:

• other text books

• reference books

• newspapers

• magazines

Have students make a display of any graphs that they can bring to the classroom.

Parents can use the Web site at **www.parent.mathsurf.com**.

At the end of this chapter, you may wish to distribute the Letter Home from *Home and Community Connections.*

Animal Calendar

Students will collect data to make a decision about a calendar cover.

Student Materials Colored markers (1 set per group), *Optional Assessment Sourcebook 10* (How We Worked in Our Group)

Introduce the Project

Calendars with beautiful photographs or prints related to a wide variety of subjects and interests have become very popular. Show three different calendars to students and invite them to vote for their favorite. Tell students their votes create data for a small survey.

Review the steps in the project, discuss the questions, and preview the self-assessment checklist below.

Self-Assessment Checklist

__ Create a survey

__ Accurately collect and record data

__ Use the data to prepare a finished product

Complete the Project

Have groups compare and contrast data. Discuss why the sets of data were similar or different.

ANIMAL calendar

A wildlife club has asked your class to design a cover for next year's animal calendar. What animal will your class choose for the cover? Take a class survey and then design a cover.

a Plan

- What questions will you ask in your survey?
- Will you give people a list of animals to choose from?

It Out

1. Write your questions. Then survey your class.
2. Use the data you collect to figure out which animal to put on the cover.
3. Design your calendar cover.

bout It

- How many animals did you have to choose from?
- Was it easy to decide which animal to put on the cover? Explain.

the Project

- Display your team's calendar cover. Did every team choose the same animal? Why or why not?

Science Connection

Have students find out more about the animals on their covers. Each group should write a short paragraph about the animal to serve as a caption.

Cooperative Learning

As a group, have students design the survey. Have group members work in pairs—surveyor and recorder—to conduct the survey. Then have the whole group interpret the results, design the calendar cover, and draw and color it. One student in each group can report the process and results to the class.

Distribute *Assessment Sourcebook 10* (How We Worked in Our Group) and have students fill it out for the skill Listen to Others. Review the characteristics of this skill. Invite students to judge themselves on the skill as they work together.

Reading Graphs and Facts Review

Reading Graphs

Review addition and subtraction facts.
Find each sum or difference.

1. $8 + 4$ 12   2. $15 - 6$ 9   3. $7 + 9$ 16

4. $17 - 8$ 9   5. $7 + 8$ 15   6. $16 - 9$ 7

7. $6 + 9$ 15   8. $11 - 6$ 5   9. $3 + 5$ 8

Skills Checklist

In this section, you will:

☐ Review Basic Addition and Subtraction Facts

☐ Read Pictographs, Bar Graphs, and Line Graphs

☐ Learn About Ordered Pairs

☐ Read Line Plots and Stem-and-Leaf Plots

☐ Solve Problems by Using a Guide

☐ Solve Problems by Choosing an Operation

9

Reading Graphs and Facts Review

In this section, students will read different types of graphs and plots, then solve problems by using a guide and choosing an operation.

Subskills

The work in this section builds on…

• Counting by 2s, 5s, and 10s

2, 4, 6, 8, 10, …

• Reading a scale

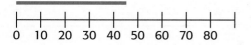

0 10 20 30 40 50 60 70 80

• Putting a number together using place value

4 tens 2 ones = 42

Use the Section Opener

Discuss how animals are helpful as companions, guides, trackers, and visual assistants. They can guide people from place to place, alert people to dangers, and retrieve items for them.

Skills Trace

(Red numbers indicate pages in this section.)

Lesson and Skill	First Introduced	Grade Four			
		Introduce	Develop	Practice/Apply	Review
1-1 Read pictographs and bar graphs.	Grade 2	10, 11	10, 26	11, 27, 40, 41, 558	24, 42, 45, 89, 195, 208, 287
1-2 Read points as ordered pairs on a coordinate grid.	Grade 3	12, 13	12	13	24, 43, 44, 143, 381
1-3 Read line graphs.	Grade 3	14, 15	14	15, 40, 41, 558	24, 44
1-4 Read line plots.	Grade 4	16, 17	16, 28, 29	17, 29	24, 42
1-5 Read stem-and-leaf plots.	Grade 4	18, 19	18	19, 558	44
1-6 Solve problems by using a guide.	Grade 3	20, 21	20	21	24, 44
1-7 Solve problems by choosing an operation.	Grade 2	22, 23	22, 452	23, 452, 453	24, 47

Mixed Review: Basic Facts exercises for this chapter occur on pages 9, 11, 13, 15, 17, 19, 39.

Multi-Age Classrooms Use pages 9–24 in Grade 3 or pages 9–24 in Grade 5 to relate to the content of this section.

Pictographs and Bar Graphs

At-A-Glance Planning

Lesson Planning Checklist

Objective Read pictographs and bar graphs.

Vocabulary pictograph, bar graph, key, scale

Student Book Lesson Materials *Optional* Transparencies of graphs on pages 10, 11; Lesson Enhancement Transparency 1, calculators

Materials for pages 10A and 10B Common examples of numerical scales (on kitchen or bathroom scale, thermometer, rulers), ruler, transparency of bar graph from page 10

Subject Connections science—egg-laying, animal life spans, bird flight speeds

Strand Connection using data

	Before Lesson	During Lesson	After Lesson
Daily Math			
p. 10A Problem of the Day			
p. 10A Math Routines			
p. 10A Mental Math			
Teaching Options			
p. 10 Student Book Lesson			
p. 10B Another Way to Learn…			
Options for Reaching All Learners			
p. 10B Language Development			
p. 10B Inclusion			
Subject Connections			
p. 10A Science Connection			
Assessment Options			
p. 10 Talk About It			
p. 11 Error Intervention			
p. 11 Journal			
p. 11 Quick Check			
Resources			
1-1 Practice			
1-1 Reteaching			
1-1 Enrichment			
1-1 Problem Solving			
1-1 Daily Transparency			

Problem of the Day

Problem of the Day

Lesson 1-1

Carla is 4 years younger than Amy. Liz is 5 years older than Amy. Order these girls from oldest to youngest.

See Problem of the Day Teaching Guide for an extension.

Liz, Amy, Carla

Math Routines

Measurement Hold up a ruler horizontally. Ask where zero should be written. Have students name the place you would finish if you traveled various numbers of units "to the right."

Calendar Have students list the number of Mondays, Tuesdays, and so on for the current month. Does the month have the same number of each day?

Mental Math

Have students picture a line of people waiting for a bus. Then have them give the position of the person who is

• halfway between the 1st and 5th person on line 3rd

• two people ahead of the 10th person 8th

Science Connection

Reptiles can lay their eggs on land. Amphibians, like frogs and salamanders, lay their eggs in the water.

Have students research the gestation periods for different amphibian and reptile eggs. Students can prepare bar graphs of their findings.

Another Way to **Learn** Lesson 1-1

Use as an alternative or in addition to pages 10 and 11.

Learning Style Visual

- Share Level 4 of the Assessment Rubric with students before they begin their work.
- Show students the sample graphs below.

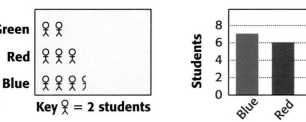

Students' Favorite Color

Green | ♀ ♂
Red | ♀ ♂ ♀
Blue | ♀ ♂ ♀ ♀

Key ♀ = 2 students

Students' Favorite Color

- Ask a volunteer to read the title on the pictograph. Have another student rephrase the title, saying: This pictograph shows… Repeat using the bar graph.
- Ask students how the titles of these two graphs are the same or different.
- Point out the key on the pictograph. Ask what value one symbol stands for. Then discuss the data.

- Discuss the bar graph's scale and how to use it to determine the value of each bar.
- Assign Check and Practice on Student Book page 11 or *Practice Master 1-1*.
- Assess using the following rubric.

Assessment Rubric
4 Full Accomplishment • reads and interprets data shown in pictographs and bar graphs
3 Substantial Accomplishment • with prompting, reads and interprets most data shown in pictographs and bar graphs
2 Partial Accomplishment • reads and interprets some data shown in pictographs and bar graphs
1 Little Accomplishment • does not read or interpret data shown in pictographs and bar graphs

Options for Reaching All Learners

Language Development

Scales

Use objects to develop understanding of the term **scale***.*

Materials Common examples of numerical scales (on kitchen or bathroom scale, thermometer, rulers)

Learning Style Visual

- Introduce the word *scale* as you show examples.
- Discuss what is the same and different about these scales: All the scales are marked in increments numbered in order; the size of the increments varies.
- Ask students to compare these scales to scales on bar graphs. Elicit that both show how much of something there is.

The Multilingual Handbook, with its glossary of math terms, illustrations, and worked-out examples, can help you with students who have limited English skills. The glossary is provided in multiple languages.

Inclusion

Reading Bar Graphs

Use a ruler to strengthen skills in reading a bar graph.

Materials Ruler, transparency of bar graph from page 10

Learning Style Visual

- Students may have difficulty determining the value represented by a bar that ends between two marked increments.
- Use a transparency of the life spans bar graph from page 10 to model how to place a ruler or the edge of a piece of paper across the top of the bar for the killer whale so that it intersects the vertical axis.
- Help students use the scale to estimate the life span of the killer whale.
- Have volunteers repeat the process for the other animals shown on the graph.

Lesson Organizer

Objective Read pictographs and bar graphs.

Student Materials None

Teacher Materials *Optional* Transparencies of graphs on pages 10, 11; Lesson Enhancement Transparency 1, calculators

Vocabulary pictograph, bar graph, key, scale

Assignment Guide

Basic 4, 5, 7, 8, 11, 14–23

Average 4–8, 11, 12, 14–23

Enriched 5, 6, 9–23

1 Introduce

Review

What is one-half of each number?

1. 10 5   **2.** 20 10

3. 40 20   **4.** 100 50

5. 30 15   **6.** 50 25

Build on Prior Knowledge

After students review dividing numbers in half, draw a rudimentary pictograph symbol—a face, a square—on the board. Tell the class that the symbol stands for 10 objects. Erase half the symbol and ask what it stands for now. 5 objects

2 Teach

See Another Way to Learn...on page 10B.

Learn

Have students identify the title, labels, and scale or key of the examples and discuss what function each serves in helping to read the data displayed.

It may be helpful to make and use transparencies of the graphs shown in the Student Book for discussion purposes.

Talk About It Ongoing Assessment

Listen for answers that discuss the value of a symbol and its use in pictographs.

Answers for Talk About It

1 5 eggs

2 Let each picture or symbol stand for a specific number of years.

Chapter 1 Lesson 1

Pictographs and Bar Graphs

You Will Learn
how to read pictographs and bar graphs

Vocabulary
pictograph
a graph that uses pictures or symbols to show data

bar graph
a graph that uses bars to show data

key
part of a pictograph that tells what quantity each symbol stands for

scale
numbers that show the units used on a graph

Did You Know?
A female sea horse lays about 200 eggs at one time. The "nest" is a pouch on the male sea horse.

Learn

Some reptiles and amphibians lay just a few eggs at one time. Others lay hundreds of eggs.

Pictographs and **bar graphs** can help you compare data.

Marbled salamander

Example

This pictograph helps you compare the numbers of eggs that some animals lay. How many eggs does a frog lay?

Eggs Laid by Animals	
Python	◯ ◯ ◖
Turtle	◯ ◯ ◯ ◯ ◯ ◯ ◯ ◯ ◯ ◯
Frog	◯ ◯ ◯ ◯ ◯ ◯
Salamander	◯ ◯ ◯ ◯ ◯ ◖

Each symbol stands for 10 eggs.

So, a frog lays 60 eggs.

Key ◯ = 10 eggs

This bar graph compares the life spans of some animals. Which animal lives 40 years?

The bar for the Asian elephant reaches 40 on the **scale**. So, the Asian elephant lives 40 years.

Animal Life Spans

(bar graph with y-axis Years: 0, 10, 20, 30, 40, 50, 60, 70; x-axis: Killer whale, Polar bear, Asian elephant, Black rhinoceros)

Talk About It

1. What does ◖ stand for in the pictograph?

2. How might a pictograph show the data in the graph?

10   Chapter 1 • Data, Graphs, and Facts Review

Practice 1-1

Name _____

Practice 1-1

Pictographs and Bar Graphs

Use the bar graph of land mammal weights to answer **1–4**.

Heaviest Land Mammals

(bar graph, y-axis Weight (tons): 1–6; x-axis: Elephant, Rhinoceros, Hippopotamus, Giraffe)

1. Which land mammals are heavier than the hippopotamus?
The elephant, the rhinoceros

2. a. Which land mammal is the heaviest? **The elephant**
   b. About how much does it weigh? **Between 5 and 6 tons**

3. Which of the mammals listed is the lightest? **The giraffe**

4. About how much does a giraffe weigh?
A little more than 1 ton

Use the pictograph to answer **5–8**.

Largest Pet Litters

Dog	● ● ● ● ● ◖
Cat	● ● ● ● ◖
Gerbil	● ● ● ◖
Hamster	● ● ● ● ● ● ◖

● = 4 Babies

5. Which animal had 19 babies? **Cat**

6. Which animal had the most babies? **Hamster**

7. How many babies did the hamster have? **26**

8. Draw the symbols that show 18 babies. ● ● ● ● ◖

Reteaching 1-1

Name _____

Another Look 1-1

Pictographs and Bar Graphs

This **bar graph** shows the number of skyscrapers in some major cities. The **pictograph** shows the same data.

How many skyscrapers are there in Chicago, IL?

To find the data on the bar graph, follow the bar next to Chicago. It ends at 50, so there are **50** skyscrapers in Chicago.

Cities with the Most Skyscrapers

(bar graph; cities: New York, NY; Chicago, IL; Houston, TX; Los Angeles, CA; Hong Kong; x-axis: Number of Skyscrapers 0–140)

To find the data on the pictograph, find Chicago on the left. There are 5 symbols next to Chicago. Each symbol shows 10 skyscrapers. Count 1 ten for each symbol. 10...20... 30...40...50.... Chicago has **50** skyscrapers.

Cities with the Most Skyscrapers

New York, NY	♦♦♦♦♦♦♦♦♦♦♦♦♦
Chicago, IL	♦♦♦♦♦
Houston, TX	♦♦♦♦
Los Angeles, CA	♦♦♦
Hong Kong	♦♦

♦ = 10 skyscrapers

Use the graphs to answer the questions.

1. Which city has about 30 skyscrapers? **Houston, TX**

2. Do Chicago, Houston, Los Angeles, and Hong Kong all together have more skyscrapers than New York? **No**

3. Which cities have fewer than 50 skyscrapers?
Houston, Los Angeles, and Hong Kong

4. Suppose your town has 20 skyscrapers. How many symbols would you draw in the pictograph? **2**

Use the graphs on page 10 for **1** and **2**.

1. Which animals lay more than 30 eggs? **Turtle, frog**

2. Which animals live longer than 35 years? **Killer whale, Asian elephant**

3. **Reasoning** Suppose each 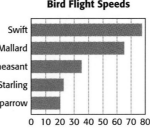 stands for 100 ants.

   a. Draw a picture to show 200 ants. **Picture should show 2 ants.**

   b. Draw a picture to show 50 ants. **Picture should show half an ant.**

PRACTICE AND APPLY

Practice

Skills and Reasoning

6. It is easier to compare when the numbers are in order. You can look at the bar lengths.

Use the bar graph of bird flight speeds for **4–6**.

Bird Flight Speeds

4. Which birds are faster than the pheasant? **Mallard, swift**

5. How fast does the starling fly? **About 20 mi/hr**

6. Why do you think the graph shows the birds from fastest to slowest?

Using Data Use the Data File on page 6 for **7–10**.

7. Which animals got 15 votes? **Monkey, macaw**

8. How many people voted? **95 people**

9. How many people wanted to hold a koala? **30 people**

10. How many symbols would be needed to show 25 votes? **5 symbols**

Problem Solving and Applications

11. **Using Data** Use the pictograph on page 10. List the animals in order by the number of eggs laid. Start with the fewest eggs.
Salamander, python, frog, turtle

12. **Critical Thinking** Use the *Did You Know?* and pictograph on page 10. If you add the sea horse egg data to the graph, how many eggs would you draw? **20 eggs**

13. **What If** You don't have the scale from the bar graph on page 10. What data could you still get from the graph? **Possible answer: Which animal lives longer than others**

Mixed Review: Basic Facts

Add or subtract.

14. $3 + 8$ **11**   15. $5 + 7$ **12**   16. $10 - 1$ **9**   17. $12 - 4$ **8**   18. $6 + 7$ **13**

19. $12 - 7$ **5**   20. $5 + 9$ **14**   21. $13 - 4$ **9**   22. $7 + 8$ **15**   23. $15 - 6$ **9**

Skills Practice Bank, page 559, Set 1   Lesson 1-1   **11**

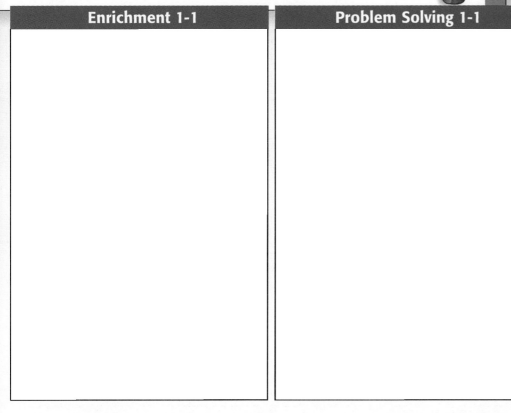

65 mi/hr

19 mi/hr

Enrichment 1-1	Problem Solving 1-1

Check

Exercises 1 and 2 Remind students that numbers ending in 5 are represented by half a symbol or are found between the marks on the scale.

Error Intervention Ongoing Assessment

Observation Students may count the eggs in the pictograph as 1s instead of 10s.

How to Help Have students use a calculator and enter ⊕ ① ⓪ for each symbol to find the total value represented by each row of eggs.

Practice

Exercises 7–10 You can use Lesson Enhancement Transparency 1 to illustrate the Data File.

For Early Finishers Challenge early finishers to make a pictograph to use the data from the bar graph on page 10 to find how much longer an Asian elephant lives than a polar bear. **20 years**

3 Close and Assess

Journal

Have students explain how pictographs and bar graphs are the same and different. Explanations should include how data is shown using symbols or bars and a key or scale and how it can be compared using the values of symbols or size of bars.

Quick Check

Number Sense If ☆ means 20 awards, which sets of symbols in the Skill exercises show more than 50 awards? **Exercises 1, 4**

Skill Find the value of each set of symbols if each ☆ means 4 awards.

1. ☆☆☆ **12**   2. ☆☆ **8**

3. ☆☆⚊ **10**   4. ☆☆☆⚊ **14**

Ordered Pairs

At-A-Glance Planning

Lesson Planning Checklist

Objective Read points as ordered pairs on a coordinate grid.

Vocabulary coordinate grid, ordered pair

Student Book Lesson Materials *Optional* Lesson Enhancement Transparencies 2, 3

Materials for pages 12A and 12B Teaching Tool Transparencies 6, 23 (Centimeter Grid Paper, Map of the United States), paper strips with straight edges (2 per student)

Subject Connection science—dinosaurs

Strand Connections geometry readiness, using data

	Before Lesson	During Lesson	After Lesson
Daily Math			
p. 12A Problem of the Day			
p. 12A Math Routines			
p. 12A Mental Math			
Teaching Options			
p. 12 Student Book Lesson			
p. 12B Another Way to Learn…			
Options for Reaching All Learners			
p. 12B Reading Assist			
p. 12B Cultural Connection			
Technology Options			
p. 12A *Logical Journey of the Zoombinis*			
Assessment Options			
p. 12 Talk About it			
p. 13 Error Intervention			
p. 13 Portfolio			
p. 13 Quick Check			
Resources			
1-2 Practice			
1-2 Reteaching			
1-2 Enrichment			
1-2 Problem Solving			
1-2 Daily Transparency			

Problem of the Day

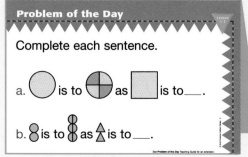

Complete each sentence.

a. ⬡ is to ⊕ as ▢ is to ___.

b. ⧂ is to ⧃ as △ is to ___.

For solution art, see Additional Answers, pages D1–D4, at the back of the Teacher's Edition.

Math Routines

Patterns If one tree symbol represents 2 trees, how many symbols are needed to represent 8 trees? 10 trees? 12 trees? What do $6\frac{1}{2}$ tree symbols represent? 4, 5, 6; 13 trees

Calendar Have students use up, down, left, and right arrows to describe moves between any two dates.

Mental Math

Name the total value of each. Explain.

3 dimes, 3 nickels $0.45

6 dimes, 4 nickels $0.80

9 dimes, 8 nickels $1.30

💿 Logical Journey of the Zoombinis

Have students play *Mudball Wall*, located on The Deep, Dark Forest Trail. Players must get the Zoombinis over the wall by selecting the mudballs that will hit the correct targets.

Another Way to **Learn** Lesson 1-2

Use as an alternative or in addition to pages 12 and 13.

Materials Teaching Tool Transparency 6 (Centimeter Grid Paper)

Learning Style Kinesthetic, Visual

- If students are not already seated in a grid pattern, rearrange their chairs or have students stand in rows and columns. Ask all students in the second column to raise their right hands. Then ask all students in the third row to raise their left hands. Point out that one student raised both hands.

- Model the connection between this activity and coordinate grids. Write the ordered pair (2, 3) and demonstrate how to locate it using Teaching Tool Transparency 6 (Centimeter Grid Paper).

- Repeat the activity and the symbolic recording for (3, 2).

- Prepare coordinate grids with the ordered pairs (2, 3) and (3, 2) marked and labeled. Have students locate and label these additional points on their grids.

   A (5, 1)   B (1, 5)   C (0, 7)   D (7, 0)

- Discuss with students how points A and B and points C and D are different.

- Assign Check and Practice on Student Book page 13 or *Practice Master 1-2.*

- Assess using the following rubric.

Assessment Rubric
4 Full Accomplishment • reads points on a coordinate grid as ordered pairs
3 Substantial Accomplishment • reads points on a coordinate grid as ordered pairs with some prompting
2 Partial Accomplishment • reads some points on a coordinate grid as ordered pairs
1 Little Accomplishment • does not read points on a coordinate grid as ordered pairs

Options for Reaching All Learners

Reading Assist

Read Graphs

Use a straight edge to read a coordinate grid.

Materials Paper strips with straight edges (2 per student)

Learning Style Visual, Kinesthetic

If students are having difficulty locating a point on a coordinate grid, have them try the following strategy for the grid on page 12.

- Have students place a paper strip so that the left end intersects the horizontal axis at the first number in the ordered pair.

- Have students place a second paper strip on the grid so that the lower end intersects the vertical axis at the second number in the ordered pair.

- Point out that the edges of the paper strips intersect at the location of the point named by the ordered pair.

Cultural Connection

Maps and Coordinate Grids

Use a map and grid paper to strengthen understanding of maps and coordinate grids.

Materials Teaching Tool Transparencies 6, 23 (Centimeter Grid Paper, Map of the United States)

Learning Style Visual, Verbal

Polynesian Islanders in the South Pacific used reeds to make maps. Shells represented islands, and palm leaves signified ocean currents.

- Use Teaching Tool Transparency 6 (Centimeter Grid Paper) to prepare a blank coordinate grid.

- On the overhead, place this grid over Teaching Tool Transparency 23 (Map of the United States).

- Name ordered pairs and invite volunteers to locate the points and name the states in which they fall.

Lesson Organizer

Objective Read points as ordered pairs on a coordinate grid.

Student Materials None

Teacher Materials *Optional* Lesson Enhancement Transparencies 2, 3

Vocabulary coordinate grid, ordered pair

Assignment Guide

Basic 8–13, 17–21, 23, 25–34

Average 10–20, 22, 23, 25–34

Enriched 12–34

1 Introduce

Review

Name the value of each point marked on the number line.

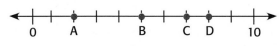

A 2, B 5, C 7, D 8

Build on Prior Knowledge

After students review how to name points on a number line, ask them if locating points would be different if the number line were positioned vertically. No

2 Teach

See Another Way to Learn…on page 12B.

Learn

You can use Lesson Enhancement Transparency 2 to illustrate Dinosaur sites and model finding ordered pairs.

For Example 1, show students how to move their fingers on the grid 2 spaces to the right and 12 spaces up. For Example 2, have students guide you to locate (4, 7) on the grid.

Talk About It **Ongoing Assessment**

Listen for explanations that indicate an understanding of the importance of the order of numbers within an ordered pair.

Answer for Talk About It

No; (2, 8) is 2 to the right and 8 up; (8, 2) is 8 to the right and 2 up.

Ordered Pairs

You Will Learn
how to read points as ordered pairs on a coordinate grid

Vocabulary

coordinate grid
a graph used to locate points

ordered pair
a number pair that names a point on a coordinate grid

Did You Know?
Tyrannosaurus rex, one of the largest dinosaurs, had teeth that were 7 inches long.

Learn

You can follow dinosaur tracks and find dinosaur fossils near Moab, Utah.

A **coordinate grid** helps you locate points.

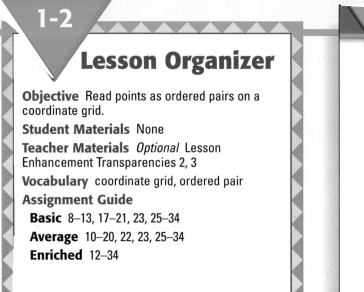

Dinosaur Sites
Moab, Utah

You can locate a point using an **ordered pair**.

Example 1

What ordered pair names where the Sauropod tracks are located?

The first number in the ordered pair shows how far to the right of 0 a point is.

The second number shows how far up from 0 a point is.

So, the Sauropod tracks are located at (2,12).

You can name a point using an ordered pair.

Example 2

What point does the ordered pair (4, 7) name?

The ordered pair names the point for the Mill Canyon Dinosaur Trail.

Talk About It

Do the ordered pairs (8, 2) and (2, 8) name the same point? Explain.

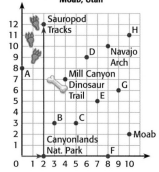

Practice 1-2

Name _____

Practice 1-2

Ordered Pairs
Use the coordinate grid. Name the ordered pair for each point.

1. L __(5,6)__   2. O __(9,8)__   3. B __(2,4)__

4. F __(4,7)__   5. A __(6,7)__   6. J __(7,5)__

7. C __(1,0)__   8. H __(1,10)__   9. K __(1,6)__

Give the letter of the point named by each ordered pair.

10. (1,0) __C__   11. (8,9) __G__   12. (10,5) __M__

13. (0,3) __E__   14. (6,2) __D__   15. (4,3) __I__

16. Jeff said (2,6) was the ordered pair for point D. What was his mistake?

__He gave the numbers of the ordered pair in the__

__incorrect order.__

17. Suppose you locate a point on a coordinate grid by only moving over 7. What is the ordered pair for this point? __(7,0)__

Reteaching 1-2

Name _____

Another Look 1-2

Ordered Pairs
Ordered pairs can help you find a location on a coordinate grid.

An ordered pair gives you directions.

Give the letter of the point named by (2,3).

Start at 0.

Move **right** ↑ Then move **up** 3 units

2 units → (2,3)

Coordinate Grid

The point is labeled with a letter. What letter do you see? __B__

Name the ordered pair for point A.

Find the horizontal and vertical lines that pass through point A.

How many units **right** do you move on the *horizontal* line? __4__

How many units **up** do you move on the *vertical* line? 6

The ordered pair for point A is __(4,6)__

Use the coordinate grid. Name the ordered pair for each point.

1. C __(1, 7)__   2. E __(8, 9)__   3. J __(2, 1)__

Give the letter of the point named by each.

4. (6,2) __D__   5. (9,1) __H__   6. (3,9) __I__

7. (7,5) __G__   8. (10,8) __F__   9. (2,1) __J__

Check

Use the coordinate grid on page 12. Name the ordered pair for each point.

1. A (0, 8)   **2.** B (3, 3)   **3.** H (10, 11) **4.** E (7, 5)

Give the letter of the point named by each.

5. (9, 6) G   **6.** (5, 3) C   **7.** (6, 9) D   **8.** (8, 0) F

9. Reasoning Where is the point (0, 0) located on a grid?
Lower left corner

Practice

Skills and Reasoning

Use this coordinate grid. Name the ordered pair
for each point.

10. A(0, 7) **11.** H(4, 9) **12.** E(2, 8) **13.** J(5, 3) **14.** B(0, 0)

Give the letter of the point named by each.

15. (1, 5) C   **16.** (6, 9) K   **17.** (7, 1) N

18. (9, 7) O   **19.** (2, 1) G   **20.** (6, 0) L

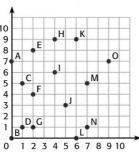

21. Salina gave (1, 7) as the ordered pair for point N.
What was her mistake?

22. Suppose you can locate a point on a
coordinate grid by only moving up 4.
What is the ordered pair for this point?
(0, 4)

21. She gave the incorrect order of
the numbers in the ordered pair.
The ordered pair for N is (7,1).

Problem Solving and Applications

23. Geometry Readiness Use grid paper to locate
these points on a coordinate grid. Connect
them in order: (2, 1), (2, 4), (5, 4), (5, 1),
and back to (2, 1). What shape do they make? **Square**

7 inches

24. Using Data Use the data from the *Did You Know?* on
page 12. Find something in your classroom that is
about as long as a tooth of the *Tyrannosaurus rex.* Possible answers:
Pencil, book or paper width

Mixed Review: Basic Facts

Find each sum or difference.

25. $9 - 3$ 6   **26.** $5 + 8$ 13   **27.** $16 - 9$ 7   **28.** $6 + 6$ 12   **29.** $15 - 8$ 7

30. $11 - 4$ 7   **31.** $8 + 9$ 17   **32.** $13 - 6$ 7   **33.** $2 + 4$ 6   **34.** $7 + 5$ 12

Enrichment 1-2

Problem Solving 1-2

Check

Exercises 1 and 8 Be sure students
understand the meaning of the zeros in the
ordered pairs. For (2, 0), you move two units
to the right and do not move up. For (0, 2)
you do not move to the right, but you do
move up two units.

Error Intervention Ongoing Assessment

Observation Students reverse the
numbers in an ordered pair.

How to Help Have students write (right,
up) or ($\rightarrow$,$\uparrow$) at the top of their papers.

Practice

Exercises 10–21 You can use Lesson
Enhancement Transparency 3 to illustrate
the coordinate grid.

Exercises 15–20 Some students may find it
helpful to place tracing paper over the grid
on page 13 and draw the moves indicated
by the ordered pairs.

For Early Finishers Challenge early finishers
to repeat Exercise 23 using any three
ordered pairs to produce a triangle.

③ Close and Assess

Portfolio

Have students repeat Exercise 23 for the
following points: (4,2), (4,4), (8,4), (8,2) and
back again to (4,2). Students can place the
grids in their portfolios. Rectangle

Quick Check

Spatial Sense Which ordered pairs are on
the same grid line: (2, 5), (5, 2), (2, 7)?
Explain. (2, 5) and (2, 7); They are both 2 to
the right.

Skill Name the ordered pair for each point.

A (3, 1)   B (0, 4)   C (6, 6)   D (7, 0)

Reading Line Graphs

At-A-Glance Planning

Lesson Planning Checklist

Objective Read line graphs.

Vocabulary line graph

Student Book Lesson Materials None

Materials for pages 14A and 14B Transparency of sample line graph

Subject Connections science—Seeing Eye® dogs, sharks, elephants

Strand Connections estimation, using data

	Before Lesson	During Lesson	After Lesson
Daily Math			
p. 14A Problem of the Day			
p. 14A Math Routines			
p. 14A Mental Math			
Teaching Options			
p. 14 Student Book Lesson			
p. 14B Another Way to Learn…			
Options for Reaching All Learners			
p. 14B Language Development			
p. 14B Inclusion			
Subject Connections			
p. 14A Social Studies Connection			
Assessment Options			
p. 14 Talk About It			
p. 15 Error Intervention			
p. 15 Interview			
p. 15 Quick Check			
Resources			
1-3 Practice			
1-3 Reteaching			
1-3 Enrichment			
1-3 Problem Solving			
1-3 Daily Transparency			

Problem of the Day

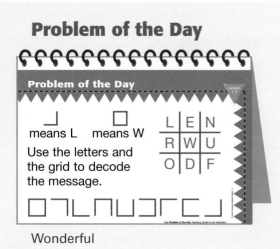

means L   means W

Use the letters and the grid to decode the message.

L	E	N
R	W	U
O	D	F

Wonderful

Math Routines

Money Name amounts of money. Ask students how much money will they have in 6 weeks if they earn the same amount every week.

Time Ask students to name the amount of time left in a 2-hour movie after the following lengths of time have passed: 15 minutes, 45 minutes, 1 hour 15 minutes. 1 hr 45 min; 1 hr 15 min; 45 min

Mental Math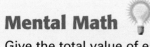

Give the total value of each. Explain.

1 dollar, 9 dimes, 2 nickels $2.00

1 dollar, 12 dimes, 1 nickel $2.25

1 dollar, 3 dimes, 9 nickels $1.75

Social Studies Connection

The cost of caring for a pet depends in part on the kind and amount of food it eats. Tell students that a graph showing the amount of money a family spent on food for their dog over several years slopes upward gradually. What might this mean? The cost of dog food has increased.

Another Way to **Learn** Lesson 1-3

Use as an alternative or in addition to pages 14 and 15.

Materials Transparency of sample line graph

Learning Style Visual, Logical

- Make a transparency of the sample line graph below.
- Show students the graph. Ask students to read the title, then the labels along the axes. Trace the line to emphasize that a line graph shows changes.

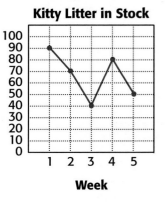

Kitty Litter in Stock

- Ask students to describe the line—does it go up, down, or remain horizontal? Use the scale to show students how the line's slope shows a changing value.
- Ask students what predictions they can make based on the data shown. Between 40 to 90 lbs of kitty litter will likely be in stock in the future.

- Invite students to make up questions that can be answered by reading the graph.
- Assign Check and Practice on Student Book pages 14 and 15 or *Practice Master 1-3*.
- Assess using the following rubric.

Assessment Rubric

4 Full Accomplishment
- reads and interprets data shown in line graphs

3 Substantial Accomplishment
- with prompting, reads and interprets data shown in line graphs

2 Partial Accomplishment
- reads and interprets some data shown in line graphs

1 Little Accomplishment
- reads but does not interpret data shown by line graphs

Options for Reaching All Learners

Language Development

Words of Change

Use common situations to develop understanding of the terms **increase, decrease,** *and* **no change.**

Learning Style Visual, Verbal

- Demonstrate *increase* by having a group of 5 students stand in front of the class and then have 3 more students join them.
- Demonstrate *decrease* by having 4 students leave the group.
- Demonstrate *no change* by keeping the group exactly as it is for a moment. Show variation of *no change* by having 2 students join the group and 2 other students leave the group.
- Challenge students to describe other examples of changes. Encourage them to use the words *increase, decrease,* and *no change.*

Inclusion

Story Lines

Use storytelling to strengthen ability to interpret line graphs.

Learning Style Verbal, Logical

- Draw this line graph on the board without a scale on either axis.

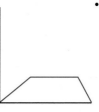

- Share the following with students: A boy collects 1 pebble at the beach each day for one week. During the next week, he keeps his pebbles but doesn't collect any more. Then he gives 2 pebbles away each day until he has none.
- Repeat the story, one sentence at a time. Have volunteers label the graph.

Lesson Organizer

Objective Read line graphs.
Student Materials None
Vocabulary line graph
Assignment Guide
  Basic 3–5, 7, 9–29
  Average 4–7, 9–29
  Enriched 5–29

1 Introduce

Review

Name the ordered pair for each point.

A (3, 0) B (2, 7) C (1, 4) D (8, 8)

Build on Prior Knowledge After students review ordered pairs, ask which point in the Review exercise is closest to the origin and which point is farthest away. Point A, Point D

2 Teach

See Another Way to Learn...on page 14B.

Learn

Pronunciation note: Michelle Drolet (mee-SHEL drō-LAY)

Discuss with students how to describe the value for points that fall between numbers on the vertical axis.

Talk About It Ongoing Assessment

Listen for answers that show an understanding of previous trends.

Answer for Talk About It

Yes; The number of dogs has stayed between 200 and 300 for five years in the 1990s.

Check

Exercise 2 Watch for students who are looking only at the direction of the line rather than comparing numerical values.

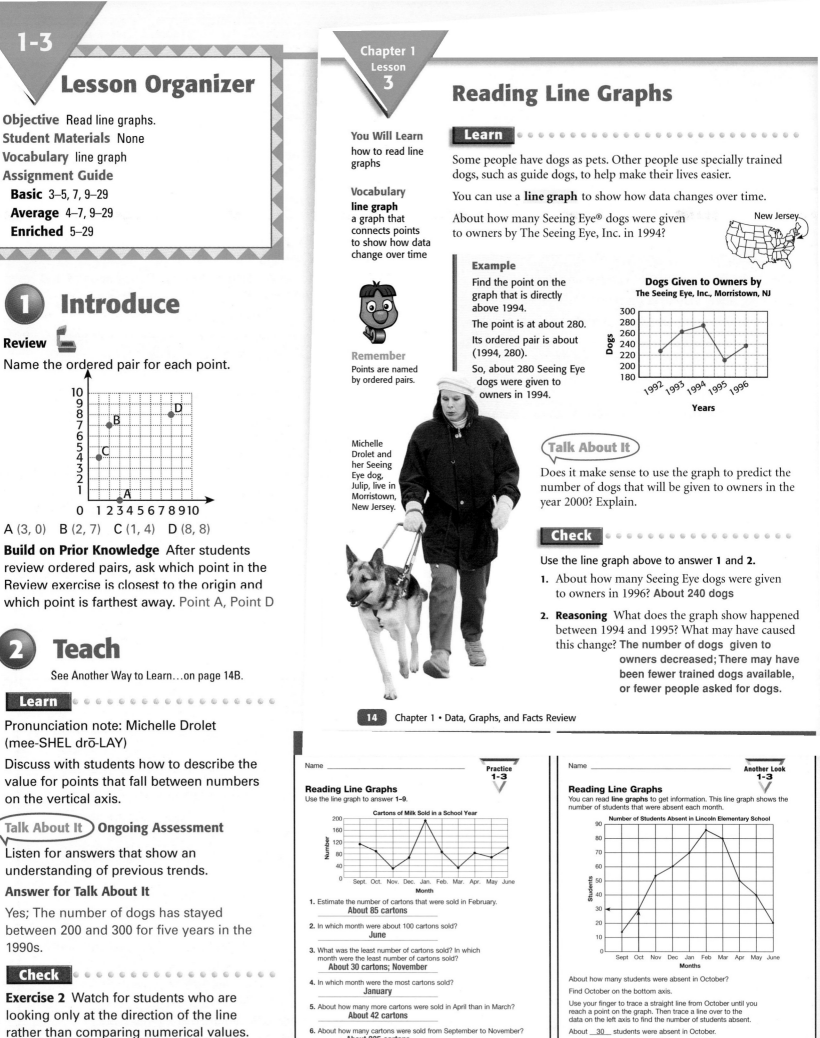

Reading Line Graphs

You Will Learn
how to read line graphs

Vocabulary
line graph
a graph that connects points to show how data change over time

Remember
Points are named by ordered pairs.

Learn

Some people have dogs as pets. Other people use specially trained dogs, such as guide dogs, to help make their lives easier.

You can use a **line graph** to show how data changes over time.

About how many Seeing Eye® dogs were given to owners by The Seeing Eye, Inc. in 1994?

Example
Find the point on the graph that is directly above 1994.

The point is at about 280.

Its ordered pair is about (1994, 280).

So, about 280 Seeing Eye dogs were given to owners in 1994.

Dogs Given to Owners by The Seeing Eye, Inc., Morristown, NJ

Michelle Drolet and her Seeing Eye dog, Julip, live in Morristown, New Jersey.

Talk About It

Does it make sense to use the graph to predict the number of dogs that will be given to owners in the year 2000? Explain.

Check

Use the line graph above to answer **1** and **2**.

1. About how many Seeing Eye dogs were given to owners in 1996? **About 240 dogs**

2. **Reasoning** What does the graph show happened between 1994 and 1995? What may have caused this change? **The number of dogs given to owners decreased; There may have been fewer trained dogs available, or fewer people asked for dogs.**

Name _____

Practice 1-3

Reading Line Graphs
Use the line graph to answer **1–9**.

Cartons of Milk Sold in a School Year

1. Estimate the number of cartons that were sold in February.
   About 85 cartons

2. In which month were about 100 cartons sold?
   June

3. What was the least number of cartons sold? In which month were the least number of cartons sold?
   About 30 cartons; November

4. In which month were the most cartons sold?
   January

5. About how many more cartons were sold in April than in March?
   About 42 cartons

6. About how many cartons were sold from September to November?
   About 235 cartons

7. About how many cartons were sold from April through June?
   About 255 cartons

8. Were the cartons sold in any month less than 40? Which month(s)?
   Yes; In November and March

9. Were more than 200 cartons sold in any month? Which month(s)?
   No

Name _____

Another Look 1-3

Reading Line Graphs
You can read **line graphs** to get information. This line graph shows the number of students that were absent each month.

Number of Students Absent in Lincoln Elementary School

About how many students were absent in October?

Find October on the bottom axis.

Use your finger to trace a straight line from October until you reach a point on the graph. Then trace a line over to the data on the left axis to find the number of students absent.

About __30__ students were absent in October.

1. About how many students were absent in December? **About 60 students**

2. About how many students were absent in March? **About 80 students**

3. In which month were about 50 students absent? **April**

4. In which month were about 40 students absent? **May**

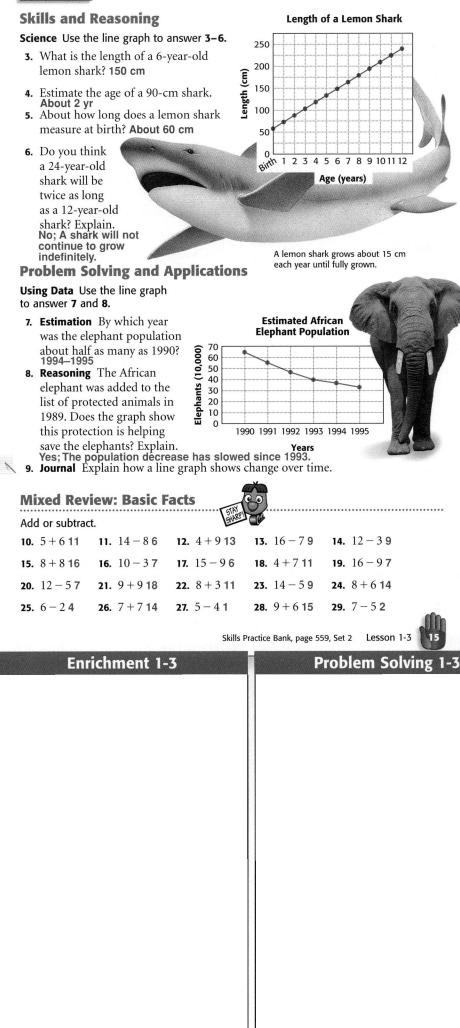

Skills and Reasoning

Science Use the line graph to answer **3–6.**

3. What is the length of a 6-year-old lemon shark? **150 cm**

4. Estimate the age of a 90-cm shark. **About 2 yr**

5. About how long does a lemon shark measure at birth? **About 60 cm**

6. Do you think a 24-year-old shark will be twice as long as a 12-year-old shark? Explain. **No; A shark will not continue to grow indefinitely.**

Length of a Lemon Shark

A lemon shark grows about 15 cm each year until fully grown.

Problem Solving and Applications

Using Data Use the line graph to answer **7** and **8.**

7. Estimation By which year was the elephant population about half as many as 1990? **1994–1995**

8. Reasoning The African elephant was added to the list of protected animals in 1989. Does the graph show this protection is helping save the elephants? Explain. **Yes; The population decrease has slowed since 1993.**

Estimated African Elephant Population

9. Journal Explain how a line graph shows change over time.

Mixed Review: Basic Facts

Add or subtract.

10. $5 + 6$ **11** **11.** $14 - 8$ **6** **12.** $4 + 9$ **13** **13.** $16 - 7$ **9** **14.** $12 - 3$ **9**

15. $8 + 8$ **16** **16.** $10 - 3$ **7** **17.** $15 - 9$ **6** **18.** $4 + 7$ **11** **19.** $16 - 9$ **7**

20. $12 - 5$ **7** **21.** $9 + 9$ **18** **22.** $8 + 3$ **11** **23.** $14 - 5$ **9** **24.** $8 + 6$ **14**

25. $6 - 2$ **4** **26.** $7 + 7$ **14** **27.** $5 - 4$ **1** **28.** $9 + 6$ **15** **29.** $7 - 5$ **2**

Skills Practice Bank, page 559, Set 2   Lesson 1-3   **15**

PRACTICE AND APPLY

Enrichment 1-3	**Problem Solving 1-3**

Observation Students read the graphed data incorrectly.

How to Help Have students hold a strip of paper across the graph so that it intersects the point and the scale.

Practice ● ○ ● ○ ● ○ ● ○ ● ○ ● ○ ● ○ ● ○ ● ○ ● ○

Exercise 6 Students will not find the answer to this question on the graph. They must interpret and think about the data.

For Early Finishers Challenge early finishers to write a problem based on the data shown in one of the graphs on page 15. Have them trade and solve problems.

3 Close and Assess

Interview

Have students use the line graph on page 14 to find the intervals for which there was an increase in the number of dogs given to owners. 1992–1993; 1993–1994; 1995–1996

Quick Check

Number Sense Describe the change shown in the graph of the time spent walking a dog between December 7 and 8. It decreased.

Skill Use the graph to answer each question.

Time Spent Walking Dog

1. For about how many minutes was the dog walked on December 5? About 30 min

2. On which date was the dog walked about 35 minutes? December 7

ANSWERS

9 A line going up to the right indicates an increase. A line going down to the right indicates a decrease. A line that stays level indicates no change.

Reading Line Plots

At-A-Glance Planning

Lesson Planning Checklist

Objective Read line plots.

Vocabulary line plot, cluster

Student Book Lesson Materials *Optional* Transparency of line plot on page 16

Materials for pages 16A and 16B Color cubes (20 per group), index cards (7 per group), common examples of objects in clusters and not in clusters (such as a ring or pin with stones in a cluster and one with stones spaced out), enlarged line plot (1 per student)

Subject Connection science—slugs

Strand Connections using data, measurement, time

	Before Lesson	During Lesson	After Lesson
Daily Math			
p. 16A Problem of the Day			
p. 16A Math Routines			
p. 16A Mental Math			
Teaching Options			
p. 16 Student Book Lesson			
p. 16B Another Way to Learn…			
Options for Reaching All Learners			
p. 16B Language Development			
p. 16B Inclusion			
Subject Connections			
p. 16A Science Connection			
Assessment Options			
p. 16 Talk About it			
p. 17 Error Intervention			
p. 17 Journal			
p. 17 Quick Check			
Resources			
1-4 Practice			
1-4 Reteaching			
1-4 Enrichment			
1-4 Problem Solving			
1-4 Daily Transparency			

Problem of the Day

Problem of the Day

Which garden needs the most fencing around it?

Garden A — 5 ft, 4 ft, 5 ft
Garden B — 2 ft, 2 ft, 4 ft, 4 ft, 6 ft, 2 ft
Garden C — 2 ft, 2 ft, 9 ft

Garden C

Math Routines

Measurement Have students estimate and then measure the length of most pencils in the classroom in centimeters.

Time Have students estimate and then time how long it takes them to eat lunch.

Mental Math

Name the total value of each. Explain.

15 dimes, 12 pennies $1.62

8 quarters, 5 nickels $2.25

10 quarters, 5 nickels $2.75

Science Connection

To test the elasticity of rubber balls, scientists drop several from the same height and measure the first bounce.

• Reproduce the line plot shown and ask students what heights these balls usually bounce to. 4 or 5 ft

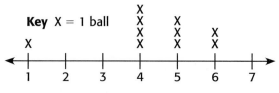

Key X = 1 ball

Rubber Ball Bounce Heights (ft)

Another Way to **Learn** Lesson 1-4
Use as an alternative or in addition to pages 16 and 17.

Materials Color cubes (20 per group), index cards (7 per group)

Learning Style Kinesthetic, Visual, Social

- Draw this line plot on the chalkboard.

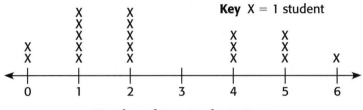

Key X = 1 student

Number of Pets Students Own

- Ask a volunteer to read the title and restate it to tell what the plot shows. Tells how many pets, if any, students own
- Have each group make a number card for each number on the line plot.
- Have students arrange the cards in order on the desk. For each X on the number plot, students place a cube above the appropriate number.

- Have group members ask each other questions that can be answered using the "line plot" they made with cubes or the line plot with Xs.
- Ask groups to look for and explain sections of the line plot that have clusters, or many Xs or cubes. Greatest cluster shows most students own 1 or 2 pets.
- Assign Check and Practice on Student Book pages 16 and 17 or *Practice Master 1-4*.
- Assess using the following rubric.

Assessment Rubric
4 Full Accomplishment • reads and interprets data shown in line plots
3 Substantial Accomplishment • with prompting, reads and interprets data shown in line plots
2 Partial Accomplishment • reads and interprets some data shown in line plots
1 Little Accomplishment • reads but does not interpret data shown in line plots

Options for Reaching All Learners

Language Development

Cluster Muster

Use common objects to develop understanding of the word **cluster**.

Materials Common examples of objects in clusters and not in clusters (such as a ring or pin with stones in a cluster and one with stones spaced out)

Learning Style Visual

- Show students the cluster ring or pin, a cluster of 5 students, or other examples. Then show the ring or pin with stones spaced out, a row of 5 students evenly spaced apart, or other examples of nonclusters.
- Have students discuss how the sets are alike and different. Introduce the word *cluster*. Challenge students to name other objects that may appear in clusters and sketch them.

Inclusion

X Marks How Many

Use enlarged line plots to strengthen understanding of data on a line plot.

Materials Enlarged line plot (1 per student)

Learning Style Visual, Auditory

Some students may confuse the values along the number line with the values of the Xs above the number line.

- Enlarge and duplicate the line plot of banana slug lengths on page 16. Ask students what the numbers on the line plot represent. Lengths of slugs
- Ask students what the X above the 13 means. One banana slug was 13 cm long.
- Have students write above each group of Xs the number of slugs shown—1 slug, 1 slug, 2 slugs, and so on.
- Model reading the labels as sentences. For example, "Two slugs were 12 centimeters long."

Lesson Organizer

Objective Read line plots.

Student Materials None

Teacher Materials *Optional* Transparency of line plot on page 16

Vocabulary line plot, cluster

Assignment Guide

Basic 4–7, 9–11, 14–38

Average 4–11, 14–38

Enriched 6–38

1 Introduce

Review 📖

Tell whether each is true for a bar graph, pictograph, and/or a line graph.

1. Compares data. Bar graph, pictograph

2. Shows change. Line graph

3. Uses symbols to represent numbers. Pictograph

Build on Prior Knowledge

After students review ways to show data in graphs, ask how a tally chart is like a pictograph. A tally chart uses tally marks in groups of 5, and a pictograph uses symbols to represent a certain number.

2 Teach

See Another Way to Learn…on page 16B.

Learn ● ○ ○ ○ ○ ○ ○ ○ ○ ○ ○ ○ ○ ○ ○ ○ ○ ○ ○

Have students explain how the statements about slugs in the Example were based on the line plot. For discussion, it may be helpful to make and use a transparency of the line plot shown on page 16.

Talk About It **Ongoing Assessment**

Listen for students to recognize what a cluster on a line plot looks like.

Answer for Talk About It

Yes, around 14–17 cm; 15 of the 24 lengths are in this interval.

Check ● ○ ○ ○ ○ ○ ○ ○ ○ ○ ○ ○ ○ ○ ○ ○ ○

Exercise 3 Students might expect the length of the slug to be one of the lengths that form a cluster. However, they should be aware that some other length is possible.

Reading Line Plots

You Will Learn
how to read line plots

Vocabulary
line plot
a graph that shows data along a number line

cluster
a group of data that appear often on a line plot

Did You Know?
Banana slugs are the largest American slugs. European slugs can reach a length of 30 cm.

Learn ● ○ ○ ○ ○ ○ ○ ○ ○ ○ ○

When is a banana not a banana? When it's a banana slug! Angela and her friends measure some slugs. Then they compare the lengths.

A **line plot** shows data along a number line. Data that appear often may form a **cluster**.

Banana slugs, found in the forests of western North America, can be very large.

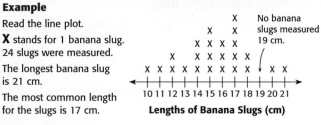

Example

Read the line plot.

X stands for 1 banana slug. 24 slugs were measured.

The longest banana slug is 21 cm.

The most common length for the slugs is 17 cm.

Lengths of Banana Slugs (cm)

Talk About It

Do the data for lengths of banana slugs form any clusters? Explain.

Check ● ○

Use the line plot above to answer **1–3**.

1. How long is the shortest banana slug? **10 cm**

2. What is the difference in length between the longest and shortest banana slugs? **11 cm**

3. **Reasoning** Suppose you measured another banana slug. What would you expect the length to be? **Between 14 and 17 cm; That is where most lengths cluster.**

Practice 1-4	Reteaching 1-4

Practice

Skills and Reasoning

Use the Great Gray Slug line plot for **4–8**.

4. What is the difference between the shortest and longest lengths? **5 cm**

5. What is the most common length? **10 cm**

6. Where do the data on this line plot form a cluster?
Around 9–10 cm

7. How many slugs measured 7 cm? **1 slug**

8. Suppose you found a great gray slug. Would you expect the length to be less than 7 cm or more than 9 cm? Why?
More than 9 cm because most slugs measured 9–12 cm

```
              x
          x   x
          x x x x
        x x x x x
      x x x x x x
      ┼─┼─┼─┼─┼─┼─►
      7 8 9 10 11 12
```
Lengths of Great Gray Slugs (cm)

Problem Solving and Applications

Use this line plot for **9–12**.

9. How many slugs crawled 19 cm in 1 minute? **1 slug**

10. How many slugs crawled 11 cm in 1 minute? **0 slugs**

11. What were the two most common lengths crawled? **16 cm, 17 cm**

```
                      x x
                    x x x
                x   x x x x x
            x   x x x x x x x x
          ┼─┼─┼─┼─┼─┼─┼─┼─┼─┼─┼─►
          10 11 12 13 14 15 16 17 18 19
```
Distances Banana Slugs Crawled (cm/min)

12. **Critical Thinking** A great gray slug can crawl about four times as fast as a banana slug. What is the shortest distance you would expect a great gray slug to crawl in one minute? **40 cm**

13. **Using Data** Use the data from the *Did You Know?* and the line plot on page 16. About how much longer is a European slug than the longest banana slug? **About 9 cm**

Mixed Review: Basic Facts

Find each sum or difference.

14. 9 + 6 **15**	15. 5 + 8 **13**	16. 9 + 2 **11**	17. 3 + 8 **11**	18. 8 + 4 **12**
19. 14 − 6 **8**	20. 13 − 6 **7**	21. 12 − 6 **6**	22. 11 − 6 **5**	23. 10 − 6 **4**
24. 9 + 9 **18**	25. 17 − 9 **8**	26. 9 + 7 **16**	27. 15 − 9 **6**	28. 9 + 5 **14**
29. 8 + 6 **14**	30. 16 − 7 **9**	31. 10 − 3 **7**	32. 13 − 5 **8**	33. 4 + 7 **11**
34. 1 + 7 **8**	35. 9 − 9 **0**	36. 8 + 5 **13**	37. 11 − 4 **7**	38. 6 + 0 **6**

Lesson 1-4   **17**

PRACTICE AND APPLY

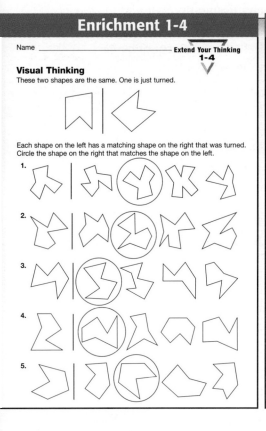

Enrichment 1-4

Name _____ Extend Your Thinking 1-4

Visual Thinking
These two shapes are the same. One is just turned.

Each shape on the left has a matching shape on the right that was turned. Circle the shape on the right that matches the shape on the left.

1.
2.
3.
4.
5.

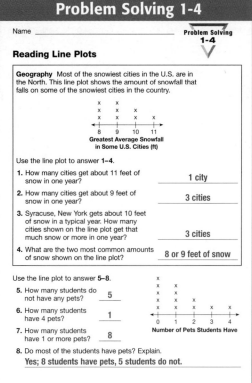

Problem Solving 1-4

Name _____ Problem Solving 1-4

Reading Line Plots

Geography Most of the snowiest cities in the U.S. are in the North. This line plot shows the amount of snowfall that falls on some of the snowiest cities in the country.

```
        x   x
        x   x   x
        x   x   x   x
      ┼───┼───┼───┼───►
      8   9   10  11
```
Greatest Average Snowfall in Some U.S. Cities (ft)

Use the line plot to answer **1–4**.

1. How many cities get about 11 feet of snow in one year? **1 city**

2. How many cities get about 9 feet of snow in one year? **3 cities**

3. Syracuse, New York gets about 10 feet of snow in a typical year. How many cities shown on the line plot get that much snow or more in one year? **3 cities**

4. What are the two most common amounts of snow shown on the line plot? **8 or 9 feet of snow**

Use the line plot to answer **5–8**.

```
                    x
                x   x
                x   x
                x   x   x
          x     x   x   x   x
        ┼───┼───┼───┼───┼───►
        0   1   2   3   4
```
Number of Pets Students Have

5. How many students do not have any pets? **5**

6. How many students have 4 pets? **1**

7. How many students have 1 or more pets? **8**

8. Do most of the students have pets? Explain.
Yes; 8 students have pets, 5 students do not.

Error Intervention Ongoing Assessment

Observation Students think a cluster is formed around only one value, the one with the most Xs.

How to Help Use a transparency of the line plot on page 16 to help students focus on the data lying between 13 and 18.

Practice

Exercise 13 Students may round the length of a banana slug to 20 cm, based on the cluster shown in the line plot on page 16.

For Early Finishers Challenge early finishers to write a problem based on one of the line plots on page 17. Have them trade and solve problems.

③ Close and Assess

Journal

Have students write a description of what a line plot is and what kinds of information it shows. Explanations should include that an X represents each time a piece of data occurs. Readers may compare heights of columns of Xs, as well as look for clusters of data.

Quick Check

Number Sense Use the line plot below. If another student's spelling test were checked, how many words would you expect to see spelled correctly? **9 or 10**

Skill Use the line plot to answer each question.

1. How many students spelled 10 words correctly? **4**

2. Where do the data form a cluster? **Around 8–10**

3. What was the most common number of words spelled correctly? **9**

Key X = 1 student

```
                              X
                              X       X
                  X       X   X       X
          X       X   X   X   X       X
        ┼───┼───┼───┼───┼───┼───┼───►
        5       6       7       8       9       10
```
Words Students Spelled Correctly on Test

Resources

Technology Master 1

Chapter 1 • Lesson 1-4   **17**

Reading Stem-and-Leaf Plots

At-A-Glance Planning

Lesson Planning Checklist

Objective Read stem-and-leaf plots.

Vocabulary stem-and-leaf plot, stem, leaf

Student Book Lesson Materials None

Materials for pages 18A and 18B Overhead place-value blocks (10 tens, 10 ones), construction paper, scissors, markers

Subject Connection science—whales, raccoons

Strand Connection using data

	Before Lesson	During Lesson	After Lesson
Daily Math			
p. 18A Problem of the Day			
p. 18A Math Routines			
p. 18A Mental Math			
Teaching Options			
p. 18 Student Book Lesson			
p. 18B Another Way to Learn…			
Options for Reaching All Learners			
p. 18B Language Development			
p. 18B Reading Assist			
Subject Connections			
p. 18A Science Connection			
Assessment Options			
p. 18 Talk About it			
p. 19 Error Intervention			
p. 19 Journal			
p. 19 Quick Check			
Resources			
1-5 Practice			
1-5 Reteaching			
1-5 Enrichment			
1-5 Problem Solving			
1-5 Daily Transparency			

Problem of the Day

Problem of the Day

These are the Japanese words for some numbers.

1	ichi	4	shi
2	ni	10	juu
3	san	12	juu-ni

If 20 is ni-juu, what is 30? Explain.

San-juu for 3 tens

Math Routines

Calendar Starting with today's date, have students give the date for this day of the week for the next three weeks.

Patterns Ask students to give the missing numbers in the patterns.

9, 19, ■, 39, ■, ■ 29, 49, 59

■, ■, 33, 43, ■, ■ 13, 23, 53, 63

Mental Math

Name each missing number and tell the pattern. Explain your thinking.

3, 7, 11, ■, 19, ■ 15, 23; count by 4s

2, 7, ■, 17, 22, ■ 12, 27; count by 5s

Science Connection

Whales must surface to breathe air. This plot shows diving times for several gray whales.

Diving Times (min)

Stem	Leaf
0	7 8 8 6 9 8
1	1 0 2 2 1

• Ask students which diving time was observed most often. 8

Another Way to **Learn** Lesson 1-5

Use as an alternative or in addition to pages 18 and 19.

Materials Overhead place-value blocks (10 tens, 10 ones)

Learning Style Visual

- Use the sample stem-and-leaf plot provided below, which shows the height, in inches, of 12 students.

Heights of Students (in.)

Stem	Leaf
4	5 8 1 8
5	4 9 0 4 8 7
6	0 2

- Use the plot to explain that the stem represents the tens place and the leaves are all ones. Each stem-and-leaf combination represents a 2-digit number.

- Use overhead place-value blocks to model several numbers from the plot. For example, model 45 with 4 tens and 5 ones. To model 48, leave the 4 tens in place and remove all 5 ones. Replace them with 8 ones.

- After you have modeled some of the data, call on volunteers to read other data on the plot.

- Have students count the number of leaves to find the total number of items represented in the plot. 12

- Have students list all data presented in the plot. Discuss how the plot is more compact than their list.

- Assign Check and Practice on Student Book pages 18 and 19 or *Practice Master 1-5*.

- Assess using the following rubric.

Assessment Rubric
4 Full Accomplishment • reads and interprets data shown in stem-and-leaf plots
3 Substantial Accomplishment • reads and interprets data shown in stem-and-leaf plots with some prompting
2 Partial Accomplishment • reads and interprets some data shown in stem-and-leaf plots
1 Little Accomplishment • reads but does not interpret data shown in stem-and-leaf plots

Options for Reaching All Learners

Language Development

Garden Plots

Use a common visual image to develop understanding of the terms **stem** *and* **leaf**.

Materials Construction paper, scissors, markers

Learning Style Visual, Verbal/Auditory

- Demonstrate showing 72, 76, 76, and 78 as the stem and leaves of a plant.

- Group students acquiring English with fluent speakers.

- Have groups make a garden by cutting out construction-paper plants to display the data given in the stem-and-leaf plot on page 18. Students should cut out and label 7 stems and 9 leaves. Be sure students label 4 leaves with a zero.

- Have each member of the group read aloud each number as he or she points first to the stem and then to a leaf.

Reading Assist

Read Graphs

Use paired reading to strengthen skills reading stem-and-leaf plots.

Learning Style Kinesthetic, Verbal/Auditory

- Have pairs read the stem-and-leaf plot on page 18.

- Ask students to count the numbers in the leaf column. This tells how many entries there are on the plot. 9

- Tell students that stems represent tens and leaves represent ones. Ask how many numbers have 5 tens. 3 What are these numbers? 50, 50, 58

- Have pairs continue reading, listing the numbers as they identify them.

1-5

Lesson Organizer

Objective Read stem-and-leaf plots.
Student Materials None
Vocabulary stem-and-leaf plot, stem, leaf
Assignment Guide
Basic 3–6, 10–24
Average 4–8, 10–24
Enriched 5–24

1 Introduce

Review

Tell how many tens and ones in each.

1. 38 **3 tens 8 ones**   2. 59 **5 tens 9 ones**
3. 52 **5 tens 2 ones**   4. 30 **3 tens 0 ones**

Build on Prior Knowledge

After students review how tens and ones are represented in 2-digit numbers, ask how they could sort 38, 59, 52, and 30 into two groups. Possible answers: Even and odd numbers; By the number of tens

2 Teach

See Another Way to Learn…on page 18B.

Learn

Have volunteers read aloud each piece of data shown in the stem-and-leaf plot. Ask students what the two zeros on the 5 stem represent. There are two different species of whales that are 50 ft long.

Talk About It Ongoing Assessment

Listen for students to explain why no leaves for the stems 4 and 7 is different from the leaf 0 for the stem 2.

Answer for Talk About It

There are no whales between 40 and 49 ft or between 70 and 79 ft.

Check

Exercise 2 Be sure students identify the shortest whale as 20 feet and then add 40 feet. Students should then show the length of a full-size whale as stem 6 and leaf 0.

 18   *Chapter 1 • Lesson 1-5*

Reading Stem-and-Leaf Plots

You Will Learn
how to read stem-and-leaf plots

Vocabulary

stem-and-leaf plot
a graph that uses place value to organize data

stem
shows the tens digit of a number

leaf
shows the ones digit of a number

Remember
A two-digit number has a tens digit and a ones digit.

Tens digit Ones digit
       ↓   ↓
       6   8

Learn

Have you ever heard anyone say, "That's a whale of a fish"? Whales are very large, but they are mammals, not fish.

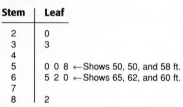

You can use a **stem-and-leaf plot** to organize and compare data.

Example
How much longer is the longest whale than the shortest?

Lengths of Some Species of Whales (ft)

Stem	Leaf
2	0
3	3
4	
5	0 0 8 ←Shows 50, 50, and 58 ft.
6	5 2 0 ←Shows 65, 62, and 60 ft.
7	
8	2

In the stem-and-leaf plot, 82 is the greatest number, and 20 is the least.
$82 - 20 = 62$

So, the longest whale is 62 ft longer than the shortest whale.

Talk About It

Why are there no leaves for the stems 4 and 7?

Check

Use the stem-and-leaf plot above to answer **1** and **2**.

1. What is the length of the next-to-shortest whale? **33 ft**

2. **Reasoning** The shortest whale shown is a pygmy right whale. A full-size right whale is 40 ft longer. How would you show the length of a full-size right whale in the stem-and-leaf plot? **Write another zero in the row that has the stem 6.**

Practice 1-5

Name _____

*Practice
1-5*

Reading Stem-and-Leaf Plots
Use this stem-and-leaf plot for **1–4.**

Number of Dogs Competing in Dog Shows

Stem	Leaf
1	6 2 0 2 4
2	5 2 9 5
3	1 6 6
4	0 5

1. What was the least number of dogs at a dog show?
   10 dogs

2. What was the greatest number of dogs at a dog show?
   45 dogs

3. How many dog shows are reported in the stem-and-leaf plot?
   14 dog shows

4. How many dog shows had between 20 and 29 dogs?
   4 dog shows

Use this stem-and-leaf plot for **5–8.**

**Shoulder Heights (in inches)
of Dogs That Won Ribbons**

Stem	Leaf
0	5 8 6 9
1	4 9 5
2	2 8 6
3	6 2

5. How many heights of dogs does the stem-and-leaf plot show?
   12 heights

6. What is the difference in shoulder heights between the tallest and the shortest dog?
   31 inches

7. How many dogs were taller than 26 inches?   **3 dogs**

8. Was there any dog 25 inches tall?   **no**

Reteaching 1-5

Name _____

*Another Look
1-5*

Reading Stem-and-Leaf Plots
This stem-and-leaf plot shows the number of points scored by the Green Bay Packers in their games during the 1995 season.

The numbers in the stem are tens digits.   The numbers in the leaf are ones digits.

Stem	Leaf
1	4 4 6 0 ——— Shows 14, 14, 16, and 10 points.
2	7 4 4 4 4 4
3	0 8 5 1 5 4

You can use the stem-and-leaf plot to find the greatest number of points the Green Bay Packers scored in one game in 1995.

First look for the greatest tens digit in the stem. __3__

Then look for the greatest one digit in its leaf. __8__

The greatest number of points scored by the Green Bay Packers in 1995 was __38 points__.

1. What was the least number of points scored by the Green Bay Packers in 1995? **10 points**

2. In how many games did the Packers score 14 points? **2 games**

3. What would you say is a typical score for the Green Bay Packers? **24 points**

4. In how many games did the Green Bay Packers score more than 25 points? **7 games**

5. What was the difference in points between Green Bay's best and worst scores? **28 points**

Skills and Reasoning

Science Use this stem-and-leaf plot for **3–5**.

3. What is the difference between the greatest weight of a raccoon and the least weight? **41 pounds**

4. How many raccoons weighed less than 30 lb? More than 30 lb? **13; 13**

5. Why might you want to redo the leaf part of your graph and put the leaves in each row in order from least to greatest?

Raccoon Weights (lb)

Stem	Leaf
0	9 6 9
1	9 5 5 7 0
2	6 1 0 6 9
3	4 8 9 3 8 8
4	3 4 3 2 7 3 2

Problem Solving and Applications

Science A group of whales swimming together is called a *school* or *pod*. Use this stem-and-leaf plot to answer **6–9**.

Number of Whales in Schools

Stem	Leaf
1	8 9 8
2	2 5 4 2 0 1 5 5 8 9 2 0 1 4 5 9 8 7 6
3	3 4 5 3 5 3 6 2 6 1 7 8 9 0 7
4	2 5 0 2

6. Which is greater: The number of schools with fewer than 20 whales or the number of schools with 40 or more whales? **Number of schools with 40 or more whales**

7. How many schools have 25 whales? **4 schools**

8. How many schools have between 23 and 33 whales? **15 schools**

9. **What If** You want to show the data about whales in a bar graph. From the stem-and-leaf plot, how can you tell which bar would be the longest? Explain. **Bar for 25; More 25s than any other number**

Mixed Review: Basic Facts

Find each sum or difference.

10. $16 - 9$ **7**
11. $5 + 8$ **13**
12. $7 + 8$ **15**
13. $12 - 4$ **8**
14. $5 + 7$ **12**
15. $9 + 8$ **17**
16. $18 - 9$ **9**
17. $17 - 8$ **9**
18. $16 - 7$ **9**
19. $8 + 3$ **11**
20. $11 - 7$ **4**
21. $6 + 8$ **14**
22. $5 + 4$ **9**
23. $15 - 9$ **6**
24. $10 - 6$ **4**

Skills Practice Bank, page 559, Set 3   Lesson 1-5   **19**

Enrichment 1-5

Name _____ **Extend Your Thinking 1-5**

Visual Thinking
Draw the missing figure.

Example
1. ___ is to ___ as ___ is to ___
2. ___ is to ___ as ___ is to ___
3. ___ is to ___ as ___ is to ___
4. ___ is to ___ as ___ is to ___
5. ___ is to ___ as ___ is to ___

Problem Solving 1-5

Name _____ **Problem Solving 1-5**

Reading Stem-and-Leaf Plots

Science The largest animals known were dinosaurs. From their skeletons, scientists can estimate how long they were.

Lengths of the Largest Dinosaurs (meters)

Stem	Leaf
1	5 2 2
2	7 5 5 1
3	6 0 0

Use the stem-and-leaf plot to answer **1–4**.

1. The Seismosaurus is the longest known dinosaur. About how many meters long was a Seismosaurus? **About 36 meters**

2. The Tyrannosaurus and Spinosaurus were the same length. How many meters long could they have been? **About 12 meters, 25 meters, or 30 meters long**

3. How many types of dinosaurs were longer than 15 meters? **7 types**

4. Suppose a new dinosaur was discovered tomorrow. If its length is 10 meters, would it be one of the 9 largest dinosaurs? Explain. **Possible answer: No; There are 10 dinosaurs shown in the stem-and-leaf plot and all are greater than 10 meters long.**

Use the stem-and-leaf plot to answer **5–7**.

Lengths of the Longest Snakes (ft)

Stem	Leaf
1	1 2 4 6
2	4
3	3

5. The python is the longest snake. What is its length? **33 feet**

6. How many snakes are longer than 16 feet? **2**

7. How many snakes are between 11 and 24 feet long? **3**

Error Intervention Ongoing Assessment

Observation Some students may not read a stem and leaf together as a 2-digit number.

How to Help Have students write *tens* and *ones* on small pieces of paper and place them on page 18 over the words *stem* and *leaf*, respectively, on the plot.

Practice •

Exercise 5 To see the value of reordering, students can reorder from least to greatest the leaves of the raccoon weight plot in order to check their answer to Exercise 3.

For Early Finishers Challenge early finishers to find the least, greatest, and most common numbers in the Number of Whales in Schools. **18; 45; 25**

③ Close and Assess

Journal

Have students tell how they read data displayed in a stem-and-leaf plot. Explanations should describe reading a 2-digit number with the stem representing its tens digit and the leaf its ones digit.

Quick Check

Number Sense Which numbers could you write in the stem-and-leaf plot below without creating any new stems: 10, 25, 72? **10, 25**

Skill Use the stem-and-leaf plot to answer each question.

Length of Some Sharks (feet)

Stem	Leaf
1	2 2 4 7
2	0 1 9
3	7
4	0

1. What is the most common length? **12 ft**

2. What is the difference in length between the longest and the next to the longest shark? **3 ft**

ANSWERS

5 Possible answers: Might make it easier to see a pattern in the data; Might see some groups of weights easier

Analyze Word Problems:
Introduction to Problem Solving Guide

At-A-Glance Planning

Objective Solve problems by using a guide.

Student Book Lesson Materials *Optional* Teacher's Edition Transparency A (Problem-Solving Guide), Lesson Enhancement Transparency 1

Materials for pages 20A and 20B Place-value blocks (15 tens, 20 ones per group), Teacher's Edition Transparency A (Problem-Solving Guide), soup spoon, teaspoon

Subject Connection science—endangered and threatened species, snakes

Strand Connection using data

	Before Lesson	During Lesson	After Lesson
Daily Math			
p. 20A Problem of the Day			
p. 20A Math Routines			
p. 20A Mental Math			
Teaching Options			
p. 20 Student Book Lesson			
p. 20B Another Way to Learn…			
Options for Reaching All Learners			
p. 20B Reading Assist			
p. 20B Language Development			
Subject Connections			
p. 20A Geography Connection			
Assessment Options			
p. 20 Talk About It			
p. 21 Quick Check			
Resources			
1-6 Practice			
1-6 Reteaching			
1-6 Enrichment			
1-6 Problem Solving			
1-6 Daily Transparency			

Problem of the Day

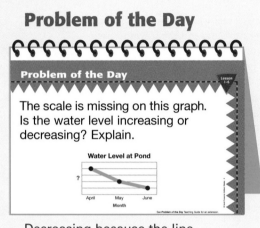

Problem of the Day   Lesson 1-6

The scale is missing on this graph. Is the water level increasing or decreasing? Explain.

Water Level at Pond

See Problem of the Day Teaching Guide for an extension.

Decreasing because the line slants down

Math Routines

Money Pose problems such as the following: If you left home with $1.00, found $0.75, and spent $1.25, did you have more or less money when you returned home than when you left? less

Measurement Ask: How high is your desk in inches? Estimate, then measure to check. How close were you?

Mental Math

Tell how much money you would have left. Explain your thinking.

Have	Spend	
$0.50	$0.30	$0.20
$0.75	$0.60	$0.15
$1.00	$0.79	$0.21

Geography Connection

Species of animals are now endangered due to changes in their natural habitats.

• Have pairs or small groups of students each research one endangered species.

• On a classroom map of the world, have students show where their animal lives. Have them use numbers to describe the decrease and, if now appropriate, increase in the animal's population.

Another Way to  Learn Lesson 1-6

Use as an alternative or in addition to pages 20 and 21.

Materials Place-value blocks (15 tens, 20 ones per group), Teacher's Edition Transparency A (Problem-Solving Guide)

Learning Style Kinesthetic

- Show students the line graph below and ask: Were there more birds spotted in 1992 or 1993?

Birds Spotted by the Bird-Watching Club

- Have students use place-value blocks to represent the number of birds spotted in 1992 and 1993.

- As you show each step on Teacher's Edition Transparency A (Problem-Solving Guide) and ask the accompanying questions, have students refer to their place-value models and answer in their groups.

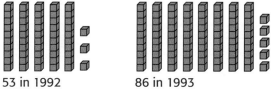

53 in 1992   86 in 1993

86 > 53, so there were more birds spotted in 1993.

- Assign Check and Practice on Student Book page 21 or *Practice Master 1-6.*
- Assess using the following rubric.

Assessment Rubric
4 Full Accomplishment • solves problems and explains steps used
3 Substantial Accomplishment • with prompting, solves problems and explains steps used
2 Partial Accomplishment • solves some problems but does not explain steps used
1 Little Accomplishment • does not solve problems or explain steps used

Options for Reaching All Learners

Reading Assist

Word Meaning
Use analogies to understand the word **species**.

Materials Soup spoon, teaspoon

Learning Style Visual

Some students may be confused by the distinction made between different species of animals.

- Explain that a *species* is a specific kind of living thing that is part of a larger, more general group.

- Hold up a soup spoon and a teaspoon. Point out that each has its own name. Although both are spoons, they are different kinds of spoons.

- Explain that a species of plant or animal is like a kind of spoon or car—generally the same, but with its own special qualities. You may wish to brainstorm species of bird, snake, bear, butterfly, or tree.

Language Development

Read and Restate
Use paired reading to understand vocabulary.

Learning Style Verbal, Social

Some students may have difficulty following the vocabulary in the Using Data section on page 21.

- Encourage partners to read the questions together and make a list of the words that are unfamiliar to them.

- Students can look up and draw or write explanations of the unfamiliar words on word cards.

- As the students finish their lists, they can reread the questions together, restating them in their own terms.

- Suggest that students add to their lists as they encounter other new words.

Lesson Organizer

Objective Solve problems by using a guide.

Student Materials None

Teacher Materials *Optional* Teacher's Edition Transparency A (Problem-Solving Guide), Lesson Enhancement Transparency 1

Assignment Guide

Basic 2–4, 7

Average 2–5, 7

Enriched 3–7

1 Introduce

Review

On a line graph, what change does each show?

1. a line that goes down to the right A decrease

2. a line that stays level No change

3. a line that goes up to the right An increase

Build on Prior Knowledge

After students review how change is shown on a line graph, ask what it means if one point on a graph is higher than another. The higher point represents a greater number.

2 Teach

See Another Way to Learn…on page 20B.

Learn ·

As you go over page 20 with students, use Teacher's Edition Transparency A (Problem-Solving Guide) to reinforce the steps in the problem-solving process.

Talk About It **Ongoing Assessment**

Listen for students to recognize the value of working in an organized manner.

Answer for Talk About It

Possible answer: Helps you understand what you know and need to find; Helps you plan how to find the answer, solve the problem, and check the answer

---

Chapter 1
Lesson 6

Problem Solving

Analyze Word Problems: Introduction to Problem Solving Guide

You Will Learn
how using a guide can help you solve problems

Reading Tip
Read the scale along the bottom of the graph to find the years in the problem.

Learn · · · · · · · · · · ·

Be a problem solver! Using a guide can help you solve any problem.

Were there more new listings of endangered and threatened species in 1991 than in 1990?

New Listings of Endangered and Threatened Species in the U.S.

Number Listed (vertical axis: 0 to 140)

Data points: 1990: 53, 1991: 86, 1992: 82, 1993: 73, 1994: 128, 1995: 49

Years (horizontal axis): 1990 1991 1992 1993 1994 1995

Work Together

▶ **Understand** | What do you know? | There were 53 new listings in 1990 and 86 new listings in 1991.
| What do you need to find? | Were there more new listings in 1991 than in 1990?

▶ **Plan** | Decide how you will find the answer. | You need to compare 86 to 53.

▶ **Solve** | Find the answer. Write your answer. | 86 is greater than 53, so there were more new listings in 1991 than in 1990.

▶ **Look Back** | Check to see if your answer makes sense. | Look at the line graph. The point for 1991 is higher than the one for 1990.

Talk About It

How did the steps in the guide help you solve the problem?

Practice 1-6

Name _____

Practice 1-6

Analyze Word Problems: Introduction to Problem Solving Guide

Use the graph below to answer 1–5.

Bones of the Human Body

Number of Bones (vertical axis: 0 to 26)

Body Part (horizontal axis): Face, Back, Chest, Shoulder, Arm

1. a. Which part of the body in the graph has the fewest bones?
Arm

b. How many bones does this part of the body have?
3 bones

2. How would you find the total number of bones in the face, back, chest, shoulders and arm?

a. What will your plan be?
Find the sum of 14 + 26 + 25 + 4 + 3.

b. What is the total number of bones in these parts?
72

3. How many more bones are in the back than in the face?
12

4. Which two body parts have the most bones?
Back, chest

5. Put the parts of the body in order by number of bones from greatest to least.
Back, chest, face, shoulder, arm

Reteaching 1-6

Check

Problem Solving
Understand
Plan
Solve
Look Back

Use the graph on page 20. Plan how you will solve the problem. Then solve.

1. **a.** Which year had the most new listings for endangered and threatened species? **1994**

   b. How many listings were in that year? **128 listings**

Problem Solving Practice

Use the graph on page 20 for **2–4.** Plan how you will solve each problem. Then solve.

Problem Solving Strategies
- Use Objects/Act It Out
- Draw a Picture
- Look for a Pattern
- Guess and Check
- Use Logical Reasoning
- Make an Organized List
- Make a Table
- Solve a Simpler Problem
- Work Backward

Choose a Tool

2. **a.** Which year had the fewest new listings for endangered and threatened species? **1995**

   b. How many listings were in that year? **49 listings**

3. Find the total number of new listings from 1990 to 1995. **471**

4. In 1996, there were 92 new listings of endangered and threatened species. Is this more or less than the number of new listings in 1995? **More**

Using Data Use the bar graph to answer **5** and **6**.

5. **Science** San Francisco garter snakes are an endangered species. How much longer is the San Francisco garter snake than the Florida pygmy rattlesnake? **30 inches**

6. What is the difference in length between the San Francisco garter snake and the Texas blind snake? **40 inches**

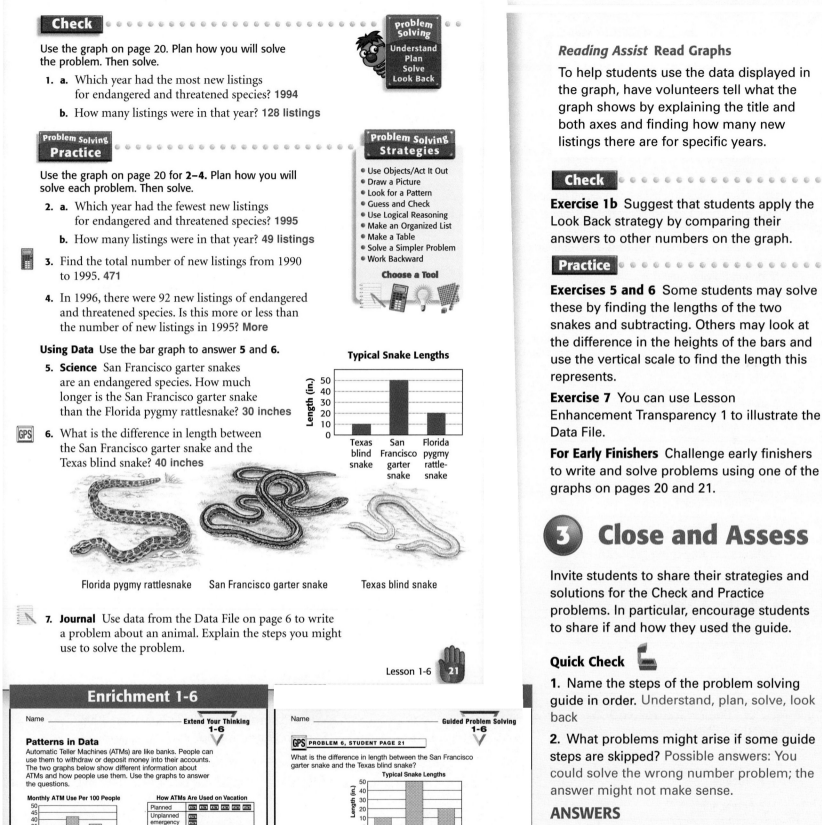

Florida pygmy rattlesnake   San Francisco garter snake   Texas blind snake

7. **Journal** Use data from the Data File on page 6 to write a problem about an animal. Explain the steps you might use to solve the problem.

Lesson 1-6   **21**

Enrichment 1-6

Name _____   **Extend Your Thinking 1-6**

Patterns in Data
Automatic Teller Machines (ATMs) are like banks. People can use them to withdraw or deposit money into their accounts. The two graphs below show different information about ATMs and how people use them. Use the graphs to answer the questions.

Monthly ATM Use Per 100 People

How ATMs Are Used on Vacation

Planned	
Unplanned emergency	
Unplanned convenience	

ATM = 5 people

1. How often do the greatest number of people use ATMs? **2–5 times a month**

2. Why does the largest group of people use ATMs while they are on vacation? **Unplanned convenience**

3. **a.** Which sentences describe the average ATM user? **II.**

   I. "I use ATM's about once a month. On vacation I only use them for emergencies."

   II. "I use ATM's 4 times a month. On vacation I use them for convenience."

   b. Explain your reasoning. **Possible answer:** Statement II relates to the greatest number on each graph.

4. About how many people per hundred use ATMs more than 6 times a month? **36**

5. How does the second largest group of people use ATMs while on vacation? **Planned use**

Name _____   **Guided Problem Solving 1-6**

GPS PROBLEM 6, STUDENT PAGE 21

What is the difference in length between the San Francisco garter snake and the Texas blind snake?

Typical Snake Lengths

— **Understand** —
1. What facts do you know? **Length of San Francisco garter snake: 50 in., and Texas blind snake: 10 in.**

2. What do you need to find out? **The difference in the length between the 2 snakes**

— **Plan** —
3. What operation do you use to find a difference? **Subtraction**

— **Solve** —
4. Find the difference. **50 − 10 = 40**
5. Write your answer. **The San Francisco garter snake is 40 inches longer than the Texas blind snake.**

— **Look Back** —
6. How can you check to see if your answer makes sense? **Add to check. 40 + 10 = 50**

SOLVE ANOTHER PROBLEM

Find the difference in length between the Florida rattlesnake and the Texas blind snake. **10 inches**

Reading Assist **Read Graphs**

To help students use the data displayed in the graph, have volunteers tell what the graph shows by explaining the title and both axes and finding how many new listings there are for specific years.

Check

Exercise 1b Suggest that students apply the Look Back strategy by comparing their answers to other numbers on the graph.

Practice

Exercises 5 and 6 Some students may solve these by finding the lengths of the two snakes and subtracting. Others may look at the difference in the heights of the bars and use the vertical scale to find the length this represents.

Exercise 7 You can use Lesson Enhancement Transparency 1 to illustrate the Data File.

For Early Finishers Challenge early finishers to write and solve problems using one of the graphs on pages 20 and 21.

3 Close and Assess

Invite students to share their strategies and solutions for the Check and Practice problems. In particular, encourage students to share if and how they used the guide.

Quick Check

1. Name the steps of the problem solving guide in order. Understand, plan, solve, look back

2. What problems might arise if some guide steps are skipped? Possible answers: You could solve the wrong number problem; the answer might not make sense.

ANSWERS

7 Answers should include: A problem about an animal; Steps identifying the problem, making a plan, carrying out the plan, solving the problem, and checking that the answer makes sense.

Chapter 1 • Lesson 1-6   **21**

At-A-Glance Planning

Lesson Planning Checklist

Objective Solve problems by choosing an operation.

Student Book Lesson Materials *Optional* Teacher's Edition Transparency A (Problem-Solving Guide)

Materials for pages 22A and 22B Counters (12 per group), index cards (3 per pair), Teacher's Edition Transparency A (Problem-Solving Guide)

Subject Connection science—animals

Strand Connection money

	Before Lesson	During Lesson	After Lesson
Daily Math			
p. 22A Problem of the Day			
p. 22A Math Routines			
p. 22A Mental Math			
Teaching Options			
p. 22 Student Book Lesson			
p. 22B Another Way to Learn…			
Options for Reaching All Learners			
p. 22B Reading Assist			
p. 22B Gifted & Talented			
Subject Connections			
p. 22A Literature Connection			
Assessment Options			
p. 22 Talk About It			
p. 23 Quick Check			
Resources			
1-7 Practice			
1-7 Reteaching			
1-7 Enrichment			
1-7 Problem Solving			
1-7 Daily Transparency			

Problem of the Day

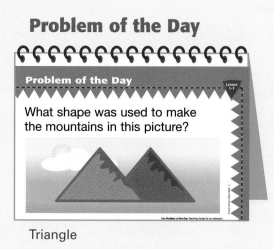

Problem of the Day — Lesson 1-7

What shape was used to make the mountains in this picture?

Triangle

Math Routines

Calendar Name a holiday. Have students tell how they would find the number of days since or until that day.

Patterns Ask students to name the next number and identify the operation they used to determine it.

2, 6, 10, 14, ■ 18; add 4

15, 12, 9, 6, ■ 3; subtract 3

2, 4, 8, 16, ■ 32; multiply by 2

Mental Math

Will the sum be greater or less than 100? Explain your thinking.

89 + 9	Less	32 + 59	Less
73 + 85	Greater	93 + 15	Greater

Literature Connection

In Louis Sachar's *Sideways Stories from Wayside School,* Dana has lots of itchy mosquito bites. She counts 75 on one side of her body and 49 on the other.

• What operation is needed to find out how many mosquito bites Dana has in all? Addition

Another Way to **Learn** Lesson 1-7

Use as an alternative or in addition to pages 22 and 23.

Materials Counters (12 per group), Teacher's Edition Transparency A (Problem-Solving Guide)

Learning Style Kinesthetic

- Present students with this problem: Juan has 3 pets. Mary has 5 more pets than Juan. How many pets does Mary have? Use the Problem-Solving Guide. Have students answer the Understand and Plan questions.

- To solve have students use counters to represent the number of pets and model the problem by first showing Juan's 3 pets and then the 5 more pets that Mary has.

- Model the problem on the overhead projector or chalkboard using a number line and write the number sentence.

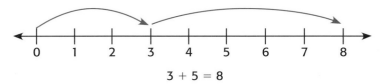

$$3 + 5 = 8$$

- Have students talk about which operation they used to solve this problem and why. Then have them write a problem about Juan and Mary's pets that could be solved by subtraction.

- Assign Check and Practice on Student Book page 23 or *Practice Master 1-7*.

- Assess using the following rubric.

Assessment Rubric
4 Full Accomplishment • chooses an operation to solve a problem • consistently solves word problems
3 Substantial Accomplishment • with prompting, chooses an operation to solve a problem • solves most word problems
2 Partial Accomplishment • chooses an operation to solve some problems • solves some word problems
1 Little Accomplishment • does not choose an operation to solve a problem • does not solve word problems

Options for Reaching All Learners

Reading Assist

Find Main Idea with Supporting Details
Use paraphrasing to help students understand questions.

Learning Style Social, Verbal

- Point out that the main idea of a word problem is the question being asked. The supporting details are the numbers and relationships described in the problem.

- Have students work in pairs to paraphrase word problems on page 23.

- One student can read a question aloud, then paraphrase it. The partner can tell whether he or she feels the paraphrase includes all necessary information.

Gifted & Talented

The Problem with Cards
Use a card game to strengthen understanding of problems that can be solved using addition or subtraction.

Materials Index cards (3 per pair)

Learning Style Verbal

- Give each pair of students three cards. Have students write a plus or minus sign on one card. Then have them write one number from 0 through 20 on each of the other two cards.

- Pairs use their cards to make an expression. Students then write word problems that could be represented by their expression.

- Have pairs trade and solve problems. Pairs can share their strategies and solutions.

Lesson Organizer

Objective Solve problems by choosing an operation.

Student Materials None

Teacher Materials *Optional* Teacher's Edition Transparency A (Problem-Solving Guide)

Assignment Guide

Basic 3–7

Average 3–7

Enriched 3–7

1 Introduce

Review

Give the missing operation sign.

1. 3 ▨ 2 = 5 +
2. 10 ▨ 5 = 5 –
3. 9 ▨ 1 = 8 –
4. 7 ▨ 4 = 11 +

Build on Prior Knowledge

After students review how to decide whether an addition or subtraction sign is missing, ask which operation they would use to find how many years are 3 more than 5. Addition

2 Teach

See Another Way to Learn…on page 22B.

Learn ● ● ● ● ● ● ● ● ● ● ● ● ● ● ● ● ● ● ●

Pronunciation note: Shiba Inu (SHEE-bah EE-noo)

You may wish to use Teacher's Edition Transparency A (Problem-Solving Guide) to review the steps in the problem solving process.

Talk About It **Ongoing Assessment**

Listen for the ability to identify the main action described in the problem.

Answer for Talk About It

If you are comparing, taking away, or finding a missing part you will subtract. If you are putting things together, you will add.

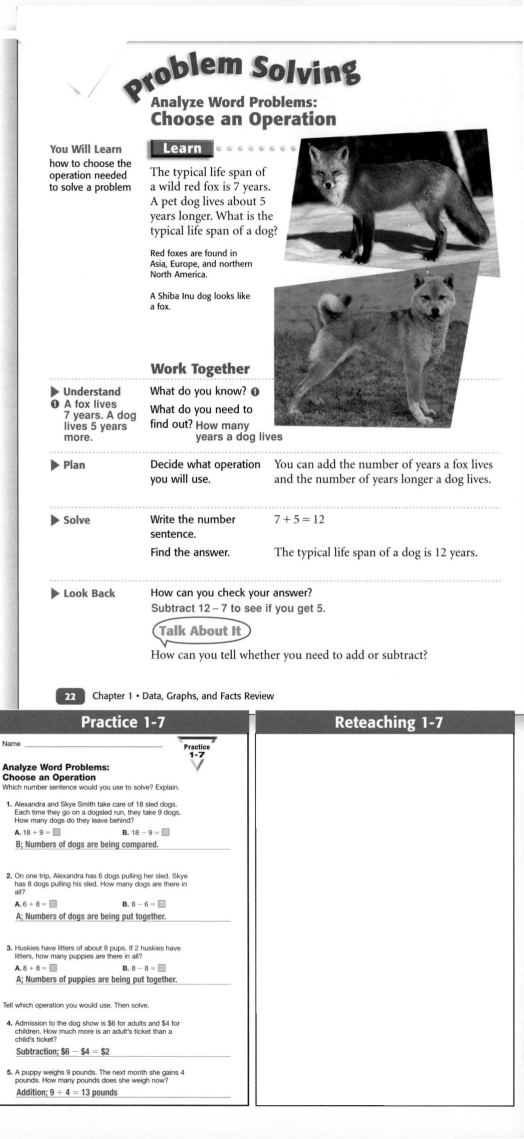

Problem Solving

Analyze Word Problems: Choose an Operation

You Will Learn
how to choose the operation needed to solve a problem

Learn ● ● ● ● ● ● ● ●

The typical life span of a wild red fox is 7 years. A pet dog lives about 5 years longer. What is the typical life span of a dog?

Red foxes are found in Asia, Europe, and northern North America.

A Shiba Inu dog looks like a fox.

Work Together

▶ **Understand** What do you know? ❶
❶ A fox lives 7 years. A dog lives 5 years more.

What do you need to find out? How many years a dog lives

▶ **Plan** Decide what operation you will use.

You can add the number of years a fox lives and the number of years longer a dog lives.

▶ **Solve** Write the number sentence.

$7 + 5 = 12$

Find the answer. The typical life span of a dog is 12 years.

▶ **Look Back** How can you check your answer?

Subtract $12 - 7$ to see if you get 5.

Talk About It

How can you tell whether you need to add or subtract?

Practice 1-7

Name _____

Practice 1-7

Analyze Word Problems: Choose an Operation

Which number sentence would you use to solve? Explain.

1. Alexandra and Skye Smith take care of 18 sled dogs. Each time they go on a dogsled run, they take 9 dogs. How many dogs do they leave behind?

   A. 18 + 9 = ▧   **B.** 18 − 9 = ▧

   B; Numbers of dogs are being compared.

2. On one trip, Alexandra has 6 dogs pulling her sled. Skye has 8 dogs pulling his sled. How many dogs are there in all?

   A. 6 + 8 = ▧   **B.** 8 − 6 = ▧

   A; Numbers of dogs are being put together.

3. Huskies have litters of about 8 pups. If 2 huskies have litters, how many puppies are there in all?

   A. 8 + 8 = ▧   **B.** 8 − 8 = ▧

   A; Numbers of puppies are being put together.

Tell which operation you would use. Then solve.

4. Admission to the dog show is $6 for adults and $4 for children. How much more is an adult's ticket than a child's ticket?

   Subtraction; $6 − $4 = $2

5. A puppy weighs 9 pounds. The next month she gains 4 pounds. How many pounds does she weigh now?

   Addition; 9 + 4 = 13 pounds

Reteaching 1-7

Check

Problem Solving: Understand, Plan, Solve, Look Back

Which number sentence would you use to solve? Explain.

1. The typical life span of a lion is 15 years. This is 8 years longer than the life span of a kangaroo. How long does a kangaroo usually live?

   Ⓐ 15 + 8 = ■ Ⓑ 15 − 8 = ■

2. **Science** A wolf is one of the largest members of the dog family. The typical weight of a wolf is about 90 pounds. A gray fox typically weighs about 10 pounds. How much more does a wolf weigh than a fox?

   Ⓐ 90 + 10 = ■ Ⓑ 90 − 10 = ■

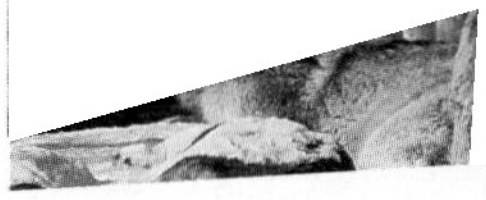

Wolves live in family groups called *packs.*

1. B; 15 − 8 = 7; Life spans of lion and kangaroo are being compared.
2. B; 90 − 10 = 80; Weights of wolf and fox are being compared.

Problem Solving Practice

Problem Solving Strategies
- Use Objects/Act It Out
- Draw a Picture
- Look for a Pattern
- Guess and Check
- Use Logical Reasoning
- Make an Organized List
- Make a Table
- Solve a Simpler Problem
- Work Backward

Choose a Tool

Which number sentence would you use to solve? Explain.

3. **Money** A dog show costs \$6 for adults and \$4 for children. How much will it cost for one of each?

   Ⓐ \$6 + \$4 = ■ Ⓑ \$6 − \$4 = ■
   A; \$6 + \$4 = \$10; Cost of tickets are being put together.

4. **Science** The gray fox is the only member of the dog family that often climbs trees. If a gray fox climbs 8 feet up a tree, and then climbs another 3 feet, how many feet has it climbed in all?

   Ⓐ 8 + 3 = ■ Ⓑ 8 − 3 = ■
   A; 8 + 3 = 11; Height increases.

Write which operation you would use. Then solve.

GPS 5. **Science** Fennecs, the smallest kind of foxes, are about 16 inches long. A red fox is about 25 inches long. What is the difference in length between a fennec and a red fox? **Subtraction; 9 inches**

6. On Saturday, there were 15 dogs at the city animal shelter. If 9 were adopted, how many were left?
   Subtraction; 6 dogs

Sahara Desert
AFRICA
Indian Ocean
South Atlantic Ocean

Fennecs live in the Sahara Desert in Africa.

7. **Journal** Write a problem that you could solve using 17 − 9 = 8.

PROBLEM SOLVING PRACTICE

Skills Practice Bank, page 559, Set 6

Enrichment 1-7

Name ______ **Extend Your Thinking 1-7**

Decision Making

Janice has 6 dogs to feed. Each dog eats 2 pounds of food a week. Which food should she buy?

Dog's Delicacy	Dog Delight	Nature's Best
\$4 for 3 pounds	\$3 for 2 pounds	\$5 for 4 pounds
We add important vitamins your dog needs!	All natural! Your dog will live years longer.	Dogs love our tasty food!!

1. What is the total amount of food the dogs eat per week? 12 pounds
2. Compare costs.
   a. weekly supply of Dog's Delicacy costs \$16.
   b. weekly supply of Dog Delight costs \$18.
   c. weekly supply of Nature's Best costs \$15.
3. Why might Janice buy Dog's Delicacy? Possible answer: Medium priced, added vitamins
4. Why might Janice buy Dog Delight? Possible answer: All natural
5. Why might Janice buy Nature's Best? Possible answer: Lowest priced, tasty
6. Which dog food should she buy? Explain. Look for answers that consider both price and the food's benefits.
7. Which part or parts of each ad is probably opinion? Possible answers: Vitamins your dog needs; dog will live longer; tasty food dogs love

Name ______ **Guided Problem Solving 1-7**

GPS **PROBLEM 5, STUDENT PAGE 23**

Fennecs, the smallest kind of foxes, are about 16 inches long. A red fox is about 25 inches long. What is the difference in length between a fennec and a red fox?

— Understand —
1. What do you know? The length of a fennec and a red fox
2. What is the length of a fennec? 16 in.
3. What is the length of a red fox? 25 in.
4. What are you asked to find? The difference in length between a fennec and a red fox

— Plan —
5. Which operation is used to find the *difference* between two numbers? Subtraction
6. Looking at the two numbers, can you estimate their difference? Yes, about 10 inches

— Solve —
7. Write the number sentence. 25 − 16 = 9
8. What is the difference in length between a fennec and a red fox? 9 inches

— Look Back —
9. How can you check your answer? Add 16 + 9 to see if you get 25.

SOLVE ANOTHER PROBLEM

On Monday morning, there were 12 dogs at the city animal shelter. During the day, 9 more dogs were brought in. How many dogs are at the shelter now? 21 dogs

***Reading Assist* Word Meaning**

Before students begin these problems, review the term *typical life span.* Help them recognize that the life span of any one animal of a species may be longer or shorter than the typical, or average, life span.

Check

Exercise 1 Be sure students read carefully to recognize that the life span of a lion is longer than that of a kangaroo.

Practice

Exercises 3–6 Watch that students read and follow directions carefully.

For Early Finishers Challenge early finishers to write a word problem that they could solve using the option for Exercise 3 or 4 that did not help to solve the exercise.

3 Close and Assess

Invite students to share their strategies and solutions for the Check and Practice problems. Encourage students to share how they chose the operation they used.

Quick Check

1. How can the problem solving guide help you choose an operation? Understanding what you know and what you need to find out helps you plan what operation to use.
2. When do you add to solve a problem? When you are putting things together
3. When do you subtract to solve a problem? When you are comparing, finding differences, taking away, or finding a missing part

ANSWERS

7 Answers should include a problem that can best be solved using subtraction.

Section A
Review and Practice

Use the Skills Checklist

Review the **Skills Checklist** on the page with students. Then ask questions such as the following:

- In which problems will you compare data? Exercises 3, 8
- In which problems will you use ordered pairs? Exercise 5
- What operation will you use in Exercise 8? Possible answer: Subtraction

Assess

You may wish to use this information to assess students' understanding of the lesson objectives.

Item Analysis		
Lesson Objective		Items
1-1	Read pictographs and bar graphs.	1–3, 10
1-2	Read points as ordered pairs on a coordinate grid.	5
1-3	Read line graphs.	4, 5, 10
1-4	Read line plots.	6–8
1-5	Read stem-and-leaf plots.	
1-6	Solve problems by using a guide.	3, 8, 9
1-7	Solve problems by choosing an operation.	9

Resources

Practice Masters
- Practice Chapter 1 Section A

Assessment Sourcebook
- Quiz Chapter 1 Section A

TestWorks: Test and Practice Software

ANSWERS

10 Bar graph for comparing data; Line graph for showing change over time

---

SECTION A
Review and Practice

(Lesson 1) Use the bar graph to answer **1–3**.

1. How many 4th graders were absent? **3**
2. How many grades are shown in the graph? **4**
3. Which grade had the greatest number of absent students? **3rd grade**

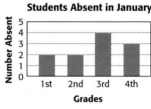
Students Absent in January

(Lessons 2 and 3) Use the line graph to answer **4** and **5**.

4. How many hours did Krista volunteer at the animal shelter in week 3? **2 hr**
5. **Reasoning** What does the ordered pair (5, 4) stand for? **In week 5, Krista volunteered for 4 hours.**

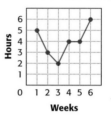
Time Krista Volunteered

(Lesson 4) Use the line plot to answer **6–8**.

Weights of Puppies (lb)

6. How many puppies weighed 16 lb? **3 puppies**
7. What does it mean that there is no **X** above 14? **No puppy weighed 14 lb.**
8. What is the difference in weight between the lightest puppies and the heaviest puppy? **5 lb**

(Lessons 6 and 7) Write which operation you would use. Then solve.

9. If a dog eats 3 cups of dry food a day, how much does it eat in 5 days? **Addition or multiplication; 3 + 3 + 3 + 3 + 3; 15 cups**
10. **Journal** Use the graphs on this page. Which graph helps you compare data? Which graph shows how data change over time? Explain.

REVIEW AND PRACTICE

Practice

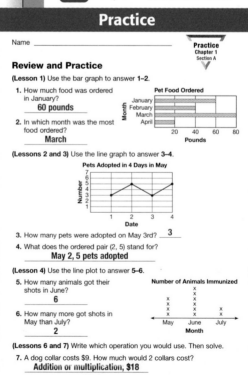

Making Graphs, Describing Data, and Facts Review

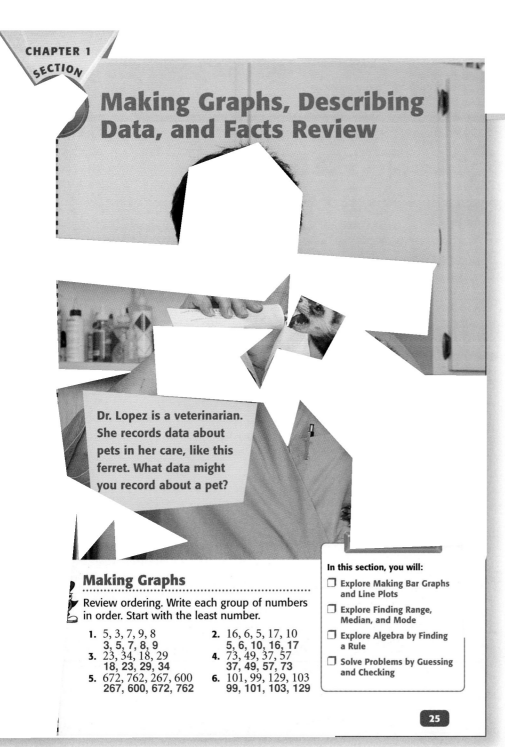

Dr. Lopez is a veterinarian. She records data about pets in her care, like this ferret. What data might you record about a pet?

Making Graphs

Review ordering. Write each group of numbers in order. Start with the least number.

1. 5, 3, 7, 9, 8
   3, 5, 7, 8, 9
2. 16, 6, 5, 17, 10
   5, 6, 10, 16, 17
3. 23, 34, 18, 29
   18, 23, 29, 34
4. 73, 49, 37, 57
   37, 49, 57, 73
5. 672, 762, 267, 600
   267, 600, 672, 762
6. 101, 99, 129, 103
   99, 101, 103, 129

In this section, you will:

☐ Explore Making Bar Graphs and Line Plots

☐ Explore Finding Range, Median, and Mode

☐ Explore Algebra by Finding a Rule

☐ Solve Problems by Guessing and Checking

25

Making Graphs, Describing Data, and Facts Review

In this section students will make bar graphs and line plots, find range, median, and mode, explore algebra by looking for a pattern to find the rule, and solve problems by guessing and checking.

Subskills

The work in this section builds on...

• Reading bar graphs and line plots

Key X = 1 student

```
              X
        X   X   X        3 students
   X        X   X   X    completed
   ―――――――――――――――       9 problems
   6   7   8   9   10
Number of Problems Completed
```

• Ordering numbers from least to greatest
  9, 1, 12, 4, 8 → 1, 4, 8, 9, 12

• Using addition and subtraction facts
  $4 - 2 = 2$ $3 + 5 = 8$

Use the Section Opener

Encourage students to discuss what data they or veterinarians might record about pets. Possible answers: Weight, height, number of vaccinations

Skills Trace

(Red numbers indicate pages in this section.)

Lesson and Skill	First Introduced	Grade Four			
		Introduce	Develop	Practice/Apply	Review
1-8 Make bar graphs.	Grade 2	26, 27	26, 27	27, 40, 41, 44, 559	42
1-9 Make line plots.	Grade 4	28, 29	28, 29	29	42
1-10 Find range, median, and mode.	Grade 4	30, 31	30, 31	31, 44, 328, 329, 559	42, 43, 44, 471
1-11 Explore algebra by looking for a pattern to find the rule.	Grade 2	32, 33	32, 33, 234–237	33, 136, 137, 234–237, 462, 463	42, 102, 143, 208, 241, 339, 287
1-12 Solve problems by using guessing and checking.	Grade 2	36–39	37–39	38, 39, 188, 189, 559	42, 44

Mixed Review: Basic Facts exercises for this chapter occur on pages 11, 13, 15, 17, 19, 39.

🏃 **Multi-Age Classrooms** Use pages 30, 31, 34, 35, 38–42, 120, 121 in Grade 3 or pages 16, 17, 22, 23, 26–29, 156, 157 in Grade 5 to relate to the content of this section.

Exploring Making Bar Graphs

At-A-Glance Planning

Lesson Planning Checklist

Objective Make bar graphs.

Student Book Lesson Materials Teaching Tool Transparency 6 (Centimeter Grid Paper), ruler (1 per group), *optional Reading Strategies for Math* Chart 23 (Making a Bar Graph)

Materials for pages 26A and 26B Color cubes (20 per group), Teaching Tool Transparency 6 (Centimeter Grid Paper), world map

Subject Connection science—teeth

Strand Connection using data

	Before Lesson	During Lesson	After Lesson
Daily Math			
p. 26A Problem of the Day			
p. 26A Math Routines			
p. 26A Mental Math			
Teaching Options			
p. 26B Facilitating and Assessing…			
Options for Reaching All Learners			
p. 26B Inclusion			
p. 26B Gifted & Talented			
Subject Connections			
p. 26A Science Connection			
Assessment Options			
p. 26 Talk About It			
p. 27 Error Intervention			
p. 27 Performance Assessment			
Resources			
1-8 Practice			
1-8 Reteaching			
1-8 Enrichment			
1-8 Problem Solving			
1-8 Daily Transparency			

Problem of the Day

Problem of the Day

Jack has 2 pennies and 6 dimes. Tony has 1 quarter, 1 nickel, and 1 dime. What coins can Jack give to Tony so that they have the same amount of money?

1 dime and 1 penny

Math Routines

Calendar Ask students to find their birthday on a current calendar. Take a survey of the days of the week on which their birthdays fall, tallying the data on the chalkboard. Ask students to name the most and least common day.

Patterns Have students practice skip counting by 2s, 5s, and 10s, beginning at a variety of numbers.

Mental Math

Will the missing number be greater or less than 100? Explain your thinking.

$74 + \blacksquare = 158$ Less

$105 + \blacksquare = 213$ Greater

$417 + \blacksquare = 601$ Greater

$397 + \blacksquare = 552$ Greater

Science Connection

Have students work in groups to look up and graph interesting animal facts, such as how fast certain animals run, how many limbs they have, or how long they incubate before birth. Groups may share complete graphs with the class.

Facilitating and Assessing Explore Lesson 1-8

Use with pages 26 and 27.

Get Started You may wish to assign the roles of graph designer, data reader, and recorder.

Observe Because the scale on the partially completed bar graph on page 26 is on the vertical axis, students should draw vertical bars.

Discuss Point out that each bar ends between the nearest multiples of 5 to the number being plotted.

Assess using the following rubric. See sample for Practice Exercise 1.

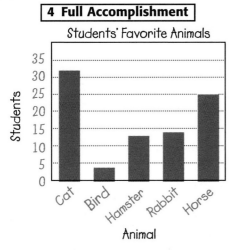

4 Full Accomplishment

Students' Favorite Animals

Assessment Rubric

4 Full Accomplishment
- draws and labels the bar graph and completes the scale
- draws bars to correct height to display data

3 Substantial Accomplishment
- with prompting, draws and labels the bar graph and completes the scale
- with prompting, draws bars to correct height to display data

2 Partial Accomplishment
- draws and labels the bar graph incorrectly and partially completes the scale
- draws some bars to correct height to display data

1 Little Accomplishment
- does not draw and label the bar graph or complete the scale
- does not draw bars to display data

Options for Reaching All Learners

Inclusion

Cube Graphs
Use cubes to make a bar graph.

Materials Color cubes (20 per group), Teaching Tool Transparency 6 (Centimeter Grid Paper)

Learning Style Kinesthetic

- Provide students with a set of data in multiples of 5.

- Have students write a title, label the axes, and complete the scale for a bar graph on a piece of grid paper.

Animals	Number of Students Who Have Pets
Cats	JHT JHT JHT JHT
Dogs	JHT JHT JHT
Fish	JHT JHT JHT
Birds	JHT

- Have students represent the data with color cubes, with each cube representing 5. Have students count by 5s, putting 1 cube in a row on grid paper for each number they say.

Gifted & Talented

Survey Display
Use a bar graph to display collected data.

Materials Teaching Tool Transparency 6 (Centimeter Grid Paper), world map

Learning Style Visual

- Have each group prepare a survey about where clothing is made. Students can check labels in their own clothing and clothing of family members. Groups can then make a tally chart of their survey data.

- Have groups display their results in a bar graph.

- Place the bar graphs on a bulletin board with a world map. You may wish to identify the countries on the graphs with flags or pushpins.

Lesson Organizer

Objective Make bar graphs.

Suggested Grouping 2 to 4

Student Materials Teaching Tool Transparency 6 (Centimeter Grid Paper), ruler (1 per group)

Teacher Materials *Optional Reading Strategies for Math* Chart 23 (Making a Bar Graph)

Assignment Guide

Basic 1–3, 5

Average 1–5

Enriched 1–5

1 Introduce

Review

Between which two multiples of 5 is each number?

1. 23 **20 and 25**   **2.** 39 **35 and 40**

3. 47 **45 and 50**   **4.** 52 **50 and 55**

Build on Prior Knowledge

After students review multiples of 5, ask where the top of the bar representing 27 on a graph with a scale marked in 5s would be. Between 25 and 30, closer to 25 than 30

2 Teach

See Facilitating and Assessing…on page 26B.

Explore • • • • • • • • • • • • • • • • • •

Ask students how they decided how tall to make the bars.

Answers for Work Together

1 Check students' graphs. The scale should be marked in 5s, and the bar for Dog should be tallest, followed by Hyena, Human, and Walrus.

Talk About It **Ongoing Assessment**

Listen for students to compare the data to the numbers written in the scale.

Answers for Talk About It

3 Use the numbers from the chart and the scale along the side of the graph.

4 Make it taller so the scale includes numbers up to 100.

Chapter 1 Lesson 8

Exploring Making Bar Graphs

Problem Solving Connection

■ Make a Table

■ Draw a Picture

Materials

grid paper

On land, a group of walruses is called a *rookery*. In water, it's called a *herd*.

Problem Solving Hint

When you make a number scale for a bar graph, look at the greatest number in the data.

Explore •

You can learn a lot from teeth! The number of teeth can help classify an animal.

Work Together

Make a bar graph to compare the number of teeth for different animals. Use the data in the table.

Animal	Teeth
Dog	42
Human	32
Hyena	34
Walrus	18

1. Copy and complete the bar graph. Use grid paper.

   a. Write a title across the top of your graph.

   b. Write a label on the left side of the graph. Write a label at the bottom for each bar.

   c. Complete the scale. Count by fives.

   d. Draw a bar for each animal. Use the scale to make each bar the correct height. Color the bars.

2. Which animal shown on the graph has the most teeth? **Dog**

Talk About It

3. How did you decide on the height for each bar?

4. Crocodiles have 100 teeth. If you wanted to add crocodiles to your bar graph, how would you change your graph?

26   Chapter 1 • Data, Graphs, and Facts Review

Practice 1-8

Name _____

Practice 1-8

Exploring Making Bar Graphs

Use the bar graph for 1–3.

Dinosaur Heights

Tyrannosaurus rex
Apatosaurus
Stegosaurus
Plesiosaurus

0   5   10   15   20   25   30
Feet

1. What does this bar graph compare? **Dinosaur heights**

2. What scale does the graph use? **5**

3. Is this bar graph vertical or horizontal? **Horizontal**

Make a bar graph to compare weights of prehistoric animals. Use the data in the table.

Weights of Prehistoric Animals				
Tyrannosaurus rex (TR)	Stegosaurus (S)	Hairy Mammoth (HM)	Giant Ground Sloth (GGS)	Plesiosaurus (P)
7 tons	2 tons	7 tons	3 tons	1 ton

4. Use grid paper to make the bar graph. **Check students' graphs.**

   a. Write a title.

   b. Write labels for the bars.

   c. Choose a scale. Count by 1s or 2s.

   d. Draw a bar for each animal. Use the scale to make each bar the correct height. Color the bars.

Title: **Weights of Prehistoric Animals**

Label: Tons 8 6 4 2 0

TR S HM GGS P

Label: **Animal**

5. Which prehistoric animal weighs the least? **Plesiosaurus**

6. Are your bars vertical or horizontal? **Possible answer: Vertical**

Reteaching 1-8

Name _____

Another Look 1-8

Exploring Making Bar Graphs

In your book you learned how to show data using a bar graph. Here is another way to draw the bars to show the data.

To draw a bar that shows the number of students who own Birds look at the scale for Students. You need to draw a bar that goes up to the line for 6.

Draw an arrow to the bar for birds.

Animal	Number of Students Who Own Animals
Bird	6
Cat	9
Dog	10
Pony	2
Gerbil	3

How can you draw a bar to show that 9 students own cats? The scale does not show odd numbers. Since 9 is between 8 and 10, make the top of the bar halfway between 8 and 10.

Title — **Number of Students Who Own Animals**

Students Scale(count by 2s) 10 8 6 4 2 0

Bird Cat Dog Pony Gerbil
Animals

Labels for the Bars

1. Complete the graph above.

   a. Draw the bar for the number of students who own dogs.

   b. Draw the bar for the number of students who own ponies.

   c. Draw the bar for the number of students who own gerbils.

2. Complete the bar graph to show the data in the table below.

Student	Hours Spent on Pet Care Weekly
Anika	9
Corine	14
Martin	16
Priscilla	4

Hours Spent on Pet Care Weekly

Hours 16 12 8 4 0

Anika Corine Martin Priscilla
Students

The bars on a bar graph can be horizontal or vertical.

**Number of Books
We Have Read**

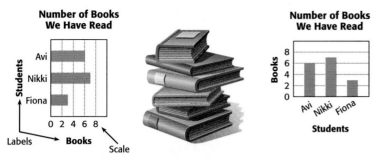

Avi
Nikki
Fiona

Students

0 2 4 6 8

Labels → **Books**
Scale

**Number of Books
We Have Read**

8
6
4
2
0

Books

Avi Nikki Fiona

Students

PRACTICE AND APPLY

Practice

Make a bar graph to compare students' favorite animals. Use the data in the table for 1–4.

1. Copy and complete the bar graph. Use grid paper.
   a. Write a title.
   b. Write labels for the bars.
   c. Complete the scale. Count by fives.
   d. Draw a bar for each animal. Use the scale to make each bar the correct height. Color the bars.

Animal	Student Votes
Cat	32
Bird	4
Hamster	13
Rabbit	14
Horse	25

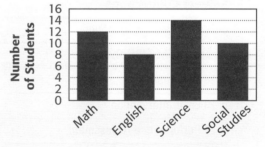

2. Which animal is most popular? **Cat**

3. Are your bars vertical or horizontal? **Vertical**

4. If you wanted to add a different animal to your graph, how many bars would the new graph have? **6**

5. **Journal** If you make a graph with data of 2 lb, 15 lb, 7 lb, and 10 lb, how will you decide what numbers to use for your scale?

Title: _____

Label:
20
15
10
5
0

Cat

Label: _____

Skills Practice Bank, page 559, Set 4   Lesson 1-8   **27**

Connect

Have students compare the two graphs of Number of Books We Have Read.

Error Intervention Ongoing Assessment

Observation Students draw bars with incorrect heights.

How to Help Encourage students to check the heights of their bars by placing a ruler across the top or end of the bar so that it intersects the axis with the scale.

Practice

Exercise 1 You may wish to have students use *Reading Strategies for Math* Chart 23 (Making a Bar Graph).

For Early Finishers Challenge early finishers to write and answer two other questions based on the bar graph of favorite animals.

③ Close and Assess

Performance Assessment

Make a bar graph of favorite subjects. Mark the scale in 2s.

Subject	Number of Students
Math	12
English	8
Science	14
Social Studies	10

Students' Favorite Subjects

16
14
12
10
8
6
4
2
0

Number of Students

Math   English   Science   Social Studies

Assess using the rubric on page 26B.

ANSWERS

1

Students' Favorite Animals

35
30
25
20
15
10
5
0

Students

Cat Bird Hamster Rabbit Horse

Animal

5 Possible answer: Make the scale from 0 to 20, going up by intervals of 5.

Chapter 1 • Lesson 1-8   **27**

Exploring Making Line Plots

At-A-Glance Planning

Objective Make line plots.

Student Book Lesson Materials *Optional* Teaching Tool Transparency 6 (Centimeter Grid Paper), Lesson Enhancement Transparency 1

Materials for pages 28A and 28B Color cubes (at least 20 per group), Teaching Tool Transparency 6 (Centimeter Grid Paper)

Subject Connection science—pelicans, animal speeds

Strand Connection using data

	Before Lesson	During Lesson	After Lesson
Daily Math			
p. 28A Problem of the Day			
p. 28A Math Routines			
p. 28A Mental Math			
Teaching Options			
p. 28B Facilitating and Assessing…			
Options for Reaching All Learners			
p. 28B Inclusion			
p. 28B Reading Assist			
Technology Options			
p. 28 Interactive CD-ROM Lesson 1			
Subject Connections			
p. 28A Literature Connection			
Assessment Options			
p. 28 Talk About It			
p. 29 Error Intervention			
p. 29 Performance Assessment			
Resources			
1-9 Practice			
1-9 Reteaching			
1-9 Enrichment			
1-9 Problem Solving			
1-9 Daily Transparency			

Problem of the Day

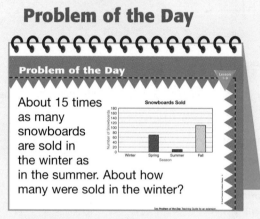

Problem of the Day

About 15 times as many snowboards are sold in the winter as in the summer. About how many were sold in the winter?

About 150 snowboards

Math Routines

Time Have students list the activities they are planning for the coming weekend. Have them label the activities with the times they will occur and then put them in chronological order.

Measurement Ask students which is longer: Foot or mile? mile Meter or centimeter? meter Decimeter or centimeter? decimeter

Mental Math

Will the missing number be greater or less than 100? Explain your thinking.

355 − ■ = 249 Greater

891 − ■ = 745 Greater

673 − ■ = 580 Less

Literature Connection

Any Number Can Play by George Sullivan gives the name and jersey numbers of record setting home-run hitters.

• Have students make a line plot of these numbers: Hank Aaron (44), Babe Ruth (3), Willie Mays (24), Reggie Jackson (44), Mike Schmidt (20), Mickey Mantle (7), Willie McCovey (44).

Facilitating and Assessing **Explore** Lesson 1-9

Use with pages 28 and 29.

Get Started You may wish to assign the roles of plot designer, data reader, and recorder.

Observe Watch that students write one X for each tally mark shown. Students should recognize that, unlike pictographs in which one symbol can represent more than one piece of data, an X in a line plot represents 1.

Discuss Students should recognize that a cluster includes the different data that occurs most often. Any data outside the cluster usually occurs less frequently.

Assess Use the rubric to assess students' work. See sample for Practice Exercise 1.

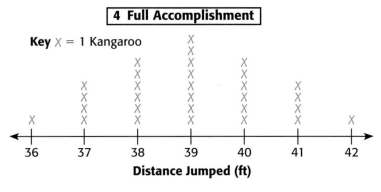

4 Full Accomplishment

Key X = 1 Kangaroo

Distance Jumped (ft)

Assessment Rubric

4 Full Accomplishment
- draws and labels axis of line plot and completes the scale
- correctly draws Xs to display data

3 Substantial Accomplishment
- with prompting, draws and labels axis of line plot and completes the scale
- draws Xs to display data with prompting

2 Partial Accomplishment
- draws and labels axis of line plot incorrectly and partially completes the scale
- draws some Xs to display data

1 Little Accomplishment
- does not draw and label axis of line plot or complete the scale
- does not draw Xs to display data

Options for Reaching All Learners

Inclusion

Color Plots

Use color cubes to facilitate making a line plot.

Materials Color cubes (at least 20 per group), Teaching Tool Transparency 6 (Centimeter Grid Paper)

Learning Style Kinesthetic

- Help students collect data about classmates. They might survey number of siblings, number of pets, or number of clocks in their homes.
- Guide students to make a line plot on grid paper to display their data. Instead of writing Xs, students will place color cubes above the axis.
- For each person surveyed, students should place a color cube above the appropriate label on the axis.
- Ask students questions that can be answered using their plots.

Reading Assist

Read Tables and Graphs

Use partner reading to transfer data to a line plot.

Materials Teaching Tool Transparency 6 (Centimeter Grid Paper)

Learning Style Visual, Verbal/Auditory

- Have students work together to read the tally chart on page 28.
- Have partners ask each other questions such as: Where is the greatest number of tally marks?
- Then have one student draw the line plot by asking the partner: How many pelicans weighed 12 pounds? and then counting aloud "one, two" as he or she writes the two Xs.
- Have the reader check the completed plot by asking his or her partner questions about the data it shows.

Lesson Organizer

Objective Make line plots.

Suggested Grouping 2 to 4

Student Materials *Optional* Teaching Tool Transparency 6 (Centimeter Grid Paper), Lesson Enhancement Transparency 1

Assignment Guide

Basic 1–4, 7

Average 1, 3–5, 7

Enriched 1, 3–7

1 Introduce

Review

Use the line plot to answer the questions.

Key X = 1 Nest

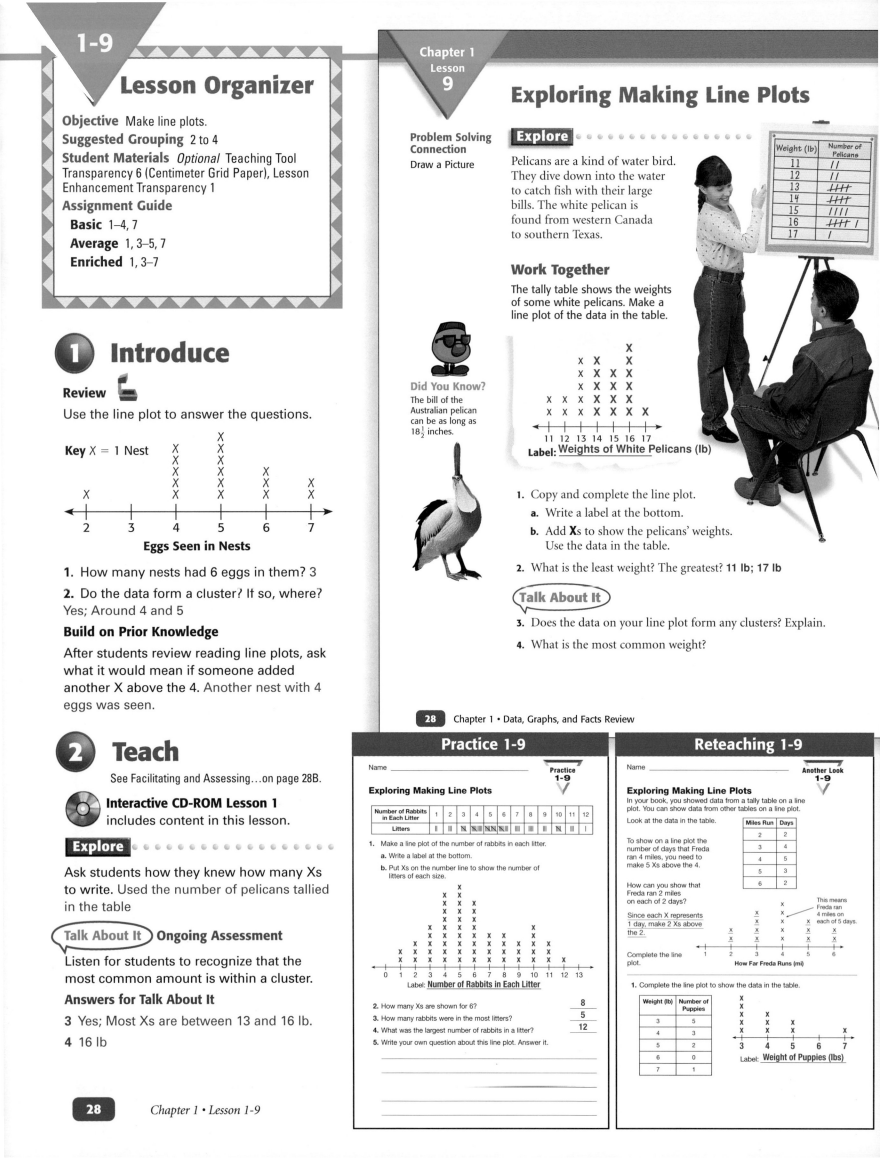

Eggs Seen in Nests

1. How many nests had 6 eggs in them? 3

2. Do the data form a cluster? If so, where? Yes; Around 4 and 5

Build on Prior Knowledge

After students review reading line plots, ask what it would mean if someone added another X above the 4. Another nest with 4 eggs was seen.

2 Teach

See Facilitating and Assessing…on page 28B.

Interactive CD-ROM Lesson 1 includes content in this lesson.

Explore

Ask students how they knew how many Xs to write. Used the number of pelicans tallied in the table

Talk About It) Ongoing Assessment

Listen for students to recognize that the most common amount is within a cluster.

Answers for Talk About It

3 Yes; Most Xs are between 13 and 16 lb.

4 16 lb

28 *Chapter 1 • Lesson 1-9*

Exploring Making Line Plots

Problem Solving Connection

Draw a Picture

Explore

Pelicans are a kind of water bird. They dive down into the water to catch fish with their large bills. The white pelican is found from western Canada to southern Texas.

Weight (lb)	Number of Pelicans
11	//
12	//
13	////
14	////
15	////
16	//////
17	/

Did You Know?
The bill of the Australian pelican can be as long as $18\frac{1}{2}$ inches.

Work Together

The tally table shows the weights of some white pelicans. Make a line plot of the data in the table.

Label: Weights of White Pelicans (lb)

1. Copy and complete the line plot.

   a. Write a label at the bottom.

   b. Add **X**s to show the pelicans' weights. Use the data in the table.

2. What is the least weight? The greatest? **11 lb; 17 lb**

Talk About It

3. Does the data on your line plot form any clusters? Explain.

4. What is the most common weight?

28 Chapter 1 • Data, Graphs, and Facts Review

Practice 1-9

Name _____

Practice 1-9

Exploring Making Line Plots

Number of Rabbits in Each Litter	1	2	3	4	5	6	7	8	9	10	11	12
Litters	||	|||	|||||	|||||||	|||||||	|||||||	||||	||||	|||	|||||	||		

1. Make a line plot of the number of rabbits in each litter.

   a. Write a label at the bottom.

   b. Put Xs on the number line to show the number of litters of each size.

Label: Number of Rabbits in Each Litter

2. How many Xs are shown for 6? ___8___

3. How many rabbits were in the most litters? ___5___

4. What was the largest number of rabbits in a litter? ___12___

5. Write your own question about this line plot. Answer it.

Reteaching 1-9

Name _____

Another Look 1-9

Exploring Making Line Plots

In your book, you showed data from a tally table on a line plot. You can show data from other tables on a line plot.

Look at the data in the table.

Miles Run	Days
2	2
3	4
4	5
5	3
6	2

To show on a line plot the number of days that Freda ran 4 miles, you need to make 5 Xs above the 4.

How can you show that Freda ran 2 miles on each of 2 days?

Since each X represents 1 day, make 2 Xs above the 2.

Complete the line plot.

How Far Freda Runs (mi)

This means Freda ran 4 miles on each of 5 days.

1. Complete the line plot to show the data in the table.

Weight (lb)	Number of Puppies
3	5
4	3
5	2
6	0
7	1

Label: Weight of Puppies (lbs)

Connect

Common running speeds for many animals are between 30 and 35 miles per hour.

The data from this table of animal speeds was used to make the line plot.

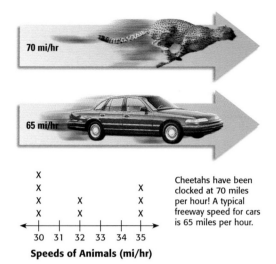

70 mi/hr

65 mi/hr

Animal	Speed (mi/hr)
Cat	30
Grizzly bear	30
Warthog	30
Deer	30
Giraffe	32
Reindeer	32
Jackal	35
Mule deer	35
Rabbit	35

```
X
X                    X
X        X           X
X        X           X
+--+--+--+--+--+--+
30 31 32 33 34 35
```

Cheetahs have been clocked at 70 miles per hour! A typical freeway speed for cars is 65 miles per hour.

Speeds of Animals (mi/hr)

Practice

Using Data Use the Data File on page 7.

1. Copy and complete the line plot of distances jumped.
   a. Write a label at the bottom.
   b. Put **X**s on the number line to show how many kangaroos jumped each distance.

2. How many **X**s are shown for 37? **4 Xs**

3. How many feet did most kangaroos jump? **39 ft**

4. How far did the winning kangaroo jump? **42 ft**

5. How much longer is the longest jump than the shortest jump? **6 ft**

6. **What If** Another kangaroo jumped 43 feet. How would you change the line plot to show this? **Add 43 to the number scale and put an X above it.**

7. **Journal** How do you know which numbers to use on your number line?

```
                    X
                    X
            X  X  X
            X  X  X
         X  X  X  X  X
         X  X  X  X  X
         X  X  X  X  X
      X  X  X  X  X  X  X
      +--+--+--+--+--+--+
      36 37 38 39 40 41 42
```
Distances Jumped
Label: by Kangaroos (ft)

Lesson 1-9 **29**

Connect

Be sure students understand why the scale in the line plot includes all whole numbers 30–35, although only 30, 32, and 35 appear in the table. Students also should recognize that the data do not form a cluster.

Error Intervention Ongoing Assessment

Observation Students write an incorrect number of Xs on a line plot.

How to Help Encourage students to count the Xs for each number in the scale and compare it to the number of tallies.

Practice

Exercise 1–6 Lesson Enhancement Transparency 1 reproduces the Data File.

For Early Finishers Challenge early finishers to write and answer two more questions based on the data on kangaroo jumps.

3 Close and Assess

Performance Assessment

Use this data to make a line plot. Write statements about the data.

Daily Low Temperatures	
Temperature (°F)	Number of Days
5°	II
6°	I
7°	IIII
8°	HHT I
9°	HHT III
10°	HHT HHT

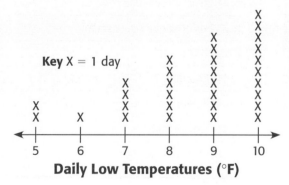

Key X = 1 day

```
                                    X
                           X        X
                           X        X
                           X        X
                    X      X        X
            X       X      X        X
   X        X       X      X        X
   X    X   X       X      X        X
   +----+---+-------+------+--------+
   5    6   7       8      9        10
```
Daily Low Temperatures (°F)

Possible answer: It was 10°F on most days

Assess using the rubric on page 28B.

ANSWERS

7 Use the least and greatest numbers for the data and the numbers in between.

Chapter 1 • Lesson 1-9 **29**

Exploring Range, Median, and Mode

At-A-Glance Planning

Lesson Planning Checklist

Objective Find range, median, and mode.
Vocabulary mode, median, range
Student Book Lesson Materials Scissors, crayons, *optional Assessment Sourcebook 10* (How We Worked in Our Group)
Materials for pages 30A and 30B Similar items of different sizes such as books of different weights and pencils of different lengths, counters (101 per group)
Subject Connections careers—veterinarian, science—animal weights
Strand Connection using data

	Before Lesson	During Lesson	After Lesson
Daily Math			
p. 30A Problem of the Day			
p. 30A Math Routines			
p. 30A Mental Math			
Teaching Options			
p. 30B Facilitating and Assessing…			
Options for Reaching All Learners			
p. 30B Language Development			
p. 30B Inclusion			
Subject Connections			
p. 30A Geography Connection			
Assessment Options			
p. 30 Talk About It			
p. 31 Error Intervention			
p. 31 Performance Assessment			
Resources			
1-10 Practice			
1-10 Reteaching			
1-10 Enrichment			
1-10 Problem Solving			
1-10 Daily Transparency			

Problem of the Day

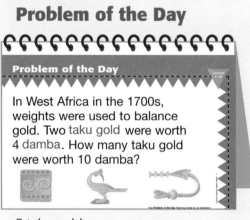

Problem of the Day

In West Africa in the 1700s, weights were used to balance gold. Two taku gold were worth 4 damba. How many taku gold were worth 10 damba?

5 taku gold

Math Routines

Time Ask students to estimate the number of minutes it takes them to get to school. List the data. Ask: How many minutes did most students list?

Calendar Have students write the number of months until their birthday. Ask what is the greatest number anyone could have written, and what is the least number.

Mental Math

Is the missing number greater or less than 400? Explain your thinking.

■ – 236 = 105 Less
■ – 242 = 271 Greater
■ – 190 = 300 Greater
■ – 270 = 122 Less

Geography Connection

Provide students with the top seven winning countries in the 1994 Winter Olympics: Norway (26), Germany (24), Russia (23), Italy (20), United States (13), Canada (13), Austria (10).

• Have students find the range, mode, and median of the number of medals.
  range: 16; mode:13; median: 20

Facilitating and Assessing Explore Lesson 1-10

Use with pages 30 and 31.

Get Started Have students work on group skills of Listen to Others and Disagree in an Agreeable Way. Have students fold sheets of paper into fourths to make 4 cards from each sheet and make cards for the cat weights. Then have students arrange the cards in order.

Observe Observe whether any students are having difficulty putting the data in order. Ask these students to begin by finding the smallest number.

Discuss Direct the focus of the discussion to the idea that arranging numbers in order allows you to compare them and find patterns. Use the material in Connect to define *mode*, *median*, and *range*.

Assess Use the rubric to assess students' work. See sample for Practice Exercise 1.

4 Full Accomplishment

345, 388, 440, 457, 471, 550, 556

1. 556
   − 345
   ─────
    211   The range is 211 pounds.

2. 457 is in the middle, so 457 pounds is the median weight.

3. Each weight occurs once, so there is no mode.

Assessment Rubric

4 Full Accomplishment
- clearly defines *range*, *median*, and *mode*
- finds the range, median, and mode of data

3 Substantial Accomplishment
- with prompting, defines *range*, *median*, and *mode*
- with prompting, finds the range, median, and mode of data

2 Partial Accomplishment
- incompletely defines *range*, *median*, and *mode*
- struggles to find the range, median, and mode of data

1 Little Accomplishment
- does not define *range*, *median*, and *mode*
- does not find the range, median, and mode of data

Options for Reaching All Learners

Language Development

Orderly Words

Use common items to strengthen understanding of the terms least, greatest, *and* in order.

Materials Similar items of different sizes such as books of different weights and pencils of different lengths

Learning Style Kinesthetic, Visual

- Show students books of different weights arranged from lightest to heaviest. Have students handle each in order of increasing weight. Then show students an assortment of pencils arranged in order from shortest to longest.

- Have students discuss what is the same about these arrangements. Introduce or review the terms *least*, *greatest*, and *in order*.

- Challenge students to find other examples and use them to show objects in order from least to greatest.

Inclusion

Weighty Stacks

Use manipulatives to help complete the activity on page 30.

Materials Counters (101 per group)

Learning Style Kinesthetic, Visual

- Have groups build a stack of counters to represent each weight shown on page 30.

- Have group members arrange the stacks in order from shortest to tallest.

- For Items 3 and 4, have students place the shortest and tallest stacks side by side to find the difference in heights.

- For Item 5, have students identify the stack height that occurs most often.

- For Item 6, have students identify the stack in the middle of the arrangement.

Lesson Organizer

Objective Find range, median, and mode.

Suggested Grouping 2 to 4

Student Materials Scissors, crayons (1 pair/set per group), *Optional Assessment Sourcebook 10* (How We Worked in Our Group)

Vocabulary mode, median, range

Assignment Guide

Basic 1–3, 6–9, 11

Average 1–3, 5–9, 11

Enriched 4–11

1 Introduce

Review

Write each set of numbers in order from least to greatest.

1. 9, 5, 7 5, 7, 9

2. 24, 56, 31 24, 31, 56

3. 128, 115, 207 115, 128, 207

Build on Prior Knowledge

After students review ordering numbers, ask them to find the difference between the greatest and least numbers in the first set of numbers. 9 − 5 = 4

2 Teach

See Facilitating and Assessing…on page 30B.

Explore • • • • • • • • • • • • • • • • • • •

Ask students how they know which weights occur most often and how they find the middle weight.

Answers for Work Together

2 6 lb: Rainbow; 7 lb: Sox, Sunny; 9 lb: Dusty, Hector, Midnight; 10 lb: Tiger, Caesar, Bigfoot; 11 lb: Elmer; 13 lb: Muffin

Talk About It **Ongoing Assessment**

Listen for students to recognize that by putting the numbers in order, they will be less likely to overlook a piece of data.

Answer for Talk About It

Possible answers: 3, 4, 5, 6; It helps to see the numbers in order to find the least and greatest; The order helps show the middle number.

Exploring Range, Median, and Mode

Problem Solving Connection

Use Objects/ Act It Out

Materials

- paper
- scissors
- crayons

Vocabulary

mode
the number that occurs most often in the data

median
the middle number when the data are put in order

range
the difference between the greatest and least numbers in the data

Did You Know?

The largest domestic cat on record weighed nearly 47 pounds and was 38 inches long.

Explore • • • • • • • • • •

About one in three homes in the United States has a cat. Veterinarians like Dr. Maria Lopez keep a record of animals' weights. What do you think is the typical weight for a cat?

Work Together

Suppose these are the weights of 11 cats that Dr. Lopez saw. Organize the data to compare the cats' weights.

Dr. Maria Lopez cares for animals in Miami, Florida.

1. Make a card for each of the cats.

   a. Cut out 11 cards.

   b. Write the name and weight of a cat on each.

2. Arrange them in order. Start with the least weight.

3. What is the least weight? The greatest weight? **6 lb; 13 lb**

4. What is the difference between the greatest and least weights? **7 lb**

5. What weight or weights occur most often? **9 lb, 10 lb**

6. When the weights are in order from least to greatest, what weight is in the middle? **9 lb**

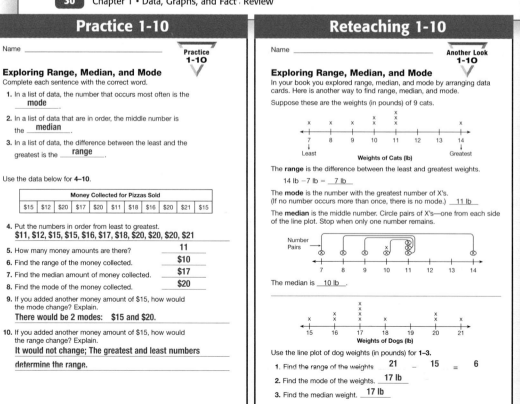

Dusty 9 lb
Rainbow 6 lb
Tiger 10 lb
Muffin 13 lb
Hector 9 lb
Sox 7 lb
Sunny 7 lb
Caesar 10 lb
Midnight 9 lb
Elmer 11 lb
Bigfoot 10 lb

Talk About It

Which questions would be difficult to answer if you had not put the cards in order? Why?

Practice 1-10

Name _____

Practice 1-10

Exploring Range, Median, and Mode

Complete each sentence with the correct word.

1. In a list of data, the number that occurs most often is the **mode**.

2. In a list of data that are in order, the middle number is the **median**.

3. In a list of data, the difference between the least and the greatest is the **range**.

Use the data below for **4–10**.

Money Collected for Pizzas Sold										
$15	$12	$20	$17	$20	$11	$18	$16	$20	$21	$15

4. Put the numbers in order from least to greatest.
   $11, $12, $15, $15, $16, $17, $18, $20, $20, $20, $21

5. How many money amounts are there? **11**

6. Find the range of the money collected. **$10**

7. Find the median amount of money collected. **$17**

8. Find the mode of the money collected. **$20**

9. If you added another money amount of $15, how would the mode change? Explain.
   There would be 2 modes: $15 and $20.

10. If you added another money amount of $15, how would the range change? Explain.
    It would not change; The greatest and least numbers determine the range.

Reteaching 1-10

Name _____

Another Look 1-10

Exploring Range, Median, and Mode

In your book you explored range, median, and mode by arranging data cards. Here is another way to find range, median, and mode.

Suppose these are the weights (in pounds) of 9 cats.

| 7 | 8 | 9 | 10 | 11 | 12 | 13 | 14 |
Least   Greatest
Weights of Cats (lb)

The **range** is the difference between the least and greatest weights.

14 lb − 7 lb = **7 lb**

The **mode** is the number with the greatest number of X's. (If no number occurs more than once, there is no mode.) **11 lb**

The **median** is the middle number. Circle pairs of X's—one from each side of the line plot. Stop when only one number remains.

| 7 | 8 | 9 | 10 | 11 | 12 | 13 | 14 |

The median is **10 lb**.

| 15 | 16 | 17 | 18 | 19 | 20 | 21 |
Weights of Dogs (lb)

Use the line plot of dog weights (in pounds) for **1–3**.

1. Find the range of the weights. **21** − **15** = **6**

2. Find the mode of the weights. **17 lb**

3. Find the median weight. **17 lb**

Connect

Suppose these are the weights of 15 cats in Dr. Lopez's records.

5, 6, 6, 6, 6, 7, 9, ⑨, 9, 11, 11, 12, 13, 14, 15   15 − 5 = 10

Math Tip
If no number in the data occurs more than once, there is no mode.

Mode	**Median**	**Range**
The number that occurs most often	The middle number when the data are in order	The greatest value minus the least value

Practice

Use the data of tortoise weights for **1–4**.

550 lb
457 lb
388 lb
440 lb
345 lb
471 lb
556 lb

1. Find the range of weights. **211 lb**

2. Find the median weight. **457 lb**

3. Find the mode of the weights. **There is none.**

4. **What If** A tortoise that weighs 550 lb joins the group. Now what is the range? What is the mode?
Range: 211 lb; Mode: 550 lb

5. **Using Data** Use the data from the *Did You Know?* on page 30. Include this in the data from page 30 on the 11 cats that Dr. Lopez saw. What is the range of weights? **41 lb**

Use the line plot of greyhound weights for **6–9**.

```
                    X
                X   X           X
 X          X   X   X   X       X
 X      X   X   X   X   X   X   X
 +---+---+---+---+---+---+---+---+---+---+---+
 60  61  62  63  64  65  66  67  68  69  70
```
Adult Greyhound Weights (lb)

6. How many greyhounds are shown on the line plot? **18 greyhounds**

7. What is the mode of the greyhound weights? **66 lb**

8. What is the range of weights? **9 lb**

9. What is the median weight? **65 lb**

10. **Critical Thinking** Why do you think pet owners might want to know the normal range of weights of cats?

11. **Journal** Define *range*, *median*, and *mode* in your own words.

Skills Practice Bank, page 559, Set 5   Lesson 1-10   31

Connect

Guide students to connect these terms to the weights they found on page 30.

Error Intervention Ongoing Assessment

Observation Some students may confuse the terms *mode* and *median*.

How to Help Some students find it helpful to think of **Most Often** for **mode**. A sketch of the location of the median of a highway can help some students recall that the median is the piece of data in the middle.

Practice

Exercises 1, 4 Allow students to use calculators to find the range. Ask them which operation they would use. Subtraction

Exercises 6–9 Have students talk about whether it is easier to find the range, median, and mode if data is given in a table or given in a line plot.

For Early Finishers Challenge early finishers to find the range, median, and mode of the data for Exercises 6–9 if data on three more greyhounds, each weighing 71 pounds, were added. 11; 66; 66

③ Close and Assess

Performance Assessment

During one afternoon, a veterinarian saw dogs with these weights in pounds:

32, 25, 7, 52, 78, 10, 40, 25, 15.

Find the range and mode of the weights and the median weight. 71 pounds; 25 pounds; 25 pounds

Assess using the rubric on page 30B.

ANSWERS

10 Possible answer: Comparing an individual cat's weight with the range helps an owner know if the cat is getting enough or too much food.

11 Answers should include: Mode is the number that occurs the most; range is the difference between the least and greatest; median is the middle number when the data are put in order.

Enrichment 1-10	**Problem Solving 1-10**

Exploring Algebra: What's the Rule?

At-A-Glance Planning

Lesson Planning Checklist

Objective Explore algebra by looking for a pattern to find the rule.

Vocabulary variable

Student Book Lesson Materials Index cards or strips of paper (5 per pair), envelopes (2 per pair)

Materials for pages 32A and 32B None

Subject Connection economics—earnings and savings

Strand Connections money, algebra

	Before Lesson	During Lesson	After Lesson
Daily Math			
p. 32A Problem of the Day			
p. 32A Math Routines			
p. 32A Mental Math			
Teaching Options			
p. 32B Facilitating and Assessing…			
Options for Reaching all Learners			
p. 32B Inclusion			
p. 32B Language Development			
Technology Options			
p. 32A *Logical Journey of the Zoombinis*			
Assessment Options			
p. 32 Talk About It			
p. 33 Error Intervention			
p. 33 Performance Assessment			
Resources			
1-11 Practice			
1-11 Reteaching			
1-11 Enrichment			
1-11 Problem Solving			
1-11 Daily Transparency			

Problem of the Day

Problem of the Day   Lesson 1-11

How many apples were purchased in Week 5 so that the median number of apples is 3?

Week	1	2	3	4	5
Apples	4	6	1	3	?

See Problem of the Day Teaching Guide for an extension

0, 1, 2, or 3 apples

Math Routines

Money Tell students a story: I took $1.75 with me from home. After I bought a snack, I had $1.25. How much did I spend? $0.50 Continue with other stories.

Calendar Tell students that you always make up a test the same number of days in advance. If you are giving a test on the 17th, you make it up on the 12th. If you are giving a test on the 29th, you make it up on the 24th. Ask them to tell the rule. Test is made up 5 days in advance.

Mental Math

Find each sum. Explain your thinking.

1,270 + 20 1,290   963 + 30 993

1,413 + 80 1,493   427 + 60 487

Logical Journey of the Zoombinis

Have students play any of the three games on *The Big, the Bad, and the Hungry Trail*. To play *Allergic Cliffs, Cave Guards*, and *Pizza Trolls*, students must guess the rule as they use deduction to find a hidden requirement.

Facilitating and Assessing Explore Lesson 1-11

Use with pages 32 and 33.

Get Started Before starting play, have students draw several gameboards, or tables with **In** and **Out** rows. You may wish to provide the gameboards for some students.

Observe As students play "Guess My Rule," watch for students who forget their original rule. Encourage them to write it down but keep it out of sight of their partners.

Also listen for students who wildly guess rules. Help them to focus first on the operation and then on the number to be added or subtracted. Some students may find it helpful to write operation signs and numbers in their tables.

In	4	5	6	7
Rule	−2	−2	−2	−2
Out	2	3	4	

Discuss As students discuss how they discovered each rule, guide them to recognize that they can use number sense to determine the operation. The **Out** number will be greater than the **In** number if addition is used. It will be less if subtraction is used.

Be sure that students check rules for more than one pair of numbers.

Assess Use the rubric to assess students' work. See sample for Practice Exercise 2.

4 Full Accomplishment

In	9	10	11	12	13
Out	5	6	7	8	9

$9 - 4 = 5$ $10 - 4 = 6$

Subtract 4.

Assessment Rubric

4 Full Accomplishment
- writes rules to identify and extend patterns

3 Substantial Accomplishment
- with prompting, writes rules to identify and extend patterns

2 Partial Accomplishment
- extends patterns without writing rules

1 Little Accomplishment
- does not write rules to identify or extend patterns

Options for Reaching All Learners

Inclusion

Group Rules
Use groups of students to demonstrate finding a rule.

Learning Style Visual

- Draw a blank In/Out table on the chalkboard.
- Have 3 students stand in a group while you (or a volunteer) record 3 in the **In** row of the table. Have 2 more join the group while you record the total 5 in the **Out** row.
- Repeat for original groups of 2, 5, and 4.
- Have students identify what happened with the group each time and lead them to record 2 more students joining the group as add 2, or $n + 2$.
- Repeat for other addition and subtraction rules.

Language Development

Story Rules
Use storytelling to identify situations that can be described by a rule.

Learning Style Verbal

- Group two students acquiring English together.
- Have each pair discuss and choose one of the rules they wrote for "Guess My Rule."
- Have partners write one or more stories based on the rules. For example, a possible story line for the rule add 3: Start with an empty aquarium, buy 3 fish, and end up with 3 fish in the aquarium.
- Students may make up stories with different numbers for the same rule.
- Have pairs take turns telling their stories to the class. Have the class guess the rule being told.

Lesson Organizer

Objective Explore algebra by looking for a pattern to find the rule.

Suggested Grouping Pairs

Student Materials Index cards or strips of paper (5 per pair), envelopes (2 per pair)

Vocabulary variable

Assignment Guide
Basic 1–4, 6
Average 2–5, 6
Enriched 4–6

---

1 Introduce

Review

Find each missing number.

1. $5 - \blacksquare = 1$ 4

2. $8 + \blacksquare = 10$ 2

3. $12 - \blacksquare = 5$ 7

4. $9 + \blacksquare = 13$ 4

Build on Prior Knowledge

After students review how to find missing numbers, ask how they would figure out an operation sign that was also missing.

Possible answer: Compare the first number to the answer; if the answer is less, the operation is subtraction. If it is greater, the operation is addition.

---

2 Teach

See Facilitating and Assessing…on page 32B.

Explore

You may wish to give students copies of *Reading Strategies for Math* Chart 29 (Number Machine) to use for their In/Out tables.

Talk About It Ongoing Assessment

Listen for students to focus on checking to make sure that the rule that works for one pair of numbers works for all pairs of numbers.

Answer for Talk About It

Possible answer: Thought about what was done to first number to get the second; checked to see if this worked for other number pairs

---

Exploring Algebra: What's the Rule?

Problem Solving Connection
- Look for a Pattern
- Make a Table

Materials
- index cards
- 2 envelopes

Explore

A rule describes what to do to the **In** number to get the **Out** number. The rule for this table is to *subtract 2*.

In	4	5	6	7
Out	2	3	4	5

Work Together

1. Play "Guess My Rule."

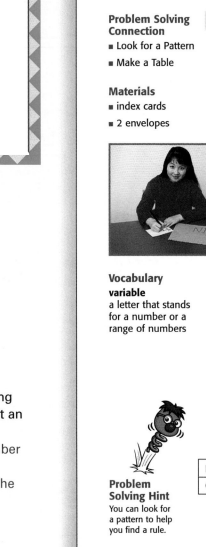

Vocabulary
variable
a letter that stands for a number or a range of numbers

a. Write a number on an index card. Draw an arrow next to it. Put it in an envelope labeled **In**. Send it to a partner.

b. Your partner thinks of a rule, uses it with your number, writes the answer on the same card, and sends it to you in an envelope labeled **Out**.

c. Start a table of your number pairs. Continue to send the cards back and forth. Your partner uses the same rule for each of your numbers. Write the number pairs in your table.

d. Continue to play until you find the rule.

e. Play again. Your partner picks a number and guesses your rule.

2. Complete these tables. Give the rules for each.

In	2	3	4	5	6	7
Out	5	6	7	8	9	10

Add 3

In	19	16	12	10	8
Out	12	9	5	3	1

Subtract 7

Problem Solving Hint
You can look for a pattern to help you find a rule.

Talk About It

How did you find each rule?

Practice 1-11

Name _____

Exploring Algebra: What's the Rule?

Complete each table. Write the rule for each table with words and with a variable.

1. Rule in words: **Add 4.**   Rule with a variable: $n + 4$

In	2	3	9	4	8	7
Out	6	7	13	8	12	11

2. Rule in words: **Subtract 2.**   Rule with a variable: $n - 2$

In	8	9	11	10	13	15
Out	6	7	9	8	11	13

3. Rule in words: **Subtract 7.**   Rule with a variable: $n - 7$

In	11	14	10	18	12	15
Out	4	7	3	11	5	8

4. Rule in words: **Add 5.**   Rule with a variable: $n + 5$

In	0	4	8	3	2	7
Out	5	9	13	8	7	12

5. Rule in words: **Add 8.**   Rule with a variable: $n + 8$

In	1	6	3	4	5	10
Out	9	14	11	12	13	18

6. Rule in words: **Subtract 6.**   Rule with a variable: $n - 6$

In	13	10	7	12	8	15
Out	7	4	1	6	2	9

Reteaching 1-11

Name _____

Exploring Algebra: What's the Rule?

In your book you explored finding a rule for number pairs by playing "Guess My Rule." Here is another way to find the rule for number pairs.

In	3	5	8	4
Out	7	9	12	

Step 1 Look at the first pair of numbers, 3 and 7. Think: What can you do to 3 to get 7? You can add 4 to 3 to get 7.

Step 2 Check your rule with the next pairs of numbers. Since $5 + 4 = 9$ and $8 + 4 = 12$, the rule checks.

Step 3 Write your rule in words. Write the operation and the number.

   add 4

Write your rule with a variable. Use a letter in the place of the In number, then follow with the operation sign and the number.

   $n + 4$

Step 4 Use your rule to complete the table. $4 + 4 = 8$

Answer the questions, then complete the table.

In	8	10	11	6	9	14
Out	5	7	8	3	6	11

1. What can you do to 8 to get 5?   **Subtract 3.**

2. What can you do to 10 to get 7?   **Subtract 3.**

3. Write the rule in words.   **Subtract 3.**

4. Write the rule using a variable. $n - 3$

5. Use the rule to complete the table.

Connect

You can use a **variable** to stand for a number or a range of numbers.

In	Earnings in Dollars	n	6	9	10	13
Out	Savings in Dollars	$n-5$	1	4	5	

If $6 was earned, how much was saved?

$n-5$
$\downarrow$
$6-5=1$ $1 was saved.

If $13 was earned, how much was saved?

$n-5$
$\downarrow$
$13-5=8$ $8 was saved.

Practice

Copy and complete each table. Use the rule.

1.

In	n	9	4	8	5	7
Out	$n+3$	12	7	11	8	10

2.

In	n	9	10	11	12	13
Out	$n-4$	5	6	7	8	9

Copy and complete each table. Write the rule.

3.

In	n	4	5	6	7	8
Out		9	10	11	12	13

Add 5 or $n+5$.

4.

In	n	1	3	7	9	11
Out			7	9	13	15	17

Add 6 or $n+6$.

5. Danielle feeds the goldfish when her neighbors are away. Each time she is paid, she spends only $2 and saves the rest. Complete the table to show her savings.

In	Earnings	n	4	6	13	7
Out	Savings	$n-2$	2	4	11	5

6. Journal Is it important to test a rule on all numbers in the table? Explain.

Lesson 1-11   **33**

Connect

Elicit that *n* is called a variable because the number it stands for varies. Then have students use a variable to write the rules they found in Item 2 on page 32.

Error Intervention Ongoing Assessment

Observation Students write and apply an incorrect rule.

How to Help Guide students to understand the need to check if a rule works for all pairs. Have students look at the first pair of numbers in the table at the top of page 32. The rule could also be multiply by 2. A check shows that this doesn't work for the other number pairs.

Practice

Exercise 1 Students should recognize that the **In** numbers are not in numerical order.

For Early Finishers Challenge early finishers to make tables like those in Practice, then trade, try to find each other's rule, and complete the tables.

③ Close and Assess

Performance Assessment

Copy and complete the table. Write the rule.

In	2	5	6	7	10
Out	6	9	10	11	14

Add 4 or $n + 4$

Assess using the rubric on page 32B.

Resources

Technology Master 2

ANSWER

6 Possible answer: Yes; A rule that works for one pair of numbers may not work for others.

Enrichment 1-11

Name _____ Extend Your Thinking 1-11

Patterns in Numbers
Tell what rule was used to make the pattern. What are the next three numbers?

1. 5; 50; 500; ___5,000___ ; ___50,000___ ; ___500,000___
Rule: **Increase the value by powers of 10.**

2. 12, 24, 36, ___48___ , ___60___ , ___72___
Rule: **Add 12.**

3. 120, 240, 360, 480, ___600___ , ___720___ , ___840___
Rule: **Add 120.**

4. 401; 801; 1,201; ___1,601___ ; ___2,001___ ; ___2,401___
Rule: **Add 400.**

5. 1,100; 950; 800; ___650___ ; ___500___ ; ___350___
Rule: **Subtract 150.**

6. 45, 90, 135, ___180___ , ___225___ , ___270___
Rule: **Add 45.**

7. 100,000; 10,000; 1,000; ___100___ ; ___10___ ; ___1___
Rule: **Decrease the value by powers of 10.**

Write three addition or subtraction patterns of your own. Give your rule.

8. _____
Rule: _____

9. _____
Rule: _____

10. _____
Rule: _____

Problem Solving 1-11

Name _____ Problem Solving 1-11

Exploring Algebra: What's the Rule?
A rule can use addition or subtraction. It can also use multiplication or division.

In	4	1	6	7	2
Out	12	3	18	21	6

1. a. Write the table's rule in words.   **Multiply by 3.**

b. Write the table's rule with a variable. $n \times 3$

c. Complete the table.

d. Describe how you discovered the rule.
Possible answer: Looked at what was done to the first number to get the second and checked to see if this worked for all pairs of numbers.

In	8	10	14	6	18	20
Out	4	5	7	3	9	10

2. a. Write a rule for the first pair of numbers that doesn't work for the second pair.   **Subtract 4.**

b. Write a rule with a variable that works for all pairs of numbers. $n \div 2$

c. Complete the table.

3. Make your own table. Your rule can use addition, subtraction, multiplication, or division. Leave some spaces blank. Give your table to a classmate to complete. **Check students' tables. Look for a consistent rule.**

In					
Out					

Rule: **Rule should match table.**

Chapter 1 • Lesson 1-11   **33**

Chapter 1
Stop and Practice

Students will practice skills taught in Lessons 1 through 11.

Find Each Sum or Difference

Some students may have more success if they do all the addition exercises first. Then they can go back and complete the subtraction exercises.

Error Search

ANSWERS

61 14; Subtracted instead of added, or failed to write 1 in the tens place

62 Correct

63 15; Incorrect fact

64 5; Added instead of subtracted

65 6; Multiplied instead of added

 **and Practice**

Find each sum or difference.

1. 3 $+6$ $\overline{9}$	**2.** 5 $+2$ $\overline{7}$	**3.** 8 -2 $\overline{6}$	**4.** 9 -3 $\overline{6}$	**5.** 16 -7 $\overline{9}$
6. 12 -5 $\overline{7}$	**7.** 11 -6 $\overline{5}$	**8.** 7 $+7$ $\overline{14}$	**9.** 3 $+4$ $\overline{7}$	**10.** 18 -9 $\overline{9}$
11. 8 -5 $\overline{3}$	**12.** 17 -9 $\overline{8}$	**13.** 9 $+4$ $\overline{13}$	**14.** 2 $+7$ $\overline{9}$	**15.** 15 -8 $\overline{7}$
16. 9 $+9$ $\overline{18}$	**17.** 6 $+2$ $\overline{8}$	**18.** 14 -6 $\overline{8}$	**19.** 7 $+8$ $\overline{15}$	**20.** 9 -7 $\overline{2}$
21. 7 $+6$ $\overline{13}$	**22.** 15 -6 $\overline{9}$	**23.** 5 $+4$ $\overline{9}$	**24.** 10 -3 $\overline{7}$	**25.** 6 -5 $\overline{1}$
26. 5 $+7$ $\overline{12}$	**27.** 8 $+3$ $\overline{11}$	**28.** 6 $+6$ $\overline{12}$	**29.** 14 -8 $\overline{6}$	**30.** 6 $+4$ $\overline{10}$

31. $12-7\ 5$ **32.** $8-5\ 3$ **33.** $6+2\ 8$ **34.** $5-3\ 2$ **35.** $16-8\ 8$

36. $9-5\ 4$ **37.** $11-8\ 3$ **38.** $6+6\ 12$ **39.** $1+5\ 6$ **40.** $13-8\ 5$

41. $5+4\ 9$ **42.** $17-8\ 9$ **43.** $2+4\ 6$ **44.** $7+5\ 12$ **45.** $15-6\ 9$

46. $5+5\ 10$ **47.** $8+8\ 16$ **48.** $13-6\ 7$ **49.** $8+5\ 13$ **50.** $6+8\ 14$

51. $3+8\ 11$ **52.** $10-6\ 4$ **53.** $14-9\ 5$ **54.** $6+6\ 12$ **55.** $7-7\ 0$

56. $14-6\ 8$ **57.** $7+9\ 16$ **58.** $6+5\ 11$ **59.** $8-3\ 5$ **60.** $3+9\ 12$

 Error Search

Find each sum or difference that is not correct. Write it correctly and explain the error.

61. $9+5=4$ **62.** $16-7=9$ **63.** $7+8=13$ **64.** $11-6=17$ **65.** $3+3=9$

Neck and Neck!

Add or subtract to solve the riddle. Match each letter to its answer in the blank below to find out which animal has the same number of neck bones as a person. Some letters are not used.

66. $15 - 8$ [F] **7**   **67.** $8 + 5$ [O] **13**   **68.** $3 + 6$ [E] **9**   **69.** $13 - 7$ [B] **6**

70. $16 - 8$ [R] **8**   **71.** $9 - 7$ [I] **2**   **72.** $12 - 6$ [M] **6**   **73.** $9 + 2$ [W] **11**

74. $13 - 9$ [A] **4**   **75.** $4 + 8$ [D] **12**   **76.** $9 - 9$ [K] **0**   **77.** $11 - 8$ [F] **3**

78. $7 + 7$ [L] **14**   **79.** $8 - 7$ [P] **1**   **80.** $6 + 8$ [H] **14**   **81.** $14 - 9$ [G] **5**

5	2	8	4	7	3	9
g	i	r	a	f	f	e

Remember the Facts!

These activities can help you remember your basic facts.

1. **Who Knows the Fact?** Sit in a circle with three or more students. Think of an addition fact, such as $7 + 5$. Clap your hands as you say each word, "Seven plus five." Then the student sitting next to you clicks his or her fingers and says, "Equals 12." Continue playing. Keep the rhythm of clapping your hands and clicking your fingers as you say the fact and give the answer.

2. **Spin Around** Use a spinner with 3, 4, 5, 6, 7, and 8 on it. Spin it twice. Use the two numbers to write an addition or subtraction fact. Repeat several times.

Stop and Practice 35

Neck and Neck!

Some students may find all the sums and differences. Others may look only for the number sentences that have the sums or differences shown below the blanks. Giraffes and humans have 7 bones in their necks.

Remember the Facts!

Have small groups try using each activity at this time to be sure they understand what to do. Small groups or pairs may then independently use the activities at other times to review facts.

For Early Finishers Challenge early finishers to create their own animal riddles to compile into a class riddle book. They may use the facts and letters given, or make up a new set.

Resources

TestWorks: Test and Practice Software

At-A-Glance Planning

Lesson Planning Checklist

Objective Solve problems by using guessing and checking.

Student Book Lesson Materials *Optional* Teacher's Edition Transparency A (Problem-Solving Guide)

Materials for pages 36A and 36B Counters in two colors (20 of each color per group)

Subject Connection science—animals

Strand Connections money, using data

	Before Lesson	During Lesson	After Lesson
Daily Math			
p. 36A Problem of the Day			
p. 36A Math Routines			
p. 36A Mental Math			
Teaching Options			
p. 36 Student Book Lesson			
p. 36B Another Way to Learn			
Options for Reaching All Learners			
p. 36B Inclusion			
p. 36B Gifted & Talented			
Technology Options			
p. 36A *Logical Journey of the Zoombinis*			
p. 38 Interactive CD-ROM Journal			
Assessment Options			
p. 37 Talk About It			
p. 39 Quick Check			
Resources			
1-12 Practice			
1-12 Reteaching			
1-12 Enrichment			
1-12 Problem Solving			
1-12 Daily Transparency			

Problem of the Day

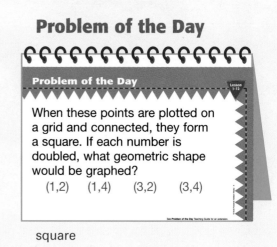

Problem of the Day Lesson 1-12

When these points are plotted on a grid and connected, they form a square. If each number is doubled, what geometric shape would be graphed?

(1,2)   (1,4)   (3,2)   (3,4)

square

Math Routines

Time Tell the class you are thinking of a time and then provide several clues. (Include in the clues several times that cross over 12 o'clock.) If you are thinking of 3 o'clock, you might give clues such as: 5 hours earlier is 10 o'clock, and 3 hours later is 6 o'clock. (Include times not exactly on the hour.)

Money If you have five coins whose total value is $0.40, what coins could they be? Repeat with other totals and combinations. 3 dimes, 2 nickels

Mental Math

Compare these numbers. Which is greater? Explain your thinking.

567, 377 567

497, 499 499

369, 355 369

4,890, 4,840 4,890

Logical Journey of the Zoombinis

Have students play puzzle games in *Who's Bayou?—The North Trek* to apply the guess and check strategy.

Another Way to **Learn** Lesson 1-12

Use as an alternative or in addition to pages 36–39.

Materials Counters in two colors (20 of each color per group)

Learning Style Kinesthetic

- Present the following problem to the class:
  Mari has a brother and a sister. The brother is older than the sister. The sum of their ages is 24. The difference in their ages is 4. How old are Mari's brother and sister?
  brother:14, sister:10

- Have students use red and yellow counters to represent the years in the brother's age and sister's age, respectively, and act out the problem presented.

- Ask students to tell you their guesses. Show their suggestions on the overhead using R and Y and the number sentences.

- Ask students why they chose certain numbers to start and why they changed the numbers as they did.

16 + 8 = 24 OK
16 – 8 = 8 No!

- Assign Check and Practice on Student Book pages 37–39 or *Practice Master 1-12*.

- Assess using the following rubric.

Assessment Rubric

4 Full Accomplishment
- solves problems by guessing and checking
- explains how to use the guess and check strategy

3 Substantial Accomplishment
- solves most problems by guessing and checking
- with prompting, explains how to use the guess and check strategy

2 Partial Accomplishment
- solves some problems by guessing and checking
- does not fully explain how to use the guess and check strategy

1 Little Accomplishment
- does not solve problems by guessing and checking
- does not explain how to use the guess and check strategy

Options for Reaching All Learners

Inclusion

Guess Tables
Use a table to organize guesses and checks.

Learning Style Logical

- Guide students to make a table in which to record their guesses and checks so they do not forget what they guessed or the results of their guesses.

- For example: Cynthia has a dog and a cat. The sum of the dog's and cat's ages is 22. The difference between the cat's age and the dog's age is 6 years.

Cat's Age	Dog's Age	Sum	Difference
13	9	22 OK	4 No
16	6	22 OK	10 No
14	8	22 OK	6 OK

Gifted & Talented

Mystery Stories
Use the guess and check strategy to solve mystery stories.

Learning Style Verbal, Logical

- Have each group write a short mystery story that involves several clues.

- Have groups trade all but the endings of their stories.

- Then have groups use the clues in the stories to guess the endings. They should check their solutions against the clues before confirming with the stories' writers.

Additional Resources for the Teacher
Problem-Solving Experiences in Mathematics, Grade 4, Randall Charles, et al. Menlo Park, CA: Addison-Wesley Publishing Company.

Lesson Organizer

Objective Solve problems by using guessing and checking.

Suggested Grouping 2 to 4

Student Materials *Optional* Teacher's Edition Transparency A (Problem-Solving Guide)

Assignment Guide

Basic 3, 4, 6–9, 12–33

Average 3–9, 12–33

Enriched 3–5, 8–33

1 Introduce

Review

Answer each question.

1. Which pairs of numbers have a sum of 12? B, D

2. Which pairs of numbers have a difference of 6? A, C, D

Ⓐ 13 and 7 Ⓑ 7 and 5
Ⓒ 12 and 6 Ⓓ 3 and 9

Build on Prior Knowledge

After students have reviewed finding the sum and difference of a pair of numbers, ask them to look again at their answers and identify the pair that has a sum of 12 and a difference of 6. D

2 Teach

See Another Way to Learn...on page 36B.

Learn ● ● ● ● ● ● ● ● ● ● ● ● ● ● ● ● ● ●

Use Teacher's Edition Transparency A (Problem-Solving Guide) to review and reinforce the steps in the problem solving process.

Reading Assist Make Predictions

Have students focus on how the information given in the problem can be used to make good guesses. Ask them why 15 and 6 was a good first guess. Their sum is 21.

Then ask why 17 and 4 would not have been a good guess to make next. The difference between 17 and 4 is more than 10, which is far from 5.

Problem Solving

Analyze Strategies: **Guess and Check**

You Will Learn
how to solve problems using the guess and check strategy

Reading Tip
Use the Glossary at the back of the book to find the meanings of *sum* and *difference*.

Learn ●

Jo has both a pet frog and a parrot. The frog is older than the parrot. The sum of the frog's and parrot's ages is 21 years. The difference of their ages is 5 years. How old is each animal?

Work Together

▶ **Understand**

What do you know? ❶

What do you need to find out?
Each animal's age

❶ The frog is older than the parrot.
The sum of their ages is 21.
The difference of their ages is 5.

▶ **Plan**

You may be able to solve the problem by guessing and checking.

Guess a pair of numbers. Check if they work.

▶ **Solve**

Use the facts you know. The sum of their ages is 21.

Guess 15 and 6. Check $15 + 6 = 21$.
$15 - 6 = 9$. The difference is not 5.

Guess 13 and 8. Check $13 + 8 = 21$.
$13 - 8 = 5$. That checks!

Write the answer. The frog is 13 years old.
The parrot is 8 years old.

▶ **Look Back**

Check to see if your answer makes sense.

The sum of their ages is 21: $13 + 8 = 21$.
The difference is 5: $13 - 8 = 5$.

36 Chapter 1 • Data, Graphs, and Facts Review

Managing Time

Have groups complete the Learn, Check, and Practice problems 3–11 in class. Have them complete problems 12–33 as homework.

Another Example

Steven and Brian are starting an endangered species card collection. Together they have 18 cards. The difference in the number of cards they have is 4. If Steven has more cards than Brian, how many cards does each boy have?

What You Read	What You Do
They have a total of 18 cards.	First guess: $10 + 8 = 18$
The difference in the number of cards they have is 4.	$10 - 8 = 2$ The difference must be 4. Second guess: $11 + 7 = 18$ $11 - 7 = 4$ That works!
Steven has more cards than Brian.	Steven has 11 cards. Brian has 7 cards.

Talk About It

1. How do you decide what your first guess will be?

2. How does your first guess help you make the second guess?

Check

Problem Solving
Understand
Plan
Solve
Look Back

Use guess and check to solve.

1. Jo walked her dog for 10 minutes more on Saturday than on Sunday. For both days she walked a total of 30 minutes. For how many minutes did she walk her dog on Sunday?
10 minutes

2. The record jumps for a gray kangaroo and a red kangaroo total 18 feet. The red kangaroo's record jump is 2 feet higher than the gray kangaroo's record jump.

Red kangaroos are the most common kind of kangaroos found in Australia.

Darwin
AUSTRALIA
Perth
Sydney
Canberra

a. Which kangaroo jumped higher? **Red**

b. Which numbers will you guess first?

c. What should the difference between the two numbers be? **2**

d. Which two numbers have a sum of 18 and a difference of 2? **8, 10**

e. What is the record jump for each kangaroo? **Red: 10 feet; Gray: 8 feet**

2b. Possible answers: 9, 9; 8, 10; 7, 11; 6, 12; 5, 13; 4, 14; 3, 15; 2, 16; 1, 17

Lesson 1-12 **37**

Have students compare the vocabulary used in this example to that used in the example on page 36.

• What terms are used to indicate addition? *Sum, together*

• What terms are used to indicate subtraction? *Difference*

• What terms are used to indicate the greater number? *Is older, has more*

Talk About It **Ongoing Assessment**

Listen for students to recognize that they may start with either part of the problem and should use number sense to make the first guess as well as to revise their subsequent guesses.

Answers for Talk About It

1 Possible answer: Use a pair of numbers that works for one part of the problem.

2 Possible answer: The first guess helps you make a more reasonable second guess.

Check

Encourage students to record their guesses and checks to refer to as they make revised guesses.

Meeting Individual Needs

Learning Style	Teaching Approach
Verbal	Have students make a list of words on pages 36–39 that they do not understand. Students can look up the words in a dictionary and make their own definitions for reference while doing the problems.
Social	As students work in small groups, assign the roles of guesser, checker, and reviser. The guesser makes the first guess and records it. The checker tests the guess. If necessary, the reviser makes the next guess and the checker tests it. Have students alternate roles for each problem.

Exercise 4 Be sure students understand that they are to find the number of cards Steven gave to his sister. "Gave away" in this context tells about the total number of cards Steven gave away; it does not mean subtraction.

Exercises 10 and 11 Some students may find it helpful to draw pictures based on their guesses and check by looking at their drawings. For Exercise 10, help students see that Mai Ling starts 2 blocks earlier than Jackie.

Interactive CD-ROM Journal
Students may want to use Interactive CD-ROM Journal Tool to answer Exercise 13. They can use the Spreadsheet/Grapher tool to create tables to illustrate their explanations.

For Early Finishers Challenge early finishers to write a problem involving their own friends or family members similar to Exercises 3 or 4.

Problem Solving
Practice •

Apply the Strategy

Use guess and check to help you solve each problem.

GPS **3.** Dmitri and Wayne spent a total of $12 for books. Dmitri spent $2 more than Wayne. How much did each spend? **Dmitri: $7; Wayne: $5**

4. Steven gave away 5 of his endangered species cards. He gave his sister 1 more card than he gave his friend. How many cards did he give his sister? **3 cards**

Choose a Strategy

Use any strategy to solve each problem. Use the pet catalog to answer 5–9.

5. Shalia ordered from the catalog. She spent $5 on two different items. She did not buy a bone. What did she order? **Collar, biscuits**

6. Stacy wanted to buy the biscuits and a bone. She had $3. What size bone could she order? **Small**

7. Rita ordered a dog dish and one other item. She paid a total of $9. What other items could Rita have ordered? **Collar or medium bone**

8. Kim ordered 3 bones in 3 different sizes. How much did she pay in all? **$8**

9. Suppose you have $15 and want to spend all of it. What would you order from the catalog? **Answers will vary but should total $15.**

10. Every morning, Jackie walks 12 blocks to school. She walks the last 9 blocks with Mai Ling. If Mai Ling walks 2 blocks farther than Jackie, how far does Mai Ling walk before meeting Jackie? **5 blocks**

11. A bike shop has a total of 5 bicycles and tricycles to repair. There are 12 wheels. What strategy would you use to find the number of bicycles and tricycles?

Problem Solving Strategies
- Use Objects/Act It Out
- Draw a Picture
- Look for a Pattern
- Guess and Check
- Use Logical Reasoning
- Make an Organized List
- Make a Table
- Solve a Simpler Problem
- Work Backward

Choose a Tool

The Pet Promenade
For all your dog's needs

Nylon collar	$3.00
Nylon leash	$5.00
Biscuits	$2.00
Bandana	$5.00
Rawhide bone	
small	$1.00
medium	$3.00
large	$4.00
Dish	$6.00

38 Chapter 1 • Data, Graphs, and Facts Review

Practice 1-12

Name _____

Practice 1-12

Analyze Strategies: Guess and Check
Use guess and check to solve.

1. Erin earned $9 for washing two cars. She received $1 more for the second car. How much was she paid for washing each car?

a. Which two numbers have a sum of $9?
$0 and $9, $1 and $8, $2 and $7, $3 and $6, $4 and $5

b. Which of these pairs of numbers also have a difference of $1?
$4 and $5

c. How much did Erin earn for the first car? **$4**

d. How much did Erin earn for the second car? **$5**

2. Antonio found money yesterday and today. He found 25¢ in all. Yesterday he found 7¢ less than today. How much did he find each day? Explain.
yesterday: 9¢; today: 16¢; 9¢ + 16¢ = 25¢,

Use any strategy to solve each problem.

3. Gary has a gray cat and a striped cat. The sum of their ages is 18. The difference of their ages is 0. How old is each cat?
9 years old

4. Alex and Francine had a swimming race. Francine swam 10 feet farther than Alex. Altogether they swam 54 feet. How far did each person swim?
Alex: 22 ft; Francine: 32 ft

5. In the triple jump, the athlete jumps three times. Suppose Matt jumps a total of 30 feet. Each jump is 1 foot longer than the jump before it. How far does he jump for each of the three jumps?
first jump: 9 ft; second jump: 10 ft; third jump: 11 ft

Reteaching 1-12

Name _____

Another Look 1-12

Analyze Strategies: Guess and Check
Every morning, Rosie meets Tammi on their way to school. The girls walk a total of 11 blocks. They meet after Rosie walks 3 blocks. How far does each girl live from school?

Guesses		Sum	Difference
Rosie	Tammi	11	3
8	3	11	5
6	5	11	1
7	4	11	3

Rosie walks 3 blocks further than Tammi each day.

Guess: Find any two numbers whose sum is 11. _8 + 3 = 11_

Write your guess in the table.

Check: What is the difference between the two numbers? _8 − 3 = 5_

What should the difference be between the numbers? _3_

Keep guessing until you find the pair that works.

How far does Rosie walk? _7 blocks_ Tammi Lee? _4 blocks_

Use the table to record your guesses. Keep guessing until you find a pair that works.

1. Sam earned $8 in two days for helping his neighbor. On Friday he earned $2 more than on Saturday. How much did he earn each day?

Guesses		Sum	Difference
Friday	Saturday	$8	$2

Friday _$5_
Saturday _$3_

2. Millen swam a total of 30 yards in two tries. The second time she swam 10 yards farther than the first time. How far did she swim each time?

Guesses		Sum	Difference
First Time	Second Time	30	10

1st time _10 yd_
2nd time _20 yd_

Problem Solving and RECREATION

For more than 100 years, people have ridden carved animals on carousels.

Most carousels have 3 rings, with an equal number of animals on each ring. The animals on the 2 inside rings are called "jumpers." They move up and down.

12. A carousel has 36 zebras, horses, and camels.

a. How many animals are on each ring? **12 animals**

b. Each ring has an equal number of zebras, horses, and camels. How many of each kind of animal are on each ring? **4 of each**

c. How many jumpers are there? **24 jumpers**

d. A jumper has a blue or a red saddle. Six more jumpers have blue saddles than have red saddles. How many blue saddles are there? **15 have blue saddles.**

13. Journal Explain how you would use guess and check to solve problem **12d.**

Mixed Review: Basic Facts

Find each sum or difference.

14. 9 + 7 16	**15.** 4 − 1 3	**16.** 4 + 3 7	**17.** 6 − 0 6	**18.** 8 + 9 17
19. 17 − 8 9	**20.** 8 + 5 13	**21.** 12 − 8 4	**22.** 15 − 8 7	**23.** 6 + 7 13
24. 9 − 0 9	**25.** 5 + 1 6	**26.** 7 + 8 15	**27.** 6 + 8 14	**28.** 7 + 9 16
29. 2 + 9 11	**30.** 5 + 7 12	**31.** 13 − 6 7	**32.** 14 − 5 9	**33.** 4 + 7 11

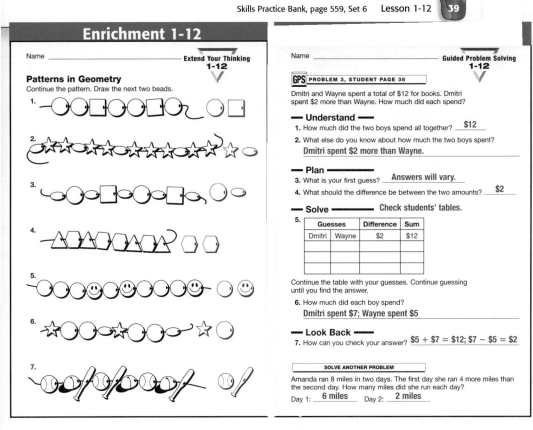

Enrichment 1-12

Name _____   Extend Your Thinking 1-12

Patterns in Geometry
Continue the pattern. Draw the next two beads.

1.
2.
3.
4.
5.
6.
7.

Name _____   Guided Problem Solving 1-12

GPS PROBLEM 3, STUDENT PAGE 38

Dmitri and Wayne spent a total of $12 for books. Dmitri spent $2 more than Wayne. How much did each spend?

— Understand —
1. How much did the two boys spend all together? **$12**
2. What else do you know about how much the two boys spent?
Dmitri spent $2 more than Wayne.

— Plan —
3. What is your first guess? **Answers will vary.**
4. What should the difference be between the two amounts? **$2**

— Solve —   **Check students' tables.**
5.

Guesses		Difference	Sum
Dmitri	Wayne	$2	$12

Continue the table with your guesses. Continue guessing until you find the answer.

6. How much did each boy spend?
Dmitri spent $7; Wayne spent $5

— Look Back —
7. How can you check your answer? **$5 + $7 = $12; $7 − $5 = $2**

SOLVE ANOTHER PROBLEM

Amanda ran 8 miles in two days. The first day she ran 4 more miles than the second day. How many miles did she run each day?
Day 1: **6 miles**   Day 2: **2 miles**

Merry-go-rounds, or carousels, are the oldest amusement park rides that are still popular today. The first known use of the term merry-go-round is from a poem that was printed in an English newspaper in 1729. The first American carousel was opened in Salem, Massachusetts, in 1799.

3 Close and Assess

Invite one member of each group to report on one problem they solved using the guess and check strategy. Have reporters include the solution; how the group made guesses, checked, and revised them; and what was the easiest and most difficult part of using this strategy.

Quick Check

1. Describe a problem that the guess and check strategy would help you solve. Possible answer: One in which you would need to check your work against a given fact; one that doesn't give all the information

2. How do you use the guess and check strategy to solve a problem? Find a pair of numbers that work for one part of the problem; check if they work for the other part. If they work, the problem is solved. If not, use number sense to guess another pair of numbers and repeat the check. Repeat as often as needed.

ANSWERS

11 Guess a number of tricycles. There will be 3 wheels for each. Guess a number of bicycles. There will be 2 wheels for each. Keep guessing until the total number of wheels is 12. 3 bicycles, 2 tricycles

13 Guess a number of red saddles and a number of blue saddles. Check that the number of red saddles plus 6 equals the number of blue saddles. Check that the total number of saddles is 24.

Chapter 1: Technology

Students will use graphing software to graph data and choose the most appropriate graph.

Student Materials *DataWonder!* or other graphing software

Preparation

To gain familiarity with the tools and tasks required, you may wish to work through this lesson before using it with your class. This lesson was written for the Macintosh version of *DataWonder!* If your students are using the Windows version of *DataWonder!* (which differs slightly in certain respects), or software other than *DataWonder!*, you may wish to modify some of the lesson steps to fit its features. Check your user's manual or online helper for assistance, if needed.

Introduce the Task

Have students open *DataWonder!* and select the Simple Data Table. Practice:

- pulling down the menu options
- entering data in cells
- changing the width of a column (not available in Windows)
- navigating across the rows with the tab key
- moving down the columns with the return key (students using the Windows version can use arrow keys)
- reducing the size of the table window
- selecting more than one cell

Work Together

Guide students through the activity. You may wish to begin with a discussion about what sandhill cranes are, where their natural habitat is, why we are concerned about their eggs, and so on.

Encourage them to click on each of the different graph buttons before selecting one for their report.

While students could justifiably select any of the three types of graphs for the crane egg data, a pictograph would not be appropriate for the crane mass data because of the great difference in numbers.

Technology

Making Graphs

Suppose you're writing a report on sandhill cranes. You write, "Sandhill cranes laid 5 eggs in February, 55 in March, 30 in April, and 10 in May."

Which type of graph would you use to show this data?

Materials
DataWonder! or other graphing software

Work Together

Use your graphing software to select the best graph to show the data.

1 Copy the table below to create a **Simple Data Table.**

2 Click on the different graph buttons in the graph window. Select the best graph for your report.

3 Insert the table and graph into the **Report** window. Then give your graph and report a title.

Report
Show Report
Insert Graph
Insert Table

Cooperative Learning

If you have only one computer station in your classroom, you may assign the following cooperative roles for groups of students to work together:

- reader/reporter—reads the task and the data to input
- data processor—enters data
- grapher—uses software to write the report, including inserting the table and graph into the report

Exercises

Answer **1–3** in the **Report** window below your graph. When you are finished, choose **Print Report** from the File menu.

1. Which graph did you choose to show the data? Explain.
   Possible answer: Pictograph; Data are small numbers and countable.
2. During which month were the most eggs laid? **March**

3. How many more eggs were laid in April than in May? **20 eggs**

Extensions

Make a **Full Data Table** graph to show the mass data in the table.
Answer **4–7** in the **Report** window. Print your report when you are finished.

4. What graph did you choose to show the data? Explain.

5. What was the mass of the crane at 2 weeks? At 8 weeks?
   287 g; 2,754 g
6. How many grams did the crane gain in the first 2 weeks? **285 g**

Sandhill Cranes

Age (weeks)		Mass (grams)
1	Birth	2
2	2	287
3	4	1,145
4	6	2,035
5	8	2,754

7. Which kind of graph best shows changes over time? **Line graph**

8. **Write Your Own Problem** Write a problem that can be answered using your graph. Give the answer. **Answers will vary.**

4. Possible answer: Line graph because data shows growth over a period of time

Technology **41**

Exercises

Exercise 1 Point out to students that line graphs are used to show change in a data set over time. The eggs laid in March are not counted among the eggs laid in April, so a line graph of the egg data might mislead people reading it.

Extensions

Exercise 4 The mass data changes dramatically as time goes by, so a pictograph might not be the most practical choice when presenting it.

Exercise 5 Have students talk about whether they could determine the exact weights from the table and/or the graph.

Resources

Technology Master 3

Section B
Review and Practice

Use the Skills Checklist

Review the **Skills Checklist** on the page with students. Then ask questions such as the following:

- In which problems do you need to know how to make bar graphs and line plots? Exercises 1, 3
- In which problems do you need to know the meaning of the words range, median, and mode? Exercises 4–6, 9
- In which problems will you use algebra? Exercise 7
- Where could you solve a problem using the Guess and Check Strategy? Exercises 7, 8

Assess

You may wish to use this information to assess students' understanding of the lesson objectives.

Item Analysis

Lesson Objective		Items
1-8	Make bar graphs.	1, 2
1-9	Make line plots.	3
1-10	Find range, median, and mode.	4–6, 9
1-11	Explore algebra by looking for a pattern to find the rule.	7
1-12	Solve problems by using guessing and checking.	7, 8

Resources

Practice Masters

- Practice Chapter 1 Section B

Assessment Sourcebook

- Quiz Chapter 1 Section B

TestWorks: Test and Practice Software

ANSWERS

2, 4–6, 9 See pages D1–D4.

Review and Practice

REVIEW AND PRACTICE

(Lesson 8) Make a bar graph.

1. Use the data in the table.
   Copy and complete the bar graph.

Animal Life Spans	
Chipmunk	6 yr
Rabbit	5 yr
Kangaroo	7 yr

Title: **Animal Life Spans**

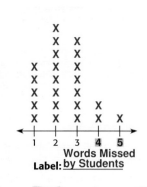

Label: **Years**

2. How could you use the life spans data to make a pictograph?

(Lesson 9) Make a line plot.

3. Use the data in the table.
   Copy and complete the line plot.

Number of Words Missed on Spelling Test	Number of Students
1	5
2	8
3	7
4	2
5	1

```
            X
            X   X
            X   X
    X   X   X
    X   X   X
    X   X   X
    X   X   X   X
    X   X   X   X   X
  +---+---+---+---+---+--->
    1   2   3   4   5
       Words Missed
Label: by Students
```

(Lesson 10) Find the range, median, and mode of each set of numbers.

4. 2, 5, 8, 4, 3, 9, 3   5. 2, 4, 6, 3, 1, 4, 4   6. 7, 3, 2, 7, 6, 7, 1

(Lesson 11) Copy and complete the table. Write the rule.

7.

In	n	10	13	8	9	12	15
Out		4	7	2	3	6	9

$n - 6$ or subtract 6

(Lesson 12) Solve.

8. The sum of two numbers is 13, and their difference is 3. What are the two numbers? **5, 8**

9. **Journal** Explain how to find the range, median, and mode for 2, 9, 7, 6, 2, 4, 2.

Skills Checklist

In this section, you have:

☑ Explored Making Bar Graphs and Line Plots

☑ Explored Finding Range, Median, and Mode

☑ Explored Algebra by Finding a Rule

☑ Solved Problems by Guessing and Checking

Practice

Name _____

Practice
Chapter 1
Section B

Review and Practice

(Lesson 8) Use the data in the table. Complete the bar graph.

1.

Number of Pets Adopted	
Dogs	12
Cats	16
Gerbils	7

Pets Adopted

```
Dogs
Cats
Gerbils
      5  10  15 20 25 30
          Number
```

(Lesson 9) Use the data in the table. Complete the line plot.

2.

Number of Books Read Last Month	Number of Students
1	3
2	6
3	1
4	8

Books Read Last Month

```
                X
                X
        X       X
        X       X
        X       X
    X   X       X
    X   X       X
    X   X   X   X
  +---+---+---+---+
    1   2   3   4
   Number of Students
```

(Lesson 10) Find the range, median, and mode of this set of numbers. 3, 5, 3, 1, 2

3. Range: **4**   Median: **3**   Mode: **3**

(Lesson 11) Complete each table. Write the rule with words and with a variable.

4.

In	2	4	6	8
Out	5	7	9	11

Rule: **Add 3, $n + 3$**

5.

In	14	15	13	12
Out	9	10	8	7

Rule: **Subtract 5, $n - 5$**

(Mixed Review) Find each sum or difference.

6. $5 + 8 =$ **13**   7. $16 - 7 =$ **9**   8. $14 - 6 =$ **8**

Choose at least one. Use what you have learned in this chapter.

1 Range Riddle

From the seven numbers below, pick five for which the following are true.

a. Their range is 4.
b. Their mode is 5.
c. Their median is 6.

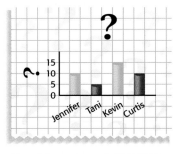

3 A Short Story

At Home Use the data displayed in this graph to write a story. Title the graph and complete the labels. Share your story with family and friends. Have them tell a different story about the graph.

1a. Possible answer: 4, 5, 6, 7, 8
1b. Possible answer: 4, 5, 5, 6, 7
1c. Possible answer: 5, 5, 6, 7, 8

2 Picture This

Check out **www.mathsurf.com/4/ch1**. Discover how explorers today are finding treasure at archaeological sites and in sunken ships. Design a treasure hunt. Use a coordinate grid. Give clues to find your treasure by using ordered pairs.

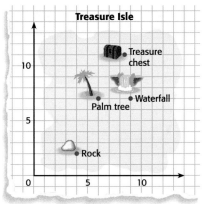

4 What's the Value of a Name?

Assign a number to each letter of your first name: A = 1, B = 2, C = 3, and so on. Add the numbers. You may use a calculator. Try to find a classmate whose name is different from yours but has the same total value.

Chapter 1 • Your Choice   43

Your Choice

Students will review the skills and concepts of the chapter using learning style strengths.

This page of activities is a good opportunity for portfolio assessment.

1 Range Riddle

Learning Style Logical

a Possible answer: 4, 5, 6, 7, 8

b Possible answer: 4, 5, 5, 6, 7

c Possible answer: 5, 5, 6, 7, 8

Challenge students to pick five numbers for which statements a–c are all true. Possible answer: 5, 5, 6, 8, 9

2 Picture This

Learning Style Visual

Clues will vary depending on treasure map.

3 A Short Story

Learning Style Visual, Verbal

Stories will depend upon what the scale numbers represent.

4 What's the Value of a Name?

Learning Style Verbal

To start, students may want to make a table of letters and values.

Answers will vary with names. Possible answer: Anna (1 + 14 + 14 + 1 = 30)

REVIEW AND PRACTICE

World Wide Web

For Picture This, suggest that students extend their research using some of the following key words: treasure, exploration, archaeology. Have students work in pairs to make directories of Web addresses which contain data relevant to treasure discoveries.

Home-School Connection

Have students collect data about their friends or family for which they complete a bar graph similar to the one in A Short Story. Have them share their graphs with the class.

Parents can use the Web site at **www.parent.mathsurf.com**.

Chapter 1
Review/Test

This page may be used to review or assess students' knowledge of Chapter 1.

Item Analysis

Lesson Objective	Items
1-1 Read pictographs and bar graphs.	4, 5
1-2 Read points as ordered pairs on a coordinate grid.	1, 2, 6, 7
1-3 Read line graphs.	6, 7
1-4 Read line plots.	
1-5 Read stem-and-leaf plots.	3, 8, 9
1-6 Solve problems by using a guide.	10–12
1-7 Solve problems by choosing an operation.	10–12
1-8 Make bar graphs.	
1-9 Make line plots.	
1-10 Find range, median, and mode.	8, 9
1-11 Explore algebra by looking for a pattern to find the rule.	
1-12 Solve problems by using guessing and checking.	10–12

Resources

Reading Strategies for Math
Chart 6 (Preparing for a Test)

Assessment Sourcebook
Chapter 1 Tests
- Forms A and B (free response)
- Form C (multiple choice)
- Form E (mixed response)
- Form F (cumulative chapter test)

TestWorks: Test and Practice Software

Home and Community Connections
- Letter Home for Chapter 1 in English and Spanish

Review/Test

Vocabulary Copy and complete.

1. (2, 3) is called an _____. **ordered pair**

2. (2, 3) can be found on a _____. **coordinate grid**

3. The _____ shows the tens digit in a stem-and-leaf plot. **stem**

(Lesson 1) Use the bar graph to answer **4** and **5**.

4. How much taller is the giraffe than the elephant? **2 m**

5. Which animal is taller than the lion but shorter than the elephant? **Moose**

Animal Heights

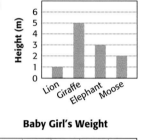

(Lessons 2 and 3) Use the line graph to answer **6** and **7**.

6. What was the baby's weight at 6 months? **About 16 or 17 lbs**

7. What ordered pair shows the baby's weight at 9 months? **(9, 19)**

(Lessons 5 and 10) Use the stem-and-leaf plot to answer **8** and **9**.

Claire's Scores

Stem	Leaf
1	0 7 6
2	1 3 1 8
3	1 6 4

Baby Girl's Weight

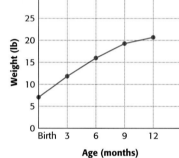

8. What is the mode of Claire's scores? **21**

9. How many times did Claire score 21? **Twice**

(Lessons 6, 7, and 12) Solve. Choose any strategy.

10. Two puppies weigh 15 lb all together. The larger puppy weighs 3 lb more than the smaller one. How much does each puppy weigh? **Larger: 9 lb; Smaller: 6 lb**

11. What is the difference in length between an elephant seal measuring 20 feet and a walrus measuring 12 feet? **8 ft**

12. **Science**. A seal can hold its breath underwater for about an hour. Can a seal swim underwater for 75 min without coming up for air? Explain. **No; 75 min is longer than 60 min or 1 hour.**

REVIEW/TEST

Assessment

Name _____

Date _____ Score _____

Chapter 1 Test
Form A

Vocabulary: In 1–3, match each with its meaning.

1. variable   **a.** a group of data that appear often on a line plot   1. __c__

2. cluster   **b.** numbers that show the units on a graph   2. __a__

3. scale   **c.** a letter that stands for a number or a range of numbers   3. __b__

In 4–6, use the bar graph.

4. Which color was chosen most often? **Blue**

Favorite Colors
Purple, Red, Blue, Yellow
0 2 4 6 8 10 12
Number of Persons

5. How many more people chose yellow than red? **2 more**

6. Add a bar to show that 4 persons chose purple as their favorite color.

In 7–9, use the line graph.

7. What ordered pair shows the height of the plant for Day 6? **(6, 8)**

Plant Growth
Height (in.)
10 8 6 4 2
0 1 2 3 4 5 6 7 8 9
Day

8. What was the plant's height on Day 3? **4 in.**

9. Which operation will you use to find how much the plant grew from Day 2 to Day 9? **Subtraction**

Name _____

In 10–12, use the line plot.

10. How many students scored 90 points? **4 students**

×
× × × ×
× × × × × ×
× × × × × ×
80 85 90 95 100 **105**
Game Scores (points)

11. What is the most common score? **95 points**

12. Two students scored 105. Add their scores to the line plot.

In 13–14, use the stem-and-leaf plot.

13. How many birthdays are on the 20th day? 13. __2 birthdays__

Birthdays

stem	leaf
0	1 2 5 8 9
1	2 6 9 9 7
2	0 9 0 3 6 7 8 3

14. How many birthdays are shown in the plot? 14. __18 birthdays__

15. Find the range, median, and mode for the set of numbers. Use this set of numbers. 2 9 7 1 3 2 8

Range __8__   Median __3__   Mode __2__

16. Complete the table. Write the rule. **Subtract 3.**

In	18	16	14	12	10
Out	15	13	**11**	**9**	7

17. Su earned $18 in two weeks. She earned $4 more this week than last week. How much did Su earn each week?

Last week __$7__   This week __$11__

18. **Explain Your Thinking** On a bar graph showing students' favorite sports, explain how you can tell the sport most often chosen. **It is shown by the longest bar.**

Performance Assessment

In which month are most people born? Survey several people to find out. Ask each person in what month he or she was born. Show the data on a graph.

1. **Decision Making** Decide how many people you will survey. Decide which people you will ask.

2. **Recording Data** Copy and complete the table. Include all 12 months. Record the total number of people born in each month. Then use the data you collect to make a bar graph.

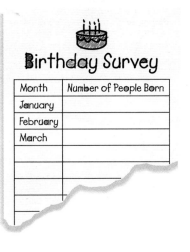

Birthday Survey

Month	Number of People Born
January	
February	
March	

Title: _____

Label: _____

12
11
10
9
8
7
6
5
4
3
2
1
0

January February March

Label: _____

3. **Explain Your Thinking** How did you decide on the title and labels for your bar graph? Based on your bar graph, in which month are most people born? In which month are the fewest people born? Write your own question that can be answered using your graph.

4. **Critical Thinking** Would you expect to get the same results if you surveyed more people? Compare your results with those of two other students. **Students are likely to get similar results, depending on how many people they survey.**

REVIEW/TEST

Assessment

Name _____ Chapter 1 Test
Form
Date _____ Score _____ D

Some of your friends may have many brothers and sisters. Others may be only children. How do the sizes of the families of your friends and relatives compare?

a. **Recording Data** Make a list of the last names of 12 families. Write how many people are in each family after each name.

b. **Recording Data** Copy the line plot shown. Use your data to complete the line plot. Add more numbers to the number line if you need to.

1 2 3 4 5 6 7 8 9
Number of People
in Family

c. **Analyzing Data** Use the line plot to answer these questions.

How many people are in the largest family?

What is the median family size?

What is the mode family size?

d. **Think Critically**

Do the data form a cluster? If so, describe the cluster.

Will your line plot look like other students' line plots? Explain.

e. **Making Decisions** You want to help raise money for school computers. How can you use your line plot to decide whether it would be better to raise money selling pizzas for $10 each or baseball tickets for $5 each to your family and friends? How might the size of the families influence your decision? Explain.

Chapter 1 Performance Assessment

Students will show their understanding of chapter concepts, including data, graphs, facts review, and problem solving by collecting, graphing, and analyzing data.

Student Materials Teaching Tool Transparency 6 (Centimeter Grid Paper)

Introduce the Task

Review Exercises 1–4 with students to be sure they understand the work they are to do. Share Level 4 of the rubric with students before they begin.

Facilitate and Assess

Before students work, you may wish to ask questions such as the following:

• How will you decide whom to survey?

• How will you record survey results?

• How will you decide on the title, labels, and scale for your graph?

Assessment Rubric

4 Full Accomplishment
• collects, organizes, and graphs data appropriately
• analyzes data and solves and writes problems using the graph

3 Substantial Accomplishment
• collects, organizes, and graphs data with few errors
• answers questions about data and with prompting, solves and writes problems

2 Partial Accomplishment
• collects, organizes, and graphs data only with help
• analyzes data, solves, and writes problems only with help

1 Little Accomplishment
• does not collect, organize or graph data
• does not analyze data, solve, nor write problems using the graph

Resources

Assessment Sourcebook

Chapter 1 Test

• Form D (performance assessment)

Math Magazine

Students will use a Venn diagram to classify data.

Teacher Materials *Optional* Lesson Enhancement Transparency 4

Science Note

Many animals that live on land and in water are amphibians. Most amphibians start their lives living in the water, breathing through gills. Some continue living in the water as adults, while others move onto land and breathe through lungs.

All amphibians can absorb oxygen through their skin, and for some adult amphibians, this is their only way to get oxygen. Other adult amphibians have both gills and lungs.

Cultural Link

Ask students which animals on the list are familiar to them. Have students find the places in which these animals live, and help the students locate the places on a globe or map. Have students contribute any specialized knowledge they may have of particular places and their animals.

Answer for Try These!

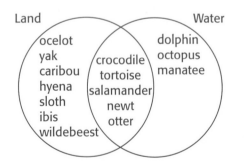

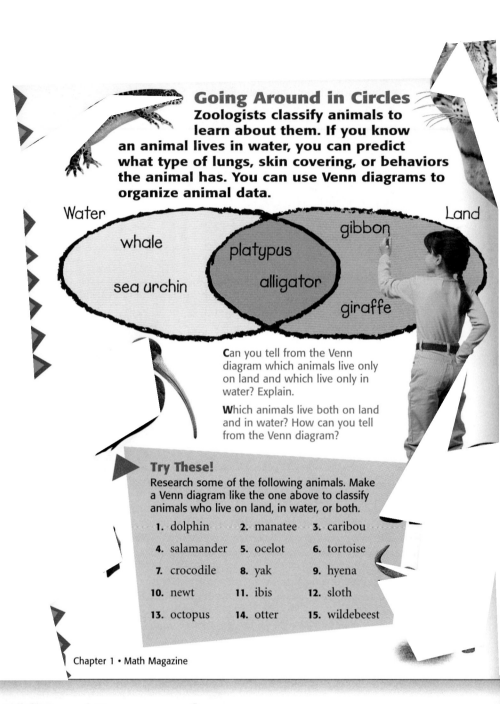

Going Around in Circles

Zoologists classify animals to learn about them. If you know an animal lives in water, you can predict what type of lungs, skin covering, or behaviors the animal has. You can use Venn diagrams to organize animal data.

Can you tell from the Venn diagram which animals live only on land and which live only in water? Explain.

Which animals live both on land and in water? How can you tell from the Venn diagram?

Try These!

Research some of the following animals. Make a Venn diagram like the one above to classify animals who live on land, in water, or both.

1. dolphin	**2.** manatee	**3.** caribou
4. salamander	**5.** ocelot	**6.** tortoise
7. crocodile	**8.** yak	**9.** hyena
10. newt	**11.** ibis	**12.** sloth
13. octopus	**14.** otter	**15.** wildebeest

Chapter 1 • Math Magazine

Additional Resources for the Teacher

Connections Game: Math and Science in Nature, Jean Morman Unsworth. Menlo Park, CA: Dale Seymour Publications.

Daily Math Adventure, Marcy Cook. White Plains, NY: Cuisenaire Company of America.

Test Prep Strategy: Make Smart Choices

Look for patterns.
Give the next three numbers in this pattern.   1, 4, 7, 10, ▨, ▨, ▨

Ⓐ 17, 27, 44   Ⓑ 11, 12, 13   Ⓒ 13, 16, 19   Ⓓ 14, 18, 22

Try adding 3
$1 + 3 = 4$
$4 + 3 = 7$
$7 + 3 = 10$
The pattern is add 3.
So, the answer is Ⓒ.

Write the letter of the correct answer. Look for patterns
or use any strategy to help.

1. Sally baked 5 dozen chocolate chip cookies. James baked 4 dozen
   sugar cookies. Gretchen baked 2 dozen oatmeal cookies. How
   many cookies did they bake all together? **D**
   Ⓐ 6 dozen   Ⓑ 7 dozen   Ⓒ 9 dozen   Ⓓ 11 dozen

2. Team A scored 17 points. Team B scored 8 points. How many
   points ahead is team A? **B**
   Ⓐ 8 points   Ⓑ 9 points   Ⓒ 25 points   Ⓓ not here

3. Give the next three numbers in this pattern. 2, 6, 10, ▨, ▨, ▨ **B**
   Ⓐ 12, 14, 16   Ⓑ 14, 18, 22   Ⓒ 1, 3, 5   Ⓓ not here

4. Which sum is the same as the difference between 14 and 6? **A**
   Ⓐ $7 + 1$ Ⓑ $10 + 10$ Ⓒ $5 + 4$ Ⓓ $14 + 6$

5. Which sum is 1 less than the sum of 8 and 3? **D**
   Ⓐ $8 + 3$ Ⓑ $6 + 6$ Ⓒ $5 + 6$ Ⓓ $6 + 4$

6. A tailed frog commonly lays 60 eggs. A Burmese python
   commonly lays 25 eggs. What operation would you use
   to find how many more eggs the frog lays than the python? **C**
   Ⓐ addition   Ⓑ multiplication
   Ⓒ subtraction   Ⓓ division

7. A hearing guide dog worked for 7 years with one owner and
   3 years with a different owner. How long did it work in all? **B**
   Ⓐ 2 years   Ⓑ 10 years   Ⓒ 80 years   Ⓓ 90 years

8. The largest gerbil litter was 15. If there were 8 females, how many
   males were there? **B**
   Ⓐ 7 females   Ⓑ 7 males   Ⓒ 8 males   Ⓓ 23 males

Test Prep Strategies
- Read Carefully
- Follow Directions
- Make Smart Choices
- Eliminate Choices
- Work Backward from an Answer

REVIEW AND PRACTICE

Chapter 1 • Cumulative Review   **47**

Practice

Name _____   **Practice** Chapter 1

Cumulative Review

(Chapter 1 Lesson 3) Use the line graph to answer each question.
1. On which dates were the
   temperatures less than
   30 degrees?
   December 1, 2, and 3

   Temperatures in December (1st week)

2. On which dates were the
   temperatures 40 degrees?
   December 4 and 6

(Chapter 1 Lessons 1 and 8) Use the data to complete the bar graph.

3.
Number of Pets	
Marsha	2
Penny	1
Lenny	5
William	6

Students' Pets

4. How many more pets does William have than Penny? __5__

(Chapter 1 Lesson 10) Find the range, median, and mode for
each set of numbers.

5. 114, 114, 112, 113, 115
   Range: __3__ Median: __114__ Mode: __114__

6. 4, 5, 4, 5, 4, 6, 3, 8, 1
   Range: __7__ Median: __4__ Mode: __4__

(Facts Review) Find each sum or difference.
7. $8 + 5 =$ __13__   8. $9 + 7 =$ __16__   9. $14 - 5 =$ __9__   10. $17 - 8 =$ __9__
11. $17 - 9 =$ __8__   12. $6 + 8 =$ __14__   13. $15 - 7 =$ __8__   14. $9 + 3 =$ __12__

Chapter 1
Cumulative Review

Students review and maintain skills and
concepts taught in Chapter 1 and practice
test-taking strategies. Special attention is
given here to the Test Prep Strategy, Make
Smart Choices: Look for Patterns.

Introduce the Test Prep Strategy

Make Smart Choices: Look for Patterns Read
and discuss the Test Prep Strategy note.
After students work through the example,
present the following problem:

Give the next three numbers in this pattern:

22, 20, 18, 16, ___, ___, ___ B
Ⓐ 16, 18, 20   Ⓑ 14, 12, 10
Ⓒ 12, 10, 8   Ⓓ not here

Encourage students to find other problems
on this page where Make Smart Choices:
Look for Patterns might be a helpful
strategy.

Some students may prefer another strategy
for some of the identified items. Have them
tell which strategy they would use and
explain why.

Review and Assess

Item Analysis	
Item	Lesson
1	1-7
2	1-7
3	1-11
4	1-12
5	1-12
6	1-7
7	1-7
8	1-7

Resources

Practice Masters
• Cumulative Review Chapter 1

Section	Pacing	Lessons			Your Test	Materials	
	Day	Lesson/Page	Objective		Correlation	Student Book	Another Way to Learn
A **Understanding Place Value** Students develop their understanding of place value through millions. **Problem Solving Connection** *Draw a Picture* *Look for a Pattern* *Problem Solving Strategy* *Make an Organized List*	Day 1	2-1	52–53	Read and write numbers in the thousands.		9-Digit PV* Chart (optional)	Paper cups, stirring sticks or straws, 9-Digit PV Chart
	Day 2	2-2	54–55	Explore place-value relationships.			PV blocks
	Day 3	2-3	56–57	Read and write numbers through the hundred millions.		9-Digit PV Chart (optional)	Centimeter Grid Paper, 9-Digit PV Chart
	Day 4	2-4	58–61	**Problem Solving** Solve problems by making an organized list.			Transparency Guided Problem Solving 1, 2
B **Building Number Sense** Students build number sense by comparing, ordering, and rounding numbers. **Problem Solving Connection** *Draw a Picture* *Use Logical Reasoning*	Day 5	2-5	66–67	Compare numbers to find which is greater.		Number Lines (optional)	Digit cards 0-9, PV blocks
	Day 6	2-6	68–69	Order a group of numbers.		9-Digit PV Chart (optional)	9-Digit PV Chart
	Day 7	2-7	70–71	Explore rounding.			Rulers
C **Making Sense of Time** Students tell time in different ways, compare units of time, find elapsed time, schedule time, and read calendars. **Problem Solving Connection** *Look for a Pattern* *Use Logical Reasoning* *Decision Making*	Day 8	2-8	74–75	Tell time to the minute and identify A.M. and P.M.			Paper-plate clocks
	Day 9	2-9	76–77	Explore estimating and comparing time.			
	Day 10	2-10	78–79	Find elapsed time.			Paper-plate clocks
	Day 11	2-11	80–81	Explore the calendar.		Calendar	
	Day 12	2-12	82–83	**Problem Solving** Solve problems by creating a schedule for making an audio tape.			
Chapter Assessment	Day 13		86–87	Assess student understanding and skills for Chapter 2.			

Also in this Chapter **Data File,** pp. 48–49, **Projects/Extensions,** pp. 50, 88

* PV = Place Value

Chapter 2
Key Math Idea

Place value is explored through millions. Numbers can be described, compared, and ordered. Time can be shown and read in different ways.

Looking Ahead
Grade 4 Chapter 3 Students will add and subtract 3- and 4-digit numbers.
Grade 5 Place value through billions and decimals through thousandths are explored.

Connections		Section Resources	
Strand	**Subject**	**Technology**	**Review and Assessment**
Geometry Readiness, Patterns, Algebra Readiness	Social Studies, Language, Culture	**Performance Math: Addition and Subtraction** 💿 **World Wide Web** 🌐 www.mathsurf.com/4/ch2 Chapter Opener, p. 48 **Calculator** 🖩 Practice Game, pp. 62–63 **Interactive CD-ROM** 💿 Exploring Place-Value Relationships, p. 55 **Logical Journey of the Zoombinis** 💿 Analyze Strategies, p. 58A	**Review** Section A Opener, p. 51 Mixed Review and Test Prep, pp. 53, 57, 61 Practice Game, pp. 62-63 Section A Review and Practice, p. 64 Skills Practice Bank, p. 560 **Ongoing Assessment** *Teacher's Edition,* all lessons *Assessment Sourcebook,* Quiz Chapter 2 Section A
Using Data	Science, Literature, Language		
Using Data, Patterns, Collecting Data	Fine Arts, Social Studies, Language		
Using Data, Collecting Data, Algebra Readiness	Fine Arts, Geography, Reading		
Using Data, Collecting Data, Algebra Readiness	Social Studies, Language Arts, Reading	**Performance Math: Addition and Subtraction** 💿 **Interactive CD-ROM Lesson 2** 💿 Comparing Numbers, p. 66 Ordering Numbers, p. 68 **Interactive CD-ROM** 💿 **Spreadsheet/Grapher Tool** Comparing Numbers, p. 67 Ordering Numbers, p. 69	**Review** Section B Opener, p. 65 Mixed Review and Test Prep, pp. 67, 69 Section B Review and Practice, p. 72 Skills Practice Bank, p. 560 **Ongoing Assessment** *Teacher's Edition,* all lessons *Assessment Sourcebook* Quiz Chapter 2 Section B
Logic, Using Data, Algebra Readiness	Social Studies Literature		
	Science, Language, Culture		
Patterns, Algebra Readiness	History, Health, Literature, Language	**World Wide Web** 🌐 www.mathsurf.com/4/ch2 Decision Making, p. 83 Your Choice, p. 85 **Math Workshop™** 💿 Exploring Time: Exact or Estimate?, p. 76A	**Review** Section C Opener, p. 73 Mixed Review and Test Prep, pp. 75, 79 Section C Review and Practice, p. 84 Your Choice, p. 85 Skills Practice Bank, p. 560 **Ongoing Assessment** *Teacher's Edition,* all lessons *Assessment Sourcebook,* Quiz Chapter 2 Section C
	Science, Health, Reading, Language		
Mental Math, Using Data, Estimation	Health, Geography, Social Studies		
	History, Language		
	Geography, Communications, Culture		
		TestWorks 💿	Chapter Review/Test, p. 86 Performance Assessment, p. 87 Cumulative Review, p. 89

Manipulatives

Using the Manipulatives

Place-Value Blocks (Base 10 Blocks) Students use place-value blocks to explore place-value relationships and patterns. By showing and counting the ones, tens, hundreds, and thousands in a number, students discover that our place-value system is based on groups of ten.

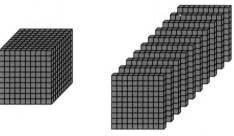

1,000 = 1 thousand = 10 hundreds

Number Lines Students use number lines and halfway points to help them round numbers to the nearest hundred thousand and develop their estimation skills.

50,000   57,000   60,000

57,000 is closer to 60,000 than to 50,000.

Suggested Materials	Alternatives
Place-value blocks	Grid paper
Number Lines	Lined notebook paper
Clocks	Paper-plate clocks with fastened paper strips

Clocks Students use analog and digital clocks to show time to the nearest minute. They find elapsed time by counting forward from the start time or backward from the end time.

Start Time	**End Time**	**Elapsed Time**
2:25 P.M.	4:17 P.M.	1 hr 52 min

Literature

A Week in the Life of an Airline Pilot

William Jaspersohn. Boston: Little, Brown & Co., 1991.

Use with Lesson 2-2 Gives information and numerical data about pilots, planes, and flying.

Little Town on the Prairie

Laura Ingalls Wilder. New York: Harper and Row, 1953.

Use with Lesson 2-6 Laura Ingalls wrote about growing up on the harsh prairie frontier during the 1870s. Before becoming a teacher and a writer, she earned $6 a month sewing shirts.

Ramona the Pest

Beverly Cleary. New York: Dell Publishing Company Inc., 1982.

Use with Lesson 2-8 Beverly Cleary's popular character Ramona Quimby makes going to school an adventure, even if she has difficulty arriving on time.

Additional Resources

Quest 2000: Exploring Mathematics, Grade 4, Randall Charles, et al. Menlo Park, CA: Addison-Wesley Publishing Company. *Unit 2.*

Investigations in Number, Data, and Space: Landmarks in the Thousands (The Number System), Susan Jo Russell and Andee Rubin.; **Investigations in Number, Data, and Space: Mathematical Thinking at Grade 4 (Introduction),** Cornelia Tierney. Menlo Park, CA: Dale Seymour Publications.

ScottForesman ESL: Accelerating English Language Learning, Grade 4, Anna Uhl Chamot, et al. Glenview, IL: ScottForesman. *pp. 110–111.*

Time and Money: Problem-Solving Focus, Carole Greenes, et al. Menlo Park, CA: Dale Seymour Publications.

Your Days Are Numbered In Calendar Math, Helene Silverman and Sheila Siderman. White Plains, NY: Cuisenaire Company of America.

Technology

For the Teacher

 ### Teacher's Resource Planner CD-ROM

The Teacher's Resource Planner CD-ROM allows you to create customized lesson plans tailored to your own class's needs. It also allows you to preview any supplement page, edit if you wish, and print it.

World Wide Web

Visit **www.teacher.mathsurf.com** for additional activities, links to lesson plans from teachers and other professionals, NCTM information, and other useful sites.

 ### TestWorks Test and Practice Software

A database of questions allows you to generate personalized practice worksheets and tests.

For the Student

Interactive CD-ROM

Use with Lesson 2-2 Students can use the Journal Tool in conjunction with the Place-Value Block Tool to demonstrate their understanding of place-value relationships.

Use with Lessons 2-5 and 2-6 Using the Spreadsheet/Grapher Tool gives students a visual aid for comparing and ordering numbers.

World Wide Web

Use with Chapter Opener Have students go online to the Scott Foresman•Addison Wesley Web site at **www.mathsurf.com/4/ch2** to learn more about coloring and crayons.

Use with Lesson 2-12 Students can go online to find out more about Malawi and other African countries.

Use with Your Choice Students search for Web sites with greater numbers that they can order in tables.

Performance Math

Use daily throughout Chapter 2 Students can practice every day to increase their familiarity with basic addition and subtraction facts.

 ### Logical Journey of the Zoombinis

Use with Lesson 2-4 Students use the Make an Organized List strategy to solve the puzzle *Captain Cajun's Ferry Boat.*

 ### Math Workshop™

Use with Lesson 2-9 Students will play *Bowling for Numbers* to answer questions requiring estimation.

 Calendar Time Kit

Time

One of the concepts in this chapter is elapsed time. You may use the Calendar Time Kit to reinforce this concept with the following activity:

Use digital and analog clocks to record and find elapsed time.

- As a class, choose an activity that will take place during class time.
- Have students read the wall clock to determine the hour and minute they begin the chosen activity. Then have them write the start time in their digital clocks and show it on their analog clocks.
- Have students repeat these steps for the end time.
- Have students find and record the elapsed time.
- Repeat this process for other daily activities.

It took 34 minutes.

Technology Centers

Preparing for Work on the Computer

Review the basics of the software for this chapter.

- Lesson 2-4 suggests using the *Logical Journey of the Zoombinis.* Preview the puzzle suggested, *Captain Cajun's Ferry Boat,* and review the relevant pages in the software's Teacher's Guide. Do a quick check at various difficulty levels so you can see the skills required.
- First, do a whole-class demonstration of the software. Then, before giving students access, review the important steps and commands.

Bulletin Board

Objective Compare activities in different time zones.

Materials World map of time zones, push pins, index cards, analog clocks made from paper plates and brads

- Have students work in pairs to choose a city from the world map, mark its location with a push pin, and write it on an index card.
- Have students brainstorm a list of activities and the times when each might be done. As a class, pick one activity from the list. Using their home town as a reference, each pair determines the corresponding time in the chosen city and shows it on the analog clocks.
- Have each pair describe an event that might be occurring in the chosen city and post it below the clock.

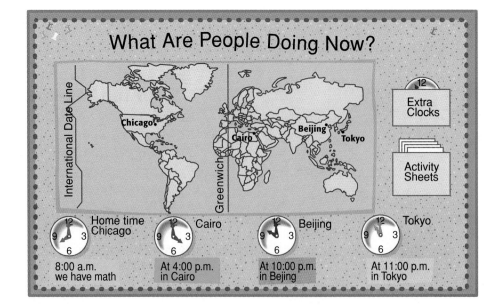

Traditional Assessment	
Review and Practice	Student Edition: pages 64, 72, 84
Cumulative Review	Student Edition: page 89; Assessment Sourcebook: Form F
Section Quizzes	Assessment Sourcebook: Section Quizzes A, B, C
Chapter Tests **Free Response** **Multiple Choice** **Mixed Response**	Student Edition: page 86; Assessment Sourcebook: Forms A and B Assessment Sourcebook: Form C Assessment Sourcebook: Form E

Alternative Assessment	
Ongoing Assessment	Teacher's Edition: every core lesson; Assessment Sourcebook: 11–13, 16–19, 21
Portfolio	Student Edition: page 85; Teacher's Edition: page 57; Assessment Sourcebook: pages 9, 13, 14, 16, 23
Interview and Observation	Teacher's Edition: pages 53, 67, 69, 79; Assessment Sourcebook: pages 18, 20
Journal	Student Edition: pages 55, 61, 64, 71, 72, 77, 81, 84; Teacher's Edition: pages 75, 83; Assessment Sourcebook: pages 8–11, 15
Performance Assessment	Student Edition: page 87; Teacher's Edition: pages: 55, 71, 77, 81; Assessment Sourcebook: Form D

NCTM Assessment Standards

Focus on Openness

Performance Teachers must make clear to students how they will be evaluated and what skills they should demonstrate. Performance assessment activities provide opportunities for teachers to highlight how students may expect to be assessed. Performance assessment opportunities occur on pages 55, 71, 77 and 81.

Test Prep

- The Test Prep Strategy **Follow Directions: Watch for Words Like *Not*** is introduced and practiced in the Cumulative Review on page 89.
- Mixed Review and Test Prep occurs throughout this chapter.

TestWorks

TestWorks can create personalized multiple-choice tests, free-response tests, and practice worksheets.

Standardized-Test Correlation		ITBS	CTBS	CAT	SAT	MAT
Lesson/Objective		Form M	4th Ed.	5th Ed.	9th Ed.	7th Ed.
2-1	Read and write numbers in the thousands.	●	●	●	●	●
2-2	Explore place-value relationships.	●	●	●	●	
2-3	Read and write numbers through the hundred millions.					
2-4	Solve problems by making an organized list.					
2-5	Compare numbers to find which is greater.	●	●	●	●	●
2-6	Order a group of numbers.	●	●	●	●	●
2-7	Explore rounding.	●	●	●	●	●
2-8	Tell time to the minute and identify A.M. and P.M.	●	●	●		●
2-9	Explore estimating and comparing time.		●	●	●	●
2-10	Find elapsed time.	●	●	●	●	●
2-11	Explore the calendar.					
2-12	Solve problems by creating a schedule for making an audio tape.					

Key
ITBS Iowa Test of Basic Skills **CTBS** Comprehensive Test of Basic Skills **CAT** California Achievement Test
SAT Stanford Achievement Test **MAT** Metropolitan Achievement Test

Find the Next Number

Task Students find the next numbers in a place-value pattern.

Objective Explore place-value concepts.

Parallel Student Book Lessons Lessons 2-1 and 2-2

Materials

Teaching Tool Transparency 12 (10 × 10 Grids, at least 100 copies per class)

Place-Value Blocks (10 hundreds, 10 tens, 10 ones per group)

scissors

tape

butcher paper

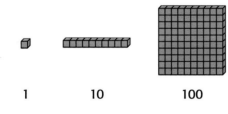

| 1 | 10 | 100 |

1 Introduce the Investigation

Explore Ones as Tens and Tens as Hundreds

1. Distribute place-value blocks to groups to examine and compare. Draw a picture of each block on the chalkboard, and list words students use to describe each one.

2. Encourage students to describe each block in terms of place value. Ask questions such as: How many ones are in 1 ten? How many rows of ones? How many columns? How many tens are in 1 hundred? How many rows of tens? How many columns?

Discuss Place-Value Patterns

3. Have students discuss the relationship among the three different place-value blocks. Challenge students to find equal relationships by building a ten from 10 ones and a hundred from 10 tens. Make sure students understand that 10 of the lesser place-value block make 1 of the *next* greater block in the series.

 Investigate

Define the Task

4. Provide scissors, tape, and ten copies of the 10 × 10 Grids to each group. On the overhead, arrange 1 one, 1 ten, and 1 hundred in a row. Tell students that their task is to use the grids to make a model of the next greater place value.

Extend the Pattern

5. Have groups meet as a class to share their models and discuss the number represented. Students should tape together 10 hundreds in a strip to make 1 thousand.

6. Have the class work together to create the next model in the pattern using their thousand models. Students should tape together 10 of their thousand strips to form a square ten thousand model.

Extend the Investigation

7. Have students write a description and create a sketch of the next numbers in the pattern and its model.

Error Intervention Ongoing Assessment

Observation Students may not follow the square, strip, square, strip pattern while creating the models.

How to Help Show students a unit square, a ten strip, and a hundred square. Then ask them to predict the next shape after the hundred square and so on.

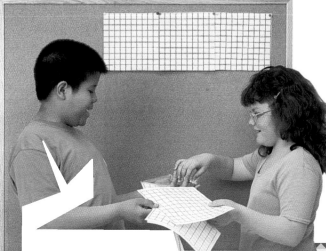

❸ Close and Assess

Discuss

Discuss how to write the numbers for each model students created. Ask:

- What number did you create with 10 hundreds? 1,000
- How did you figure out what number it was? Possible answer: Skip counted by hundreds
- How is 1,000 related to 100? 1,000 is made from 10 hundreds.
- What number was represented by the second model? 10,000
- How is 10,000 related to 1,000, 100, 10, and 1. 10,000 is made from 10 thousands, 100 hundreds, 1,000 tens, or 10,000 ones.
- If 1,000 is the first 4-digit number and 10,000 is the first 5-digit number, what do you think the first 6-digit number is? 100,000
- How do you think 100,000 is related to 10,000? 10 ten thousands will make 100,000.

Assessment Rubric

4 Full Accomplishment
- uses place-value relationships to find the next number in a pattern
- clearly explains relationship among 1, 10, 100, 1,000, and 10,000

3 Substantial Accomplishment
- uses place-value relationships to find the next number in a pattern
- with prompting, explains relationship among 1, 10, 100, 1,000, and 10,000

2 Partial Accomplishment
- has difficulty using place-value relationships to find the next number in a pattern
- has difficulty fully explaining relationship among 1, 10, 100, 1,000, and 10,000

---

1 Little Accomplishment
- does not use place-value relationships to find the next number in a pattern
- does not explain relationship among 1, 10, 100, 1,000, and 10,000

Place Value and Time

Theme: Amazing Facts

Teacher Materials *Optional* Lesson Enhancement Transparency 5

Introduce the Chapter

Interesting number facts are used to cover place-value concepts with whole numbers and skills and concepts related to time. Students learn to identify the place value of a digit in a number, compare two numbers, order a list of numbers, round a number to a given place, and make organized lists to solve problems.

Activate Prior Knowledge

Ask volunteers to name a very large number. Is the number used to count something or to measure something? Record students' ideas on the overhead or chalkboard.

Use the Data File

You may wish to use Lesson Enhancement Transparency 5 and the following questions to discuss the Data File.

- How are the numbers represented on pages 48 and 49? Time line, tables, schedule

- Have students suggest what high-tech crayon might be invented by the year 2000. Accept all reasonable answers.

- Use the table to find which Asian groups had more than 1 million immigrants to the United States in 1990. Chinese, Filipino

- Bus, train, and plane schedules have certain things in common. What are they? They all name the cities to which you can travel and tell the arrival and departure times.

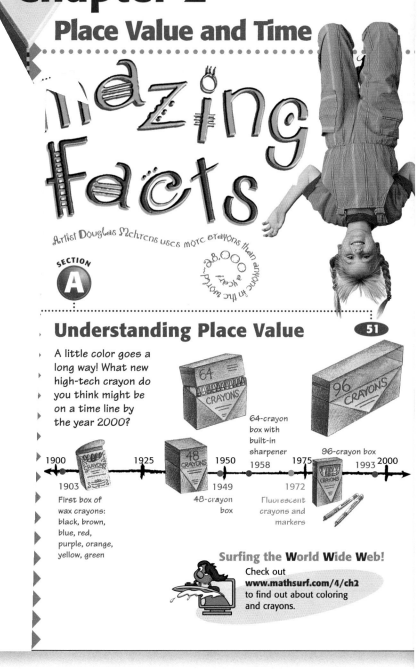

Chapter 2
Place Value and Time

Amazing Facts

Artist Douglas Mehrens uses more crayons than anyone in the world—28,000 a year!

SECTION A

Understanding Place Value — 51

A little color goes a long way! What new high-tech crayon do you think might be on a time line by the year 2000?

64-crayon box with built-in sharpener
96-crayon box

1900 · 1925 · 1950 · 1958 · 1975 · 1993 2000

1903 First box of wax crayons: black, brown, blue, red, purple, orange, yellow, green

1949 48-crayon box

1972 Fluorescent crayons and markers

Surfing the World Wide Web!
Check out www.mathsurf.com/4/ch2 to find out about coloring and crayons.

Extensions

Geography Connection

Have students look at a map of Florida and estimate the distances between the towns listed on the train schedule. Have them write the distances in a table and compare to the elapsed times in the schedule.

Performance Math: Addition and Subtraction

Students can build their fluency with basic addition and subtraction facts using Performance Math 10 minutes per day. They can keep track of their own progress by periodically checking the progress reports.

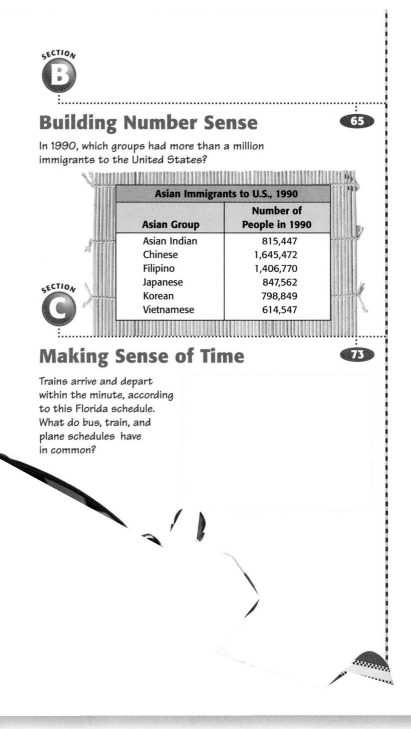

Math in the Community

School-Community Connection

Research Where You Live Have small groups use library resources or contact local officials to collect statistical information about their city or town. Students should look for population and area facts.

Students can use their experience with reading, writing, and comparing greater numbers to report their findings to the class.

Community Project The Chapter 2 community project is available in *Home and Community Connections*.

Home-School Connection

Greater Numbers in Your World
Ask students to find examples of numbers greater than 999 at home and in their neighborhoods. In class, brainstorm a list of likely locations. Possibilities include:

- page numbers in long books
- newspaper or magazine articles on population, area, employment
- nutrition information on food packages

Parents can use the Web site at **www.parent.mathsurf.com**.

At the end of this chapter, you may wish to distribute the Letter Home from *Home and Community Connections*.

It's A Matter of Fact

Students will describe a real-world model that shows 1,000.

Student Materials Collection of 10 or more of the same object, ruler, *optional Assessment Sourcebook 10* (How We Worked in Our Group)

Teacher Materials Place-value blocks (1 one, 1 ten, 1 hundred, 1 thousand)

Introduce the Project

Students may have used place-value blocks in earlier grades. Hold up the models for 1, 10, 100, and 1,000. The basic unit is a cubic centimeter. Point out that the blocks are one way to model the relative sizes of 1, 10, 100, and 1,000.

Explain that in this project students will find other ways to show 1,000. Go over the steps of the project, discuss the questions, and preview the self-assessment checklist below. Invite students to help set the standard for their work.

Self-Assessment Checklist

__ Describe a physical model that shows 1,000

__ Accurately measure the basic unit

__ Clearly and accurately report the process and results

Complete the Project

Have volunteers present the objects they chose to describe 1,000. Make a class list or display of the different objects chosen by the students.

ANSWERS

Possible Answer for Carry It Out

10 paper clips are about 10 inches long, so 1,000 paper clips will be 1,000 inches long, or about 83 feet.

Possible Answer for Talk About It

You would need more objects to show 1,000.

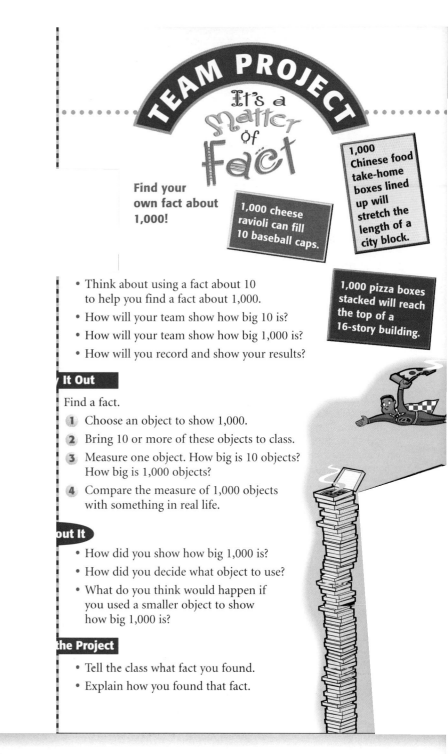

TEAM PROJECT

It's a **Matter of Fact**

Find your own fact about 1,000!

1,000 cheese ravioli can fill 10 baseball caps.

1,000 Chinese food take-home boxes lined up will stretch the length of a city block.

1,000 pizza boxes stacked will reach the top of a 16-story building.

- Think about using a fact about 10 to help you find a fact about 1,000.
- How will your team show how big 10 is?
- How will your team show how big 1,000 is?
- How will you record and show your results?

It Out

Find a fact.

1. Choose an object to show 1,000.
2. Bring 10 or more of these objects to class.
3. Measure one object. How big is 10 objects? How big is 1,000 objects?
4. Compare the measure of 1,000 objects with something in real life.

out It

- How did you show how big 1,000 is?
- How did you decide what object to use?
- What do you think would happen if you used a smaller object to show how big 1,000 is?

the Project

- Tell the class what fact you found.
- Explain how you found that fact.

Literature Connection

Students may be familiar with the fairy tales of *Aladdin, Ali Baba and the 40 Thieves*, and *Sinbad the Sailor.* Tell students that these stories come from an ancient Arabic collection called *The Thousand and One Nights*, in which a girl named Scheherazade tells the Sultan stories for that length of time. Sometimes she told several stories in a night; sometimes she would tell one long story over several nights.

- Show students a picture book. Have them find out how high a stack of 1,001 books would be.

Cooperative Learning

As students work together, one can measure and the other can record the results.

Distribute *Assessment Sourcebook 10* (How We Worked in Our Group) and have students fill it out for the skill Explain and Summarize. Invite students to judge themselves on the skill as they work together.

Understanding Place Value

The word *crayon* can be written in many languages.

German: *wachsmalkreide*
Spanish: *tiza de color*
Portuguese: *lápis de pastel*
Danish: *tegnekridt*
Cantonese: *laapbee*

How can you tell if there are between 10 and 100, or 100 and 1,000 crayons on this page?

Understanding Place Value

In this section, students will read and write numbers through hundred millions and identify the places and place values of digits.

Subskills

The work in this section builds on...

• Reading and writing whole numbers through hundreds

275 is read as two hundred, seventy-five

• Identifying the place and value of a digit in a number.

In 673, the digit 7 is in the tens place. It has a value of 70.

• Using place-value models to represent numbers

The number 456 can be shown with 4 hundreds blocks, 5 tens blocks, and 6 ones blocks.

Use the Section Opener

The crayons pictured on this page are made of pigment, or coloring matter, and wax. Ask how students can tell about how many crayons are in the picture. Possible answers: Count each crayon; Count number of crayons in 1 box, count number of boxes, then use repeated addition to find the total.

Reading and Writing Greater Numbers

Review counting. Copy and write the missing numbers.

1. 234, 235, 236, ■, ■, ■ 237, 238, 239

2. 989, ■, 991, ■, 993, ■ 990, 992, 994

3. ■, 487, 486, ■, 484, ■, 482 488, 485, 483

Skills Checklist

In this section, you will:

☐ Learn About Place Value Through Millions

☐ Explore Place-Value Relationships

☐ Solve Problems by Making an Organized List

51

Skills Trace

(Red numbers indicate pages in this section.)

Lesson and Skill	First Introduced	Grade Four			
		Introduce	Develop	Practice/Apply	Review
2-1 Read and write numbers in the thousands.	Grade 3	52, 53	52	50, 53, 62–64, 88, 560	64, 86, 89
2-2 Explore place-value relationships.	Grade 3	54, 55	54, 55	55, 64, 85, 87, 560	64, 85, 86
2-3 Read and write numbers through the hundred millions.	Grade 4	56, 57	56	57, 64, 85, 87, 560	64, 85, 86, 89
2-4 Solve problems by making an organized list.	Grade 4	58, 59	58, 59	60, 61, 64, 560	64, 86

Mixed Review and Test Prep exercises for this chapter occur on pages 53, 57, 61, 67, 69, 75, 79.

🚶 **Multi-Age Classrooms** Use pages 51–62 in Grade 3 or pages 51–64 in Grade 5 to relate to the content of this section.

Place Value Through Thousands

At-A-Glance Planning

Lesson Planning Checklist

Objective Read and write numbers in the thousands.

Vocabulary place value, digit, period, expanded form, standard form, word name

Student Book Lesson Materials Teaching Tool Transparency 3 (9-Digit Place-Value Chart)

Materials for pages 52A and 52B Paper cups (6 per group), stirring sticks or straws (54 per group), Teaching Tool Transparency 3 (9-Digit Place-Value Chart), index cards with word names *one* to *nine* (1 set per group), multiples of 10 from *twenty* to *ninety* (1 set per group), *hundred, thousand* (1 each per student)

Subject Connection social studies—games/recreation

Strand Connections geometry readiness, patterns, algebra readiness

	Before Lesson	During Lesson	After Lesson
Daily Math			
p. 52A Problem of the Day			
p. 52A Math Routines			
p. 52A Mental Math			
Teaching Options			
p. 52 Student Book Lesson			
p. 52B Another Way to Learn…			
Options for Reaching All Learners			
p. 52B Language Development			
p. 52B Cultural Connection			
Subject Connections			
p. 52A Social Studies Connection			
Assessment Options			
p. 52 Talk About It			
p. 53 Error Intervention			
p. 53 Interview			
p. 53 Quick Check			
Resources			
2-1 Practice			
2-1 Reteaching			
2-1 Enrichment			
2-1 Problem Solving			
2-1 Daily Transparency			

Problem of the Day

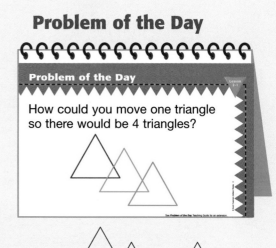

Problem of the Day

How could you move one triangle so there would be 4 triangles?

Math Routines

Measurement Use a meter stick to show that a decimeter is 10 times as great as a centimeter, and a meter is 10 times as great as a decimeter. Ask students to name objects with lengths equal to each unit.

Money Have students make a list of the first five things they would buy if they won $50,000.

Mental Math

Is the sum odd or even? Explain.

15 + 8	12 + 12	23 + 7
Odd	Even	Even
19 + 6	36 + 26	29 + 43
Odd	Even	Even

Social Studies Connection

The population of a city, town, or state is usually a number with 4 to 6 digits.

- Have teams use reference materials to find the populations of five cities or states.

- Students can use the populations to practice identifying the places and values of digits.

Another Way to **Learn** Lesson 2-1

Use as an alternative or in addition to pages 52 and 53.

Materials Paper cups (6 per group), stirring sticks or straws (54 per group), Teaching Tool Transparency 3 (9-Digit Place-Value Chart)

Learning Style Kinesthetic

- Share Level 4 of the Assessment Rubric with students before they begin their work.

- Have groups label their cups: ones, tens, hundreds, thousands, ten thousands, hundred thousands.

- Remind students that numbers are made up of digits. Explain that they are going to use the cups and sticks to show different numbers.

- Tell students to put between zero and nine sticks in each cup. Then ask a student to name the number shown. Write the number on the overhead place-value chart, showing how each digit goes in its place.

- Have groups create 10 different numbers with 2, 3, 4, 5, or 6 digits. They should record each number in these forms: 305 = 3 hundreds 0 tens 5 ones, and three hundred five.

- Assign Check and Practice on Student Book page 53 or *Practice Master 2-1*.

- Assess using the following rubric.

Assessment Rubric
4 Full Accomplishment • reads and writes numbers in the thousands correctly • correctly identifies place and value of digits in numbers
3 Substantial Accomplishment • reads and writes most numbers in the thousands correctly • correctly identifies place and value of digits in most numbers
2 Partial Accomplishment • reads and writes some numbers in the thousands correctly • sometimes misnames place or value of digits in numbers
1 Little Accomplishment • does not read or write numbers in thousands • does not identify place and value of digits in numbers

Options for Reaching All Learners

Language Development

Make the Number

Use index cards to reinforce word names.

Materials Index cards with word names *one* to *nine* (1 set per group), multiples of 10 from *ten* to *ninety* (1 set per group), *hundred, thousand* (1 each per student)

Learning Style Verbal

- Group students acquiring English with more fluent speakers. Students in each group stack both sets of index cards face down in the center of a table.

- Each student draws one card from each stack and combines the two words drawn with *hundred* and *thousand* cards to make a number. For example, *four* and *seventy* might make the number 70,400.

- As students make their numbers, they must say them aloud and show how they are written.

Cultural Connection

Cultural Number Systems

Use Babylonian symbols to develop understanding of place value and digits.

Learning Style Visual, Logical

Early Babylonians used a positional system based on 60. They could write all the numbers from 1 to 60 using only a hook (▼) and a wedge (◄). The hook (▼) was used for numbers 1 to 9 and 60. The wedge (◄), combined with the hook, was used for numbers 11 to 59.
▼▼▼ = 3   ◄▼ = 11   ◄◄▼▼▼▼ = 26

- Ask students how many number symbols our place-value system uses. 10; 0 to 9

- Have students find out how other number systems work. Possibilities include the Maya based on 20, the binary system based on 0 and 1.

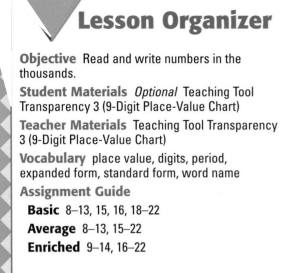

Lesson Organizer

Objective Read and write numbers in the thousands.

Student Materials *Optional* Teaching Tool Transparency 3 (9-Digit Place-Value Chart)

Teacher Materials Teaching Tool Transparency 3 (9-Digit Place-Value Chart)

Vocabulary place value, digits, period, expanded form, standard form, word name

Assignment Guide

Basic 8–13, 15, 16, 18–22

Average 8–13, 15–22

Enriched 9–14, 16–22

1 Introduce

Review

Identify the number of hundreds, tens, and ones in each number.

1. 306   3 hundreds 0 tens 6 ones

2. 870   8 hundreds 7 tens 0 ones

3. 515   5 hundreds 1 ten 5 ones

Build on Prior Knowledge

Ask students to identify the digit in the tens place in each of the three numbers above. Repeat with the ones place and the hundreds place. 0, 7, 1; 6, 0, 5; 3, 8, 5

2 Teach

See Another Way to Learn...on page 52B.

Explore

Use Teaching Tool Transparency 3 (9-Digit Place-Value Chart) for demonstration if desired. When discussing the place-value charts in the examples, emphasize that the place of a digit determines its value.

(Talk About It) Ongoing Assessment

Listen to students' discussions to check that they understand that multiplying a digit by its place gives its value.

Answer for Talk About It

4,000; 400; 4

Chapter 2 Lesson 1

Place Value Through Thousands

You Will Learn
how to read and write numbers in the thousands

Vocabulary

place value
value given to the place a digit has in a number

digits
0, 1, 2, 3, 4, 5, 6, 7, 8, 9

period
group of 3 digits in a number, separated by a comma

Ways to Write a Number
expanded form
standard form
word name

Math Tip
Use commas to separate periods when you write a number.

Learn

Jigsaw puzzles can be fun but complicated to put together. It took about a week for students at Gravenvoorde School in the Netherlands to put together a giant jigsaw puzzle with 204,484 pieces!

Place value can help you understand the value of the **digits** in the number of puzzle pieces used.

Example

Thousands Period			Ones Period		
hundred thousands	ten thousands	thousands	hundreds	tens	ones
2	0	4 ,	4	8	4

Here are some ways you can write this number.

expanded form	$200{,}000 + 4{,}000 + 400 + 80 + 4$
standard form	204,484
word name	two hundred four thousand, four hundred eighty-four

(Talk About It)

What is the value of each 4 in 204,484?

Practice 2-1	Reteaching 2-1

Check

Write the word name for each number.

1. 4,663   2. 23,509   3. 400,806   4. 56,803

5. Write 300,000 + 7,000 + 200 + 6 in standard form. **307,206**

6. Write the value of the red digit in 31,645. **30,000**

7. **Reasoning** In the number 9,026, what does the zero tell you?
There are no hundreds, 0 is a place holder.

Practice

Skills and Reasoning

Write the word name for each number.

8. 29,763   9. 78,321   10. 532,971   11. 96,673

12. Write 20,000 + 4,000 + 900 + 30 + 2 in standard form. **24,932**

13. Write the value of the red digit in 54,389. **4,000**

14. Write a 6-digit number with 5 in the ten-thousands place and 2 in the thousands place. **Possible answer: 152,980**

Problem Solving and Applications

15. **Geometry Readiness** Write the color of the missing jigsaw piece. **Green**

16. Wei XuChong was the winner of the world's largest musical chairs game, which was played at the Anglo-Chinese School in Singapore. The game started with 8,238 people. Write the word name for that number. **Eight thousand, two hundred thirty-eight**

17. **Patterns** What number comes next? 548, 5,480, 54,800 **548,000**

Mixed Review and Test Prep

Algebra Readiness Find each missing number.

18. 15 + 4 = n **19**   19. 18 − 4 = n **14**   20. 12 + 7 = n **19**   21. 19 − 8 = n **11**

22. What is the mode of the spelling test scores?
87, 85, 84, 87, 86, 87, 86, 85 **D**

  Ⓐ 84   Ⓑ 85   Ⓒ 86   Ⓓ 87

Lesson 2-1   **53**

Enrichment 2-1

Name _____   Extend Your Thinking 2-1

Visual Thinking   Accept reasonable estimates.
Estimation About how many shapes are in each drawing?

1. About 120   2. About 30

3. About 1,000   4. About 400

5. About 60   6. About 700

Problem Solving 2-1

Name _____   Problem Solving 2-1

Place Value Through Thousands

Careers Here are the number of Americans who work in each career. Write the word name for each number.

1. Actors/directors/producers—129,000 people
One hundred twenty-nine thousand

2. Aircraft pilots—85,000 people
Eighty-five thousand

3. Auto mechanics—739,000 people
Seven hundred thirty-nine thousand

4. Bank tellers—525,000 people
Five hundred twenty-five thousand

5. All these numbers have been rounded to what place?
The thousands place

Patterns What number comes next?

6. 23; 230; 2,300 **23,000**   7. 439; 4,390; 43,900 **439,000**

8. 124; 1,240; 12,400 **124,000**   9. 309; 3,090; 30,900 **309,000**

10. 31; 313; 3,131 **31,313**   11. 472; 1,472; 10,472 **100,472**

12. 100; 1,000; 10,000 **100,000**

13. 700; 700,000; 700,000,000 **700,000,000,000**

14. The letters of the word "wonderful" have each been assigned a number. Using the chart, write the number for each word below, then write its word name.

W O N D E R F U L
1 2 3 4 5 6 7 8 9

a. FOLDER **729,456; seven hundred twenty-nine thousand, four hundred fifty-six**

b. LOWER **92,156; ninety-two thousand, one hundred fifty-six**

Check

Exercise 7 If students have difficulty, have them say the number aloud first.

Error Intervention Ongoing Assessment

Observation Students may have difficulty with numbers that include zeros.

How to Help Provide blank 9-digit place-value charts and have students write each digit in its proper place. They then use the number to give the word name or expanded form.

Practice

Exercise 14 Point out that this problem has more than one possible answer.

For Early Finishers Challenge early finishers to write the word names for the numbers in Exercises 12 and 13. twenty-four thousand, nine hundred thirty-two; fifty-four thousand, three hundred eighty-nine

③ Close and Assess

Interview

Ask students to write any 6-digit number. Then ask them to explain the place and value of each digit in the number.

Quick Check

Number Sense Explain how the digits 5, 0, and 3 can be used to make more than one 3-digit number. Possible answer: The digits can be used in different places.

Skill Write the value of the digit 5 in each number.

1. 45,677 **5,000**   2. 211,536 **500**

3. 510,627 **500,000**   4. 152,630 **50,000**

ANSWERS

1 Four thousand, six hundred sixty-three

2 Twenty-three thousand, five hundred nine

3 Four hundred thousand, eight hundred six

4 Fifty-six thousand, eight hundred three

8 Twenty-nine thousand, seven hundred sixty-three

9 Seventy-eight thousand, three hundred twenty-one

10 Five hundred thirty-two thousand, nine hundred seventy-one

11 Ninety-six thousand, six hundred seventy-three

Exploring Place-Value Relationships

At-A-Glance Planning

Lesson Planning Checklist

Objective Explore place-value relationships.

Student Book Lesson Materials Place-value blocks (10 hundreds, 20 tens, 20 ones per group), overhead place-value blocks

Materials for pages 54A and 54B Play money (30 $1 bills, 30 $10 bills, 30 $100 bills per pair), adding-machine tape (10 meters per group), scissors, metric rulers, markers (1 of each per group)

Subject Connection science—migration

Strand Connections patterns, using data

	Before Lesson	During Lesson	After Lesson
Daily Math			
p. 54A Problem of the Day			
p. 54A Math Routines			
p. 54A Mental Math			
Teaching Options			
p. 54B Facilitating and Assessing...			
Options for Reaching All Learners			
p. 54B Language Development			
p. 54B Inclusion			
Technology Options			
p. 55 Interactive CD-ROM Journal			
Subject Connections			
p. 54A Literature Connection			
Assessment Options			
p. 54 Talk About It			
p. 55 Error Intervention			
p. 55 Performance Assessment			
Resources			
2-2 Practice			
2-2 Reteaching			
2-2 Enrichment			
2-2 Problem Solving			
2-2 Daily Transparency			

Problem of the Day

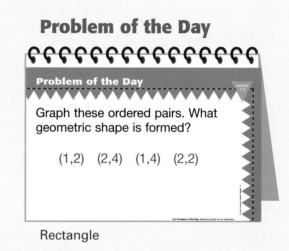

Problem of the Day

Graph these ordered pairs. What geometric shape is formed?

(1,2)   (2,4)   (1,4)   (2,2)

Rectangle

Math Routines

Time Ask students how many hours have elapsed since 3 days ago at the same time. 72 hr

Patterns Have students predict which pattern below will reach 1,000 first, then have them check their predictions.

A: 100, 200, 300, 400...

B: 10, 20, 40, 80...

B will reach 1,000 in 8 steps, A in 10.

Mental Math

Is the difference odd or even? Explain.

31 − 12	42 − 28	34 − 21
Odd	Even	Odd
46 − 38	21 − 16	57 − 29
Even	Odd	Even

Literature Connection

A Week in the Life of an Airline Pilot by William Jaspersohn states that a Boeing 747-100 airplane weighs 377,000 pounds empty and 805,000 pounds full.

- Write the weight of the empty plane in expanded form. 300,000 + 70,000 + 7,000

- What is the place value of the 8 in 805,000? Hundred thousands

Facilitating and Assessing **Explore** Lesson 2-2

Use with pages 54 and 55.

Get Started You may wish to assign roles such as reader, materials manager, and recorder. However, all students should have hands-on experience with the place-value blocks.

Observe Students may use different methods to check that they have the correct number of ones, tens, or hundreds for each number. Some students will count; others may be able to multiply mentally.

Discuss Focus the discussion on different ways to show numbers. For 2-digit numbers such as 80, students can use all ones or all tens. For 3-digit numbers such as 600, students can use all ones, all tens, or all hundreds. By the time they get to 4-digit numbers it will be difficult to model with ones or even tens. Hundreds and thousands blocks will be easier.

Assess Use the rubric to assess students' work. See sample for Practice Exercise 3.

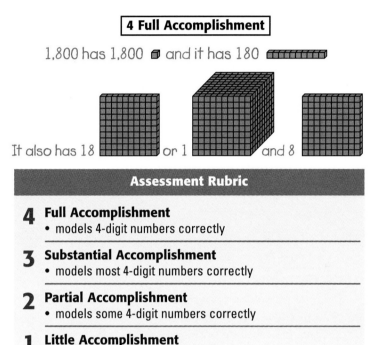

4 Full Accomplishment

1,800 has 1,800 ▱ and it has 180 ▱▱▱▱▱

It also has 18 ▱ or 1 ▱ and 8 ▱

Assessment Rubric

4 Full Accomplishment
- models 4-digit numbers correctly

3 Substantial Accomplishment
- models most 4-digit numbers correctly

2 Partial Accomplishment
- models some 4-digit numbers correctly

1 Little Accomplishment
- does not model 4-digit numbers

Options for Reaching All Learners

Language Development

Fair Exchange
Use play money to name place-value relationships.

Materials Play money (30 $1 bills, 30 $10 bills, 30 $100 bills per pair)

Learning Style Visual, Social, Kinesthetic

- Work with only three pairs at a time. Ask partners to divide the money equally.

- Have one student count out 7 hundreds, 6 tens, and 4 ones, saying each amount clearly.

- Have the second student ask for 1 of the tens by offering ones of equal value and saying: 1 ten for 10 ones. Now you have 7 hundreds, 5 tens, and 14 ones.

- Then have the second student offer a similar exchange of tens for 1 hundred, saying: 1 hundred for 10 tens. Now you have 6 hundreds, 15 tens, and 14 ones.

- Partners can reverse roles for other numbers.

Inclusion

Metric Models
Use lengths of tape to show place-value relationships.

Materials Adding-machine tape (10 meters per group), scissors, metric rulers, markers (1 of each per group)

Learning Style Kinesthetic

- Tell students that they are to use the materials to create models that show ones, tens, and hundreds using units of length. If necessary, remind them that 10 centimeters = 1 decimeter, and that 100 centimeters = 10 decimeters = 1 meter.

- Students can create models by measuring and marking lengths on the tape in various ways. For example, a 10-centimeter strip could be 10, a 1-centimeter length 1, and a 100-centimeter strip 100.

- Have students use their models to show numbers such as 261 or 357.

Lesson Organizer

Objective Explore place-value relationships.

Suggested Grouping 2 to 4

Student Materials Place-value blocks (10 hundreds, 20 tens, 20 ones per group)

Teacher Materials Overhead place-value blocks

Assignment Guide

Basic 1–5, 7–9

Average 1–5, 7–9

Enriched 2–9

1 Introduce

Review

Write each in standard form.

1. 30,000 + 5,000 + 400 + 90 + 3 35,493

2. 400,000 + 500 + 7 400,507

3. 600,000 + 1,000 + 70 601,070

Build on Prior Knowledge

Discuss with students the kinds of models they have used to show ones, tens, and hundreds, such as play money or place-value blocks. Have students model a few 3-digit numbers with place-value blocks.

2 Teach

See Facilitating and Assessing…on page 54B.

Explore ● ● ● ● ● ● ● ● ● ● ● ● ● ● ● ● ●

Use overhead place-value blocks if desired. You may wish to ask questions such as the following as you observe students.

• How are 40 tens related to 400? How can you use the place-value blocks to show this? 40 tens = 400

• What is the greatest number of tens in a 2-digit number? In a 3-digit number? How do you know? 9; 99

Talk About It **Ongoing Assessment**

Listen for students to explain how ones, tens, or hundreds can show a number.

Answers for Talk About It

3 Each place has a value equal to 10 times the place to the right, 100 times the place two places to the right, and so on.

4 10 tens make 100, so 90 tens make 900.

Exploring Place-Value Relationships

Problem Solving Connection

■ Draw a Picture

■ Look for a Pattern

Materials

place-value blocks

Math Tip

Look for place-value patterns.

Explore

You can explore place-value patterns by using place-value blocks or by drawing pictures.

Work Together

1. Use place-value blocks or draw pictures to show your answers.

a. How many ones are in 10? 10

b. How many tens are in 100? 10

c. How many tens are in 200? 20

d. How many hundreds are in 300? 3

e. How many hundreds are in 1,000? 10

2. Use patterns or draw pictures to show your answers.

a. How many tens are in 400? 40

b. How many hundreds are in 4,000? 40

c. How many tens are in 1,000? 100

d. How many hundreds are in 3,600? 36

Talk About It

3. Describe the place-value patterns you found.

4. Suppose you don't have place-value blocks or paper and pencil. How can you find the number of tens in 900?

54 Chapter 2 • Place Value and Time

Practice 2-2

Name _____

Practice 2-2

Exploring Place-Value Relationships

1. Draw pictures to show how many hundreds in 1,100.
Look for 11 pictures, each one representing 100.

Complete the table. You may use place-value blocks or draw pictures to help you.

	Number	Hundreds	Tens	Ones
2.	200	2	20	200
3.	700	7	70	700
4.	1,300	13	130	1,300
5.	5,400	54	540	5,400
6.	7,900	79	790	7,900
7.	9,800	98	980	9,800

8. What is the least number of place-value blocks you need to show 4,200? The greatest?

Possible answer: 4 thousands and 2 hundreds;

4,200 ones blocks

9. What is the least number of place-value blocks you need to show 5,950? The greatest?

Possible answer: 5 thousands, 9 hundreds, and

5 tens; 5,950 ones blocks

Reteaching 2-2

Name _____

Another Look 2-2

Exploring Place-Value Relationships

In your book, you used place-value blocks or pictures to explore number patterns. Here is another way to explore place-value patterns.

Example 1

How many tens are in 500?

Draw a line to the right of the digit in the tens place.

50|0

Read the number to the left of the line.

There are __50 tens__ in 500.

Example 2

How many hundreds are in 6,000?

Draw a line to the right of the digit in the hundreds place.

60|00

Read the number to the left of the line.

There are __60 hundreds__ in 6,000.

Write how many.

1. How many tens are in 400? __40__

2. How many hundreds are in 9,000? __90__

3. a. How many tens are in 6,000? __600__

b. How many hundreds are in 6,000? __60__

4. a. How many tens are in 700? __70__

b. How many hundreds are in 700? __7__

5. a. How many tens are in 1,400? __140__

b. How many hundreds are in 1,400? __14__

6. a. How many tens are in 1,800? __180__

b. How many hundreds are in 1,800? __18__

Connect
Our place-value system is based on groups of 10.

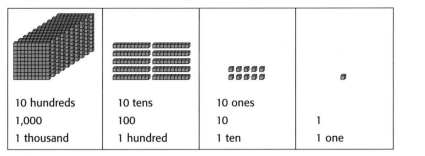

10 hundreds	10 tens	10 ones	
1,000	100	10	1
1 thousand	1 hundred	1 ten	1 one

Practice
Copy and complete the table. You may use place-value blocks or draw pictures to help you.

	Number	Hundreds	Tens	Ones
1.	300	3	30	300
2.	500	5	50	500
3.	1,800	18	180	1,800
4.	2,400	24	240	2,400

5. What is the least number of place-value blocks you need to show 5,000? The greatest?
5 one thousand blocks; 5,000 one blocks

Using Data Use the pictograph for **6–8.**

Distances Traveled to Warmer Climates	
Gray whale	○ ○ ○ ○ ○ ○
White stork	○ ○ ○ ○ ○ ○ ○ ○
Monarch butterfly	○ ○
European eel	○ ○ ○ ○

○ = 1,000 miles

6. Which travels farther, the white stork or the gray whale? **white stork**

7. How far does the European eel travel? **4,000 miles**

8. How far does the monarch butterfly fly? **2,000 miles**

9. **Journal** Suppose you had 1,200 index cards. Explain how you could stack the cards into stacks of 10, 100, and 1,000.

Lesson 2-2   55

Connect
Point out that the place-value blocks increase by 10—there are 10 ones in 1 ten; there are 10 tens in 1 hundred. Connect this to the place values of a 3-digit number such as 546. Each place is 10 times the place to its right.

Error Intervention Ongoing Assessment

Observation Listen for students who have trouble understanding that each place is 10 times the value of the place to its right.

How to Help Point out the relationships shown in the first line of the diagram in Connect. The first line shows how each place relates to the place to its right.

Practice

Exercises 6–8 Ask students to explain the symbol key to make sure they understand that each symbol stands for 1,000 miles.

Exercise 9 Students should realize that they are to stack the index cards in three different ways.

Interactive CD-ROM Journal Students can use the Journal Tool to record and print out their journal explanations. They can use the Place-Value Block Tool to illustrate their work.

For Early Finishers Challenge early finishers to add 5 tens to a number in the table they made for Exercises 1–4 and write the new number as ones, tens, and hundreds in as many ways as they can. Possible answer: 350 = 3 hundreds 5 tens; 3 hundreds 50 ones; 35 tens; 350 ones; 30 tens 50 ones

3 Close and Assess

Performance Assessment

Use place-value blocks or a drawing to show 1,400 with hundreds blocks. Then show 1,400 with the least possible number of blocks. Students' models or drawings should show 14 hundreds blocks and then 1 thousand block and 4 hundreds blocks.

Assess using the rubric on page 54B.

Resources

Technology Master 4

ANSWERS

9 120 stacks of 10; 12 stacks of 100; 1 stack of 1,000 with 200 left over

Place Value Through Millions

At-A-Glance Planning

Objective Read and write numbers through the hundred millions.

Student Book Lesson Materials Teaching Tool Transparency 3 (9-Digit Place-Value Chart)

Materials for pages 56A and 56B Teaching Tool Transparencies 6, 3 (Centimeter Grid Paper, 9-Digit Place-Value Chart)

Subject Connection fine art—crayons

Strand Connections using data, patterns, collecting data, algebra readiness

	Before Lesson	During Lesson	After Lesson
Daily Math			
p. 56A Problem of the Day			
p. 56A Math Routines			
p. 56A Mental Math			
Teaching Options			
p. 56 Student Book Lesson			
p. 56B Another Way to Learn…			
Options for Reaching All Learners			
p. 56B Language Development			
p. 56B Inclusion			
Subject Connections			
p. 56A Social Studies Connection			
Assessment Options			
p. 56 Talk About It			
p. 57 Error Intervention			
p. 57 Portfolio			
p. 57 Quick Check			
Resources			
2-3 Practice			
2-3 Reteaching			
2-3 Enrichment			
2-3 Problem Solving			
2-3 Daily Transparency			

Problem of the Day

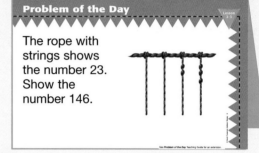

Problem of the Day

Lesson 2-3

The rope with strings shows the number 23. Show the number 146.

For solution art, see pages D1–D4.

Math Routines

Patterns Have students make up six numbers, using the digit 6 once in each. The 6 should have a different value in each number.

Time Ask students to estimate how long 1,000,000 seconds are in days. About 10 days When they have made their estimates, tell them that one day is close to 100,000 seconds (86,400). Have them refine their estimates.

Mental Math

Is each product odd or even? Explain.

12 × 3 Even	11 × 4 Even	20 × 2 Even
7 × 9 Odd	13 × 3 Odd	11 × 5 Odd

Social Studies Connection ◐

In 1991, the population of Calcutta, capital of the Indian state of West Bengal and the world's ninth largest city, was 11,898,000. The population in 1990 of Washington, DC was 606,900. Have students write the word name for each population. Eleven million, eight hundred ninety-eight thousand; Six hundred six thousand, nine hundred

Another Way to Learn Lesson 2-3

Use as an alternative or in addition to pages 56 and 57.

Materials Teaching Tool Transparencies 6, 3 (Centimeter Grid Paper, 9-Digit Place-Value Chart)

Learning Style Visual

- Give each group a supply of centimeter grid paper. Tell students that their task is to find a way to show a million. They can use the grid paper or any type of drawing or diagram.

- Allow groups to work independently until they discover that they will not be able literally to show 1 million squares or other objects. They will need to invent some new model. For example, they might agree that each centimeter square will stand for 1,000. Then they will need 1,000 squares to show 1 million.

- If students do not think of using a place-value chart, suggest that this is another way to show greater numbers. Use the Teaching Tool Transparency 3 (9-Digit Place-Value Chart) on the overhead. Then lead a discussion in which students talk about various ways to show numbers equal to or greater than 1 million.

- Ask each group to create five numbers that each have 7 to 9 digits. They should write the word name for each number and label the places and values of the digits.

- Assign Check and Practice on Student Book pages 56 and 57 or *Practice Master 2-3*.

- Assess using the following rubric.

Assessment Rubric
4 **Full Accomplishment**   • reads and writes numbers through hundred millions
3 **Substantial Accomplishment**   • reads and writes most numbers through hundred millions
2 **Partial Accomplishment**   • reads and writes some numbers through hundred millions
1 **Little Accomplishment**   • does not read and write numbers through hundred millions

Options for Reaching All Learners

Language Development

Patterns in Number Words
Use tables to analyze patterns in word names.

Learning Style Verbal, Visual

- Have students make a three-column table headed: 2 two, 12 twelve, 22 twenty-two.

- In the first column, ask students to write the numbers and word names for 3 through 9. In the second column they write the numbers and word names for 13 through 19, and in the third column the numbers and word names for 23 through 29.

- When the tables are completed, have students look across each row and notice the similarities among the word names. For example, *six, sixteen,* and *sixty* all contain the word *six*.

Inclusion

A Million Times More
Use personal numbers and place-value relationships to create numbers in the millions.

Learning Style Individual, Visual

- Have each student list five numbers that are less than 1,000. Students can choose numbers that they like or that are important to them; for example, their ages, numbers of brothers and sisters, heights in inches. Have students label or describe each number.

- Then have students create another list in which each of their numbers "grows" a million times. For example, a student might write: I have 13 cousins. If I had a million times that many, I would have 13,000,000 cousins.

- Students can illustrate their work with drawings or cartoons.

Lesson Organizer

Objective Read and write numbers through the hundred millions.

Student Materials None

Teacher Materials Teaching Tool Transparency 3 (9-Digit Place-Value Chart), *optional* Lesson Enhancement Transparency 5

Assignment Guide

Basic 7–12, 15–18, 20–23

Average 9–18, 20–23

Enriched 9–10, 13–23

1 Introduce

Review

For each number, name the place of the digit 6.

1. 461,230 Ten thousands

2. 72,106 Ones

3. 6,311 Thousands

Build on Prior Knowledge

Ask students in which of the three exercises above the 6 has the greatest value. Have students explain how they compared the values of the different 6s. 461,230

2 Teach

See Another Way to Learn…on page 56B.

Learn ● ● ● ● ● ● ● ● ● ● ● ● ● ● ● ●

Use Teaching Tool Transparency 3 (9-Digit Place-Value Chart) on the overhead. Demonstrate how to use the period names in reading a number: 349,568,172 is read 349 million, 568 thousand, 172. Have students write the standard form and the word name for the number. Three hundred forty-nine million, five hundred sixty-eight thousand, one hundred seventy-two

Talk About It **Ongoing Assessment**

Watch to see that students understand the difference between the value of a digit and the name of that digit's place. For example, in 483,261, the digit 8 is in the ten thousands place. It has a value of 8 ten thousands, or 80 thousands, or 80,000.

Answer for Talk About It

Each has hundreds, tens, and ones places.

Check ● ● ● ● ● ● ● ● ● ● ● ● ● ● ●

Allow students to use a place-value chart.

Place Value Through Millions

You Will Learn
how to read and write numbers through the hundred millions

Learn ● ● ● ● ●

What is the greatest number of crayons you've ever used to make a drawing? You might like to visit a crayon factory that made 145,432,279 crayons in a month!

Place value can help you understand this number.

If 145,432,279 crayons were put in a row, they would almost reach from Washington, D.C., to Calcutta, India.

Millions Period			Thousands Period			Ones Period		
hundred millions	ten millions	millions	hundred thousands	ten thousands	thousands	hundreds	tens	ones
1	4	5 ,	4	3	2 ,	2	7	9

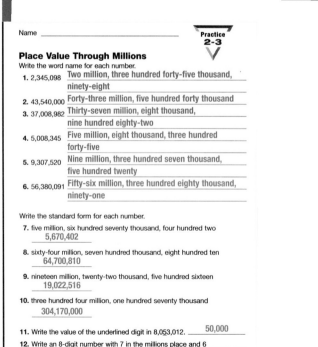

Math Tip
When you read a number, read the number in each period and then the period name.

standard form 145,432,279

word name one hundred forty-five million, four hundred thirty-two thousand, two hundred seventy-nine

Talk About It

What do the three periods—the millions, the thousands, and the ones—have in common?

Check ●

Write the word name for each number.

1. 36,921,438 **2.** 400,000 **3.** 8,200,000

4. Write five million, one hundred thousand in standard form. 5,100,000

5. Write the value of the red digit in 43,261,800. 3,000,000

6. **Reasoning** What is the greatest place value of an 8-digit number? ten millions

---

Name _____

Practice 2-3

Place Value Through Millions

Write the word name for each number.

1. 2,345,098 Two million, three hundred forty-five thousand, ninety-eight

2. 43,540,000 Forty-three million, five hundred forty thousand

3. 37,008,982 Thirty-seven million, eight thousand, nine hundred eighty-two

4. 5,008,345 Five million, eight thousand, three hundred forty-five

5. 9,307,520 Nine million, three hundred seven thousand, five hundred twenty

6. 56,380,091 Fifty-six million, three hundred eighty thousand, ninety-one

Write the standard form for each number.

7. five million, six hundred seventy thousand, four hundred two
5,670,402

8. sixty-four million, seven hundred thousand, eight hundred ten
64,700,810

9. nineteen million, twenty-two thousand, five hundred sixteen
19,022,516

10. three hundred four million, one hundred seventy thousand
304,170,000

11. Write the value of the underlined digit in 8,0_5_3,012. 50,000

12. Write an 8-digit number with 7 in the millions place and 6 in the thousands place. Possible answers: 17,006,000; 97,546,039

13. In the number 19,853,372, which digit has the least value? 2

Skills and Reasoning

Write the word name for each number.

7. 9,253,074   **8.** 10,634,000   **9.** 23,046,116   **10.** 15,306,108

Write the standard form for each number.

11. four million, seven hundred thousand, nine hundred fifty **4,700,950**

12. five million, three hundred ninety thousand, seven **5,390,007**

13. Write the value of the red digit in 10,100,110. **10,000,000**

14. Write a 7-digit number with 4 in the ten-thousands place and 4 in the thousands place. **Possible answer: 3,244,900**

15. In the number 12,345,678, which digit has the greatest value? **1**

Problem Solving and Applications

16. Using Data Use the Data File on page 48. Write the word name for the number of crayons Douglas Mehrens uses. **twenty-eight thousand**

Patterns Look for a pattern. Write the number that comes next.

17. 429, 4,290, 42,900   **18.** 5,625,000, 562,500, 56,250
429,000   **5,625**

19. Collecting Data Find a fact that uses a number in the millions. Write the standard form or the word name for the number. **Answers will vary.**

20. Critical Thinking A certain number has six digits. Can the number be in the millions? Explain. **No; Millions is the seventh place value.**

Mixed Review and Test Prep

Find each answer.

21. 3 + 8 = n **11**

22. 18 − 8 = n **10**

23. Find the median weight of the soccer players. **C**

Ⓐ 72 lb

Ⓑ 70 lb

Ⓒ 63 lb

Ⓓ 61 lb

70 lb   63 lb   72 lb   61 lb   60 lb

Skills Practice Bank, page 560, Set 1   Lesson 2-3   **57**

Enrichment 2-3

Name _____   Extend Your Thinking 2-3

Critical Thinking
Estimation How much is a million? Read each situation. Circle your best guess. Explain what you could do to check your estimate.

1. If one million kids climbed onto each other's shoulders they would be:
a. as tall as a 110-story building
b. farther up than airplanes can fly
c. past the moon
Possible answer: Find out about how tall 100 kids would be, then multiply by 10,000.

2. If you wanted to count from one to one million, it would take you about:
a. 12 days
b. 2 years
c. 95 years
Possible answer: Find out how long it takes you to count to 100 or 1,000, then multiply by 10,000 or 1,000.

3. The world's largest peanut measured 4 in. How far would a million similar peanuts stretch if they were laid end to end?
a. 1 mile
b. 63 miles
c. 40 feet
Possible answer: Find the number of feet, then miles equal to 4 million inches.

Problem Solving 2-3

Name _____   Problem Solving 2-3

Place Value Through Millions

Science The Earth is $4\frac{1}{2}$ billion years old. Scientists divide the Earth's history into time periods according to the fossils they find in rocks. Use the table of periods in Earth's history to solve the problems.

Time Period	When It Began
Late Triassic Period	225,000,000 years ago
Jurassic Period	213,000,000 years ago
Cretaceous Period	144,000,000 years ago
Tertiary Period	65,000,000 years ago

1. Write the word name for the number that tells when the Tertiary period began. **Sixty-five million**

2. Which period began one hundred forty-four million years ago? **Cretaceous period**

3. Which two periods began more than two-hundred million years ago? **Jurassic and Late Triassic periods**

Solve the riddles.

4. I'm a seven-digit number with digits from 1 to 7. Each digit is used once. From left to right the digits go from least to greatest. What number am I? **1,234,567**

5. I'm an odd six-digit number whose tens digit is less than the tens digit in 345,211. My ones digit is greater than the ones digit in 345,208. The rest of my digits are the same as these two numbers. What number am I? **345,209**

6. I'm a number that ends in 0 or 5. I have exactly three 1s and three 0s for digits. What number could I be?
Possible answers: 111,000; 110,100; 100,110; 1,000,115

Error Intervention **Ongoing Assessment**

Observation Some students may have difficulty writing numbers that contain several zeros, as in Exercise 4.

How to Help Remind students that there are always three digits after a comma.

Practice • • • • • • • • • • • • • • • • • • •

Exercise 16 Lesson Enhancement Transparency 5 reproduces the Data File.
Exercises 17 and 18 Remind students to identify the pattern in the given numbers before writing the next number.

For Early Finishers Have students write the word names for the numbers in Exercise 17.
four hundred twenty-nine; four thousand, two hundred ninety; forty-two thousand, nine hundred

③ Close and Assess

Portfolio
Have students create 9-digit numbers and identify the periods, the place names, and values of each digit.

Quick Check

Number Sense One number begins with 8 in the thousands place. Another number begins with 3 in the ten thousands place. Which number is greater? The one that begins with 3 in the ten thousands place

Skill Write the value of the 9 in each.

1. 4,697,125 90,000

2. 291,536,736 90,000,000

3. 10,629,512 9,000

4. 211,956,010 900,000

ANSWERS

1 thirty-six million, nine hundred twenty-one thousand, four hundred thirty-eight

2 four hundred thousand

3 eight million, two hundred thousand

7 nine million, two hundred fifty-three thousand, seventy-four

8 ten million, six hundred thirty-four thousand

9 twenty-three million, forty-six thousand, one hundred sixteen

10 fifteen million, three hundred six thousand, one hundred eight

At-A-Glance Planning

Objective Solve problems by making an organized list.

Student Book Lesson Materials Teaching Tool Transparencies 1, 2 (Guided Problem Solving)

Materials for pages 58A and 58B Teaching Tool Transparencies 1, 2 (Guided Problem Solving), Power Polygons (1 triangle, 1 rectangle, 1 square, and 1 parallelogram per pair), index cards (8 per pair)

Subject Connections fine arts—crayons, Arcimboldo; geography—mapmaking

Strand Connections using data, patterns, logic, collecting data, algebra readiness

	Before Lesson	During Lesson	After Lesson
Daily Math			
p. 58A Problem of the Day			
p. 58A Math Routines			
p. 58A Mental Math			
Teaching Options			
p. 58 Student Book Lesson			
p. 58B Another Way to Learn…			
Options for Reaching All Learners			
p. 58B Inclusion			
p. 58B Reading Assist			
Technology Options			
p. 58A *Logical Journey of the Zoombinis*			
Assessment Options			
p. 59 Talk About It			
p. 61 Quick Check			
Resources			
2-4 Practice			
2-4 Reteaching			
2-4 Enrichment			
2-4 Problem Solving			
2-4 Daily Transparency			

Problem of the Day

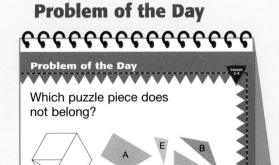

D

Math Routines

Calendar Have students list three consecutive days in the month and form as many even numbers as possible. For example, May 2, 3, and 4 make 234; July 16, 17, and 18 make 161, 718.

Money Have students find the total cost of a $1.95 magazine and a $0.35 pretzel. Then have them list five different ways they could pay for these items without using pennies. $2.30; Possible answer: 8 quarters, 3 dimes; 20 dimes, 6 nickels

Mental Math

Is each quotient odd or even? Explain.

$25 \div 5$	$21 \div 7$	$49 \div 7$
Odd	Odd	Odd
$24 \div 3$	$48 \div 8$	$64 \div 8$
Even	Even	Even

Logical Journey of the Zoombinis

Students can use the Make an Organized List strategy to solve *Captain Cajun's Ferry Boat.* The Zoombinis are arranged on the ferry boat according to their attributes. Students can list common and uncommon attributes to help them discover the rules for the arrangement.

Another Way to **Learn** Lesson 2-4

Use as an alternative or in addition to pages 58-61.

Materials Teaching Tool Transparencies 1, 2 (Guided Problem Solving)

Learning Style Kinesthetic

- Ask eight volunteers to come to the front of the room. Then pose this problem: If each student shakes hands with every other student, how many handshakes will there be? Have students suggest methods of solving the problem. List their methods.

- Have students solve the problem by acting it out. There will be 28 handshakes in all.

- Then ask students how they could solve the problem without actually having people shake hands. Highlight or share the method of using a list.

- Have pairs of students make a list for the problem.

- Have students discuss when using the strategy Make an Organized List is useful. Use Teaching Tool Transparencies 1, 2 (Guided Problem Solving) to review the steps in solving problems.

Student	Shakes With...						
1	2	3	4	5	6	7	8
2	3	4	5	6	7	8	
3	4	5	6	7	8		
4	5	6	7	8			
5	6	7	8				
6	7	8					
7	8						
8							

- Assign Check and Practice on Student Book pages 59–61 or *Practice Master 2-4*.

- Assess using the following rubric.

Assessment Rubric

4 Full Accomplishment
- solves problems by making an organized list

3 Substantial Accomplishment
- solves most problems by making an organized list

2 Partial Accomplishment
- solves simple problems using an organized list

1 Little Accomplishment
- does not use a list to solve problems

Options for Reaching All Learners

Inclusion

How Many Pairs?
Use polygons to find the number of possible pairs in a set.

Materials Power Polygons (1 triangle, 1 rectangle, 1 square, and 1 parallelogram per pair)

Learning Style Kinesthetic

- Have students start with the triangle, rectangle, and square. Ask them to find and record all the combinations of two different shapes. 3 pairs: TR, TS, RS

- Have students use all four shapes and find all possible pairs. 6 pairs: TR, TS, TP, RS, RP, SP

- Show students how to organize their results by making a list for each problem. Emphasize that the items in the list should be organized.

Reading Assist

Make Predictions
Use index cards to make predictions.

Materials Index cards (8 per pair)

Learning Style Logical, Visual

- Have students write these color names on index cards: red, orange, yellow, green, blue, purple, brown, black.

- Ask students to predict how many two-color combinations they can make using these 8 colors. Remind students that red-orange and orange-red are the same color pair.

- Students can use the cards to produce all combinations and check predictions. 28 combinations: RO, RY, RG, RBl, RP, RBr, RBlk, OY, OG, OBl, OP, OBr, OBlk, YG, YBl, YP, YBr, YBlk, GBl, GP, GBr, GBlk, BlP, BlBr, BlBlk, PBr, PBlk, BrBlk

Lesson Organizer

Objective Solve problems by making an organized list.

Suggested Grouping 2 to 4

Student Materials None

Teacher Materials Teaching Tool Transparencies 1, 2 (Guided Problem Solving)

Assignment Guide
Basic 3–5, 8, 10–21
Average 4–6, 8–21
Enriched 4–21

1 Introduce

Review

Arrange the letters A and B and the numbers 1, 2, and 3 to form as many letter-number pairs as possible. A1, A2, A3, B1, B2, B3

Build on Prior Knowledge

After students have found all the letter-number pairs, ask them how organizing their work can help solve the problem. Possible answer: List the pairs that start with A, then the pairs that start with B. Listing pairs in an organized way helps to make sure all possibilities are found and none are duplicated.

2 Teach

See Another Way to Learn...on page 58B.

Learn ●

Use Teaching Tool Transparencies 1, 2 (Guided Problem Solving) to review the problem solving steps. As students work on page 58, relate the steps on the overhead to those on the text page.

Reading Assist **Understand**

Organizational Devices

Write these color words on the overhead or chalkboard: *yellow, green, blue, purple.* Ask students if they can use a single letter to represent each color. Yes: Y, G, B, P

Next to each color, write the letter that represents it. Students can refer to the list as they work on page 58.

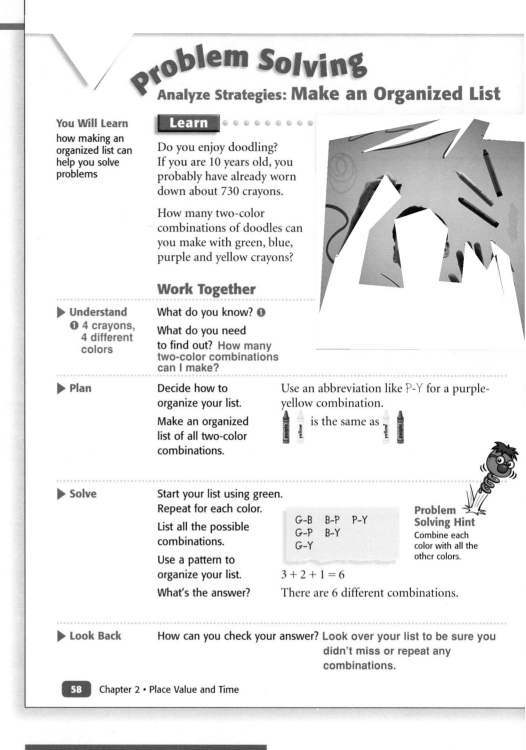

Analyze Strategies: Make an Organized List

You Will Learn
how making an organized list can help you solve problems

Learn ● ● ● ● ● ● ● ● ●

Do you enjoy doodling? If you are 10 years old, you probably have already worn down about 730 crayons.

How many two-color combinations of doodles can you make with green, blue, purple and yellow crayons?

Work Together

▶ **Understand** | What do you know? ❶
❶ 4 crayons, 4 different colors | What do you need to find out? How many two-color combinations can I make?

▶ **Plan** | Decide how to organize your list. | Use an abbreviation like P-Y for a purple-yellow combination.
| Make an organized list of all two-color combinations. | is the same as

▶ **Solve** | Start your list using green. Repeat for each color.
List all the possible combinations.
Use a pattern to organize your list.
What's the answer? |

G-B	B-P	P-Y
G-P	B-Y	
G-Y		

$3 + 2 + 1 = 6$

There are 6 different combinations.

Problem Solving Hint
Combine each color with all the other colors.

▶ **Look Back** | How can you check your answer? Look over your list to be sure you didn't miss or repeat any combinations.

Managing Time

To teach this lesson in one day, work through page 58 and Exercises 1, 3, 5, and 7–9 on pages 59–61 in the first half of the period. Then discuss the top of page 59 and assign the remaining exercises. Some may be done for homework.

Another Example

Here's another chance to be an artist. Shirts come in red, white, or blue. Letters on the shirts can be purple or green. Can you design 7 different two-color shirts?

What You Read	What You Do
a. Shirts come in red, white, or blue. Lettering can be purple or green.	Make a list. RP WP BP RG WG BG
b. Can you design 7 different two-color shirts?	Count the entries
No, you can only make 6 different shirts.	There are 6 entries.

Talk About It

Why is making an organized list a good strategy to use to solve the problems in the Examples?

Check

Use an organized list to help solve each problem.

Problem Solving
Understand
Plan
Solve
Look Back

1. How many two-color combinations can you make with one primary and one secondary color?

Primary colors

Secondary colors

1a. Red, blue, or yellow
1b. RG, RP, RO, BG, BP, BO, YG, YP,
a. To start your list, pick a primary color.
b. Combine that color with each secondary color. Then for each other primary color, write its combinations with each secondary color.
c. How many different ways did you find? **9 ways**
d. Did you find them all? **Answers will vary.**

2. At Picasso's Art Shop, paint brushes are packed in boxes of 10, 100, or 1,000 brushes. There is an order for 1,150 paint brushes.
a. Find three different ways to fill the order.
b. What is the fewest number of boxes needed to fill the order? **7**
c. What is the greatest number of boxes needed to fill the order? **115**

Lesson 2-4   59

Another Example

It may be simpler for students to write out the chart using words rather than single letters to represent colors. If time permits, have students draw and color an example of each shirt.

Talk About It Ongoing Assessment

Make sure students understand that an organized list helps to find all the possibilities in each category.

Answer for Talk About It

Possible answers: It helps keep track of the data. It helps you see patterns. When you look for missing parts or a pattern, it helps you find all the answers. You can make sure you don't list anything twice.

Check

Exercise 2 Be sure students understand that there are many different ways to pack the paint brushes, which means there isn't just one correct answer.

Meeting Individual Needs

Learning Style	Teaching Approach
Visual	Have students create a diagram or make a drawing to solve the problem at the top of page 59. Then they can compare their work with the list approach in the text.
Kinesthetic	Students might use counters, color cubes, or scraps of paper to represent possible choices, then combine choices in an array, creating a list as they go.

Practice

Practice

Reading Assist Word Meaning

If necessary, explain that *neon* is a gas that is used in some electric lights. Neon markers do not actually contain neon. Their ink is the color of neon lights.

Exercise 5 Check that students can identify the names of the different kinds of fruits and vegetables.

Exercise 10 Suggest students create problems that require finding a set of possible combinations.

For Early Finishers Challenge early finishers to find and list the number of two-color combinations possible with 9, 10, 11, and 12 different colors. 36, 45, 55, 66

Problem Solving Practice

Apply the Strategy

Make an organized list to solve each problem.

[GPS] **3.** Suppose you have 5 neon markers: green, purple, blue, yellow, and pink. You choose 2 markers to make a drawing.

   a. How many different choices do you have? 10

   b. If one color must be green, how many choices do you have? 4

   c. If someone gave you an orange marker so you had 6 markers in all, how many choices do you have? 15

4. At the store, paper is packed in boxes of 10, 100, or 1,000 sheets. Suppose a customer orders 2,250 sheets.

   a. Find three ways the order can be filled.

   b. What is the fewest boxes needed to fill the order? 9

   c. What is the most boxes needed to fill the order? 225

4a. Possible answer: 2 large boxes, 2 medium boxes, 5 small boxes; 22 medi boxes, 5 small boxes, 225 small boxes

Choose the Strategy

Make an organized list or use any strategy to solve each problem.

5. **Fine Arts** How many different faces can you make?

Pairs of eyes:

Noses:

Mouth:

Explain the strategy you used.

6. Mike and Nadi have a total of 15 markers. Nadi has 3 less than Mike. How many markers do each have? Mike has 9; Nadi has 6.

Problem Solving Strategies

- Use Objects/Act It Out
- Draw a Picture
- Look for a Pattern
- Guess and Check
- Use Logical Reasoning
- Make an Organized List
- Make a Table
- Solve a Simpler Problem
- Work Backward

Choose a Tool

Painting by Italian artist Giuseppe Arcimboldo (1527–1593)

60   Chapter 2 • Place Value and Time

Practice 2-4	Reteaching 2-4

Problem Solving and GEOGRAPHY

When maps are drawn, areas that touch are given different colors. To fill in any map, you need at most four different colors.

7. How many four-color combinations are possible with 5 crayons? **5**

8. Delaware has 20 counties fewer than Wyoming. How many counties does Delaware have? **3**

9. **Collecting Data** What states border Wyoming? **Montana, South Dakota, Nebraska, Colorado, Utah, Idaho**

The state of Wyoming has 23 counties, which are shown here.

10. **Journal** Use the art supplies to write a problem that can be solved by making an organized list.

Art Supplies
Crayon
Paint
Chalk
Chart paper
Poster board

Mixed Review and Test Prep

Algebra Readiness Find each sum or difference.

11. $9 + 3 = n$ **12**
12. $14 - 9 = n$ **5**
13. $8 + 4 = n$ **12**
14. $17 - 6 = n$ **11**
15. $8 + 7 = n$ **15**
16. $17 - 8 = n$ **9**
17. $6 + 8 = n$ **14**
18. $18 - 9 = n$ **9**

Using Data Use the bar graph to answer 19–21.

19. Which is the most popular color? **Blue**

20. Which color had 2 more votes than violet? **Red**

21. How many students were asked which was their favorite color? **D**
    Ⓐ 12 Ⓑ 22
    Ⓒ 32 Ⓓ 42

Our Favorite Colors

(bar graph: Red, Violet, Green, Blue, Pink, Black — Number of Students 0–12)

Skills Practice Bank, page 560, Set 6   Lesson 2-4   **61**

Historical Note

The Four-Color Theorem states that no more than four colors are needed to color a flat map so that no areas that touch have the same color. This theorem was proved in 1976 using a computer, although the proof is still being challenged. If a map is drawn on a three-dimensional object such as a torus (a doughnut-shaped solid), more colors may be needed. For example, a map drawn on a torus requires seven colors.

③ Close and Assess

Ask students to discuss how they might find all the different two-color combinations using a set of 6 colors of paint. Encourage suggestions that lead to making an organized list.

Quick Check

1. When you are listing two-color combinations, how can you keep your list organized? Possible answer: Write all the combinations that start with one color before listing the combinations that start with the next color.

2. When listing two-color combinations for 4 crayons, a student found three possibilities for each color. What did the student do wrong? Possible answer: The student listed the same pairs twice, for example red-orange and orange-red.

ANSWERS

2a Possible answers: 1 box of 1,000, 1 box of 100, 5 boxes of 10; 11 boxes of 100, 5 boxes of 10; 1 box of 1,000, 15 boxes of 10

5 There are 6 different faces. Make an organized list or draw a picture.

10 Answers should include problems that use combinations of paper and crayon, paint, or chalk.

Enrichment 2-4

Name _____ Extend Your Thinking **2-4**

Patterns in Numbers
Tell what rule was used to make the pattern. What are the next two numbers?

1. 30, 40, 50, 60, ___ **70** , ___ **80**
   Rule: **Add 10.**

2. 1; 10; 100; 1,000; ___ **10,000** ; ___ **100,000**
   Rule: **Multiply by 10.**

3. 2, 4, 8, 16, ___ **32** , ___ **64**
   Rule: **Multiply by 2.**

4. 26; 260; 2,600; 26,000; ___ **260,000** ; ___ **2,600,000**
   Rule: **Multiply by 10.**

5. 22,195; 22,190; 22,185; 22,180; ___ **22,175** ; ___ **22,170**
   Rule: **Subtract 5.**

6. 3; 30; 300; 3,000; ___ **30,000** ; ___ **300,000**
   Rule: **Multiply by 10.**

7. 360,000; 36,000; 3,600; ___ **360** ; ___ **36**
   Rule: **Divide by 10.**

8. 520,000; 52,000; 5,200; ___ **520** ; ___ **52**
   Rule: **Divide by 10.**

Make up your own number patterns. Leave some blank spaces. Give them to a classmate to solve. **Answers will vary. Check students' patterns.**

9. ___ , ___ , ___ , ___ , ___

10. ___ , ___ , ___ , ___ , ___

Problem Solving 2-4

Name _____ Guided Problem Solving **2-4**

GPS PROBLEM 3, STUDENT PAGE 60

Suppose you have 5 neon markers: green, purple, blue, yellow, and pink. You choose 2 markers to make a drawing.

a. How many different choices do you have?

b. If one color must be green, how many choices do you have?

— **Understand** —
1. What do you know?
   Part a. **5 markers of different colors, you choose 2**
   Part b. **1 marker must be green.**
2. What must you find?
   Part a. **Number of choices you have**
   Part b. **Number of choices you have if one must be green**

— **Plan** —
How can you organize your answers? **Make an organized list.**

— **Solve** —
List your choices. How many are there?
   Part a. **G Pu, G B, G Y, G Pi; Pu B, Pu Y, Pu Pi; B Y, B Pi; Y P; 10**
   Part b. **G Pu, G B, G Y , G Pi; 4**

— **Look Back** —
How can you check your answers? **Use markers or crayons.**

SOLVE ANOTHER PROBLEM

What if the same set of 5 markers had 2 blue markers and no green markers? What are your choices?
B Pu, B Pi, B Y, B B; Pu Pi, Pu Y; Pi Y

Chapter 2
Practice Game

Students will strengthen number sense and place value skills as they play the practice game.

Learning Style Logical

Student Materials Calculator, Teaching Tool Transparency 18 (Chapter 2 Game Board), 2 markers, set of digit cards 1–9, *optional Assessment Sourcebook 10 (How We Worked in Our Group)*

Preparation

Use index cards to make a set of digit cards for each group of students.

How to Play

Provide each group with one calculator, one copy of the gameboard, 2 markers, and a set of digit cards. Have students read the game rules and make sure they understand both the rules of the game and the goal. To win, a player or team must make *exactly* 10,000 points. Let students know they can use the calculator to check the addition for their scores.

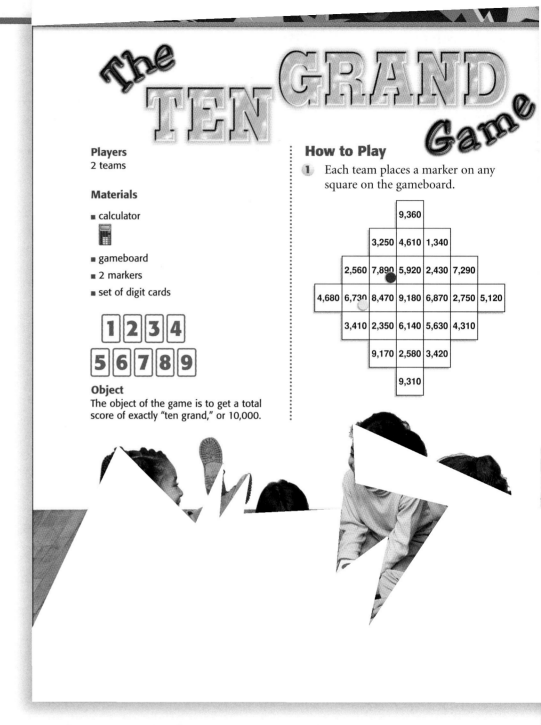

The TEN GRAND Game

Players
2 teams

Materials
- calculator
- gameboard
- 2 markers
- set of digit cards

1 2 3 4
5 6 7 8 9

Object
The object of the game is to get a total score of exactly "ten grand," or 10,000.

How to Play
1. Each team places a marker on any square on the gameboard.

		9,360				
	3,250	4,610	1,340			
	2,560	7,890	5,920	2,430	7,290	
4,680	6,730	8,470	9,180	6,870	2,750	5,120
	3,410	2,350	6,140	5,630	4,310	
		9,170	2,580	3,420		
		9,310				

Math Center Option

As an alternative, set up this game in a math center for students to play independently. Post a recording sheet for students to record their scores and the strategies they devised for playing the game.

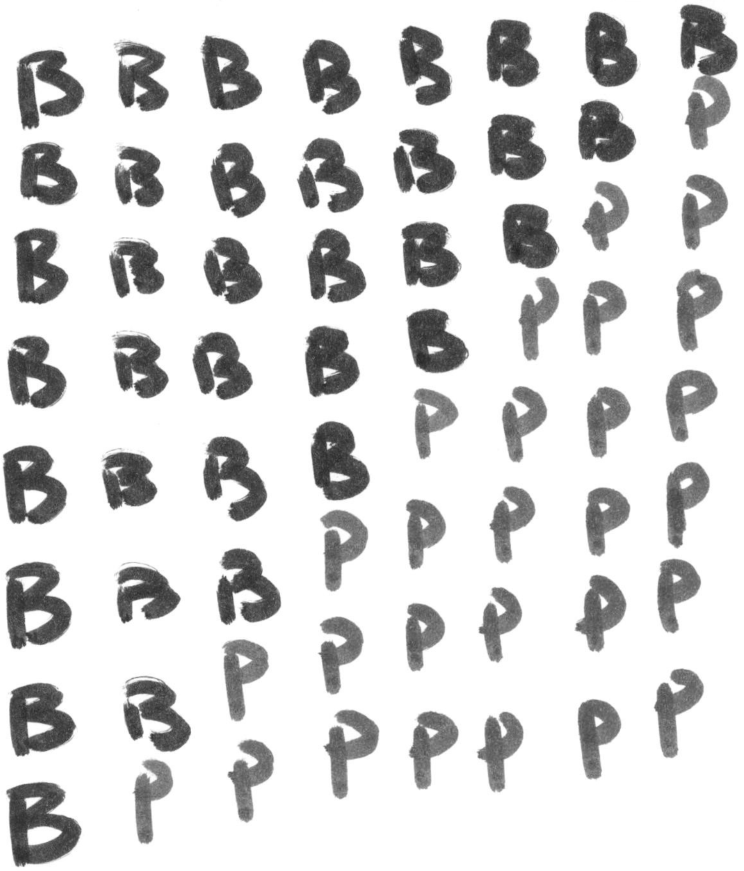

2 Each team draws a digit card and returns it to the stack. The team with the greater number goes first.

3 Each team draws a digit card. A team may move its marker to any "touching" square with a matching digit. The marker may be moved up, down, left, right, or diagonally.

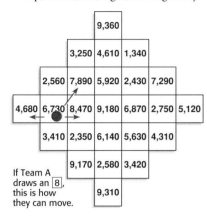

If Team A draws an 8, this is how they can move.

4 If no "touching" square has the digit, the team loses a turn.

5 Each team scores the place value of the matching digit.

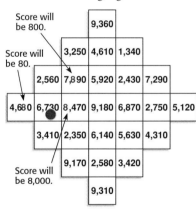

Score will be 800.

Score will be 80.

Score will be 8,000.

6 Both teams record their scores and return the digit cards to the stack.

7 Both teams continue to take turns. Each team adds its scores. The first team to score exactly 10,000 wins. If a team goes over 10,000, it loses.

Talk About It

1. Did you always choose to move to the greatest number? Explain.

2. What strategies did you use to get to 10,000 without "going over"?

More Ways to Play

- Play again. Make a 0 digit card for the stack.

- Play again. Change your goal from 10,000 to 20,000.

- Make your own gameboard by copying the grid and putting your own 4-digit numbers in the squares.

Reasoning

1. Suppose your score was 8,000 and your digit card was 2. Would 2,560 or 3,420 be a better choice for your move? Explain.

2. Suppose your score was 8,000 and your digit card was 3. Would 3,420 or 9,310 be a better choice for your move? Explain.

3. If your score was 6,800, what numbers would you need to win in two moves? In three moves?

The Ten Grand Game  63

Cooperative Learning

Distribute *Assessment Sourcebook 10* (How We Worked in Our Group) and have students fill it out for the skill Disagree in an Agreeable Way. Review the characteristics of this skill. Invite students to judge themselves on the skill as they work together.

Section A
Review and Practice

Use the Skills Checklist

Review the **Skills Checklist** on the page with students. Then ask questions such as the following:

- In which exercises will you need to understand or use the following words:

  word name? Exercises 4–9

  period? Exercise 1

  standard form? Exercise 2

  expanded form? Exercise 3, 10–11

- In which problems will you identify place value? Exercises 12–16
- In which problems will you use a table or a list? Exercises 10–11, 17

Assess

You may wish to use this information to assess students' understanding of the lesson objectives.

Item Analysis

Lesson Objective		Items
2-1	Read and write numbers in the thousands.	2–8
2-2	Explore place-value relationships.	10, 11, 18
2-3	Read and write numbers through the hundred millions.	1, 9, 12–16
2-4	Solve problems by making an organized list.	17

Resources

Practice Masters

- Practice Chapter 2 Section A

Assessment Sourcebook

- Quiz Chapter 2 Section A

TestWorks: Test and Practice Software

ANSWERS

5–9, 18 See pages D1–D4.

Review and Practice

Vocabulary Match each with its example.

1. number with three periods **c**
2. standard form **b**
3. expanded form **d**
4. word name **a**

a. twenty-five thousand, one hundred eleven
b. 2,154
c. 100,000,000
d. $50,000 + 2,000 + 600 + 40 + 3$

(Lesson 1) Write the word name for each number.

5. 14,913   6. 892,211   7. 3,479   8. 555,000   9. 5,006,390

(Lesson 2) Copy and complete the table.

	Number	Hundreds	Tens	Ones
10.	4,000	40	400	4,000
11.	2,900	29	290	2,900

(Lesson 3) Write the value of each red digit.

12. 86,987,002
80,000,000

13. 72,989,920
2,000,000

14. 900,900,020
900,000,000

15. 362,481
60,000

16. **Science** Earth is about 93,000,000 miles from the sun. Mercury is about 36,000,000 miles from the sun and is the planet closest to the sun. Write the value of the digit 3 in each number. 3,000,000; 30,000,000

(Lesson 4) Make an organized list or use any strategy to solve.

17. Cards are packed in boxes of 10, 100, or 1,000 cards.
    a. Find three different ways to fill an order for 1,750 cards.
    b. What is the fewest number of boxes needed to fill the order? 13
    c. What is the greatest number of boxes needed to fill the order? 175

18. **Journal** How would you explain to a friend what place value means? What tools or pictures would you use?

17a. Possible answer: 1 box of 1,000, 7 boxes of 100, 5 boxes of 10; 17 boxes of 100, 5 boxes of 10, 1 box of 1,000, 75 boxes of 10

Skills Checklist

In this section, you have:

☑ Learned About Place Value Through Millions

☑ Explored Place-Value Relationships

☑ Solved Problems by Making an Organized List

REVIEW AND PRACTICE

64   Chapter 2 • Review and Practice

Practice

Name _____

Practice
Chapter 2
Section A

Review and Practice

Vocabulary Write true or false for each statement.

1. 25,206,102 has two periods. __false__
2. The expanded form of 1,367 is one thousand, three hundred sixty-seven. __false__
3. The standard form of 40,000 + 7,000 + 4 is 47,004. __true__

(Lessons 1 and 3) Write the value of each underlined digit.

4. 23,189 __3,000__   5. 36,345,899 __30,000,000__

6. Write the word name for 6,382.
   six thousand, three hundred eighty-two

(Lesson 2) Complete the table.

	Number	Hundreds	Tens	Ones
7.	3,500	35	350	3,500
8.	700	7	70	700

(Lesson 4) Make an organized list or use any strategy to solve.

9. Name all the different outfits can you make from this set of clothing: red shirt (RS), green shirt (GS), brown pants (BP), blue jeans (BJ), crew socks (CS), and tube socks (TS).
   (RS) (BP) (CS); (RS) (BP) (TS); (RS) (BJ) (CS); (RS) (BJ) (TS);
   (GS) (BP) (CS); (GS) (BP) (TS); (GS) (BJ) (CS); (GS) (BJ) (TS)

(Mixed Review) Find the range, median, and mode for each set of numbers.

10. 11, 13, 5, 4, 6, 6, 2 __11__ ; __6__ ; __6__
11. 3, 5, 5, 5, 3, 8, 2, 1 __7__ ; __4__ ; __5__
12. 0, 0, 4, 0, 3, 4, 7, 4, 0, 0 __5__ ; __4__ ; __3, 4__

Building Number Sense

In the past 50 years, the population of Springfield, Missouri, has grown from almost 67,000 people to more than 150,000.

Make a list of different ways you can show that your city is larger or smaller than Springfield.

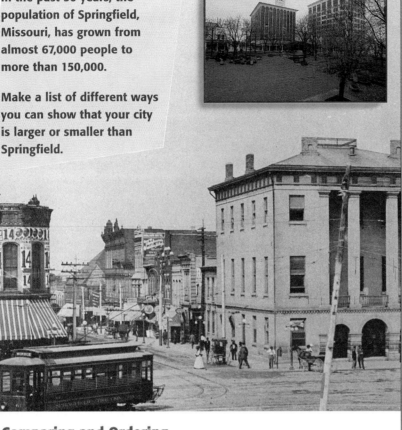

Comparing and Ordering Numbers

Review place value. Which number do you say first when you count from 1?

1. 19 or 91
19

2. 47 or 41
41

3. 45 or 43
43

4. 29 or 39
29

5. 160 or 150
150

6. 225 or 235
225

Skills Checklist

In this section, you will:
☐ Compare Numbers
☐ Order Numbers
☐ Explore Rounding

65

Building Number Sense

In this section, students will compare and order greater numbers. They will also round numbers to the nearest hundred or thousand.

Subskills

The work in this section builds on...

- Understanding place value through thousands

204,431 = two hundred four thousand, four hundred thirty-one

- Understanding place value through millions

145,432,279 = one hundred forty-five million, four hundred thirty-two thousand, two hundred seventy-nine

Use the Section Opener

In 1810, the population of the entire state of Missouri was 19,783. By 1990, the population was more than 5 million! Ask students how they might compare the size of their own home town or city to that of Springfield. Compare number of people, amount of land, number of buildings.

Use the **Skills Checklist** and **GET READY** to preview the skills taught in Section B and to assess students' readiness for Lesson 2–5.

Skills Trace

(Red numbers indicate pages in this section.)

Lesson and Skill	First Introduced	Grade Four			
		Introduce	Develop	Practice/Apply	Review
2-5 Compare numbers to find which is greater.	Grade 3	66, 67	66	67, 72, 560	72, 86, 89
2-6 Order a group of numbers.	Grade 3	68, 69	68	69, 72, 85, 560	72, 85, 86, 89
2-7 Explore rounding.	Grade 3	70, 71	70, 71	71, 72, 85, 560	72, 85, 86, 89

Mixed Review and Test Prep exercises for this chapter occur on pages 53, 57, 61, 67, 69, 75, 79.

Multi-Age Classrooms Use pages 63–72 in Grade 3 or pages 51–64 in Grade 5 to relate to the content of this section.

Comparing Numbers

At-A-Glance Planning

Lesson Planning Checklist

Objective Compare numbers to find which is greater.

Vocabulary compare

Student Book Lesson Materials *Optional* Teaching Tool Transparency 5 (Number Lines)

Materials for pages 66A and 66B Digit cards 0–9 (1 set per group), place-value blocks (1 set per group), Teaching Tool Transparency 3 (9-Digit Place-Value Chart)

Subject Connection social studies—census data

Strand Connections using data, collecting data, algebra readiness

	Before Lesson	During Lesson	After Lesson
Daily Math			
p. 66A Problem of the Day			
p. 66A Math Routines			
p. 66A Mental Math			
Teaching Options			
p. 66 Student Book Lesson			
p. 66B Another Way to Learn…			
Options for Reaching All Learners			
p. 66B Reading Assist			
p. 66B Inclusion			
Technology Options			
p. 66 Interactive CD-ROM Lesson 2			
p. 67 Interactive CD-ROM Spreadsheet/Grapher Tool			
Subject Connections			
p. 66A Language Arts Connection			
Assessment Options			
p. 66 Talk About It			
p. 67 Error Intervention			
p. 67 Observation			
p. 67 Quick Check			
Resources			
2-5 Practice			
2-5 Reteaching			
2-5 Enrichment			
2-5 Problem Solving			
2-5 Daily Transparency			

Problem of the Day

a. $8 + 6 - 2 = 12$
b. $8 - 3 + 5 = 10$
c. $9 - 1 - 3 = 5$
d. $5 - 5 + 2 = 2$

Math Routines

Measurement Ask five students to tell the number of minutes their trip to school takes. Then have all students write as many statements as they can comparing and ordering the given numbers.

Calendar Ask students on which day of the month they were born. Ask if this number is before, after, or the same as today's date.

Mental Math

Find the total number of letters in your first and last names. Give five number sentences that equal that total.

Language Arts Connection

• Have pairs create a chart showing words used to compare objects or quantities.

Two Things	Three or More Things
more	most
greater	greatest
less	least
fewer	fewest
taller	tallest

• Create a class chart. Students may note the suffixes *-er* and *-est*.

Another Way to **Learn** Lesson 2-5

Use as an alternative or in addition to pages 66 and 67.

Materials Digit cards 0–9 (1 set per group), place-value blocks (1 set per group)

Learning Style Kinesthetic

- Write the symbols > and < on the overhead or chalkboard and review the meaning of each symbol.

- Have each group mix up the digit cards and stack them facedown in the center of the table.

- Two students draw 4 digit cards each. They each make a 4-digit number with the cards drawn. Then two other students show the numbers using drawings or place-value blocks.

- The group decides which number is greater and records its work. Groups repeat the activity several times and then discuss and agree on a method for comparing two numbers.

- When groups are finished, lead a class discussion in which students suggest ways to extend their comparison method to numbers with more than 4 digits.

- Assign Check and Practice on Student Book page 67 or *Practice Master 2-5.*

- Assess using the following rubric.

Options for Reaching All Learners

Reading Assist

Understand Organizational Devices

Use illustrations to remember meaning of symbols.

Learning Style Visual, Musical

- Tell students that they often must read symbols when reading mathematics. It is helpful to use memory devices and illustrations to remember their meanings.

- With respect to > and <, tell students to think: The pointed part of each symbol always *points* toward the lesser number.

- Tell students another way to remember the meaning of the symbols is to draw a picture such as an alligator opening its mouth toward the greater number.

- Students with musical backgrounds may make the analogies that *crescendo* (louder) looks like <, and *diminuendo* (softer) looks like >.

Inclusion

Chart It

Use place-value charts to compare two numbers.

Materials Teaching Tool Transparency 3 (9-Digit Place-Value Chart)

Learning Style Logical, Visual

- Have students write the numbers in the chart.

- Have students find the first place where the digits differ.

hundred thousands	ten thousands	thousands	hundreds	tens	ones
greater → 8	7 ,	0	2	1
(no digit)	9 ,	9	8	3
6 / 6	5	4 ,	6	0	0
	5	3 ,	9	8	7

greater

different digits 4>3

Lesson Organizer

Objective Compare numbers to find which is greater.

Student Materials None

Teacher Materials *Optional* Teaching Tool Transparency 5 (Number Lines)

Vocabulary compare

Assignment Guide
Basic 6–18, 20, 21, 24–28
Average 8–21, 24–28
Enriched 10–28

1 Introduce

Review

Which number is greater?

1. 350 or 530   **2.** 418 or 481   **3.** 870 or 87
530   481   870

Build on Prior Knowledge

After students compare 2- and 3-digit numbers, ask them how they decided which number was greater. Review the meanings of > (is greater than) and < (is less than). Discuss how they might compare greater numbers.

2 Teach

See Another Way to Learn...on page 66B.

Interactive CD-ROM Lesson 2 includes content in this lesson.

Learn ● ● ● ● ● ● ● ● ● ● ● ● ● ● ● ● ● ● ●

Use Teaching Tool Transparency 5 (Number Lines) for demonstration, if desired. When discussing Example 1, point out that students can reverse the numbers and the symbol. For example, 10,525 > 10,515 can also be written as 10,515 < 10,525.

Talk About It Ongoing Assessment

Be sure students understand that when comparing digits, they must begin at the left because left-hand digits have the greatest place value. Use 549 < 721 to illustrate why beginning with the digits on the right does not work.

Answer for Talk About It

Digits at the left have the greater place value.

Comparing Numbers

You Will Learn
how to compare numbers to find which is greater

Vocabulary
compare
to decide which of two numbers is greater

Math Tip
> means "is greater than"
< means "is less than"

Learn ●

On which day of the week were you born?

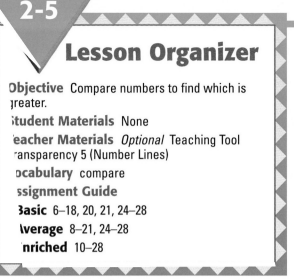

Number of Babies Born in a Typical Week in U.S.						
Mon.	Tue.	Wed.	Thurs.	Fri.	Sat.	Sun.
10,243	10,730	10,515	10,476	10,525	8,799	8,532

You can use a number line to **compare** numbers.

Example 1

Were there more babies born on Wednesday than on Friday?

```
        10,515   10,525
   ←─┼───┼───┼───┼───┼───┼───┼───┼───┼───┼───┼───→
   10,500   Wed. Fri.      10,550          10,600
```

10,525 > 10,515   More babies were born on Friday than on Wednesday.

You can also use place value to compare numbers.

Example 2

Compare 41,572 and 43,245.

Step 1	Step 2
Begin at the left. Compare.	Find the first place where the digits are different. Compare.
41,572	41,572
43,245	43,245
Both numbers have 4 ten thousands or 40,000.	1 thousand < 3 thousands
So, 41,572 < 43,245 or 43,245 > 41,572	

Talk About It

Why do you begin at the left to compare digits?

Practice 2-5

Name _____

Comparing Numbers
Compare. Write >, <, or =.

1. 459 < 468
2. 49,010 > 48,010
3. 54,193 > 54,183
4. 66,439 = 66,439
5. 8,192 < 8,193
6. 4,999 < 5,001
7. 72,698 = 72,698
8. 99,678 > 99,670
9. 125 < 215
10. 3,479 < 3,497
11. 52,391 > 52,319
12. 67,465 = 67,465
13. 4,032 < 4,230
14. 82,321 > 82,312
15. 3,762 < 37,620
16. 88,161 > 86,816
17. 25,112 > 25,111
18. 3,731 > 3,713

19. List three numbers that are greater than 10,000.
Answers will vary.

20. List three numbers that are less than 66,100.
Answers will vary.

21. List three numbers that are greater than 1,121.
Answers will vary.

22. Is a 4-digit number always less than a 5-digit number? Explain.
Yes; least 5-digit number is 10,000; greatest 4-digit number is 9,999.

23. Is a 3-digit number always greater than a 2-digit number?
Yes; greatest 2-digit number is 99; least 3-digit number is 100.

Reteaching 2-5

Name _____

Comparing Numbers
You can use a place-value chart to compare numbers.
Compare 14,260 and 14,306. Find which is greater.

Thousands Period			Ones Period		
hundreds	tens	ones	hundreds	tens	ones
	1	4	2	6	0
	1	4	3	0	6

Begin at the left. Compare.
How many ten thousands does 14,260 have? ___1___
How many ten thousands does 14,306 have? ___1___
How many thousands does 14,260 have? ___4___
How many thousands does 14,306 have? ___4___
How many hundreds does 14,260 have? ___2___
How many hundreds does 14,306 have? ___3___

14,306 _>_ 14,260 because 14,306 has more hundreds than 14,260. 14,306 > 14,260

Compare. Write >, <, or =.

1. 3,210 < 3,401

Thousands Period			Ones Period		
hundreds	tens	ones	hundreds	tens	ones
		3	2	1	0
		3	4	0	1

2. 52,348 > 51,348

Thousands Period			Ones Period		
hundreds	tens	ones	hundreds	tens	ones
	5	2	3	4	8
	5	1	3	4	8

Check

Compare. Use a number line to help. Write >, <, or =.

1. 9,110 ● 9,190 < **2.** 8,950 ● 9,220 < **3.** 9,210 ● 9,190 > **4.** 35,952 ● 53,952 <

5. Reasoning Write a 5-digit number greater than 12,247 and less than 12,427. **Possible answer: 12,345**

Practice

Skills and Reasoning

Compare. Use a number line to help. Write >, <, or =.

6. 455 ● 426 > **7.** 32,111 ● 31,222 > **8.** 75,491 ● 83,491 <

9. 67,094 ● 63,215 > **10.** 30,034 ● 30,035 < **11.** 9,999 ● 10,000 <

12. 81,032 ● 81,132 < **13.** 94,738 ● 94,638 > **14.** 6,514 ● 6,514 =

15. 32,334 ● 32,443 < **16.** 1,468,092 ● 9,579 > **17.** 4,237 ● 42,370 <

Using Data Use the baby data on page 66 for **18** and **19**.

18. List numbers less than 10,000. **8,532, 8,799**

19. List numbers greater than 10,520. **10,525, 10,730**

20. Is a 6-digit number always greater than a 5-digit number? Explain. **Yes; Greatest 5-digit is 99,999; Least 6-digit is 100,000**

Problem Solving and Applications

Using Data Use the table for **21** and **22**.

21. Do more people have the name Rivera or Long? **Rivera**

22. Do more people have the name López or Cox? **Cox**

23. Collecting Data Ask your classmates on which days of the week they were born. Make a bar graph. Compare it with the data on page 66. **Answers will vary.**

Number of People in U.S. with the Same Last Names	
Last Name	**Number**
Long	229,615
López	254,535
Rivera	238,457
Cox	256,842

Mixed Review and Test Prep

Algebra Readiness Copy and complete.

24. $12 + 5 = n$ **17** **25.** $16 - n = 11$ **5** **26.** $n - 4 = 12$ **16** **27.** $n + 9 = 16$ **7**

28. Which number has 4 in the thousands place and 3 in the tens place? **C**

Ⓐ 13,542 Ⓑ 34,215 Ⓒ 24,531 Ⓓ 43,152

Lesson 2-5   **67**

Enrichment 2-5	**Problem Solving 2-5**

Check

Make sure students know the meanings of > and < before they begin the exercises.

Error Intervention Ongoing Assessment

Observation Watch for students who have difficulty comparing digits in like places for problems written in the form 9,210 ● 9,190.

How to Help Suggest that students write one number directly below the other or in a place-value chart. This makes it much easier to compare the digits.

Practice

Exercise 23 Students can use a perpetual calendar in any almanac to find their day of birth.

Interactive CD-ROM Spreadsheet/ Grapher-Tool Students can use the Spreadsheet/Grapher Tool to make bar graphs for Exercise 23.

For Early Finishers Have students create new math sentences for Exercises 12–17 by reversing the numbers and the symbols. For example, they would write 426 < 455 for Exercise 6. 81,132 > 81,032; 94,638 < 94,738; 6,514 = 6,514; 32,443 > 32,334; 9,579 < 1,468,092; 42,370 > 4,237

③ Close and Assess

Observation

Watch that students are comparing place value, not simply digits. Suggest they write one number underneath the other and align place values.

Quick Check

Number Sense In which place can you stop comparing digits in each Skill exercise below? Thousands; Tens; Hundreds; Hundreds

Skill Compare. Write >, <, or =.

1. 16,890 ● 18,690 <

2. 7,427 ● 7,472 <

3. 36,403 ● 36,043 >

4. 8,525 ● 8,252 >

Ordering Numbers

At-A-Glance Planning

Lesson Planning Checklist

Objective Order a group of numbers.

Vocabulary order

Student Book Lesson Materials *Optional* Teaching Tool Transparency 3 (9-Digit Place-Value Chart)

Materials for pages 68A and 68B Teaching Tool Transparency 3 (9-Digit Place-Value Chart), lined notebook paper

Subject Connections social studies—population, literature—Laura Ingalls Wilder

Strand Connections logic, using data, algebra readiness

	Before Lesson	During Lesson	After Lesson
Daily Math			
p. 68A Problem of the Day			
p. 68A Math Routines			
p. 68A Mental Math			
Teaching Options			
p. 68 Student Book Lesson			
p. 68B Another Way to Learn…			
Options for Reaching All Learners			
p. 68B Inclusion			
p. 68B Gifted & Talented			
Technology Options			
p. 68 Interactive CD-ROM Lesson 2			
p. 69 Interactive CD-ROM Spreadsheet/Grapher Tool			
Subject Connections			
p. 68A Literature Connection			
Assessment Options			
p. 68 Talk About It			
p. 69 Error Intervention			
p. 69 Interview			
p. 69 Quick Check			
Resources			
2-6 Practice			
2-6 Reteaching			
2-6 Enrichment			
2-6 Problem Solving			
2-6 Daily Transparency			

Problem of the Day

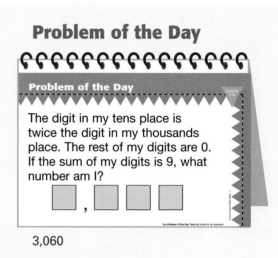

Problem of the Day

The digit in my tens place is twice the digit in my thousands place. The rest of my digits are 0. If the sum of my digits is 9, what number am I?

3,060

Math Routines

Calendar Have students add the numbers corresponding to the day and month on which they were born. Then give five number sentences that equal that total. For example, if born on July 18, add 7 (for July) and 18.

Money Have students name sums of money less than $1. Write the amounts on the chalkboard and have the class order amounts from greatest to least.

Mental Math

Which is the greater number? Explain your thinking.

4,673 or 4,763 4,763

20,456 or 24,056 24,056

3,092 or 3,920 3,920

Literature Connection

In her autobiography *Little Town on the Prairie*, Laura Ingalls Wilder describes life during the late 1800s. She earned $6 a month sewing shirts. Soon after, she taught three terms of school, for which she was paid $20, $30, and $25 per month.

- Order Wilder's monthly salaries from greatest to least. $30, $25, $20, $6

Another Way to **Learn** Lesson 2-6

Use as an alternative or in addition to pages 68 and 69.

Materials Teaching Tool Transparency 3 (9-Digit Place-Value Chart)

Learning Style Visual

- List population data for several nearby cities or counties, including the school's location, in a table on the chalkboard or overhead. Have students read and discuss the data.
- Ask students what they can see about the sizes of the numbers.
- Ask students how Teaching Tool Transparency 3 (9-Digit Place-Value Chart) can help them put the numbers in order. Possible answer: The chart keeps the digits lined up so that it is easier to compare digits in the same place.
- Have students put the population numbers in order from greatest to least using the place-value chart.
- Repeat the activity with a new set of numbers or population data from nearby states.
- Assign Check and Practice on Student Book page 69 or *Practice Master 2-6.*

- Assess using the following rubric.

Assessment Rubric
4 Full Accomplishment • orders numbers with the same or different number of digits • explains a method for ordering a list of numbers
3 Substantial Accomplishment • orders most numbers with the same or different number of digits with assistance • explains a method for ordering a list of numbers with prompting
2 Partial Accomplishment • orders only some numbers with the same or different number of digits • has difficulty explaining a method for ordering a list of numbers
1 Little Accomplishment • does not order numbers • does not explain a method for ordering a list of numbers

Options for Reaching All Learners

Inclusion

Line Up the Digits
Use lined paper to order numbers.

Materials Lined notebook paper

Learning Style Visual

- Some students may have difficulty ordering numbers. Show them how to use a piece of lined paper to help.
- Students can turn the paper sideways so that the lines run up and down. Then they write the digits in the columns.
- Have students use this method to order the population data on page 68. They should write numbers far enough apart so that there is plenty of room to insert numbers.
- Repeat for the data on page 69.

Gifted & Talented

In Between
Use a math sentence to show the order of three numbers.

Learning Style Logical

- Show students the math sentence $42 < 45 < 53$. Point out that a math symbol appears twice in this sentence. One meaning of the sentence is: 45 is between 42 and 53.
- Have students use the population data on page 68 to write sentences of this type. Students can also reverse the order of numbers, for example, $53 > 45 > 42$.
- Challenge students to write three-number math sentences using the population data from this lesson.
- Extend the activity by having students find and use population data of local areas.

Lesson Organizer

Objective Order a group of numbers.

Student Materials None

Teacher Materials *Optional* Teaching Tool Transparency 3 (9-Digit Place-Value Chart)

Vocabulary order

Assignment Guide

Basic 3, 5, 7, 10–11, 13–17

Average 3, 5, 8–10, 13–17

Enriched 4, 6, 8, 9, 12–17

1 Introduce

Review

Order these numbers from least to greatest.

45, 54, 48, 41, 84, 14   14, 41, 45, 48, 54, 84

Build on Prior Knowledge

Ask students what strategy they would use to put the numbers above in order from greatest to least. Some students may suggest using slips of paper. Others may try finding the greatest number, crossing it out, and continuing in that manner.

2 Teach

See Another Way to Learn…on page 68B.

Interactive CD-ROM Lesson 2 includes content in this lesson.

Learn

Use Teaching Tool Transparency 3 (9-Digit Place-Value Chart) for demonstration, if desired. For example, you can write the numbers 156,983 and 70,487 on the chart, reminding students of the names of the places. Point out that some students may want to start by sorting the five numbers into 5-digit and 6-digit groups.

(Talk About It) Ongoing Assessment

Ask students if they know other ways to order a list of numbers. Some students may prefer scanning the list to find the greatest number, then the next greatest, and so on.

Answer for Talk About It

Possible answer: You can compare only two things at a time.

Check

Exercise 1 Before students begin, ask them how many numbers are to be compared.

Ordering Numbers

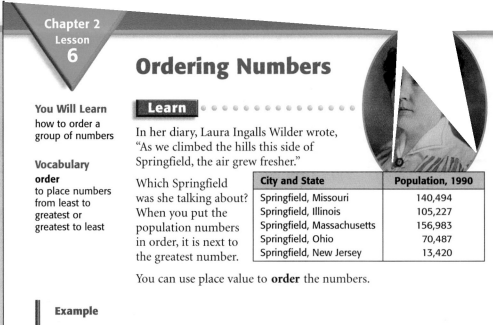

You Will Learn
how to order a group of numbers

Vocabulary
order
to place numbers from least to greatest or greatest to least

Learn

In her diary, Laura Ingalls Wilder wrote, "As we climbed the hills this side of Springfield, the air grew fresher."

Which Springfield was she talking about? When you put the population numbers in order, it is next to the greatest number.

City and State	Population, 1990
Springfield, Missouri	140,494
Springfield, Illinois	105,227
Springfield, Massachusetts	156,983
Springfield, Ohio	70,487
Springfield, New Jersey	13,420

You can use place value to **order** the numbers.

Example

Step 1	Step 2	Step 3
Compare the numbers two at a time to find the greatest number.	Continue comparing the other numbers.	Then order the numbers from greatest to least.
$140,494 > 105,227$	$140,494 > 105,227$	156,983
$156,983 > 140,494$	$105,227 > 70,487$	140,494
$156,983 > 70,487$	$70,487 > 13,420$	105,227
$156,983 > 13,420$		70,487
		13,420

If 156,983 is the greatest number, 140,494 is the next greatest number. So, Wilder wrote about Springfield, Missouri!

(Talk About It)

Why did you begin by comparing two numbers at a time?

Did You Know?
There are more than 20 places named Springfield in the United States!

Check

1. Order the numbers from least to greatest.
524,500, 524,050, 524,505, 524,550
524,050, 524,500, 524,505, 524,550
2. Write three numbers that are more than 80,000 but less than 81,000. **Possible answer: three numbers that are in the eighty-thousands**

Practice 2-6	Reteaching 2-6

Skills and Reasoning

Order the numbers from least to greatest.

3. 70,000, 70,700, 77,000, 70,770   **4.** 41,253, 714,253, 542,708, 312,649
70,000, 70,700, 70,770, 77,000   41,253, 312,649, 542,708, 714,253

Order the numbers from greatest to least.

5. 40,000, 44,000, 40,400, 40,440
44,000, 40,440, 40,400, 40,000
6. 343,343, 334,434, 334,343, 343,433
343,433, 343,343, 334,434, 334,343
7. Write a number between 14,250 and 14,750.
Possible answer: 14,260
8. These numbers are ordered from greatest to least:
147,211, 144,936, 141,587, 139,894. Between which
two numbers is 143,768? **Between 144,936 and 141,587**

Problem Solving and Applications

9. Logic Use the digits 7, 7, 5, and 5. Create as many 4-digit
numbers as you can. Order them from greatest to least.
7,755, 7,575, 7,557, 5,775, 5,757, 5,577

Using Data Use the table for 10–12.

State	Number of People	Area (square miles)
Alaska	603,617	570,374
Delaware	717,197	1,982
North Dakota	641,367	68,994
Utah	1,951,408	82,168
Wyoming	480,184	97,105

10. Name the states in order from fewest people to most people.
Wyoming, Alaska, North Dakota, Delaware, Utah
11. Name the states in order from least area to greatest area.
Delaware, North Dakota, Utah, Wyoming, Alaska
12. Critical Thinking Do the states with the fewest people
also have the least area? Explain. No; Possible answer: Delaware has the second
most people but least area.

Mixed Review and Test Prep

Algebra Readiness Find each answer.

13. $17 - 6 = n$ 11   **14.** $15 - 8 = n$ 7   **15.** $8 + 3 + 4 = n$ 15   **16.** $2 + 7 + 5 = n$ 14

17. Name the period shown by the red digits in 413,296,083. B

Ⓐ ones   Ⓑ thousands   Ⓒ millions   Ⓓ not here

Skills Practice Bank, page 560, Set 2   Lesson 2-6   **69**

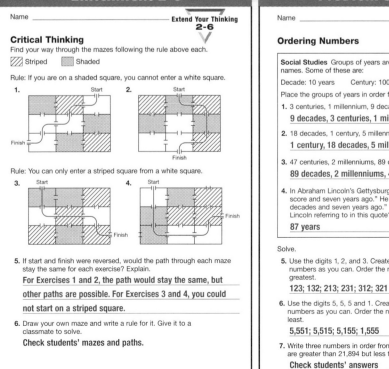

Enrichment 2-6

Name _____   **Extend Your Thinking 2-6**

Critical Thinking
Find your way through the mazes following the rule above each.

▨ Striped   ▦ Shaded

Rule: If you are on a shaded square, you cannot enter a white square.

1. Start   **2.** Start

Finish   Finish

Rule: You can only enter a striped square from a white square.

3. Start   **4.** Start

Finish   Finish

5. If start and finish were reversed, would the path through each maze
stay the same for each exercise? Explain.

For Exercises 1 and 2, the path would stay the same, but

other paths are possible. For Exercises 3 and 4, you could

not start on a striped square.

6. Draw your own maze and write a rule for it. Give it to a
classmate to solve.

Check students' mazes and paths.

Problem Solving 2-6

Name _____   **Problem Solving 2-6**

Ordering Numbers

Social Studies Groups of years are sometimes given
names. Some of these are:

Decade: 10 years   Century: 100 years   Millennium: 1,000 years

Place the groups of years in order from shortest to longest.

1. 3 centuries, 1 millennium, 9 decades

9 decades, 3 centuries, 1 millennium

2. 18 decades, 1 century, 5 millenniums

1 century, 18 decades, 5 millenniums

3. 47 centuries, 2 millenniums, 89 decades

89 decades, 2 millenniums, 47 centuries

4. In Abraham Lincoln's Gettysburg Address he said "four
score and seven years ago." He could have said "eight
decades and seven years ago." How many years was
Lincoln referring to in this quote?

87 years

Solve.

5. Use the digits 1, 2, and 3. Create as many 3-digit
numbers as you can. Order the numbers from least to
greatest.

123; 132; 213; 231; 312; 321

6. Use the digits 5, 5, 5 and 1. Create as many 4-digit
numbers as you can. Order the numbers from greatest to
least.

5,551; 5,515; 5,155; 1,555

7. Write three numbers in order from least to greatest that
are greater than 21,894 but less than 42,189.

Check students' answers

Error Intervention Ongoing Assessment

Observation Students may make errors in
copying greater numbers such as 5- and
6-digit numbers.

How to Help Tell students to check each
number after they have written it.

Practice ·

Exercise 9 Point out that each number must
have exactly two 7s and two 5s. For
example, the numbers 5,777 and 5,557
would not be correct answers.

**Interactive CD-ROM Spreadsheet/
Grapher Tool** Students can use the
Spreadsheet/Grapher Tool to graph the data
in Exercises 10–12.

For Early Finishers Challenge early finishers
to order the numbers in Exercise 3 from
greatest to least and Exercise 5 from least to
greatest. Exercise 3: 77,000; 70,770; 70,700;
70,000; Exercise 5: 40,000; 40,400; 40,440;
44,000

③ Close and Assess

Interview

Ask students why someone might need to
sort a list of numbers from greatest to least.
Encourage students to give a specific
application in which someone might want to
know which was the greatest or least
quantity. Possible answers: to find the
highest-scoring player in a game or to find
the least-expensive product on a shelf.

Quick Check

Number Sense In Skill Exercise 1, how many
digits from the left do you need to check to
find the least number? The greatest
number? 2; 4

Skill

1. Order these numbers from least to
greatest. 37,642; 37,462; 34,462; 37,624
34,462; 37,462; 37,624; 37,642

2. Order these numbers from greatest to
least. 787,800; 878,700; 787,080; 878,800
878,800; 878,700; 787,800; 787,080

Resources

Technology Master 5

Exploring Rounding

At-A-Glance Planning

Lesson Planning Checklist

Objective Explore rounding.

Vocabulary estimate, rounding

Student Book Lesson Materials Rulers, *optional* Lesson Enhancement Transparency 6

Materials for pages 70A and 70B Counters, 2 index cards with *about* and *exactly* written on them

Subject Connection science—insects

Strand Connections using data, estimation

	Before Lesson	During Lesson	After Lesson
Daily Math			
p. 70A Problem of the Day			
p. 70A Math Routines			
p. 70A Mental Math			
Teaching Options			
p. 70B Facilitating and Assessing…			
Options for Reaching All Learners			
p. 70B Language Development			
p. 70B Cultural Connection			
Subject Connections			
p. 70A Science Connection			
Assessment Options			
p. 70 Talk About It			
p. 71 Error Intervention			
p. 71 Performance Assessment			
Resources			
2-7 Practice			
2-7 Reteaching			
2-7 Enrichment			
2-7 Problem Solving			
2-7 Daily Transparency			

Problem of the Day

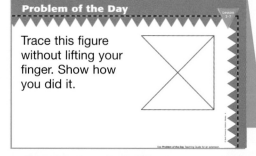

Problem of the Day

Trace this figure without lifting your finger. Show how you did it.

For solution art, see pages D1–D4.

Math Routines

Time Ask students what number of minutes past the hour it is. Have them round this number to the nearest ten minutes.

Money Ask students if they could buy a new bike with 100,000 pennies. Yes

Mental Math

In the set 10, 20, 30, the number 20 is halfway between 10 and 30. Name each missing number if the second number is halfway between the first and third.

____, 6, 9 3   ____, 8, 12 4

20, 25, ____ 30   45, 60, ____ 75

Science Connection

There are many fascinating facts about insects. Here are a few; have students round each number to the nearest hundred and thousand. The tiny midge beats its wings 62,760 times per minute. 62,800; 63,000 Scientists recognize 1,830 varieties of fleas. 1,800; 2,000 There is a record of a butterfly flying 2,133 miles. 2,100; 2,000

Facilitating and Assessing **Explore** Lesson 2-7

Use with pages 70 and 71.

Get Started For Exercise 1, have half the students in each group copy and complete number lines a and b. Have the other students copy and complete number lines c and d. Have students share their results.

Observe As students work on Exercise 2, you may want them to estimate each answer first before they use their number line to check. Listen to assess students' previous knowledge of rounding.

Discuss Use Teaching Tool Transparency 6 (Number Lines) to discuss each problem in Exercise 2 with the class. Have students compare rounding to the nearest ten with rounding to the nearest hundred. Ask them how the methods are alike and how they are different. Repeat by having students compare rounding to the nearest hundred with rounding to the nearest thousand.

Assess Use the rubric to assess students' work. See sample for Practice Exercise 7.

---

4 Full Accomplishment

8,045

8,000   8,500   9,000

8,045 is closer to 8,000. The hundreds digit is 0 and that is less than 5.

Assessment Rubric

4 Full Accomplishment
- rounds numbers to any given place

3 Substantial Accomplishment
- rounds most numbers to the nearest ten, hundred, or thousand

2 Partial Accomplishment
- rounds some numbers to the nearest ten, hundred, or thousand

1 Little Accomplishment
- does not round numbers to nearest ten, hundred, or thousand

---

Options for Reaching All Learners

Language Development

Exact or Estimate?
Use counters to strengthen understanding of exact and estimated amounts.

Materials Counters, 2 index cards with *about* and *exactly* written on them

Learning Style Logical

- Review the words *about*, *exactly*, and *estimate*.

- Have one member of the group place a handful of counters on the table, and ask the student to his or her right to use the index card labeled *about* and tell *about* how many counters there are. Then have the student who put the counters on the table use the index card *exactly* and tell *exactly* how many there are.

- For the next round, have students ask each other questions that can be answered by an estimate. Possibilities include *about* how many days of school and students in school.

Cultural Connection

About How Many?
Use an example of African estimation to discuss accuracy in estimation.

Learning Style Logical

Sometimes, how accurately we estimate the number or amount of something depends on what we are counting. The Kpelle people of West Africa are able to give highly accurate estimates of the amount of rice in a variety of containers because measuring rice is an activity integral to their daily lives.

- Ask students to create a list of situations when people might estimate how much, how many or how long.

- Discuss the example of the Kpelle people's estimation of rice. Ask them whether they think their estimates might be more accurate in some situations than others and why.

Lesson Organizer

Objective Explore rounding.

Suggested Grouping 2 to 4

Student Materials Rulers

Teacher Materials *Optional* Lesson Enhancement Transparency 6, and Teaching Tool Transparency 5

Vocabulary estimate, rounding

Assignment Guide

Basic 1–10, 16–18, 21

Average 1–5, 10–16, 18, 19, 21

Enriched 1–3, 8–12, 16–21

1 Introduce

Review

Round each number to the nearest ten.

1. 39 40   **2.** 81 80   **3.** 54 50

Build on Prior Knowledge

Ask students how they would round numbers such as 25 or 45 to the nearest ten. Remind them that numbers that end in 5 are rounded to the next greater ten.

2 Teach

See Facilitating and Assessing…on page 70B.

Explore •

You may wish to use Lesson Enhancement Transparency 6, which reproduces the Work Together time lines, for modeling and discussion.

Talk About It **Ongoing Assessment**

Watch for students who realize they can find the halfway point by folding their number line in half.

Answers for Talk About It

3 Possible answer: Counted to the fifth mark after the first number

4 Decide if 2,493 is greater or less than 2,500.

Exploring Rounding

Problem Solving Connection

- Draw a Picture
- Use Logical Reasoning

Materials
ruler

Vocabulary
estimate
to find a number that is close to the exact number

rounding
replacing a number with a number that tells about how many or how much

Did You Know?
You can hear the "tsh-ee-EEEE-e-ou" sound of the male cicada from about 450 yards away.

Explore • • • • • • • • • • • • • • • • • • •

Don't let it bug you, but new insects are discovered all the time. Scientists discover about 7,000 new kinds of insects every year!

In this case, the number 7,000 is not an exact number. It is an **estimate**.

Rounding is one way to estimate.

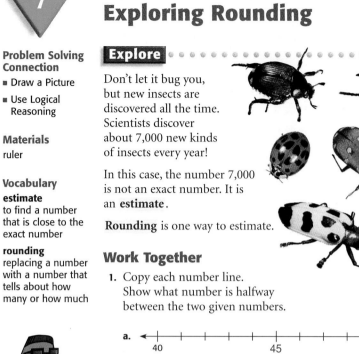

Work Together

1. Copy each number line. Show what number is halfway between the two given numbers.

a.
```
40        45        50
```

b.
```
200       250       300
```

c.
```
1,000     1,500     2,000
```

d.
```
60,000    65,000    70,000
```

2. Use your number lines to help answer each.

a. Is 48 closer to 40 or 50? **50**   **b.** Is 241 closer to 200 or 300? **200**

c. Is 1,392 closer to 1,000 or 2,000? **1,000**

d. Is 65,017 closer to 60,000 or 70,000? **70,000**

Talk About It

3. How did you find each halfway number?

4. Explain how you decide if 2,493 is closer to 2,000 or 3,000.

70   Chapter 2 • Place Value and Time

Practice 2-7

Reteaching 2-7

Connect

Here is a method for rounding.

Example
Round the number to the nearest hundred.

Step 1	Step 2
Find the digit in the place to which you are rounding. 635 ↑ Round to the nearest hundred.	Look at the digit to the right. 635 ↑ Round down, if the number is less than 5. or Round up, if the number is 5 or greater. 3 < 5 So, 6 stays the same.

635 rounds to 600.

Practice

Round each number to the nearest hundred.

1. 276
300
2. 552
600
3. 385
400
4. 197
200
5. 545
500

Round each number to the nearest thousand.

6. 4,000
4,000
7. 8,045
8,000
8. 4,984
5,000
9. 5,409
5,000
10. 5,555
6,000
11. 6,514
7,000
12. 3,251
3,000
13. 6,189
6,000
14. 8,073
8,000
15. 6,438
6,000

16. Is 56,053 closer to 50,000 or 60,000? Explain.
60,000; 56,053 is greater than the halfway number 55,000.
17. Is 213,900 closer to 210,000 or 220,000? Explain.
210,000; 213,900 is less than the halfway number 215,000.
18. **Reasoning** Write five numbers that round to 200 when rounded to the nearest hundred.
Possible answer: in the 150–249 range
19. **Science** There are 136,800 kinds of butterflies and crickets.

   a. Round this number to the nearest ten thousand.
140,000
   b. Round this number to the nearest hundred thousand.
100,000
20. **Critical Thinking** I am a 3-digit number. Use the clues to find me.

   • I am greater than 700.
   • I am less than 757.
   753
   • My ones digit is a 3.
   • I am 800 when rounded to the nearest hundred.

21. **Journal** You want to round 462 to the nearest hundred. How does it help to know what number is halfway between 400 and 500?

Skills Practice Bank, page 560, Set 3   Lesson 2-7   **71**

Connect

Use Teaching Tool Transparency 5 to show an overhead number line from 600 to 700, marked in intervals of 10. Mark the place for 635. Then have students compare the number line with the method for rounding on page 71.

Error Intervention Ongoing Assessment

Observation Look for students who are not sure which digit to examine when they are deciding how to round.

How to Help Have students copy the number to be rounded and circle the digit in the place to which they are rounding, then underline the digit to the right of the circled place. For example, ②7̲6.

Practice

Exercise 6 Point out that no further rounding to the thousands can be done.

Exercise 19 Point out that 136,800 has probably been rounded to the nearest hundred. It is highly unlikely that the exact number of insects is 136,800.

For Early Finishers Challenge early finishers to round the numbers in Exercises 1–5 to the nearest ten, then round the numbers in Exercises 11–15 to the nearest hundred.
280, 550, 390, 200, 550;
6,500; 3,300; 6,200; 8,100; 6,400

3 Close and Assess

Performance Assessment

Draw a number line showing the hundreds from 6,000 through 7,000. Use it to round each number to the nearest thousand. Check students' number lines.

6,236	6,498	6,500	6,802
6,000	6,000	7,000	7,000

Assess using the rubric on page 70B.

ANSWERS

21 Explanations should include the need to compare 462 to the halfway number 450.

Name _____   **Problem Solving 2-7**

Exploring Rounding
Show the height of each of these famous mountains on a number line. On each number line, show the number that is the mountain's height rounded to the nearest thousand. Then answer the questions. Check students' answers.

Famous Mountains of the World

Mountain	Height in feet
Mt. Everest	29,028
Mt. McKinley	20,320
Mt. Ararat	16,946
Mt. Olympus	9,550
Mt. Rushmore	5,725

1. How did you decide where to show Mt. Ararat's rounded height on the number line?
Possible answer: 16,946 rounded to 17,000 which is less than halfway between 15,000 and 20,000.

2. You are climbing Mt. Olympus, and are at 6,405 ft high. Round this number to the nearest 1,000. Show your position on the Mt. Olympus number line. About how far from the mountain top are you? How do you know?
6,000 feet; point (on number line) should be close to 5,000;
About 4,000, since the difference between my point and
Mt. Olympus' point is 10,000 is 4,000.

3. Explain how to decide if Mt. Rushmore's height is closer to 5,000 feet or 10,000 feet.
Possible answer: 7,500 is halfway between 5,000 and 10,000.
5,725 is less than 7,500, so it is closer to 5,000.

Chapter 2 • Lesson 2-7   **71**

Section B
Review and Practice
Use the Skills Checklist

Review the **Skills Checklist** on the page with students. Then ask questions such as the following:

- In which problems will you compare or order numbers? Exercises 3–13, 23
- In which problems will you round numbers? Exercises 14–22
- In which problems do you need to think about place value? Exercises 1–24

Assess

You may wish to use this information to assess students' understanding of the lesson objectives.

Item Analysis		
Lesson Objective		Items
2-5	Compare numbers to find which is greater.	2, 3–10, 24
2-6	Order a group of numbers.	2, 11–13, 23
2-7	Explore rounding.	1, 14–22

Resources

Practice Masters
- Practice Chapter 2 Section B

Assessment Sourcebook
- Quiz Chapter 2 Section B

TestWorks: Test and Practice Software

ANSWERS

24 Possible answer: First compare the digits in the thousands place. If these are equal, compare the digits in the hundreds place. Repeat until you find two unequal digits. The greater of these will indicate which 4-digit number is greater.

Review and Practice

Vocabulary Choose the best word to complete each exercise.

Word List
order
rounds
compare

1. 4,932 _____ to 5,000
   rounds
2. You can _____ 4,932, 4,923, and 4,329 to find which number is greatest. Then you can put them in _____ from greatest to least.
   compare; order

(Lesson 5) Compare. Write >, <, or =.

3. 80,001 ⬤ 80,100 **<**   4. 4,990 ⬤ 4,929 **>**   5. 7,332,878 ⬤ 7,323,878 **>**

6. 455,311 ⬤ 455,331 **<**   7. 2,999 ⬤ 3,001 **<**   8. 629,348 ⬤ 629,348 **=**

9. Write the greatest number using the digits 1, 7, 9, 3, and 2. **97,321**

10. Write the least number using the digits 8, 4, 6, 1, 9, and 7. **146,789**

(Lesson 6) Order each set of numbers from least to greatest.

11. 880,000, 80,000, 800,000
    80,000, 800,000, 880,000
12. 314,500, 632,070, 504,707
    314,500, 504,707, 632,070
13. **Logic** Use the digits 6, 9, 5. Create as many 3-digit numbers as you can. Order the numbers from greatest to least.
    965, 956, 695, 659, 596, 569

(Lesson 7) Round each number to the nearest hundred.

14. 529 **500** 15. 879 **900** 16. 497 **500** 17. 634 **600** 18. 821 **800**

Round each number to the nearest thousand in **19–21.**

19. The largest teddy bear picnic was attended by 18,116 bears. **18,000**

20. The largest balloon sculpture had 25,344 colored balloons. **25,000**

21. **History** At a New Year's Day Celebration in 1907, President Roosevelt shook hands with 8,513 people. **9,000**

22. **Reasoning** Write four numbers that when rounded to the nearest thousand would be 3,000. **Possible answer: in the 2,500 to 3,499 range**

23. **Using Data** Use the Data File on page 49. Which group had the greatest number of people coming to the United States in 1990? The least number of people? **Chinese; Vietnamese**

24. **Journal** Describe how you can compare two 4-digit numbers.

Skills Checklist
In this section, you have:
☑ Compared Numbers
☑ Ordered Numbers
☑ Explored Rounding

REVIEW AND PRACTICE

Practice

Name _____

Practice
Chapter 2
Section B

Review and Practice
Vocabulary Match each with its definition.

1. **b**   compare   **a.** to replace a number with one that tells about how many

2. **a**   round   **b.** to decide which of two numbers is greater

3. **c**   order   **c.** to place numbers from least to greatest or greatest to least

(Lesson 5) Compare. Write >, <, or =.

4. 3,623 **>** 3,539   5. 2,300 **<** 3,100

6. 2,556 **<** 2,655   7. 8,900 **=** 8,900

8. Write the greatest number using the digits 6, 5, 3, 7, and 0.
   76,530

(Lesson 6) Order each set of numbers from least to greatest.

9. 38,808; 38,299; 35,315 **35,315; 38,299; 38,808**

10. 209,453; 209,053; 354,998 **209,053; 209,453; 354,998**

11. Use the digits 6, 2 and 7. Create as many 3-digit numbers as you can. Order the numbers from least to greatest.
    267, 276, 627, 672, 726, 762

(Lesson 7) Round each number to the nearest hundred.

12. 852 **900**   13. 739 **700**   14. 460 **500**

Round each number to the nearest thousand.

15. Communication satellites can relay over 17,890 telephone calls over the whole United States. **18,000**

16. The largest lake is the Caspian Sea. It covers 143,550 square miles. **144,000**

(Mixed Review) Write >, <, or =.

17. 7 + 9 **=** 9 + 7   18. 8 − 4 **>** 9 − 6   19. 7 − 3 **>** 3

Making Sense of Time

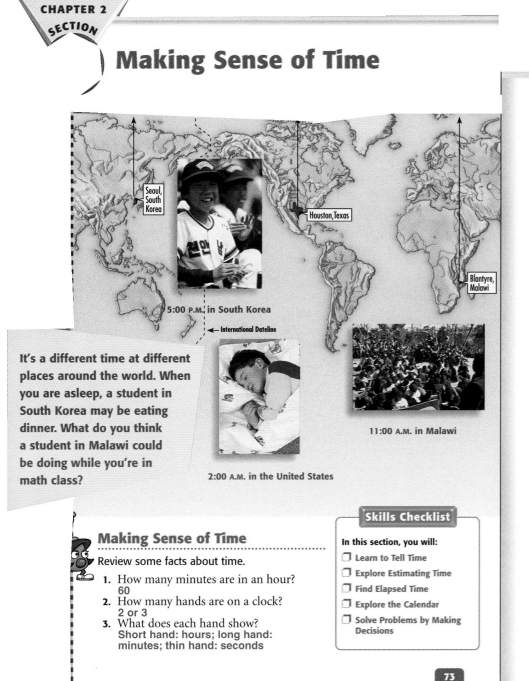

5:00 P.M. in South Korea

Seoul, South Korea

Houston, Texas

Blantyre, Malawi

← International Dateline

11:00 A.M. in Malawi

2:00 A.M. in the United States

It's a different time at different places around the world. When you are asleep, a student in South Korea may be eating dinner. What do you think a student in Malawi could be doing while you're in math class?

Making Sense of Time

Review some facts about time.

1. How many minutes are in an hour?
   60
2. How many hands are on a clock?
   2 or 3
3. What does each hand show?
   Short hand: hours; long hand: minutes; thin hand: seconds

Skills Checklist

In this section, you will:

☐ Learn to Tell Time
☐ Explore Estimating Time
☐ Find Elapsed Time
☐ Explore the Calendar
☐ Solve Problems by Making Decisions

73

Making Sense of Time

In this section, students will write the time in different forms. They will also estimate reasonable lengths of time for activities, find elapsed time, and read calendars.

Subskills

The work in this section builds on...

• Comparing numbers to find which number is greater

300 is greater than 258

• Understanding the meaning of estimate

When you estimate, you find a number close to the exact number.

485 is close to 500.

Use the Section Opener

Malawi is a nation in southeastern Africa. Almost one-fifth of Malawi is covered by Lake Nyasa. Ask students what someone in Malawi might be doing while they are in math class. Possible answers: Eating, reading, sleeping

To expand on this idea, ask students to find countries on a globe that they may have lived in, visited or know about and then compare the time there and in the United States.

Skills Trace

(Red numbers indicate pages in this section.)

Lesson and Skill	First Introduced	Grade Four			
		Introduce	Develop	Practice/Apply	Review
2-8 Tell time to the minute and identify A.M. and P.M.	Grade 3	74, 75	74	75, 84, 87, 560	84, 86, 89
2-9 Explore estimating and comparing time.	Grade 3	76, 77	76, 77	77, 84, 560	84, 86, 89
2-10 Find elapsed time.	Grade 3	78, 79	78	79, 84, 87, 560	84, 86, 89
2-11 Explore the calendar.	Grade 3	80, 81	80, 81	81, 84, 85, 87, 560	84, 85, 86, 89
2-12 Solve problems by creating a schedule for making an audio tape.	Grade 3	82, 83	82, 83	83, 84, 87, 560	84, 86, 89

Mixed Review and Test Prep exercises for this chapter occur on pages 53, 57, 61, 67, 69, 75, 79.

Multi-Age Classrooms Use pages 73–86 in Grade 3 or the Math Routines in Grade 5 to relate to the content of this section.

Telling Time

At-A-Glance Planning

Objective Tell time to the minute and identify A.M. and P.M.

Vocabulary analog clock, digital clock, A.M., P.M.

Student Book Materials *Optional* Teacher's Edition Transparency B (Clock)

Materials for pages 74A and 74B Paper plate (1 per student), fasteners (1 per student), index card (1 per student), strip of paper (1 per student), scissors (1 per group), classroom clock or Teacher's Edition Transparency B (Clock)

Subject Connections history—clocks, health—calories

Strand Connections patterns, algebra readiness

	Before Lesson	During Lesson	After Lesson
Daily Math			
p. 74A Problem of the Day			
p. 74A Math Routines			
p. 74A Mental Math			
Teaching Options			
p. 74 Student Book Lesson			
p. 74B Another Way to Learn…			
Options for Reaching All Learners			
p. 74B Inclusion			
p. 74B Language Development			
Subject Connections			
p. 74A Literature Connection			
Assessment Options			
p. 74 Talk About It			
p. 75 Error Intervention			
p. 75 Journal			
p. 75 Quick Check			
Resources			
2-8 Practice			
2-8 Reteaching			
2-8 Enrichment			
2-8 Problem Solving			
2-8 Daily Transparency			

Problem of the Day

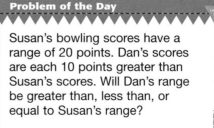

Problem of the Day

Susan's bowling scores have a range of 20 points. Dan's scores are each 10 points greater than Susan's scores. Will Dan's range be greater than, less than, or equal to Susan's range?

Equal to

Math Routines

Time Name some times that are multiples of 5 minutes but are not half hours or hours. For each time, ask students to name the length of time to the next half hour and the next hour.

Calendar Name some dates that are not multiples of 5. For each date, have students count on by 2s, 5s, and 10s.

Mental Math

Name the number that is 100 more than each. Explain your thinking.

198	207	964	902
298	307	1,064	1,002

Literature Connection

In Beverly Cleary's *Ramona the Pest*, Ramona's mother tells her to leave for school at quarter past eight. Ramona leaves when the minute hand points to 5. She thinks that 25 minutes past the hour is a quarter past because there are 25 cents in the coin called a quarter.

- What time should Ramona have left the house? What time did she leave? 8:15; 8:25

- Was she early or late? 10 minutes late

Another Way to [Learn] Lesson 2-8

Use as an alternative or in addition to pages 74 and 75.

Materials Paper plate (1 per student), fasteners (1 per student), index card (1 per student), strips of paper (3 per student), scissors (1 per group)

Learning Style Kinesthetic

- Have students work in small groups. Each student makes a paper-plate analog clock. The hour and minute hands are cut from paper and attached to the plate with a fastener. (Save these clocks for Lesson 2-10.) Then each student makes a digital clock using an index card and strips of paper.

- Each student shows a time on his or her clock. The group records the times twice, writing A.M. and P.M. after each time.

- The group then lists events that might happen for each time they have recorded.

- Assign Check and Practice on Student Book pages 74 and 75 or *Practice Master 2-8.*

- Assess using the following rubric.

Assessment Rubric

4 Full Accomplishment
- writes clock times in numbers and in words
- uses A.M. and P.M. notations to record times

3 Substantial Accomplishment
- writes most clock times in numbers and in words
- uses A.M. and P.M. notations to record most times

2 Partial Accomplishment
- writes some clock times in numbers but has difficulty writing times in words
- sometimes confuses A.M. and P.M. when recording times

1 Little Accomplishment
- does not write most clock times in numbers or in words
- does not use A.M. and P.M. notations to record times

Options for Reaching All Learners

Inclusion

Before or After?
Use a clock to arrange events in sequential order.

Materials Classroom clock or Teacher's Edition Transparency B (Clock)

Learning Style Individual

- Display a time such as 10:00 A.M. Each student writes one event that might happen before that time and one event that might happen after that time.

- Repeat the activity with a time in the afternoon.

- As students work, watch for students who have trouble identifying reasonable times for events to occur.

- Invite students to display times for the class.

Language Development

Different Names for Times
Use a classroom clock to develop number and word names for the same time.

Materials Classroom clock or Teacher's Edition Transparency B (Clock)

Learning Style Verbal

- Display a time such as 10:45 A.M. Each group brainstorms as many different ways as possible to express the time.

- Compile a class list of all the ways students found to write that time. Watch for students who need additional time to practice writing the ways time is expressed.

- Repeat the activity with times such as 2:15 P.M., 7:20 A.M., and 9:40 P.M.

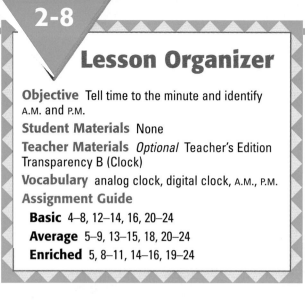

Lesson Organizer

Objective Tell time to the minute and identify A.M. and P.M.

Student Materials None

Teacher Materials *Optional* Teacher's Edition Transparency B (Clock)

Vocabulary analog clock, digital clock, A.M., P.M.

Assignment Guide

Basic 4–8, 12–14, 16, 20–24

Average 5–9, 13–15, 18, 20–24

Enriched 5, 8–11, 14–16, 19–24

1 Introduce

Review

Draw clock faces to show times half an hour later than each time listed. Check students' drawings.

1. 2:30 3:00   **2.** 8:15 8:45

3. 4:00 4:30   **4.** 10:45 11:15

Build on Prior Knowledge

After students have finished the Review exercises, have them find times half an hour earlier than each time listed. Remind students to write each time using a colon. 2:00, 7:45, 3:30, 10:15

2 Teach

See Another Way to Learn...on page 74B.

Learn ● ● ● ● ● ● ● ● ● ● ● ● ● ● ● ● ● ● ●

Use Teacher's Edition Transparency B (Clock) for demonstration, if desired. You may wish to draw a time line to show one full day from midnight until midnight. Mark the first half of the time line A.M. and the second half P.M.

Talk About It   Ongoing Assessment

Students should suggest that Danielle will be sleeping at 4:30 A.M. Have students discuss as a class what they usually do at 4:30 P.M.

Answer for Talk About It

Possible answer: Sleeping

Check ● ● ● ● ● ● ● ● ● ● ● ● ● ● ● ● ● ●

Exercises 1 and 2 Remind students that time can be expressed as minutes after the hour or minutes before the hour.

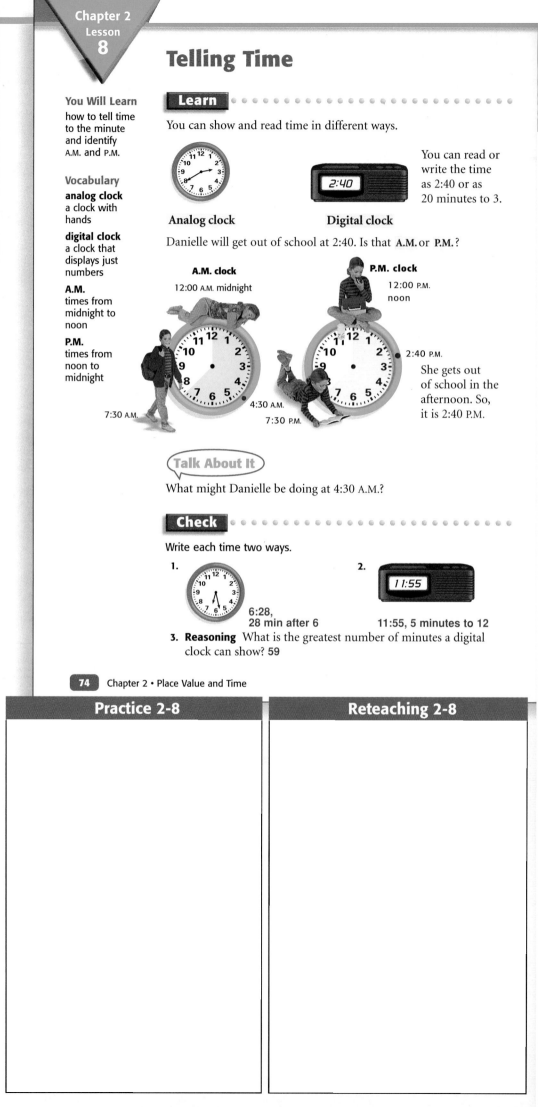

Chapter 2 Lesson 8

Telling Time

You Will Learn
how to tell time to the minute and identify A.M. and P.M.

Vocabulary

analog clock a clock with hands

digital clock a clock that displays just numbers

A.M. times from midnight to noon

P.M. times from noon to midnight

Learn ●

You can show and read time in different ways.

Analog clock   **Digital clock**   2:40

You can read or write the time as 2:40 or as 20 minutes to 3.

Danielle will get out of school at 2:40. Is that A.M. or P.M.?

A.M. clock
12:00 A.M. midnight

7:30 A.M.

4:30 A.M.

7:30 P.M.

P.M. clock
12:00 P.M. noon

2:40 P.M.

She gets out of school in the afternoon. So, it is 2:40 P.M.

Talk About It

What might Danielle be doing at 4:30 A.M.?

Check ●

Write each time two ways.

1. 6:28, 28 min after 6

2. 11:55   11:55, 5 minutes to 12

3. Reasoning What is the greatest number of minutes a digital clock can show? **59**

74   Chapter 2 • Place Value and Time

Practice 2-8	Reteaching 2-8

Practice

Skills and Reasoning

Write each time two ways.

4.

5:59, 1 minute to 6

5. `4:54`

4:54, 6 minutes to 5

Write a reasonable time for each. Use A.M. or P.M. **Possible answers are given:**

6. Eat lunch 11:30 A.M. **7.** Start school 8:30 A.M. **8.** Play outside 4:00 P.M.

9. Do homework 7:00 P.M. **10.** Have recess 10:30 A.M. **11.** Look at the moon 9:30 P.M.

Draw an analog clock and a digital clock for each time.

12. quarter to four **13.** half past midnight **14.** eleven twenty

15. How many times in one day will a clock show the time 3:48? **Twice**

16. What time is 1 minute earlier than 3 o'clock? **2:59**

Problem Solving and Applications

17. Patterns Danielle hears the weather forecast at 8:08 A.M., 8:18 A.M., and 8:28 A.M. When will the next forecast be? **8:38 A.M.**

18. Danielle and Lorenzo met for lunch. Danielle arrived at 15 min before 1 P.M. Lorenzo arrived at 12:43 P.M. Who got there first? **Lorenzo**

19. History Among the oldest working clocks in Europe are the Salisbury Cathedral clock built in 1386, and the Wells Cathedral clock built in 1392. Which clock is older? **Salisbury Cathedral clock**

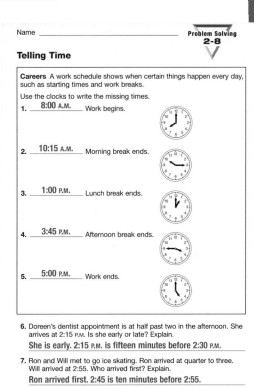

Wells Cathedral clock

Mixed Review and Test Prep

Algebra Readiness Find each missing number.

20. $16 - 9 = n$ **7** **21.** $14 - 8 = n$ **6** **22.** $15 - 4 = n$ **11** **23.** $18 - 5 = n$ **13**

24. Health In which country do people eat the most calories daily? **C**

Ⓐ Bulgaria
Ⓑ United States
Ⓒ Ireland
Ⓓ Greece

Country	Daily Calories (per person)
Bulgaria	3,634
United States	3,642
Ireland	3,692
Greece	3,688

Skills Practice Bank, page 560, Set 4   Lesson 2-8 **75**

Name _____   **Problem Solving 2-8**

Telling Time

Careers A work schedule shows when certain things happen every day, such as starting times and work breaks.

Use the clocks to write the missing times.

1. __8:00 A.M.__ Work begins.

2. __10:15 A.M.__ Morning break ends.

3. __1:00 P.M.__ Lunch break ends.

4. __3:45 P.M.__ Afternoon break ends.

5. __5:00 P.M.__ Work ends.

6. Doreen's dentist appointment is at half past two in the afternoon. She arrives at 2:15 P.M. Is she early or late? Explain.
She is early. 2:15 P.M. is fifteen minutes before 2:30 P.M.

7. Ron and Will met to go ice skating. Ron arrived at quarter to three. Will arrived at 2:55. Who arrived first? Explain.
Ron arrived first. 2:45 is ten minutes before 2:55.

Error Intervention Ongoing Assessment

Observation Watch for students who have difficulty translating times using *quarter* and *half*.

How to Help Draw a circular clock face and divide it into four quarters. Point out that 15 minutes is one-fourth of an hour. *One-quarter* is another name for *one-fourth*. Repeat with the term *half*.

Practice

Exercise 17 If necessary, have students use a clock face or draw a time line to find that the forecasts are 10 minutes apart.

For Early Finishers Challenge early finishers to describe activities or events that could take place at the times shown in Exercises 4 and 5. Have them list at least one A.M and P.M. activity. Possible answers: 5:59 A.M. waking up, 5:59 P.M. eating dinner; 4:54 A.M. sleeping, 4:54 P.M. doing homework

3 Close and Assess

Journal

Have students each choose one activity they do in the morning, one in the afternoon, and one at night. They can describe the activity and then write the approximate time they do it.

Quick Check

Number Sense Which of these times is earlier, quarter to 9 in the morning or 8:30 A.M.? 8:30 A.M.

Skill Write each time using a colon and A.M. or P.M.

1. quarter to six in the evening 5:45 P.M.

2. a half hour before midnight 11:30 P.M.

3. half past ten in the morning 10:30 A.M.

ANSWERS

12 Clock hands should be at 9 and $\frac{3}{4}$ of way between 3 and 4, 3:45

13 Clock hands should be at 6 and halfway between 12 and 1, 12:30

14 Clock hands should be at 4 and $\frac{1}{3}$ of way between 11 and 12, 11:20

Chapter 2 • Lesson 2-8   **75**

Exploring Time: Exact or Estimate?

At-A-Glance Planning

Objective Explore estimating and comparing time.
Student Book Lesson Materials None
Materials for pages 76A and 76B Index cards (5 per student)
Subject Connections science—plants, health—bacteria
Strand Connections time, estimation, using data, mental math

	Before Lesson	During Lesson	After Lesson
Daily Math			
p. 76A Problem of the Day			
p. 76A Math Routines			
p. 76A Mental Math			
Teaching Options			
p. 76B Facilitating and Assessing…			
Options for Reaching All Learners			
p. 76B Reading Assist			
p. 76B Language Development			
Technology Options			
p. 76A Math Workshop			
Assessment Options			
p. 76 Talk About It			
p. 77 Error Intervention			
p. 77 Performance Assessment			
Resources			
2-9 Practice			
2-9 Reteaching			
2-9 Enrichment			
2-9 Problem Solving			
2-9 Daily Transparency			

Problem of the Day

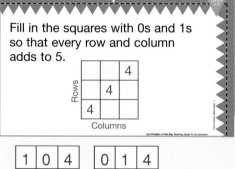

Fill in the squares with 0s and 1s so that every row and column adds to 5.

1	0	4
0	4	1
4	1	0

0	1	4
1	4	0
4	0	1

Math Routines

Time Ask students to tell how long it takes to do some everyday activities. For each one, ask them whether the time they named is an exact time or an estimate.

Measurement Have students close their eyes. Say *start* and have them raise their hands when they think 30 seconds have passed. Discuss the difference between their estimates and the actual duration.

Mental Math

Name the number that is 100 less than each. Explain your thinking.

751 651   662 562

1,073 973   1,153 1,053

 ## Math Workshop

• Have students play *Bowling for Numbers*.

• By selecting the ≈ symbol, they can answer questions dealing with estimation. Some of these questions will require students to estimate the amount of time it would take for certain events to take place.

Facilitating and Assessing **Explore** Lesson 2-9

Use with pages 76 and 77.

Get Started You may wish to begin by leading a whole-class discussion about the time units listed in the table at the top of page 77. Then have pairs or groups of students begin work on Exercises 1 and 2 on page 76.

Observe Watch to see that students understand they should fill in the blanks in Exercise 1 with a unit (such as seconds) rather than a quantity (such as 10).

Discuss During a class discussion, focus students' attention on the idea of a reasonable unit of time. Point out that students' opinions of the most reasonable answer may vary in some of the examples.

Assess Use the rubric to assess students' work. See sample for Practice Exercise 5.

4 Full Accomplishment

2 years ● 100 weeks

2 years = 365 x 2 = 730 days

100 weeks = 100 x 7 = 700 days

730 > 700

2 years > 100 weeks

Assessment Rubric

4 Full Accomplishment
- chooses the appropriate unit of time
- estimates a reasonable time for an activity

3 Substantial Accomplishment
- chooses the appropriate unit of time, with prompting
- estimates a reasonable time for an activity, with prompting

2 Partial Accomplishment
- has difficulty choosing the appropriate unit of time
- estimates reasonable times for some activities and units but not for others

1 Little Accomplishment
- does not choose the appropriate unit of time
- does not estimate a reasonable time for an activity

Options for Reaching All Learners

Reading Assist

Recognize Sequence

Use index cards to identify chronological order in a sequence of events.

Materials Index cards (5 per student)

Learning Style Logical

- Each student writes five events that happen in a typical day. Each event is written on a separate index card.
- Partners trade index cards and list the events in a logical order from first to last.
- After pairs are finished, have volunteers share their activity lists and the strategies they used for putting partners' events in order.

Language Development

Keeping a Diary

Use dates and times to write or illustrate diary entries.

Learning Style Verbal, Visual

- Students write diary entries for a typical school day. Students who are fluent in English can model their entries on the one shown on page 76. Allow students who are less fluent in English to illustrate their diary entries with drawings or pictures cut from magazines. Encourage them to add some words to their picture diaries. Tell students to include approximate times for their activities.
- Have students repeat the activity for a typical Saturday.
- Check that students use reasonable lengths of time.

Lesson Organizer

Objective Explore estimating and comparing time.

Suggested Grouping 2 to 4

Student Materials None

Assignment Guide

Basic 1–9, 12

Average 1–7, 9, 10, 12

Enriched 1–6, 9–12

1 Introduce

Review

Put these units of time in order from least to greatest.

1. minute, hour, day, second Sec, min, hr, d

2. month, day, hour, week Hr, d, wk, mo

3. month, day, year, week D, wk, mo, yr

Build on Prior Knowledge

After students have the units above in order, write the numbers 1, 7, 12, 24, 30, and 60 on the board. Ask students to pick one number and use it to relate two units of time. For example, a student might say that 1 week equals 7 days. Encourage students to create as many sentences as possible.

2 Teach

See Facilitating and Assessing…on page 76B

Explore •

Be sure groups read Exercises 1 and 2 before they start working. You may wish to ask questions such as the following as you observe students at work.

• In Exercise 1, what are possible choices for each of the blanks in the story? Second, minute, hour, day, week, month, year

Answers for Work Together

1a sec	**1b** sec or min	**1c** sec
1d hr	**1e** min	**1f** sec or min
1g sec	**1h** hr	**1i** hr
1j hr	**1k** sec or min	

Talk About It Ongoing Assessment

Watch for students who write events for which only one time unit is reasonable.

Answer for Talk About It

Check students' answers.

Exploring Time: Exact or Estimate?

Problem Solving Connection

■ Look for a Pattern

■ Use Logical Reasoning

Remember
The units of time are seconds, minutes, hours, days, weeks, months, and years.

Explore •

Work Together

1. Read the paragraph. Write the most reasonable unit of time for each activity.

Spot's Diary, June 15

6:00: Woke up. Yawned and stretched for 15 **a.** . Scratched my ears for 2 or 3 **b.** .
6:05: Went to find Louie. Barked for 30 **c.** until Louie took me out. 6:30: Tired. Went back to sleep for 2 **d.** . 8:30: Yawned. Tired. Went back to sleep for 45 **e.** . 9:15: Stared at food bowl for 15 **f.** until Louie fed me. 9:30: Ate. Took about 90 **g.** . Went back to sleep. 11:10: Chewed on a bone. After 6 **h.** of chewing, it's pretty slimy. 12:00: Took long walk with Louie for about 2 **i.** . Chased a little kid. I'm still a puppy, but I am almost 6 **j.** old in human years. I sat and thought about that for a **k.** , and decided it's a dog's life.

2. Write some time statements of your own.

a. Think of events that take you different times to do.

b. Make a list of the events. Leave a blank for the unit of time.

c. Trade lists with a partner. Fill in the blanks.

Talk About It

For which events on your partner's list was it reasonable to have different units of time? Why?

76 Chapter 2 • Place Value and Time

Practice 2-9

Name _____

Exploring Time: Exact or Estimate?

Match each time unit with its definition. Draw a line to connect them.

1. 1 century — **A.** 365 days
2. 1 day — **B.** 24 hours
3. 1 week — **C.** 10 years
4. 1 year — **D.** 100 days
5. 1 decade — **E.** 7 days

Compare. Write >, < or =.

6. 1 week (<) 1 month   **7.** 90 minutes (>) 1 hour
8. 350 days (<) 1 year   **9.** 50 years (<) 1 century
10. 1 century (>) 1 year   **11.** 60 seconds (=) 1 minute
12. 36 hours (>) 1 day   **13.** 9 years (<) 1 decade

All of the following information is given in seconds. What unit would be more reasonable for measuring each event?

14. I slept for 86,400 seconds last night. __Hours__
15. The movie lasted for 7,200 seconds. __Minutes or hours__
16. Only 259,200 seconds until my birthday __Days__
17. I am almost 283,824,000 seconds old. __Years__

Choose the most reasonable unit of time for each sentence and write it in the blank.

18. Dentists recommend that you brush your teeth for 2 __minutes__ every morning and night.
19. You can find a year ending in "–99" in every __century__ .
20. Noon happens once a __day__ .
21. The 1970's were more than a __decade__ ago.

Reteaching 2-9

Name _____

Exploring Time: Exact or Estimate?

It takes about :   1 second to blink your eyes.
1 minute to walk a block.
1 hour to do homework.
1 day to drive across Texas.
1 week for a plant to sprout.

Using this data as reference, you know that you cannot tie your shoe in 1 second. You may not need a full minute either. You can probably tie your shoe in a few seconds. So the most reasonable unit of time to tie your shoe is seconds.

Fill in the blanks with one of the following units of time: seconds, minutes, hours, days, weeks, months, or years.

1. A weekend lasts for 2 __days__
2. A cup of hot chocolate lasts for about 5 __minutes__
3. You can keep library books for 2 or 3 __weeks__
4. Each night, most people sleep for 8–10 __hours__
5. Most television commercials last for about 20 __seconds__
6. I threw a ball in the air and I caught it in 2 __seconds__
7. I rode my bike for 30 __minutes__
8. Recess lasts 20 __minutes__
9. Movies are usually about 2 __hours__ long.
10. My summer vacation from school lasts 2 __months__
11. I have been going to this school for 3 __years__
12. I put my sweater on in about 5 __seconds__
13. Your hair grows about an inch in 4 __weeks__
14. Dentists like to check your teeth every 6 __months__

Connect

Time is measured in different units.

1 minute (min) = 60 seconds (sec)
1 hour (hr) = 60 minutes
1 day (d) = 24 hours
1 week (wk) = 7 days
1 month (mo) = about 4 weeks
1 year (yr) = 12 months
1 year = 365 days
1 leap year = 366 days
1 decade = 10 years
1 century = 100 years

There are 86,400 seconds in 1 day.

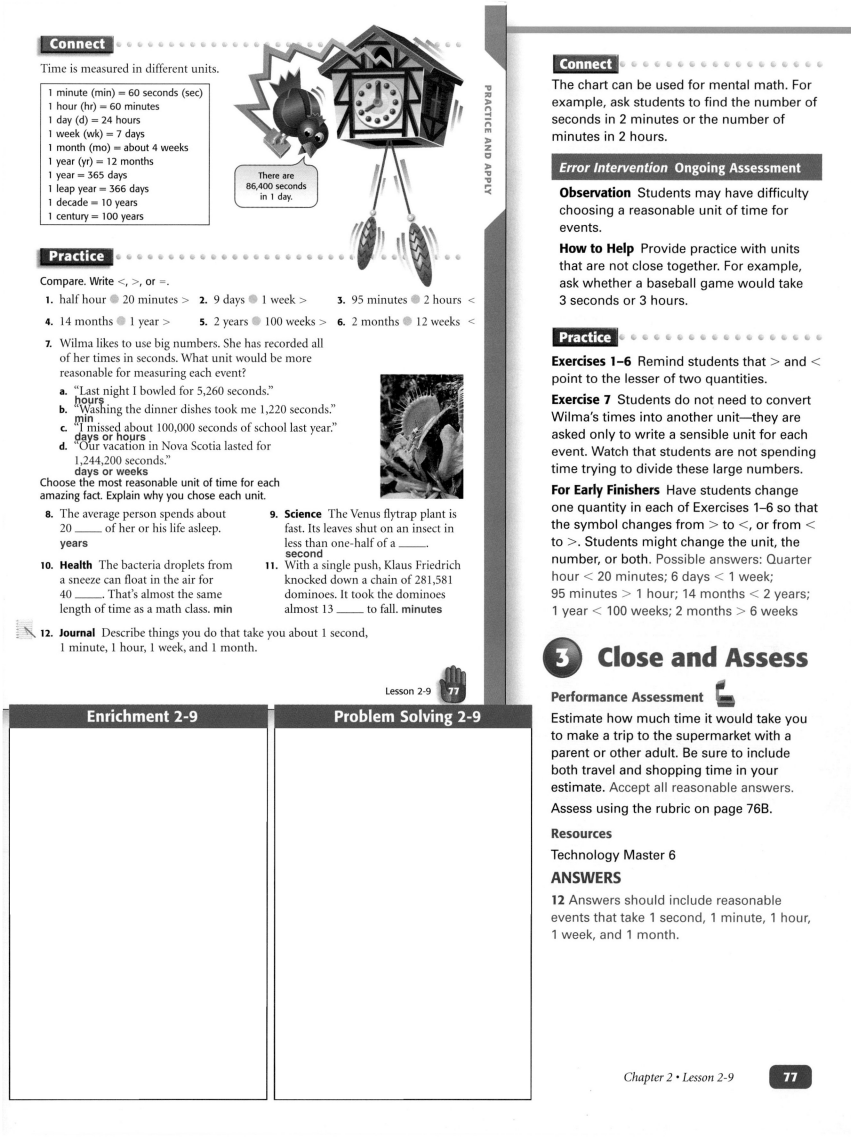

Practice

Compare. Write <, >, or =.

1. half hour ● 20 minutes >
2. 9 days ● 1 week >
3. 95 minutes ● 2 hours <
4. 14 months ● 1 year >
5. 2 years ● 100 weeks >
6. 2 months ● 12 weeks <

7. Wilma likes to use big numbers. She has recorded all of her times in seconds. What unit would be more reasonable for measuring each event?

   a. "Last night I bowled for 5,260 seconds."
   hours
   b. "Washing the dinner dishes took me 1,220 seconds."
   min
   c. "I missed about 100,000 seconds of school last year."
   days or hours
   d. "Our vacation in Nova Scotia lasted for 1,244,200 seconds."
   days or weeks

Choose the most reasonable unit of time for each amazing fact. Explain why you chose each unit.

8. The average person spends about 20 ____ of her or his life asleep.
   years

9. **Science** The Venus flytrap plant is fast. Its leaves shut on an insect in less than one-half of a ____.
   second

10. **Health** The bacteria droplets from a sneeze can float in the air for 40 ____. That's almost the same length of time as a math class. **min**

11. With a single push, Klaus Friedrich knocked down a chain of 281,581 dominoes. It took the dominoes almost 13 ____ to fall. **minutes**

12. **Journal** Describe things you do that take you about 1 second, 1 minute, 1 hour, 1 week, and 1 month.

Lesson 2-9   77

Enrichment 2-9

Problem Solving 2-9

Connect

The chart can be used for mental math. For example, ask students to find the number of seconds in 2 minutes or the number of minutes in 2 hours.

Error Intervention Ongoing Assessment

Observation Students may have difficulty choosing a reasonable unit of time for events.

How to Help Provide practice with units that are not close together. For example, ask whether a baseball game would take 3 seconds or 3 hours.

Practice

Exercises 1–6 Remind students that > and < point to the lesser of two quantities.

Exercise 7 Students do not need to convert Wilma's times into another unit—they are asked only to write a sensible unit for each event. Watch that students are not spending time trying to divide these large numbers.

For Early Finishers Have students change one quantity in each of Exercises 1–6 so that the symbol changes from > to <, or from < to >. Students might change the unit, the number, or both. Possible answers: Quarter hour < 20 minutes; 6 days < 1 week; 95 minutes > 1 hour; 14 months < 2 years; 1 year < 100 weeks; 2 months > 6 weeks

3 Close and Assess

Performance Assessment

Estimate how much time it would take you to make a trip to the supermarket with a parent or other adult. Be sure to include both travel and shopping time in your estimate. Accept all reasonable answers.

Assess using the rubric on page 76B.

Resources

Technology Master 6

ANSWERS

12 Answers should include reasonable events that take 1 second, 1 minute, 1 hour, 1 week, and 1 month.

Elapsed Time

At-A-Glance Planning

Lesson Planning Checklist

Objective Find elapsed time.

Vocabulary elapsed time

Student Book Lesson Materials *Optional* Teacher's Edition Transparency B (Clock), Lesson Enhancement Tansparency 7

Materials for pages 78A and 78B Paper-plate clocks from Lesson 2-8 (1 per student), examples of schedules, map of the United States showing time zones and major cities

Subject Connections geography—train travel, health— exercise

Strand Connections mental math, using data, estimation, patterns

	Before Lesson	During Lesson	After Lesson
Daily Math			
p. 78A Problem of the Day			
p. 78A Math Routines			
p. 78A Mental Math			
Teaching Options			
p. 78 Student Book Lesson			
p. 78B Another Way to Learn…			
Options for Reaching All Learners			
p. 78B Inclusion			
p. 78B Gifted & Talented			
Subject Connections			
p. 78A Social Studies Connection			
Assessment Options			
p. 78 Talk About It			
p. 79 Error Intervention			
p. 79 Observation			
p. 79 Quick Check			
Resources			
2-10 Practice			
2-10 Reteaching			
2-10 Enrichment			
2-10 Problem Solving			
2-10 Daily Transparency			

Problem of the Day

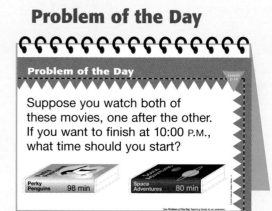

Problem of the Day

Suppose you watch both of these movies, one after the other. If you want to finish at 10:00 P.M., what time should you start?

Perky Penguins 98 min

Space Adventures 80 min

7:02 P.M.

Math Routines

Calendar Have students name dates during the current month. Give an elapsed time, such as 3 weeks 5 days, that will carry them into the next month. Have students find the end date.

Time Ask students to tell the length of time some after-school activities take and the times they begin. Ask others to find the ending times.

Mental Math

Name the number that is 500 more than each. Explain your thinking.

349 849   498 998

621 1,121   840 1,340

Social Studies Connection

Supply students with train, bus, or plane schedules. Have them plan a trip to a place at least 200 miles away. Have them compare the lengths of time, costs, convenience, and availability of the various modes of transportation and come up with a recommendation on how to arrive at their destinations.

Another Way to **Learn** Lesson 2-10

Use as an alternative or in addition to pages 78 and 79.

Materials Paper-plate clocks from Lesson 2-8 (1 per student), examples of schedules

Learning Style Kinesthetic

- Each student shows a time on his or her clock. Then partners work together to find the difference between their two times. There will be various answers for each pair of times, depending on which time is earlier and whether the times are A.M., P.M., or both.

- After partners have had a chance to find at least one solution, have volunteers explain how they found the difference between the times. Explain that the difference is called the *elapsed time*.

- Provide pairs with an example of a bus schedule, television listings, or other schedule. Ask them to choose two entries and find the elapsed time. Repeat with other entries.

- If time permits, have each pair write and act out a story that involves finding the elapsed time.

- Assign Check and Practice on Student Book pages 78 and 79 or *Practice Master 2-10*.

- Assess using the following rubric.

Assessment Rubric
4 **Full Accomplishment** • finds elapsed times • reads and uses a schedule to find elapsed time
3 **Substantial Accomplishment** • finds most elapsed times • reads and uses a schedule to find elapsed time
2 **Partial Accomplishment** • finds some elapsed times but only to hours or half hours • has difficulty reading a schedule
1 **Little Accomplishment** • does not find elapsed times • does not read a schedule

Options for Reaching All Learners

Inclusion

Are We There Yet?
Use clocks to help practice finding time.

Materials Paper-plate clocks from Lesson 2–8 (1 per student)

Learning Style Kinesthetic

- Have students imagine they are taking a car trip that starts in the morning and ends in the afternoon. Pairs of students can work together to find the time the journey will take.

- One student picks a time in the morning; the other picks a time in the afternoon. Have students pick times that are on the half hour or hour and draw clock faces to record their times.

- Students should then move the hands on paper-plate clocks from their start times to their end times, counting half hours with every half-turn of the hour hand. Students then write the elapsed time.

Gifted & Talented

Times Across the Country
Use a map to introduce time zones.

Materials Map of the United States showing time zones and major cities

Learning Style Logical

- Each partner chooses one city in different time zones.

- Students use the map to determine and record the current time in each city.

- Students write and solve two problems about travel between the chosen cities. For example: A plane leaves New York at 10:00 A.M. It flies six hours and lands in Los Angeles. What time is it in Los Angeles when the plane lands? 1 P.M.

Lesson Organizer

Objective Find elapsed time.

Student Materials None

Teacher Materials *Optional* Teacher's Edition Transparency B (Clock), Lesson Enhancement Transparency 7

Vocabulary Elapsed time

Assignment Guide

Basic 4–9, 11, 13, 15, 17–21

Average 4–8, 10, 11, 14, 15, 17–21

Enriched 6–12, 15–21

1 Introduce

Review

Tell how long each baseball game lasts.

1. Starts at 1:00 P.M. Ends at 4:00 P.M. **Three hours**

2. Starts at 9:00 A.M. Ends at 12:30 P.M. **Three and one-half hours**

3. Starts at 5:30 P.M. Ends at 7:00 P.M. **One and one-half hours**

Build on Prior Knowledge

Ask volunteers to explain how they solved the Review exercises. Some students will count by half hours; others may count whole hours first and then add the half hours.

2 Teach

See Another Way to Learn…on page 78B.

Learn

You may wish to use Lesson Enhancement Transparency 7 to discuss the example.

Talk About It) Ongoing Assessment

Listen for students who are able to subtract, but keep in mind that counting on is easier for most students.

Answer for Talk About It

Possible answer: Count minutes first, then hours.

Check

Remind students that it is important to note the A.M. and P.M. notations when finding elapsed times.

Elapsed Time

You Will Learn
how to find elapsed time

Vocabulary
elapsed time
the difference between two times

Learn

Here's a man who loved to read train schedules. Never traveling on the same track, John E. Ballenger of Florida traveled 76,485 miles by train.

When you read train schedules, it is useful to know how to find **elapsed time**.

Arrival/Departure Times	
Orlando	11:15 A.M.
Winter Haven	12:37 P.M.
West Palm Beach	3:02 P.M.
Fort Lauderdale	3:55 P.M.
Miami	4:44 P.M.

Example

Find the time it takes to travel between Orlando and Miami starting at 11:15 A.M.

Step 1	**Step 2**	**Step 3**
Count the hours.	Count the minutes.	Write the elapsed time.
11:15 → 4:44	4:15 → 4:44	5 hours 29 minutes

A trip from Orlando to Miami takes 5 hours and 29 minutes.

Math Tip
You can skip count by fives to help you count the number of minutes on a clock.

Talk About It

Describe another way to find the elapsed time from Orlando to Miami.

Check

Find each elapsed time.

1. 3:15 P.M. to 5:54 P.M.
2 hr 39 min

2. 6:30 A.M. to 2:05 P.M.
7 hr 35 min

3. Reasoning Explain how you counted the minutes between 6:30 A.M. and 2:05 P.M. **Possible answer: Count hours from 6:30 to 1:30, count minutes.**

Name _____

Elapsed Time

Find each elapsed time.

1. 7:15 P.M. to 11:30 P.M.	4 hours and 15 minutes
2. 3:20 A.M. to 9:48 A.M.	6 hours and 28 minutes
3. 12:30 P.M. to 10:55 P.M.	10 hours and 25 minutes
4. 4:10 P.M. to 5:17 P.M.	1 hour and 7 minutes
5. 10:45 A.M. to 5:55 P.M.	7 hours and 10 minutes
6. 6:12 P.M. to 12:32 A.M.	6 hours and 20 minutes
7. 9:05 P.M. to 1:04 A.M.	3 hours and 59 minutes
8. 11:59 A.M. to 12:17 P.M.	18 minutes
9. 9:00 A.M. to 11:30 A.M.	14 hours and 30 minutes
10. 1:30 P.M. to 5:30 P.M.	4 hours

11. Explain why it was easy to find the elapsed times in **9** and **10** mentally. **They both use half-hour and hour time amounts.**

Complete.

	Start Time	End Time	Elapsed Time
12.	1:22 P.M.	1:28 A.M.	12 hr 6 min
13.	9:00 A.M.	1:12 P.M.	4 hr 12 min
14.	8:50 A.M.	12:15 P.M.	3 hr 25 min
15.	9:56 A.M.	7:16 P.M.	9 hr 20 min
16.	7:35 A.M.	9:45 A.M.	2 hr 10 min
17.	2:56 P.M.	3:23 P.M.	27 min

Name _____

Elapsed Time

Departure Time	Arrival Time
Boston 1:00	Cleveland 4:10

How long does it take to fly from Boston to Cleveland?
Use a clock to help you.

From 1:00 P.M. until 4:00 P.M. is 3 hours.
Count 10 minutes from 4:00 P.M. until 4:10 P.M.

It takes __3 hours and 10 minutes__ to fly from Boston to Cleveland.

Write each elapsed time. Use a clock to help you.

1. 9:15 P.M. to 10:30 P.M.
9:00 P.M. to 10:00 P.M. is ___1___ hour(s).
:15 to :30 is ___15___ minutes
1 hour and 15 minutes

2. 5:15 P.M. to 8:30 P.M.
5:00 P.M. to 8:00 P.M. is ___3___ hour(s).
:15 to :30 is ___15___ minutes.
3 hours and 15 minutes

3. 1:00 P.M. to 10:30 P.M. __9 and a half hours__

4. 8:30 P.M. to 9:15 P.M. __45 minutes__

5. 7:20 A.M. to 10:05 A.M. __2 hours and 45 minutes__

6. 10:15 A.M. to 1:00 P.M. __2 hours and 45 minutes__

Practice

Skills and Reasoning

Find each elapsed time.

4. 7:44 A.M. to 10:50 A.M.
3 hr 6 min

5. 1:25 P.M. to 6:15 P.M.
4 hr 50 min

6. 5:03 A.M. to 1:56 P.M.
8 hr 53 min

7. 8:10 P.M. to 2:08 A.M.
5 hr 58 min

Mental Math Find each elapsed time.

8. 4:00 P.M. to 5:30 P.M.
1 hr 30 min

9. 4:15 P.M. to 9:15 P.M.
5 hr

10. Explain why it was easy to find the elapsed times in **8** and **9** mentally. **all half-hour and hour time amounts**

Copy and complete.

	Start Time	End Time	Elapsed Time
11.	8:22 P.M.	11:55 P.M.	3 hr 33 min
12.	3:06 P.M.	9:00 P.M.	5 hr 54 min

Problem Solving and Applications

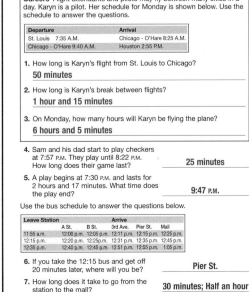

13. Health Doctors recommend at least 20 minutes of aerobic exercise a day. Phil starts jogging at 8:52 A.M. and jogs until 9:15 A.M. Has he met the 20-minute aerobic exercise requirement for that day? Explain. **Yes; he jogged for 23 min.**

14. Jed rides a unicycle. Suppose he starts riding at 10:20 A.M. and rides for 6 hr and 32 min. When will he stop? **4:52 P.M.**

Using Data Use the Data File on page 49 for **15** and **16**.

15. Estimation If you get on the *Silver Star* in Sanford and get off the train in Sebring, about how long are you on the train? **3 hours 2 min**

16. If you get on the train in Palatka and get off 2 hours and 10 minutes later, where will you be? **Orlando**

Mixed Review and Test Prep

Find each sum.

17. 8 + 4 + 3 **15**   **18.** 7 + 2 + 4 **13**   **19.** 5 + 7 + 6 **18**   **20.** 2 + 6 + 9 **17**

21. Patterns What is the missing number in the number pattern?

58, 49, 40, ▥, 22, 13, … **B**

Ⓐ 29   Ⓑ 31   Ⓒ 39   Ⓓ 42

Skills Practice Bank, page 560, Set 5   Lesson 2-10   **79**

Error Intervention **Ongoing Assessment**

Observation Watch for students who frequently get answers that are one hour or one minute too long.

How to Help Remind students to begin counting on the hour or minute *after* the given hour or minute. For example, to find the number of hours from 11 A.M. to 2 P.M., students should count "12, 1, 2" to get a total of three hours.

Practice

Exercise 13 Explain that aerobic exercise increases the heart and breathing rates.

For Early Finishers Challenge early finishers to find the time that is about midway between each pair of times shown in Exercises 4–7. Possible answers: About 9:45 A.M.; About 4:00 P.M.; About 9:30 A.M.; About 11:00 P.M.

③ Close and Assess

Observation

Give a student a clock with movable hands. Have him or her use the clock to find the elapsed time between 10:20 A.M. and 2:30 P.M. Watch to see how the student counts or moves the clock hands in solving the problem. **4 hr 10 min**

Quick Check

Number Sense Which of these times is more than 2 hours later than 11:15 A.M.? **1:30 P.M.**

1:10 P.M.   12:20 P.M.   1:30 P.M.

Skill Find each elapsed time.

1. 3:50 P.M. to 6:00 P.M. **2 hr 10 min**

2. 10:15 A.M. to 1:25 P.M. **3 hr 10 min**

3. 9:15 A.M. to 10:10 P.M. **12 hr 55 min**

Enrichment 2-10

Name _____   **Extend Your Thinking 2-10**

Patterns in Data
Find a pattern to answer each question. Then write the rule.

1. Eric takes his medicine at 8:15 A.M., 11:15 A.M., and 2:15 P.M. When will he take his medicine next?   **5:15 P.M.**
Rule: **Every 3 hours**

2. WRKO plays Carla's favorite song at 10:05 A.M., 10:35 A.M. and 11:05 A.M. When will they probably play it next?   **11:35 A.M.**
Rule: **Every 30 minutes**

3. A news program is on the radio at noon, 6:00 P.M., and midnight. When will the news be on again?   **6:00 A.M.**
Rule: **Every 6 hours**

4. Anita's grandmother drinks a glass of water at 8:30 A.M., 10:30 A.M., and 12:30 P.M. When will she have another?   **2:30 P.M.**
Rule: **Every 2 hours**

5. Mayflies hatch in the stream at 5:12 A.M., 5:18 A.M., 5:30 A.M., and 5:54 A.M. When will mayflies hatch again?   **6:42 A.M.**
Rule: **Add 6 minutes then double the number of minutes added each time.**

6. Mr. Kim, the baker, takes bread out of the oven at 4:30 A.M., 5:30 A.M., 7:00 A.M., 8:00 A.M., and 10:30 A.M. When will he take bread out of the oven again?   **11:30 A.M.**
Rule: **Add one hour, then one hour and 30 minutes.**

Problem Solving 2-10

Name _____   **Problem Solving 2-10**

Elapsed Time

Careers Flight attendants and pilots may fly between many cities in a day. Karyn is a pilot. Her schedule for Monday is shown below. Use the schedule to answer the questions.

Departure	Arrival
St. Louis 7:35 A.M.	Chicago - O'Hare 8:25 A.M.
Chicago - O'Hare 9:40 A.M.	Houston 2:55 P.M.

1. How long is Karyn's flight from St. Louis to Chicago?
50 minutes

2. How long is Karyn's break between flights?
1 hour and 15 minutes

3. On Monday, how many hours will Karyn be flying the plane?
6 hours and 5 minutes

4. Sam and his dad start to play checkers at 7:57 P.M. They play until 8:22 P.M. How long does their game last?   **25 minutes**

5. A play begins at 7:30 P.M. and lasts for 2 hours and 17 minutes. What time does the play end?   **9:47 P.M.**

Use the bus schedule to answer the questions below.

Leave Station	Arrive				
	A St.	B St.	3rd Ave.	Pier St.	Mall
11:55 a.m.	12:00 p.m.	12:05 p.m.	12:11 p.m.	12:15 p.m.	12:25 p.m.
12:15 p.m.	12:20 p.m.	12:25p.m.	12:31 p.m.	12:35 p.m.	12:45 p.m.
12:35 p.m.	12:40 p.m.	12:45 p.m.	12:51 p.m.	12:55 p.m.	1:05 p.m.

6. If you take the 12:15 bus and get off 20 minutes later, where will you be?   **Pier St.**

7. How long does it take to go from the station to the mall?   **30 minutes; Half an hour**

Chapter 2 • Lesson 2-10   **79**

Exploring the Calendar

At-A-Glance Planning

Lesson Planning Checklist

Objective Explore the calendar.

Vocabulary ordinal number

Student Book Lesson Materials Teacher's Edition Transparency C (Calendar), *optional Assessment Sourcebook 10* (How We Worked in Our Group)

Materials for pages 80A and 80B Current year calendar, Teacher's Edition Transparency C (Calendar)

Subject Connection history—calendars

Strand Connections patterns, using data

	Before Lesson	During Lesson	After Lesson
Daily Math			
p. 80A Problem of the Day			
p. 80A Math Routines			
p. 80A Mental Math			
Teaching Options			
p. 80B Facilitating and Assessing…			
Options for Reaching All Learners			
p. 80B Language Development			
p. 80B Inclusion			
Subject Connections			
p. 80A History Connection			
Assessment Options			
p. 80 Talk About It			
p. 81 Error Intervention			
p. 81 Performance Assessment			
Resources			
2-11 Practice			
2-11 Reteaching			
2-11 Enrichment			
2-11 Problem Solving			
2-11 Daily Transparency			

Problem of the Day

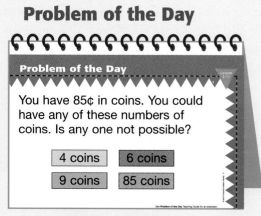

Problem of the Day

You have 85¢ in coins. You could have any of these numbers of coins. Is any one not possible?

| 4 coins | 6 coins |
| 9 coins | 85 coins |

Each number of coins shown can be used to form 85¢.

Math Routines

Measurement Tell students there are 3 ft in 1 yd. Have students tell how many feet are in each number of yards.

5 yd 15 ft   10 yd 30 ft   3 yd 9 ft

Patterns Describe these patterns using ordinals. Ask students to continue each for three more ordinals.

2nd, 5th, 8th, ■, ■, ■, 11th, 14th, 17th

4th, 9th, 14th, ■, ■, ■, 19th, 24th, 29th

Mental Math

Name the number that is 500 less than each. Explain your thinking.

604	899	1,286	1,459
104	399	786	959

History Connection

Have students research the history of the calendar we use today and compare it to other calendars. Encourage students who have familiarity with other calendars to display or explain how these calendars work.

Facilitating and Assessing Explore Lesson 2-11

Use with pages 80 and 81.

Get Started Provide each group with a calendar (Teacher's Edition Transparency C). You may wish to assign roles such as reader, recorder, and materials manager, as well as the group skill Check for Understanding that students can practice.

Observe As students work, check that they know a week is any 7 days and that they are familiar with the idea of a leap year. If necessary, review leap years for the class.

Discuss Focus the discussion on the difference between *day* and *date*. In the phrase "Monday, August 6," Monday is a *day* and August 6 is a *date*.

Assess Use the rubric to assess students' work. See sample for Practice Exercise 2.

Assessment Rubric
4 **Full Accomplishment** • uses a calendar to solve problems • accurately reads days and dates from a calendar
3 **Substantial Accomplishment** • uses a calendar to solve most problems • reads days and dates from a calendar
2 **Partial Accomplishment** • uses a calendar to solve some problems • has difficulty reading days and dates from a calendar
1 **Little Accomplishment** • does not use a calendar to solve problems • does not read days and dates from a calendar

4 Full Accomplishment

January   February   March
April   May   June
July   August   September
October   November   December

The second, fourth, sixth, ninth, and eleventh months do not have 31 days.

Options for Reaching All Learners

Language Development

Let's Celebrate!
Use vocabulary to describe when holidays occur.

Materials Current year calendar

Learning Style Verbal

• Group students acquiring English with fluent speakers. You may need to prepare additional activities with ordinal numbers for some students.

• Discuss the language often used to describe the day and date of a holiday. For example, the Fourth of July *falls on* Monday; Thanksgiving *is observed on* a Thursday in November.

• Have students compare and contrast holidays from other cultures that they know about or have celebrated. Then ask each student to pick a favorite holiday, find the day and date it occurs in the current year, and describe the holiday.

Inclusion

Planning Your Homework
Use a calendar to plan a homework assignment.

Materials Teacher's Edition Transparency C (Calendar)

Learning Style Logical

• Students vary greatly in their ability to make long-range plans. Have students choose an assignment such as reading a short book or making part of a class mural. Tell them they have a week to complete the project.

• Students work in small groups to plan the seven days they have to do the assignment. They mark their own calendars with their schedules.

• Groups can meet more than once to revise their plans during the week.

Lesson Organizer

Objective Explore the calendar.

Suggested Grouping 2 to 4

Student Materials Teacher's Edition Transparency C (Calendar), *optional Assessment Sourcebook 10* (How We Worked in Our Group)

Teacher Materials Teacher's Edition Transparency C (Calendar)

Vocabulary ordinal number

Assignment Guide

Basic 1–2, 4–6, 8

Average 2, 3, 5–8

Enriched 2, 3, 5–8

1 Introduce

Review

Answer each question. Answers will vary.

1. What day of the week is today?
2. What is today's date?
3. What is the date of your birthday?

Build on Prior Knowledge

If necessary, review with students the difference between a *day* and a *date*. Then discuss how people know the current day and date. Possible methods: Use a radio, television, newspaper, watch, or calendar.

2 Teach

See Facilitating and Assessing…on page 80B.

Explore

Use Teacher's Edition Transparency C (Calendar), if desired. Be sure groups read Exercises 1–6 before they start working. You may wish to ask questions such as the following as you observe students at work.

- Why is it impossible to tell the day of the week from just a date? Possible answer: The months don't have exactly four weeks, so the dates are not in a pattern.

Talk About It Ongoing Assessment

Showing students calendars for different years will help with the second question. Point out that 7 × 52 = 364, and this is 1 day fewer than 365.

Answer for Talk About It

Falls on same day; Not true in leap years

Exploring the Calendar

Problem Solving Connection

- Look for Patterns
- Use Logical Reasoning

Materials
calendar

Vocabulary
ordinal number a number used to tell order—for example, second or third

Did You Know?
During a leap year, February has 29 days.

Explore

We use a calendar created under Julius Caesar in 46 B.C. Every fourth year is usually a leap year and has an extra day. Years ending in 00, however, are not leap years unless they can be divided by 400.

1600 and 2000 are leap years. 1700 is not.

When you read a calendar, you use **ordinal numbers**, such as first, fifth, and twentieth, to read the dates.

Felt Hat Day is on the fifteenth of September. September is the ninth month of the year.

Work Together

Use the calendar in your classroom.

1. Which day of the week occurs most often in December? **Answer depends on calendar.**

2. Which month is the seventh month of the year? **July**

3. Thanksgiving always falls on the fourth Thursday of November. What is Thanksgiving's date? **Answer depends on calendar.**

4. Which months have five Sundays? **Answer depends on calendar.**

5. Is this year a leap year? Explain. **Answer depends on calendar.**

6. If September 5 falls on a Wednesday, what is the date two weeks later? **September 19**

Talk About It

What do you notice about the first and last days of this year? Is this true for all years? Explain.

Practice 2-11

Name _____

Practice 2-11

Exploring the Calendar
Use the calendar at home or in your classroom to answer these questions.

1. September, April, June, and November all have 30 days. Which months have 31 days?
   January, March, May, July, August, October, December

2. How can you remember the number of days in each month?
   Answers will vary. Possible answer: Make up a rhyme or song to remember it.

3. How many days are in a regular year? __365__

4. In which month will you find the extra day in a leap year?
   February

5. How often does a leap year happen?
   Every 4 years

6. How many months have 30 days? __4__

7. How many months have 31 days? __7__

8. How many months have neither 30 or 31 days? __1__

9. What are the ordinal numbers of the months that have 31 days?
   1st, 3rd, 5th, 7th, 8th, 10th, 12th

10. Suppose you want to take a karate. The first class is January 16th. The class meets every week for 6 weeks. What's the date of the last class?
    February 20th

11. Seth is going to his aunt's house two weeks after the third to last day in July. What day is he going?
    August 11th

Reteaching 2-11

Name _____

Another Look 2-11

Exploring the Calendar
Use the calendar to answer each question.

July

Sun.	Mon.	Tues.	Wed.	Thu.	Fri.	Sat.
				1	2	3
4	5	6	7	8	9	10
11	12	13	14	15	16	17
18	19	20	21	22	23	24
25	26	27	28	29	30	31

How many Fridays are in this month?
Count the squares under Friday. __There are 5__.

Write the date of the third Wednesday.
Count the first 3 Wednesdays and write the date. __July 21__

Write the day of the week of July 7th.
Find the number 7 and look at the top of the column to see the day of the week. __Wednesday__

1. How many Mondays are in July? __4__
2. How many Wednesdays? __4__
3. How many Thursdays? __5__
4. Write the dates of these days.
   a. the fourth Tuesday __July 27__
   b. the second Monday __July 12__
   c. the fifth Friday __July 30__
5. Write the days of the week of these dates.
   a. July 18th __Sunday__
   b. July 1st __Thursday__
   c. July 10th __Saturday__

Connect

Here are two ways to remember the number of days in each month.

Some people use an old rhyme.

> Thirty days hath
> September, April,
> June, and November;
> All the rest have
> thirty-one,
> Excepting February
> alone, Which hath but
> twenty-eight, in fine,
> Till leap year gives it
> twenty-nine.

Some people count on their knuckles.

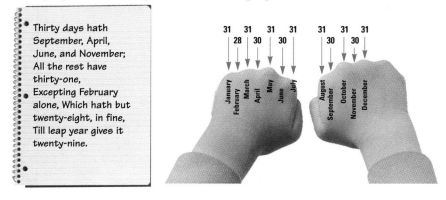

Practice

Use the calendar in your classroom.

1. How many days are in a leap year? **366 days**

2. Use ordinal numbers to name the months of the year that do *not* have 31 days. **2nd, 4th, 6th, 9th, 11th**

3. Benjamin was born in 1988. He jokingly says that he has a birthday only every four years. On which day do you think Benjamin was born? **Feb. 29, 1988**

4. In 1997, the National Shrimp Festival in Gulf Shores, Alabama, was October 9–12. A nearby town wanted to hold a festival 4 weeks later. When would their festival start? **November 6**

5. Suppose you take your puppy to a training class that meets every other week on Wednesdays. If the first class is on March 15th, what are the dates of the next three classes? **Mar. 29, Apr. 12 and 26**

6. If July 4 falls on a weekend, workers are often given Friday or Monday off. Did it happen this year? Explain. **Answer depends on calendar.**

7. December, January, and February are winter months. Which are the months in spring? In summer? In fall? **Spring: March, April, May; summer: June, July, August; Fall: September, October, November**

8. **Journal** Explain how you can find the elapsed time from the last day of third grade until the first day of fourth grade.

Lesson 2-11 **81**

Connect

Make certain students understand that there can be 28, 29, 30, or 31 days in a month.

Error Intervention Ongoing Assessment

Observation Watch for students who cannot remember the number of days in a particular month.

How to Help Suggest that students always check a calendar to find the number of days in a particular month or that they use the ways suggested on page 81 to remember.

Practice

Exercise 2 Remind students that an ordinal number shows position, for example, *first, second, third,* and *fourth.*

Exercise 7 Since the seasons usually begin on the 20th or 21st of a month, expect some variation in answers.

For Early Finishers Have students use a current calendar and find the days of the week for October 9–12 and March 15. Answers depend on the year.

3 Close and Assess

Performance Assessment

Use a calendar to find the day and date that is one week before your birthday. Answers will vary according to students' birthday dates.

Assess using the rubric on page 80B.

ANSWERS

8 Explanations should include: Use of calendar, number of days in a month, date of last day in third grade, date of first day in fourth grade

---

Enrichment 2-11

Name _____ **Extend Your Thinking 2-11**

Critical Thinking

A Chinese one-year calendar has 12 months. It is based on cycles of the moon. It is similar to the calendar you use every day, but only has 29 or 30 days in each month.

Each year is named after one of 12 animals.

Rooster	Dog	Pig	Rat	Ox	Tiger
1981	1982	1983	1984	1985	1986
1993	1994	1995	1996	1997	1998
2005	2006	2007	2008	2009	2010

Rabbit	Dragon	Snake	Horse	Sheep	Monkey
1987	1988	1989	1990	1991	1992
1999	2000	2001	2002	2003	2004
2011	2012	2013	2014	2015	2016

1. Look at the years in the calendar. Find a pattern. Then fill in the next year for each animal.

2. Describe the pattern you found.
   Possible answer: The cycle repeats itself every 12 years.

3. What animal is this year named after? **Check students' work.**

4. Name the animal for which the year you were born is named. **Check students' work.**

5. What animal will 2018 be named for? Explain how you found your answer. **Dog; Possible answer: The monkey was the animal for 2016 so I counted over two more.**

6. What animal was 1978 named for? **Horse; Possible answer: 1978 + 12 = 1990; The animal named for 1990 was the animal for 1978.**

Problem Solving 2-11

Name _____ **Problem Solving 2-11**

Exploring the Calendar

June is a busy month! It's time to fill in the calendar!

Sunday	Monday	Tuesday	Wednesday	Thursday	Friday	Saturday
						1
P 2	3	4	S 5	6	7	C 8
9	10	11	12	13	OFF 14	15
P FD 16	17	B 18	19	20	21	22
23	24	25	26	K 27	28	29
P 30						

Find the correct date for each Special Day listed below and follow the *What to do* directions to mark it on the calendar.

Special Day	When	What to do
Swimming pool opens	the first Wednesday	Write an "S."
Craft Fair	the second Saturday	Write a "C."
Puppet Show	every other Sunday, starting June 2	Write a "P."
Bike Race	the third Tuesday	Write a "B."
Camera Day at Park	9 days after bike race	Write a "K."
Flag Day	1 day before new moon	Draw a flag.
The full moon	4 weeks after the first puppet show	Draw a circle.
The new moon	1 week after craft fair	Draw a dark circle.
Summer begins!	1 week before camera day	Draw a sun.
Father's Day	the third Sunday	Write "FD."

If Flag Day falls on a weekend, workers are given Friday and Monday off. Otherwise, workers just get Flag Day off. Write "off" on the calendar on each day workers will have off.

Chapter 2 • Lesson 2-11 **81**

Decision Making: Scheduling Time

At-A-Glance Planning

Objective Solve problems by creating a schedule for making an audio tape.

Student Book Lesson Materials *Optional* Teacher's Edition Transparency B (Clock), *optional Assessment Sourcebook 10* (How We Worked in Our Group)

Materials for pages 82A and 82B Clock with second hand

Subject Connections geography—Malawi, communications—audio tapes

Strand Connections estimation, collecting data, using data

	Before Lesson	During Lesson	After Lesson
Daily Math			
p. 82A Problem of the Day			
p. 82A Math Routines			
p. 82A Mental Math			
Teaching Options			
p. 82B Facilitating and Assessing…			
Options for Reaching All Learners			
p. 82B Inclusion			
p. 82B Cultural Connection			
Technology Options			
p. 83 World Wide Web			
Subject Connections			
p. 82A Geography Connection			
Assessment Options			
p. 83 Journal			
Resources			
2-12 Practice			
2-12 Reteaching			
2-12 Enrichment			
2-12 Problem Solving			
2-12 Daily Transparency			

Problem of the Day

Problem of the Day

Two weeks and two days from today will be May 26. What is today's date?

May — S M T W T F S

㉖

See Problem of the Day Teaching Guide for an extension.

May 10

Math Routines

Time Have students describe activities for a typical evening in 15-minute intervals. Have them begin at 5:00 P.M. and end at 7:00 P.M. Tell them to write the schedule as follows:

5:00–5:15   I_____

5:15–5:30   I_____

and so on.

Measurement Have each student name one activity they do every day and how long it takes to do it.

Mental Math

Give five addition sentences with a sum of 50. Explain how you chose the numbers to add.

Geography Connection

Have students use library materials or online reference sources to find information about the African country of Malawi. You might ask each student to find five different facts and then work as a group to create a Malawi notebook.

Facilitating and Assessing [Explore] Lesson 2-12

Use with pages 82 and 83.

Get Started You may wish to assign roles such as timekeeper, recorder, or team captain, as well as the group skill Explain and Summarize for students to practice as they work.

Observe If groups have trouble getting started, suggest that they might begin with a schedule that includes an introduction, three speeches, and a conclusion. Then they could revise their schedule to add or change the sections.

Discuss Have a volunteer from each group post the group's schedule and point out any features of interest. Discuss with the class the challenges of trying to agree on just one schedule for the whole class. Ask for ideas on how such an agreement might be reached. Possible answers: By class vote; By voting for a small committee to create the plan

Assess Use the rubric to assess students' work. See sample.

4 Full Accomplishment	
Introduction	3 minutes
People in Our Class	2 minutes
People in Our School	5 minutes
People in Our Town	5 minutes
Conclusion	3 minutes

$3 + 2 + 5 + 5 + 3 = 18$. We have 12 minutes left to use on the tape. We could add 4 minutes to each main section or add two 6-minute sections on people in our state and in our country.

Assessment Rubric

4 **Full Accomplishment**
- creates a schedule to help make decisions

3 **Substantial Accomplishment**
- with prompting, creates a schedule to help make decisions

2 **Partial Accomplishment**
- has trouble creating a schedule to help make decisions

1 **Little Accomplishment**
- does not create a schedule to help make decisions

Options for Reaching All Learners

Inclusion

Your Turn
Use projects to estimate lengths of time.

Materials Clock with second hand

Learning Style Verbal, Visual, Musical, Kinesthetic

- Have each student do an activity that he or she estimates will take 2 minutes. The activity could be to play a piece of music, make a drawing, give a speech, or make an object such as a paper snowflake.

- Then have students time each other to see how close their estimates are. They may revise their projects, if needed, to come closer to the 2-minute time limit.

- Make a class list of 2-minute projects. If students have created products, use these products to decorate the list.

Cultural Connection

Students Around the World
Use student-made tapes to strengthen understanding of cultures, especially those represented in the classroom.

Learning Style Social

- In the student lesson, students plan a 30-minute audio tape directed to students in a country in Africa. Have students choose one or two other places to direct their tape.

- Students should outline the following and explain their answers:

How would the tape be the same for a place other than Africa? How would the tape be different?

Would it be better to make a video tape rather than an audio tape? Why or why not?

Lesson Organizer

Objective Solve problems by creating a schedule for making an audio tape.

Suggested Grouping 2 to 4

Student Materials *Optional Assessment Sourcebook 10* (How We Worked in Our Group)

Teacher Materials *Optional* Teacher's Edition Transparency B (Clock)

Assignment Guide

Basic 1–15

Average 1–15

Enriched 1–15

1 Introduce

Review

Find the elapsed time for each speech part.

1. Introduction 8:50 to 8:52 2 minutes

2. Facts About Our Class 8:52 to 9:01 9 minutes

3. What Our School Looks Like 9:01 to 9:07 6 minutes

Build on Prior Knowledge

After students find the elapsed time of individual events, ask them how they could find the elapsed time of consecutive events. Possible answers: Add the elapsed time of each event; find the elapsed time from start of first event to end of last event.

2 Teach

See Facilitating and Assessing...on page 82B.

Explore • • • • • • • • • • • • • • • • •

Show students the location of Malawi on a map or globe. During the lesson, you may wish to use Teacher's Edition Transparency B (Clock) to model times.

As students do the activity, watch to make sure they understand that their task is only to plan the schedule for the tape. Students should not start to actually write scripts.

Reading Assist

Main Idea and Supporting Details

Suggest that students read with a partner to identify the main ideas and supporting details of what they read.

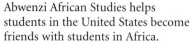

Problem Solving
Decision Making: **Scheduling Time**

You Will Learn
how creating a schedule can help you make decisions

Did You Know?
Abwenzi is the word for "friends" in the Chichewa language of Malawi, Africa.

Explore •

Abwenzi African Studies helps students in the United States become friends with students in Africa.

Suppose your class decides to join this exciting project by sending an audio tape to a class in Malawi. You want to make a 30-minute tape of information about your class.

Decide how you will introduce yourselves. What is important to tell about your class? How will you schedule your time so that your tape is about 30 minutes long?

Here's a sample schedule:

Event	Time (min)	Total Time (min)
Class song	3	3
Hello speech	5	8
Classroom tour	5	13

82

Work Together

▶ **Understand**

1. What do you know? Tape is 30 min long.

2. What do you need to decide? Taping time schedule.

3. What information will you need to help you make a decision? What to put on the tape and how much time each part takes.

▶ **Plan and Solve**

4. What are some things about yourselves that you would like to tell the class in Malawi? Possible answer: Description of students' home, school, and community lives?

5. Make a list of the speakers and what they will do.

6. How can counting the minutes of each speaker help you plan your tape? Helps make a schedule.

7. One student has an idea. "I think each of us should just get 5 minutes." If your class follows this idea, how long will your tape be?

8. Another student has an idea. "Let's talk on one side of the tape and put our favorite songs on the other side." If your class follows this idea, will you have enough tape to include 10 songs? Explain.

9. Should you include extra time in your schedule? Why or why not? Yes; Possible answer: Someone may talk longer than planned.

▶ **Make a Decision**

10. Write a final list of the order of the speakers.

11. Make a schedule to help guide your taping.

▶ **Present Your Decision**

12. Show your schedule to the class.

13. Does your schedule allow enough time to tell about your class?

14. Compare the different group schedules. What was the longest tape time? The shortest?

15. Check out www.mathsurf.com/4/ch2 to find out more about Malawi and other African countries.

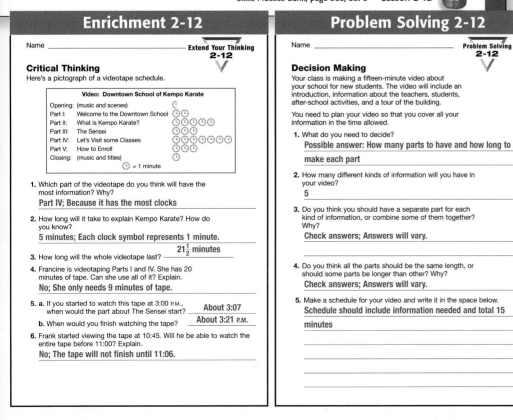

Skills Practice Bank, page 560, Set 6   Lesson 2-12   **83**

Reading Assist **Recognize Sequence**

Help students recognize and evaluate the sequence of activities by asking and discussing the following:

• Did you first divide the 30 minutes into sections of different time lengths? Or did you first decide on the topics you want to include? Does one method work better? Why?

Exercise 15 Students may try looking under the more general topic of Africa first and narrow the search to Malawi. Then encourage students to use a map of Africa and search for information on nearby countries. Invite students to share their findings with classmates.

③ Close and Assess

Journal

Summarize what you have learned in this lesson. Include a short copy of your final schedule. Answers should include how student scheduled the time and decided on topics. They should also include student's final schedule.

Assess using the rubric on page 82B.

ANSWERS

7 Five times as long as the number of students in the class

8 It depends on whether the combined lengths of the songs is shorter than the length of one side of the tape.

Enrichment 2-12

Name _____   **Extend Your Thinking 2-12**

Critical Thinking

Here's a pictograph of a videotape schedule.

Video: Downtown School of Kempo Karate	
Opening: (music and scenes)	
Part I: Welcome to the Downtown School	
Part II: What is Kempo Karate?	
Part III: The Sensei	
Part IV: Let's Visit some Classes	
Part V: How to Enroll	
Closing: (music and titles)	

🕐 = 1 minute

1. Which part of the videotape do you think will have the most information? Why?
   Part IV; Because it has the most clocks

2. How long will it take to explain Kempo Karate? How do you know?
   5 minutes; Each clock symbol represents 1 minute.

3. How long will the whole videotape last? **21½ minutes**

4. Francine is videotaping Parts I and IV. She has 20 minutes of tape. Can she use all of it? Explain.
   No; She only needs 9 minutes of tape.

5. a. If you started to watch this tape at 3:00 P.M., when would the part about The Sensei start? **About 3:07**
   b. When would you finish watching the tape? **About 3:21 P.M.**

6. Frank started viewing the tape at 10:45. Will he be able to watch the entire tape before 11:00? Explain.
   No; The tape will not finish until 11:06.

Problem Solving 2-12

Name _____   **Problem Solving 2-12**

Decision Making

Your class is making a fifteen-minute video about your school for new students. The video will include an introduction, information about the teachers, students, after-school activities, and a tour of the building.

You need to plan your video so that you cover all your information in the time allowed.

1. What do you need to decide?
   Possible answer: How many parts to have and how long to make each part

2. How many different kinds of information will you have in your video?
   5

3. Do you think you should have a separate part for each kind of information, or combine some of them together? Why?
   Check answers; Answers will vary.

4. Do you think all the parts should be the same length, or should some parts be longer than other? Why?
   Check answers; Answers will vary.

5. Make a schedule for your video and write it in the space below.
   Schedule should include information needed and total 15 minutes

_____

_____

_____

_____

Section C
Review and Practice

Use the Skills Checklist

Review the **Skills Checklist** on the page with students. Then ask questions such as the following:

- In which problems will you use the skills of reading clocks or telling time? Exercises 4–5, 15

- In which problems will you compare times? Exercises 6–9

- In which problem will you recognize or find elapsed time? Exercises 3, 10–11

Assess

You may wish to use this information to assess students' understanding of the lesson objectives.

Item Analysis

Lesson Objective	Items
2-8 Tell time to the minute and identify A.M. and P.M.	1, 2, 4, 5, 15
2-9 Explore estimating and comparing time.	6–9, 15
2-10 Find elapsed time.	3, 10, 11, 15
2-11 Explore the calendar.	12–14
2-12 Solve problems by creating a schedule for making an audio tape.	

Resources

Practice Masters

- Practice Chapter 2 Section C

Assessment Sourcebook

- Quiz Chapter 2 Section C

TestWorks: Test and Practice Software

ANSWERS

15 Check to see that students' answers show their understanding of elapsed time and the difference between A.M. and P.M.

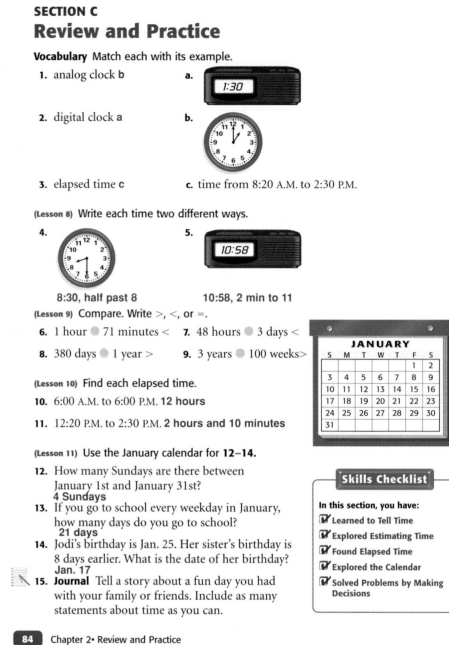

Review and Practice

Vocabulary Match each with its example.

1. analog clock **b**

2. digital clock **a**

3. elapsed time **c**

a.

b.

c. time from 8:20 A.M. to 2:30 P.M.

(Lesson 8) Write each time two different ways.

4.

8:30, half past 8

5.

10:58, 2 min to 11

(Lesson 9) Compare. Write >, <, or =.

6. 1 hour ● 71 minutes <   7. 48 hours ● 3 days <

8. 380 days ● 1 year >   9. 3 years ● 100 weeks >

(Lesson 10) Find each elapsed time.

10. 6:00 A.M. to 6:00 P.M. **12 hours**

11. 12:20 P.M. to 2:30 P.M. **2 hours and 10 minutes**

(Lesson 11) Use the January calendar for **12–14.**

12. How many Sundays are there between January 1st and January 31st?
 4 Sundays
13. If you go to school every weekday in January, how many days do you go to school?
 21 days
14. Jodi's birthday is Jan. 25. Her sister's birthday is 8 days earlier. What is the date of her birthday?
 Jan. 17
15. **Journal** Tell a story about a fun day you had with your family or friends. Include as many statements about time as you can.

JANUARY

S	M	T	W	T	F	S
					1	2
3	4	5	6	7	8	9
10	11	12	13	14	15	16
17	18	19	20	21	22	23
24	25	26	27	28	29	30
31						

Skills Checklist

In this section, you have:

- ✓ Learned to Tell Time
- ✓ Explored Estimating Time
- ✓ Found Elapsed Time
- ✓ Explored the Calendar
- ✓ Solved Problems by Making Decisions

REVIEW AND PRACTICE

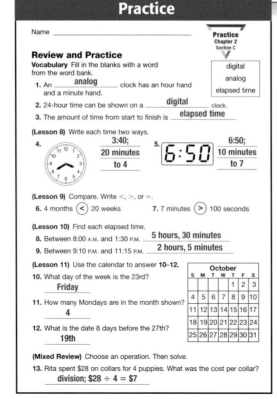

Practice

Name _____

Practice
Chapter 2
Section C

Review and Practice
Vocabulary Fill in the blanks with a word from the word bank.

digital
analog
elapsed time

1. An ___analog___ clock has an hour hand and a minute hand.

2. 24-hour time can be shown on a ___digital___ clock.

3. The amount of time from start to finish is ___elapsed time___.

(Lesson 8) Write each time two ways.

4. 3:40; 20 minutes to 4

5. `6:50` 6:50; 10 minutes to 7

(Lesson 9) Compare. Write <, >, or =.

6. 4 months ⊘ 20 weeks

7. 7 minutes ⊘ 100 seconds

(Lesson 10) Find each elapsed time.

8. Between 8:00 A.M. and 1:30 P.M. 5 hours, 30 minutes

9. Between 9:10 P.M. and 11:15 P.M. 2 hours, 5 minutes

(Lesson 11) Use the calendar to answer 10–12.

10. What day of the week is the 23rd?
 Friday

11. How many Mondays are in the month shown?
 4

12. What is the date 8 days before the 27th?
 19th

October

S	M	T	W	T	F	S
				1	2	3
4	5	6	7	8	9	10
11	12	13	14	15	16	17
18	19	20	21	22	23	24
25	26	27	28	29	30	31

(Mixed Review) Choose an operation. Then solve.

13. Rita spent $28 on collars for 4 puppies. What was the cost per collar?
 division; $28 ÷ 4 = $7

YOUR CHOICE

Choose at least one. Use what you have learned in this chapter.

① Math Big-tionary

Make your own number dictionary. Make a page for each place value, including the hundred millions. For each place give an example or two. Your examples can be pictures, stories, or amazing facts.

TENS
5o Number of states in U.S.
76 How old my grandmother is

② Number Round-Up

Challenge a partner to think of a situation where a number rounds to a chosen number. For example, if you choose 300: "There are 275 baseball cards in my collection!" Then switch roles.

③ Number Cube

Use the digits 1, 2, 3. Use each digit only once. Find the missing numbers for the other sides of the cube. Then make your own number cube, using different digits.
132, 312, 231

④ Calendar Clues

At Home Pick one day of the year (don't tell). Give clues to help someone guess the day.

• in a month that begins with J
• 2-digit date
• not a week-end day … (and so on)

Challenge a friend or family member to guess your day.

⑤ Cyber Search

Look at **www.mathsurf.com/4/ch2** for sites with big numbers. The sites might show population, world records, or distances in outer space. Order the numbers. Put the ordered numbers in a table. Give your table a title.

REVIEW AND PRACTICE

World Wide Web

For Cyber Search, you may wish to give students a narrower topic for their searches. Suggest that they begin at **www.mathsurf.com/4/ch2**. For example, the class might agree to look for facts about soccer that have numbers with more than four digits.

Home-School Connection

For Calendar Clues, have each student count the number of clocks (or other devices that show the time) at home. The data can be used for a class graph. You and your students may be surprised at how many items show time!

Parents can use the Web site at **www.parent.mathsurf.com**.

Your Choice

Students will review the skills and concepts of the chapter using learning style strengths. This page of activities is a good opportunity for portfolio assessment.

① Math Big-tionary

Learning Style Verbal, Visual, Individual

Note that students' dictionaries must have at least 9 pages (one for each place value). Allow them to use more pages if they wish.

② Number Round-Up

Learning Style Social, Logical

Students should tell their partners whether the chosen number is rounded to the nearest ten, hundred, or thousand.

③ Number Cube

Learning Style Logical

When students make their own cubes, they must choose three different nonzero digits in order to get six different numbers. 132, 312, 231

④ Calendar Clues

Learning Style Social

Remind students that their clues must result in just one possible answer.

Possible answer: In a month that has only 3 letters; 2-digit date; 3 in the tens place; not the last day of the month (May 30)

⑤ Cyber Search

Learning Style Visual

Web sites with population data are good places for students to look for large numbers.

Chapter 2
Review/Test

This page may be used to review or assess students' knowledge of Chapter 2.

Item Analysis		
Lesson Objective		**Items**
2-1	Read and write numbers in the thousands.	1, 3–8
2-2	Explore place-value relationships.	4–8
2-3	Read and write numbers through the hundred millions.	8
2-4	Solve problems by making an organized list.	9
2-5	Compare numbers to find which is greater.	10–12
2-6	Order a group of numbers.	13–14
2-7	Explore rounding.	15–19
2-8	Tell time to the minute and identify A.M. and P.M.	2
2-9	Explore estimating and comparing time.	20–22
2-10	Find elapsed time.	23, 24
2-11	Explore the calendar.	25
2-12	Solve problems by creating a schedule for making an audio tape.	

Resources

Reading Strategies for Math

Chart 6 (Preparing for a Test)

Assessment Sourcebook

Chapter 2 Tests

• Forms A and B (free-response)

• Form C (multiple choice)

• Form E (mixed response)

• Form F (cumulative chapter test)

TestWorks: Test and Practice Software

Home and Community Connections

• Letter Home for Chapter 2 in English and Spanish

Review/Test

Vocabulary Match each with its meaning.

1. standard form **c**
2. digital clock **b**
3. period **a**

   a. a group of three digits in a number, separated by a comma

   b. shows the time with digits

   c. a way to write a number

(Lessons 1, 2, and 3) Give the value of each red digit.

4. 2,556	**5.** 1,812	**6.** 7,985	**7.** 10,031	**8.** 7,301,299
2,000	800	80	10,000	90

(Lesson 4) Solve. Use any strategy.

9. How many combinations of pants and shirts can you make? Write the combinations. Use the table. **4; JR; JC; SR; SC**

Clothes Choices	
Pants	**Shirts**
Jeans	Red
Shorts	Checked

(Lesson 5) Compare. Write >, <, or =.

10. 2,003 ● 2,005 **<**   11. 65,656 ● 65,565 **>**   12. 933,771 ● 1,399,771 **<**

(Lesson 6) Order the numbers from least to greatest.

13. 6,161, 6,661, 6,116   14. 42,887, 41,987, 42,779
   6,116, 6,161, 6,661   41,987, 42,779, 42,887

(Lesson 7) Round each number to the nearest thousand.

15. 9,226	**16.** 5,811	**17.** 3,600	**18.** 1,846	**19.** 2,376
9,000	6,000	4,000	2,000	2,000

(Lessons 8 and 9) Compare. Write >, <, or =.

20. 72 hours ● 4 days **<**   21. 28 minutes ● half hour **<**   22. 359 days ● 1 year **<**

(Lesson 10) Find each elapsed time for **23** and **24**.

23. 10:30 A.M. to 12:30 P.M. **2 hours**

24. Belva went to a square dance that started at 2:15 P.M. and ended at 5:00 P.M. How long was she at the dance? **2 hours and 45 minutes**

25. **(Lesson 11)** **Reasoning** If a month starts on a Monday, how many Mondays are in the month? **5; not true for February, unless in a leap year and starting on a Monday**

Assessment

Performance Assessment

A Place Value

Read the story about Handley School. Use numbers in the clouds to fill in each blank. One number will not be used.

a. 452
b. 904
c. 1,152
d. 98,000
e. 42,000

360,000

42,000

904

At Handley School, there are just under 500 students. The school gives the __a.__ students 2 pencils a year, or __b.__ pencils.
The teachers use __c.__ pieces of chalk, a little more than the number of pencils used by the students.
Each year the school serves almost 100,000 pints of milk and 50,000 lunches.
That's __d.__ pints of milk and __e.__ lunches.

1,152

452

98,000

1. **Explain Your Thinking** How did you choose the numbers to put in the blanks? **Possible answer. Used place value.**

2. **Decision Making** Write a story with numbers in the hundreds, thousands, and millions. Leave blanks for each number. Exchange stories with a partner and fill in the best number for each blank. **Answers may vary.**

3. **Critical Thinking** Suppose there were twice as many students at Handley School. How would you rewrite the story? **Double all the numbers in the story except for the 2 pencils.**

B Time

Make a schedule of your activities on a Saturday. Write the start and end time for each activity. Include at least 5 events.

4. **Decision Making** Decide which activities to include. When does the activity begin? When does it end? How long is each activity? **Answers may vary.**

5. **Explain Your Thinking** Explain how you find the elapsed time for each activity. **Answers may vary. Example: You could use clocks to count the hours and minutes.**

6. **Critical Thinking** How long do you play outside in a day? In a week? **Answers may vary. Example: You could multiply your answer for a day by 7 for a week.**

REVIEW/TEST

Assessment

Name _____
Date _____ Score _____

Chapter 2 Test
Form
D

How do you spend your time in one week? These are the activities that some fourth graders have listed.

being in school	sleeping	reading
doing homework	playing baseball	watching television
practicing piano	riding my bike	playing computer games
eating meals	playing with friends	roller blading

a. **Recording Data** First make a list of the things you usually do in one week during the school year. Then make a table like the one below. The number of rows depends on the number of activities in your list. Write your list in the Activities column and write the length of the activity to the nearest hour.

Hours I Spend on Activities During the School Year							
Activities	Sun.	Mon.	Tues.	Wed.	Thurs.	Fri.	Sat.
Total hours	24 hr	24 hr	24 hr	24hr	24 hr	24hr	24 hr

b. **Recording Data** Estimate the number of hours you spend on each activity each week. Write your estimates for each day in the table. Make sure that the sum in each column is 24 hours.

c. **Analyzing Data** Use the table to answer these questions.
Which activity takes the most time in a week?
Which activity takes the least time in a week?
Which days do you spend the most time in after-school activities?

d. **Analyzing Data** List the times you spend on the activities for one day from least to greatest.

e. **Making Decisions** Would you like to spend more or less time on any of the activities that you listed? Explain.

Chapter 2 Performance Assessment

Students will show their understanding of place value and comparing and ordering through millions. They will show their understanding of estimating, telling, and using time and calendars.

Introduce the Task

- Allow students time to read all the instructions. For Exercise 2, discuss the idea that children should give clues in their stories that will help a partner match the numbers to the situation.

  Share Level 4 of the rubric with students before they begin.

Facilitate and Assess

Before students begin work, you may wish to ask questions such as the following:

- How can you make sure that none of your numbers will go in more than one blank?

- How will you decide which activities to use for your Saturday schedule?

- How will you know that the numbers you choose for your story are reasonable?

Assessment Rubric

4 Full Accomplishment
- chooses numbers and lengths of time that are reasonable and appropriate
- completes all parts of the task

3 Substantial Accomplishment
- chooses most numbers or lengths of time that are reasonable and appropriate
- completes most parts of the task

2 Partial Accomplishment
- chooses several numbers or lengths of time that are not reasonable or appropriate
- does not complete all parts of the task

1 Little Accomplishment
- chooses few numbers or lengths of time that are reasonable or appropriate
- does not complete the task

Resources

Assessment Sourcebook

Chapter 2 Test
- Form D (performance assessment)

Chapter 2   **87**

Math Magazine

Students will use Roman numerals to write numbers.

Student Materials Encyclopedia

Historical Note

Roman numerals are used for the copyright notices on books and movies. They are sometimes found on buildings to show the dates the buildings were constructed. Here are some examples of dates written in Roman numerals:

MDCCC	1800
MCM	1900
MCML	1950
MCMLXXX	1980
MCMXC	1990

Cultural Link

Encourage students to compare other number systems to the base-ten system. The base-ten system is *positional,* meaning that the position of a digit changes its value. Other systems students may find are often not positional. In such systems, symbols have the same value no matter where they occur.

No Place for Zeros

Ancient Romans used a number system that used these symbols:

I	V	X	L	C	D	M
1	5	10	50	100	500	1,000

From these symbols, you can make other numbers, but the system does not use place value or zeros.

When in Rome, do as the Romans did! Read and write Roman numerals. When a symbol meaning less is to the right, add.

Additional Resources for the Teacher

Discovery in Mathematics, Robert B. Davis. Menlo Park, CA: Dale Seymour Publications.

Connections Game: Architecture, Jean Morman Unsworth. Menlo Park, CA: Dale Seymour Publications.

Cumulative Review

Test Prep Strategy: Follow Directions!

Watch for words like *not*.
Write a number that is not between 42,931 and 42,941. **A**

(A) 42,930   (B) 42,940   (C) 42,939   (D) 42,932

Choices (B), (C), and (D) are between 42,931 and 42,941. (A) is *not* between 42,931 and 42,941. The answer is (A). **STAY SHARP!**

Write the letter of the correct answer. Use any strategy.

1. Which number is not less than 2,555,999? **B**

(A) 2,499,999   (B) 2,556,005
(C) 2,554,999   (D) 2,500,005

2. Which number rounded to the nearest thousand is greater than 3,000? **C**

(A) 3,334   (B) 3,198   (C) 3,502   (D) 3,099

3. How many hours are there in 3 days? **B**

(A) 48   (B) 72
(C) 720   (D) 180

Use the pictograph to answer **4–7.**

4. Who did not collect twenty or more diskettes? **C**

(A) Martin   (B) Eric
(C) Steve   (D) Salima

5. Who collected the same number of diskettes as Martin? **D**

(A) Eric   (B) Bobby
(C) Salima   (D) Leah

6. How many diskettes did Eric and Salima collect combined? **A**

(A) 80   (B) 90
(C) 70   (D) 60

7. What was the mode of the diskettes collected? **B**

(A) 40   (B) 30   (C) 20   (D) 10

Test Prep Strategies

- Read Carefully
- Follow Directions
- Make Smart Choices
- Eliminate Choices
- Work Backward from an Answer

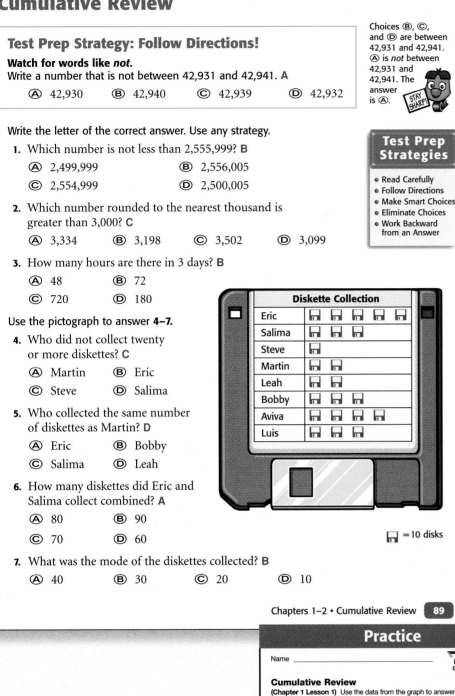

Diskette Collection

Eric	🖫 🖫 🖫 🖫 🖫
Salima	🖫 🖫 🖫
Steve	🖫
Martin	🖫 🖫
Leah	🖫 🖫
Bobby	🖫 🖫 🖫
Aviva	🖫 🖫 🖫 🖫
Luis	🖫 🖫 🖫

🖫 = 10 disks

REVIEW AND PRACTICE

Practice

Name _____

Practice Chapter 1–2

Cumulative Review
(Chapter 1 Lesson 1) Use the data from the graph to answer each question.

1. How many activities are the favorite of more than 5 students? **2**

2. What activity is the favorite of 4 students? **Puzzles**

Favorite Activity
Reading
Board games
Soccer
Puzzles
0 1 2 3 4 5 6 7 8 9 10
Number of Students

(Chapter 1 Lesson 10) Find the range, mode, and median for each set of numbers.

3. 11, 24, 11, 29, 15, 11 __18__, __11__, __13__,

4. 29, 26, 23, 20, 26 __9__, __26__, __26__

(Chapter 1 Lesson 12) Solve. Use any strategy.

5. Rodney is 3 times as old as his sister. A year ago, he was 4 times as old. How old are Rodney and his sister now?
Rodney is 9; sister is 3

(Chapter 2 Lesson 3) Write the value of each underlined digit.

6. 4,645,861 __40,000__   **7.** 5,293,862 __5,000,000__

(Chapter 2 Lesson 6) Order from least to greatest.

8. 337,655; 37,650; 438,530; 299,999
37,650; 299,999; 337,655; 438,530

9. 54,670; 155,839; 54,668; 55,355
54,668; 54,670; 55,355; 155,839

(Chapter 2 Lesson 8) Write each time in two ways.

10. **5:55;**
5 minutes before 6

11. **6:25;**
25 minutes after 6

Chapters 1–2 Cumulative Review

Students review and maintain skills and concepts taught in Chapters 1–2 and practice test-taking strategies. Special attention is given here to the Test Prep Strategy, Follow Directions: Watch for Words Like *Not*.

Introduce the Test Prep Strategy

Follow Directions: Watch for Words Like *Not*
Read and discuss the Test Prep Strategy note. After students work through the example, present the following problem:
Which number is *not* greater than 36,406? B

(A) 36,604   (B) 36,046
(C) 360,400   (D) 36,460

Encourage students to find other problems on this page where Follow Directions: Watch for Words Like *Not* might be a helpful strategy.

Some students may prefer another strategy for some of the identified items. Have them tell which strategy they would use and explain why.

Review and Assess

Item Analysis	
Item	Lesson
1	2-5
2	2-7
3	2-9
4	1-1
5	1-1
6	1-1
7	1-10

Resources

Practice Masters

• Cumulative Review Chapters 1–2

Section	Pacing Day	Lessons Lesson/Page Objective			Your Test Correlation	Materials Student Book	Another Way to Learn
A **Understanding Addition and Subtraction** Students find and estimate sums and differences. **Problem Solving Skill** *Exact or Estimate?*	Day 1	3-1	94–95	Explore addition and subtraction problems.		Calculators	
	Day 2	3-2	96–97	Explore adding and subtracting on a thousand chart.		Thousand chart, counters, calculators	
	Day 3	3-3	98–99	Estimate sums and differences using rounding.			PV* blocks
	Day 4	3-4	100–101	**Problem Solving** Solve problems needing exact answers or estimates.			Newspapers, magazines, scissors, paste
B **Adding and Subtracting** Students develop the algorithms through 3- and 4- digit numbers. **Problem Solving Skill** *Multiple-Step Problems*	Day 5	3-5	104–107	Add 3-digit and 4-digit numbers.			PV blocks
	Day 6	3-6	108–109	Add 3 and 4 addends.			PV blocks
	Day 7	3-7	110–113	Subtract 3-digit and 4-digit numbers.			PV blocks
	Day 8	3-8	114–115	Subtract from numbers with zeros.			9-Digit PV Chart
	Day 9	3-9	118–119	**Problem Solving** Solve multiple-step problems.			Large bag of beans
	Day 10	3-10	120–121	Add and subtract numbers mentally.			Calculators
	Day 11	3-11	122–123	Choose a calculation method.		Calculators	Calculators
C **Using Money** Students add and subtract money. **Problem Solving Connection** *Use Objects/Act It Out* **Problem Solving Strategy** *Look for a Pattern*	Day 12	3-12	126–127	Count and compare money.		Play money	Play money
	Day 13	3-13	128–129	Add and subtract money amounts.			Play money
	Day 14	3-14	130–131	Explore making change.		Play money	
	Day 15	3-15	134–135	Explore algebra by balancing number sentences.		Counters, envelope	
	Day 16	3-16	136–137	**Problem Solving** Solve problems by looking for a pattern.			Number Lines, Power Polygons
Chapter Assessment	Day 17		140–141	Assess student understanding and skills for Chapter 3.			

Also in this Chapter **Data File,** pp. 90–91, **Projects/Extensions,** pp. 92, 142

* PV = Place Value

Chapter 3
Key Math Idea

Addition involves combining and regrouping numbers to find a sum. Subtraction involves taking away and comparing.

Connections		Section Resources	
Strand	**Subject**	**Technology**	**Review and Assessment**
Algebra, Money, Geometry	Literature, Language	**Performance Math: Addition and Subtraction** 💿	**Review**
Logic	Fine Arts, Social Studies, Reading, Culture	**World Wide Web** 🌐 www.mathsurf.com/4/ch3 Chapter Opener, p. 91	Section A Opener, p. 93 Mixed Review and Test Prep, p. 99 Section A Review and Practice, p. 102 Skills Practice Bank, p. 561
Reasoning, Using Data, Time, Logic	Careers, Reading, Language	**Calculator** 🖩 Addition and Subtraction Patterns, pp. 94–95 Exploring Adding and Subtracting on a Thousand Chart, pp. 96	**Ongoing Assessment** *Teacher's Edition,* all lessons *Assessment Sourcebook,* Quiz Chapter 3 Section A
Using Data, Collecting Data	Careers, Reading	**Math Workshop** 💿 Analyze Word Problems, p. 100A	
Mental Math, Using Data, Geometry	Literature, Language	**Performance Math: Addition and Subtraction** 💿	**Review**
Logic, Mental Math	Art, Language	**Math Workshop** 💿 Subtracting, p. 110A	Section B Opener, p. 103 Mixed Review and Test Prep, pp. 107, 109, 113, 115, 121, 123
Using Data, Algebra, Mental Math, Patterns	Careers, Science	**Calculator** 🖩 Subtracting, p. 112	Practice Game, pp. 116–117 Section B Review and Practice, p. 124 Skills Practice Bank, p. 561
Using Data, Algebra	Music, Science, Geography, Language	**Interactive CD-ROM Lesson 3** 💿 Subtracting with Middle Zeros, p. 114	
Using Data, Collecting Data, Time	Careers, Language		**Ongoing Assessment** *Teacher's Edition,* all lessons *Assessment Sourcebook,* Quiz Chapter 3 Section B
Mental Math, Algebra, Measurement	Careers, Science, Language		
Using Data, Geometry, Patterns	Careers, Science, Reading		
Patterns, Time	Careers, Literature	**Performance Math: Addition and Subtraction** 💿	**Review**
Using Data, Patterns	Careers, Literature, Language	**Calculator** 🖩 Exploring Algebra, p. 135 Your Choice, p. 139	Section C Opener, p. 125 Mixed Review and Test Prep, pp. 127, 129 Stop and Practice, pp. 132–133 Section C Review and Practice, p. 138
Using Data	Careers, Reading	**Math Workshop** 💿 Analyze Strategies, p. 136A	Your Choice, p. 139 Skills Practice Bank, p. 561
Patterns, Mental Math	Science	**World Wide Web** 🌐 www.mathsurf.com/4/ch3 Your Choice, p. 139 Math Magazine, p. 142	**Ongoing Assessment** *Teacher's Edition,* all lessons *Assessment Sourcebook,* Quiz Chapter 3 Section C
	Language		
		TestWorks 💿	Chapter Review/Test, p. 140 Performance Assessment, p. 141 Cumulative Review, p. 143

Manipulatives

Using the Manipulatives

Play Money Students use play money throughout Section C to practice addition and subtraction with money.

$$\$5 + \$1 + \$0.25 + \$0.20 = \$6.45$$

Power Polygons Power Polygons are set up in various patterns in Another Way to Learn in Lesson 3-16 to enhance students' understanding of the problem solving strategy Look for a Pattern.

Suggested Materials	Alternatives
Calculators	————
Counters	Buttons, beans, beads, coins
Play money	Index cards with values marked
Place-value blocks	Grid paper
Power Polygons	————

Literature

Knock! Knock!

Jackie Carter. New York: Scholastic, Inc., 1993.

Use with Lesson 3-1 Old friends come to visit the mother and daughter who have just moved into a new home and each one brings them a gift. Farmer Harden brings spinach and Brussels sprouts.

Homework Machine

From *A Light in the Attic*. Shel Silverstein. New York: HarperCollins, 1981.

Use with Lesson 3-5 The poet describes a machine that can do mathematical problems.

Smart

From *Where the Sidewalk Ends: Poems and Drawings*. Shel Silverstein. New York: HarperCollins, 1974.

Use with Lesson 3-12 A boy gets a $1 bill from his father and trades what he has for more coins. With each trade he receives amounts of lesser and lesser value.

A Job for Jenny Archer

Ellen Conford. Boston: Little, Brown and Company, 1988.

Use with Lesson 3-13 Jenny goes to a garage sale to find a birthday present for her mother and finds a beautiful lace collar for $3.25.

Additional Resources

Quest 2000: Exploring Mathematics, Grade 4, Randall Charles, et al. Menlo Park, CA: Addison-Wesley Publishing Company. *Unit 4.*

Investigations in Number, Data, and Space: Money, Miles, and Large Numbers (Addition and Subtraction), Karen Economopoulos, et al. Menlo Park, CA: Dale Seymour Publications.

Nimble With Numbers, Leigh Childs and Laura Choate. Menlo Park, CA: Dale Seymour Publications.

Number SENSE: Simple Effective Number Sense Experiences, Grade 3–4; Number SENSE: Simple Effective Number Sense Experiences, Grades 4–6, Alistair McIntosh, et al. Menlo Park, CA: Dale Seymour Publications.

Target Practice®, Grades 1–5, Margo Seymour and Dale Seymour. Menlo Park, CA: Dale Seymour Publications.

The Money Book, June H. Campbell. Menlo Park, CA: Dale Seymour Publications.

Math By-Lines, Grades 3–4, Carole Greenes, et al. Menlo Park, CA: Dale Seymour Publications.

Time and Money: Problem-Solving Focus, Carole Greenes, et al. Menlo Park, CA: Dale Seymour Publications.

For the Teacher

 Teacher's Resource Planner CD-ROM

The Teacher's Resource Planner CD-ROM allows you to create customized lesson plans tailored to your own class's needs. It also allows you to preview any supplement page, edit if you wish, and print it.

 **World Wide Web**

Visit **www.teacher.mathsurf.com** for additional activities, links to lesson plans from teachers and other professionals, NCTM information, and other useful sites.

 TestWorks Test and Practice Software

A database of questions allows you to generate personalized practice worksheets and tests.

For the Student

 **Interactive CD-ROM**

Use with Lesson 3-8 Students use the Place-Value Blocks Tool to reinforce their understanding of regrouping which is necessary when subtracting across zeros.

World Wide Web

Use with Chapter Opener, Your Choice, and Math Magazine Have students go online at **www.mathsurf.com/4/ch3** to learn about different jobs, to begin planning a dream vacation, and to learn more about currencies from around the world.

 **Performance Math**

Use daily throughout Chapter 3 Students can practice daily to increase their familiarity with basic addition and subtraction facts.

Math Workshop

Use with Lessons 3-4, 3-7, and 3-16 Students can play *Bowling for Numbers* to develop their estimation and subtraction skills. *Puzzle Patterns* will allow students to practice solving problems involving patterns.

📅 Calendar Time Kit

Money

One of the concepts in this chapter is counting money. You may use the Calendar Time Kit to reinforce this concept with the following activity:

Use coins to determine change from five dollars.

- Name a money amount less than five dollars and an item that might have that actual cost.
- Have volunteers make that amount two ways using play money and show it in a money chart.
- On alternate days, name the previous day's item and tell students that they paid for it with a five-dollar bill. Have them determine how much change they would get and show it using two different coin and bill combinations in a money chart.

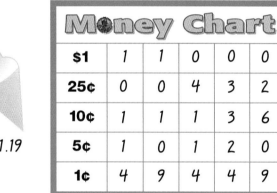

Money Chart

$1	1	1	0	0	0
25¢	0	0	4	3	2
10¢	1	1	1	3	6
5¢	1	0	1	2	0
1¢	4	9	4	4	9

$1.19

Technology Centers

Establish Computer Basics

Determine what students already know about computers.

- A basic knowledge of computers is a prerequisite for learning from programs such as *Performance Math* and *Math Workshop*. You may want to create a pre-test about computer terms and concepts to gauge skill levels. Use the data you collect to determine those students who may need help getting acquainted with computer technology and those who may be able to serve as helpers.

- Have students name and describe parts of the computer. You may want to have knowledgeable students make labels to paste on and near the computers.

Name: _____ Date: _____

Computers

1. You use the _____ to point and click.
2. You can store information on a _____.
3. Describe a CD-ROM. What does it look like? What does it do? _____ _____ _____
4. What is a menu on a computer? _____ _____
5. What do you want to find out about using a computer? _____ _____ _____

Bulletin Board

Objective Calculate the cost of a meal from a menu.

Materials Restaurant menus, construction paper

- Post menus from three or four restaurants on the bulletin board.
- Have groups choose a menu and "order" a meal, listing their choices and prices on paper strips.
- Ask students to find the total cost of their orders and calculate change from the next multiple of five dollars. Students can post their strips by the menu.
- During the course of the chapter, change the activity. Tell students they have $10 to spend and have them list possible choices for a meal.

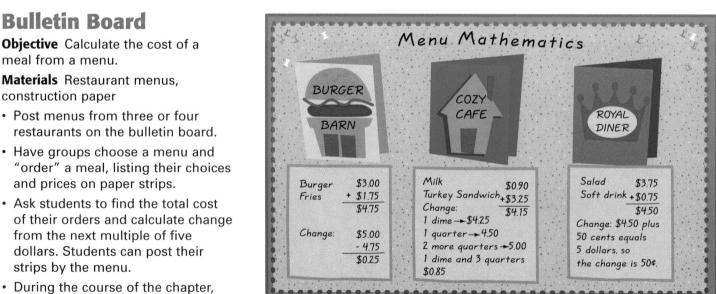

Traditional Assessment	
Review and Practice	Student Edition: pages 102, 124, 138
Cumulative Review	Student Edition: page 143; Assessment Sourcebook: Form F, Quarterly Test Chapters 1–3
Section Quizzes	Assessment Sourcebook: Section Quizzes A, B, C

Chapter Tests
  Free Response
  Multiple Choice
  Mixed Response
	Student Edition: page 140; Assessment Sourcebook: Forms A and B
	Assessment Sourcebook: Form C
	Assessment Sourcebook: Form E

Alternative Assessment	
Ongoing Assessment	Teacher's Edition: every core lesson; Assessment Sourcebook: pages 11–13, 16–19, 21
Portfolio	Student Edition: page 139; Teacher's Edition: pages 107, 113; Assessment Sourcebook: pages 9, 13, 14, 16, 23
Interview and Observation	Teacher's Edition: pages 115, 121, 123, 127, 129; Assessment Sourcebook: pages 18, 20
Journal	Student Edition: pages 95, 97, 101, 102, 107, 113, 124, 131, 135, 138; Teacher's Edition: pages 99, 109; Assessment Sourcebook: pages 8–11, 15
Performance Assessment	Student Edition: page 141; Teacher's Edition: pages 95, 97, 131, 135; Assessment Sourcebook: Form D

NCTM Assessment Standards

Focus on Learning

Journal Assessment activities should be matched to the development in the instruction. Journal writing provides a record of the key learning that occurs throughout the year. Journal opportunities appear throughout Chapter 3.

Test Prep

- The Test Prep Strategy **Make Smart Choices: Use Mental Math** is introduced and practiced in the Cumulative Review on page 143.
- Mixed Review and Test Prep occurs throughout the chapter.

 **TestWorks**

TestWorks can create personalized multiple-choice tests, free-response tests, and practice worksheets.

Standardized-Test Correlation		ITBS Form M	CTBS 4th Ed.	CAT 5th Ed.	SAT 9th Ed.	MAT 7th Ed.
Lesson/Objective						
3-1	Explore addition and subtraction problems.	●	●	●	●	●
3-2	Explore adding and subtracting on a thousand chart.					
3-3	Estimate sums and differences using rounding.	●	●	●	●	●
3-4	Solve problems needing exact answers or estimates.	●	●	●	●	●
3-5	Add 3-digit and 4-digit numbers.	●	●	●	●	●
3-6	Add 3 and 4 addends.	●	●	●	●	●
3-7	Subtract 3 and 4 digit numbers.	●	●	●	●	
3-8	Subtract from numbers with zeros.	●	●	●	●	
3-9	Solve multiple-step problems.	●	●	●	●	●
3-10	Add and subtract numbers mentally.					
3-11	Choose a calculation method.	●	●	●	●	●
3-12	Count and compare money.	●	●	●	●	●
3-13	Add and subtract money amounts.	●	●	●	●	●
3-14	Explore making change.		●	●	●	●
3-15	Explore algebra by balancing number sentences.	●	●		●	
3-16	Solve problems by looking for a pattern.	●	●	●	●	●

Adding and Subtracting Whole Numbers and Money

Theme: On the Job

Teacher Materials *Optional* Lesson Enhancement Transparency 8

Introduce the Chapter

The role of math in a variety of careers provides a context for adding and subtracting whole numbers. Students review and extend addition and subtraction skills, and solve problems involving money. Problem solving continues to be an emphasis, including exact answers or estimation, multiple-step problems, and patterns.

Activate Prior Knowledge

Ask students to discuss different jobs they know about and what skills and education are needed to perform them.

Use The Data File

You may wish to use Lesson Enhancement Transparency 8 along with the following questions to discuss the Data File.

- What are the three ways in which data are represented in the data file? Double-bar graph, table, line graph

- Name a job you would like to have when you grow up. Use the job statistics double-bar graph to find the category in which your job would fall. Answers will vary.

- Use the Take Our Daughters to Work® data to decide whether the program is popular. Predict whether a similar program for sons would be popular. Answers will vary.

- Use the Earnings by the Hour line graph to describe the changes in hourly wages and to predict future changes. Pay per hour has risen and will continue to rise.

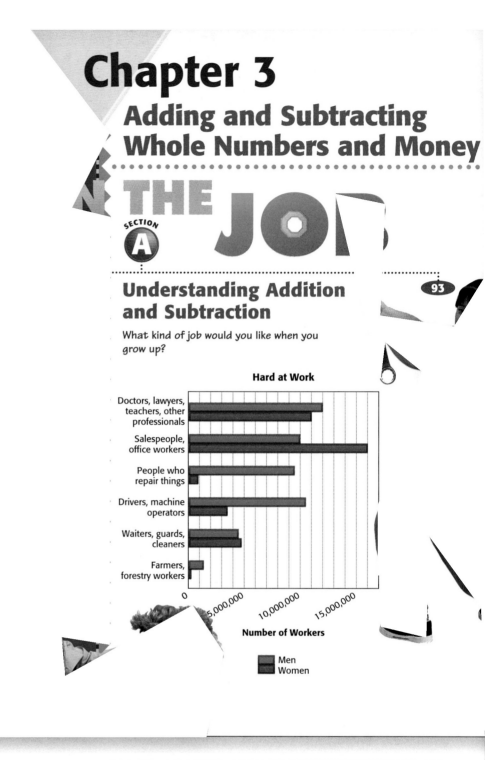

Chapter 3
Adding and Subtracting Whole Numbers and Money

SECTION A

Understanding Addition and Subtraction

93

What kind of job would you like when you grow up?

Hard at Work

Number of Workers

Men
Women

Extensions

Career Connection

Use the question on page 90 as a starting point for a class discussion on math in the workplace. Ask students which jobs they think would require them to work with numbers. Professional athletes are always working with numbers, since all sports are scored numerically. Architects and artists work with such concepts as ratio, proportion, and geometry.

Performance Math: Addition and Subtraction

Offer students who need work on their basic addition and subtraction skills the opportunity to practice with *Performance Math* for 10 minutes each day. Students can keep track of their own progress and keep these progress reports in their portfolios.

Adding and Subtracting
`103`

Americans celebrate Take Our Daughters to Work® day in April. How popular is the program? How can you tell? How popular would such a program be for sons?

After the 1995 Take Our Daughters to Work day, a poll showed that:

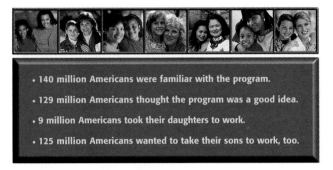

- 140 million Americans were familiar with the program.
- 129 million Americans thought the program was a good idea.
- 9 million Americans took their daughters to work.
- 125 million Americans wanted to take their sons to work, too.

Surfing the World Wide Web!

Have you ever visited the workplace of your parents or another adult? Want to learn more about jobs? Check out **www.mathsurf.com/4/ch3** to find out more.

Using Money
`125`

How has the average hourly wage changed in the United States? Predict how it will change in the future.

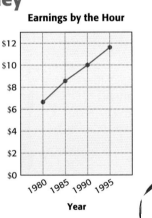

Earnings by the Hour

Pay per Hour: $12, $10, $8, $6, $4, $2, $0

Year: 1980, 1985, 1990, 1995

Preview the Sections

(A) Understanding Addition and Subtraction

Students will explore addition and subtraction patterns, model problems on a thousand chart, estimate sums and differences, and solve problems needing exact answers or estimates.

(B) Adding and Subtracting

Students will add and subtract greater numbers, add multiple addends, subtract with zeros, add and subtract mentally, choose a calculation method, and solve multiple-step problems.

(C) Using Money

Students will review counting, adding, and subtracting money; explore making change; balance algebraic sentences by finding the missing numbers; and solve problems by looking for patterns.

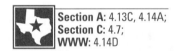

Section A: 4.13C, 4.14A;
Section C: 4.7;
WWW: 4.14D

Math in the Community

School-Community Connection

Teenagers' Part-Time Jobs Have students work in small groups. They can use library resources and surveys to learn more about the kinds of part-time jobs available to teenagers. Have students create a bar graph using the data from their surveys. Have them show the number of students employed in different part-time jobs.

Community Project The Chapter 3 community project is available in *Home and Community Connections.*

Home-School Connection

Money in Your World Ask students to name examples of common living expenses. They may suggest such things as:

- rent or mortgage payments
- food
- clothing
- entertainment
- transportation
- maintenance of home and/or vehicle

Have students ask friends or family members if they can add to the list.

Parents can use the Web site at **www.parent.mathsurf.com**.

At the end of this chapter, you may wish to distribute the Letter Home from *Home and Community Connections.*

Math Comics: Why Estimate?

Students will draw comics that show situations in which estimation is appropriate.

Student Materials Paper, markers or colored pencils, *optional Assessment Sourcebook 10* (How We Worked in Our Group)

Introduce the Project

Poll students to see how many regularly enjoy reading comic books or comics in the newspaper.

Have students discuss comic books or newspaper comics and describe the characteristics of the comics. Drawings, with captions in speech balloons or printed under the picture.

Ask students to look at the comics on page 92 and tell why situations require estimation. The amount of time it will take to buy the popcorn can only be estimated, so the comparison can only be estimated; it would be impossible to count all the stars.

Explain that in this project students will choose a situation where estimation is necessary, then draw a humorous comic showing the situation.

Self-Assessment Checklist

__ Identify a situation that requires estimating

__ Draw a comic representation of the situation, showing appropriate numbers

__ Clearly and accurately report the process and results

Complete the Project

Have teams present their comics to the class. Discuss how each situation requires estimation. Comics can be displayed on the bulletin board so that students can have fun looking at one another's work.

ANSWERS

Possible Answers for Talk About It

Answers will vary, but should include reasons to estimate listed at the top of page 92.

Art Connection

Have students write math comics in the style of their favorite newspaper strips. Students can use the strips' characters and visual style. You might wish to have students prepare analyses of their chosen strips, describing the main characters, style of humor, and visual "look" of the strip.

Cooperative Learning

Distribute *Assessment Sourcebook 10* (How We Worked in Our Group) and have students fill it out for the skill Listen to Others. Review the characteristics of this skill. Invite students to judge themselves on this skill as they work together.

TEAM PROJECT — MATH COMICS: WHY ESTIMATE?

Do you enjoy reading comics? Make your own funny drawings to show when you might estimate.

You might estimate when:

• You aren't able to use a calculator
• A "rough" answer is good enough
• You need an answer quickly

a Plan

• How will your team make a funny comic that shows estimation?
• How will you share the writing and the drawing?

It Out

1. Discuss your ideas.
2. Decide on an estimating situation.
3. Decide how you can make the situation funny.
4. Draw a comic. Write a caption.

Will there be time to buy popcorn before the movie starts?

out It

• How does your comic show an estimating situation?
• Have you ever used estimation in a similar way? Explain.

the Project

• Share your estimation situation with the class.

How many stars are in the sky?

Understanding Addition and Subtraction

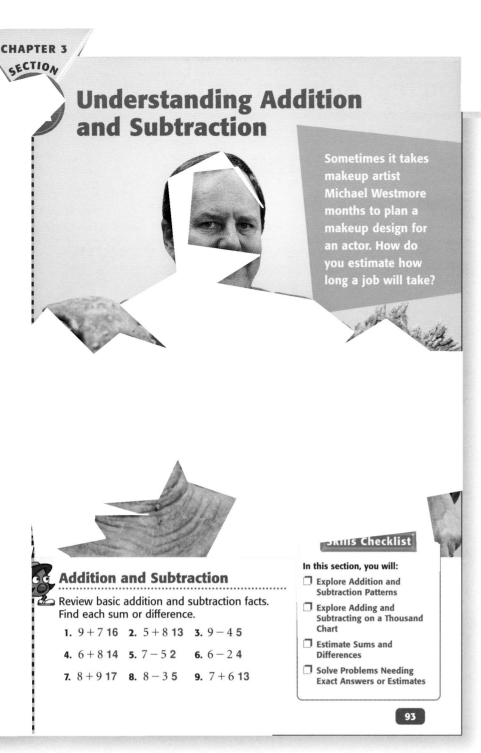

Sometimes it takes makeup artist Michael Westmore months to plan a makeup design for an actor. How do you estimate how long a job will take?

Addition and Subtraction

Review basic addition and subtraction facts. Find each sum or difference.

1. $9 + 7$ **16** 2. $5 + 8$ **13** 3. $9 - 4$ **5**

4. $6 + 8$ **14** 5. $7 - 5$ **2** 6. $6 - 2$ **4**

7. $8 + 9$ **17** 8. $8 - 3$ **5** 9. $7 + 6$ **13**

Skills Checklist

In this section, you will:

☐ Explore Addition and Subtraction Patterns

☐ Explore Adding and Subtracting on a Thousand Chart

☐ Estimate Sums and Differences

☐ Solve Problems Needing Exact Answers or Estimates

93

Understanding Addition and Subtraction

In this section, students will explore addition and subtraction patterns, model addition and subtraction on a thousand chart, estimate sums and differences, and solve problems needing exact or estimated answers.

Subskills

The work in this section builds on...

• Using addition and subtraction facts

• Modeling addition and subtraction with place-value blocks

• Rounding to the nearest ten

Use the Section Opener

Have students brainstorm ideas about estimating the length of time Michael Westmore needs to design makeup for an actor. Then ask students how they estimate the length of time any job will take. Past knowledge of time required to perform similar tasks, time required to perform portions of the task.

Skills Trace

(Red numbers indicate pages in this section.)

Lesson and Skill	First Introduced	Grade Four			
		Introduce	Develop	Practice/Apply	Review
3-1 Explore addition and subtraction patterns.	Grade 3	94, 95	94, 95	95, 102, 132, 133, 139, 561	102, 139, 140, 143
3-2 Explore adding and subtracting on a thousand chart.	Grade 4	96, 97	96, 97	97, 102, 561	102, 140, 143
3-3 Estimate sums and differences using rounding.	Grade 3	98, 99	92, 98	99, 102, 116, 117, 561	102, 140, 143
3-4 Solve problems needing exact answers or estimates.	Grade 3	100, 101	92, 100, 101	101, 102, 116, 117 132, 133, 139, 561	102, 139, 140, 143

Mixed Review and Test Prep exercises for this chapter occur on pages 99, 107, 109, 113, 115, 121, 123, 127, 129.

🏃 **Multi-Age Classrooms** Use pages 95–104 in Grade 3 or pages 82–87 in Grade 5 to relate to the content of this section.

Exploring Addition and Subtraction Patterns

At-A-Glance Planning

Lesson Planning Checklist

Objective Explore addition and subtraction patterns.
Vocabulary sum, difference
Student Book Lesson Materials Calculators, *optional*
Teaching Tool Transparency 9 (Hundred Chart)
Materials for pages 94A and 94B Calculators
Strand Connections mental math, patterns, algebra readiness, money, geometry readiness

	Before Lesson	During Lesson	After Lesson
Daily Math			
p. 94A Problem of the Day			
p. 94A Math Routines			
p. 94A Mental Math			
Teaching Options			
p. 94B Facilitating and Assessing…			
Options for Reaching All Learners			
p. 94B Language Development			
p. 94B Gifted & Talented			
Subject Connections			
p. 94A Literature Connection			
Assessment Options			
p. 94 Talk About It			
p. 95 Error Intervention			
p. 95 Performance Assessment			
Resources			
3-1 Practice			
3-1 Reteaching			
3-1 Enrichment			
3-1 Problem Solving			
3-1 Daily Transparency			

Problem of the Day

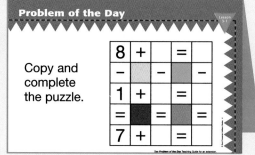

For solution art, see pages D1–D4.

Math Routines

Patterns Have students identify the rule, then continue this pattern: 2, 5, 9, 14, 20, ■, ■, ■, … Ask them to make up other, similar patterns. Add 3, add 4, …; 27,35,44

Money If you received $10 for every day of the month so far, how much money would you have?

Mental Math

Name the greater amount. Explain your thinking.

$0.45 + $0.55 or $0.90 $0.45 + $0.55
$0.34 + $0.56 or $0.80 $0.34 + $0.56
$0.22 + $0.39 or $0.65 $0.65
$0.81 + $0.18 or $1.00 $1.00

Literature Connection

Family and friends come to visit a mother and daughter in *Knock! Knock!* by Jackie Carter. Farmer Harden brought 2 bowls of spinach and 1 bowl of brussels sprouts. How many bowls in all if Farmer Harden had brought 20 bowls of spinach and 10 bowls of brussels sprouts? 200 bowls of spinach and 100 bowls of brussels sprouts? 30 bowls, 300 bowls

Facilitating and Assessing **Explore** Lesson 3-1

Use with pages 94 and 95.

Get Started You may wish to assign the group skill Check for Understanding for students to practice. Have students take turns entering the numbers in the calculator and recording each answer.

Share Level 4 of the Assessment Rubric with students before they begin their work.

Observe For Exercise 2, be sure students are completing each part of the problem using patterns before checking their answers with a calculator. Listen for students who demonstrate recognition of the patterns as they complete the exercises.

Discuss Ask students who readily completed the exercises to explain the patterns and how they recognized them. Use the overhead projector to review each step of Exercise 2. Have students give a rule about adding with a pattern of zeros. Ask if the rule holds true for subtraction. You might want to write the rules on the chalkboard or a poster. Then give some examples and have students give examples of their own and explain the similarities between the rules.

Assess Use the rubric to assess students' work. See sample for Practice Exercise 1.

4 Full Accomplishment
$70 + 10 = 80$
$700 + 100 = 800$
$7,000 + 1,000 = 8,000$

Assessment Rubric

4 Full Accomplishment
- uses basic facts and patterns to solve addition and subtraction equations

3 Substantial Accomplishment
- uses basic facts and patterns to solve most addition and subtraction equations

2 Partial Accomplishment
- uses basic facts and patterns to solve some addition and subtraction equations

1 Little Accomplishment
- does not consistently use basic facts and patterns to solve addition and subtraction equations

Options for Reaching All Learners

Language Development

Verbal Patterns
Use oral and written language skills to reinforce the recognition of patterns.

Materials Calculators

Learning Style Verbal, Visual

- Read aloud a group of addition or subtraction problems such as $13 + 8$; $130 + 80$; $1,300 + 800$; and $13,000 + 8,000$. Have individual students repeat each problem slowly and clearly after you. Students should write each problem and find the answer using patterns and place value. They can check their answers on the calculator.

- Have students describe the patterns they used. Ask for descriptions of how place value helped in finding the sums.

- Challenge students to make their own subtraction exercises following a similar pattern.

Gifted & Talented

More Patterns
Use a calculator to discover other addition and subtraction patterns.

Materials Calculators

Learning Style Visual

- Give students an addition fact such as $5 + 3 = 8$. Have them use their calculators to make a pattern by adding one zero at a time to only one of the addends. $50 + 3 = 53$; $500 + 3 = 503$; $5,000 + 3 = 5,003$

- Have students describe this new pattern. How is the placement of the zero or zeros in the answer different from other patterns they have studied? The zeros are now in the middle of the number instead of at the end.

- Have them repeat the activity using a subtraction fact. What happens? There is a pattern of an increasing number of 9s in the middle of the differences.

Lesson Organizer

Objective Explore addition and subtraction patterns.

Suggested Grouping 2 to 4

Student Materials Calculators

Teacher Materials *Optional* Teaching Tool Transparency 9 (Hundred Chart)

Vocabulary sum, difference

Assignment Guide

Basic 1–9, 13, 16, 18, 19

Average 1–3, 7–19

Enriched 1–2, 8–19

1 Introduce

Review

Find each sum or difference.

1. 14 − 8 6　　**2.** 7 + 9 16

3. 15 − 7 8　　**4.** 4 + 9 13

Build on Prior Knowledge

After students review basic addition and subtraction facts, model an example such as 23 + 34 on the overhead using a hundred chart. Then ask students to describe any patterns they can find in the chart. Possible answers: All the numbers at the right end in zero. The numbers in each column show 10 more from one row to the next.

2 Teach

See Facilitating and Assessing…on page 94B.

Explore ● (

You may wish to use drawings of place-value blocks on the overhead to model the patterns.

Talk About It **Ongoing Assessment**

Listen for comments noting the use of basic facts and the increasing number of zeros.

Answers for Talk About It

3 Answers should relate to basic facts and place value.

4 Possible answer: Use the fact 7 + 8 = 15 and patterns of zeros to find 15,000.

5 Possible answer: Use the fact 9 − 5 = 4 and patterns of zeros. 9,000 − 5,000 = 4,000

Exploring Addition and Subtraction Patterns

Problem Solving Connection
Look for a Pattern

Materials
calculator

Vocabulary
sum
the number obtained by adding numbers

difference
the number obtained by subtracting one number from another

Remember
Think about using basic facts.

Explore ●

How can you use patterns to add and subtract tens, hundreds, and thousands mentally?

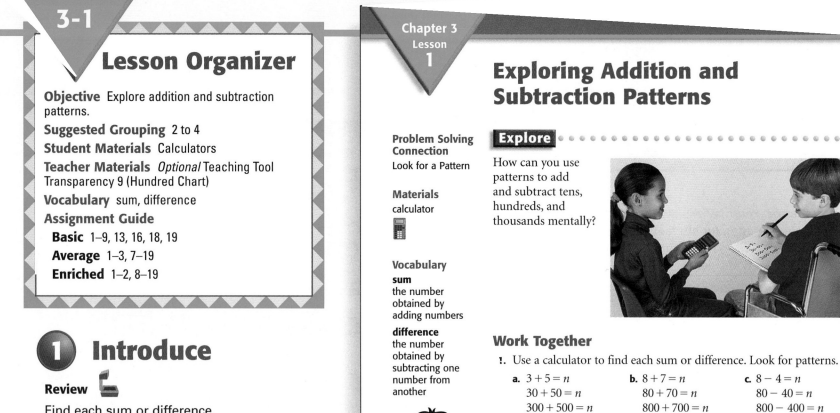

Work Together

1. Use a calculator to find each sum or difference. Look for patterns.

a. $3 + 5 = n$
$30 + 50 = n$
$300 + 500 = n$
$3,000 + 5,000 = n$
8, 80, 800, 8,000

b. $8 + 7 = n$
$80 + 70 = n$
$800 + 700 = n$
$8,000 + 7,000 = n$
15, 150, 1,500, 15,000

c. $8 - 4 = n$
$80 - 40 = n$
$800 - 400 = n$
$8,000 - 4,000 = n$
4, 40, 400, 4,000

2. Look for patterns to help you find each sum or difference. Use a calculator to check your answers.

a. $10 - 8 = n$
$100 - 80 = n$
$1,000 - 800 = n$
$10,000 - 8,000 = n$
2, 20, 200, 2,000

b. $14 + 4 = n$
$140 + 40 = n$
$1,400 + 400 = n$
$14,000 + 4,000 = n$
18, 180, 1,800, 18,000

c. $9 - 3 = n$
$90 - 30 = n$
$900 - 300 = n$
$9,000 - 3,000 = n$
6, 60, 600, 6,000

Talk About It

3. What patterns did you find?

4. Explain how to add $7,000 + 8,000$ mentally.

5. If you know the difference between 9 and 5, how can you find the difference between 9,000 and 5,000?

Practice 3-1	Reteaching 3-1

Connect

You can use mental math to add and subtract.

Find the **sum** of 200 and 500.　　Find the **difference** between 6,000 and 4,000.

$200 + 500 = n$　　　　　　$6,000 - 4,000 = n$

Think: $2 + 5 = 7$.　　　　　**Think:** $6 - 4 = 2$.

So, $200 + 500 = 700$.　　　　So, $6,000 - 4,000 = 2,000$.

Practice

Copy and complete.

1. $70 + 10 = n$ **80**　　　2. $n + 40 = 90$ **50**　　　3. $90 + n = 170$ **80**
   $700 + 100 = n$ **800**　　　$n + 400 = 900$ **500**　　　$900 + n = 1,700$ **800**
   $7,000 + 1,000 = n$ **8,000**　$n + 4,000 = 9,000$ **5,000**　$9,000 + n = 17,000$ **8,000**

Find each sum or difference.

4. $5,000 + 5,000$ **10,000**　5. $8,000 + 1,000$ **9,000**　6. $6,000 + 2,000$ **8,000**

7. $3,000 + 9,000$ **12,000**　8. $9,000 - 7,000$ **2,000**　9. $5,000 - 3,000$ **2,000**

10. $80,000 - 40,000$ **40,000** 11. $50,000 - 30,000$ **20,000** 12. $30,000 + 60,000$ **90,000**

Algebra Readiness Find each missing number.

13. $90 - n = 80$ **10**　　　14. $n - 20 = 50$ **70**　　　15. $90 - n = 30$ **60**
    $900 - n = 800$ **100**　　　$700 - 200 = n$ **500**　　　$900 - 600 = n$ **300**
    $9,000 - 1,000 = n$ **8,000**　$7,000 - n = 5,000$ **2,000**　$n - 6,000 = 3,000$ **9,000**

16. **Money** A new CD player costs $90. Three CDs cost $40 all together. How much will the CD player and the three CDs cost in all? **$130**

17. **Critical Thinking** What do you notice about the sums for the following pairs: $500 + 600$ and $600 + 500$? **Possible answer: The sum is the same, regardless of the order of numbers.**

18. **Geometry Readiness** Copy and complete the pattern.

▲ ■ ■ ▲ ◆ ▲ ■ □G □G □G

19. **Journal** Use patterns and place value to explain how adding $7,000 + 4,000$ is like adding $70,000 + 40,000$. How is it different?

Lesson 3-1 **95**

Connect

Name a basic addition or subtraction fact, then have students write their own groups of addition or subtraction sentences that show a pattern.

Error Intervention Ongoing Assessment

Observation Students may not write the correct number of zeros in the sum.

How to Help Students may benefit from rewriting the problems in vertical form. Stress correct alignment of digits that have the same place value.

Practice

Exercise 13 Point out that students can think about the basic fact first. Try $9 - n = 8$, then solve the problem.

For Early Finishers Challenge early finishers to extend the patterns for Exercises 7–9 to the next place value. 120,000; 20,000; 20,000

3 Close and Assess

Performance Assessment

Find the sums and differences for hundreds and thousands. Look for a pattern.

$5 + 7 = 12$

$50 + 70 = 120$

$500 + 700 = 1,200$

$5,000 + 7,000 = 12,000$

$17 - 9 = 8$

$170 - 90 = 80$

$1,700 - 900 = 800$

$17,000 - 9,000 = 8,000$

Assess using the rubric on page 94B.

ANSWERS

19 Both problems use the same basic fact. The place values are different.

Chapter 3 • Lesson 3-1 **95**

Exploring Adding and Subtracting on a Thousand Chart

At-A-Glance Planning

Lesson Planning Checklist

Objective Explore adding and subtracting on a thousand chart.

Student Book Lesson Materials Thousand chart, counters, calculator, *optional* Teaching Tool Transparency 9 (Hundred Chart)

Materials for pages 96A and 96B Thousand chart, 4 strips of cardboard, 4 pieces of string, 40 buttons, *optional* Teaching Tool Transparency 9 (Hundred Chart)

Subject Connection fine arts—murals

Strand Connections patterns, mental math, logic

	Before Lesson	During Lesson	After Lesson
Daily Math			
p. 96A Problem of the Day			
p. 96A Math Routines			
p. 96A Mental Math			
Teaching Options			
p. 96B Facilitating and Assessing…			
Options for Reaching All Learners			
p. 96B Reading Assist			
p. 96B Cultural Connection			
Subject Connections			
p. 96A Social Studies Connection			
Assessment Options			
p. 96 Talk About It			
p. 97 Error Intervention			
p. 97 Performance Assessment			
Resources			
3-2 Practice			
3-2 Reteaching			
3-2 Enrichment			
3-2 Problem Solving			
3-2 Daily Transparency			

Problem of the Day

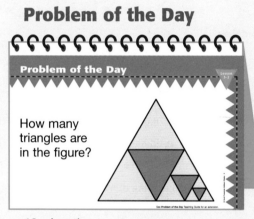

Problem of the Day

How many triangles are in the figure?

13 triangles

Math Routines

Calendar Name a date on the current month's calendar. Ask students to name the date that was 1 week ago, 1 week 3 days ago, 3 weeks 4 days ago, and so on.

Money Tell students that they have $1 and are buying items for 15 cents. Ask them to start with $1, and continue to count back for each item they buy. Ask how many items they could buy for $1. 6 items

Mental Math

Tell how much more money is needed.

Have $1.09	Need $1.25 $0.16
Have $1.15	Need $1.90 $0.75
Have $2.25	Need $3.05 $0.80

Social Studies Connection

The Great Wall of China was built to defend the northern frontier of China. By about 204 B.C., about 1,200 miles of wall had been built. When work ended centuries later, the wall was about 1,500 miles long.

• Ask students how many miles of wall were built after 204 B.C. About 300 miles

Facilitating and Assessing **Explore** Lesson 3-2

Use with pages 96 and 97.

Get Started Distribute thousand charts to each group or show students how to turn a hundred chart into a thousand chart by writing a zero after each number. The chart will go from 10 to 1,000 by tens. Assign the roles of reader, calculator, and recorder.

Observe Students may add or subtract the tens before the hundreds, or they may begin with the hundreds. Either method is acceptable.

210	220	230	240	250	260	270	280	290	300
310	320	330	340	350	360	370	380	390	400
410	420	430	440	450	460	470	480	490	500

$$230 + 180 = 410$$

Discuss Ask volunteers to use the overhead to show how they used the thousand chart to solve Exercise 2. You may also wish to have students demonstrate that the answers to both problems are the same, whether they begin with tens or hundreds.

Assess Use the rubric to assess students' work. See sample for Practice Exercise 2.

4 Full Accomplishment

740	750	760	770	780
840	850	860	870	880
940	950	960	970	980

$$970 - 220 = 750$$

Assessment Rubric

4 Full Accomplishment
- uses a thousand chart to find sums and differences

3 Substantial Accomplishment
- with prompting, uses a thousand chart to find sums and differences

2 Partial Accomplishment
- uses a thousand chart to find some sums and differences

1 Little Accomplishment
- does not use a thousand chart to find sums or differences

Options for Reaching All Learners

Reading Assist

Find Main Idea with Supporting Details
Use word problems to find the main idea.

Learning Style Verbal, Visual

- Have students work in pairs.
- Have one student read through part a of Exercise 17 aloud, then restate the question. You may wish to write pertinent information on the chalkboard for students' reference.
- Have pairs identify the information and numbers they need to find the answer. Number of teenagers: 250; number of adults: 50
- Then have them solve the problem. 250 − 50 = 200 more teenagers
- Discuss how pairs choose the numbers and the operation needed to solve the problem.
- Repeat the activity for part b of Exercise 17.

Cultural Connection

Counting Without Numbers
Use an abacus to add and subtract hundreds.

Materials 4 strips of cardboard, 4 pieces of string, 40 buttons

Learning Style Kinesthetic

Tell students that the abacus is a counting board often used in Japan, China, and Russia instead of a calculator.

- As a class project, make a simple Russian abacus.
- To add, move counters to the left. To subtract, move counters to the right. Students can exchange 10 ones for 1 ten, 10 tens for 1 hundred, and so on.

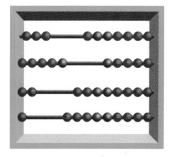

3,521

Lesson Organizer

Objective Explore adding and subtracting on a thousands chart.

Suggested Grouping 2 to 4

Student Materials Thousand chart, counters

Teacher Materials Teaching Tool Transparency 9 (Hundred Chart), counters

Assignment Guide

Basic 1–8, 13, 16–18

Average 5–13, 16–18

Enriched 7–18

1 Introduce

Review

Find each sum.

1. 4 + 8 **12**

2. 40 + 80 **120**

3. 400 + 800 **1,200**

4. 4,000 + 8,000 **12,000**

Build on Prior Knowledge

Show students a hundred chart and a thousand chart. Discuss how the charts are alike and how they are different. Possible answer: Both charts have 100 squares; the hundred chart shows ones, and the thousand chart shows tens.

2 Teach

See Facilitating and Assessing...on page 96B.

Explore ● ● ● ● ● ● ● ● ● ● ● ● ● ● ● ● ● ●

Using the overhead and a thousand chart, model addition problems such as 230 + 350, then subtraction problems such as 480 − 340. Have students follow along using their thousand charts and counters.

Talk About It **Ongoing Assessment**

Listen for students to indicate that they must move by tens and by hundreds on the chart.

Answers for Talk About It

4 Possible answer: Place a counter on 470 and move it forward 1 hundred and 2 tens to 590. 470 + 120 = 590

5 Possible answers: Start with 340 and move forward 2 hundreds and 8 tens. Start with 280 and move forward 3 hundreds and 4 tens. 340 + 280 = 620

Exploring Adding and Subtracting on a Thousand Chart

Problem Solving Connection
- Use Objects/ Act It Out
- Look for a Pattern

Materials
- thousand chart
- counters

Math Tip
Think about counting by tens and hundreds.

Explore ●

You can use a thousand chart to help find sums and differences.

Work Together

1. Use a thousand chart to find each sum or difference. Record your answers.

   a. Find 430 + 300.

      Put a counter on 430.

      Move forward 3 hundreds.

      Where did your counter land? **730**

   b. Find 680 − 240.

      Put a counter on 680.

      Move back 2 hundreds.

      Then move back 4 tens.

      What square did you land on? **440**

440	450	460	470	480	490	500
540	550	560	570	580	590	600
640	650	660	670	680	690	700

2. Use a thousand chart to find each sum or difference.

   a. 230 + 180 **410** b. 370 + 130 **500** c. 600 − 120 **480** d. 720 − 190 **530**

   e. 160 + 470 **630** f. 430 − 190 **240** g. 300 − 180 **120** h. 410 + 410 **820**

3. Place a counter on a number that has a 5 in the hundreds place. Place another counter on a number that has a 5 in the tens place. What is the difference between the two numbers? **Possible answer: 510 − 450 = 60**

Talk About It

4. How would you use a thousand chart to show 470 + 120?

5. Explain two ways to find 340 + 280 on a thousand chart.

96 Chapter 3 • Adding and Subtracting Whole Numbers and Money

---

Practice 3-2	**Reteaching 3-2**

Connect

Here are two different ways to subtract numbers.

Find $540 - 130$.

You can use mental math.

540 minus 100 is 440.

Subtract 30 more.

$440 - 30 = 410$

You can use a thousand chart.

Start at 540 and move back 1 hundred to 440. Then move back 3 tens to 410.

310	320	330	340	350
410	420	430	440	450
510	520	530	540	550

Practice

Find each sum or difference. Use a thousand chart or mental math.

1. $160 + 300$ **460**   2. $970 - 220$ **750**   3. $600 - 430$ **170**   4. $560 + 150$ **710**

5. $720 + 190$ **910**   6. $650 - 560$ **90**   7. $470 - 280$ **190**   8. $760 - 390$ **370**

9. $800 + 140$ **940**   10. $610 + 240$ **850**   11. $630 - 370$ **260**   12. $590 + 310$ **900**

13. Find the difference between 540 and 370. **170**

14. **Logic** Jan places two counters on her chart. The counters are apart by 240. One of them is on 720. Where is the other counter? **960 or 480**

15. **Critical Thinking** What number is equally far from 630 and 410? Explain how you can use a thousand chart to find the number. **520; Place counters on each number and count to find the square halfway between the two.**

16. **Write Your Own Problem** Write a set of clues that will help a partner guess where a counter is on your thousand chart. **Answers will vary.**

17. **Fine Arts** "The Great Wall" in Los Angeles is the longest mural in the world. It is 2,500 feet long. It took 250 teenagers and 50 adults 10 years to finish painting this wall.

17a. 200 more teenagers

a. How many more teenagers than adults worked on this mural?

b. If some teenagers were 13 years old when the painting began, how old were they when the mural was finished? **23 years old**

18. **Journal** Explain how you can use a thousand chart or mental math to find $440 + 460$ and $830 - 150$.

Lesson 3-2   **97**

Connect

Point out that the thousands chart shows only multiples of 10, so mental math is easier.

Error Intervention Ongoing Assessment

Observation Students may have difficulty using a thousand chart.

How to Help Use the overhead and a thousand chart to model adding and subtracting by tens. Start at 10 and count forward, then backward, by tens to demonstrate addition and subtraction. Focus on what happens at the end of a row.

Practice

Exercise 14 There are two possible answers to this question.

For Early Finishers Challenge early finishers to subtract, instead of adding, in Exercises 4, 9, 10, and 12. **410, 660, 370, 280**

3 Close and Assess

Performance Assessment

Find each sum or difference. Use a thousand chart.

1. $270 + 560$ 830; Students should move down 5 squares and to the right 6 squares.

2. $880 - 310$ 570; Students should move up 3 squares and to the left 1 square.

Assess using the rubric on page 96B.

ANSWERS

18 Answers should include adding 4 hundreds and 6 tens to 440 on a thousand chart and subtracting 1 hundred and 5 tens from 830 on a thousand chart. Adding and subtracting mentally uses basic facts and place value.

Enrichment 3-2

Extend Your Thinking 3-2

Name _____

Critical Thinking

Mel's Music World had a sale for five days. On day 1, the store sold 200 of its supply of tapes. On day 2, half of the remaining amount was sold. The same thing happened on days 3, 4 and 5. At the end of the sale, Mel counted the number of tapes left in the store. He discovered there were only 50 tapes left.

1. Mel wanted a record of the sale. He made a chart for the five days of the sale. But, he was so busy waiting on customers that he forgot to fill in the chart! He only recorded the number of tapes left at the end of day 5. How can Mel figure out the number of tapes left at the end of each of the other days?

Possible answer: Work Backward

2. Use the plan you described above to complete the chart.

Day	Total Number of Tapes Left
1	800
2	400
3	200
4	100
5	50

3. Suppose Mel decided to hold the sale for one additional day. If the same pattern of sales continues, how many tapes will be left in the store at the end of day 6? **25**

4. Mel also had a sale on CDs. He sold 120 the first day, twice that number on the second day and twice as many on the third day as on the second. How many CDs did he sell on the third day? **480**

Problem Solving 3-2

Problem Solving 3-2

Name _____

Exploring Adding and Subtracting on a Thousand Chart

Marty saves baseball cards. He has a total of 730 cards in his collection. He wants to give 180 cards to his friend Marie.

1. Marty wants to know how many cards he will have left in his collection after he gives Marie 180 cards.

a. How could Marty use a thousand chart to find his new card total?
   Start at 730 and move back 1 hundred and 8 tens.

b. How could Marty use mental math to find his new card total?
   $730 - 200 = 530$; $530 + 20 = 550$

c. Use mental math or a thousand chart to find Marty's new card total. **550**

2. Marie had 260 of her own cards. Then Marty gave her 180 cards from his collection.

a. Describe two ways Marie could use a thousand chart to find her new card total.
   Possible answers: Start at 260 and move forward 1 hundred and 8 tens; start at 180 and move forward 2 hundreds and 6 tens.

b. How could Marie use mental math to find her new card total?
   $260 + 100 = 360$; $360 + 80 = 440$

c. Use mental math or a thousand chart to find Marie's new card total. **440**

3. Who has more cards, Marty or Marie? How many more? **Marty; 110 more**

4. Marty buys another 170 cards and Marie buys another 90. Now how many do each have? **Marty: 720, Marie: 530**

Chapter 3 • Lesson 3-2   **97**

Estimating Sums and Differences

At-A-Glance Planning

Objective Estimate sums and differences using rounding.

Vocabulary estimate

Student Book Lesson Materials *Optional* Lesson Enhancement Transparency 8

Materials for pages 98A and 98B Place-value blocks (10 hundreds per group), index cards (4); red, yellow, blue, and green crayons or markers (1 of each)

Subject Connection careers—makeup artists

Strand Connections estimation, using data, time, logic

	Before Lesson	During Lesson	After Lesson
Daily Math			
p. 98A Problem of the Day			
p. 98A Math Routines			
p. 98A Mental Math			
Teaching Options			
p. 98 Student Book Lesson			
p. 98B Another Way to Learn...			
Options for Reaching All Learners			
p. 98B Reading Assist			
p. 98B Language Development			
Subject Connections			
p. 98A Career Connection			
Assessment Options			
p. 98 Talk About It			
p. 99 Error Intervention			
p. 99 Journal			
p. 99 Quick Check			
Resources			
3-3 Practice			
3-3 Reteaching			
3-3 Enrichment			
3-3 Problem Solving			
3-3 Daily Transparency			

Problem of the Day

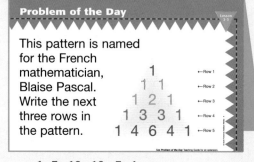

Problem of the Day

This pattern is named for the French mathematician, Blaise Pascal. Write the next three rows in the pattern.

```
        1           ←Row 1
       1 1          ←Row 2
      1 2 1         ←Row 3
     1 3 3 1        ←Row 4
    1 4 6 4 1       ←Row 5
```

1 5 10 10 5 1
1 6 15 20 15 6 1
1 7 21 35 35 21 7 1

Math Routines

Time State various starting times for events such as ball games, movies, and music lessons. Ask students what time they should arrive to be half an hour early.

Measurement Remind students that 1 quart equals 4 cups. Ask how many cups of juice could be served if they had 4, 5, or $6\frac{1}{2}$ quarts. 16, 20, 26 cups

Mental Math

Add or subtract. Explain your thinking.

50 + 80 130   70 − 30 40

49 + 81 130   71 − 29 42

Career Connection

It takes makeup artist Michael Westmore and his assistants three hours to do the makeup for a full-headed alien; a humanoid alien can be done in an hour or less.

• How many minutes does it take one makeup artist to do two full-headed aliens at 180 minutes each? 360 minutes

• What is the total time it takes to do three humanoid aliens whose individual makeup times are 57 minutes, 49 minutes, and 64 minutes? 170 minutes

Another Way to **Learn** Lesson 3-3

Use as an alternative or in addition to pages 98 and 99.

Materials Place-value blocks (10 hundreds per group)

Learning Style Visual, Kinesthetic

- Briefly review rounding to hundreds by asking students to round 389, 144, 209, and 473 to the nearest hundred. Allow students to use hundreds blocks.

- Have groups model estimating 219 + 178, rounding to the nearest hundred using the hundreds place-value blocks. They should show the rounding of each number and then show the addition with the hundreds blocks. 200, 200; 200 + 200 = 400

- Have groups model estimating 488 − 331, first showing their rounding of each number to the nearest hundred using the hundreds place-value blocks. They should then subtract the rounded numbers. 500, 300; 500 − 300 = 200

- Have groups continue to model addition and subtraction exercises you write on the chalkboard. As students become more comfortable in the activity, ask them to solve a few of the problems without using the blocks.

- Help students recognize that the same rounding process can be used to add and subtract thousands. Then have them estimate 2,898 − 1,234 by rounding to the nearest thousand. 3,000 − 1,000 = 2,000

- Assign Check and Practice on Student Book page 99 or *Practice Master 3-3*.

- Assess using the following rubric.

Assessment Rubric

4 Full Accomplishment
- estimates sums and differences correctly using rounding

3 Substantial Accomplishment
- estimates most sums and differences correctly using rounding

2 Partial Accomplishment
- estimates some sums and differences using rounding

1 Little Accomplishment
- does not estimate, round, or calculate consistently

Options for Reaching All Learners

Reading Assist

Recognize Sequence
Use role-playing to review sequence words: **first, when, then, in response**.

Materials Index cards (4); red, yellow, blue, and green crayons or markers (1 of each)

Learning Style Visual, Kinesthetic

Students having trouble with Exercise 23 might benefit from a review of sequence words.

- Write the word *alien* on each card, once each in red, yellow, blue and green.

- Ask four volunteers to choose one card each.

- Then direct them to act out their part, in sequence, as described in Exercise 23.

- Students should say each sequencing word aloud as they act out the sequence.

Language Development

Word Meaning
Use partner reading to interpret and understand word problems.

Learning Style Visual, Verbal

The Problem Solving and Applications exercises on page 99 may be difficult for some students, because they contain words not usually found in everyday spoken English, such as *makeup artist, alien, screeched,* and *response*.

- Pair students acquiring English with fluent speakers. Encourage students to draw or act out any words unfamiliar to their partners.

- Encourage partners to read together and restate the problems. In some cases you may want to encourage fluent English speakers to paraphrase the problems using more common words.

Lesson Organizer

Objective Estimate sums and differences using rounding.

Student Materials None

Teacher Materials *Optional* Lesson Enhancement Transparency 8

Vocabulary estimate

Assignment Guide

Basic 10–19, 21, 24–27

Average 12–21, 23–27

Enriched 12–15, 18–27

1 Introduce

Review

Round each number to the nearest hundred.

1. 273 300   **2.** 795 800

3. 539 500   **4.** 641 600

Round each number to the nearest thousand.

5. 2,746 3,000   **6.** 5,427 5,000

7. 4,289 4,000   **8.** 3,622 4,000

Build on Prior Knowledge

After students have reviewed rounding, ask how they think they could use rounded numbers to find sums and differences.
Possible answer: Then use basic facts and patterns

2 Teach

See Another Way to Learn…on page 98B.

Learn

Use the overhead to work through the examples with students. Stress that rounding appropriately is the foundation of the activity.

Talk About It Ongoing Assessment

Watch for those students who can easily perform the rounding and addition or subtraction as mental math.

Answer for Talk About It

Greater than 300. Both numbers rounded to lesser numbers.

Estimating Sums and Differences

You Will Learn
how to estimate sums and differences using rounding

Vocabulary
estimate
to find a number close to an exact answer

Remember
You can use a number line to help you round numbers.

138 is closer to 100 than to 200.

Learn

Let the cameras roll! First, makeup artists have to plan ahead. They can **estimate** about how many people will need special makeup for a big movie scene.

You can round to estimate sums.

Makeup artist Michael Westmore creates alien faces for actors in his studio in Hollywood, California.

Example 1

About how many actors will need special makeup for the crowd scene?

Estimate 138 + 224 by rounding to the nearest hundred.

$$138 \longrightarrow 100$$
$$+224 \longrightarrow +200$$
$$\overline{300}$$

About 300 actors will need makeup.

EXTRAS NEEDED
For Alien Crowd Scene

Actors	Number Signed Up
Scaly aliens	138
Hairy aliens	224

You can also use rounding to estimate differences.

Other Examples

A. Estimate 1,252 – 564.
Round to the nearest hundred.

$$1,252 \longrightarrow 1,300$$
$$- 564 \longrightarrow - 600$$
$$\overline{700}$$

B. Estimate 2,975 – 1,778.
Round to the nearest thousand.

$$2,975 \longrightarrow 3,000$$
$$-1,778 \longrightarrow -2,000$$
$$\overline{1,000}$$

Talk About It

Is the total number of actors for the crowd scene greater than or less than 300? Explain.

Name _____

Practice 3-3

Estimating Sums and Differences

Estimate. Round to the nearest hundred.

1. 413 + 387   800   **2.** 954 – 450   500   **3.** 581 + 417   1,000   **4.** 693 – 482   200

5. 217 + 581   800   **6.** 438 – 160   200   **7.** 577 – 328   300   **8.** 181 + 444   600

9. 413 – 129   300   **10.** 391 + 649   1,000   **11.** 852 – 781   100   **12.** 551 + 109   700

Estimate. Round to the nearest thousand.

13. 5,221 + 2,746   8,000   **14.** 8,441 – 6,099   2,000   **15.** 6,911 – 2,562   4,000

16. 2,601 + 5,814   9,000   **17.** 1,099 + 4,623   6,000   **18.** 5,715 – 2,839   3,000

19. 8,764 – 4,369   5,000   **20.** 3,233 + 5,118   8,000   **21.** 2,612 – 1,011   2,000

22. Estimate the difference between 758 and 436 to the nearest hundred.   400

23. Estimate the sum of 5,244 and 1,609 to the nearest thousand.   7,000

24. Is the difference of 1,261 and 724 greater than or less than 500? Explain.
Greater than 500; 1,300 – 700 = 600, 600 > 500

Name _____

Another Look 3-3

Estimating Sums and Differences

You can use a number line to help you estimate sums and differences.

Estimate 248 + 457.

Is 248 closer to 200 or 300?
Since 248 < 250, it is closer to 200.

Is 457 closer to 400 or 500?
Since 457 > 450, it is closer to 500.

Estimate the sum by adding the rounded addends.

200 + 500 = 700

Estimate by rounding to the nearest hundred.

1. 548 – 160

   a. Is 548 closer to 500 or 600?   500

   b. Is 160 closer to 100 or 200?   200

   c. 500 – 200 = 300

2. 814 – 335   800 – 300 = 500   **3.** 329 + 221   300 + 200 = 500

4. 624 + 919   600 + 900 = 1,500   **5.** 735 + 589   700 + 600 = 1,300

6. 911 – 732   200   **7.** 852 – 499   400   **8.** 328 + 271   600

9. 729 – 356   300   **10.** 615 – 138   500   **11.** 521 + 411   900

12. 298 – 157   100   **13.** 362 + 621   1,000   **14.** 417 + 388   800

Check

Estimate each sum or difference. Round to the nearest hundred.

1. $385 + 224$ **600** 2. $585 - 157$ **400** 3. $721 + 137$ **800** 4. $915 - 228$ **700**

Estimate each sum or difference. Round to the nearest thousand.

5. $4,424 - 2,788$ **1,000** 6. $7,881 + 1,589$ **10,000** 7. $3,580 - 1,625$ **2,000** 8. $4,292 + 1,114$ **5,000**

9. **Reasoning** Estimate the sum of 551 and 475. Will the exact answer be less than or greater than your estimate? Explain.
1,100; The exact answer will be less. You round both numbers up.

Practice

Skills and Reasoning

Estimate each sum or difference. Round to the nearest hundred.

10. $567 + 241$ **800** 11. $842 - 390$ **400** 12. $410 + 710$ **1,100** 13. $674 - 221$ **500**

Estimate each sum or difference. Round to the nearest thousand.

14. $3,387 + 4,835$ **8,000** 15. $9,394 - 6,240$ **3,000** 16. $2,111 + 1,753$ **4,000** 17. $8,887 - 3,721$ **5,000**

18. Estimate the difference between 821 and 379 to the nearest hundred. **400**
19. Estimate the sum of 3,921 and 4,693 to the nearest thousand. **9,000**
20. Is the sum of 327 and 215 greater than or less than 500? Explain.
Possible answer: greater than 500; both numbers round

Problem Solving and Applications

21. **Using Data** Use the Data File on page 90. Which job group has almost the same number of women as men?
Waiters, guards, cleaners
22. **Time** Makeup artists often start work at 4:00 A.M., so the actors will be ready for filming at 10:00 A.M. How much time do the artists spend at work before filming begins? **6 hours**
23. **Logic** The yellow alien held its ears and said nothing when the green alien screeched, "No!" in response to the blue alien. Then the red alien yelled, "Yes!" Which alien spoke first? **Blue alien**

Mixed Review and Test Prep

Compare. Write >, <, or =.

24. $8,919 \bullet 8,199$ **>** 25. $9,770 \bullet 9,070$ **>** 26. $7,500 \bullet 9,509$ **<**

27. Which number is between 198,247 and 199,274? **B**
Ⓐ 197,472 Ⓑ 198,742 Ⓒ 199,742 Ⓓ not here

Lesson 3-3 99

Name _____

Problem Solving 3-3

Estimating Sums and Differences

Social Studies The chart shows the number of inventions registered in the United States between 1800 and 1860. Use the chart to answer the questions below.

Year	Number of Inventions
1800	41
1810	223
1820	155
1830	544
1840	458
1850	883
1860	4,357

1. About how many more inventions were created in 1850 than in 1820? **700**
2. About how many inventions were created from 1810 through 1820? **400**
3. About how many more inventions were created in 1860 than from 1810 through 1830? **3,000**
4. In which years were there almost the same number of inventions? **1810, 1820; 1830, 1840**

The Zigot company makes bicycles. The chart shows how many bicycles were made over a five-day period.

Day	Monday	Tuesday	Wednesday	Thursday	Friday
Bicycles Made	1,745	2,319	2,832	1,601	1,459

5. About how many bicycles were made during the first two days of the week? **4,000**
6. What is the approximate difference between the greatest and the least number of bicycles made during the week? **About 2,000**

Check

Remind students that numbers 500 or greater round to the next-greater thousand. Numbers less than 500 round to the lesser thousand.

Error Intervention Ongoing Assessment

Observation Students may have a difficult time remembering the rounded numbers, even though they can correctly round to the nearest hundred or thousand.

How to Help Encourage students to write the rounded numbers.

Practice

Exercises 10–17 Remind students to watch for the operation sign in these mixed addition and subtraction exercises.

Exercise 21 You may wish to use Lesson Enhancement Transparency 8 to display the Data File on page 90.

For Early Finishers Challenge early finishers to repeat Exercises 14–17, rounding to the nearest hundred. **8,200; 3,200; 3,900; 5,200**

③ Close and Assess

Journal

Have students describe how they know when the exact sum or difference will be greater than or less than the estimated sum or difference, then give examples.

Quick Check

Number Sense In which Skill exercise below do you know that the estimate will be greater than the actual sum or difference? Explain. Exercise 4, because the first number rounds to the greater thousand, 7,000, and the second number rounds to the lesser thousand, 3,000, so the estimated difference is greater.

Skill Estimate each sum or difference. Round to the nearest thousand.

1. $4,285 + 2,733$ **7,000**
2. $7,451 - 4,669$ **2,000**
3. $5,229 + 3,801$ **9,000**
4. $6,840 - 3,229$ **4,000**

Resources

Technology Master 7

Chapter 3 • Lesson 3-3 **99**

At-A-Glance Planning

Lesson Planning Checklist

Objective Solve problems needing exact answers or estimates.

Student Book Lesson Materials None

Materials for pages 100A and 100B Magazines and newspapers (several per pair), construction paper, scissors, paste, posterboard (1 sheet)

Subject Connections careers—food service, health, history

Strand Connections using data, collecting data, estimation

	Before Lesson	During Lesson	After Lesson
Daily Math			
p. 100A Problem of the Day			
p. 100A Math Routines			
p. 100A Mental Math			
Teaching Options			
p. 100 Student Book Lesson			
p. 100B Another Way to Learn...			
Options for Reaching All Learners			
p. 100B Inclusion			
p. 100B Reading Assist			
Technology Options			
p. 100A *Math Workshop*			
Assessment Options			
p. 100 Talk About It			
p. 101 Quick Check			
Resources			
3-4 Practice			
3-4 Reteaching			
3-4 Enrichment			
3-4 Problem Solving			
3-4 Daily Transparency			

Problem of the Day

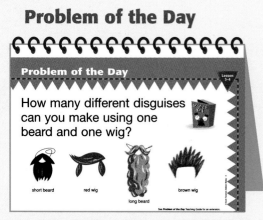

4 different disguises are possible

Math Routines

Time Tell students that a movie starts at 7:45 P.M. and that it usually takes about 30 minutes to get to the theater. Have them name and explain a reasonable time to leave home. 7:15 P.M. because it is about 30 minutes earlier than 7:45 P.M.

Money Tell students that they are cashiers at a fair. A customer buys an item for $1.79 with a $5 bill. Ask them to explain how to find the amount of change to give. $3.21; Possible answer: Subtract $1.79 from $5.

Mental Math

Add 90. Explain your thinking.

80	120	230	550
170	210	320	640

Math Workshop

Students can use *Bowling for Numbers* to practice solving problems using estimation. They can push the ≈ button to select questions involving estimation. Students will be asked questions about estimating time, weight, and linear measurement.

Another Way to **Learn** Lesson 3-4

Use as an alternative or in addition to pages 100 and 101.

Materials Magazines and newspapers (several per pair), construction paper, scissors, paste

Learning Style Visual, Logical

- Post several numbers and their references from newspapers or magazines on the bulletin board. These should include some estimated numbers ("60,000 Watch Golf Match") as well as some exact numbers ("Buddy Burgers—Only $1.95").

- Allow students several minutes to examine the clippings. Discuss which numbers might be estimated, or rounded, and which might be exact. Have students give reasons why a number might be an estimate or exact.

- Present a word problem based on your bulletin board numbers. First ask students whether an estimated or exact answer is needed, then as a group solve the problem.

- Have pairs present word problems to the class. They should tell whether they think answers should be estimated or exact, and give their reasons.

- Assign Check and Practice on Student Book page 101 or *Practice Master 3-4*.

- Assess using the following rubric.

Assessment Rubric
4 Full Accomplishment • solves problems needing exact or estimated answers
3 Substantial Accomplishment • solves most problems needing exact or estimated answers
2 Partial Accomplishment • solves some problems needing exact or estimated answers
1 Little Accomplishment • does not solve problems needing exact or estimated answers

Options for Reaching All Learners

Inclusion

Number Notebook
Use a number notebook to promote identification of estimated and exact numbers.

Learning Style Verbal/Auditory, Individual

- Help students make a number notebook by stapling together several pieces of paper.

- Ask students to record and describe numbers they hear on television, see in video games, hear on the radio, or see in stores—anywhere outside the classroom.

- Numbers may be kept in two lists, *Estimated Numbers* and *Exact Numbers*. You may want to suggest that estimated numbers always be written in red and exact numbers be written in blue.

- Review notebooks periodically and have students explain their number sorting.

Reading Assist

Read Tables
Use a class data table to strengthen understanding of how to read tables.

Materials Posterboard (1 sheet)

Learning Style Visual, Verbal

- Make a table with each student's name down the left side and three blank columns to the right. Label the columns *Favorite Color*, *Favorite Snack*, and *Favorite TV Show*, or similar subjects.

- Students can write their choices in the table during free time. Review the completed table. Ask volunteers to find other students' favorites.

- Ask students to explain how they read the table.

Lesson Organizer

Objective Solve problems needing exact answers or estimates.

Suggested Grouping 2 to 4

Student Materials None

Assignment Guide

Basic 4, 6, 7, 10

Average 4, 5, 7, 8, 10

Enriched 5, 7–10

1 Introduce

Review

Estimate each sum or difference.

1. 388 + 210 600   **2.** 812 − 492 300

3. 949 − 279 600   **4.** 721 − 383 300

Build on Prior Knowledge

Quickly review estimating and ask students to name some times when estimating is appropriate, both in math and in their daily lives.

2 Teach

See Another Way to Learn…on page 100B.

Learn ● ● ● ● ● ● ● ● ● ● ● ● ● ● ● ● ● ●

Read or have students read the introduction at the top of the page. Have a volunteer rephrase the question and discuss what students are being asked to find. Review the Work Together strategy step by step and relate it to the problem.

Reading Assist Find Main Idea with Supporting Details

On a separate piece of paper, have students write the numbers and information they need to solve the word problem. Stress that they should not copy the problem but should write the important information.

(Talk About It) Ongoing Assessment

Listen for students to recognize that an estimate is not always close enough. Sometimes an exact answer is needed.

Answer for Talk About It

Possible answer: If students ordered their lunches in advance, workers would know exactly how many lunches to prepare.

Problem Solving

Analyze Word Problems: **Exact or Estimate?**

You Will Learn
how to decide if you need an exact answer or an estimate

Learn ●

School cafeteria workers know what most students like to eat: chicken nuggets!

The cafeteria workers keep track of how many lunches they serve each day. How many chicken nugget lunches should they plan for next week?

Day	Lunch	Number Served
Monday	Hamburgers	285
Tuesday	Baked chicken	189
Wednesday	Spaghetti	329
Thursday	Chicken nuggets	423
Friday	Pizza	397

❶ How many chicken nugget lunches were served last week

Patricia Scro serves school lunches in Jefferson Township, New Jersey.   New Jersey

Work Together

▶ **Understand** What do you know? ❶

What do you need to find out? How many chicken nugget lunches to plan for next week

▶ **Plan** Do you need an exact answer or will an estimate do?

Estimate. You don't know exactly how many students will eat lunch.

▶ **Solve** Decide if your estimate should be greater than or less than the number served last week. What's the answer?

To be sure enough chicken nugget meals are available, the estimate should be greater than 423. Workers should plan 430 lunches.

▶ **Look Back** Is your answer reasonable? Yes, the cafeteria will serve about the same number of lunches next week as last week.

(Talk About It)

How could cafeteria workers plan for the exact number of lunches?

Name _____   **Practice 3-4**

Analyze Word Problems: Exact or Estimate?

Decide if you need an exact answer or an estimate. Solve.

1. If 5 containers of chicken nuggets serve about 20 students, how many will 20 containers serve?   **About 80 students**

2. The cafeteria manager knows that about 200 students buy lunch each day. About how many student lunches will be sold in a 5-day week?   **About 1,000**

Use the table below. Solve.

Lunches Served in a Week		
Day	**Lunch**	**Number Served**
Monday	Pita Pocket	217
Tuesday	Chef Salad	162
Wednesday	Fish Sticks	305
Thursday	Grilled Ham and Cheese	257
Friday	Vegetable Pizza	321

3. Last week, the cafeteria served 35 fewer grilled ham and cheese lunches than it did this week. How many were served last week?   **222**

Estimate or use any strategy to solve **4** and **5**.

4. Two slices of vegetable pizza contain about 1,100 milligrams of sodium. A serving of fish sticks has about 400. About how much more sodium does two slices of vegetable pizza have than a serving of fish sticks?   **About 700 milligrams**

5. Ron stands behind Tim in the lunch line. Maria stands right in front of Bill. Tim and Bill stand next to each other. What are the students order in line? What strategy did you use to solve the problem?

Maria, Bill, Tim, Ron; Possible answers: Draw a Picture, Make a List.

Name _____   **Another Look 3-4**

Analyze Word Problems: Exact or Estimate?

Cindy has a dentist's appointment at 4:00. She plans to go shopping and then to the library beforehand. She wants to shop for about an hour and a half and study at the library for about an hour.

Travel Time	
Home ► Store	20 min.
Store ► Library	18 min.
Library ► Dentist	13 min.

Can Cindy estimate the time she should leave, or does she need an exact answer?

Cindy does not know exactly how long she will be shopping or studying, so she doesn't have to leave the house at an exact time. Since she wants to make sure she's at the dentist by 4:00, she should overestimate.

For each problem, tell if you need an exact answer or an estimate.

1. Ron has given 3 recitals this month. At his last recital, he had 118 guests. At the recital before that, he had 180 guests. 165 people came to the first recital. About how many guests have come to Ron's recitals?

Exact or estimate? __**Estimate**__

2. Karen is the owner of City Diner. She is planning to bake pies for the upcoming week. Last week 57 people ordered pie. One pie serves 8 people.

   a. How many pies should Karen bake?

   Exact or estimate? __**Estimate**__

   b. What is the greatest number of people Karen can serve if she bakes 8 pies?

   Exact or estimate? __**Exact**__

3. Ann has $3.40. She would like to buy a juice which costs $0.75 and a sandwich which costs $2.55. Does she have enough?

Exact or estimate? __**Exact**__

Decide if you need an exact answer or an estimate. Solve.

Problem Solving
Understand
Plan
Solve
Look Back

1. If 10 pizzas serve 80 students, how many students will 20 pizzas serve? **Estimate; About 160 students**

2. Use the table on page 100. The cafeteria serves salad with each spaghetti lunch. How many salads were served last week? **Exact; 329 salads**

3. Use the table on page 100. If the cafeteria plans to serve baked chicken next week, about how many such lunches should the cooks plan for? **Estimate; About 200**

Problem Solving Practice •

Using Data Use the table on page 100 for **4** and **5**.

4. The cafeteria served 22 fewer chicken nuggets lunches two weeks ago than it did last week. How many were served that week? **401 lunches**

GPS 5. The cafeteria provides milk with each meal. It also sells milk to students who bring bag lunches. Last Wednesday, 20 students bought milk. How many cartons of milk did the cafeteria need that day? **349 cartons**

6. **Health** There are 11,000 international units (I.U.) of vitamin A in a carrot. A sweet potato has about 9,000. About how much more vitamin A does a carrot have than a sweet potato? **About 2,000 I.U.**

7. **History** Sweet potatoes were first grown in southern Mexico and Central America. Spanish explorers of the 1500s introduced them to other parts of the world. About how long ago was that?
About 500 years ago

8. **Collecting Data** Make a chart of cafeteria lunches at your school. Log the number of lunches served each day for a week. Find the most and least popular meals.
Answers will vary.

9. Jackson stands between Ko and Sita in the hot lunch line. Jackson is ahead of Ko. Which of these three students is third in line? What strategy did you use?
Ko; Possible strategy: draw a picture or use logical reasoning.

10. **Journal** Write about a problem you solved using estimates. Tell why you used estimates. Then tell how you solved the problem.

Problem Solving Strategies

● Use Objects/Act It Out
● Draw a Picture
● Look for a Pattern
● Guess and Check
● Use Logical Reasoning
● Make an Organized List
● Make a Table
● Solve a Simpler Problem
● Work Backward

Choose a Tool

PROBLEM SOLVING PRACTICE

Name _____

Extend Your Thinking
3-4

Patterns in Data
Mia is reading a 128 page book. She is keeping a record of how many pages she reads each day.

Complete the chart.

Day	Page Number
1	6
2	14
3	24
4	30
5	38
6	48
7	**54**
8	**62**
9	**72**
10	78

1. If Mia continues the same reading pattern, to what page will she read on Day 7?   **54**

2. To what page will Mia read on Day 8?   **62**

3. To what page will Mia read on Day 9?   **72**

4. At the end of Day 13, on what page will Mia be?   **102**

5. At this rate, how long will it take Mia to finish the book? Explain how you know.
17; Because continuing the pattern shows that she will finish reading the 128 page book on the 17th day

6. Describe the pattern in the number of pages Mia reads each day.
She reads in patterns of 6 pages, then 8 pages, then 10 pages.

Check ◦

Exercise 1 Students can use mental math to solve.

Practice ◦ ◦ ◦ ◦ ◦ ◦ ◦ ◦ ◦ ◦ ◦ ◦ ◦ ◦ ◦ ◦ ◦ ◦ ◦

Exercise 8 The scope of this problem could be narrowed to collecting data from the class rather than the entire school.

For Early Finishers Challenge early finishers to use the table on page 100. Assume each cafeteria lunch comes with a carton of milk. Find out how many cartons of milk would be needed on Thursday if students who brought bag lunches bought 17 cartons of milk. $423 + 17 = 440$; 440 cartons

(3) Close and Assess

Discuss when exact answers were needed and when estimates were enough. Ask questions such as: Have you ever needed to measure something but didn't have a ruler? Have you ever guessed about how much money you had? Listen for students who understand the meaning of estimate and exact.

Quick Check

• Would you use an estimate or an exact number to talk about the number of words or letters in a newspaper? Why?
Estimate; There are too many to count.

• Would you use an estimate or an exact number to talk about the score in a baseball game? Why? Exact number; Games require exact scores to determine the winners.

ANSWERS

10 Answers should include situations in which an exact answer is not necessary. Students will round to estimate.

Section A
Review and Practice

Use the Skills Checklist

Review the **Skills Checklist** on the page with students. Then ask questions such as the following:

- Which problems will you solve by finding a pattern? Exercises 4–6
- For which problems could you use a thousand chart to help you add and subtract? Exercises 7–19
- In which problems will you use your estimation skills? Exercises 20–26
- How might you use the vocabulary words in your journal answer? Do they all apply to the topic for discussion? Possible answers: *Estimate* will be used easily when discussing estimation. Either *sum* or *difference* may be used, but probably not both. All three words can apply.

Assess

You may wish to use this information to assess students' understanding of the lesson objectives.

Item Analysis		
Lesson Objective		Items
3-1	Explore addition and subtraction patterns.	2, 3, 4–6
3-2	Explore adding and subtracting on a thousand chart.	7–19
3-3	Estimate sums and differences using rounding.	20–23
3-4	Solve problems needing exact answers or estimates.	1, 24–26

Resources

Practice Masters
- Practice Chapter 3 Section A

Assessment Sourcebook
- Quiz Chapter 3 Section A

TestWorks: Test and Practice Software

ANSWERS

26 Answers should include situations in which an exact answer is not necessary.

Review and Practice

Vocabulary Match each word with its meaning.

1. estimate **c**   **a.** number obtained by adding
2. sum **a**   **b.** number obtained by subtracting
3. difference **b**   **c.** to find a number close to an exact answer

(Lesson 1) Copy and complete each number sentence.

4. $2 + 1 = n$ **3**
   $20 + 10 = n$ **30**
   $200 + 100 = n$ **300**
   $2,000 + 1,000 = n$ **3,000**

5. $9 - 7 = n$ **2**
   $90 - 70 = n$ **20**
   $900 - 700 = n$ **200**
   $9,000 - 7,000 = n$ **2,000**

6. $3 + 2 = n$ **5**
   $30 + 20 = n$ **50**
   $300 + 200 = n$ **500**
   $3,000 + 2,000 = n$ **5,000**

(Lesson 2) Mental Math Find each sum or difference.

7. $120 + 200$ **320**
8. $330 - 100$ **230**
9. $840 - 110$ **730**
10. $460 + 250$ **710**
11. $770 - 220$ **550**
12. $580 + 120$ **700**
13. $490 - 130$ **360**
14. $550 + 310$ **860**
15. $320 + 210$ **530**
16. $640 - 200$ **440**
17. $270 + 120$ **390**
18. $930 - 520$ **410**

19. **Science** In three months, a dolphin at the Dolphin Research Center ate about 120 pounds of butter fish and 480 pounds of herring. How many pounds of fish did the dolphin eat in all? **600 pounds**

(Lesson 3) Estimate each sum or difference. Round to the nearest thousand.

20. $2,663 + 1,422$
    4,000
21. $1,585 - 1,400$
    1,000
22. $2,357 + 3,042$
    5,000
23. $3,310 - 697$
    2,000

(Lesson 4) Decide if an exact answer or an estimate is needed. Explain.

24. You want to buy a sandwich, milk, and an apple. You need to know quickly if you have enough money.
    Estimate; It is enough for a quick answer.
25. You time yourself to find how long it takes to run 100 yards. You want to see if you can better your time, so you run 100 yards again.
    Exact answer; You need exact times to compare
26. **Journal** Describe a situation in which you might estimate.

REVIEW AND PRACTICE

Skills Checklist
In this section, you have:
☑ Explored Addition and Subtraction Patterns
☑ Explored Adding and Subtracting on a Thousand Chart
☑ Estimated Sums and Differences
☑ Solved Problems Needing Exact Answers or Estimates

Practice

Name _____

Practice
Chapter 3
Section A

Review and Practice
Vocabulary Write true or false for each statement.
1. A good estimate for the sum of 447 and 316 is 131.   **False**
2. A good estimate for the difference between 447 and 316 is 100.   **True**

(Lesson 1) Complete each number sentence.
3. $7 + 8 =$ **15**
   $70 + 80 =$ **150**
   $700 + 800 =$ **1,500**
   $7,000 + 8,000 =$ **15,000**
4. $3 + 9 =$ **12**
   $30 + 90 =$ **120**
   $300 + 900 =$ **1,200**
   $3,000 + 4,000 =$ **12,000**

(Lesson 2) Mental Math Find each sum or difference.
5. $300 + 80 =$ **380**
6. $280 - 120 =$ **160**
7. $440 - 130 =$ **310**
8. $270 + 120 =$ **390**

(Lesson 3) Estimate each sum or difference. Round to the nearest thousand.
9. $6,847 + 3,283$ **7,000** + **3,000** = **10,000**
10. $7,482 - 1,521$ **7,000** − **2,000** = **5,000**

(Lesson 4) Decide if an exact answer or an estimate is needed. Explain.
11. Grace was given 16 words to write in sentences. She has used 9 of them. How many more does she need to use?
    Exact; Grace must use all the words in sentences.
12. Mitch's family drove 383 miles on Monday and 339 miles on Tuesday. About how far did they drive in all?
    Estimate; They only want to know "about" how far they drove.

(Mixed Review) Write >, <, or =.
13. $4,067$ **(>)** $4,009$
14. $3,545$ **(=)** $3,545$
15. $6,300$ **(>)** 660
16. $7,739$ **(<)** $7,909$

Adding and Subtracting

Helen Chavez-Hansen is president of her own company. Her factory makes tortillas, a kind of flat bread made from flour or corn.

Suppose you had your own food business. How would you use math to fill orders?

Addition with Greater Numbers

Review regrouping. Copy and complete.

1. 8 ones + 3 ones = ⬛ tens, ⬛ ones

                        1   1

2. 7 ones + 6 ones = ⬛ tens, ⬛ ones

                        1   3

3. 8 tens + 3 tens = ⬛ hundreds, ⬛ tens

                        1   1

4. 7 tens + 6 tens = ⬛ hundreds, ⬛ tens

                        1   3

Skills Checklist

In this section, you will:

- ☐ Add and Subtract Greater Numbers
- ☐ Subtract with Middle Zeros
- ☐ Solve Multiple-Step Word Problems
- ☐ Add and Subtract Mentally
- ☐ Choose a Calculation Method

103

Adding and Subtracting

In this section, students will add and subtract greater numbers, subtract from numbers with zeros, use mental math to add and subtract, choose a calculation method, and solve multiple-step problems.

Subskills

The work in this section builds on...

- Identifying addition and subtraction patterns

  $2 + 5 = 7$

  $20 + 50 = 70$

  $200 + 500 = 700$

- Using place-value concepts to add and subtract

  $530 - 210 = 320$

- Estimating sums and differences

  $395 - 209$

  ↓   ↓

  $400 - 200 = 200$

Use the Section Opener

Ask students how they think they might use math if they had a business of their own. Possible answer: Add prices, subtract the number of items you sell from the total number you have.

Skills Trace

(Red numbers indicate pages in this section.)

Lesson and Skill	First Introduced	Grade Four			
		Introduce	Develop	Practice/Apply	Review
3-5 Add 3-digit and 4-digit numbers.	Grade 3	104–107	104, 105	106, 107, 109, 116-117, 121, 124, 132, 133, 139, 561	124, 139, 140, 143, 245, 381
3-6 Add 3 and 4 addends.	Grade 3	108, 109	108	109, 121, 124, 132, 133, 561	124, 140, 143
3-7 Subtract 3-digit and 4-digit numbers.	Grade 3	110–113	110, 111	112, 113, 116-117, 124, 132, 133, 139, 561	124, 139, 140, 143, 245, 287, 381, 427
3-8 Subtract from numbers with zeros.	Grade 3	114, 115	114	115, 124, 132, 133, 561	124, 140, 143
3-9 Solve multiple-step problems.	Grade 3	118, 119	118, 119	119, 124, 133, 189, 561	124, 140, 143
3-10 Add and subtract numbers mentally.	Grade 3	120, 121	120	121, 124, 561	124, 140, 143
3-11 Choose a calculation method.	Grade 3	122, 123	122	123, 124, 132, 133, 139, 561	124, 139, 140, 143

Mixed Review and Test Prep exercises for this chapter occur on pages 99, 107, 109, 113, 115, 121, 123, 127, 129.

🚶 **Multi-Age Classrooms** Use pages 161–194 in Grade 3 or pages 81–102 in Grade 5 to relate to the content of this section.

Adding

At-A-Glance Planning

Lesson Planning Checklist

Objective Add 3-digit and 4-digit numbers.

Student Book Lesson Materials *Optional* Lesson Enhancement Transparency 9

Materials for pages 104A and 104B Place-value blocks (15 ones, 15 tens, 10 hundreds, 1 thousand per group), algorithm mats (1 per student)

Subject Connections careers—biologist; social studies—Paricutín volcano

Strand Connections mental math, using data, geometry readiness

	Before Lesson	During Lesson	After Lesson
Daily Math			
p. 104A Problem of the Day			
p. 104A Math Routines			
p. 104A Mental Math			
Teaching Options			
p. 104 Student Book Lesson			
p. 104B Another Way to Learn…			
Options for Reaching All Learners			
p. 104B Inclusion			
p. 104B Language Development			
Subject Connections			
p. 104A Literature Connection			
Assessment Options			
p. 105 Talk About It			
p. 105 Error Intervention			
p. 107 Portfolio			
p. 107 Quick Check			
Resources			
3-5 Practice			
3-5 Reteaching			
3-5 Enrichment			
3-5 Problem Solving			
3-5 Daily Transparency			

Problem of the Day

Problem of the Day

1. Write your age in years.
2. Write two zeros after it.
3. Add 250.
4. Add a number less than 50.
5. Subtract 365.
6. Add 115.
7. What do you notice?

The first two digits are the age. The last two digits represent the chosen number in Step 4.

Math Routines

Measurement Remind students that 16 ounces = 1 pound. Ask how many pounds and ounces three 12 oz packages of crackers weigh. 2 lb 4 oz

Patterns Have students give each sum.

$1 + 3$ 4 $1 + 3 + 5$ 9 $1 + 3 + 5 + 7$ 16

Have students name the pattern and find the next two sums. The next consecutive odd number is added each time; 25, 36

Mental Math

Name the number that is 111 greater. Explain your thinking.

20 131   **39** 150   **59** 170   **99** 210

Literature Connection

In the poem "Homework Machine," Shel Silverstein describes a machine that will do math problems. According to the machine, $9 + 4 = 3$.

- What is the correct answer? 13

- Explain the machine's mistake. Possible answer: It ignored the tens place.

Another Way to [Learn] Lesson 3-5
Use as an alternative or in addition to pages 104–107.

Materials Place-value blocks (15 ones, 15 tens, 10 hundreds, 1 thousand per group)

Learning Style Kinesthetic, Visual

- Ask groups to model the numbers 257 and 385 using place-value blocks. Then ask them to put the blocks together and tell how many of each kind of place-value block they have. 5 hundreds, 13 tens, 12 ones

- Help students see that they can trade 10 ones for 1 ten, then trade 10 tens for 1 hundred. Ask a volunteer to tell the new number of each type of block and the number the blocks represent. 6 hundreds, 4 tens, 2 ones; 642

- Model the algorithm for the addition problem on the chalkboard or overhead, inviting volunteers to help.

- Ask groups to model the addition problem 1,372 + 256 using the place-value blocks, then write the algorithm.

```
  1,372
+   256
  1,628
```

- Ask students to suggest things they might have to watch for when adding 3-digit numbers. Regrouping, correct alignment of addends

- Assign Check and Practice on Student Book pages 105–107 or *Practice Master 3-5*.

- Assess using the following rubric.

Assessment Rubric
4 **Full Accomplishment** • consistently finds sums of 3-digit and 4-digit numbers
3 **Substantial Accomplishment** • finds sums of most 3-digit and 4-digit numbers
2 **Partial Accomplishment** • finds sums of some 3-digit and 4-digit numbers but does not regroup consistently
1 **Little Accomplishment** • does not find sums of 3-digit and 4-digit numbers consistently

Options for Reaching All Learners

Inclusion

Between the Lines
Use algorithm mats to strengthen addition skills.

Materials Algorithm mats (1 per student)

Learning Style Visual

- Prepare a page of several algorithm mats for students to use when adding 3-digit and 4-digit numbers. Make a copy for each student.

	thousands	hundreds	tens	ones
Regrouped Number	1	1	1	
Problem	3, + 4,	6 5	8 4	9 7
Sum	8,	2	3	6

- Students can use the mats to keep track of regrouping and to keep columns of numbers correctly aligned.

Language Development

Talking About Math
Use model sentences to improve communication of math processes.

Learning Style Verbal

- Encourage students to use the correct phrases in math by modeling. For example, in Example 1, Step 1, if a student says, "I put the number on top," rephrase the student's words as, "I regrouped the ones and wrote a 1 above the 9 in the tens place."

- You may wish to show model sentences to describe math processes on the chalkboard or on a poster overhead, where students can refer to them quickly.

Lesson Organizer

Objective Add 3-digit and 4-digit numbers.
Student Materials None
Teacher Materials *Optional* Lesson Enhancement Transparency 9
Assignment Guide
Basic 22–44, 49, 53, 54, 56, 60, 62–66
Average 25–50, 52–54, 56, 57, 59, 60, 62–66
Enriched 31–66

1 Introduce

Review

Estimate each sum.

1. 328 + 479 800
2. 209 + 142 300
3. 756 + 211 1,000
4. 934 + 158 1,100
5. 749 + 751 1,500

Build on Prior Knowledge

Ask students to explain what an estimate tells them. Then ask if it would be useful to estimate before finding an exact answer. It gives an idea of about how many; yes, you would know if your answer was about right.

2 Teach

See Another Way to Learn…on page 104B.

Learn ● ● ● ● ● ● ● ● ● ● ● ● ● ● ● ● ●

Pronunciation note: Phyllis Ha (HAH)

• Read, or have volunteers read, the introduction and the word problem. Discuss how they know that they need to use addition to find the answer. Ask students to explain the steps as you model the algorithm of the problem on the chalkboard or overhead projector. Ask students to explain why the regrouped numbers are written over the next greater place in the problem. So they can be added in the correct place more easily, and so they are not forgotten in the addition of the numbers in the next place

• You can use Lesson Enhancement Transparency 9 to illustrate Example 1.

Adding

You Will Learn
how to add 3-digit and 4-digit numbers

Learn ● ● ● ● ● ● ● ● ● ● ●

Wildlife biologists can spend all day counting. They count birds, fish, trees, and other things. Why? The counts help them keep track of populations of species from year to year.

Phyllis counts nests for two kinds of albatrosses, which are sea birds. In one area, she counts 696 Laysan albatross nests and 175 black-footed albatross nests. How can you find out how many nests she counts in all?

Phyllis Ha works for the U.S. Fish and Wildlife Service in Honolulu, Hawaii.

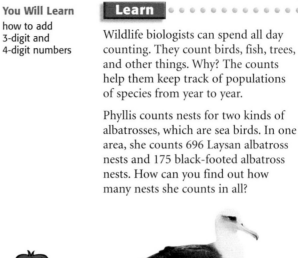  

Remember
10 ones = 1 ten
10 tens = 1 hundred

You add because you need to put together amounts to find the total.

Example 1
Find 696 + 175.

Step 1	Step 2	Step 3
Add the ones. Regroup as needed.	Add the tens. Regroup as needed.	Add the hundreds.

1		1 1	1 ten	1 1	1 hundred	
696	6 ones	696	9 tens	696	6 hundreds	
+ 175	+ 5 ones	+ 175	+ 7 tens	+ 175	+ 1 hundred	
1	1 ten, 1 one	71	1 hundred, 7 tens	871	8 hundreds	

696 + 175 = 871   **Estimate** to check. 700 + 200 = 900
Since 871 is close to 900, the answer is reasonable.

So, Phyllis counted 871 nests in all.

Managing Time

Use the first half of the period to cover Learn and Check. Use the second half for selected Practice exercises. Assign the remaining exercises as homework.

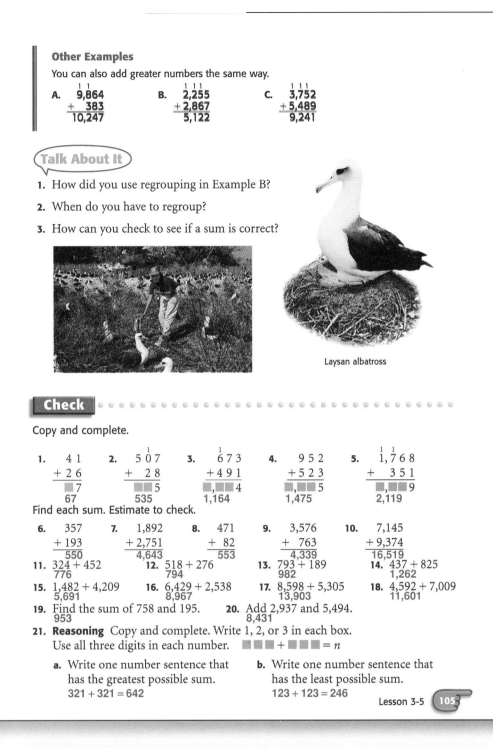

Other Examples

You can also add greater numbers the same way.

A.
```
  1 1
  9,864
+   383
 10,247
```

B.
```
  1 1 1
  2,255
+ 2,867
  5,122
```

C.
```
  1 1 1
  3,752
+ 5,489
  9,241
```

Talk About It

1. How did you use regrouping in Example B?

2. When do you have to regroup?

3. How can you check to see if a sum is correct?

Laysan albatross

Check

Copy and complete.

1.
```
   4 1
 + 2 6
  ▮ 7
   67
```

2.
```
    1
  5 0 7
 +  2 8
  ▮▮ 5
   535
```

3.
```
    1
  6 7 3
 + 4 9 1
 ▮,▮▮ 4
  1,164
```

4.
```
  9 5 2
 +5 2 3
 ▮,▮▮ 5
  1,475
```

5.
```
   1 1
  1,7 6 8
 +   3 5 1
 ▮,▮▮ 9
  2,119
```

Find each sum. Estimate to check.

6.
```
   357
 + 193
   550
```

7.
```
   1,892
 + 2,751
   4,643
```

8.
```
   471
 +  82
   553
```

9.
```
   3,576
 +   763
   4,339
```

10.
```
   7,145
 + 9,374
  16,519
```

11. 324 + 452
776

12. 518 + 276
794

13. 793 + 189
982

14. 437 + 825
1,262

15. 1,482 + 4,209
5,691

16. 6,429 + 2,538
8,967

17. 8,598 + 5,305
13,903

18. 4,592 + 7,009
11,601

19. Find the sum of 758 and 195.
953

20. Add 2,937 and 5,494.
8,431

21. **Reasoning** Copy and complete. Write 1, 2, or 3 in each box. Use all three digits in each number. ▮▮▮ + ▮▮▮ = n

a. Write one number sentence that has the greatest possible sum.
321 + 321 = 642

b. Write one number sentence that has the least possible sum.
123 + 123 = 246

Lesson 3-5 **105**

Other Examples

Ask students:

• Do the rules for subtracting 3-digit numbers apply to subtracting 4-digit numbers? Yes

• What would you expect to be different about adding 4-digit numbers? You might have to add digits in the thousands place; there is a chance you will regroup thousands into the ten-thousands place.

Talk About It Ongoing Assessment

Listen for students to recognize when regrouping is necessary.

Answers for Talk About It

1 12 ones were regrouped as 1 ten 2 ones; 12 tens were regrouped as 1 hundred 2 tens; 11 hundreds were regrouped as 1 thousand 1 hundred.

2 When there are 10 or more in a place

3 Estimate, add the addends in a different order, or subtract one addend from the sum.

Check

Exercises 1–5 Although the ones places of the answers are given for students, encourage them to add as usual. This will prevent them from missing any regrouping that is required.

Exercises 11–20 Have students rewrite these problems in vertical format.

Error Intervention Ongoing Assessment

Observation Students may not record their regrouping correctly.

How to Help As they add, have students write each fact separately to the side of their paper. They can then decide which digit to write as part of the sum and which digit to regroup to the next place.

Practice

Exercises 58 and 59 Students will need to read the information carefully. The initial 10 meters should not be added to 150 + 290, as the 150-meter figure includes this initial height.

Exercise 62 Watch for regrouping of all place values.

For Early Finishers Challenge early finishers to find how many more silversides than mullet Phyllis and her partner counted in Exercise 54. **59**

Practice

Skills and Reasoning

Find each sum.

22.
$$\begin{array}{r} 8\,4 \\ +\ 3\,1 \\ \hline \blacksquare\blacksquare5 \\ 115 \end{array}$$

23.
$$\begin{array}{r} \overset{1\ 1}{9\,8\,6} \\ +\ \ 8\,5 \\ \hline \blacksquare,\blacksquare\blacksquare1 \\ 1,071 \end{array}$$

24.
$$\begin{array}{r} 4\,0\,2 \\ +2\,9\,0 \\ \hline \blacksquare\blacksquare2 \\ 692 \end{array}$$

25.
$$\begin{array}{r} \overset{1\ 1}{1\,7\,9} \\ +4\,4\,4 \\ \hline \blacksquare\blacksquare3 \\ 623 \end{array}$$

26.
$$\begin{array}{r} \overset{1}{3,\,4\,9\,0} \\ +\ \ \ 3\,2\,2 \\ \hline \blacksquare,\blacksquare\blacksquare2 \\ 3,812 \end{array}$$

27.
$$\begin{array}{r} 3,094 \\ +8,371 \\ \hline 11,465 \end{array}$$

28.
$$\begin{array}{r} 390 \\ +611 \\ \hline 1,001 \end{array}$$

29.
$$\begin{array}{r} 4,218 \\ +\ \ 303 \\ \hline 4,521 \end{array}$$

30.
$$\begin{array}{r} 650 \\ +772 \\ \hline 1,422 \end{array}$$

31.
$$\begin{array}{r} 6,598 \\ +2,602 \\ \hline 9,200 \end{array}$$

32.
$$\begin{array}{r} 499 \\ +517 \\ \hline 1,016 \end{array}$$

33.
$$\begin{array}{r} 7,821 \\ +\ \ 699 \\ \hline 8,520 \end{array}$$

34.
$$\begin{array}{r} 989 \\ +555 \\ \hline 1,544 \end{array}$$

35.
$$\begin{array}{r} 3,271 \\ +3,185 \\ \hline 6,456 \end{array}$$

36.
$$\begin{array}{r} 2,203 \\ +9,034 \\ \hline 11,237 \end{array}$$

37. $571 + 225$
796

38. $842 + 398$
1,240

39. $384 + 295$
679

40. $245 + 83$
328

41. $948 + 575$
1,523

42. $4,921 + 3,038$
7,959

43. $8,480 + 1,842$
10,322

44. $4,421 + 355$
4,776

45. $7,565 + 7,565$
15,130

46. $2,549 + 9,805$
12,354

47. $3,821 + 5,096$
8,917

48. $6,002 + 7,777$
13,779

49. Find the sum of 356 and 489.
845

50. Add 1,827 and 945.
2,772

51. Copy and complete. Write 4, 5, 6, 7, 8, or 9 in each box. Use each digit only once. $\blacksquare\blacksquare\blacksquare + \blacksquare\blacksquare\blacksquare = n$

    a. Write a number sentence that has the greatest sum.
    $974 + 865 = 1,839$

    b. Write a number sentence that has the least sum.
    $469 + 578 = 1,047$

Problem Solving and Applications

Mental Math Write $<$, $>$, or $=$.

52. $453 + 198 \ \bullet\ 453 + 199$ $<$

53. $453 + 200 \ \bullet\ 200 + 453$ $=$

54. Phyllis and her partner count fish at the mouth of a river in Hawaii. They count 217 silversides and 158 mullet. How many fish is this? **375 fish**

55. Phyllis counts 1,392 Laysan albatross and 350 black-footed albatross. How many albatrosses is this? **1,742 albatrosses**

Using Data Use the table for **56** and **57**.

56. **Mental Math** How many clams did the biologists count? **650 clams**

57. How many more clams did they count at Site 2 than at Site 1? **100 clams**

Wildlife Refuge
Population Counts
for Giant Clams

Site	Number of Giant Clams
Site 1	200
Site 2	300
Site 3	150

Practice 3-5

Name _____

Adding
Find each sum.

1.
$$\begin{array}{r} 6\,7 \\ +2\,1 \\ \hline 8\,8 \end{array}$$

2.
$$\begin{array}{r} 4\,6\,8 \\ +3\,5\,4 \\ \hline 8\,2\,2 \end{array}$$

3.
$$\begin{array}{r} 8\,0\,5 \\ +2\,8\,0 \\ \hline 1,0\,8\,5 \end{array}$$

4.
$$\begin{array}{r} 2\,3\,7 \\ +5\,5\,5 \\ \hline 7\,9\,2 \end{array}$$

5.
$$\begin{array}{r} 4,2\,1\,0 \\ +\ \ 9\,4\,5 \\ \hline 5,1\,5\,5 \end{array}$$

6.
$$\begin{array}{r} 4,0\,1\,7 \\ +9,5\,6\,4 \\ \hline 13,5\,8\,1 \end{array}$$

7.
$$\begin{array}{r} 8\,2\,0 \\ +2\,4\,4 \\ \hline 1,0\,6\,4 \end{array}$$

8.
$$\begin{array}{r} 3,5\,7\,2 \\ +\ \ 6\,1\,9 \\ \hline 4,1\,9\,1 \end{array}$$

9.
$$\begin{array}{r} 5\,3\,0 \\ +9\,8\,6 \\ \hline 1,5\,1\,6 \end{array}$$

10.
$$\begin{array}{r} 7,3\,8\,1 \\ +2,6\,1\,5 \\ \hline 9,9\,9\,6 \end{array}$$

11. $462 + 233 =$ **695**

12. $758 + 435 =$ **1,193**

13. $148 + 326 =$ **474**

14. $337 + 98 =$ **435**

15. $915 + 608 =$ **1,523**

16. $2,801 + 7,955 =$ **10,756**

17. Find the sum of 627 and 261. **888**

18. Add 2,658 and 695. **3,353**

19. Complete. Write 1, 2, 3, 4, 5, 6, 7, 8, or 9 in each box. Use each digit only once.

    a. Write a number sentence that has the greatest sum.
    $9,864 + 753 =$ **10,617**

    b. Write a number sentence that has the least sum.
    $1,357 + 246 =$ **1,603**

Write $>$, $<$, or $=$.

20. $357 + 219 \ \textcircled{<}\ 357 + 110 + 110$

21. $632 + 412 \ \textcircled{>}\ 632 + 411$

22. Ron and Will are collecting cans of food for the food drive at their school. So far Ron has 177 cans and Will has 209. How many cans is this? **386**

Reteaching 3-5

Name _____

Adding
You can use place-value blocks to add numbers.

476 + 829

6 ones + 9 ones = 15 ones
Regroup 15 ones as 1 ten and 5 ones
1 ten + 7 tens + 2 tens = 10 tens
Regroup 10 tens as 1 hundred
1 hundred + 4 hundreds + 8 hundreds = 13 hundreds

$$\begin{array}{r} \overset{1\ 1}{4\,7\,6} \\ +8\,2\,9 \\ \hline 1,3\,0\,5 \end{array}$$

Use the place value blocks to find each sum.

1. 518 + 853 = **1,371**

2. 573 + 744 = **1,317**

3. 904 + 124 = **1,028**

Problem Solving and SOCIAL STUDIES

One February morning in 1943, a farmer in Mexico noticed a volcano forming in his field. The next morning it had grown another 10 meters. After a week, it was 150 meters high. It grew another 290 meters in the first year. By 1952, it had stopped growing.

The Paricutín (pah ree koo TEEN) volcano in Mexico is one of the youngest volcanoes on Earth.

58. How high was the volcano after the first year?
440 meters
59. Paricutín continued to grow another 77 meters until it stopped in 1952. How tall is it now?
517 meters
60. **Geography** Use the map. Is Paricutín closer to Mexico City or Guadalajara?
Guadalajara
61. **Geometry Readiness** What geometric shape do you think the volcano most looks like— a pyramid, a cone, or a rectangular prism?
Cone

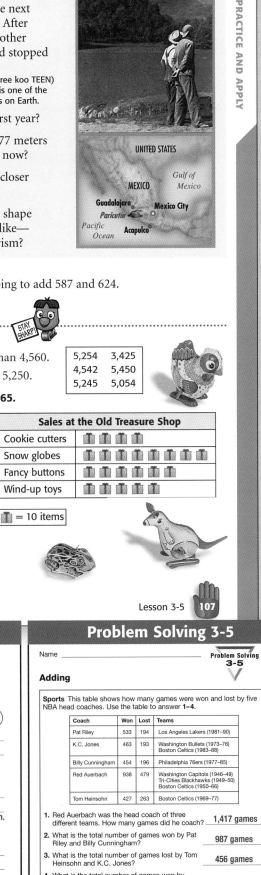

UNITED STATES

MEXICO

Gulf of Mexico

Guadalajara
Paricutín • Mexico City
Pacific Ocean
Acapulco

62. **Journal** Explain how you use regrouping to add 587 and 624.

Mixed Review and Test Prep

63. Use the numbers in the box.
   a. List the numbers that are greater than 4,560.
   5,254, 5,245, 5,450, 5,054
   b. List the numbers that are less than 5,250.
   4,542, 5,245, 3,425, 5,054

5,254	3,425
4,542	5,450
5,245	5,054

Using Data Use the pictograph for **64** and **65**.

64. How many snow globes and wind-up toys did the shop sell? **130**

65. How many more buttons than cookie cutters did the shop sell?
20 more

66. Which is a 7-digit number with a 4 in the hundred thousands place and a 0 in the hundreds place? **A**
   Ⓐ 3,467,074   Ⓑ 3,764,047
   Ⓒ 437,604   Ⓓ 3,067,474

Sales at the Old Treasure Shop	
Cookie cutters	🎁🎁🎁🎁
Snow globes	🎁🎁🎁🎁🎁🎁🎁🎁
Fancy buttons	🎁🎁🎁🎁🎁🎁
Wind-up toys	🎁🎁🎁🎁🎁

🎁 = 10 items

Historical Note

The volcano Paricutín (pah-REE-koo-TEEN) is a well documented volcano. People witnessed its birth and recorded its development. During the nine years of eruptions, the nearby town of Paricutín was buried, and the town of San Juan Parangaricutiro was partially buried. Paricutín spewed lava and volcanic ash over an 18-square-mile area. Its maximum height was 2,808 m above sea level.

③ Close and Assess

Portfolio

Have students select two problems from Practice Exercises 22–50 and solve, showing all their work.

Quick Check

Number Sense Estimate if each sum will be in the hundreds, thousands, or ten-thousands.

1. 437 + 219 Hundreds
2. 735 + 327 Thousands
3. 6,349 + 3,119 Thousands
4. 5,028 + 7,397 Ten-thousands

Skill Find each sum.

1. 473 + 845 1,318
2. 794 + 299 1,093
3. 2,749 + 6,359 9,108
4. 3,851 + 3,718 7,569

ANSWERS

62 Regroup 11 ones as 1 ten, 1 one. Regroup 11 tens as 1 hundred 1 ten. 587 + 624 = 1,211

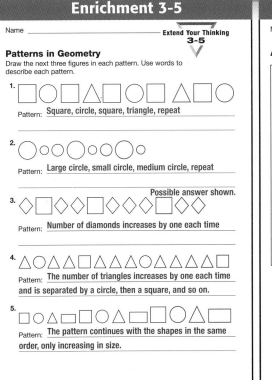

Enrichment 3-5

Name _____   Extend Your Thinking **3-5**

Patterns in Geometry
Draw the next three figures in each pattern. Use words to describe each pattern.

1. □○□△□□○△□○
   Pattern: **Square, circle, square, triangle, repeat**

2. ○∘○◯∘∘◯∘
   Pattern: **Large circle, small circle, medium circle, repeat**

   Possible answer shown.
3. ◇□◇□◇◇◇□◇◇
   Pattern: **Number of diamonds increases by one each time**

4. △○△△□△△○△△△□
   Pattern: **The number of triangles increases by one each time and is separated by a circle, then a square, and so on.**

5. □○△□□○△□□○△□
   Pattern: **The pattern continues with the shapes in the same order, only increasing in size.**

Problem Solving 3-5

Name _____   Problem Solving **3-5**

Adding

Sports This table shows how many games were won and lost by five NBA head coaches. Use the table to answer **1–4**.

Coach	Won	Lost	Teams
Pat Riley	533	194	Los Angeles Lakers (1981–90)
K.C. Jones	463	193	Washington Bullets (1973–76) Boston Celtics (1983–88)
Billy Cunningham	454	196	Philadelphia 76ers (1977–85)
Red Auerbach	938	479	Washington Capitols (1946–49) Tri-Cities Blackhawks (1949–50) Boston Celtics (1950–66)
Tom Heinsohn	427	263	Boston Celtics (1969–77)

1. Red Auerbach was the head coach of three different teams. How many games did he coach? **1,417 games**

2. What is the total number of games won by Pat Riley and Billy Cunningham? **987 games**

3. What is the total number of games lost by Tom Heinsohn and K.C. Jones? **456 games**

4. What is the total number of games won by all five coaches? **2,815 games**

5. Frieda makes beaded necklaces. She has 325 blue beads and 219 red beads. How many beads does she have in all? **544 beads**

6. **Choose a strategy** For the high school football games on Saturday and Sunday, 257 and 394 tickets were sold. How many more tickets were sold for the Sunday game than the Saturday game?
   • Use Objects/Act It Out
   • Draw a Picture
   • Look for a Pattern
   • Guess and Check
   • Use Logical Reasoning
   • Make an Organized List
   • Make a Table
   • Solve a Simpler Problem
   • Work Backward

   a. What strategy would you use to solve the problem?
   Strategies will vary.

   b. Answer the problem. **137 games**

Column Addition

At-A-Glance Planning

Lesson Planning Checklist

Objective Add 3 and 4 addends.

Vocabulary addends, front-end estimation

Student Book Lesson Materials None

Materials for pages 108A and 108B Place-value blocks (1 thousand, 10 hundreds, 30 tens, 30 ones per group)

Subject Connection careers—desktop publishing

Strand Connections money, logic, mental math

	Before Lesson	During Lesson	After Lesson
Daily Math			
p. 108A Problem of the Day			
p. 108A Math Routines			
p. 108A Mental Math			
Teaching Options			
p. 108 Student Book Lesson			
p. 108B Another Way to Learn…			
Options for Reaching All Learners			
p. 108B Inclusion			
p. 108B Language Development			
Subject Connections			
p. 108A Art Connection			
Assessment Options			
p. 108 Talk About It			
p. 109 Error Intervention			
p. 109 Journal			
p. 109 Quick Check			
Resources			
3-6 Practice			
3-6 Reteaching			
3-6 Enrichment			
3-6 Problem Solving			
3-6 Daily Transparency			

Problem of the Day

Problem of the Day

After getting up, Jan exercised for 28 minutes, did math homework for 31 minutes, and got dressed in 13 minutes. It was then 8:22 A.M. What time did Jan get up?

7:10 A.M.

Math Routines

Measurement Have students find the total in feet and inches: 3 in. + 5 in. + 7 in. 1 ft 3 in.

Patterns Have students continue the pattern and give the rule. 4, 54, 554, 5,554, ■, ■, 55,554, 555,554; add 50; 500; 5,000; 50,000; 500,000

Mental Math

Name the number that is 99 greater. Explain your thinking.

38 137   123 222   326 425   449 548

Art Connection

Bring in some brochures for businesses, tourist attractions, or restaurants.

- Ask students how using a computer makes it easier to create the type, art, and layout for a brochure. It is easier to adjust copy, art, photos or layouts.

- Ask how you might use addition to order from a brochure. You could find the total of several prices.

Another Way to **Learn** Lesson 3-6

Use as an alternative or in addition to pages 108 and 109.

Materials Place-value blocks (1 thousand, 10 hundreds, 30 tens, 30 ones per group)

Learning Style Visual, Kinesthetic

- Have students model the following numbers using the place-value blocks: 493, 314, 205.

- Ask students how they could find out how many blocks they have in all. Combine the blocks and count them.

- Have students combine the place-value blocks to determine the total amount. 1,012

- Discuss how combining the same value blocks would help students add. Which blocks would they add first? Which would they add next? Why?

- Have students write the problem and find the sum. Stress that numbers should be correctly aligned.

- Model how to use front-end estimation and adjusting to see what kind of answer they should expect. Remind them that estimation helps them find a number close to the exact answer. $400 + 300 + 200 = 900$; $90 + 10 = 100$; $900 + 100 = 1,000$

- Assign Check and Practice on Student Book page 109 or *Practice Master 3-6*.

- Assess using the following rubric.

Assessment Rubric

4 Full Accomplishment
- consistently finds and estimates sums of three or four addends

3 Substantial Accomplishment
- finds and estimates most sums of three or four addends

2 Partial Accomplishment
- finds and estimates some sums of three or four addends

1 Little Accomplishment
- does not find sums of three or four addends consistently

Options for Reaching All Learners

Inclusion

Front-End Estimation

Use front-end estimation to predict answers.

Learning Style Logical

- Write $532 + 378$ on the chalkboard.

- Ask students to use estimation to predict what the answer will be. How many digits will there be? What number will the sum be close to? Will the number be greater than 800? Will the number be less than 900?

- Repeat, using two 4-digit numbers and one 3-digit and one 4-digit number.

Language Development

It's Hard to Say...

Use individual instruction to strengthen correct pronunciation of difficult math words.

Learning Style Verbal/Auditory

Both of the vocabulary words in this lesson, *addends* and *front-end estimation*, may be difficult to pronounce.

- Listen for students who have difficulty pronouncing these words or who are pronouncing them incorrectly. Meet privately with these students to help them learn and use the correct pronunciations. Model the use of each term by using it in a sentence.

- To help students with the pronunciation of difficult words, you might break up the words into syllables, clap the syllables, then put the parts of the words together.

Lesson Organizer

Objective Add 3 and 4 addends.
Student Materials None
Vocabulary addends, front-end estimation
Assignment Guide
  Basic 7–15, 19, 22–25
  Average 10–17, 20–25
  Enriched 11–18, 20–25

1 Introduce

Review

Find each sum.

1. 476 + 299 775
2. 247 + 493 740
3. 573 + 720 1,293

Build on Prior Knowledge

After students review adding 3-digit numbers, have them round each addend to the nearest hundred and estimate to see if their answers are reasonable. 800; 700; 1,300

2 Teach

See Another Way to Learn…on page 108B.

Learn

Model adding 442 + 339 = 781, then 781 + 628 = 1,409. Ask students if they can suggest a faster way to add more than two addends. Lead students to see that the sum can be found by adding all three numbers at once.

Remind students that they can use front-end estimation to check that their sums are reasonable.

Talk About It Ongoing Assessment

Listen to see that students recognize the importance of place value in addition.

Answer for Talk About It

It makes it easier to add numbers of the same place value.

Column Addition

You Will Learn
how to add 3 or 4 addends

Vocabulary
addends
numbers that are added together to make a sum

front-end estimation
a way to estimate by first looking at the leading digits

Learn

"Don't get in over your head," reads Jonathan's ad. His ad reaches many people who don't know how to use computers. Jonathan prints 442 flyers, 339 brochures, and 628 bookmarks. How many items does he print in all?

Jonathan runs a desktop publishing business in Farmersville, Illinois.

You can add three **addends** to find the total number of items. Use **front-end estimation** to check.

Example
Find 442 + 339 + 628.

Step 1	Step 2	Step 3
Add the ones. Regroup as needed.	Add the tens. Regroup as needed.	Add the hundreds.
$\begin{array}{r} {\scriptstyle 1} \\ 442 \\ 339 \\ + 628 \\ \hline 9 \end{array}$	$\begin{array}{r} {\scriptstyle 1\,1} \\ 442 \\ 339 \\ + 628 \\ \hline 09 \end{array}$	$\begin{array}{r} {\scriptstyle 1\,1} \\ 442 \\ 339 \\ + 628 \\ \hline 1,409 \end{array}$

Round to the front-end, or leading, digits.

$$\begin{array}{rcr} 442 & \longrightarrow & 400 \\ 339 & \longrightarrow & 300 \\ + 628 & \longrightarrow & + 600 \\ \hline & & 1,300 \end{array}$$

Adjust your estimate.

$$\begin{array}{rcr} 442 & \longrightarrow & 40 \\ 339 & \longrightarrow & 40 \\ + 628 & \longrightarrow & + 30 \\ \hline & & 110 \end{array}$$

1,300 + 110 = 1,410

Since 1,409 is close to 1,410, the answer is reasonable.

Jonathan needs to print 1,409 items.

Talk About It

Why do you line up the ones, tens, and hundreds before you add?

Practice 3-6	Reteaching 3-6

Find each sum. Estimate to check.

1. 32	**2.** 472	**3.** 984	**4.** 75	**5.** 3,004
41	208	27	348	12
+ 26	+ 325	+ 3,845	+ 590	+ 8,984
99	1,005	4,856	1,013	12,000

6. Reasoning When you add three or more addends, does it matter if you change the order of the addends? Explain. No, you can add in any order and still get the same sum.

Practice

Skills and Reasoning

Find each sum. Estimate to check.

7. 51	**8.** 487	**9.** 280	**10.** 3,298	**11.** 7,855
41	564	85	2,408	4,080
+ 85	+ 812	+ 946	+ 6,091	+ 28
177	1,863	1,311	11,797	11,963

12. 43 + 27 + 74 144
13. 205 + 398 + 190 793
14. 147 + 2,490 + 3,580 6,217
15. Find the sum of 2,220 and 540 and 217. 2,977

16. Write this number sentence in another way so it has the same sum. 245 + 678 + 2,503 = 3,426 Answers should show addends in a different sequence.

Mental Math Write >, <, or =. Decide without finding the sum.

17. 59 + 34 + 82 ● 49 + 24 + 72 >
18. 422 + 659 + 394 ● 427 + 664 + 402 <

Problem Solving and Applications

19. Suppose Jonathan prints 35 forms, 148 brochures, and 268 flyers. How many items does he print? 451 items

20. Money Jonathan charged $25 for flyers, $18 for charts, and $22 for banners. What was the total? $65

21. Logic If you use one sheet of paper in an envelope, how many different color combinations can you make? 6 combinations

Mixed Review and Test Prep

Mental Math Find each sum or difference.

22. 6,000 + 5,000 11,000
23. 20,000 − 10,000 10,000
24. 70,000 − 20,000 50,000
25. Find the number that means 3 hundreds, 8 tens, and 6 ones. C

Ⓐ 3,086   Ⓑ 317   Ⓒ 386   Ⓓ not here

Check

Be sure students are using front-end estimation or rounding correctly when they estimate to check their sums.

Error Intervention Ongoing Assessment

Observation Students do not align the digits of the numbers correctly.

How to Help Suggest that students write the exercises on lined paper turned sideways.

Practice

Exercises 12–15 Students may want to rewrite the exercises in vertical form.

For Early Finishers Challenge early finishers to find the sum of the sums for Exercises 7–9. 3,351

③ Close and Assess

Journal

Have students write three rules they would teach to a younger student about the most important things to remember when adding three or four numbers. Encourage them to explain their reasons for selecting these rules.

Quick Check

Number Sense Explain how to use front-end estimation to estimate the sum of 305 + 956 + 322. Then find the sum. Possible answer: Use 300 for 305, 900 for 956, and 300 for 322. Adjust the estimate: 0 + 50 + 20 = 70. Then add to get 1,570.

Skill Find each sum. Use estimation to check your answer.

1. 439 + 97 + 2,634 3,170
2. 3,610 + 823 + 59 4,492
3. 72 + 538 + 7,346 7,956
4. 5,826 + 519 + 688 + 3,752 10,785

Enrichment 3-6

Name _____ Extend Your Thinking 3-6

Patterns in Numbers
Fill in the blanks to complete the pattern. Tell what rule was used to make the pattern.

1. 23, 56, 89, __122__, __155__, __188__
Rule: Add 33.

2. 123, 199, 275, __351__, __427__, __503__
Rule: Add 76.

3. 154, 376, 598, __820__, __1,042__, __1,264__
Rule: Add 222.

4. 12, 24, 48, 96, __192__, __384__, __768__
Rule: Add number to itself, or multiply number by 2.

5. 12, 23, 34, 45, __56__, __67__, __78__
Rule: Add 11.

6. 1, 2, 4, 7, __11__, __16__, __22__
Rule: Add 1, 2, 3, 4, and so on.

7. 25, 22, 32, 29, 39, __36__, __46__, __43__
Rule: Subtract 3, add 10.

8. 10, __23__, __36__, 49, 62, 75, __88__
Rule: Add 13.

Problem Solving 3-6

Name _____ Problem Solving 3-6

Column Addition

History Marco Polo is known for his 4-year journey from Italy to China in the 13th century. He returned to Italy 24 years later where he shared his knowledge of useful Chinese customs. The map below shows the approximate path of Marco Polo's trip.

1. Marco Polo began his journey in Venice. How far did he travel to arrive at Hormuz? The distance from Acre to Hormuz is 3,029 miles. 4,794 miles

2. How far did Marco Polo travel to arrive at Kashgar? 6,853 miles

3. Was the distance from Venice to Hormuz greater or less than the distance from Hormuz to Cambaluc? Explain.
The distance is greater from Hormuz to Cambaluc. 2,059 + 2,824 = 4,883 miles; 1,765 + 3,029 = 4,794 miles; 4,883 mile > 4,794 miles

5. Landon has a coin collection with 789 pennies, 231 nickels, 408 dimes, and 149 quarters. How many coins does he have in his collection? 1,577 coins

6. Patti's school library has 27 encyclopedias, 14 dictionaries, 348 fiction books, and 13 atlases. How many books are in the library? 402 books

Subtracting

At-A-Glance Planning

Objective Subtract 3-digit and 4-digit numbers

Student Book Lesson Materials *Optional* Lesson Enhancement Transparencies 10, 11

Materials for pages 110A and 110B Place-value blocks (30 ones, 20 tens, 10 hundreds, 1 thousand per group), algorithm mat (1 per student), index cards (1 per student)

Subject Connections careers—lifeguard, science—marine animals

Strand Connections using data, algebra readiness, mental math, critical thinking

	Before Lesson	During Lesson	After Lesson
Daily Math			
p. 110A Problem of the Day			
p. 110A Math Routines			
p. 110A Mental Math			
Teaching Options			
p. 110 Student Book Lesson			
p. 110B Another Way to Learn…			
Options for Reaching All Learners			
p. 110B Inclusion			
p. 110B Gifted & Talented			
Technology Options			
p. 110A *Math Workshop*			
Assessment Options			
p. 111 Talk About It			
p. 111 Error Intervention			
p. 113 Portfolio			
p. 113 Quick Check			
Resources			
3-7 Practice			
3-7 Reteaching			
3-7 Enrichment			
3-7 Problem Solving			
3-7 Daily Transparency			

Problem of the Day

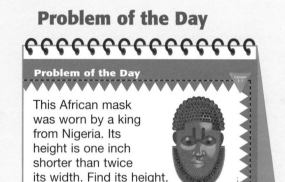

Problem of the Day

This African mask was worn by a king from Nigeria. Its height is one inch shorter than twice its width. Find its height.

4 in.

7 inches

Math Routines

Calendar Have students give the date 6, 16, and 26 days before today.

Time Ask students to tell what time it was 15 minutes ago, 1 hour 15 minutes ago, and 3 hours 15 minutes ago.

Mental Math

Name the number that is 101 greater. Explain your thinking.

66 167   84 185

210 311   279 380

 **Math Workshop**

Have students play the subtraction part of *Bowling for Numbers*. Students will develop their subtraction skills as they work through various levels of problems.

Another Way to [Learn] Lesson 3-7

Use as an alternative or in addition to pages 110–113.

Materials Place-value blocks (30 ones, 20 tens, 10 hundreds, 1 thousand per group)

Learning Style Kinesthetic, Visual

- Have students use place-value blocks to model 453. Tell students to subtract 368 from 453.

- Ask what they need to do to subtract 8 ones from 3 ones. Have them exchange 1 ten for 10 ones from the 5 tens in 453, then subtract 8 from 13, getting 5.

- Have them model subtracting tens, this time exchanging 1 hundred for 10 tens.

- Have students record their work using the usual algorithm. Model it for them first on the overhead if necessary.

- Model how to use estimation to see what kind of difference they should expect.

- Repeat the activity for other problems.

- Assign Check and Practice on Student Book pages 111–113 or *Practice Master 3-7*.

- Assess using the following rubric.

Assessment Rubric
4 **Full Accomplishment** • consistently finds differences of 3-digit and 4-digit numbers
3 **Substantial Accomplishment** • finds differences of most 3-digit and 4-digit numbers
2 **Partial Accomplishment** • finds differences of some 3-digit and 4-digit numbers but does not regroup consistently
1 **Little Accomplishment** • does not find differences of 3-digit and 4-digit numbers consistently

Options for Reaching All Learners

Inclusion

Between the Lines
Use algorithm mats to strengthen subtraction skills.

Materials Algorithm mat (1 per student)

Learning Style Visual

- Prepare a page of algorithm mats for students to use when subtracting 3-digit and 4-digit numbers. Make a copy for each student.

	thousands	hundreds	tens	ones
Regrouped Numbers	4	11 1̸	10 ∅	13
Problem	5̸, −2,	2̸ 6	1̸ 8	3̸ 7
Difference	2,	5	2	6

- Students can use the mats to keep track of regrouping and to keep numbers aligned.

Gifted & Talented

Can You Subtract?
Use a game to strengthen 3-digit and 4-digit subtraction skills.

Materials Index cards (1 per student)

Learning Style Social, Visual

- Write each of these numbers on a separate index card: 797, 44, 949, 196, 1,986, 1,233, 1,180 and 427.

- Write = 753 on the chalkboard.

- Give each student a card and tell students that their job is to pair up with a classmate to create a subtraction problem whose difference is 753.

- Have students find the classmate with a match to their card. Encourage them to use estimation and mental math to help them find the match to their number card.

- Have pairs share their subtraction sentences with the class.

Lesson Organizer

Objective Subtract 3-digit and 4-digit numbers.

Student Materials None

Teacher Materials *Optional* Lesson Enhancement Transparencies 10, 11

Assignment Guide

Basic 19–42, 51, 54, 55, 57, 59–65

Average 26–48, 51, 53–58, 59–65

Enriched 28–65

1 Introduce

Review

Find each sum. In which exercises did you need to regroup? 1, 3, 4

1. 345 + 7,891 8,236

2. 2,217 + 3,450 5,667

3. 689 + 37 726

4. 4,325 + 387 4,712

Build on Prior Knowledge

Discuss with students how addition and subtraction are related. Ideas raised might include: they are opposites; one can be used to check the other. Ask if they think they will ever need to regroup when they subtract.

2 Teach

See Another Way to Learn…on page 110B.

Learn

• Read or have students read the introduction and the word problem. Discuss how they can tell that they need to use subtraction to find the answer. Ask students to explain why regrouped numbers are written over both the place they are subtracting in and the next greater place in the problem. Because both these place values are affected by the regrouping

• You can use Lesson Enhancement Transparencies 10 and 11 to illustrate Examples 1 and 2.

Subtracting

You Will Learn
how to subtract 3-digit and 4-digit numbers

Learn •

Ernest Johnson's classes make a splash! He teaches swimming and works as a lifeguard. In 1996, 358 children signed up for swim classes at Ernest's club. In 1995, 189 children signed up. How many more children signed up in 1996?

Lifeguard Ernest Johnson lives in Homestead, Florida.

Subtract to compare the number of swimmers.

Remember
18 ones is the same as 1 ten, 8 ones.

Example 1

Find 358 − 189.

Step 1	Step 2	Step 3
Subtract the ones. Regroup as needed.	Subtract the tens. Regroup as needed.	Subtract the hundreds.

4 18 Regroup
3 5̸ 8̸ 5 tens as
−1 8 9 4 tens,
    9 10 ones.
	14
	 2 4̸ 18 Regroup
	3̸ 5̸ 8̸ 3 hundreds as
	−1 8 9 2 hundreds,
	  6 9 10 tens.
		14
		 2 4̸ 18
		3̸ 5̸ 8̸
		−1 8 9
		 1 6 9

358 − 189 = 169	**Estimate** to check.	

358 − 189 = 169 is about 400 − 200 = 200

Since 169 is close to 200, the answer is reasonable.

In 1996, 169 more swimmers signed up than in 1995.

Managing Time

Use the first half of the lesson for the Learn and Check exercises. Use the second half of the lesson for selected Practice exercises. Assign the remaining problems for homework.

Example 2

You can subtract greater numbers using the same steps.

Find 4,925 − 1,862.

Step 1	Step 2	Step 3	Step 4
Subtract ones. Regroup as needed.	Subtract tens. Regroup as needed.	Subtract hundreds. Regroup as needed.	Subtract thousands.
4,925 − 1,862 3	8 12 4,9̸2̸5 − 1,862 6 3	8 12 4,9̸2̸5 − 1,862 0 6 3	8 12 4,9̸2̸5 − 1,862 3,0 6 3

4,925 − 1,862 = 3,063 You can use addition to check.

$$\begin{array}{r} 3,063 \\ + 1,862 \\ \hline 4,925 \end{array}$$

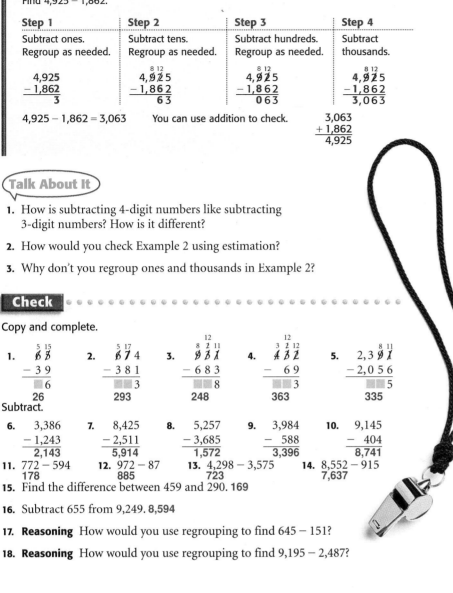

Talk About It

1. How is subtracting 4-digit numbers like subtracting 3-digit numbers? How is it different?

2. How would you check Example 2 using estimation?

3. Why don't you regroup ones and thousands in Example 2?

Check

Copy and complete.

1. 5 15
6̸5̸
− 3 9
■ 6
26

2. 5 17
6̸7̸4
− 3 8 1
■■3
293

3. 12
8 2 11
9̸3̸1̸
− 6 8 3
■■8
248

4. 12
3 2 12
4̸3̸2̸
− 6 9
■■3
363

5. 8 11
2,3̸9̸1̸
− 2,0 5 6
■■5
335

Subtract.

6. 3,386
− 1,243
2,143

7. 8,425
− 2,511
5,914

8. 5,257
− 3,685
1,572

9. 3,984
− 588
3,396

10. 9,145
− 404
8,741

11. 772 − 594 **178**

12. 972 − 87 **885**

13. 4,298 − 3,575 **723**

14. 8,552 − 915 **7,637**

15. Find the difference between 459 and 290. **169**

16. Subtract 655 from 9,249. **8,594**

17. **Reasoning** How would you use regrouping to find 645 − 151?

18. **Reasoning** How would you use regrouping to find 9,195 − 2,487?

Skills Practice Bank, page 561, Set 2 Lesson 3-7 **111**

Talk About It Ongoing Assessment

Listen for students to recognize when regrouping is necessary.

Answers for Talk About It

1 It is the same, except that with 4-digit numbers you may have to regroup thousands.

2 Round each number to the nearest thousand to find 5,000 − 2,000 = 3,000.

3 You can subtract without regrouping. 5 − 2 = 3; 4 thousands − 1 thousand = 3 thousands

Check

Exercises 1–5 Although the ones places of the differences have been completed for students, encourage them to start with the ones place and subtract as usual. This will prevent them from missing any regrouping that is required.

Error Intervention Ongoing Assessment

Observation Students may not record their regrouping correctly.

How to Help As they regroup, be sure students are crossing out the original digit in the number they are regrouping and writing the new digit above that number. Correct alignment may also help prevent confusion.

ANSWERS

17 Regroup 6 hundreds as 5 hundreds and 10 tens. The difference is 494.

18 Regroup 9 tens as 8 tens and 10 ones. Regroup 9 thousands as 8 thousands and 10 hundreds. The difference is 6,708.

Meeting Individual Needs

Learning Style	Teaching Approach
Visual	As you model the algorithm on the overhead or chalkboard, use different colors of markers or chalk for different place values to help students keep track of the numbers. Draw arrows as a number is regrouped and changed.
Kinesthetic	Have students use number cards to build models of the problem. They can trade cards for others to show regrouping.

Chapter 3 • Lesson 3-7 **111**

Practice

Exercises 54–58 Before students work on these exercises, direct their attention to the data on diving depths at the top of page 113. To provide auditory reinforcement of the data, have volunteers read each entry in the order in which it appears.

Exercise 59 Be sure students use the table at the bottom of page 112 as the basis for their responses.

For Early Finishers Challenge early finishers to answer the following: What if the anchor in Exercise 58 fell to the seafloor in an area where the seafloor was 900 feet below the boat? What animals might be used? Fin whale, porpoise, Weddell seal

Practice

Skills and Reasoning

Subtract.

19. 5 7̶2̶ − 5 6 = ▧▧6 **516**
20. 8̶3̶8 − 1 5 5 = ▧▧3 **683**
21. 8̶4̶1̶ − 6 4 2 = ▧▧9 **199**
22. 1,6̶3̶4 − 9 4 3 = ▧▧1 **691**
23. 8,2̶3̶4̶ − 6,3 6 5 = ▧,▧▧9 **1,889**

24. 285 − 162 = **123**
25. 478 − 259 = **219**
26. 851 − 587 = **264**
27. 119 − 54 = **65**
28. 633 − 49 = **584**

29. 6,295 − 2,174 = **4,121**
30. 7,221 − 5,321 = **1,900**
31. 3,936 − 2,878 = **1,058**
32. 1,111 − 674 = **437**
33. 7,462 − 189 = **7,273**

34. 852 − 451 **401**
35. 579 − 498 **81**
36. 265 − 77 **188**
37. 7,839 − 2,842 **4,997**
38. 523 − 56 **467**
39. 7,359 − 367 **6,992**
40. 4,138 − 197 **3,941**
41. 8,347 − 1,358 **6,989**
42. 931 − 78 **853**
43. 532 − 69 **463**
44. 1,634 − 943 **691**
45. 4,254 − 2,965 **1,289**

46. Find the difference between 4,148 and 2,891. **1,257**

47. How would you regroup 3 tens to find the difference between 232 and 128? **Regroup as 2 tens and 10 ones; 232 − 128 = 104**

48. **Algebra Readiness** Find the rule. Complete the table.

In	470	550	630	710
Out	490	570	650	730

Rule: Add 20.

Patterns Copy and complete.

49. 287, 278, 269, ▧, ▧, ▧ **260, 251, 242**
50. 1,092, 1,097, 1,102, ▧, ▧, ▧ **1,107, 1,112, 1,117**

Problem Solving and Applications

Using Data Use the table for 51–53.

51. In which year did the lifeguards make the fewest rescues at this Florida beach? **1995**

52. **Mental Math** What is the difference between the number of rescues in 1992 and the number in 1993? **8**

53. **Calculator** In the four-year period, how many people were rescued at this Florida beach? **974 people**

Florida Beach Rescues	
Year	Number of People Rescued
1992	251
1993	259
1994	260
1995	204

Practice 3-7

Name _____

Practice 3-7

Subtracting

Subtract.

1. 852 − 575 = **277**
2. 321 − 58 = **263**
3. 928 − 749 = **179**
4. 2,414 − 923 = **1,491**
5. 394 − 253 = **141**
6. 267 − 119 = **148**
7. 744 − 498 = **246**
8. 128 − 68 = **60**
9. 4,592 − 1,497 = **3,095**
10. 1,983 − 788 = **1,195**
11. 8,214 − 5,321 = **2,893**
12. 3,465 − 2,877 = **588**

13. 764 − 332 = **432**
14. 672 − 579 = **93**
15. 115 − 46 = **69**
16. 3,723 − 1,687 = **2,036**

17. Find the difference between 5,528 and 2,681. **2,847**

18. How would you regroup 4 tens to find the difference between 341 and 228? **3 tens and 10 ones**

19. Find the rule. Complete the table.

In	260	320	380	440
Out	230	290	350	410

Rule: **Subtract 30.**

Complete.

20. 276, 283, 290, **297**, **304**, **311**
21. 584, 572, 560, **548**, **536**, **524**
22. 2,022; 2,038; 2,054; **2,070**, **2,086**, **2,102**
23. 189, 184, 179, **174**, **169**, **164**

Reteaching 3-7

Name _____

Another Look 3-7

Subtracting

If a digit in the top number is less than the digit in the same place in the bottom number, regrouping is necessary. Sometimes it's helpful to regroup before subtracting.

Find 332 − 145.

Compare the ones. Since 2 < 5, you must regroup.

2 12
33̶2̶
−115

Compare the tens. 2 > 1. Regrouping is not necessary. Subtract the ones, the tens, and the hundreds.

2 12
33̶2̶
−115
217

12 ones − 5 ones = 7 ones
2 tens − 1 ten = 1 ten
3 hundreds − 1 hundred = 2 hundred

Subtract. Regroup before subtracting to help find the difference.

1. 3 11
419
−287
 a. Compare ones. Do you need to regroup? **No**
 b. Compare tens. Do you need to regroup? **Yes**
 c. 419 − 287 = **132**

2. 565 − 178 = **387**
3. 726 − 329 = **397**
4. 487 − 198 = **289**
5. 4,621 − 1,580 = **3,041**
6. 5,644 − 4,589 = **1,055**
7. 8,211 − 1,566 = **6,645**
8. 9,213 − 4,865 = **4,348**
9. 4,329 − 1,202 = **3,127**
10. 6,413 − 2,127 = **4,286**

Problem Solving and SCIENCE

Marine animals get a seal of approval for helping in underwater rescues! Seals, whales, and other marine animals can dive deep into the ocean.

Using Data Use the graph for **54–58**.

54. Which dives deeper, a porpoise or a California sea lion? How much deeper can it dive? **Porpoise; 634 feet**

55. a. Which animal can dive to the greatest depth? The least depth? **Weddell seal; sea otter**
   b. Find the difference between these two diving depths. **1,788 feet**

56. How much deeper can a fin whale dive than a porpoise? **164 feet**

57. How much deeper can a porpoise dive than a sea otter? **804 feet**

58. Critical Thinking Suppose a boat loses its anchor. The ocean floor is about 1,500 feet below the boat. Which animals might the crew use to get the anchor? How can you tell? **Weddell seal; it's the only animal that can dive at least 1,500 feet deep.**

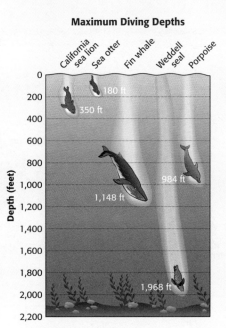

Maximum Diving Depths

California sea lion · Sea otter · Fin whale · Weddell seal · Porpoise

Depth (feet)

180 ft
350 ft
984 ft
1,148 ft
1,968 ft

59. Journal Use the table on page 112. Explain how you would find the difference in the number of rescues between any two years. How would you check your answer?

Mixed Review and Test Prep

Add or subtract.

60. 254 + 68 + 543
   865
61. 1,843 − 1,575
   268
62. 846 + 3,257 + 2,182
   6,285

Write each number in standard form.

63. nine thousand, three hundred eight
   9,308
64. seventy thousand, two hundred
   70,200
65. Over 7 years, the annual rescues at a beach were 191, 203, 410, 203, 198, 325, and 273. What is the mode? **B**

   Ⓐ 273   Ⓑ 203   Ⓒ 258   Ⓓ not here

Skills Practice Bank, page 561, Set 2   Lesson 3-7   113

Science Note

The Weddell seal is the best diver of all the true seals. In addition to diving as deep as 2,000 ft (600 m), it can remain below the surface of the water for more than an hour at a time. Like all seals, the Weddell seal is a carnivore, or meat-eater. The most common foods of seals are fish, squid, and crustaceans.

③ Close and Assess

Portfolio

Have students select two problems from Practice Exercises 19–45 for their portfolios. They should solve each problem, showing all work.

Quick Check

Number Sense Estimate to tell if a difference will be in thousands, hundreds, or tens.

1. 827 − 319 Hundreds
2. 5,595 − 2,467 Thousands
3. 3,345 − 3,279 Tens
4. 8,028 − 7,397 Hundreds

Skill Find each difference.

1. 954 − 528 426
2. 658 − 409 249
3. 3,743 − 2,959 784
4. 8,022 − 6,586 1,436

Resources

Technology Master 8

ANSWERS

59 Answers should include subtracting the lesser number from the greater number and using addition to check the answer.

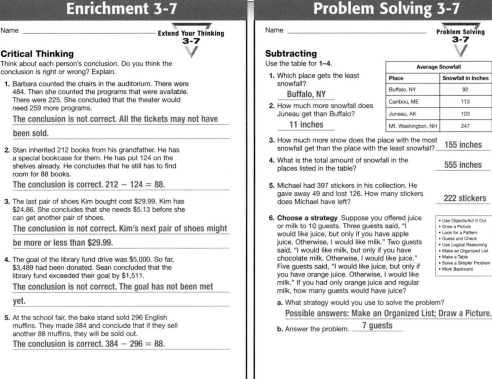

Enrichment 3-7

Name _____

Extend Your Thinking 3-7

Critical Thinking
Think about each person's conclusion. Do you think the conclusion is right or wrong? Explain.

1. Barbara counted the chairs in the auditorium. There were 484. Then she counted the programs that were available. There were 225. She concluded that the theater would need 259 more programs.
The conclusion is not correct. All the tickets may not have been sold.

2. Stan inherited 212 books from his grandfather. He has a special bookcase for them. He has put 124 on the shelves already. He concludes that he still has to find room for 88 books.
The conclusion is correct. 212 − 124 = 88.

3. The last pair of shoes Kim bought cost $29.99. Kim has $24.86. She concludes that she needs $5.13 before she can get another pair of shoes.
The conclusion is not correct. Kim's next pair of shoes might be more or less than $29.99.

4. The goal of the library fund drive was $5,000. So far, $3,489 had been donated. Sean concluded that the library fund exceeded their goal by $1,511.
The conclusion is not correct. The goal has not been met yet.

5. At the school fair, the bake stand sold 296 English muffins. They made 384 and conclude that if they sell another 88 muffins, they will be sold out.
The conclusion is correct. 384 − 296 = 88.

Problem Solving 3-7

Name _____

Problem Solving 3-7

Subtracting
Use the table for **1–4**.

Average Snowfall	
Place	Snowfall in Inches
Buffalo, NY	92
Caribou, ME	113
Juneau, AK	103
Mt. Washington, NH	247

1. Which place gets the least snowfall?
   Buffalo, NY

2. How much more snowfall does Juneau get than Buffalo?
   11 inches

3. How much more snow does the place with the most snowfall get than the place with the least snowfall? **155 inches**

4. What is the total amount of snowfall in the places listed in the table? **555 inches**

5. Michael had 397 stickers in his collection. He gave away 49 and lost 126. How many stickers does Michael have left? **222 stickers**

6. Choose a strategy Suppose you offered juice or milk to 10 guests. Three guests said, "I would like juice, but only if you have apple juice. Otherwise, I would like milk." Two guests said, "I would like milk, but only if you have chocolate milk. Otherwise, I would like juice." Five guests said, "I would like juice, but only if you have orange juice. Otherwise, I would like milk." If you had only orange juice and regular milk, how many guests would have juice?

   • Use Objects/Act It Out
   • Draw a Picture
   • Look for a Pattern
   • Guess and Check
   • Use Logical Reasoning
   • Make an Organized List
   • Make a Table
   • Solve a Simpler Problem
   • Work Backward

   a. What strategy would you use to solve the problem?
   Possible answers: Make an Organized List; Draw a Picture.

   b. Answer the problem. **7 guests**

Chapter 3 • Lesson 3-7   **113**

Subtracting with Middle Zeros

At-A-Glance Planning

Lesson Planning Checklist

Objective Subtract from numbers with zeros.

Student Book Lesson Materials *Optional* Lesson Enhancement Transparency 12

Materials for pages 114A and 114B Teaching Tool Transparency 3 (9-Digit Place-Value Chart), overhead place-value blocks, place-value blocks (1 thousand, 10 hundreds, 10 tens, 15 ones per group), classroom maps of the United States and world (or globe)

Subject Connections music—Interlochen Arts Camp, science—mockingbirds

Strand Connections using data, algebra readiness

	Before Lesson	During Lesson	After Lesson
Daily Math			
p. 114A Problem of the Day			
p. 114A Math Routines			
p. 114A Mental Math			
Teaching Options			
p. 114 Student Book Lesson			
p. 114B Another Way to Learn…			
Options for Reaching All Learners			
p. 114B Inclusion			
p. 114B Language Development			
Technology Options			
p. 114 Interactive CD-ROM Lesson 3			
Subject Connections			
p. 114A Geography Connection			
Assessment Options			
p. 114 Talk About It			
p. 115 Error Intervention			
p. 115 Interview			
p. 115 Quick Check			
Resources			
3-8 Practice			
3-8 Reteaching			
3-8 Enrichment			
3-8 Problem Solving			
3-8 Daily Transparency			

Problem of the Day

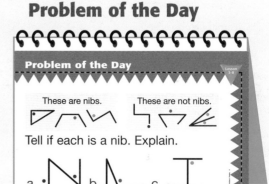

a. No, too many dots
b. Yes, 3 line segments and a dot in a corner
c. No, too many dots

Math Routines

Money Ask students to name the amount of money they could subtract from $5.00 and have $1.50 left. How much to have $2.00 left? $3.50; $3.00

Calendar Have students find the number of days left in the school year. Then have them subtract that number from the total number of school days.

Mental Math

Name the number that is 199 greater. Explain your thinking.

304 503	188 387
77 276	239 438

Geography Connection

Have a map of the United States available. Have students find and identify the states mentioned in the bar graph on page 115.

- Challenge students to use the map scale to estimate how far each state is from Michigan, the home of the arts camp.

- They should also locate their own state and estimate its distance from Michigan.

Another Way to **Learn** Lesson 3-8

Use as an alternative or in addition to pages 114 and 115.

Materials Teaching Tool Transparency 3 (9-Digit Place-Value Chart), overhead place-value blocks

Learning Style Visual, Kinesthetic

- Model the number 3,000 using the place-value chart. Ask students how many tens are in 3,000. Give students a moment to think, then cover the last zero in the number to illustrate the answer.

- Repeat the process of identifying the number of tens in other numbers, such as 4,002; 2,045; and 21,027.

- Ask students if they could find 3,005 − 216 without regrouping. Then use overhead place-value blocks to model the subtraction.

- Work through the algorithm on a place-value chart. Discuss with students the relationship of the models to the algorithm.

- Assign Check and Practice on Student Book page 115 or *Practice Master 3-8*.

- Assess using the following rubric.

Options for Reaching All Learners

Inclusion

One Step at a Time
Use a simplified regrouping method to review subtracting across zeros.

Materials Place-value blocks (1 thousand, 10 hundreds, 10 tens, 15 ones per group)

Learning Style Visual, Kinesthetic

Students who struggle with regrouping can use a one-step-at-a-time method to subtract across zeros.

- Using the example 1,003 − 256, demonstrate for students how they can determine if and at what point they need to regroup.

- Help students see that they can regroup 1 thousand to 10 hundreds; regroup 1 of those hundreds as 10 tens; then regroup 1 of those tens as 10 ones. The 10 ones should be added to the 3 ones already in the ones place.

$$\begin{array}{r} 9\,9 \\ \cancel{10}\cancel{10}13 \\ \cancel{1,003} \\ -\ \ 256 \end{array}$$

Language Development

New Surroundings
Use maps to help with pronunciations of state and country names.

Materials Classroom maps of the United States and world (or globe)

Learning Style Visual

- Help students correctly locate on the map and pronounce the names of states where they or their parents were born. Fluent speakers within a group can offer further practice and help to other students.

- Encourage students to pronounce the names of states where they have friends or relatives.

- Continue by having students who were born in another country locate that country on the world map or globe and teach classmates how to pronounce the country's name.

Lesson Organizer

Objective Subtract from numbers with zeros.

Student Materials None

Teacher Materials *Optional* Lesson Enhancement Transparency 12

Assignment Guide

Basic 7–20, 22, 26–29

Average 9–21, 23, 25–29

Enriched 11–29

1 Introduce

Review

Subtract on a thousand chart. Explain your method.

1. 340 − 50 290

2. 880 − 30 850

3. 600 − 140 460

counted back 5 tens; counted back 3 tens; counted back 14 tens

Build on Prior Knowledge

On the chalkboard, show the calculation and notation for regrouping when subtracting from a number with a zero in the ones place, such as those above. Emphasize the necessary regrouping of hundreds as tens. Encourage students to guide you through the steps.

2 Teach

See Another Way to Learn…on page 114B.

Interactive CD-ROM Lesson 3 includes material in this lesson.

Learn

On the overhead, model the two subtraction methods shown on page 114 or use Lesson Enhancement Transparency 12 to illustrate subtracting with middle zeros.

Talk About It) Ongoing Assessment

Look for students to apply the basic concept of regrouping.

Answer for Talk About It

Possible answer: Jennifer regrouped 2,001 as 1 thousand, 9 hundreds, 9 tens, and 11 ones. Philippa regrouped 2,001 as 199 tens and 11 ones.

Subtracting with Middle Zeros

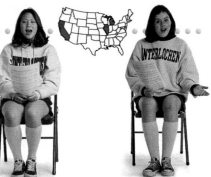

You Will Learn
how to subtract from a number that has zeros

Math Tip
2,000 is the same as 199 tens, 1 ten.

Learn

Teachers rise and shine in harmony with their students at Interlochen Arts Camp. In 1996, music, art, and dance teachers worked with 2,001 students. If 148 of these students were from other countries, how many came from the United States?

Jennifer is from Madera, California. Philippa is from Champaign, Illinois. Both studied singing at Interlochen Arts Camp in Michigan.

Jennifer and Philippa solved the problem in different ways.

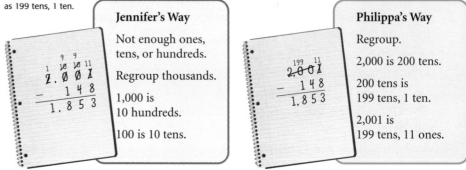

Jennifer's Way

Not enough ones, tens, or hundreds.

Regroup thousands.

1,000 is 10 hundreds.

100 is 10 tens.

Philippa's Way

Regroup.

2,000 is 200 tens.

200 tens is 199 tens, 1 ten.

2,001 is 199 tens, 11 ones.

1,853 students were from the United States.

Other Examples

A.
```
   4 10 14
   5 0 4
 − 1 8 7
   3 1 7
```
B.
```
   2   9 11
   3, 0 2 1
 − 2, 4 3 2
      5 8 9
```
C.
```
   3   9 10
   4, 0 0 6
 − 1, 2 4 4
   2, 7 6 2
```
D.
```
   5   9 9 17
   6, 0 0 7
 − 2, 7 5 8
   3, 2 4 9
```

(Talk About It)

How did Jennifer and Philippa regroup differently?

Name _____

Practice
3-8

Subtracting with Middle Zeros

Find each difference.

1. 500 − 324 **176**	**2.** 7,000 − 4,968 **2,032**	**3.** 308 − 136 **172**	**4.** 4,062 − 1,292 **2,770**
5. 6,006 − 723 **5,283**	**6.** 3,300 − 1,551 **1,749**	**7.** 5,900 − 899 **5,001**	**8.** 4,003 − 423 **3,580**
9. 7,003 − 298 **6,705**	**10.** 6,010 − 3,478 **2,532**	**11.** 4,000 − 298 **3,702**	**12.** 1,303 − 797 **506**

13. 8,000 − 4,449 = __3,551__

14. 2,000 − 376 = __1,624__

15. 601 − 208 = __393__

16. 7,040 − 2,634 = __4,406__

17. 907 − 359 = __548__

18. 3,005 − 2,228 = __777__

19. 8,070 − 688 = __7,382__

20. 5,800 − 4,390 = __1,410__

21. What number is 2,438 less than 6,108? __3,670__

22. What number is 146 less than 2,301? __2,155__

23. What number is 329 less than 5,000? __4,671__

24. How could thinking about 90 tens help you find 1,901 − 297?
90 tens can be regrouped as 89 tens plus 1 ten.

25. How could thinking about 200 tens help you find 2,004 − 1,559?
200 tens can be regrouped as 199 tens plus 1 ten.

Name _____

Another Look
3-8

Subtracting with Middle Zeros

Sometimes it's helpful to regroup before subtracting.

Find 1,003 − 317.

Compare the ones. Since 3 < 7, you must regroup.

Look for the first non-zero digit to the left of the 3. It is the 1 in the thousands place. One thousand is the same as 100 tens.

You can regroup 100 tens as 99 tens and 10 ones.

```
    99  13
  1,0 0 3
 − 3 1 7
```

Subtract the ones, the tens, and the hundreds.

```
    99  13
  1,0 0 3      13 ones − 7 ones = 6 ones
 − 3 1 7       9 tens − 1 ten = 8 tens
    6 8 6      9 hundreds − 3 hundreds = 6 hundreds
```

Find each difference.

1. 2,005 − 836

  a. Compare the ones. Since 5 < 6, you must regroup. The first non-zero digit to the left of the 5 is __2__.

  b. 2 thousands is the same as __200__ tens.

  c. You can regroup __200__ tens as __199__ tens and __10__ ones.

  d. 2,005 − 836 = __1,169__

2. 800 − 452

  a. Compare the ones. Do you need to regroup? __Yes__

  b. 800 − 452 = __348__

3. 3,008 − 1,589 = __1,419__   **4.** 8,006 − 927 = __7,079__

Find each difference.

1.	2.	3.	4.	5.
700	2,000	805	4,049	3,003
− 382	− 1,248	− 622	− 1,917	− 430
318	752	183	2,132	2,573

6. **Reasoning** How would you regroup to find 602 − 143? Solve.
   Regroup 602 as 59 tens and 12 ones. 602 − 143 = 459.

Practice ○

Skills and Reasoning

Find each difference.

7.	8.	9.	10.	11.
600	8,000	409	3,051	7,004
− 418	− 3,857	− 137	− 1,541	− 373
182	4,143	272	1,510	6,631

12. 2,100 − 1,698   13. 4,800 − 779   14. 6,008 − 338   15. 5,000 − 3,553
    402   4,021   5,670   1,447
16. 804 − 358   17. 4,006 − 3,329   18. 7,060 − 785   19. 4,900 − 3,250
    446   677   6,275   1,650
20. What number is 424 less than 1,000? 576

21. How could thinking about 300 tens help you find 3,005 − 1,827?

> You need to regroup in the ones, tens, and hundreds. 300 tens can be regrouped as 299 tens plus 1 ten. 3,005 − 1,827 = 1,178.

Problem Solving and Applications

Using Data Use the bar graph for **22–24.**

22. From which state did most students come? **Michigan**
23. How many more students came from Michigan than Indiana? **300 students**
24. **Write Your Own Problem** Use the data to write your own problem. Problems should relate to the number of students from various states.
25. **Science** Mockingbirds can sing about 200 songs. That's about 195 more songs than other birds sing. About how many songs do other birds sing? **About 5 songs**

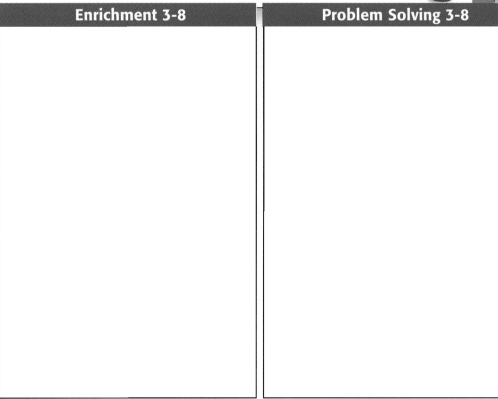

Home States of Arts Camp Students

Number of Students — Home States (Florida, Illinois, Indiana, Michigan, New York, Ohio)

Mixed Review and Test Prep

Algebra Readiness Find each missing number.

26. 629 − 380 = n **249**   27. 141 − 37 = n **104**   28. 1,588 − 1,003 = n **585**

29. Two hundred thousand, four is the word name for what number? **C**
   Ⓐ 200,400,000   Ⓑ 20,000,004   Ⓒ 200,004   Ⓓ 2,004

Skills Practice Bank, page 561, Set 3   Lesson 3-8   **115**

PRACTICE AND APPLY

Enrichment 3-8	Problem Solving 3-8

Check ○ ○ ○ ○ ○ ○ ○ ○ ○ ○ ○ ○ ○ ○ ○ ○ ○ ○ ○

Ask students which exercises will not need regrouping in all places. Exercises 3, 4, 5

Error Intervention Ongoing Assessment

Observation Students may have difficulty regrouping thousands into tens, or renaming the answer as thousands.

How to Help Students might benefit from learning to regroup one place at a time, rather than across all the zeros at once.

Practice ○ ○ ○ ○ ○ ○ ○ ○ ○ ○ ○ ○ ○ ○ ○ ○ ○ ○ ○

Remind students to look at each exercise carefully and decide how they need to regroup before proceeding.

For Early Finishers Challenge early finishers to subtract the answer to Exercise 12 from the answer to Exercise 13. 3,619

③ Close and Assess

Interview

Ask individual students to demonstrate and explain the method they use to subtract across zeros. Allow students to use place-value charts or blocks if necessary.

Quick Check

Number Sense Explain how to use regrouping to subtract 3,003 − 295. Possible answer: Regroup 300 tens as 299 tens and 13 ones; then subtract.

Skill Subtract.

1. 4,000 − 266 3,734
2. 5,002 − 419 4,583
3. 4,009 − 1,242 2,767

Chapter 3
Practice Game

Students will strengthen addition and subtraction skills as they play the practice game.

Learning Style Visual, Kinesthetic

Student Materials Digit cards 0–9 (2 sets per pair) *optional Assessment Sourcebook 10* (How We Worked in Our Group)

Preparation

Make two sets of digit cards, numbered 0–9, for each pair of students.

How to Play

Provide each pair with two sets of digit cards. Help students read the game rules and make sure they understand the object of the game. Play two demonstration rounds if necessary.

Zeroing in on Addition and Subtraction

Players
2 or more players

Materials
2 sets of digit cards

0 1 2 3 4
5 6 7 8 9
0 1 2 3 4
5 6 7 8 9

Object
The object of the game is to estimate a sum as close to the exact answer as possible.

How to Play

1. Each player draws an addition grid like this.

2. Each player shuffles a set of digit cards and places them face down. Each player then takes three cards, puts them in a row to make a three-digit number, and records the number on the grid.

Math Center Option

As an alternative, post the rules in the math center along with two envelopes of digit cards. Encourage students to play and discuss the results and how their strategies might affect the game.

3 Each player draws three more cards, makes a three-digit number in the second row, and records it on the grid.

4 Players estimate the sum to the nearest hundred. Then they find the actual sum.

5 Now players find the difference between the estimate and the sum.

Chad's Cards

Estimate: 300 [2] [8] [1]
+ 300 + [3] [4] [9]
_____ _____
600 6 3 0

6 Each player records the difference as his or her score. The player with the lowest score wins.

630 Sum
− 600 Estimate
_____
30 Difference

7 Play five or more games. Look for winning strategies.

Zeroing in on Addition and Subtraction Game **117**

(**Talk About It**)

1. What winning strategies did you find?

2. Suppose you have 247 in the first row and then pick 6, 3, and 1. What number can you make to get the lowest score? Explain.

More Ways to Play

■ Play the game using subtraction. Each player takes six cards and places them anywhere in a subtraction grid.

■ Play again. Use a grid like this.

+ [ ][ ][ ]

Reasoning

1. Suppose the number in the top row of an addition grid is 207. The cards you draw for the second row are 3, 9, and 4. What number should you make? Explain.

2. Suppose your grid looks like this. Which cards would be best to get? Explain.

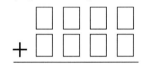

+ [7][ ][2]

1. 493; Estimate: 200 + 500 = 700; Sum: 207 + 493 = 700; Score = 0
2. Possible answer: 1, 5, 8; Arrange as 148 and 752; Estimate: 100 + 800 = 900; Sum: 148 + 752 = 900; Score = 0

(**Talk About It**) **Ongoing Assessment**

Listen for students who understand that sums ending in 0 or 00 will more closely match their estimates, resulting in a better score.

Possible Answers for Talk About It

1 Possible answer: Arrange the digits so the sum has 0 in the tens and 0 in the ones place.

2 361; 247 + 361 = 608; 608 − 600 = 8

More Ways to Play

When playing the game with subtraction, allow students to select all six digits in one drawing and then arrange the digits as they wish over the entire grid. This should prevent the possibility of a negative difference.

Reasoning

Possible Answers

1 493; Estimate: 200 + 500 = 700; Sum: 207 + 493 = 700; Score = 0

2 Possible answer: 1, 5, 8; Arrange as 148 and 752; Estimate: 100 + 800 = 900; Sum: 148 + 752 = 900; Score = 0

Cooperative Learning

Before beginning the game, distribute *Assessment Sourcebook 10* (How We Worked in Our Group) and have students fill it out for the skill Encourage and Respect Others. Review the characteristics of this skill. Invite students to judge themselves on the skill as they work together.

Analyze Word Problems: Multiple-Step Problems

At-A-Glance Planning

Objective Solve multiple-step problems.

Student Book Lesson Materials None

Materials for pages 118A and 119B Large bag of beans (1 handful per student)

Subject Connections careers—Internet publishing, media

Strand Connections using data, collecting data, time

	Before Lesson	During Lesson	After Lesson
Daily Math			
p. 118A Problem of the Day			
p. 118A Math Routines			
p. 118A Mental Math			
Teaching Options			
p. 118 Student Book Lesson			
p. 118B Another Way to Learn…			
Options for Reaching All Learners			
p. 118B Inclusion			
p. 118B Language Development			
Subject Connections			
p. 118A Career Connection			
Assessment Options			
p. 118 Talk About It			
p. 119 Quick Check			
Resources			
3-9 Practice			
3-9 Reteaching			
3-9 Enrichment			
3-9 Problem Solving			
3-9 Daily Transparency			

Problem of the Day

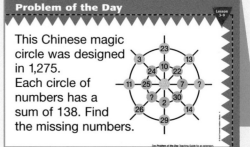

This Chinese magic circle was designed in 1,275. Each circle of numbers has a sum of 138. Find the missing numbers.

Inner circle: 18, Outer circle: 19

Math Routines

Money Name an item and a dollar amount it might cost. Then ask the class to find how much they would have to save each week for 4 weeks to buy it.

Time Name the time that is the end of the school day. Ask students to find the length of time remaining until then. Then ask them to find out how many 45-minute lessons they can do by then.

Mental Math

Name the number that is **995** greater. Explain your thinking.

455	701	568	96
1,450	1,696	1,563	1,091

Career Connection

Have students choose a topic to research, then mock up a Web page to share information with classmates. Students' pages can be done on sheets of poster paper and can incorporate text and art done by hand, printed out from computer software, or cut out of newspapers or magazines. Suggest that students invent links to other sites that feature related information.

Another Way to **Learn** Lesson 3-9

Use as an alternative or in addition to pages 118 and 119.

Materials Large bag of beans (1 handful per student)

Learning Style Visual, Kinesthetic, Logical

- Prepare a large bag of beans, counters, or other small objects. Have students form four teams—Team A, Team B, Team C, and Team D. Each student should reach into the bag and take a handful of beans.

- Tell students you want to find the difference between the number of beans the A and B Teams have and the number of beans the C and D Teams have.

- Have students discuss as a class how to solve the problem. They should write a step-by-step plan on the chalkboard for finding the difference.

- Ask students to follow their plan and solve the problem. Students should check their answers by estimating.

- Discuss the plan and solution. Did the plan recognize that it takes more than one operation to solve the problem? Which operations were involved? Was the plan logical?

- Pose other problems of a similar nature and repeat the activity until students have established plans that work consistently.

- Assign Check and Practice on Student Book page 119 or *Practice Master 3-9*.

Assessment Rubric
4 Full Accomplishment • consistently solves multiple-step problems
3 Substantial Accomplishment • with prompting, solves multiple-step problems
2 Partial Accomplishment • solves some multiple-step problems
1 Little Accomplishment • does not consistently set up or solve multiple-step problems

Options for Reaching All Learners

Inclusion

Step by Step

Use a graphic organizer to organize calculations in multiple-step problems.

Learning Style Visual, Logical

Prepare a graphic organizer to help students keep track of what they are being asked and to help organize their thoughts when solving multiple-step problems.

To find the answer, I need to know _____

In Step 1, I need to find _____

In Step 2, I need to find _____

The answer is _____

Language Development

Understand Vocabulary

Use partner reading to understand meaning in context.

Learning Style Social, Verbal

- Pair highly verbal students with those less proficient in language, vocabulary, or reading skills. Have them take turns reading the problems aloud to each other. The listener should paraphrase what she or he heard.

- Circulate through the room as students work together and listen for those having difficulty with the language, wording, or certain phrases.

- You may wish to give students photocopies of page 119 so that they can underline information that gave them clues about the steps and/or operations to use.

Lesson Organizer

Objective Solve multiple-step problems.

Suggested Grouping 2 to 4

Student Materials None

Assignment Guide

Basic 3–8

Average 4–9

Enriched 5–10

1 Introduce

Review

Find each answer.

1. Add 2 + 7. Then subtract 3. 6
2. Add 23 + 34. Then subtract 8. 49
3. Subtract 32 from 84. Then add 4. 56

Build on Prior Knowledge

Ask students how many steps they had to take to find each answer above. 2

Ask what operations they used. 1. addition, subtraction 2. addition, subtraction 3. subtraction, addition

2 Teach

See Another Way to Learn…on page 118B.

Learn ● ● ● ● ● ● ● ● ● ● ● ● ● ● ● ● ● ● ●

Have a volunteer read the introduction and problem and guide students through each step in order.

Reading Assist Find Main Idea with Supporting Details

- Students may benefit from reading the question (the last sentence of the first paragraph) first to find the main idea, or what they are expected to find. Then students can read the entire paragraph, to find the details they need to answer the question.

(Talk About It) Ongoing Assessment

Listen for students to indicate the need to perform the steps in a logical order.

Answer for Talk About It

You had to find the total hits in North America, and then compare it with the number of hits from Australia.

Analyze Word Problems: Multiple-Step Problems

You Will Learn
how to solve problems that have more than one step

Learn ● ● ● ● ● ● ● ● ● ● ● ● ● ● ● ● ● ●

Young writers can publish their stories on the World Wide Web. Look at the number of hits on this publishing website. How many more hits came from North America than Australia?

Solve this problem one step at a time.

Work Together

▶ **Understand**	What do you know? ❶
❶ **How many hits from individual countries**	What do you need to find out? The difference between total hits from North America and from Australia
▶ **Plan**	How can you find out? Find the total hits from North America.
	What's the next step? Compare the total to hits from Australia.

▶ **Solve**

Step 1: Add to find the number of hits from North America.

Canada	2,485
Mexico	10
United States	+ 1,199
	3,694

Math Tip
A *hit* is a visit to a website.

Step 2: Subtract to compare the hits from North America and Australia.

North America	3,694
Australia	− 2,465
	1,229

What's the answer? The difference is 1,229 hits.

▶ **Look Back**

Does your answer make sense? How do you know?

You can use addition to check the answer: 1,229 + 2,465 = 3,694. Or estimate: 3,700 − 2,500 = 1,200.

(Talk About It)

Since 1,229 is close to 1,200, the answer is reasonable.

Why did this problem have to be solved in two steps?

Name _____

Practice 3-9

Analyze Word Problems: Multiple-Step Problems

1. Joan wrote a science paper with 246 words. When she edited the story, she crossed out 38 words and added 77 new words.

   a. How long was the paper after she crossed out words?
   208 words

   b. How long was the paper after she added new words?
   285 words

2. How many more people attended the museum on Sunday than on Monday and Tuesday combined?
   27 people

City Museum Attendance	
Day	Number of People
Sunday	986
Monday	462
Tuesday	497
Wednesday	315
Thursday	678
Friday	359

3. During a different week, 37 more people went to the museum on Tuesday than on the Tuesday in the table. On Wednesday of that week 113 fewer people showed up than on Tuesday of that week. How many people were there on Wednesday?
   421

4. Lawrence can spend one hour researching in the library to write a paper. He spends 25 minutes gathering books and then 31 minutes writing notes. How much time does he have left?
   4 minutes

5. Mario reads an e-mail note from his brother. It takes him 76 seconds to sign on, 24 seconds to find the note, and 33 seconds to read it. Did Mario use the computer for more than 2 minutes? Explain.
   Yes; 76 + 24 + 33 = 133 seconds; 133 seconds > 120

Name _____

Another Look 3-9

Analyze Word Problems: Multiple-Step Problems

Crystal has 436 stamps in her stamp collection. Daryl has 213 stamps in his collection. Kathie has 221 stamps in her collection. Who has more stamps, Kathie and Daryl together or Crystal?

Find the total number of stamps that Kathie and Daryl have together.

```
  2 2 1   (Kathie's stamps)
+ 2 1 3   (Daryl's stamps)
  4 3 4   (Kathie and Daryl's total)
```

Compare the total to Crystal's number of stamps.

434 stamps (Kathie and Daryl) < 436 stamps (Crystal)

Crystal has more stamps than Kathie and Daryl together.

1. There are 346 students in the third grade. There are 662 students in fourth grade and 309 students in fifth grade. How many more students are there in the fourth grade than in the third and fifth grades combined?

   a. How many students are in the third and fifth grades combined?
   655 students

   b. How many students are in the fourth grade?
   662 students

   c. What is the difference between the number of fourth grade students and the number of students in the third and fifth grades?
   7 students

2. On Thursday, 113 people attended the school play. On Friday, 152 people attended. On Saturday, 270 people attended. Did more people see the play on Saturday or on Thursday and Friday combined?
   Saturday

1. Gayle's first draft of a story had 212 words. When she edited the story, she crossed out 24 words and added 47 new ones.

   a. How long was the story after she crossed out words?
   188 words
   b. How long was the story when she added new words?
   235 words

2. The publishing website got 795 hits from England. How many more hits came from Oceania than England? **2,134 hits**

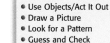

Problem Solving Practice •

GPS 3. Kyle's first published story is 117 words long. His second story is 42 words longer. His third story is 56 words shorter than his second story. How long is his third story? **103 words**

4. Emil uses a computer for 1 hour. He spends 26 minutes writing a story and 21 minutes correcting it. How much time does he have left? **13 minutes**

5. It takes Maurice 87 seconds to log on, 24 seconds to find an e-mail note, and 92 seconds to read it. Does this take more than 3 minutes? Explain.
Yes; Add 87 + 24 + 92 seconds to get 203 seconds; 203 seconds > 180 seconds (3 minutes)

Using Data Use the table for **6–8**.

6. How much more time is spent watching TV than reading books? **1,425 hours**

7. How much less time do people spend reading in general than watching TV? **1,175 hours**

8. **What If** You are a journalist. Would you have a greater audience if you worked for cable TV or for newspapers and magazines? Explain. **Cable TV; Audiences spend 201 more hours/person/year.**

9. **Collecting Data** Keep a log to find out how much time you spend with different media in a week. Share your data. Make a bar graph of class data.
Answers should include a student log and bar graph of class data.

10. **Time** Suppose you sign up for a one-day World Wide Web class. The class includes three lessons, each 1 hour long. There is a 2-hour practice session, after a 30-minute lunch break. The class ends at 3:30 P.M.

    a. What time did the class begin? **10:00 A.M.**

    b. What strategies did you use to solve this problem? **Possible answers: using objects (a clock), using logical reasoning, or working backward.**

Skills Practice Bank, page 561, Set 6   Lesson 3-9   **119**

Problem Solving Strategies
- Use Objects/Act It Out
- Draw a Picture
- Look for a Pattern
- Guess and Check
- Use Logical Reasoning
- Make an Organized List
- Make a Table
- Solve a Simpler Problem
- Work Backward

Choose a Tool

Annual Media Use	
Media	**Hours Per Person**
Network TV	925
Independent TV	149
Cable TV	451
Recorded music	274
Newspapers	166
Magazines	84
Books	100

PROBLEM SOLVING PRACTICE

You may wish to have students identify the operations required by each exercise before solving.

Practice • • • • • • • • • • • • • • • • • •

If students have difficulty solving some of the problems, suggest they look at the list of Problem Solving Strategies to find a way to approach each problem.

For Early Finishers Challenge early finishers to find the total number of hits on the Web site shown on page 118 and the total number of hours spent per person using all the media listed in the table on page 119. 6,623; 2,149

③ Close and Assess

Have students discuss how to solve multiple-step problems. Write students' ideas on the chalkboard. Encourage students to help organize their ideas in a logical order.

Quick Check

Solve the following problem. Show your work.

Jack had 9 apples. Bruce gave him 6 more. Jack then gave 12 apples to Yvonne. How many apples did Jack have in the end?
9 + 6 = 15; 15 − 12 = 3

Enrichment 3-9

Name _____   **Extend Your Thinking 3-9**

Decision Making
You and your brother have $25 to spend on a birthday gift for your mom. You have a choice of three gifts.

Gift A: a pair of earrings for $14.99 and a box of candy for $8.95

Gift B: a bird feeder for $18.95 and some birdseed for $4.50

Gift C: a potted plant for $11.99, a vase for $8.50, and cut flowers for $4.50

Extra information: You will make your own card and wrapping paper. Sales tax is included.

1. List the gifts from most expensive to least expensive. Include the total cost of each.
   Gift C ($24.99), Gift A ($23.94), Gift B ($23.45)

2. How much money would you have left over if you bought
   a. Gift A? **$1.06**
   b. Gift B? **$1.55**
   c. Gift C? **$0.01**

3. How much would Gift C cost if you didn't buy the vase? **$16.49**

4. Describe the strong and weak points of each gift choice.
   Gift A: **Answers will vary. Look for responses that consider**
   Gift B: **what the recipient would like.**
   Gift C: _____

5. Which gift would you choose? Explain your reasoning.
   Answers will vary.

6. If you had enough money for two gift choices, which two would you choose? Why?
   Answers will vary.

Problem Solving 3-9

Name _____   **Guided Problem Solving 3-9**

GPS PROBLEM 3, STUDENT PAGE 119

Kyle's first published story is 117 words long. His second story is 42 words longer. His third story is 56 words shorter than his second story. How long is his third story?

— **Understand** —
1. How long is Kyle's first story? **117 words**
2. What do you need to know to answer the question?
   The length of the second story and the third story

— **Plan** —
3. a. How will you find the length of the second story? Explain.
   Add 42 to 117 because the second story is 42 words longer than the first story.
   b. Write the number sentence. **117 + 42 = 159**
4. a. How will you find the length of the third story? Explain.
   Subtract 56 from 159 because the third story is 56 words shorter than the second story.
   b. Write the number sentence. **159 − 56 = 103**

— **Solve** —
5. How long is Kyle's second story? **159 words**
6. How long is Kyle's third story? **103 words**

— **Look Back** —
6. What strategy could you use to check your answer?
   Possible answer: Work Backward

SOLVE ANOTHER PROBLEM

Keesha's first draft of a story was 223 words long. When she edited the story, she crossed out 51 words and added 74 new ones. How long was the edited story? **246 words**

Chapter 3 • Lesson 3-9   **119**

Using Mental Math

At-A-Glance Planning

Lesson Planning Checklist

Objective Add and subtract numbers mentally.

Student Book Lesson Materials None

Materials for pages 120A and 120B Calculators

Subject Connections careers—circus performer; science—muscles, hyenas

Strand Connections mental math, algebra readiness, measurement, collecting data

	Before Lesson	During Lesson	After Lesson
Daily Math			
p. 120A Problem of the Day			
p. 120A Math Routines			
p. 120A Mental Math			
Teaching Options			
p. 120 Student Book Lesson			
p. 120B Another Way to Learn…			
Options for Reaching All Learners			
p. 120B Language Development			
p. 120B Inclusion			
Technology Options			
p. 120A Calculator Connection			
Assessment Options			
p. 120 Talk About It			
p. 121 Error Intervention			
p. 121 Interview			
p. 121 Quick Check			
Resources			
3-10 Practice			
3-10 Reteaching			
3-10 Enrichment			
3-10 Problem Solving			
3-10 Daily Transparency			

Problem of the Day

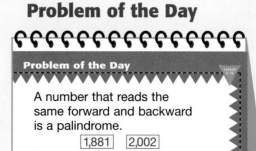

Problem of the Day

A number that reads the same forward and backward is a palindrome.

| 1,881 | | 2,002 |

Find the palindromes between 5,000 and 7,000. What other patterns do you notice?

Some possible answers: 5,005; 5,115; 5,225; 5,335; 5,445; 5,555; 5,665. First and last digits same. Middle 2 digits same.

Math Routines

Time Name several times during the school day. Then ask students to name the time a 45-minute lesson would have to begin in order to end at that time.

Calendar Name a date in the current month. Ask students to name the date 3 weeks ago, 3 weeks and 2 days ago, and so on.

Mental Math

Name the number that is 99 less. Explain your thinking.

178 79   205 106   551 452   693 594

Calculator Connection

Pair students for a brain-versus-calculator race. Give each pair five addition and subtraction problems. One student uses mental math and the other uses a calculator. Make sure that the problems are easy enough to solve mentally. Then have partners switch roles and repeat the race.

Another Way to **Learn** Lesson 3-10

Use as an alternative or in addition to pages 120 and 121.

Materials Calculators

Learning Style Verbal

- Ask groups of students to use mental math to solve a progression of addition and subtraction problems such as the following:

Addition	Subtraction
300 + 200 500	400 − 100 300
301 + 200 501	400 − 101 299
301 + 199 500	401 − 100 301
303 + 198 501	402 − 97 305

- After the groups have found each sum and difference, they should use calculators to check their work.

- Ask groups to explain how they determined each answer. Write each appropriate method on the chalkboard.

- Have groups try out each other's strategies and compare methods. Point out that there is not just one correct way; students should use whichever method they find easiest.

- Assign Check and Practice on Student Book pages 120 and 121 or *Practice Master 3-10*.

- Assess using the following rubric.

Assessment Rubric

4 Full Accomplishment
- finds sums and differences mentally and explains process used

3 Substantial Accomplishment
- finds most sums and differences mentally but needs prompting to explain process used

2 Partial Accomplishment
- finds some sums and differences mentally but does not explain process used

1 Little Accomplishment
- does not find sums and differences or explain process used

Options for Reaching All Learners

Language Development

Write On
Use written computation to explain a mental math strategy.

Learning Style Verbal, Social

- Have students use step-by-step written computation to demonstrate their mental math strategies.

- As students write each step, use simple sentences to restate the operation in the form of a question, for example: Did you add 3 to make 300? Is 300 easier for you to subtract?

- Encourage students to respond in complete sentences, such as: Yes, I added 3 to make 300 because it is easier for me to subtract 300.

Inclusion

Getting "A-Round" to It
Use ideas of rounding to develop mental math strategies.

Learning Style Individual, Logical

- Encourage students to think about rounding by asking: If you could round only one of the numbers, how would that make the problem simpler? You could add or subtract mentally more easily.

- Point out that students are not rounding numbers for these problems. They are performing an operation that results in "a round number." Stress that they are finding compatible numbers that will help them find exact numbers more easily.

Lesson Organizer

Objective Add and subtract numbers mentally.

Student Materials None

Assignment Guide

Basic 12–21, 27, 28, 31–35

Average 16–28, 31–35

Enriched 18–35

1 Introduce

Review

Find each sum or difference.

1. 25 + 25 50

2. 125 + 200 325

3. 350 − 200 150

Build on Prior Knowledge

After students review adding and subtracting, ask them why these problems were easy. What did these problems have in common? Possible answers: No regrouping; Numbers that end in zeros

2 Teach

See Another Way to Learn…on page 120B.

Learn

Ask students if they prefer Deeva's way of adding 3 to the bottom number and adjusting the difference or Kevin's way of simply adding 3 to both the top and bottom numbers.

Talk About It Ongoing Assessment

Listen for students to recognize number patterns that can be subtracted easily.

Answers for Talk About It

1 Possible answer: It's easier to subtract 200 than 197. He added 3 to each number so as not to affect the difference.

2 Possible answer: Add 200 + 50, then subtract 6.

Check

Watch that students do not automatically round all the numbers in the exercises. Ask them first to look at the exercises, then decide what changes will help them solve each.

Using Mental Math

You Will Learn
how to add and subtract numbers mentally

Did You Know?
Children in the United States laugh about 400 times a day. Adults laugh about 15 times a day.

Learn

Laughter is everybody's business at the Belfast Circus School. Students practice juggling, tumbling, unicycle riding, and clowning around.

Suppose the students make 500 fliers to advertise their shows. If they post 197 fliers, how many do they have left?

The Belfast Circus School in Northern Ireland

There are many ways to add and subtract mentally. You can invent your own ways, too.

Here is how Deeva and Kevin find 500 − 197 mentally.

Deeva's Way

I know that 500 − 200 = 300.

I took away 3 too many, so I'll add back 3.
The answer is 303.

Kevin's Way

I'll add 3 to each number.

$$500 + 3 \longrightarrow 503$$
$$\underline{-197 + 3 \longrightarrow -200}$$
$$303$$

Talk About It

1. Why did Kevin add 3 to each number before subtracting?

2. Explain how you would add 195 and 49 mentally.

Check

Add or subtract mentally. Choose any method.

1. 99 + 67   **2.** 98 + 53   **3.** 403 + 87   **4.** 695 + 125   **5.** 258 + 111
166   151   490   820   369

6. 200 − 99   **7.** 800 − 195   **8.** 805 − 150   **9.** 275 − 125   **10.** 355 − 225
101   605   655   150   130

11. Reasoning Explain two ways to find 300 − 198.
Possible answers: Subtract 300 − 200, then add 2. Add 2 to each number and subtract. 300 − 198 = 102.

Practice 3-10

Name _____

Practice 3-10

Using Mental Math
Add or subtract mentally. Choose any method.

1. 82 + 99 = __181__

2. 506 + 95 = __601__

3. 500 − 99 = __401__

4. 400 − 47 = __353__

5. 195 + 377 = __572__

6. 3,678 − 599 = __3,079__

7. 850 + 38 + 150 = __1,038__

8. 125 + 82 + 875 = __1,082__

9. 243 + 675 + 325 = __1,243__

10. 2,000 − 499 = __1,501__

11. Find the sum of 507 and 393. __900__

12. Find the difference between 604 and 296. __308__

Complete. Write >, <, or =.

13. 352 + 197 ⊲< 252 + 298

14. 101 − 99 = 201 − 199

15. 437 − 198 > 437 − 199

16. 293 + 471 < 283 + 571

17. 629 − 13 < 629 + 13

18. 746 − 123 < 646 + 123

19. 309 + 300 = 709 − 100

20. 173 + 163 > 163 + 167

21. Find the rule. Complete the table.

In	600	800	1,000	1,200
Out	450	650	850	1,050

Rule: Subtract 150.

22. Make your own table. Write your rule.

In			
Out			

Rule: _____

Reteaching 3-10

Name _____

Another Look 3-10

Using Mental Math
Follow these steps to mentally add 57 and 42:

First add the tens.   5 + 4 = 9

Then add the ones.   7 + 2 = 9

Write the total as a 2-digit number.

Follow these steps to mentally subtract 53 from 78:

First subtract the tens.   7 − 5 = 2

Then subtract the ones.   8 − 3 = 5

Write the difference as a 2-digit number. 78 − 53 = 25

To add or subtract 3-digit numbers (without regrouping) mentally, add or subtract the hundreds first, then follow the same steps.

Add or subtract mentally.

1. 546 + 213
a. 5 + 2 = [7]
b. 4 + 1 = [5]
c. 6 + 3 = [9]
546 + 213 = __759__

2. 74 − 31
a. 7 − 3 = [4]
b. [4] − 1 = [3]
c. 74 − 31 = __43__

3. 676 + 223 = __899__

4. 417 + 82 = __499__

5. 89 − 42 = __47__

6. 288 − 164 = __124__

7. 213 + 424 = __637__

8. 679 − 322 = __357__

9. 876 − 431 = __445__

10. 527 + 332 = __859__

Skills and Reasoning

💡 **Mental Math** Add or subtract mentally. Choose any method.

12. $99 + 73$
172

13. $95 + 305$
400

14. $600 - 99$
501

15. $300 - 48$
252

16. $568 + 195$
763

17. $4,768 - 599$
4,169

18. $125 + 68 + 875$
1,068

19. $133 + 550 + 450$
1,133

20. Find the sum of 406 and 394.
800

21. Find the difference between 702 and 498.
204

Copy and complete. Write >, <, or =.

22. $453 + 198 ● 353 + 299$ <

23. $536 - 198 ● 536 - 199$ >

24. $748 + 12 ● 748 - 12$ >

25. $807 - 200 ● 507 + 100$ =

ⓧ **26. Algebra Readiness** Find the rule. Complete the table.

In	500	700	900	1,100	1,300
Out	425	625	825	1,025	1,225

Rule: Subtract 75

Problem Solving and Applications

27. The Belfast Circus School performers give two shows in town. A total of 398 people go to the shows. If 202 people are at the first show, how many are at the second show? **196 people**

28. Science For humans, smiling uses 17 muscles in the face. Frowning uses 43 muscles. How many more muscles does it take to frown? **26 muscles**

29. Measurement Spotted hyenas are noisy animals. They cackle, screech, and sometimes laugh. A typical female spotted hyena weighs 173 pounds. A male weighs about 121 pounds. What is the difference in their weights? **52 pounds**

30. Collecting Data Make a tally chart of the number of times you see someone laugh during lunchtime. Record data separately for adults and children. Then compare it with the data in *Did You Know?* on page 120. **Answers will vary.**

Mixed Review and Test Prep

Add.

31. $564 + 221$ **785** **32.** $329 + 504$ **833** **33.** $781 + 178$ **959** **34.** $206 + 206$ **412**

35. Which set of numbers is ordered from greatest to least? **B**
Ⓐ 378, 738, 873   Ⓑ 873, 783, 378   Ⓒ 873, 837, 883

Lesson 3-10 **121**

Enrichment 3-10

Problem Solving 3-10

Error Intervention Ongoing Assessment

Observation Students may use compatible numbers or simple numbers as needed, add and subtract correctly, but have difficulty adjusting the answer.

How to Help Remind students to write down what they did with each number when adding or subtracting, so they can make any necessary adjustments to the answer.

Practice ● ● ● ● ● ● ● ● ● ● ● ● ● ● ● ● ● ●

Exercises 12–21 You might read these exercises aloud to encourage students' use of mental math.

For Early Finishers Challenge early finishers to find the rule for adding numbers to the top row of the table in Exercise 26, then extend the table four places. Rule: Add 200; Top row: 1,500; 1,700; 1,900; 2,100; Bottom row: 1,425; 1,625; 1,825; 2,025

③ Close and Assess

Interview

Ask individual students to explain how $602 - 297$ or $602 + 297$ can be solved mentally.

Quick Check

Number Sense In Skill Exercise 1 below, do you need to adjust the difference? No, if you subtracted 4 from 404 and added 4 to 196.

Skill Use mental math to find each sum or difference.

1. $404 + 196$ 600
2. $798 - 205$ 593
3. $549 + 223$ 772
4. $409 - 253$ 156

Choosing a Calculation Method

At-A-Glance Planning

Objective Choose a calculation method.

Student Book Lesson Materials Calculators

Materials for pages 122A and 122B Calculators, problem sheet (1 per pair), *optional* posterboard

Subject Connection careers—food industry

Strand Connections using data, geometry readiness, patterns

	Before Lesson	During Lesson	After Lesson
Daily Math			
p. 122A Problem of the Day			
p. 122A Math Routines			
p. 122A Mental Math			
Teaching Options			
p. 122 Student Book Lesson			
p. 122B Another Way to Learn…			
Options for Reaching All Learners			
p. 122B Reading Assist			
p. 122B Gifted & Talented			
Subject Connections			
p. 122A Science Connection			
Assessment Options			
p. 122 Talk About It			
p. 123 Error Intervention			
p. 123 Observation			
p. 123 Quick Check			
Resources			
3–11 Practice			
3–11 Reteaching			
3–11 Enrichment			
3–11 Problem Solving			
3–11 Daily Transparency			

Problem of the Day

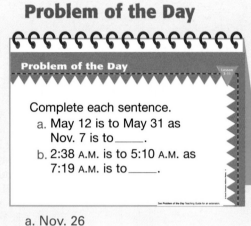

Problem of the Day

Complete each sentence.
a. May 12 is to May 31 as Nov. 7 is to _____.
b. 2:38 A.M. is to 5:10 A.M. as 7:19 A.M. is to _____.

a. Nov. 26
b. 9:51 A.M.

Math Routines

Patterns Have students complete the following pattern and give the rule. 10, 13, 11, 14, 12, 15, ■, ■, ■,… 13, 16, 14; Add 3, subtract 2

Calendar Ask students to find the age of a person born on July 3, 1960, in years, months, and days. Continue with other dates.

Mental Math

Name the number that is 101 less. Explain your thinking.

331	702	945	812
230	601	844	711

Science Connection

Bring in nutrition facts charts from a package of corn tortillas and a package of flour tortillas.

• Compare the number of calories and grams of fat in each type of tortilla.

• Have students tell which computation method they used when comparing flour and corn tortillas and why they chose this method.

Another Way to Learn Lesson 3-11

Use as an alternative or in addition to pages 122 and 123.

Materials Calculators

Learning Style Social, Kinesthetic

- Ask students to find 62,945 + 34,685. Have one group member use a calculator, one use paper and pencil, and one use mental math. They should compare their answers. Have group members rotate methods of calculation throughout the lesson as you assign additional problems.

- Ask students which method they think was easiest, and why. Answers will vary, but many will probably say the calculator.

- Ask if they think this is always true. Give them this problem: 2,000 + 3,000. Ask which method they think is easiest now and why. Answers will vary, but many will probably say mental math.

- Assign Check and Practice on Student Book pages 122 and 123 or *Practice Master 3-11*.

- Assess using the following rubric.

Assessment Rubric

4 Full Accomplishment
- finds sums and differences using an appropriate calculation method

3 Substantial Accomplishment
- finds most sums and differences using an appropriate calculation method

2 Partial Accomplishment
- finds some sums and differences but does not consistently choose an appropriate calculation method

1 Little Accomplishment
- does not find sums and differences using an appropriate calculation method

Options for Reaching All Learners

Reading Assist

Find Main Idea with Supporting Details
Use three questions to find the main idea and supporting details of word problems.

Materials *Optional* Posterboard

Learning Style Verbal, Logical

Encourage students to read the entire problem carefully before answering the following questions. You may want to put these questions on a poster.

1 *What do I want to find?* This important information is often found at the end of the problem.

2 *What do I know?* This often means the given numbers, but it may also mean finding information in another place, such as a graph or table.

3 *What do I have to do to find the answer?* Occasionally there is more information than is needed, but more often it is a matter of selecting an operation.

Gifted & Talented

Best of Both Worlds
Use a calculator and mental math to solve problems.

Materials Calculators, problem sheet (1 per pair)

Learning Style Visual, Logical

- Have pairs of students complete a problem sheet you have prepared, such as the one shown below.

- Students have to determine the operation as well as the number necessary to change the calculator readout. They can use the calculator to check their work.

What do you have to do? What number do you have to use?		
Your calculator reads:	To make it read:	Do:
1. 400	515	add 115
2. 3,578	4,000	add 422

Lesson Organizer

Objective Choose a calculation method.
Suggested Grouping 3 or 4
Student Materials Calculators
Assignment Guide
  Basic 6–15, 18, 21–28
  Average 9–18, 21–28
  Enriched 11–28

1 Introduce

Review

Find each sum or difference.

1. 5,000 − 2,000 3,000

2. 4,903 + 1,355 6,258

3. 4,001 − 1,999 2,002

4. 3,847 + 1,111 4,958

Build on Prior Knowledge

Ask students to name the methods they used to answer the Review exercises. Survey the class to see which methods students find easiest and most difficult.

2 Teach

See Another Way to Learn…on page 122B.

Learn ● ● ● ● ● ● ● ● ● ● ● ● ● ● ● ● ●

Pronunciation note: Chavez (SHAH-vez)
Ask students to read the problem at the top of the page and work through the example using paper and pencil *and* a calculator. Discuss which method they think is easier and why.

Talk About It Ongoing Assessment

Listen for students to recognize that the method of calculation chosen relates to the difficulty level of the problem. Watch for students who use a calculator for every problem and encourage them to try other methods.

Answer for Talk About It

Possible answer: When the calculation method involves more than one regrouping.

Check ● ● ● ● ● ● ● ● ● ● ● ● ● ● ● ● ●

Encourage students to try different methods of calculation as they do the exercises.

122   *Chapter 3 • Lesson 3-11*

Choosing a Calculation Method

You Will Learn
how to choose a calculation method

Learn ● ● ● ● ● ● ● ● ● ● ● ● ●

Warm them, roll them, fill them! However you eat them, tortillas are a well-rounded meal.

In a typical week, a tortilla factory produces 98,448 packages of corn tortillas and 85,178 packages of flour tortillas. How many packages does it make in all?

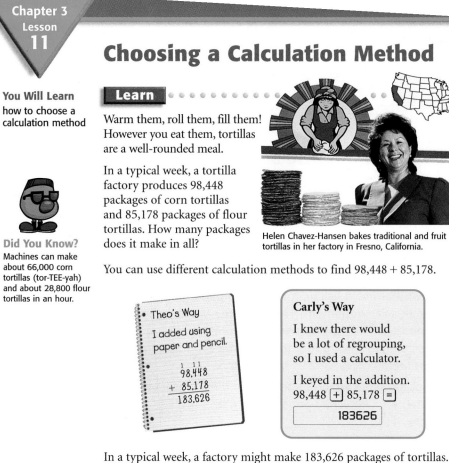

Helen Chavez-Hansen bakes traditional and fruit tortillas in her factory in Fresno, California.

Did You Know?
Machines can make about 66,000 corn tortillas (tor-TEE-yah) and about 28,800 flour tortillas in an hour.

You can use different calculation methods to find 98,448 + 85,178.

Theo's Way
I added using paper and pencil.

    1 11
    98,448
  + 85,178
  ─────────
   183,626

Carly's Way
I knew there would be a lot of regrouping, so I used a calculator.

I keyed in the addition.
98,448 [+] 85,178 [=]

    183626

In a typical week, a factory might make 183,626 packages of tortillas.

Talk About It

When might it be better to use a calculator?

Check ●

Find each sum or difference. Choose any method.

1.	**2.**	**3.**	**4.**
27,400	58,000	27,650	36,000
− 12,650	+ 30,000	+ 12,400	− 16,000
14,750	88,000	40,050	20,000

5. Reasoning Which calculation method would you use to find the difference between 12,825 and 9,948? Explain. **Possible answer: A calculator because the exercise involves regrouping three times.**

122   Chapter 3 • Adding and Subtracting Whole Numbers and Money

---

Practice 3-11	**Reteaching 3-11**
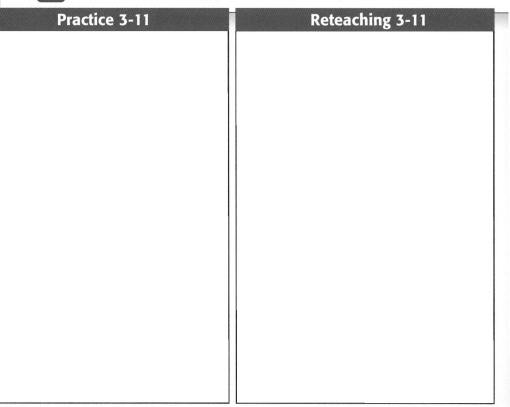

Skills and Reasoning | Choose a tool

Find each sum or difference. Choose any method.

6. 44,200 − 22,100 **22,100**	**7.** 36,584 − 6,798 **29,786**	**8.** 28,500 + 28,500 **57,000**	**9.** 76,345 − 46,345 **30,000**
10. 32,008 − 11,003 **21,005**	**11.** 91,100 − 80,000 **11,100**	**12.** 21,339 + 66,783 **88,122**	**13.** 38,911 − 29,745 **9,166**

14. Find the sum of 3,700 and 54,200. **57,900**

15. Subtract 59,000 from 89,000. **30,000**

16. What is the greatest possible sum of two 5-digit numbers?
99,999 + 99,999 = 199,998

Problem Solving and Applications

17. Using Data Use the facts from *Did You Know?* on page 122. About how many more corn tortillas than flour tortillas can a factory make in an hour? **37,200**

Using Data Use the table for **18** and **19**.

18. How many packages of the two most popular sizes of flour tortillas were made that day?
3,260 packages

19. How many packages of flour tortillas were made that day?
4,128 packages

20. Geometry Readiness Draw a picture of a tortilla folded in half. What shape is it?
Half circle

21. Using Data Use the Data File on page 91. Of the people who knew about the "Take Our Daughters to Work" program, how many did *not* take a daughter to work?
131 million

Flour Tortillas Made in One Day

Size	Number of Packages
7 inch	497
8 inch	1,591
10 inch	354
12 inch	1,669
14 inch	17

Mixed Review and Test Prep

Compare each pair of numbers. Write > or <.

22. 699 ● 669 **>**

23. 1,220 ● 1,720 **<**

24. 1,652 ● 1,662 **<**

25. 2,812 ● 1,282 **>**

26. 12,695 ● 16,692 **<**

27. 3,796 ● 3,794 **>**

28. Patterns Which pair of numbers continues the pattern? **B**
500, 1,000, 1,500, ■, ■

Ⓐ 1,600, 1,700   Ⓑ 2,000, 2,500   Ⓒ 1,000, 500   Ⓓ not here

Observation Students may not arrive at a correct answer, even though they are using calculators.

How to Help Review how entries are made. For instance, the commas separating the thousands and hundreds are never entered. Care must be taken not to register a double digit by pressing on any key for too long. Each entry should be checked for accuracy before pressing a key for the next step. Stress the importance of care and accuracy when using a calculator. For some students the use of a calculator with a paper printout would be particularly helpful.

Practice ○ ○ ○ ○ ○ ○ ○ ○ ○ ○ ○ ○ ○ ○ ○ ○ ○

Exercise 16 You may wish to prompt students by asking what is the greatest 5-digit number. 99,999

For Early Finishers Challenge early finishers to read the table, then list the tortilla sizes from least to greatest number of packages.
14 inch, 10 inch, 7 inch, 8 inch, 12 inch

③ Close and Assess

Observation

Watch closely as students work to complete their assignments. Observe which students always reach for a calculator as well as those who seriously try mental math first.

Quick Check

Number Sense Explain what calculation method you would use for each problem.

1. 3,499 + 2,200 Probably mental math

2. 4,174 − 2,478 Probably paper and pencil or calculator

Skill Find each sum or difference. Use any method you like.

1. 5,000 + 1,756 6,756

2. 4,275 − 1,001 3,274

3. 6,254 + 4,288 10,542

4. 13,386 − 8,111 5,275

Name _____

Choosing a Calculation Method

Social Studies Information about four American cities is shown in the table.

City	Population in 1994	Tallest Building	Height of Building
Boston	547,725	John Hancock Tower	790 feet
Atlanta	396,052	Nation's Bank Tower	1,050 feet
Denver	493,559	Republic Plaza	714 feet
San Francisco	734,676	Transamerica Pyramid	853 feet

Use the data to solve. Choose any method.

1. How many more people lived in San Francisco than in Denver in 1994? **241,117**

2. What was the total population of Boston and Atlanta in 1994? **943,777**

3. How many more people lived in the two cities with the greatest population than the two cities with the least population? **392,790**

4. How much taller is the Transamerica Pyramid than the John Hancock Tower? **63 ft**

5. How much taller is the tallest building listed than the shortest one? **336 ft**

6. The Toddler Toy Factory produced 57,327 toys on Monday and 62,571 toys on Tuesday.

a. How many more toys did it produce on Tuesday than on Monday? **5,244 toys**

b. How many toys did it produce all together on Monday and Tuesday? **119,898 toys**

7. Caroline had 236 building bricks, and her sister had 264. How many did they have in total? **500 bricks**

Section B
Review and Practice

Use the Skills Checklist

Review the **Skills Checklist** on the page with students. Then ask questions such as the following:

- In which problems will you use your estimation skills? Exercises 3–12
- For which problems could you subtract with middle zeros? Exercises 17–21
- For which problems might you need to choose a calculation method? Exercises 26–29

Assess

You may wish to use this information to assess students' understanding of the lesson objectives.

Item Analysis

Lesson Objective	Items
3-5 Add 3-digit and 4-digit numbers.	3–12, 26, 28
3-6 Add 3 and 4 addends.	2, 7–11
3-7 Subtract 3-digit and 4-digit numbers.	13–21, 23, 25, 27
3-8 Subtract from numbers with zeros.	17–21
3-9 Solve multiple-step problems.	22
3-10 Add and subtract numbers mentally.	23–25
3-11 Choose a calculation method.	1, 26–29

Resources

Practice Masters

- Practice Chapter 3 Section B

Assessment Sourcebook

- Quiz Chapter 3 Section B

TestWorks: Test and Practice Software

ANSWERS

29 Answers should mention the number of students who want to be scientists and the number who want to be musicians, and subtract that total from the number of classmates.

SECTION B
Review and Practice

Vocabulary Match each word with its meaning.

1. front-end estimation **b**   a. numbers added together to make a sum
2. addends **a**   b. a way to estimate using leading digits

(Lessons 5 and 6) Find each sum. Estimate to check.

3. $781 + 112$ **893**　　4. $853 + 250$ **1,103**　　5. $823 + 415$ **1,238**　　6. $646 + 789$ **1,435**

7.　　227
　　240
　　$+ 352$
　　819

8.　　2,425
　　　 55
　　$+ 436$
　　2,916

9.　　689
　　 99
　　$+ 8,324$
　　9,112

10.　　810
　　436
　　$+ 3,352$
　　4,598

11.　　1,915
　　6,485
　　$+ 9,399$
　　17,799

12. **Science** Mauna Loa volcano, in Hawaii, rises 4,170 meters above sea level. About 6,000 meters more of the volcano are underwater. How tall is the volcano in all? **About 10,170 meters**

4,170 m
6,000 m

(Lessons 7 and 8) Subtract.

13. $632 - 110$ **522**　14. $463 - 253$ **210**　15. $1,289 - 975$ **314**　16. $2,498 - 1,178$ **1,320**

17.　　203
　　$- 51$
　　152

18.　　700
　　$- 525$
　　175

19.　　6,001
　　$- 3,210$
　　2,791

20.　　2,000
　　$- 323$
　　1,677

21.　　8,100
　　$- 7,321$
　　779

(Lesson 9) Solve.

22. **Music** At Interlochen, 47 students play in the orchestra, 36 students play in the band, and 86 students sing in the chorus. How many more students sing than play musical instruments? **3 students**

(Lessons 10) **Mental Math** Add or subtract mentally.

23. $749 - 201$ **548**　　24. $99 + 75$ **174**　　25. $1,435 - 405$ **1,030**

(Lesson 11) Find each sum or difference.

26.　　5,003
　　$+ 4,210$
　　9,213

27.　　6,314
　　$- 2,831$
　　3,483

28.　　92,131
　　$+ 12,476$
　　104,607

29. **Journal** Explain how you would compare the number of classmates who want to become scientists or musicians with the total number of classmates.

REVIEW AND PRACTICE

Skills Checklist

In this section, you have:

☑ Added and Subtracted Greater Numbers

☑ Subtracted with Middle Zeros

☑ Solved Multiple-Step Word Problems

☑ Added and Subtracted Mentally

☑ Chosen a Calculation Method

Practice

Name _____

Practice
Chapter 3
Section B

Review and Practice
Vocabulary Underline the appropriate number to complete each sentence.

1. A front-end estimate of $291 + 450$ is (<u>600</u>, 800).

2. (<u>376</u>, 819) is an addend in the number sentence $443 + 376 = 819$.

(Lessons 5 and 6) Find each sum. Estimate to check.

3. $162 + 435 =$ __597__　　4. $234 + 125 =$ __359__

5.　　328
　　551
　　$+ 723$
　　1,602

6.　　491
　　607
　　$+ 356$
　　1,454

7.　　664
　　 78
　　$+ 5,337$
　　6,079

8.　　4,729
　　 920
　　$+ 4,851$
　　10,500

(Lessons 7 and 8) Subtract.

9. $568 - 312 =$ __256__　　10. $645 - 560 =$ __85__

11.　　600
　　$- 357$
　　243

12.　　9,058
　　$- 1,215$
　　7,843

13.　　7,000
　　$- 5,839$
　　1,161

14.　　4,281
　　$- 1,687$
　　2,594

(Lesson 9) Solve.

15. Of the students in 4th grade at Lampeter High School, 23 play baseball, 15 play football and 29 are in the band. How many more students play a sport than are in the band? **9 students**

(Lesson 10) Add or subtract mentally.

16. $98 + 52 =$ __150__　　17. $308 - 250 =$ __58__

(Lesson 11) Find each sum or difference.

18.　　58,900
　　$+ 50,000$
　　108,900

19.　　8,999
　　$- 457$
　　8,542

20.　　5,621
　　$+ 1,677$
　　7,298

21.　　28,400
　　$- 3,700$
　　24,700

(Mixed Review) Complete the pattern and find the rule.

22. 4,000; 8,000; 12,000; __16,000__ ; __20,000__ ; __24,000__

Rule: __Add 4,000__

Using Money

Philomena Okigbo imports arts and crafts from Africa to sell in the United States. Her work gives her a chance to teach people about African culture.

When you buy things, how can you tell that you'll have enough money? How do you know how much change you'll get back?

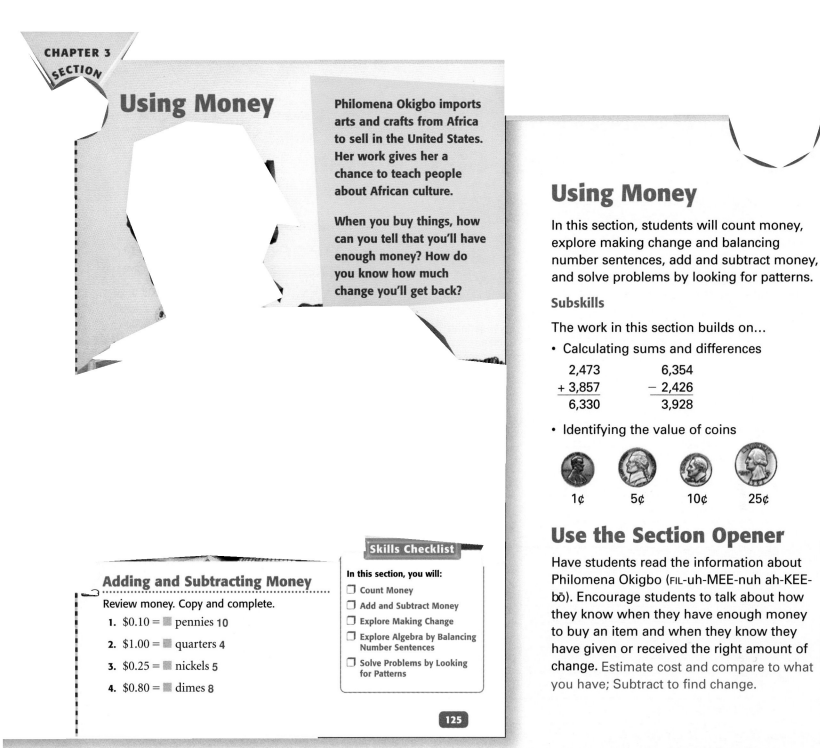

Adding and Subtracting Money

Review money. Copy and complete.

1. $0.10 = ■ pennies 10

2. $1.00 = ■ quarters 4

3. $0.25 = ■ nickels 5

4. $0.80 = ■ dimes 8

Skills Checklist

In this section, you will:

☐ Count Money

☐ Add and Subtract Money

☐ Explore Making Change

☐ Explore Algebra by Balancing Number Sentences

☐ Solve Problems by Looking for Patterns

125

Using Money

In this section, students will count money, explore making change and balancing number sentences, add and subtract money, and solve problems by looking for patterns.

Subskills

The work in this section builds on...

• Calculating sums and differences

$$
\begin{array}{r} 2{,}473 \\ +\ 3{,}857 \\ \hline 6{,}330 \end{array}
\qquad
\begin{array}{r} 6{,}354 \\ -\ 2{,}426 \\ \hline 3{,}928 \end{array}
$$

• Identifying the value of coins

1¢   5¢   10¢   25¢

Use the Section Opener

Have students read the information about Philomena Okigbo (FIL-uh-MEE-nuh ah-KEE-bō). Encourage students to talk about how they know when they have enough money to buy an item and when they know they have given or received the right amount of change. Estimate cost and compare to what you have; Subtract to find change.

Skills Trace

(Red numbers indicate pages in this section.)

Lesson and Skill	First Introduced	Grade Four			
		Introduce	Develop	Practice/Apply	Review
3-12 Count and compare money.	Grade 3	126, 127	126	127, 132, 133, 138, 141, 142, 561	138, 140, 143, 339, 557
3-13 Add and subtract money amounts.	Grade 3	128, 129	128	129, 132, 133, 138, 139, 141, 561	138, 139, 140, 143, 334, 339, 381, 427
3-14 Explore making change.	Grade 3	130, 131	130, 131	131, 138, 142, 561	138, 140, 143, 538, 557
3-15 Explore algebra by balancing number sentences.	Grade 4	134, 135	134, 135	135, 138, 561	138, 140, 143, 466
3-16 Solve problems by looking for a pattern.	Grade 3	136, 137	136, 137	137, 138, 561	138, 140, 143, 339

Mixed Review and Test Prep exercises for this chapter occur on pages 99, 107, 109, 113, 115, 121, 123, 127, 129.

Multi-Age Classrooms Use pages 123–140 in Grade 3 or pages 249–260 in Grade 5 to relate to the content of this section.

Counting Money

At-A-Glance Planning

Lesson Planning Checklist

Objective Count and compare money.

Vocabulary decimal point

Student Book Lesson Materials *Optional* Play money—pennies, nickels, dimes, quarters, $1, $5, $10, $20 bills (10 of each per group)

Materials for pages 126A and 126B Play money—pennies, nickels, dimes, quarters, $1, $5, $10, $20 bills (10 of each per group), coins (or photographs of coins) from other countries

Subject Connection careers—retail sales

Strand Connections patterns, time

	Before Lesson	During Lesson	After Lesson
Daily Math			
p. 126A Problem of the Day			
p. 126A Math Routines			
p. 126A Mental Math			
Teaching Options			
p. 126 Student Book Lesson			
p. 126B Another Way to Learn…			
Options for Reaching All Learners			
p. 126B Cultural Connection			
p. 126B Inclusion			
Subject Connections			
p. 126A Literature Connection			
Assessment Options			
p. 126 Talk About It			
p. 127 Error Intervention			
p. 127 Observation			
p. 127 Quick Check			
Resources			
3-12 Practice			
3-12 Reteaching			
3-12 Enrichment			
3-12 Problem Solving			
3-12 Daily Transparency			

Problem of the Day

Problem of the Day

Five coins were put into this meter. Which coins were used?

10 min. for 5¢
20 min. for 10¢
1 hr. for 25¢

4 dimes and 1 nickel

Math Routines

Money Ask students what coins they might give a cashier along with a $10 bill if they buy an item for $8.17. Any combination that totals $0.17 to avoid getting $0.83 in change.

Patterns Ask students how many $2 items they can buy with $10, $20, or $30. Ask what pattern they see. 5, 10, 15; multiples of $10 divided by $2

Mental Math

Name the number that is 498 less. Explain your thinking.

667 169 851 353 905 407 713 215

Literature Connection

In the poem "Smart," by Shel Silverstein, a boy trades a dollar bill for a successively greater number of coins with less and less value until he is left with 5 pennies, all the while thinking he's made a better deal. The first trade was one dollar for two quarters because "two is more than one."

• Discuss the boy's logic. Ask students how they might explain to the boy what was wrong with his reasoning.

Another Way to **Learn** Lesson 3-12

Use as an alternative or in addition to pages 126 and 127.

Materials Play money—pennies, nickels, dimes, quarters, $1, $5, $10, $20 bills (10 of each per group)

Learning Style Visual, Kinesthetic

- Have groups examine and sort the different coins and bills. Then have them tell the value of each kind.

- Have groups mix all the coins in one pile. Two students can take six coins from each pile. Ask students to count the amount of money in each group of six coins. Ask students whether it would it be easier to count the money starting with the quarters or the pennies. Why? Possible answers: Quarters; You would be counting on from a number that ends in 5 or 0.

- Ask groups to write both amounts of money and tell which amount is greater and why.

- Repeat the activity using a mixed pile of coins and bills.

- Write several money amounts, such as $5.38, $23.62, and $43.97, on the chalkboard. Ask groups to count out the bills and coins for that amount. You might have them find two ways to make the given amounts.

- Check students' understanding of the difference between quantity and value. Ask students to explain why counting the *number* of coins and bills does not tell the *amount* of money. Possible answer: Because coins and bills have different values, which affect the amount of money

- Assign Check and Practice on Student Book page 127 or *Practice Master 3-12.*

- Assess using the following rubric.

Assessment Rubric
4 **Full Accomplishment** • consistently counts, writes, and compares amounts of money
3 **Substantial Accomplishment** • counts, writes, and compares most amounts of money
2 **Partial Accomplishment** • counts some amounts of money but has difficulty in writing or comparing amounts of money
1 **Little Accomplishment** • does not count, write, or compare amounts of money

Options for Reaching All Learners

Cultural Connection

Coins from All Over

Use coins to heighten awareness of other cultures' currency.

Materials Coins (or photographs of coins) from other countries

Learning Style Visual

- Encourage students who know about coins from other places to name and describe them. If possible, bring actual coins or photographs of these coins to class.

- If foreign coins are available, have students compare U.S. and foreign coins. Ask what they notice about patterns in U.S. coins. How do foreign coins compare for ease of counting? It's easy to count by 1s, 5s, 10s, and 25s.

- You may want to suggest using encyclopedias or almanacs, or enlisting family members for help with coin research.

Inclusion

Getting a Feel for Money

Use play money to translate a visual experience into a tactile one.

Materials Play money (assorted coins and bills)

Learning Style Kinesthetic

- Help students feel and recognize coins by the size and the serrated or smooth edges. Invite visually impaired students to share their experiences.

- Bills can be folded to help distinguish between denominations. For example, fold $1 bills in half vertically. Fold $5 bills in half horizontally. Fold one corner on $10 bills. Fold two corners on $20 bills.

- Have students exchange coins and folded bills, then count the amounts of money without looking.

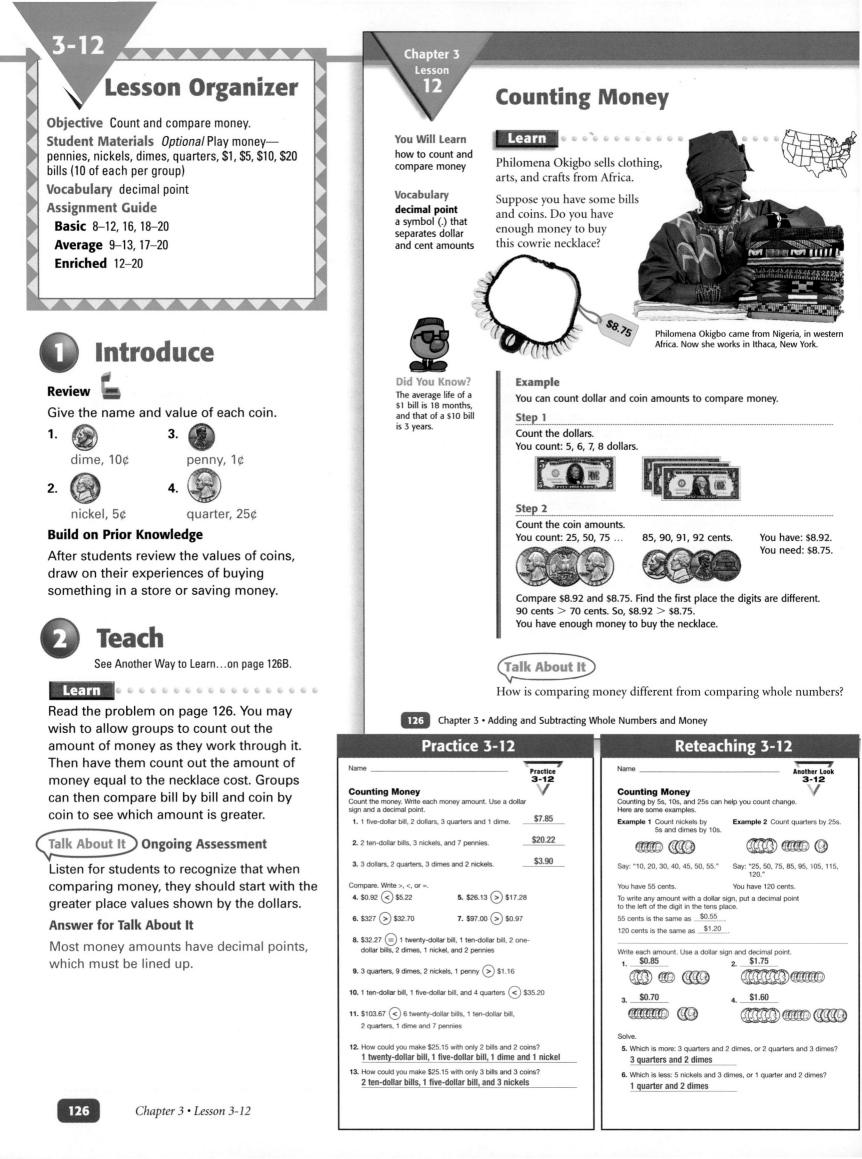

3-12

Lesson Organizer

Objective Count and compare money.

Student Materials *Optional* Play money—pennies, nickels, dimes, quarters, $1, $5, $10, $20 bills (10 of each per group)

Vocabulary decimal point

Assignment Guide

Basic 8–12, 16, 18–20

Average 9–13, 17–20

Enriched 12–20

1 Introduce

Review

Give the name and value of each coin.

1. dime, 10¢ **3.** penny, 1¢

2. nickel, 5¢ **4.** quarter, 25¢

Build on Prior Knowledge

After students review the values of coins, draw on their experiences of buying something in a store or saving money.

2 Teach

See Another Way to Learn…on page 126B.

Learn

Read the problem on page 126. You may wish to allow groups to count out the amount of money as they work through it. Then have them count out the amount of money equal to the necklace cost. Groups can then compare bill by bill and coin by coin to see which amount is greater.

Talk About It) Ongoing Assessment

Listen for students to recognize that when comparing money, they should start with the greater place values shown by the dollars.

Answer for Talk About It

Most money amounts have decimal points, which must be lined up.

Counting Money

You Will Learn
how to count and compare money

Vocabulary
decimal point
a symbol (.) that separates dollar and cent amounts

Did You Know?
The average life of a $1 bill is 18 months, and that of a $10 bill is 3 years.

Learn

Philomena Okigbo sells clothing, arts, and crafts from Africa.

Suppose you have some bills and coins. Do you have enough money to buy this cowrie necklace?

$8.75

Philomena Okigbo came from Nigeria, in western Africa. Now she works in Ithaca, New York.

Example

You can count dollar and coin amounts to compare money.

Step 1
Count the dollars.
You count: 5, 6, 7, 8 dollars.

Step 2
Count the coin amounts.
You count: 25, 50, 75 …   85, 90, 91, 92 cents.   You have: $8.92
                                                    You need: $8.75

Compare $8.92 and $8.75. Find the first place the digits are different.
90 cents > 70 cents. So, $8.92 > $8.75.
You have enough money to buy the necklace.

Talk About It

How is comparing money different from comparing whole numbers?

126 Chapter 3 • Adding and Subtracting Whole Numbers and Money

---

Practice 3-12

Name _____
Practice 3-12

Counting Money

Count the money. Write each money amount. Use a dollar sign and a decimal point.

1. 1 five-dollar bill, 2 dollars, 3 quarters and 1 dime. $7.85

2. 2 ten-dollar bills, 3 nickels, and 7 pennies. $20.22

3. 3 dollars, 2 quarters, 3 dimes and 2 nickels. $3.90

Compare. Write >, <, or =.

4. $0.92 (<) $5.22   **5.** $26.13 (>) $17.28

6. $327 (>) $32.70   **7.** $97.00 (>) $0.97

8. $32.27 (=) 1 twenty-dollar bill, 1 ten-dollar bill, 2 one-dollar bills, 2 dimes, 1 nickel, and 2 pennies

9. 3 quarters, 9 dimes, 2 nickels, 1 penny (>) $1.16

10. 1 ten-dollar bill, 1 five-dollar bill, and 4 quarters (<) $35.20

11. $103.67 (<) 6 twenty-dollar bills, 1 ten-dollar bill, 2 quarters, 1 dime and 7 pennies

12. How could you make $25.15 with only 2 bills and 2 coins?
1 twenty-dollar bill, 1 five-dollar bill, 1 dime and 1 nickel

13. How could you make $25.15 with only 3 bills and 3 coins?
2 ten-dollar bills, 1 five-dollar bill, and 3 nickels

Reteaching 3-12

Name _____
Another Look 3-12

Counting Money

Counting by 5s, 10s, and 25s can help you count change. Here are some examples.

Example 1 Count nickels by 5s and dimes by 10s.

Example 2 Count quarters by 25s.

Say: "10, 20, 30, 40, 45, 50, 55."   Say: "25, 50, 75, 85, 95, 105, 115, 120."

You have 55 cents.   You have 120 cents.

To write any amount with a dollar sign, put a decimal point to the left of the digit in the tens place.

55 cents is the same as __$0.55__.
120 cents is the same as __$1.20__.

Write each amount. Use a dollar sign and decimal point.

1. $0.85   **2.** $1.75

3. $0.70   **4.** $1.60

Solve.

5. Which is more: 3 quarters and 2 dimes, or 2 quarters and 3 dimes?
3 quarters and 2 dimes

6. Which is less: 5 nickels and 3 dimes, or 1 quarter and 2 dimes?
1 quarter and 2 dimes

Check

Count the money. Write each amount with dollar sign and decimal point.

1. 3 dollars, 2 quarters, 3 pennies **$3.53**
2. one $20.00 bill, 2 $10.00 bills, 4 dimes, 1 nickel **$40.45**

Compare. Write >, <, or =.

3. $25.94 ● $25.49 **>**
4. $94.06 ● $94.01 **>**
5. $0.38 ● $1.37 **<**
6. $42.40 ● $4.24 **>**

7. **Reasoning** How could you make $37.95 with the fewest bills and coins?
Possible answer: 1 $20 bill, 1 $10 bill, 1 $5 bill, 2 dollars, 3 quarters, 2 dimes

Practice

Skills and Reasoning

Count the money. Write each amount with dollar sign and decimal point.

8. one $10.00 bill, 1 dollar, 1 quarter, 1 nickel **$11.30**

9. 4 dollars, 2 quarters, 1 dime, 3 pennies **$4.63**

Compare. Write >, <, or =.

10. $0.77 ● $67.00 **<**
11. $75.57 ● $57.75 **>**
12. $245.00 ● $254.00 **<**

13. 3 dollars, 5 quarters, 2 nickels ● $4.35 **=**

14. $7.34 ● 1 $5.00 bill, 2 dollars, 3 dimes, 4 nickels **<**

15. How could you make $55.28 with only 4 bills and 4 coins?
2 $20 bills, 1 $10 bill, 1 $5 bill, 1 quarter, and 3 pennies

Problem Solving and Applications

16. What is the greatest number of five-dollar bills you would need to buy the medium wall art? **9 $5 bills**

17. Suppose you have 1 twenty-dollar bill, 1 ten-dollar bill, 2 five-dollar bills, 10 quarters, 7 dimes. What is the largest wall art you could buy? Write the amount you have. **Small wall art; $43.20**

Wall Art from Africa	
Small	$40.00
Medium	$45.00
Large	$50.00

Mixed Review and Test Prep

Patterns Copy and complete each pattern.

18. 3, 6, 9, 12, ■, ■, ■
15, 18, 21

19. 70, 60, 50, 40, ■, ■, ■
30, 20, 10

20. **Time** Which is the fifth month of the year? **C**
Ⓐ March   Ⓑ September   Ⓒ May   Ⓓ April

Lesson 3-12   **127**

Check

Exercises 1 and 2 Be sure students understand they are to write the total amount of money, not the individual amount for each denomination.

Error Intervention Ongoing Assessment

Observation Students may compare digits of different values when comparing.

How to Help Encourage them to align the money amounts in columns. Remind them of place values in our monetary system.

Practice

Exercise 15 Suggest that students first find the coins needed for the cents and then the bills needed for the dollars.

For Early Finishers Challenge early finishers to find four more ways to make $55.28 in Exercise 15 using any combination of bills and coins.

③ Close and Assess

Observation

Watch as students count out a specific money amount. Listen for students to count on as they use a variety of bills and coins.

Quick Check

Number Sense Tell which amount is greater.

1. $28.94 or $29.84 **$29.84**

2. $65.00 or $64.99 **$65.00**

Skill Count the money. Write each amount with a dollar sign and decimal point.

1. 5 quarters, 2 dimes, 3 pennies **$1.48**

2. $5 bill, 3 quarters, 6 nickels, 12 pennies **$6.17**

Enrichment 3-12

Name _____ **Extend Your Thinking 3-12**

Critical Thinking

The units of currency known as dollars and cents are used in other countries besides the United States, such as Australia and Canada, for example. But many countries have different currencies. Use the information given to answer each question.

1. In Germany, there are 100 pfennigs to the mark. If you had 2 marks and 70 pfennigs, and someone gave you 3 10-pfennig coins, how much money would you have?
3 marks

2. In France, there are 100 centimes to the franc. If you had 8 francs and 45 centimes, and someone gave you a 5-franc coin and a 20-centime coin, how much money would you have?
13 francs and 65 centimes

3. In Japan, the currency is called yen. If you had 490 yen and someone gave you two 500-yen coins and a 10-yen coin, how much money would you have?
1,500 yen

4. In Greece, the currency is called drachma. If you had 1,000 drachma and someone gave you one 50-drachma bill, two 20-drachma coins and three 5-drachma coins, how much money would you have?
1,105 drachma

5. In Saudi Arabia, there are 100 halalahs to the riyal. If you had 6 riyals and 34 halalahs and someone gave you a 5-riyal bill, a 50-halalah coin and three 10-halalah coins, how much money would you have?
12 riyals and 14 halalahs

6. In Zambia, there are 100 ngwee to the kwacha. If you had 54 ngwee and someone gave you one 20-ngwee coin, six 10-ngwee coins, three 2-ngwee coins and one 1-ngwee coin, how much money would you have?
1 kwacha and 41 ngwee

7. In the United Kingdom, there are 100 pence to the pound. If you had 5 pounds and someone gave you two 1-pound coins, one 20-pence coin, two 5-pence coins, six 2-pence coins and four 1-pence coins, how much money would you have?
7 pounds and 46 pence

Problem Solving 3-12

Name _____ **Problem Solving 3-12**

Counting Money

Careers Mr. Conte, the clerk at the music store, processed the following two orders:

piano lesson books for $30.99

sheet music for $67.95

1. Mr. Conte received only five-dollar bills for the books.
   a. How many bills did he receive? **7**
   b. Should he give change? **Yes**
   c. If so, how much? **$4.01**

2. Mr. Conte received 6 bills and 5 coins to pay for the sheet music. He received the exact amount. What were the bills and coins?
3 twenty-dollar bills, 1 five-dollar bill, 2 dollars, 3 quarters, and 2 dimes

3. If you pay the exact amount, what is the least number of bills and coins you could use to make a $15.27 purchase?
1 ten-dollar bill, 1 five-dollar bill, 1 quarter, and 2 pennies

4. a. If you have 3 ten-dollar bills, 8 dollars, 16 dimes, and 21 pennies, could you make a $47.56 purchase? Explain.
No; $39.81 < $47.56

   b. If you pay the exact amount, what is the least number of bills and coins you could use to make the $47.56 purchase?
2 twenty-dollar bills, 1 five-dollar bill, 2 dollars, 2 quarters, 1 nickel, and 1 penny

5. If you only had 10-dollar bills how many would you use to pay for an item that costs $56.15? **6**

Adding and Subtracting Money

At-A-Glance Planning

Lesson Planning Checklist

Objective Add and subtract money amounts.

Student Book Lesson Materials *Optional* Lesson Enhancement Transparency 8

Materials for pages 128A and 128B Teaching Tool Transparencies 21, 22 (Play Money—10 pennies, 10 nickels, 5 dimes, 4 quarters, 50 pennies, 5 $1 bills, 4 $5 bills, 2 $10 bills, 5 $20 bills per pair); catalogs or newspaper fliers; small paper bags (1 per pair)

Subject Connection careers—dog training

Strand Connections estimation, using data, patterns

	Before Lesson	During Lesson	After Lesson
Daily Math			
p. 128A Problem of the Day			
p. 128A Math Routines			
p. 128A Mental Math			
Teaching Options			
p. 128 Student Book Lesson			
p. 128B Another Way to Learn…			
Options for Reaching All Learners			
p. 128B Language Development			
p. 128B Inclusion			
Subject Connections			
p. 128A Literature Connection			
Assessment Options			
p. 128 Talk About It			
p. 129 Error Intervention			
p. 129 Observation			
p. 129 Quick Check			
Resources			
3-13 Practice			
3-13 Reteaching			
3-13 Enrichment			
3-13 Problem Solving			
3-13 Daily Transparency			

Problem of the Day

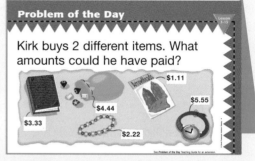

Kirk buys 2 different items. What amounts could he have paid?

$1.11
$5.55
$4.44
$3.33
$2.22

$3.33, $4.44, $5.55, $6.66, $7.77, $8.88 and $9.99

Math Routines

Measurement Ask students to name two benchmark temperatures in the Fahrenheit system and describe two activities they might do at each.

Time Ask students what time it was 35 minutes ago if the time now is 12:15. Use other examples in which both times are multiples of 5 minutes. 11:40

Mental Math

Name the number that is 999 less. Explain your thinking.

1,662	2,975	2,807	3,004
663	1,976	1,808	2,005

Literature Connection

In *A Job for Jenny Archer* by Ellen Conford, Jenny goes to a garage sale with $3.27, looking for a birthday present for her mother. She finds a lace collar.

• The woman had planned to sell it for $6. Ask students how much more money Jenny needs to buy the collar. $2.73

• The owner cuts the price to $3 and sells Jenny a box and wrapping paper for $0.25. Ask how much Jenny has left over. $0.02

Another Way to **Learn** Lesson 3-13

Use as an alternative or in addition to pages 128 and 129.

Materials Teaching Tool Transparencies 21, 22 (Play Money—10 pennies, 4 nickels, 5 dimes, 4 quarters, 5 $1 bills, 4 $5 bills, 2 $10 bills, 5 $20 bills per pair)

Learning Style Visual, Kinesthetic, Social

- Have students place all the money to one side of their work area. Pairs can decide which student will begin the activity.

- Ask one student to take $14.78 from the money supply. After that amount is counted out, ask the second student to take $6.33 from the first student's amount. Encourage students to exchange coins for others of equal value.

- Pairs should then work together to find the amount of money the first student has left.

- Model an algorithm on the chalkboard to familiarize students with the symbols. Then ask students to write their own subtraction problem to show their actions. Be sure students show the decimal points and dollar signs.

- Ask one partner to take $8.64 from the supply, and the other to take $9.22.

- Pairs can work together to find the amount of money they have in all, then write an addition problem showing the decimal point and dollar sign.

- Repeat several times using other amounts and alternating addition and subtraction operations. Allow students to solve the problems without using play money.

- Assign Check and Practice on Student Book page 129 or *Practice Master 3-13.*

- Assess using the following rubric.

Assessment Rubric
4 Full Accomplishment • consistently finds sums and differences of money amounts
3 Substantial Accomplishment • finds sums and differences of most money amounts
2 Partial Accomplishment • finds some sums and differences of money amounts but does not regroup consistently
1 Little Accomplishment • does not find sums or differences of money amounts

Options for Reaching All Learners

Language Development

The U.S. Quarter

Use play money to strengthen understanding of the relative value of the U.S. quarter.

Materials Teaching Tool Transparencies 21, 22 (Play Money—1 dollar, 4 quarters, 10 nickels, 5 dimes, 50 pennies per group)

Learning Style Verbal, Kinesthetic

Some students may come from countries with no coin equivalent to the U.S. quarter. They may need additional practice with the value of a quarter.

- Discuss the meaning of the word *quarter*, relating it to *fourth*. Then ask students to show how many quarters equal one dollar.

- Ask students to find all the possible equivalents of a quarter using play money. Challenge them to record each equivalent on a table.

Inclusion

Going Shopping

Use shopping activities to add and subtract money.

Materials Catalogs or newspaper fliers, play money, small paper bags

Learning Style Kinesthetic, Visual

- Give each pair a paper bag containing a random amount of play money. Have students count their money.

- Have students select a catalog or newspaper flier and choose at least three items.

- Ask students to find how much money they need to purchase the items and to compare that amount to how much they have. Students then calculate either the amount left over or how much more money they need to buy the items.

- Repeat the activity by having students trade money bags and select new items.

Objective Add and subtract money amounts.

Suggested Grouping 2 to 4

Student Materials None

Teacher Materials *Optional* Lesson Enhancement Transparency 8; Overhead play money

Assignment Guide

Basic 10–20, 23, 26, 28–31

Average 15–26, 28–31

Enriched 15–31

1 Introduce

Review

Find each sum or difference.

1. 385 + 384 769

2. 547 − 295 252

3. 1,473 + 4,190 5,663

4. 6,394 − 2,695 3,699

Build on Prior Knowledge

Ask students when they have had to add or subtract money. Then ask how they count money. Possible answers: Count bills, then coins; count coins first, then bills.

2 Teach

See Another Way to Learn…on page 128B.

Learn • • • • • • • • • • • • • • • • • • •

You may want to model the example using overhead play money. As you exchange coins and bills for regrouping, emphasize how this process is similar to the exchanges they have made with place-value blocks.

Talk About It **Ongoing Assessment**

Listen for students to recognize the importance of place value in adding and subtracting money.

Answer for Talk About It

To make sure you add or subtract the same place value.

Adding and Subtracting Money

You Will Learn
how to add and subtract money amounts

Did You Know?
There are at least 50 million dog owners and 58 million cat owners in the United States.

Learn • • • • • • • • • • • • • • • • •

"The secret is patience," says Ryan's mom. "Just keep trying till the puppies learn to follow your lead!"

Ryan and Aubrey help their mom with her dog training business in Royal Oak, Michigan.

A leather dog collar costs $12.69. A cloth one costs $7.95. How much more does the leather one cost?

Subtract to compare the two amounts.

Example 1

Find $12.69 – $7.95.

Step 1	Step 2	Step 3
Line up the decimals.	Subtract as you would with whole numbers.	Write the decimal point and dollar sign in the difference.
$12.69 − 7.95	$\overset{11}{\cancel{1}} 16$ $1\cancel{2}.\cancel{6}9$ − 7.95 474	$\overset{11}{\cancel{1}} 16$ $1\cancel{2}.\cancel{6}9$ − 7.95 $4.74

Estimate to check. $13.00 − $8.00 = $5.00
Since $4.74 is close to $5.00, the answer is reasonable. The leather collar costs $4.74 more.

You can add dollar amounts in the same way.

Other Examples

A.
$\overset{1}{}$
$9.29
+ 4.68
$13.97

B.
$\overset{1\ 1\ 1}{}$
$49.79
+ 7.34
$57.13

C.
$\overset{1}{}$
$98.00
+ 27.95
$125.95

Talk About It

Why do you need to line up the decimal points?

Name _____

Practice 3-13

Adding and Subtracting Money

Add or subtract. Estimate to check.

1. $12.99
+ 0.49
$13.48

2. $2.95
−1.45
$1.50

3. $1.61
+ 8.67
$10.28

4. $19.50
+ 0.68
$20.18

5. $12.62
+ 5.19
$17.81

6. $33.59
− 12.27
$21.32

7. $86.19
+ 4.98
$91.17

8. $92.11
− 79.12
$12.99

9. $4.96
− 2.18
$2.78

10. $12.28
+ 8.39
$20.67

11. $57.00
− 14.79
$42.21

12. $26.41
− 24.16
$2.25

13. $18.62 + $29.78 = __$48.40__

14. $0.25 + $17.76 = __$18.01__

15. $8.17 − $5.19 = __$2.98__

16. $19.68 − $19.52 = __$0.16__

17. Find the difference between $111.02 and $19.25. $91.77

18. Find the sum of $552 and $777. $1,329

19. Find the difference between $1,092 and $75. $1,017

20. Find the sum of $0.98 and $1.29. $2.27

21. Estimate to decide if the sum of $35.02 and $35.19 is greater than $70.00. Explain.

Yes; $35.02 and $35.19 are close to $35.00. $35 + $35 =

$70. Since the numbers were rounded to the lower

amounts, the sum will be greater than $70.00.

Name _____

Another Look 3-13

Adding and Subtracting Money

You can use play money to help you add and subtract money amounts.

$12.52
+ 7.67

Start by adding the coins. Count the quarters, then the dimes, then the nickels, then the pennies: "25, 50, 75, 100, 110, 115, 116, 117, 118, 119."

Exchange the coins for dollars. 119 cents is the same as 1 dollar and 19 cents.

Write the amount left in coins after the decimal point.

Count the bills. Count "10, 15, 16, 17, 18, 19, 20."

Write the amount in bills in front of the decimal point. $12.52 + $7.67 = $20.19

Add or subtract. Use play money to help you.

1. $4.13
+ 5.95
$10.08

2. $7.13
+ 2.27
$9.40

3. $10.82
− 6.41
$4.41

4. $6.13
− 2.79
$3.34

5. $19.32
+ 8.74
$28.06

6. $6.27
− 4.82
$1.45

7. $12.36
+ 7.55
$19.91

8. $15.47
+ 9.08
$24.55

9. $3.11
− 1.49
$1.62

Add or subtract. Estimate to check.

1. $2.25
 + 1.10
 $3.35

2. $9.94
 − 2.10
 $7.84

3. $10.59
 − 2.35
 $8.24

4. $15.38
 + 22.95
 $38.33

5. $24.66
 + 0.76
 $25.42

6. $6.42 + $13.16
 $19.58

7. $32.20 − $11.12
 $21.08

8. $47.12 − $13.98
 $33.14

9. **Reasoning** Suppose you added $15.11, $32, and $0.38 and got $15.81. Explain why this sum is incorrect.
 Placed the decimal point to the left instead of to the right of 32;
 $15.11 + $32 + $0.38 = $47.49

Skills and Reasoning

Add or subtract. Estimate to check.

10. $3.06
 + 6.20
 $9.26

11. $9.98
 − 2.11
 $7.87

12. $7.59
 − 2.32
 $5.27

13. $11.22
 + 7.88
 $19.10

14. $20.35
 + 9.63
 $29.98

15. $23.06
 + 1.10
 $24.16

16. $8.56
 − 0.92
 $7.64

17. $18.60
 − 11.49
 $7.11

18. $21.88
 − 20.81
 $1.07

19. $14.31
 + 5.39
 $19.70

20. $41.41 + $15.50
 $56.91

21. $0.87 + $145.45
 $146.32

22. $60.10 − $16.38
 $43.72

23. Find the difference between $35.60 and $17.99. **$17.61**

24. Find the sum of $856 and $1,296. **$2,152**

25. Estimate to decide if the sum of $24.73 and $24.28 is greater than $50.00. Explain.
 $24.73 is close to $25, and $24.28 is close to $24. $25 + $24 = $49, so it is less than $50.00.

Problem Solving and Applications

26. Suppose Ryan and Aubrey buy a new dog brush for $6.99. How much change will they get back from a $10 bill? **$3.01**

27. Ryan and Aubrey's mom charges $5.50 per night for a dog to sleep over. Food is $2.35 more. What is the total cost per night? **$7.85**

DOG HOTEL
$5.50 PER NIGHT
EATS $2.35

28. **Using Data** Use the Data File on page 91. About how much did the average hourly wage go up from 1980 to 1995? **About $5.00**

Mixed Review and Test Prep

STAY SHARP!

Patterns Copy and complete each pattern.

29. 75, 85, 95, ▨, ▨
 105, 115

30. 20, 300, 4,000, ▨, ▨
 50,000, 600,000

31. In the number 2,374,285, what is the value of the digit 7? **B**
 Ⓐ 7 thousands　Ⓑ 70 thousands　Ⓒ 7 hundreds　Ⓓ not here

Skills Practice Bank, page 561, Set 4　Lesson 3-13　**129**

Name _____

Problem Solving
3-13

Adding and Subtracting Money

History In November 1929, during the time in American History known as the Great Depression, you could buy a candy bar for as little as 3¢! But a worker earned only about $25 a week.

Here are some typical Depression Age prices for items you would buy today. Find the difference in prices.

	Item	Price in 1929	Price in 1997	Difference
1.	Hamburger	$0.05	$0.69	$0.64
2.	Ice cream cone	$0.03	$1.19	$1.16
3.	Ticket to the movies	$0.10	$5.50	$5.40
4.	Bus fare	$0.08	$1.00	$0.92

5. How much would a hamburger and an ice-cream cone combined cost in
 a. 1929? __$0.08__
 b. 1997? __$1.88__

6. If you pay $20 for a shirt that costs $12.79, how much change should you receive? **$7.21**

7. Sue went to a movie that cost $5.50. Her popcorn cost $2.50 and her soda cost $2.25.
 a. How much did Sue spend? **$10.25**
 b. If Sue brought $15 to the movies with her, did she have enough money left to buy a book that cost $3.29 on the way home? Explain.
 Yes; $15.00 − $10.25 = $4.75; $4.75 > $3.29

8. Write your own subtraction problem about money. Use $30.76 and $41.80. Be sure to include the answer.
 Check students' problems. $41.80 − $30.76 = $11.04

Exercise 9 Encourage students to use place value and number sense to estimate the answer.

Error Intervention Ongoing Assessment

Observation Students may forget to insert the decimal point and/or the dollar sign.

How to Help Ask students to write the dollar sign and decimal point in the answer place before adding or subtracting.

Exercises 26 and 27 Suggest that students identify the necessary operation before solving.

Exercise 28 You may wish to use Lesson Enhancement Transparency 8 to display the Data File on page 91.

For Early Finishers Challenge early finishers to find the sum of all the answers to Exercises 10–12. $9.26 + $7.87 + $5.27 = $22.40

③ Close and Assess

Observation

Watch students as they solve one addition exercise and one subtraction exercise from Exercises 10–22. Check that students regroup, write the dollar sign, and align the decimal points correctly.

Quick Check

Number Sense Identify the money value of the numbers on each side of the decimal point. The numbers to the right are cents; the numbers to the left are dollars.

Skill Find each sum or difference.

1. $35.86 + $15.36 **$51.22**

2. $71.48 + $83.67 **$155.15**

3. $96.14 − $73.56 **$22.58**

4. $82.00 − $37.58 **$44.42**

PRACTICE AND APPLY

Exploring Making Change

At-A-Glance Planning

Objective Explore making change.

Student Book Lesson Materials Play money (10 pennies, 10 nickels, 10 dimes, 10 quarters, 5 $1 bills, 5 $5 bills, 5 $10 bills, 5 $20 bills per group), Teaching Tool Transparencies 21, 22 (Play Money)

Materials for pages 130A and 130B Index cards (6 per team)

Subject Connection careers—cashier

Strand Connection using data

	Before Lesson	During Lesson	After Lesson
Daily Math			
p. 130A Problem of the Day			
p. 130A Math Routines			
p. 130A Mental Math			
Teaching Options			
p. 130B Facilitating and Assessing…			
Options for Reaching All Learners			
p. 130B Reading Assist			
p. 130B Gifted & Talented			
Subject Connections			
p. 130A Social Studies Connection			
Assessment Options			
p. 130 Talk About It			
p. 131 Error Intervention			
p. 131 Performance Assessment			
Resources			
3-14 Practice			
3-14 Reteaching			
3-14 Enrichment			
3-14 Problem Solving			
3-14 Daily Transparency			

Problem of the Day

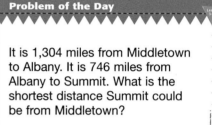

Problem of the Day

Lesson 3-14

It is 1,304 miles from Middletown to Albany. It is 746 miles from Albany to Summit. What is the shortest distance Summit could be from Middletown?

See Problem of the Day Teaching Guide for an extension.

558 miles

Math Routines

Money Have students count on from amounts of money between $0.50 and $0.75 to reach $1.00. Ask them to do it with as few coins as possible.

Calendar Ask students whether it is possible for the 21st of one month and the 7th of the following month to be on the same day of the week. Must be 21st of February in nonleap year

Mental Math

Name the number that is 195 less. Explain your thinking.

339	638	916	807
144	443	721	612

Social Studies Connection

Many people earn their living catching and selling fish. Others fish for fun.

- Have students write one mathematics problem that a person who fishes for fun might need to solve and one problem that a person who fishes for a living might need to solve.

- Have students swap problems and solve.

Facilitating and Assessing **Explore** Lesson 3-14

Use with pages 130 and 131.

Get Started Be sure students understand that an angler is someone who fishes. For Exercises 1 and 2, you might encourage groups to act out the process of paying and giving change. Be sure they put out the available cash-drawer money as described before each exchange.

Observe Watch for students who use acceptable variations of the change-giving process. Encourage them to explain their variations to the class.

Discuss Use the overhead projector and play money or a blank transparency to allow groups to show how Bob and Mike solved their problem. Discuss and compare methods, then decide if one method is always easier than the other. Offer opportunities for each student to express an opinion.

Assess Use the rubric to assess students' work. See sample for Practice Exercise 4.

	Assessment Rubric	
4	**Full Accomplishment** • makes correct change	
3	**Substantial Accomplishment** • makes most change correctly with occasional errors	
2	**Partial Accomplishment** • makes some change correctly but makes errors in subtracting	
1	**Little Accomplishment** • does not make correct change	

4 Full Accomplishment

Cost	$0.32	$12.39	$3.44	$29.80	$17.36
Amount Given	$5.00	$13.00	$20.00	$50.00	$17.50
Change	$4.68	$0.61	$16.56	$20.20	$0.14

Options for Reaching All Learners

Reading Assist

Recognize Sequence
Use lists to organize multiple-step problems.

Learning Style Verbal, Visual, Logical

• Have students read Practice Exercise 1 carefully. Then ask each pair to make a list of things they need to do before they can solve the problem. Stress that their lists should show the necessary steps in the correct order.

1 Find the price of the floating fly.

2 Find the price of the box of grasshoppers.

3 Add the prices of the floating fly and the box of grasshoppers.

4 Subtract (or count on) from the amount of money given.

• After the lists are complete, have students find the answer.

Gifted & Talented

Add up to $10.00
Use a game to explore making change.

Materials Index cards (6 per team)

Learning Style Social, Logical

• Organize students in teams of three. Each team's goal is to come up with three amounts of money totaling as close as possible to $10 without going over.

• Each team member secretly decides on an amount of money and writes it down. Two teams exchange their three money addends. Each team finds the sum of the money amounts and then finds the amount of change from $10. If a team's sum is greater than $10, that team is out. The team whose addends give the least change wins.

• Have teammates discuss their strategies (but not specific amounts) to use.

Lesson Organizer

Objective Explore making change.

Suggested Grouping 2 to 4

Student Materials Play money (10 pennies, 10 nickels, 10 dimes, 10 quarters, 5 $1 bills, 5 $5 bills, 5 $10 bills, 5 $20 bills per group)

Teacher Materials Teaching Tool Transparencies 21, 22 (Play Money)

Assignment Guide

Basic 1–3, 6, 7

Average 2–4, 6, 7

Enriched 3–7

1 Introduce

Review

Use mental math to find each difference.

1. $3.00 − $0.75 $2.25
2. $9.99 − $7.82 $2.17
3. $13.45 − $9.98 $3.47
4. $12.00 − $3.49 $8.51

Build on Prior Knowledge

Ask students if they have ever received change in a store. How did they check to make sure they got the right amount?

2 Teach

See Facilitating and Assessing…on page 130B.

Explore • • • • • • • • • • • • • • • •

For Exercise 1a, have students actually remove the quarters from their "cash drawers" before solving the problem. They should remove dollar bills for Exercise 2c.

Talk About It Ongoing Assessment

Listen for students to compare the relative ease of counting on and subtracting.

Answers for Talk About It

3 When the change involves different types of coins and bills

4 Starting with pennies gets to the nearest 5¢ or 10¢. Then it's easier to add dimes or nickels to multiples of 5¢ or 10¢, and quarters to multiples of 25¢.

Chapter 3
Lesson 14

Exploring Making Change

Problem Solving Connection

Use Objects/ Act It Out

Materials

play money: coins and bills

Explore •

You reeled in a job at Buddy's Bait Stand! That's where anglers pick up their fishing supplies.

Work Together

Work with play money, or draw pictures.

1a. Possible answer: 2 dollars, 7 dimes, 1 nickel

1. A customer buys a box of worms.

   a. The customer pays with a $5 bill. The cash drawer doesn't have any quarters. What change will you give?

   b. Suppose the customer pays with a $10 bill. You just got some quarters to put in the cash drawer. How would you count on to $10.00?

Remember
$10.00 is the same as $10.

1b. Possible answer: 3 quarters, 2 dollars, and 1 $5 bill

2. A customer buys a box of slugs and pays with a $20 bill.

   a. How much is the change? $16

   b. What is one combination of coins and bills that you could give as change?

   c. Suppose there are no dollar bills in the cash drawer. How would you give change?

   Possible answer: 1 $10 bill, 1 $5 bill, 5 quarters

2b. Possible answer: 1 $10 bill, 1 $5 bill, 1 dollar, and 1 quarter

Talk About It

3. When is counting on a helpful way to give change?

4. When counting on, why might you start with pennies and work your way up to quarters?

BUDDY'S BAIT STAND

Bait and Supplies	Price
Worms	$2.25 per box
Grasshoppers	$1.79 per box
Slugs	$3.75 per box
Fishing line	$14.99 each
Floating fly	$9.49 each
Minnow float	$6.99 each
Shrimp fly	$4.50 each

Practice 3-14	**Reteaching 3-14**

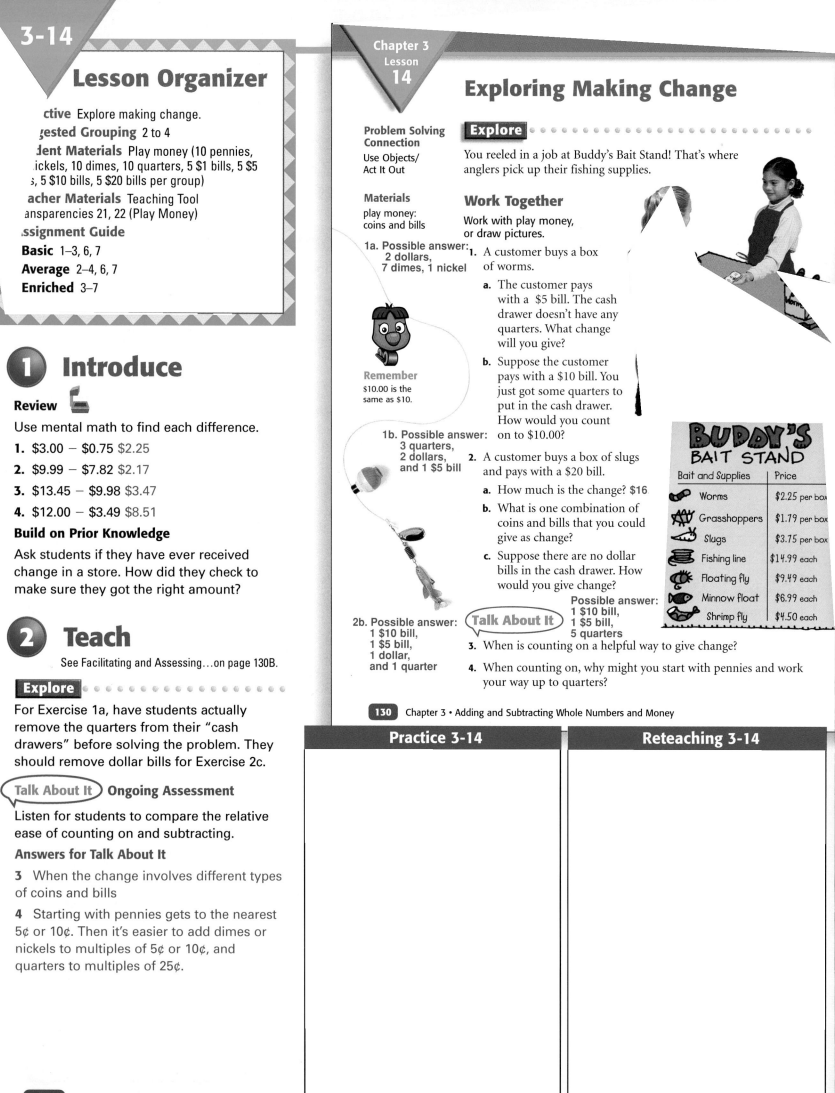

Connect

Bob and Mike also work at Buddy's. Each one serves a customer who buys a box of grasshoppers and pays with a $10 bill. Here is how Bob and Mike make change.

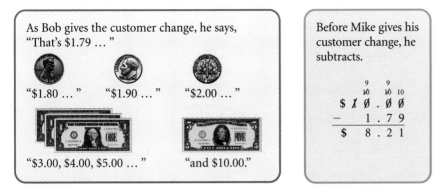

As Bob gives the customer change, he says, "That's $1.79 … "

"$1.80 … "   "$1.90 … "   "$2.00 … "

"$3.00, $4.00, $5.00 … "   "and $10.00."

Before Mike gives his customer change, he subtracts.

$$\begin{array}{r} \overset{9}{\cancel{10}} \overset{9}{\cancel{10}}\, 10 \\ \$\, \cancel{1}\, \cancel{0}\, .\, \cancel{0}\, \cancel{0} \\ -\quad 1\, .\, 7\, 9 \\ \hline \$\quad 8\, .\, 2\, 1 \end{array}$$

Bob and Mike both give $8.21 change.

Practice

Using Data Use the data on page 130 for **1–3**. Write the change for each purchase.

1. A customer buys a floating fly and a box of grasshoppers and pays with a $20 bill. **$8.72**

2. A friend buys 3 shrimp flies and pays with $15. **$1.50**

3. A family buys fishing line, a minnow float, a shrimp fly, and a box of worms. The family pays with two $20 bills. **$11.27**

4. Copy and complete the table. Write each amount of change.

Cost	$0.32	$12.39	$3.44	$29.80	$17.36
Amount Given	$5.00	$13.00	$20.00	$50.00	$17.50
Change	$4.68	$0.61	$16.56	$20.20	$0.14

5. Suppose you have this money in your pocket. List three ways you could pay for a minnow float.

6. **Critical Thinking** Why might you give a clerk $5.06 to pay for a $3.06 item? **To get two $1 bills back**

7. **Journal** Describe how you have seen people give change in stores.

Skills Practice Bank, page 561, Set 5   Lesson 3-14   **131**

Connect

Have students discuss which method of counting change they prefer and why.

Error Intervention Ongoing Assessment

Observation Students may have difficulty using the counting-on method of giving change.

How to Help Have students use play money to model counting on. Place the play money in stacks in this order: pennies, nickels, dimes, quarters, $1 bills, $5 bills, $10 bills, $20 bills.

Practice

Exercise 7 Students can also express an opinion as to which method they think is easier and which method might be more accurate.

For Early Finishers Challenge early finishers to find out how much change they would get from $50 if they bought one of every item listed at Buddy's Bait Stand. **$6.24**

3 Close and Assess

Performance Assessment

Suppose you have a $20 bill and would like to buy a package of fishing line and a box of grasshoppers. Use play money or draw coins to show the correct amount of change you should get. **$3.22**

Assess using the rubric on page 130B.

Resources

Technology Master 9

ANSWERS

5 Possible answer: 1 $5 bill and 2 dollars; 2 $5 bills; 1 $5 bill, 1 dollar, 3 quarters, 2 dimes, 4 pennies

7 Answers will vary.

Enrichment 3-14	Problem Solving 3-14

Chapter 3
Stop and Practice

Students will practice skills taught in Lessons 1 through 14.

Add or Subtract

Exercises 1–38 Caution students to take the time to look at the sign and determine whether they should add or subtract.

Exercises 13, 16–25 Students must remember to write the dollar signs in the answers.

Exercises 16–21, 30–38 Caution students to use place values to align the digits of each exercise.

Error Search

Suggest that students copy the problems and work them out on their own before looking at the given answers. This will make answers easier to compare.

ANSWERS

39 $11.16; Left out the decimal point

40 135; Added rather than subtracted

41 $34; Added an extra zero to the answer

42 Correct

STOP and Practice

Add or subtract. Estimate to check.

1. 245 − 234 11	**2.** 467 + 897 1,364	**3.** 976 − 86 890	**4.** 456 + 342 798	**5.** 308 − 175 133
6. 233 + 741 974	**7.** 808 − 256 552	**8.** 584 + 77 661	**9.** 845 − 209 636	**10.** 729 − 64 665
11. 28 43 + 62 133	**12.** 473 67 + 539 1,079	**13.** $8.95 4.13 + 2.68 $15.76	**14.** 9,634 903 + 1,823 12,360	**15.** 846 3,237 + 2,184 6,267

16. $15.12 − $9.35 **$5.77**

17. $8.95 + $8.57 **$17.52**

18. $29.49 − $15.95 **$13.54**

19. $77.89 − $14.36 **$63.53**

20. $12.45 + $18.96 **$31.41**

21. $39.49 + $10.23 **$49.72**

22. $65.18 + 55.10 $120.28	**23.** $98.01 − 10.99 $87.02	**24.** $76.83 + 12.83 $89.66	**25.** $22.90 + 7.95 $30.85
26. 9,876 + 2,134 12,010	**27.** 7,919 − 3,912 4,007	**28.** 4,817 − 2,111 2,706	**29.** 6,789 + 5,217 12,006

30. 275 − 150 **125**

31. 899 + 100 **999**

32. 230 − 149 **81**

33. 1,500 + 150 + 200 **1,850**

34. 665 + 195 + 489 **1,349**

35. 1,300 + 25 + 275 **1,600**

36. 422 + 59 + 305 **786**

37. 781 + 201 + 35 **1,017**

38. 1,469 + 23 + 140 **1,632**

Error Search

Find each sum or difference that is not correct. Write it correctly and explain the error.

39. $18.65 − 7.49 $1,116	**40.** 1,189 − 1,054 2,243	**41.** $12.00 + 22.00 $340.00	**42.** 1,022 − 889 133

39. $11.16; Left out the decimal point   41. $34; Added an extra zero to the answer

40. 135; Added rather than subtracted   42. Correct

Hog Wild!

Add or subtract. Match each letter with its answer below to solve the riddle. Some letters are not used.

What does a pig write with?

Iay OVELay ATHMay

43. 854 − 76 [G]
778

44. 352 + 276 [A]
628

45. 509 − 234 [C]
275

46. 431 + 592 [P]
1,023

47. 257 + 936 [B]
1,193

48. 454 − 323 [P]
131

49. 672 + 44 [I]
716

50. 707 − 342 [M]
365

51. 475 + 150 [D]
625

52. 692 − 88 [E]
604

53. 563 + 57 [O]
620

54. 340 − 139 [N]
201

628	1,023	716	778	131	604	201
A	P	I	G	P	E	N

Number Sense   Reasoning

Write whether each statement is true or false. Explain your answer.

55. $5.50 + $10.95 > $55.50 + $10.95 **F; $16.45 < $66.45**

56. $75.03 − $1.00 > $75.30 − $1.00 **F: $74.03 < $74.30**

57. $5.55 + $7.89 = $7.89 − $5.55 **F; $13.44 > $2.34**

58. $78.90 − $78.09 > $4.99 − $2.99 **F; $0.81 < $2.00**

59. $1.89 + $4.98 + $3.95 < $11.23 + $2.05 **T; $10.82 < $13.28**

60. $10.00 + $20.00 + $3.00 < $1.00 + $20.00 + $30.00 **T; $33.00 < $51.00**

61. $0.73 + $3.50 = $3.50 + $0.73 **T; $4.23 = $4.23**

Stop and Practice **133**

Hog Wild!

Suggest that students write out each problem vertically and then fill in the letters to solve the puzzle.

ANSWERS

51 625

52 604

53 620

54 201

Number Sense

Students will have to read carefully before drawing conclusions about whether the equations are true or false. Students who have difficulty determining the accuracy of the statements may benefit from using play money to model the exercises. Encourage students to give details as they explain their reasoning. Ask that they point out specific numbers rather than generalizing.

For Early Finishers Challenge early finishers to add instead of subtract in Exercises 1, 3, 5, 7, 9, and 10. 1. 479; 3. 1,062; 5. 483; 7. 1,064; 9. 1,054; 10. 793

Resources

TestWorks: Test and Practice Software

Exploring Algebra: Balancing Number Sentences

At-A-Glance Planning

Lesson Planning Checklist

Objective Explore algebra by balancing number sentences.

Student Book Lesson Materials Counters (30 per pair), small envelopes (1 per pair), piece of paper, overhead counters

Materials for pages 134A and 134B Calculators (1 per pair), Teacher's Edition Transparency D (Balance Scale), color cubes

Strand Connections patterns, critical thinking, mental math

	Before Lesson	During Lesson	After Lesson
Daily Math			
p. 134A Problem of the Day			
p. 134A Math Routines			
p. 134A Mental Math			
Teaching Options			
p. 134B Facilitating and Assessing…			
Options for Reaching All Learners			
p. 134B Gifted & Talented			
p. 134B Inclusion			
Technology Options			
p. 135 Interactive CD-ROM Journal			
Subject Connections			
p. 134A Science Connection			
Assessment Options			
p. 134 Talk About It			
p. 135 Error Intervention			
p. 135 Performance Assessment			
Resources			
3-15 Practice			
3-15 Reteaching			
3-15 Enrichment			
3-15 Problem Solving			
3-15 Daily Transparency			

Problem of the Day

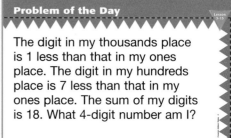

Problem of the Day

The digit in my thousands place is 1 less than that in my ones place. The digit in my hundreds place is 7 less than that in my ones place. The sum of my digits is 18. What 4-digit number am I?

7,128 or 6,057

Math Routines

Measurement Show students a meter stick. Ask one student to name a 2-digit number of centimeters. Ask another student to name the number of centimeters that must be added to the first number to equal 1 meter exactly.

Money Ask students to name two amounts, each less than one dollar, with a sum of exactly $1.00. Discuss the similarities between using the meter stick and using $1.00 as a sum.

Mental Math

Name the number that is 297 less. Explain.

335 38   782 485   940 643   693 396

Science Connection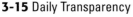

Scientists use pan balances to find mass. An object is placed on one pan and known masses are placed on the other. Scientists record the number of grams that make the pans balance.

• How many grams must be added to the left pan if it holds a 5-gram mass and the right pan has 40 grams of salt? 35 grams

Facilitating and Assessing **Explore** Lesson 3-15

Use with pages 134 and 135.

Get Started Have students make number sentence workmats. Work through Exercise 3a as a class, noting the steps needed to solve for the missing number. Model the problem on the overhead projector. If necessary, repeat for Exercise 3b.

Observe Check to be sure groups are correctly using their number sentence workmats and counters to model each algebraic number sentence. Be sure students understand that the envelope represents n, the unknown. Listen for students who easily recognize that they can subtract the known number from the total to find the missing number.

Discuss Ask students to generalize the steps they took to solve for the missing numbers. Answers should indicate that they could subtract the known number from the total to find the missing number or use their knowledge of addition to identify missing addends.

Assess Use the rubric to assess students' work. See sample for Practice Exercise 1.

4 Full Accomplishment

$$n + 6 = 11$$
$$5 + 6 = 11$$

Assessment Rubric

4 **Full Accomplishment**
• consistently finds values to balance number sentences

3 **Substantial Accomplishment**
• finds values to balance most number sentences

2 **Partial Accomplishment**
• struggles to find values to balance number sentences

1 **Little Accomplishment**
• does not find values to balance number sentences

Options for Reaching All Learners

Gifted & Talented

A Bigger Mystery
Use greater numbers and a calculator to extend the concept of balancing number sentences.

Materials Calculators (1 per pair)

Learning Style Visual, Logical, Social

• Students who have mastered the skill of finding the missing number might enjoy the challenge of finding the solutions to equations involving greater numbers, such as $199 + n = 238$. $n = 39$

• Have students make up two addition number sentences and two subtraction number sentences with 3- or 4-digit missing numbers. Pairs can trade to find the answers. Solutions should be checked with a calculator.

Inclusion

Seeing Is Believing
Use a pan balance to reinforce the concept of balancing number sentences.

Materials Teacher's Edition Transparency D (Balance Scale), color cubes

Learning Style Visual

• Give students a visual example of the basic idea that the two sides of an algebraic number sentence have to balance.

• With Teacher's Edition Transparency D (Balance Scale) as a visual aid, show students how a scale balances according to the masses on either end.

• Let volunteers add cubes to the scale. Emphasize that they must add the same number of cubes to both sides. Use the scale throughout the lesson to help students grasp the concept.

Lesson Organizer

Objective Explore algebra by balancing number sentences.

Suggested Grouping 2 to 4

Student Materials Counters (30 per pair), small envelopes (1 per pair), piece of paper

Teacher Materials Overhead counters

Assignment Guide

Basic 1–8, 11–13, 17–19, 23

Average 3–9, 11–14, 17–20, 23

Enriched 4–10, 13–16, 19–23

---

1 Introduce

Review

Find each sum or difference.

1. 7 + 5 12   **2.** 5 + 7 12

3. 12 − 5 7   **4.** 12 − 7 5

5. 9 + 6 15   **6.** 6 + 9 15

7. 15 − 9 6   **8.** 15 − 6 9

Build on Prior Knowledge

After reviewing fact families, ask students how knowing the addition facts 8 + 5 and 5 + 8 can help them find 13 − 8 and 13 − 5. Possible answer: You can use the numbers in the addition fact to find the numbers in the subtraction fact.

---

2 Teach

See Facilitating and Assessing…on page 134B.

Explore ● ● ● ● ● ● ● ● ● ● ● ● ● ● ● ● ●

Model the activity with a student at the overhead. Begin with the student putting the counters on the mat. Then switch roles and have the student "guess" the number of hidden counters.

(Talk About It) Ongoing Assessment

Listen for students to discuss how knowing the fact families helped them find the missing numbers. Ask for specific examples.

Answer for Talk About It

Possible answer: Arranged counters to stand for the numbers on both sides of the equal sign. The value for *n* is the difference between the two numbers.

Exploring Algebra: Balancing Number Sentences

Problem Solving Connection

Use Objects/ Act It Out

Materials
- counters
- small envelope
- piece of paper

Explore

A number sentence balances when the value of the left side equals the value of the right side. You can use a number sentence workmat and counters to show the values.

Work Together

1. Make a number sentence workmat.

2. Work with your partner to show $5 + n = 12$.

   a. One person places counters on the right side of the mat. That person places the same number of counters on the left side, hiding some of the counters in an envelope.

   b. The partner guesses how many counters are in the envelope.

Remember
A variable *n* can be used in place of a number.

3. Take turns finding the value for *n* in the following number sentences. Keep a record of your work.

   a. $8 + n = 12$ 4   b. $3 + n = 11$ 8   c. $5 + n = 14$ 9

   d. $15 + n = 21$ 6   e. $19 + n = 27$ 8   f. $9 + n = 12$ 3

(Talk About It)

What strategy did you use to find the value for *n*?

Practice 3-15

Name _____

Exploring Algebra:
Balancing Number Sentences
Write a number sentence that has the same meaning.

$6 + n = 14$	$n + 6 = 14$

1. $9 + n = 18$ $n + 9 = 18, 18 = 9 + n,$ or $18 = n + 9$

2. $n + 6 = 11$ $6 + n = 11, 11 = 6 + n,$ or $11 = n + 6$

Find the value of *n* in each of the following number sentences. You may use counters to help.

3. $n + 11 = 20$ _9_   **4.** $9 + n = 16$ _7_

5. $8 + n = 16$ _8_   **6.** $4 + n = 13$ _9_

7. $7 + n = 18$ _11_   **8.** $n + 7 = 15$ _8_

9. $n + 16 = 30$ _14_   **10.** $12 + n = 23$ _11_

11. $22 + n = 36$ _14_   **12.** $n + 4 = 27$ _23_

Use number patterns to find the value for each *n*.

13. a. $n + 20 = 42$ _22_   **b.** $n + 20 = 32$ _12_   **c.** $n + 20 = 22$ _2_

Find the value for *n* in each of the following.

14. $n + 4,062 = 7,063$ _3,001_   **15.** $1,912 + n = 2,840$ _928_

16. $1,492 + n = 2,000$ _508_   **17.** $n + 1,803 = 2,512$ _709_

Find the value for *n* in each of the following.

18. $n + 200 = 315$ _115_   **19.** $1,000 = n + 500$ _500_

20. $750 = 500 + n$ _250_   **21.** $32 + n = 432$ _400_

Reteaching 3-15

Name _____

Exploring Algebra:
Balancing Number Sentences
In your book you used workmats to balance number sentences. Here is another way to balance number sentences.

$6 + n = 9$

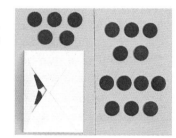

The basketball team has been practicing. They used the same number of basketballs on each side of the court. How many basketballs are in the box?

You can change the picture to solve the problem. Draw Xs over six basketballs on each side of the court.

You took 6 basketballs away from both sides of the basketball court. So, the number of basketballs on either side should be the same. How many basketballs are in the box? _3_

1. How many basketballs are in the box? _4_

$4 + n = 8$

2. How many tennis balls are in the box? _7_

$3 + n = 10$

Draw pictures to show each number sentence. Then find the value of *n*.

3. $n + 8 = 16$ $n =$ _8_   **4.** $9 + n = 11$ $n =$ _2_

The variable *n* may appear on either side of a number sentence.

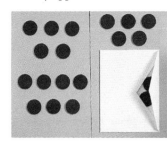

These number sentences have the same meaning:

$5 + n = 12$ $12 = 5 + n$

$n + 5 = 12$ $12 = n + 5$

PRACTICE AND APPLY

Problem Solving Hint

To find the value for *n*, look at the numbers or amounts on both sides of the number sentence.

Practice . . . .

Find the value for *n* in each of the following number sentences. You may use counters to help.

1. $n + 6 = 11$ **5**   2. $12 + n = 18$ **6**   3. $17 = 9 + n$ **8**   4. $13 = n + 4$ **9**

5. $8 + n = 15$ **7**   6. $n + 9 = 22$ **13**   7. $20 = n + 5$ **15**   8. $23 = 7 + n$ **16**

9. **Patterns** Use number patterns to find the value for each *n*.

   a. $n + 17 = 28$ **11**   b. $n + 17 = 38$ **21**   c. $n + 17 = 48$ **31**   d. $n + 17 = 58$ **41**

10. **Critical Thinking** Explain how to find the value for *n* in this number sentence. $n + n = 18$ **The value for *n* is the same for both addends, so *n* = 9.**

Calculator Find the value for *n* in each of the following.

11. $955 + n = 994$ **39**   12. $4,312 = n + 1,096$ **3,216**   13. $372 + n = 2,007$ **1,635**

14. $709 = n + 42$ **667**   15. $953 + n = 1,035$ **82**   16. $n + 687 = 741$ **54**

Mental Math Find the value for *n* in each of the following.

17. $n + 100 = 125$ **25**   18. $500 + n = 800$ **300**   19. $7,000 = n + 4,000$ **3,000**

20. $600 + n = 660$ **60**   21. $n + 75 = 575$ **500**   22. $900 = 200 + n$ **700**

23. **Journal** Compare the number sentences $n + 12 = 21$ and $21 = n + 12$. Explain why the value for *n* stays the same even when the number sentence is written in a different way. Explain how *n* can appear in any position in a number sentence.

Lesson 3-15 **135**

Ask students to identify the most important thing to remember when solving an algebraic number sentence. The values on both sides of the equals sign must be the same.

Error Intervention Ongoing Assessment

Observation Students may use the wrong operation when trying to find the value of the missing number.

How to Help Select an addition number sentence and have students write all other members of the fact family. Ask students to select one number sentence in the fact family that would help them solve for the missing number and tell what operation is used in that number sentence. Help students recognize that the opposite operation is used to find the missing number.

Practice . . . .

Interactive CD-ROM Journal Students can use the journal tool to answer Exercise 23 and illustrate their explanations using the Place-Value Blocks Tool.

For Early Finishers Challenge early finishers to make up their own number sentences using *n* and addition and then exchange and solve one another's problems.

③ **Close and Assess**

Performance Assessment

Find the value of *n*. Use counters to help.

$8 + n = 14$ **6**

$12 = n + 9$ **3**

Assess using the rubric on page 134B.

ANSWERS

23 *n* represents the same missing value; $n = 9$

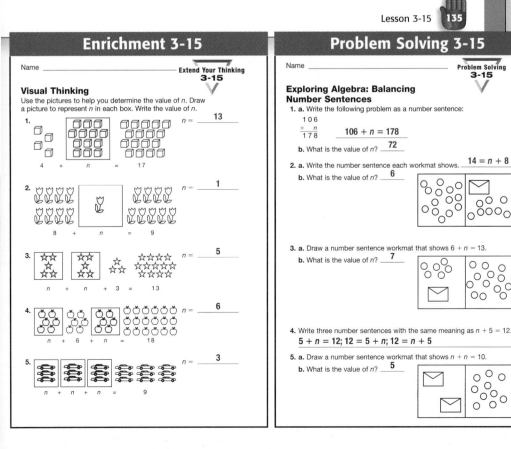

Enrichment 3-15

Name _____ Extend Your Thinking 3-15

Visual Thinking

Use the pictures to help you determine the value of *n*. Draw a picture to represent *n* in each box. Write the value of *n*.

1. $n =$ **13** $4 + n = 17$

2. $n =$ **1** $8 + n = 9$

3. $n =$ **5** $n + n + 3 = 13$

4. $n =$ **6** $n + 6 + n = 18$

5. $n =$ **3** $n + n + n = 9$

Problem Solving 3-15

Name _____ Problem Solving 3-15

Exploring Algebra: Balancing Number Sentences

1. a. Write the following problem as a number sentence:

   $\begin{array}{r} 1\,0\,6 \\ +\ n \\ \hline 1\,7\,8 \end{array}$ $106 + n = 178$

   b. What is the value of *n*? **72**

2. a. Write the number sentence each workmat shows. $14 = n + 8$

   b. What is the value of *n*? **6**

3. a. Draw a number sentence workmat that shows $6 + n = 13$.

   b. What is the value of *n*? **7**

4. Write three number sentences with the same meaning as $n + 5 = 12$. $5 + n = 12; 12 = 5 + n; 12 = n + 5$

5. a. Draw a number sentence workmat that shows $n + n = 10$.

   b. What is the value of *n*? **5**

At-A-Glance Planning

Objective Solve problems by looking for a pattern.

Student Book Lesson Materials *Optional* Lesson Enhancement Transparencies 13, 14

Materials for pages 136A and 136B Teaching Tool Transparency 5 (Number Lines), Power Polygons (1 set per group), stamps (3 or 4 designs per pair), ink pad (1 per pair), paper strips (2 per student)

Subject Connections Careers—mason

Strand Connections patterns, geometry

	Before Lesson	During Lesson	After Lesson
Daily Math			
p. 136A Problem of the Day			
p. 136A Math Routines			
p. 136A Mental Math			
Teaching Options			
p. 136 Student Book Lesson			
p. 136B Another Way to Learn…			
Options for Reaching All Learners			
p. 136B Inclusion			
p. 136B Language Development			
Technology Options			
p. 136A *Math Workshop*			
Assessment Options			
p. 136 Talk About It			
p. 137 Quick Check			
Resources			
3-16 Practice			
3-16 Reteaching			
3-16 Enrichment			
3-16 Problem Solving			
3-16 Daily Transparency			

Problem of the Day

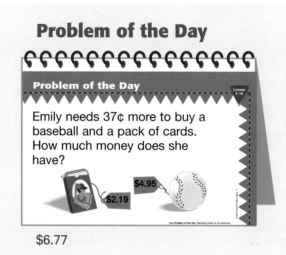

$6.77

Math Routines

Time Tell students that a baby will be fed every 4 hours, starting at 8:00 A.M. Ask students to tell when the feedings will occur. 12:00 NOON, 4:00 P.M., 8:00 P.M., and 12:00 midnight

Calendar Show students a calendar and ask whether it is possible for a month that begins on any day other than Saturday to contain 5 Saturdays. Yes, a 31-day month can begin on Thursday or Friday and still contain 5 Saturdays.

Mental Math

Name the number that is 190 less. Explain your thinking.

559 369   965 775

1,843 1,653   708 518

Math Workshop

To give students practice solving problems involving patterns, have them play *Puzzle Patterns*. A picture is divided into eight rectangular pieces. Students click and drag to rearrange puzzle pieces into a single picture.

Another Way to [Learn] Lesson 3-16

Use as an alternative or in addition to pages 136 and 137.

Materials Teaching Tool Transparency 5 (Number Lines), Power Polygons (1 set per group)

Learning Style Visual

- Have groups number their number lines from 8 to 24 and locate the numbers 8, 11, 14, 17. Have them draw arrows to show the progression of the pattern.

- Next have students identify the change between the first two numbers, the second and third number, and the third and fourth numbers.

- Discuss the amount of change between each pair of numbers and ask if they see a pattern. After students identify the pattern (add 3), ask them what the fifth and sixth numbers on the number line would be. 20, 23

- Prepare number lines for other patterns and show them on the overhead. Have students identify the rule for each. Draw arrows above the number line to show addition and below the number line to show subtraction.

$$8 \quad 9 \quad 10 \quad 11 \quad 12 \quad 13 \quad 14 \quad 15 \quad 16 \quad 17 \quad 18 \quad 19 \quad 20 \quad 21 \quad 22 \quad 23 \quad 24$$

Rule: Add 3

- When students are comfortable with the number patterns, repeat the activity with geometric patterns using Power Polygons.

- Assign Check and Practice on Student Book page 137 or *Practice Master 3-16*.

- Assess using the following rubric.

Assessment Rubric
4 **Full Accomplishment**   • consistently finds and uses patterns to solve problems
3 **Substantial Accomplishment**   • finds and uses patterns to solve most problems
2 **Partial Accomplishment**   • finds some patterns solves few problems
1 **Little Accomplishment**   • does not find or use patterns to solve problems

Options for Reaching All Learners

Inclusion

Stamp Patterns

Use stamp designs to reinforce understanding of patterns.

Materials Stamps (3 or 4 designs per pair), ink pad (1 per pair)

Learning Style Visual, Kinesthetic

- Review the meaning of *pattern* with students.

- Have pairs of students use the stamps and ink pad to create a pattern on a sheet of paper.

- Have partners exchange patterns and use the stamps and pad to continue each other's patterns. Have pairs discuss each pattern, and then write a rule to describe each one.

- If stamps are not available, students can draw patterns with colored pencils or crayons.

Language Development

Number and Alphabet Strips

Use number and alphabet strips to promote the use of mathematical vocabulary.

Materials Paper strips (2 per student)

Learning Style Verbal/Auditory

- Make (or have students make) strips of paper, one for numbers and one for letters.

134	135	136	137	138	139	140	141	142	143

A	B	C	D	E	F	G	H	I	J	K	L	M

- Have students move their fingers to show movement as you call out numbers or letters, such as: 136, then 138, or J, then G. Ask students to describe the movements in mathematical terms, such as: Add 2. Subtract 3.

Lesson Organizer

Objective Solve problems by looking for a pattern.

Suggested Grouping 2 to 4

Student Materials None

Teacher Materials *Optional* Lesson Enhancement Transparencies 13, 14

Assignment Guide

Basic 6–9
Average 6–10
Enriched 7–11

1 Introduce

Review

Find each sum or difference.

1. 6 + 8 14
2. 60 + 80 140
3. 600 + 800 1,400
4. 17,000 − 9,000 8,000
5. 1,700 − 900 800
6. 170 − 90 80

Build on Prior Knowledge

Ask students to look at Review exercises 1–3 and 4–6 and tell what the next exercises would be. 6,000 + 8,000 = 14,000; 17 − 9 = 8

2 Teach

See Another Way to Learn...on page 136B.

Learn

You can use Lesson Enhancement Transparency 13 to illustrate the number pattern table. Write the entire alphabet on the chalkboard so students can see how many letters are being skipped each time.

Reading Assist Word Meaning

To make sure students understand *pattern*, *rule*, *item*, and *relationship*, have them use the words in sentences.

Talk About It Ongoing Assessment

Students may describe a variety of patterns. Encourage students to give specific examples.

Answer for Talk About It

Possible answer: Patterns with colors, shapes, or sizes of objects

---

Problem Solving

Analyze Strategies: Look for a Pattern

You Will Learn
how to solve problems by looking for a pattern.

Learn •

Fabric and wallpaper designers, architects, and biologists all work with patterns.

Look at the table. The patterns in a row follow the same rule. Each row has a different rule. Find the rule for each row.

	Number Pattern	Figure Pattern	Letter Pattern
Row 1	134 137 140 143 ...	▫ ▫ ▫ ▫	A D G J M ...
Row 2	156 154 152 150 ...	▫ ▫ ▫ ▫	M K I G E ...
Row 3	178 180 175 177 ...	▫ ▫ ▫ ▫	T V Q S N ...

Work Together

▶ **Understand** What do you know? The patterns in a row follow the same rule. Each row has a different rule.
What do you need to find out?
The rule for each row

▶ **Plan** Identify the pattern in each row. Look at the relationship between each number, figure, or letter and the item that comes next.

▶ **Solve** Find a rule that describes the pattern in each row. Row 1: Add 3.
Row 2: Subtract 2.
Row 3: Add 2, subtract 5.

▶ **Look Back** Do the patterns in a row follow the same rule?
Yes; Check by applying the row's rule to each pattern in the row.

(**Talk About It**)

What other kinds of patterns can you make?

136 Chapter 3 • Adding and Subtracting Whole Numbers and Money

---

Practice 3-16

Reteaching 3-16

Name _____

Another Look
3-16

Analyze Strategies: Look for a Pattern
This row of letters follows a pattern:

A E I M Q

What letters of the alphabet are missing?

A$_{bcd}$E$_{fgh}$I$_{jkl}$M$_{nop}$Q

What is the pattern?

There are 3 letters of the alphabet missing between each letter.

What are the next 2 letters? Q$_{rst}$ __U__ $_{vwx}$ __Y__

1. 4 $_6$ 10 $_6$ 16 $_6$ 22 $_6$ 28

   a. Find the difference between each pair of numbers. Fill in the blanks above.
   b. What is the rule?
   Add 6 to each number.
   c. What are the next two numbers in the pattern? __34__ , __40__

2. Z $_{YX}$ W $_{VU}$ T $_{SR}$ Q $_{PO}$ N

   a. Fill in the blanks to show which letters are missing.
   b. What is the rule? **Move back 3 letters, or skip 2 letters.**
   c. What are the next 2 letters in the pattern? __K__ , __H__

3. 28 $_2$ 30 $_5$ 25 $_2$ 27 $_5$ 22

   a. Find the difference between each pair of numbers. Fill in the blanks above.
   b. What is the rule? **Add 2 then subtract 5.**
   c. What are the next two numbers in the pattern? __24__ , __19__

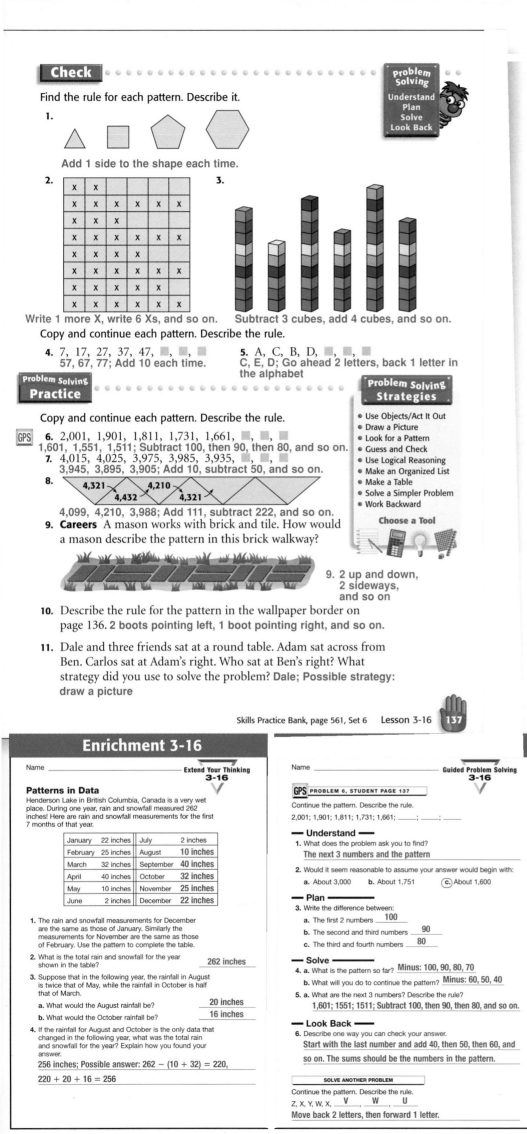

Check

Find the rule for each pattern. Describe it.

1.

Add 1 side to the shape each time.

2.

Write 1 more X, write 6 Xs, and so on.

3.

Subtract 3 cubes, add 4 cubes, and so on.

Copy and continue each pattern. Describe the rule.

4. 7, 17, 27, 37, 47, ■, ■, ■,
57, 67, 77; **Add 10 each time.**

5. A, C, B, D, ■, ■, ■,
C, E, D; **Go ahead 2 letters, back 1 letter in the alphabet**

Problem Solving Practice

Copy and continue each pattern. Describe the rule.

GPS **6.** 2,001, 1,901, 1,811, 1,731, 1,661, ■, ■, ■,
1,601, 1,551, 1,511; **Subtract 100, then 90, then 80, and so on.**

7. 4,015, 4,025, 3,975, 3,985, 3,935, ■, ■, ■,
3,945, 3,895, 3,905; **Add 10, subtract 50, and so on.**

8.
4,321, 4,210,
4,432, 4,321,
4,099, 4,210, 3,988; **Add 111, subtract 222, and so on.**

9. Careers A mason works with brick and tile. How would a mason describe the pattern in this brick walkway?

9. 2 up and down, 2 sideways, and so on

10. Describe the rule for the pattern in the wallpaper border on page 136. **2 boots pointing left, 1 boot pointing right, and so on.**

11. Dale and three friends sat at a round table. Adam sat across from Ben. Carlos sat at Adam's right. Who sat at Ben's right? What strategy did you use to solve the problem? **Dale; Possible strategy: draw a picture**

Skills Practice Bank, page 561, Set 6   Lesson 3-16   **137**

Problem Solving
Understand
Plan
Solve
Look Back

Problem Solving Strategies

• Use Objects/Act It Out
• Draw a Picture
• Look for a Pattern
• Guess and Check
• Use Logical Reasoning
• Make an Organized List
• Make a Table
• Solve a Simpler Problem
• Work Backward

Choose a Tool

Check

Exercise 1 Students may note the increase in size. Encourage them to look for another pattern.

Exercise 3 You can use Lesson Enhancement Transparency 14 to illustrate the cubes.

Exercises 4–5 Make sure students understand that the shaded boxes are used to indicate that students should give three more items for the pattern.

Practice

Exercises 6–8 Students might benefit from using a calculator. Have them record the difference between consecutive numbers.

For Early Finishers Challenge early finishers to select one of the patterns in Exercises 6–7 to extend by three numbers.

6. 1,481; 1,461; 1,451

7. 3,855; 3,865; 3,815

③ Close and Assess

Discuss with students which patterns they found easiest to continue and which were the most difficult.

Quick Check

Continue each pattern. Describe the rule.

1. 223, 246, 269, ■, ■, 292, 315; add 23

2.

Pentagon, seven-sided figure; add 2 sides, subtract 1 side

3. Explain how you can find a rule for a pattern. Explanations should include looking for a predictable relationship among consecutive items.

Enrichment 3-16

Name _____ **Extend Your Thinking 3-16**

Patterns in Data

Henderson Lake in British Columbia, Canada is a very wet place. During one year, rain and snowfall measured 262 inches! Here are rain and snowfall measurements for the first 7 months of that year.

January	22 inches	July	2 inches
February	25 inches	August	10 inches
March	32 inches	September	40 inches
April	40 inches	October	32 inches
May	10 inches	November	25 inches
June	2 inches	December	22 inches

1. The rain and snowfall measurements for December are the same as those of January. Similarly the measurements for November are the same as those of February. Use the pattern to complete the table.

2. What is the total rain and snowfall for the year shown in the table?   **262 inches**

3. Suppose that in the following year, the rainfall in August is twice that of May, while the rainfall in October is half that of March.

a. What would the August rainfall be?   **20 inches**

b. What would the October rainfall be?   **16 inches**

4. If the rainfall for August and October is the only data that changed in the following year, what was the total rain and snowfall for the year? Explain how you found your answer.

256 inches; Possible answer: 262 − (10 + 32) = 220,

220 + 20 + 16 = 256

Name _____ **Guided Problem Solving 3-16**

GPS **PROBLEM 6, STUDENT PAGE 137**

Continue the pattern. Describe the rule.

2,001; 1,901; 1,811; 1,731; 1,661; _____; _____; _____

— Understand —

1. What does the problem ask you to find?
The next 3 numbers and the pattern

2. Would it seem reasonable to assume your answer would begin with:
a. About 3,000   **b.** About 1,751   **c.** About 1,600

— Plan —

3. Write the difference between:

a. The first 2 numbers ____100____

b. The second and third numbers ____90____

c. The third and fourth numbers ____80____

— Solve —

4. a. What is the pattern so far? **Minus: 100, 90, 80, 70**

b. What will you do to continue the pattern? **Minus: 60, 50, 40**

5. a. What are the next 3 numbers? Describe the rule?
1,601; 1551; 1511; Subtract 100, then 90, then 80, and so on.

— Look Back —

6. Describe one way you can check your answer.
Start with the last number and add 40, then 50, then 60, and so on. The sums should be the numbers in the pattern.

SOLVE ANOTHER PROBLEM

Continue the pattern. Describe the rule.
Z, X, Y, W, X, ___V___, ___W___, ___U___
Move back 2 letters, then forward 1 letter.

Chapter 3 • Lesson 3-16   **137**

Section C
Review and Practice

Use the Skills Checklist

Review the **Skills Checklist** on the page with students. Then ask questions such as the following:

- For which problems will you need to count and compare money? Exercises 1–6
- In which problems will you add and subtract money? Exercises 7–18
- In which problems will you make change? Exercises 16–18, 28
- Which problems will you solve by balancing number sentences? Exercises 19–24
- Which problems will you solve by finding the pattern? Exercises 25–27

Assess

You may wish to use this information to assess students' understanding of the lesson objectives.

Item Analysis

Lesson Objective	Items
3-12 Count and compare money.	1–6
3-13 Add and subtract money amounts.	7–15
3-14 Explore making change.	16–18, 28
3-15 Explore algebra by balancing number sentences.	19–24
3-16 Solve problems by looking for a pattern.	25–27

Resources

Practice Masters

- Practice Chapter 3 Section C

Assessment Sourcebook

- Quiz Chapter 3 Section C

TestWorks: Test and Practice Software

ANSWERS

25 Drop the zero from the ones place, then add 100 to the previous 3-digit number.

28 Answers should include subtracting $6.25 from $10.00 to get $3.75, and counting on from $6.25.

Review and Practice

(Lesson 12) Count the money. Write each amount with dollar sign and decimal point.

1. 2 $20 bills, 1 $10 bill, 3 $5 bills, 2 quarters, 1 dime, 1 nickel
$65.65

2. 5 $10 bills, 1 $5 bill, 2 $1 bills, 6 dimes, 5 nickels
$57.85

Compare. Write >, <, or =.

3. $0.27 ● $26.00 <
4. $723 ● $732 <
5. $321.10 ● $321.01 >

6. **Reasoning** Suppose you have just five coins in your pocket. They add up to 51 cents. What coins are they? **1 quarter, 2 dimes, 1 nickel, 1 penny**

(Lesson 13) Add or subtract. Estimate to check.

7. $10.26 + $32.02
$42.28
8. $124.33 + $73.20
$197.53
9. $6.76 + $3.14 + $10.45
$20.35
10. $60.11 − $44.45
$15.66
11. $7.95 − $6.10
$1.85
12. $25.49 − $10.99
$14.50
13. $8.63 + $9.95
$18.58
14. $20.64 + $110.92
$131.56
15. $125.43 − $72.95
$52.48

(Lesson 14) **Using Data** Use data from the table for **16–18**.

16. Marcus bought soda and fruit drops. He gave the clerk a $10 bill. What was his change? **$6.25**

17. Carol bought 2 bags of popcorn. She gave the clerk a $5.00 bill. Did she get any change? Explain.
No; $2.50 + $2.50 = $5.00

18. **Reasoning** Nikira spent $8.00. What did she buy? **Possible answer: 1 popcorn, 2 sodas, 1 fruit drops**

Movie Theater Snacks	
Popcorn	$2.50
Soda	$1.75
Fruit drops	$2.00

(Lesson 15) **Algebra Readiness** Find the value for *n* in each of the following.

19. $n + 100 = 200$
100
20. $n + 37 = 87$
50
21. $923 = 902 + n$
21
22. $n + 77 = 100$
23
23. $785 = 734 + n$
51
24. $307 = 290 + n$
17

(Lesson 16) **Patterns** Continue each pattern. Describe the pattern.

25. 510, 51, 610, 61, ■, ■, ■
710, 71, 810

26. 10, 17, 16, 23, 22, ■, ■, ■
29, 28, 35; Add 7, then subtract 1.

27. 25, 30, 28, 33, 31, ■, ■, ■
36, 34, 39; Add 5, then subtract 2.

28. **Journal** Suppose you sell something for $6.25. The customer gives you a $10 bill. Explain the different ways you could give change.

Skills Checklist

In this section, you have:

- ☑ Counted Money
- ☑ Added and Subtracted Money
- ☑ Explored Making Change
- ☑ Explored Algebra by Balancing Number Sentences
- ☑ Solved Problems by Looking for a Pattern

REVIEW AND PRACTICE

Practice

Name _____

Practice
Chapter 3
Section C

Review and Practice
(Lesson 12) Count the money. Write each amount with dollar sign and decimal point.

1. 3 $20 bills, 2 $1 bills, 2 dimes, 4 pennies — $62.24
2. 6 $10 bills, 2 $5 bills, 3 quarters, 2 nickels — $70.85

Compare. Write >, <, or =.

3. $0.35 (<) $31.00
4. $126 (<) $162
5. $107.01 (<) $107.10

(Lesson 13) Add or subtract. Estimate to check.

6. $7.11 − $4.42 = $2.69
7. $3.76 + $5.89 = $9.65
8. $4.75 + $9.20 = $13.95
9. $7.25 − $0.78 = $6.47

(Lesson 14) Write the change for each purchase.

10. A customer buys a book for $4.95 and a pen for $2.19 and pays with a $10 bill. $2.86
11. Mallory bought a sandwich and milk for $3.21. She paid $5.01. $1.80

(Lesson 15) Find the value for *n* in each of the following.

12. $n + 12 = 37$ — 25
13. $60 − n = 54$ — 6
14. $392 + n = 500$ — 108
15. $737 = 712 + n$ — 25

(Lesson 16) Continue each pattern. Describe the pattern.

16. 500, 400, 310, 230, 160 , 100 , 50
Rule: Subtract 100, then 90, then 80 and so on.

17. 12, 20, 29, 39, 50 , 62 , 75
Rule: Add 8, then 9, then 10 and so on.

(Mixed Review) Solve.

18. A Saturday class starts at 11:00 A.M. It lasts for 2 hours and 40 minutes. What time does it finish? 1:40 P.M.

19. You give a clerk $30 for a $27.28 purchase. Tell what type of change you will receive.
2 dollars, 2 quarters, 2 dimes, 2 pennies

Choose at least one. Use what you have learned in this chapter.

1 Number Trick!

At Home Ask a family member or a friend to enter any 3-digit number on a calculator. Have that person:

- add 242
- subtract 38
- add 96

Then ask for the answer. Subtract 300 from the answer. Tell the person the starting number. How does the trick work? Make up your own tricks!

3 Puzzlemania

Make a crossword puzzle for your class using numbers on grid paper. Use addition and subtraction. Write at least ten math problems for each of the Across and Down sections. Make a key to show all of the correct answers.

Across	Down
Ⓐ 324 + 325	Ⓐ 514 + 107
Ⓑ 921 − 810	Ⓑ 623 − 498

2 Teach It

Your teacher announces that she is going to be absent tomorrow. She needs a volunteer to teach the math lesson.

Make a poster explaining how to add and subtract 3-digit numbers with and without regrouping.

4 Dream Vacation 🌐

Work in a small group. Choose a place you'd like to visit. Start your group's tour at **www.mathsurf.com/4/ch3**. Find the cost of:

- plane or train tickets
- hotels or camping
- food
- tours

How much will your "dream vacation" cost? Design a brochure to advertise your vacation spot.

REVIEW AND PRACTICE

🌐 World Wide Web

Be sure students have a specific planned destination for Dream Vacation. Suggest that they visit Web sites dedicated to their destinations for further information and/or images they can include in their brochures.

Home-School Connection

Students may recognize that calculator tricks like the one in Number Trick! are based on a set of operations that result in a net change of 0. Encourage students to challenge a family member to figure out the trick.

Parents can use the Web site at **www.parent.mathsurf.com**.

Your Choice

Students will review the skills and concepts of the chapter using learning style strengths.

This page of activities is a good opportunity for portfolio assessment.

1 Number Trick!

Learning Style Logical

Students must comprehend that the key to the trick is that numbers added to and subtracted from the starting number result in a net gain of 300. Students will have to plan their variations on this trick ahead of time to ensure success.

$242 - 38 + 96 = 300$; Adding 242 and 96 and then subtracting 38 from any number is the same as adding 300 to that number.

2 Teach It

Learning Style Verbal, Visual

Students may feel more comfortable making one poster for each category. Be sure posters are large enough to be seen by all members of the class. You may wish to display completed posters in the classroom.

3 Puzzlemania

Learning Style Logical, Visual

Students may approach the activity either by forming the puzzle and then making the clues, or by making clues and then arranging the answers in crossword form. Allow students to choose their own strategy.

4 Dream Vacation

Learning Style Social, Visual

Challenge students to search for the vacation they can find for their destination that costs the least per day.

Chapter 3
Review/Test

This page may be used to review or assess students' knowledge of Chapter 3.

Item Analysis

Lesson Objective		Items
3-1	Explore addition and subtraction patterns.	1–7
3-2	Explore adding and subtracting on a thousand chart.	4–7
3-3	Estimate sums and differences using rounding.	8–11
3-4	Solve problems needing exact answers or estimates.	
3-5	Add 3-digit and 4-digit numbers.	4, 7, 9, 11, 12–16, 21, 22
3-6	Add 3 and 4 addends.	12–16
3-7	Subtract 3-digit and 4-digit numbers.	5, 6, 8, 10, 17–20, 23
3-8	Subtract from numbers with zeros.	18–20, 23, 28
3-9	Solve multiple-step problems.	
3-10	Add and subtract numbers mentally.	4–7, 21–23
3-11	Choose a calculation method.	21–23
3-12	Count and compare money.	24–26
3-13	Add and subtract money amounts.	27–29
3-14	Explore making change.	28
3-15	Explore algebra by balancing number sentences.	30–32
3-16	Solve problems by looking for a pattern.	33

Resources

Reading Strategies for Math

Chart 6 (Preparing for a Test)

Assessment Sourcebook

Chapter 3 Tests

• Forms A and B (free response)

• Form C (multiple choice)

• Form E (mixed response)

• Form F (cumulative chapter test)

TestWorks: Test and Practice Software

Home and Community Connections

• Letter Home for Chapter 3 in English and Spanish

Review/Test

Vocabulary Match each word with its meaning.

1. addends **b**   a. the number obtained by subtracting
2. sum **c**   b. numbers that are added together to make a sum
3. difference **a**   c. the number obtained by adding

(Lessons 1 and 2) Mental Math Find each sum or difference.

4. $320 + 400$ **720**   5. $550 - 110$ **440**   6. $770 - 130$ **640**   7. $560 + 240$ **800**

(Lesson 3) Estimate each sum or difference. Round to the nearest hundred.

8. $591 - 320$ **300**   9. $419 + 333$ **700**   10. $775 - 662$ **100**   11. $314 + 106$ **400**

(Lessons 5 and 6) Find each sum. Estimate to check.

12.	486	13.	165	14.	691	15.	1,035	16.	2,395
	40		895		299		4,503		7,593
	+ 981		+ 3,420		+ 2,789		+ 1,290		+ 8,392
	1,507		**4,480**		**3,779**		**6,828**		**18,380**

(Lessons 7 and 8) Subtract. Add or estimate to check.

17. $753 - 458$ **295** 18. $460 - 182$ **278** 19. $3,204 - 2,999$ **205** 20. $4,001 - 2,432$ **1,569**

(Lessons 10 and 11) Find each sum or difference. Choose any calculation method.

21. $1,355 + 2,143$ **3,498**   22. $1,352 + 2,002$ **3,354** 23. $7,640 - 6,000$ **1,640**

(Lesson 12) Compare. Write >, <, or =.

24. $128.00 ● $12.80 **>**   25. $6.70 ● $11.99 **<**   26. $55.02 ● $52.05 **>**

(Lessons 13 and 14) Add or subtract. Estimate to check.

27. $42.78 + $15.37 **$58.15**   28. $67.00 - $43.19 **$23.81**   29. $25.25 + $25.50 + $25.75 **$76.50**

(Lesson 15) Algebra Readiness Find the value for each n.

30. $n + 17 = 58$ **41**   31. $n + n = 80$ **40**   32. $400 + n = 600$ **200**

(Lesson 16) Use any strategy to solve.

33. Ernest posted the photos of the swim team on the notice board. He put 6 in the top row, 9 in the second row, 12 in the third row, and so on. How many photos did he put in the fifth row? **18 photos**

Assessment

Name _____

Date _____ Score _____

Chapter 3 Test
Form
A

Vocabulary: In 1–3, match each word with its meaning.

1. difference   a. a way to estimate by first looking at the leading digits   1. **b**
2. estimate   b. number obtained by subtracting   2. **c**
3. front-end estimation   c. to find a number close to an exact amount   3. **a**

In 4, complete each number sentence.

4. $7 + 2 = 9$

$70 + 20 = n$ **$70 + 20 = 90$**

$700 + 200 = 900$

$7,000 + 2,000 = n$ **$7,000 + 2,000 = 9,000$**

In 5–7, find each sum or difference. Use mental math.

5. $540 + 200$ 6. $360 + 630$ 7. $780 - 420$
   740   **990**   **360**

In 8–10, estimate each sum or difference. Round to the nearest hundred.

8. $768 - 284$ 9. $933 - 645$ 10. $529 + 255$
   500   **300**   **800**

11. Jay ran a 100-yard dash in 14 seconds. Is the time an exact amount or an estimate?   11. **Exact amount**

In 12–15, find each sum. Estimate to check.

12. $723 + 538$ 12. **1,261**

13.	4,825	14.	756	15.	6,987
	+ 987		2,183		7,136
	5,812		+ 4,309		+ 123
			7,548		**14,545**

16. Find $643 - 291$.   16. **352**

Name _____

In 17–19, subtract. Add or estimate to check.

17.	829	18.	4,071	19.	6,001
	− 473		− 2,895		− 5,878
	356		**1,176**		**123**

20. Leo earned $290 mowing lawns and $340 pulling weeds. He spent $125. How much did he have left?   20. **$505**

In 21–23, find the sum or difference.

21.	8,620	22.	1,468	23.	3,200
	− 4,000		+ 3,929		+ 4,704
	4,620		**5,397**		**7,904**

In 24–25, compare. Write <, >, or =.

24. $164 ● $16.40   24. **>**

25. $7.49 ● $14.49   25. **<**

In 26–28, add or subtract. Estimate to check.

26.	$24.65	27.	$30.69	28.	$57.00
	+ 35.98		+ 29.77		− 29.88
	$60.63		**$60.46**		**$27.12**

29. Ana gives the cashier $5.00 for three items costing $1.50 each. How much change will she receive?   29. **50¢**

In 30–31, find the value for each n.

30. $18 + n = 40$ 30. **22**

31. $n + 400 = 700$ 31. **300**

32. Tiger had $10. Then he saved $4 each week. How much money did he have after 5 weeks?   32. **$30**

33. **Explain Your Thinking** Explain how Agatha could use mental math to find $700 - 196$.
Possible answer: Add 4 to each number and subtract to get 504.

Performance Assessment

Suppose you've been saving up for a new mountain bike and need $75 more. You decide to earn the money. What jobs would you do to earn $75?

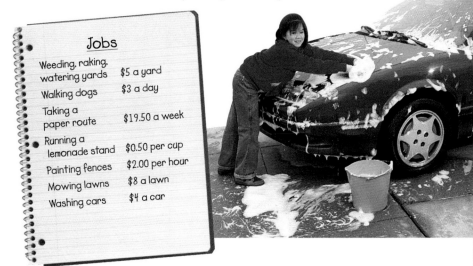

Jobs

Weeding, raking, watering yards	$5 a yard
Walking dogs	$3 a day
Taking a paper route	$19.50 a week
Running a lemonade stand	$0.50 per cup
Painting fences	$2.00 per hour
Mowing lawns	$8 a lawn
Washing cars	$4 a car

1. **Decision Making** Decide which jobs you might want to do. Estimate how much time you would have to spend at each job to earn $75.

2. **Recording Data** Copy and fill out the table below. Remember you must earn at least $75.

Job	Pay	Customers or Time Needed	Total Earnings
	Total		

3. **Explain Your Thinking** How did you decide on which jobs to do?

4. **Critical Thinking** Which job has the greatest range in how much money you could earn in a day? Why? How would a "slow" day affect your earnings with that job?

REVIEW/TEST

Assessment

Name _____ **Chapter 3 Test**
Form
Date _____ Score _____ **D**

Your aunt will take you to two of the places shown in the table.

Busch Gardens	Child (ages 3–9) $29.75	Adult $36.15
Disney World	Child (ages 2–12) $32.68	Adult $40.81
Sea World	Child (ages 3–12) $32.80	Adult $39.95
Kennedy Space Center Tour	$8 per person (children under age 2 are free)	

a. **Making Decisions** Choose two places to visit.

b. **Recording Data**

How much will tickets cost for you and your aunt to visit one of the places you chose?

How much will it cost for tickets to the other place you chose?

How much will it cost for tickets for the two of you to visit both places?

c. **Explain Your Thinking**

How did you decide whether you needed a child's ticket or an adult's ticket?

How did you find the cost of two tickets to both places?

d. **Making Decisions** Your aunt gives you $10 to spend. Which items shown would you buy? How much will these items cost?

FLORIDA $7.22

FLORIDA $3.21

Pencil Case FLORIDA $3.89

$4.26

26¢

FLORIDA $4.78

$2.96

Chapter 3 Performance Assessment

Students will practice adding and subtracting money amounts as they make plans to earn money for a bike.

Introduce the Task

Allow students time to read the introduction to the problem and scan the data, the table, and the exercise questions.

Share Level 4 of the rubric with students before they begin.

Facilitate and Assess

Before students work, you may wish to ask questions such as the following:

- How will you decide which jobs you might like to take?

- How will you decide how much time or how many customers will be needed at each job?

Assessment Rubric

4 Full Accomplishment
- completes jobs plan to achieve savings goal, calculates appropriately, and explains decisions

3 Substantial Accomplishment
- completes jobs plan to achieve goal with few calculation errors and explains decisions with prompting

2 Partial Accomplishment
- partially completes jobs plan, makes some calculation errors and does not explain decisions

1 Little Accomplishment
- does not complete jobs plan or calculate correctly and does not explain decisions

Resources

Assessment Sourcebook

Chapter 3 Test

- Form D (performance assessment)

ANSWERS

4 Possible answers: Selling lemonade depends on the number of customers. If it were a cold or cloudy day, you might not have many customers.

Math Magazine

Students will apply skills learned in this chapter as they investigate different types of currency.

Historical Note

Although the origin of minted coins is unclear, coins are thought to have been invented by the ancient Chinese. They were then "reinvented" about 700 B.C. by the Lydians in what is now Turkey.

The Chinese invented paper currency about the 11th century A.D. The Greeks and Romans used a complex monetary system; like that in the modern world, it included banks and the privilege of buying on credit. During the Middle Ages, the barter system became much more common: goods were traded rather than sold. The use of money only reemerged about the 9th century.

Cultural Link

Have students look closely at the different types of U.S. coins. Ask whether they can identify the people and symbols depicted on the coins. Bring in, or have students bring in, coins from other countries. After repeating the activity, talk about how these coins are like United States coins and how they differ. Students should note that the portraits and symbols reflect the country's history.

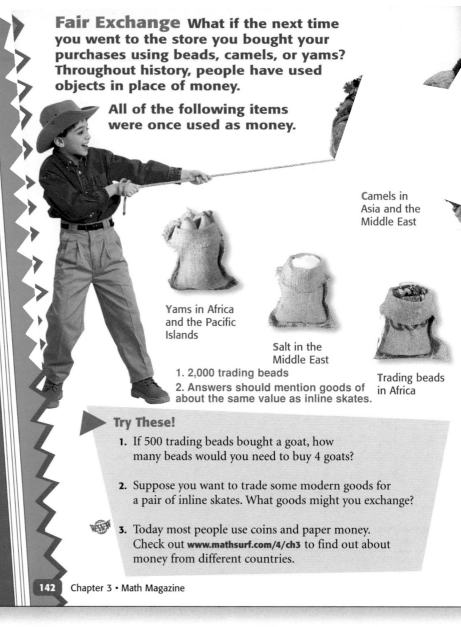

Fair Exchange What if the next time you went to the store you bought your purchases using beads, camels, or yams? Throughout history, people have used objects in place of money.

All of the following items were once used as money.

Camels in Asia and the Middle East

Yams in Africa and the Pacific Islands

Salt in the Middle East

Trading beads in Africa

1. 2,000 trading beads
2. Answers should mention goods of about the same value as inline skates.

Try These!

1. If 500 trading beads bought a goat, how many beads would you need to buy 4 goats?

2. Suppose you want to trade some modern goods for a pair of inline skates. What goods might you exchange?

3. Today most people use coins and paper money. Check out **www.mathsurf.com/4/ch3** to find out about money from different countries.

142 Chapter 3 • Math Magazine

Additional Resources for the Teacher

The Money Book, June H. Campbell. Menlo Park, CA: Dale Seymour Publications.

Time and Money: Problem-Solving Focus, Carole Greenes, et al. Menlo Park, CA: Dale Seymour Publications.

World Wide Web

Students wishing to locate other sites on the World Wide Web where they can find out more about foreign currency might begin by searching for such keywords as *currency* or *exchange rates*. This should provide them with a list of countries and their various currencies. Students can use a table showing exchange rates to investigate the worth of United States dollars versus the currency of any country of their choice.

Test Prep Strategy: Make Smart Choices

Use mental math.
The Radical Reptiles pet store had a sale on iguanas. The store sold 12 iguanas on Monday, 23 on Tuesday, 14 on Wednesday, and 25 on Thursday. How many iguanas did it sell over four days?

Ⓐ 77   Ⓑ 74   Ⓒ 48   Ⓓ 40

Start by adding the two greatest numbers mentally.
23 + 25 = 48. Add 12 more to get 60 and add 14 more to get 74. The answer is Ⓑ.

Write the letter of the correct answer.

1. What are the coordinates for the point on the graph? **D**

   Ⓐ (1, 2)
   Ⓑ (4, 3)
   Ⓒ (3, 5)
   Ⓓ (3, 4)

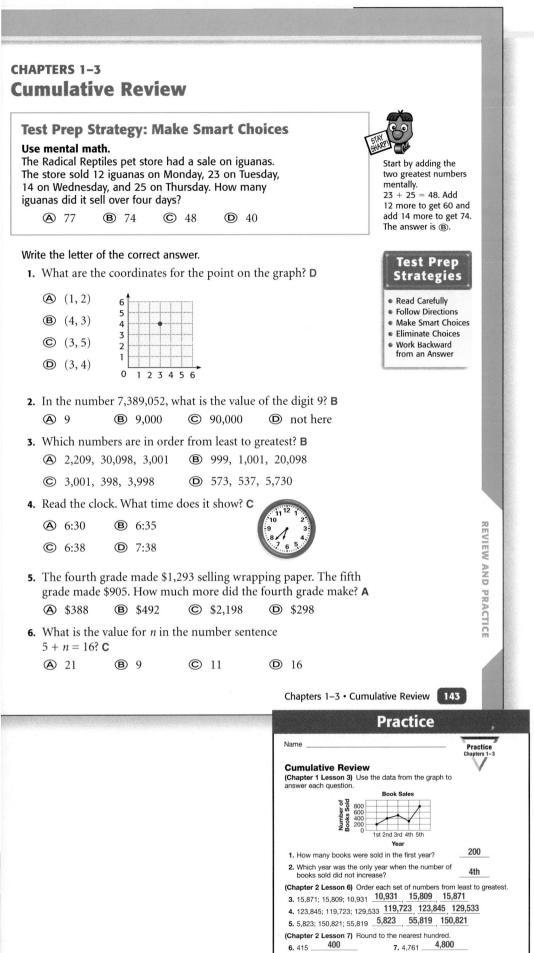

Test Prep Strategies
- Read Carefully
- Follow Directions
- Make Smart Choices
- Eliminate Choices
- Work Backward from an Answer

2. In the number 7,389,052, what is the value of the digit 9? **B**
   Ⓐ 9   Ⓑ 9,000   Ⓒ 90,000   Ⓓ not here

3. Which numbers are in order from least to greatest? **B**
   Ⓐ 2,209, 30,098, 3,001   Ⓑ 999, 1,001, 20,098
   Ⓒ 3,001, 398, 3,998   Ⓓ 573, 537, 5,730

4. Read the clock. What time does it show? **C**
   Ⓐ 6:30   Ⓑ 6:35
   Ⓒ 6:38   Ⓓ 7:38

5. The fourth grade made $1,293 selling wrapping paper. The fifth grade made $905. How much more did the fourth grade make? **A**
   Ⓐ $388   Ⓑ $492   Ⓒ $2,198   Ⓓ $298

6. What is the value for n in the number sentence
   $5 + n = 16$? **C**
   Ⓐ 21   Ⓑ 9   Ⓒ 11   Ⓓ 16

Chapters 1–3 • Cumulative Review **143**

Practice

Name _____

Practice
Chapters 1–3

Cumulative Review
(Chapter 1 Lesson 3) Use the data from the graph to answer each question.

Book Sales

1. How many books were sold in the first year? **200**
2. Which year was the only year when the number of books sold did not increase? **4th**

(Chapter 2 Lesson 6) Order each set of numbers from least to greatest.
3. 15,871; 15,809; 10,931 **10,931** , **15,809** , **15,871**
4. 123,845; 119,723; 129,533 **119,723** , **123,845** , **129,533**
5. 5,823; 150,821; 55,819 **5,823** , **55,819** , **150,821**

(Chapter 2 Lesson 7) Round to the nearest hundred.
6. 415 **400**   7. 4,761 **4,800**

Round to the nearest thousand.
8. 19,599 **20,000**   9. 17,490 **17,000**

(Chapter 3 Lessons 7 and 8) Subtract.
10. 651
    −561
    ‾‾‾‾
     90

11. 723
    −289
    ‾‾‾‾
    434

12. 487
    −208
    ‾‾‾‾
    279

13. 300
    −176
    ‾‾‾‾
    124

14. 3,192
    −1,419
    ‾‾‾‾‾
    1,773

15. 4,028
    −1,368
    ‾‾‾‾‾
    2,660

16. 8,254
    −3,249
    ‾‾‾‾‾
    5,005

17. 1,001
    − 926
    ‾‾‾‾‾
      75

(Chapter 3 Lesson 14) Write the change for each purchase.
18. Matthew gives the clerk a $10 bill for $5.32 worth of dog biscuits. **$4.68**
19. Marco pays for a $2.15 library fine with $3.00. **$0.85**

Chapters 1–3
Cumulative Review

Students review and maintain skills and concepts taught in Chapters 1–3 and practice test-taking strategies. Special attention is given here to the Test Prep Strategy, Make Smart Choices: Use Mental Math.

Introduce the Test Prep Strategy

Make Smart Choices: Use Mental Math Read and discuss the Test Prep Strategy note. After students work through the example, present the following problem:

Mrs. Ruiz ordered 15 math textbooks, 26 reading books, 17 science textbooks and 9 social studies textbooks. How many textbooks did she order? C
Ⓐ 66   Ⓑ 57
Ⓒ 67   Ⓓ 87

Encourage students to find other problems where Make Smart Choices: Use Mental Math might be a helpful strategy.

Some students may prefer another strategy for some of the identified items. Have them tell which strategy they would use and explain why.

Review and Assess

Item Analysis	
Item	Lesson
1	1-2
2	2-3
3	2-6
4	2-8
5	3-13
6	3-15

Resources

Practice Masters
- Cumulative Review Chapters 1–3

Assessment Sourcebook
- Quarterly Test Chapters 1–3

Chapter 3 **143**

REVIEW AND PRACTICE

Section	Pacing	Lessons			Your Test	Materials	
	Day	Lesson/Page		Objective	Correlation	Student Book	Another Way to Learn
A **Understanding Multiplication** Students review the meaning of multiplication and explore multiplication patterns. **Problem Solving Connection** *Look for a Pattern* *Make a Table* *Decision Making*	Day 1	4-1	148–149	Review the meaning of multiplication.			Counters, small bowls or bags
	Day 2	4-2	150–151	Explore patterns in multiplying by 0, 1, 2, 5, and 9.		Hundred Chart	
	Day 3	4-3	152–153	Multiply with 3 or 4 as a factor.			Counters
	Day 4	4-4	154–157	Multiply with 6, 7, or 8 as a factor.			Counters
	Day 5	4-5	158–159	Explore patterns in multiples of 10, 11, and 12.		Fact Table, calculators	
	Day 6	4-6	162–163	**Problem Solving** Solve problems by making decisions.		Calculators (optional)	
B **Understanding Division** Students review and explore division. **Problem Solving Connection** *Work Backward*	Day 7	4-7	166–167	Review the meaning of division.			Counters, small bowls or bags
	Day 8	4-8	168–169	Explore multiplication and division stories.			
	Day 9	4-9	170–171	Divide with 2, 5, and 9 as divisors.			Counters, small bowls or bags
	Day 10	4-10	172–173	Divide with 0 and 1.			Counters
C **Extending Multiplication and Division** Students review division and explore even and odd. **Problem Solving Connection** *Use Objects/Act It Out* *Make an Organized List* **Problem Solving Strategy** *Compare Strategies* **Problem Solving Skill** *Too Much or Too Little Information*	Day 11	4-11	176–177	Divide with 3 and 4 as divisors.			Counters
	Day 12	4-12	178–179	Divide with 6, 7, and 8 as divisors.			Counters
	Day 13	4-13	180–181	Explore even and odd numbers.		Counters	
	Day 14	4-14	184–185	Explore factors.		Grid Paper	
	Day 15	4-15	186–187	**Problem Solving** Solve problems with too much or too little information.			
	Day 16	4-16	188–189	**Problem Solving** Solve problems by comparing strategies.			
Chapter Assessment	Day 17		192–193	Assess student understanding and skills for Chapter 4.			

Looking Back
Grade 3 Multiplication and division facts were introduced. **Grade 4 Chapter 3** Addition and subtraction concepts were developed by working with 3 and 4 addends.

Chapter 4
Key Math Idea

Multiplication involves combining equal groups. It can be shown as sets or arrays. Division involves separating a group into equal sets.

Looking Ahead
Grade 4 Chapter 9 Division and multiplication will be used to find fractions of sets. **Grade 5** Multiplication is extended to include the distributive property.

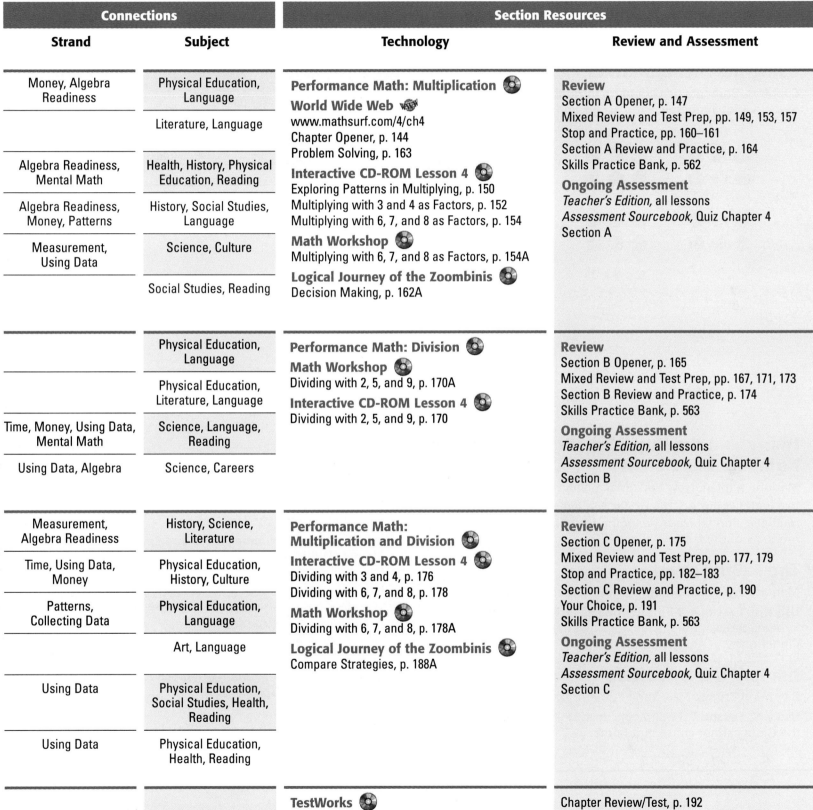

Connections		Section Resources	
Strand	**Subject**	**Technology**	**Review and Assessment**
Money, Algebra Readiness	Physical Education, Language	**Performance Math: Multiplication**	**Review** Section A Opener, p. 147
	Literature, Language	**World Wide Web** www.mathsurf.com/4/ch4 Chapter Opener, p. 144 Problem Solving, p. 163	Mixed Review and Test Prep, pp. 149, 153, 157 Stop and Practice, pp. 160–161 Section A Review and Practice, p. 164 Skills Practice Bank, p. 562
Algebra Readiness, Mental Math	Health, History, Physical Education, Reading	**Interactive CD-ROM Lesson 4** Exploring Patterns in Multiplying, p. 150 Multiplying with 3 and 4 as Factors, p. 152	**Ongoing Assessment** *Teacher's Edition,* all lessons
Algebra Readiness, Money, Patterns	History, Social Studies, Language	Multiplying with 6, 7, and 8 as Factors, p. 154 **Math Workshop** Multiplying with 6, 7, and 8 as Factors, p. 154A	*Assessment Sourcebook,* Quiz Chapter 4 Section A
Measurement, Using Data	Science, Culture	**Logical Journey of the Zoombinis** Decision Making, p. 162A	
	Social Studies, Reading		
	Physical Education, Language	**Performance Math: Division**	**Review** Section B Opener, p. 165
	Physical Education, Literature, Language	**Math Workshop** Dividing with 2, 5, and 9, p. 170A **Interactive CD-ROM Lesson 4**	Mixed Review and Test Prep, pp. 167, 171, 173 Section B Review and Practice, p. 174 Skills Practice Bank, p. 563
Time, Money, Using Data, Mental Math	Science, Language, Reading	Dividing with 2, 5, and 9, p. 170	**Ongoing Assessment** *Teacher's Edition,* all lessons
Using Data, Algebra	Science, Careers		*Assessment Sourcebook,* Quiz Chapter 4 Section B
Measurement, Algebra Readiness	History, Science, Literature	**Performance Math: Multiplication and Division**	**Review** Section C Opener, p. 175
Time, Using Data, Money	Physical Education, History, Culture	**Interactive CD-ROM Lesson 4** Dividing with 3 and 4, p. 176 Dividing with 6, 7, and 8, p. 178	Mixed Review and Test Prep, pp. 177, 179 Stop and Practice, pp. 182–183 Section C Review and Practice, p. 190
Patterns, Collecting Data	Physical Education, Language	**Math Workshop** Dividing with 6, 7, and 8, p. 178A	Your Choice, p. 191 Skills Practice Bank, p. 563
	Art, Language	**Logical Journey of the Zoombinis** Compare Strategies, p. 188A	**Ongoing Assessment** *Teacher's Edition,* all lessons *Assessment Sourcebook,* Quiz Chapter 4 Section C
Using Data	Physical Education, Social Studies, Health, Reading		
Using Data	Physical Education, Health, Reading		
		TestWorks	Chapter Review/Test, p. 192 Performance Assessment, p. 193 Cumulative Review, p. 195

Manipulatives

Using the Manipulatives

Counters Students use counters throughout Chapter 4 to model various multiplication arrays and division patterns.

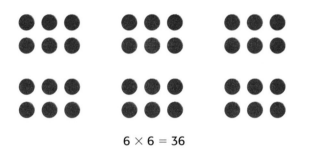

$6 \times 6 = 36$

Suggested Materials	Alternatives
Addition/Multiplication Fact Table	———
Centimeter Grid Paper	Grid paper
Counters	Buttons, beans, beads, coins, paper clips
Small bowls or plastic bags	Egg cartons

Literature

Henry and the Boy Who Thought Numbers Were Fleas

Marjorie Kaplan. New York: Macmillan, 1991.

Use with Lesson 4-2 Henry the dog helps Sam learn his multiplication tables by wagging his tail to show the products of the factors.

The 329th Friend

Marjorie Weinman Sharmat. New York: Macmillan, 1992.

Use with Lesson 4-8 Emery's guests arrive one by one and in pairs, threes, fours, fives, tens, twenties, and fifties to his dinner party.

Jim and the Beanstalk

Raymond Briggs. New York: Putnam, 1989.

Use with Lesson 4-11 Jim cuts down the beanstalk so that the Giant cannot chase him home.

Additional Resources

Quest 2000: Exploring Mathematics, Grade 4, Randall Charles, et al. Menlo Park, CA: Addison-Wesley Publishing Company. *Unit 4.*

Investigations in Number, Data, and Space: Arrays and Shares (Multiplication and Division), Karen Economopoulos, et al. Menlo Park, CA: Dale Seymour Publications.

The Super Source™: Color Tiles, Grades 3–4; Cuisenaire® Rods, Grades 3–4; Snap™ Cubes, Grades 3–4, White Plains, NY: Cuisenaire Company of America.

Math by All Means: Division, Grades 3–4, Marilyn Burns. Sausalito, CA: Math Solutions Publications.

Nimble With Numbers, Leigh Childs and Laura Choate. Menlo Park, CA: Dale Seymour Publications.

Number SENSE: Simple Effective Number Sense Experiences, Grade 3–4; Number SENSE: Simple Effective Number Sense Experiences, Grades 4–6, Alistair McIntosh, et al. Menlo Park, CA: Dale Seymour Publications.

Target Practice, Grades 1–5, Margo Seymour and Dale Seymour. Menlo Park, CA: Dale Seymour Publications.

Math By-Lines, Grades 3–4, Carole Greenes, et al. Menlo Park, CA: Dale Seymour Publications.

For the Teacher

 ### Teacher's Resource Planner CD-ROM

The Teacher's Resource Planner CD-ROM allows you to create customized lesson plans tailored to your own class's needs. It also allows you to preview any supplement page, edit if you wish, and print it.

 ### World Wide Web

Visit **www.teacher.mathsurf.com** for additional activities, links to lesson plans from teachers and other professionals, NCTM information, and other useful sites.

 ### TestWorks Test and Practice Software

A database of questions allows you to generate personalized practice worksheets and tests.

For the Student

Interactive CD-ROM

Use with Lessons 4-2 through 4-4, 4-9, 4-11, and 4-12 Students use the Geometry Tool to model multiplication and division patterns and arrays as they explore fact families.

 ### World Wide Web

Use with Chapter Opener and Lesson 4-6 Have students go online at **www.mathsurf.com/4/ch4** to find out about the fitness activities of other students and to learn about how other schools raise money for sports equipment.

 ### Performance Math

Use daily throughout Chapter 4 Students can practice daily to increase their familiarity with basic multiplication and division facts.

Logical Journey of the Zoombinis

Use with Lessons 4-6 and 4-16 Students record how they solve the Zoombini puzzles in the Zoombini Puzzle Log. This allows them to compare strategies with other students and to help them solve new challenges requiring similar problem-solving skills.

 ### Math Workshop

Use with Lessons 4-4, 4-9, and 4-12 Students can reinforce their multiplication and division skills by playing *Bowling for Numbers.* Hall of Fame certificates can be added to students' portfolios.

Calendar Time Kit

Graphing

One of the concepts in this chapter is multiplication facts. You may use the Calendar Time Kit to reinforce this concept with the following activity:

Create a graph to calculate numbers of animal legs.

- Choose four animals, each with a different number of legs, such as a spider, cricket, giraffe, and ostrich. Have students fill in those names along one axis of the graph.
- Write the name of each animal on a card. Each day, have a volunteer pick two cards at random and add the animals chosen on the graph.
- Have students use multiplication to calculate the total number of legs for each animal each day.

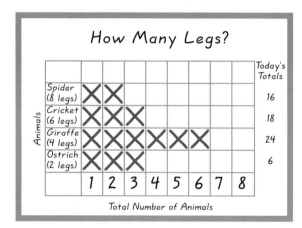

Technology Centers

Technology Resource Area

- This chapter calls for the use of *Performance Math, Math Workshop,* and *Logical Journey of the Zoombinis* to build fluency with multiplication and division facts and the use of a variety of problem solving strategies. This is a good opportunity to set up a technology resource area. Stock the area with computer supplies, materials, and books and magazines about computing.
- Post instructions for loading each of the programs and have knowledgeable students make labels to paste on and near the computers for other students to study.

Bulletin Board

Objective Students create rhymes to help them memorize multiplication and division facts.

Materials Drawing and writing supplies

- Work with students to create a "Math Fitness" bulletin board.
- Every few days, have students choose a multiplication and a division fact.
- Model a simple rhyme such as *Six times seven is forty-two/How many jumping jacks can I do?*
- Have students write rhymes of their own based on their math facts.
- Encourage students to illustrate their rhymes and post their work on the board.

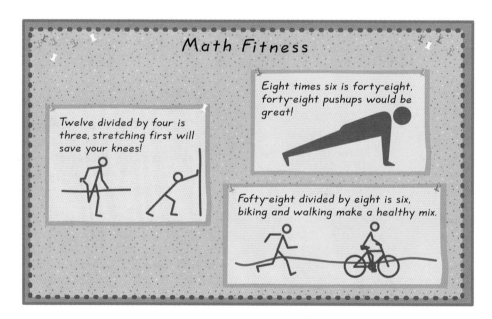

Traditional Assessment	
Review and Practice	Student Edition: pages 164, 174, 190
Cumulative Review	Student Edition: page 195; Assessment Sourcebook: Form F
Section Quizzes	Assessment Sourcebook: Section Quizzes A, B, C

Chapter Tests
  Free Response
  Multiple Choice
  Mixed Response
	Student Edition: page 192; Assessment Sourcebook: Forms A and B
	Assessment Sourcebook: Form C
	Assessment Sourcebook: Form E

Alternative Assessment	
Ongoing Assessment	Teacher's Edition: every core lesson; Assessment Sourcebook: pages 11–13, 16–19, 21
Portfolio	Teacher's Edition: pages 149, 167; Assessment Sourcebook: pages 9, 13, 14, 16, 23
Interview and Observation	Teacher's Edition: pages 153, 157, 173, 177; Assessment Sourcebook: pages 18, 20
Journal	Student Edition: pages 151, 157, 159, 164, 169, 174, 181, 185, 190; Teacher's Edition: pages 163, 171, 179; Assessment Sourcebook: pages 8–11, 15
Performance Assessment	Student Edition: page 193; Teacher's Edition: pages 151, 159, 169, 181, 185; Assessment Sourcebook: Form D

NCTM Assessment Standards

Focus on Equity

Portfolios Different assessment methods allow students to show the range of their mathematical power. A portfolio of work can reflect a student's strengths and preferred learning style. Chapter 4 portfolio opportunities occur on pages 149, 167, and 168.

Test Prep

- The Test Prep Strategy **Make Smart Choices: Use Logical Reasoning** is introduced and practiced in the Cumulative Review on page 195.
- Mixed Review and Test Prep occurs throughout the chapter.

TestWorks

TestWorks can create personalized multiple-choice tests, free-response tests, and practice worksheets.

Standardized-Test Correlation		ITBS	CTBS	CAT	SAT	MAT
Lesson/Objective		**Form M**	**4th Ed.**	**5th Ed.**	**9th Ed.**	**7th Ed.**
4-1	Review the meaning of multiplication.	●	●	●	●	●
4-2	Explore patterns in multiplying by 0, 1, 2, 5, and 9.	●	●	●	●	●
4-3	Multiply with 3 or 4 as a factor.	●	●	●	●	●
4-4	Multiply with 6, 7, or 8 as a factor.	●	●	●	●	●
4-5	Explore patterns in multiples of 10, 11, and 12.	●	●	●	●	●
4-6	Solve problems by making decisions.	●	●	●	●	●
4-7	Review the meaning of division.	●	●	●	●	●
4-8	Explore multiplication and division stories.	●	●	●	●	●
4-9	Divide with 2, 5, and 9 as divisors.	●	●	●	●	●
4-10	Divide with 0 and 1.					
4-11	Divide with 3 and 4 as divisors.	●	●	●	●	●
4-12	Divide with 6, 7, and 8 as divisors.	●	●	●	●	●
4-13	Explore even and odd numbers.	●	●	●	●	●
4-14	Explore factors.	●	●	●		●
4-15	Solve problems with too much or too little information.	●	●	●	●	●
4-16	Solve problems by comparing strategies.					

Key
ITBS Iowa Test of Basic Skills   **CTBS** Comprehensive Test of Basic Skills   **CAT** California Achievement Test
SAT Stanford Achievement Test   **MAT** Metropolitan Achievement Test

Multiplication and Division Concepts and Facts

Theme: Keeping Fit

Teacher Materials *Optional* Lesson Enhancement Transparency 15

Introduce the Chapter

Fitness activities offer contexts for the use of basic multiplication and division facts. Multiplication is related to repeated addition, and division is related to repeated subtraction and to the inverse of multiplication. Students apply multiplication and division facts to decision making and solve problems including those with too much or too little information.

Activate Prior Knowledge

Collect data from the class on how much time each day students spend doing fitness activities. Discuss ways that you could figure out how much time is spent on fitness activities in a week.

Use the Data File

You may wish to use Lesson Enhancement Transparency 15 along with the following questions to discuss the Data File.

- How are the data represented? List, table, pictograph

- Read the paragraph about Ashrita and explain how you could find out how many times you would have to travel around the court to match his record. Possible answer: Add 20 eighty-three times. Find 20 × 83. 1,660 times

- Using the soccer game data, find how many more points the Crunch scored than the Spirit. 6 points

- Use the pictograph to tell how many players should be on the court for two teams total during a volleyball game. 6 players per team; 12 players total

Chapter 4
Multiplication and Division Concepts and Facts

SECTION A

Understanding Multiplication 147

Ashrita Furman of New York has broken many world records! Here are some of the 47 records he holds.

Balancing 55 glasses on his chin for 10 seconds

Bouncing 16 miles on a pogo stick

Performing 8,341 somersaults in 10 hours, 30 minutes

Dribbling a basketball 83 miles in 24 hours

If you dribble a basketball around the outside of a basketball court 20 times, the distance will be about 1 mile. How can you find how many times you would have to travel around the outside of the court to equal Ashrita's record?

Surfing the World Wide Web!
How do you keep fit? Go to **www.mathsurf.com/4/ch4** to find out how your favorite fitness activities compare with those of other students in your grade. Share the data you find with your classmates.

Extensions

Language Arts Connection

Provide students with a copy of an article from the sports section of your local newspaper that describes a game. Have students identify the types of information given in the article. Then have students calculate the difference between the final scores of the competing athletes or teams.

Performance Math: Multiplication and Division

Have students use *Performance Math* to assess their knowledge of basic multiplication and division facts. This pre-test will allow *Performance Math* to create a learning program customized to the needs of each individual student.

You may wish to follow this pre-test with 10-minute practice periods with *Performance Math* throughout the chapter as needed.

SECTION

Understanding Division 165

This table shows the goals scored in a soccer game between the Cleveland Crunch and the Baltimore Spirit. By how many points did the Crunch beat the Spirit?

Team	Period 1	Period 2	Period 3	Period 4
Crunch	2	0	8	4
Spirit	0	4	4	0

SECTION

Extending Multiplication and Division 175

The number of players on a team is an important part of the rules of a game. In an official volleyball game, how many players should be on the court?

Official Number of Players per Team	
Basketball	👕 👕 1
Soccer	👕 👕 👕 👕 👕 1
Volleyball	👕 👕 👕
Baseball	👕 👕 👕 👕 1
Field Hockey	👕 👕 👕 👕 👕 1
Men's Lacrosse	👕 👕 👕 👕 👕
Ice Hockey	👕 👕 👕
Women's Lacrosse	👕 👕 👕 👕 👕 👕

👕 = 2 players

Preview the Sections

A Understanding Multiplication

Students will use equal groups and arrays to show multiplication and repeated addition. They will look for patterns in multiples of 1-digit numbers to help them learn basic facts. Then they will use multiplication to decide how to solve problems.

B Understanding Division

Students will use equal groups and arrays to show division as sharing, repeated subtraction, and the opposite of multiplication. They will use fact families to connect multiplication and division and to help them learn basic division facts.

C Extending Multiplication and Division

Students will extend their understanding of the connection of multiplication and division to learning more division facts, exploring even and odd numbers, and finding factors. Students will then focus on applying the strategies of Guess and Check and Draw a Picture to solve problems with too much or too little information.

Math in the Community

School-Community Connection

Parks and Recreation Department
Have groups of students research places in your community where they can go to exercise and play, such as parks, gymnasiums, or pools. Students can use multiplication, division, and other math skills to report such things as number of teams that can play at the same time and number of players per team.

Community Project The Chapter 4 community project is available in *Home and Community Connections.*

Home-School Connection

Real-Life Division and Multiplication
Ask students to find examples of multiplication and division at home. They may find examples in:
- arrangements of food on shelves or in containers
- division of food supplies
- numbers of doors or windows per room

Parents can use the Web site at **www.parent.mathsurf.com**.

At the end of the chapter, you may wish to distribute the Letter Home from *Home and Community Connections.*

Multiplication Four Square

Students will play a recess game that involves basic multiplication facts.

Student Materials Butcher paper, markers or chalk, ball (1 per group), tape, *optional Assessment Sourcebook 10 (How We Worked in Our Group)*

Introduce the Project

Have students talk about how they use numbers when they play a variety of games. They may mention keeping score or moving a marker a certain number of spaces.

Review the steps in the project, discuss the questions, and preview the self-assessment checklist below.

Self-Assessment Checklist

___ Name products of basic multiplication facts

___ Develop and use a strategy

Complete the Project

Have students share their experiences playing Multiplication Four Square and any strategies they tried. Some students may have bounced the ball to players with greater numbers to make it harder for those players to multiply.

TEAM PROJECT
Multiplication FOUR SQUARE

Play a recess game with a multiplication twist.

Four Square Rules

- A player wearing a number stands outside each square. The other players wait in line.
- A player bounces the ball into another square. The player outside that square catches it and says out loud the product of the tosser's number and his or her own number.
- If the player misses the ball or says an incorrect answer, he or she goes to the end of the line. A new player stands outside the square.

- Make sure everyone in your group knows how to play Four Square.

Try It Out

1. On butcher paper or on the playground, draw 4 equal squares about 3 feet by 3 feet each.
2. Choose a number between 1 and 9. Write the number on paper and tape it to your shirt.
3. Play the game. Remember to say the product out loud.

Talk About It

- Did you find it hard to multiply some numbers? Explain.
- Was it harder or easier to multiply numbers as the game got faster? Explain.

Wrap Up the Project

- Tell how your team played the game.
- Discuss how other recess games, such as jacks or jumping rope, involve math.

Physical Education Connection

Another children's game which involves figures outlined on the ground is hopscotch. Discuss different ways to design a hopscotch court, then ask students to suggest variations of the game that would require multiplication. Possible answer: Throw a pebble onto a number; multiply that number by the number in each square as you hop.

Cooperative Learning

Before students begin play, you may want them to discuss characteristics of good sportsmanship. Distribute *Assessment Sourcebook 10* (How We Worked in Our Group) and have students fill it out for the skill Encourage and Respect Others. Review the characteristics of this skill. Invite students to judge themselves on the skill as they work together.

Allie keeps fit by swimming. If she trains an equal number of hours each day, how could you find how many hours she trains in 3 days?

Skills Checklist

In this section, you will:

☐ Review the Meaning of Multiplication

☐ Explore Patterns in Multiplying by 0, 1, 2, 5, and 9

☐ Multiply with 3, 4, 6, 7, and 8 as Factors

☐ Explore Patterns in Multiples of 10, 11, and 12

☐ Solve Problems by Making Decisions

Multiplication

Review addition. Find each sum.

1. $3 + 3 + 3$ **9**
2. $4 + 4 + 4 + 4 + 4$ **20**
3. $6 + 6 + 6$ **18**
4. $\$9 + \$9 + \$9 + \$9$ **\$36**
5. $8 + 8 + 8 + 8$ **32**
6. $2 + 2 + 2 + 2 + 2$ **10**
7. $5 + 5 + 5$ **15**
8. $\$7 + \$7 + \$7 + \$7$ **\$28**

147

Understanding Multiplication

In this section, students will use equal groups, arrays, repeated addition, and patterns to review the meaning of multiplication. They will solve problems by making decisions.

Subskills

The work in this section builds on...

- Using counters to make models

4 groups of 2

- Adding two or more 1-digit numbers
- Identifying number patterns

11, 22, 33, 44, 55

The ones and tens digits increase by 1.

Use the Section Opener

Because Allie has spina bifida, she cannot kick when she swims. Her favorite stroke is the butterfly. Each time Allie races with her swim team, she has one goal—to beat the time she swam in the previous race.

Have students discuss how they could find how many hours Allie practices in 3 days.
Possible answers: Repeated addition; Multiplication

Skills Trace

(Red numbers indicate pages in this section.)

Lesson and Skill	First Introduced	Grade Four			
		Introduce	Develop	Practice/Apply	Review
4-1 Review the meaning of multiplication.	Grade 2	148, 149	146, 148	149, 160, 161, 164, 191, 562	164, 191, 192, 195, 208, 222, 240–242, 258, 282
4-2 Explore patterns in multiplying by 0, 1, 2, 5, and 9.	Grade 3	150, 151	146, 150, 151	151, 160, 161, 164, 182, 183, 194, 562	164, 192, 195, 245, 287, 339, 427, 468, 471
4-3 Multiply with 3 or 4 as a factor.	Grade 3	152, 153	146, 152	153, 160, 161, 164 182, 183, 562	164, 192, 195, 240–242, 287, 381, 468, 471, 523
4-4 Multiply with 6, 7, or 8 as a factor.	Grade 3	154–157	146, 154, 155	156, 157, 160, 161, 164, 182, 183, 191, 193, 194, 562	164, 192, 195, 208, 222, 240–242, 245, 287, 557
4-5 Explore patterns in multiples of 10, 11, and 12.	Grade 4	158, 159	158, 159	159, 160, 161, 164, 194, 562	164, 191, 192, 195, 538
4-6 Solve problems by making decisions.	Grade 3	162, 163	162, 163	163, 164, 562	164, 192, 195

Mixed Review and Test Prep exercises for this chapter occur on **pages 149, 153, 157, 167, 171, 173, 177, 179.**

Multi-Age Classrooms Use pages 203–230 and 239–252 in Grade 3 or pages 111–132 in Grade 5 to relate to the content of this section.

Reviewing the Meaning of Multiplication

At-A-Glance Planning

Objective Review the meaning of multiplication.

Vocabulary array, factor, product

Student Book Lesson Materials *Optional* Overhead counters (20)

Materials for pages 148A and 148B Counters (80 per group), small bowls or plastic bags (9 per group), 1 musical instrument, *optional* counters (20 per student)

Subject Connection physical education—baseball

Strand Connections money, time, algebra readiness

	Before Lesson	During Lesson	After Lesson
Daily Math			
p. 148A Problem of the Day			
p. 148A Math Routines			
p. 148A Mental Math			
Teaching Options			
p. 148 Student Book Lesson			
p. 148B Another Way to Learn…			
Options for Reaching All Learners			
p. 148B Language Development			
p. 148B Inclusion			
Subject Connections			
p. 148A Physical Education Connection			
Assessment Options			
p. 148 Talk About It			
p. 149 Error Intervention			
p. 149 Portfolio			
p. 149 Quick Check			
Resources			
4-1 Practice			
4-1 Reteaching			
4-1 Enrichment			
4-1 Problem Solving			
4-1 Daily Transparency			

Problem of the Day

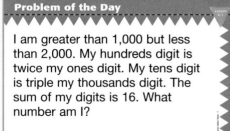

Problem of the Day

I am greater than 1,000 but less than 2,000. My hundreds digit is twice my ones digit. My tens digit is triple my thousands digit. The sum of my digits is 16. What number am I?

1,834

Math Routines

Patterns Have students solve problems such as $3 + 3$, $3 + 3 + 3$, $3 + 3 + 3 + 3$, using multiplication. $3 \times 2 = 6$, $3 \times 3 = 9$, and so on.

Calendar Choose a date during the current month. Have students count by twos, threes, fours, and fives from that date as far into the month as possible.

Mental Math

Find each sum. Explain your thinking.

$2 + 7$ 9	$20 + 70$ 90	$200 + 700$ 900
$6 + 5$ 11	$60 + 50$ 110	$600 + 500$ 1,100

Physical Education Connection

Different sports have different rules for how many players can be in play at a time.

• Have students find the number of players who can play at one time for their favorite team sport. Then have them draw a picture and write an addition and multiplication sentence to show the total number of players in an 8-team tournament.

Another Way to **Learn** Lesson 4-1

Use as an alternative or in addition to pages 148 and 149.

Materials Counters (80 per group), small bowls or plastic bags (9 per group)

Learning Style Kinesthetic

- Share Level 4 of the Assessment Rubric with students before they begin their work.

- Have groups put 6 counters in each of 3 bowls or bags and use any method to find how many in all. Invite groups to share their findings and methods with the class.

- Using counters, demonstrate on the overhead 3 groups of 6 each and an array of 3 rows of 6 each. Connect the manipulatives to the symbolic notation by writing an addition sentence and a multiplication sentence. Introduce the terms *factor, product,* and *array* during the demonstration.

- Have one group member put 5 counters in each of 4 bowls or bags. Have another member use the same number of counters to form a corresponding array. Have two others write the addition and multiplication sentences that describe the groups and array.

- Have group members alternate roles and repeat with other factors.

- Assign Check and Practice on Student Book page 149 or *Practice Master 4-1*.

- Assess using the following rubric.

Assessment Rubric
4 Full Accomplishment • writes addition and multiplication sentences from models and explains how the operations are related
3 Substantial Accomplishment • with prompting, writes addition and multiplication sentences and explains how the operations are related
2 Partial Accomplishment • writes some addition and multiplication sentences and explains in part how the operations are related
1 Little Accomplishment • does not write addition and multiplication sentences or explain how the operations are related

Options for Reaching All Learners

Language Development

Array Hunt
Use common examples to strengthen understanding of **array, factor,** *and* **product.**

Learning Style Visual, Verbal

- Show students an array in the classroom, such as equal rows of desks. Discuss why it is an array. Then write the multiplication sentence that describes the array and identify the factors and product.

- Have pairs of students find other examples of arrays in the classroom, such as rows of windowpanes, equal stacks of books, and equal rows of cubbyholes or lockers.

- For each array, have students talk about why it is an array. Have them write the multiplication sentence that describes it, and indicate which numbers are the factors and product.

Inclusion

Understanding Equal Groups
Use music to strengthen understanding of the meaning of multiplication.

Materials 1 musical instrument, *optional* counters (20 per student)

Learning Style Musical, Verbal/Auditory

- If students have difficulty focusing on printed arrays, use musical notes to represent equal groups or rows.

- Play for students several groups of the same number of equally held notes, such as 4 groups of 3 quarter notes each, with a rest in between each group.

- Have students write or say an addition and multiplication sentence to describe the total notes played.

- Students may make rows of counters to record the groups of notes.

Lesson Organizer

Objective Review the meaning of multiplication.

Student Materials None

Teacher Materials *Optional* Overhead counters (20)

Vocabulary array, factors, product

Assignment Guide

Basic 4–7, 10–14

Average 4–7, 9–14

Enriched 5–14

---

1 Introduce

Review 📖

Find each sum.

1. $2 + 2 + 2 + 2 + 2 + 2$ 12

2. $3 + 3 + 3 + 3 + 3$ 15

3. $5 + 5 + 5 + 5$ 20

Build on Prior Knowledge

After students review repeated addition, ask how else they could have found the sums in the Review Exercises. Possible answers: Skip count by the number being added; Multiply

2 Teach

See Another Way to Learn…on page 148B.

Learn ●

Have students compare the groups and the array. They should recognize that the numbers of groups and rows in the array are the same and that all the groups and all rows have the same number of counters.

After reviewing the factors and product in the multiplication sentence, have students explain how the factors and product are represented by the equal groups, the array, and the addition sentence.

You may want to use counters to demonstrate on the overhead.

Talk About It **Ongoing Assessment**

Look for examples that show students' understanding that multiplication is related to repeated addition of the same number.

Answers for Talk About It

1 Possible answer: $2 + 2 + 2 = 6$ as $3 \times 2 = 6$

2 Possible answer: $3 + 7 + 1 = 11$

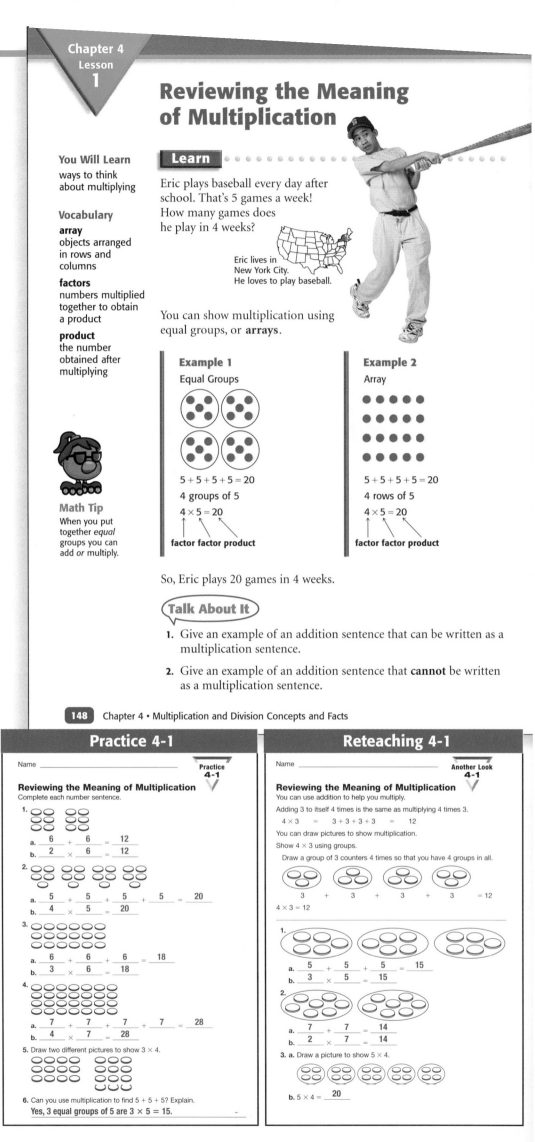

Reviewing the Meaning of Multiplication

You Will Learn
ways to think about multiplying

Vocabulary

array
objects arranged in rows and columns

factors
numbers multiplied together to obtain a product

product
the number obtained after multiplying

Math Tip
When you put together *equal* groups you can add *or* multiply.

Learn ● ● ● ● ● ● ● ● ● ●

Eric plays baseball every day after school. That's 5 games a week! How many games does he play in 4 weeks?

Eric lives in New York City. He loves to play baseball.

You can show multiplication using equal groups, or **arrays**.

Example 1
Equal Groups

$5 + 5 + 5 + 5 = 20$
4 groups of 5
$4 \times 5 = 20$
factor factor product

Example 2
Array

$5 + 5 + 5 + 5 = 20$
4 rows of 5
$4 \times 5 = 20$
factor factor product

So, Eric plays 20 games in 4 weeks.

Talk About It

1. Give an example of an addition sentence that can be written as a multiplication sentence.

2. Give an example of an addition sentence that **cannot** be written as a multiplication sentence.

148 Chapter 4 • Multiplication and Division Concepts and Facts

Practice 4-1

Name _____

Practice 4-1

Reviewing the Meaning of Multiplication
Complete each number sentence.

1.
a. $\frac{6}{} + \frac{6}{} = \frac{12}{}$
b. $\frac{2}{} \times \frac{6}{} = \frac{12}{}$

2.
a. $\frac{5}{} + \frac{5}{} + \frac{5}{} + \frac{5}{} = 20$
b. $\frac{4}{} \times \frac{5}{} = 20$

3.
a. $\frac{6}{} + \frac{6}{} + \frac{6}{} = 18$
b. $\frac{3}{} \times \frac{6}{} = 18$

4.
a. $\frac{7}{} + \frac{7}{} + \frac{7}{} + \frac{7}{} = 28$
b. $\frac{4}{} \times \frac{7}{} = 28$

5. Draw two different pictures to show 3×4.

6. Can you use multiplication to find $5 + 5 + 5$? Explain.
Yes, 3 equal groups of 5 are $3 \times 5 = 15$.

Reteaching 4-1

Name _____

Another Look 4-1

Reviewing the Meaning of Multiplication
You can use addition to help you multiply.
Adding 3 to itself 4 times is the same as multiplying 4 times 3.
$4 \times 3 = 3 + 3 + 3 + 3 = 12$
You can draw pictures to show multiplication.
Show 4×3 using groups.
Draw a group of 3 counters 4 times so that you have 4 groups in all.

$3 + 3 + 3 + 3 = 12$
$4 \times 3 = 12$

1.
a. $\frac{5}{} + \frac{5}{} + \frac{5}{} = 15$
b. $\frac{3}{} \times \frac{5}{} = 15$

2.
a. $\frac{7}{} + \frac{7}{} = 14$
b. $\frac{2}{} \times \frac{7}{} = 14$

3. a. Draw a picture to show 5×4.

b. $5 \times 4 = \frac{20}{}$

Copy and complete each number sentence.

1.

a. ■ + ■ = ■ $4 + 4 = 8$
b. ■ × ■ = ■ $2 × 4 = 8$

2.

a. ■ + ■ + ■ = ■ $7 + 7 + 7 = 21$
b. ■ × ■ = ■ $3 × 7 = 21$

3. **Reasoning** How could you use multiplication to find $6 + 6 + 6$?
Multiply 3 by 6 to get 18.

Practice ○

Skills and Reasoning

Copy and complete each number sentence.

4.

a. ■ + ■ + ■ = ■ $4 + 4 + 4 = 12$
b. ■ × ■ = ■ $3 × 4 = 12$

5.

a. ■ + ■ + ■ = ■ $5 + 5 + 5 = 15$
b. ■ × ■ = ■ $3 × 5 = 15$

6. Draw two different pictures to show $3 × 6$. **Possible answers: 18 objects in 3 groups of 6; An array of 18 with 3 rows of 6**
7. Can you use multiplication to find $10 + 10 + 10$? Explain. **Yes; 3 equal groups of 10 is $3 × 10 = 30$.**

Problem Solving and Applications

Write an addition and a multiplication sentence for each. Solve.

8. **Money** Suppose it costs $2 each to watch a baseball game. How much will a family of 5 pay? **$10; Possible answers: $2 + $2 + $2 + $2 + $2 = $10; 5 × $2 = $10**
9. **What If** Eric practices batting 3 hours a day at baseball camp. How many hours will he practice in 6 days? **18 hours; $3 + 3 + 3 + 3 + 3 + 3 = 18$; $6 × 3 = 18$**

Mixed Review and Test Prep

Algebra Readiness Find each sum or difference.

10. $116 + 18 = n$ **134**
11. $872 − 234 = n$ **638**
12. $202 + 343 = n$ **545**
13. $409 − 24 = n$ **385**
14. **Money** How much change would you get from a $10 bill, if you bought a baseball for $7.79? **D**

Ⓐ $17.79   Ⓑ $3.79   Ⓒ $3.21   Ⓓ $2.21

Lesson 4-1   **149**

Enrichment 4-1

Name _____   Extend Your Thinking **4-1**

Visual Thinking
Circle the figure with the same pattern as the figure on the left.

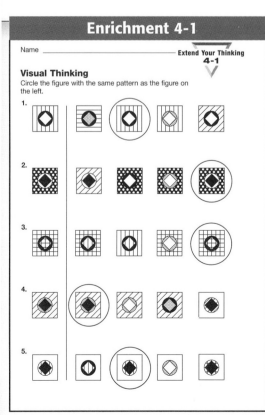

Problem Solving 4-1

Name _____   Problem Solving **4-1**

Reviewing the Meaning of Multiplication

Science Earth is not the only planet that has a moon. Most of the other planets in our solar system also have moons. In many cases, they have more than one moon.

1. In 1610, Galileo discovered 4 moons on Jupiter. Today, scientists believe that Jupiter has 4 times as many moons as Galileo saw. How many known moons does Jupiter have? **16 moons**
2. Mars has 2 known moons. Saturn is known to have 9 times as many moons as Mars. How many known moons does Saturn have? **18 moons**
3. Until 1989, scientists had only discovered 2 of Neptune's moons. Since then, scientists have found 4 times as many moons orbiting Neptune as they originally thought. How many known moons does Neptune have? **8 moons**
4. Uranus is known to have 5 times as many moons as Earth. How many known moons does Uranus have? **5 moons**
5. Suppose you go to soccer practice 5 days a week. How many days would you go to practice in 4 weeks? **20 days**
6. Suppose you work on homework 2 hours a day. How many hours would you work in 5 days? **10 hours**
7. A magazine costs $3. How much would you pay for 6 magazines? **$18**
8. A tray of blueberry muffins contains 2 cups of blueberries. How many blueberries are in 3 trays? **6 cups**

Check ○ ○ ○ ○ ○ ○ ○ ○ ○ ○ ○ ○ ○ ○

Exercises 1 and 2 Remind students to write the complete addition and multiplication sentences, not just the sum or product.

Error Intervention Ongoing Assessment

Observation Students write the number in each group or row for both factors in a multiplication sentence.

How to Help Have students write and complete a sentence such as *4 groups (or rows) of 5 make 20* to clarify their thinking.

Practice ○

Exercises 8 and 9 Encourage students who are having difficulty writing sentences to draw pictures or use counters to represent each situation.

For Early Finishers Challenge early finishers to write a word problem that could be represented by one of the expressions in Exercises 4–7.

3 Close and Assess

Portfolio

Have students choose two different numbers from 2 through 9 to represent a number of groups and the number in each group. Have them draw the groups and the corresponding array, then write the corresponding addition and multiplication sentences.

Quick Check

Number Sense Which of the following addition expressions can also be written as a multiplication expression? Explain. **Exercises 1 and 3; The same number is added.**

1. $3 + 3 + 3 + 3$
2. $1 + 2 + 3$
3. $9 + 9$
4. $5 + 6 + 5$

Skill Write the addition and multiplication sentence shown by each.

1.

$2 + 2 + 2 + 2 + 2 + 2 + 2 = 14$; $7 × 2 = 14$

2.

$12 + 12 = 24$; $2 × 12 = 24$

Resources

Technology Master 10

Exploring Patterns in Multiplying by 0, 1, 2, 5, and 9

At-A-Glance Planning

Lesson Planning Checklist

Objective Explore patterns in multiplying by 0, 1, 2, 5, and 9.

Vocabulary multiple

Student Book Lesson Materials Teaching Tool Transparency 9 (Hundred Chart), colored pencils (1 red, 1 blue, 1 yellow per group), *optional Assessment Sourcebook 10* (How We Worked in Our Group)

Materials for pages 150A and 150B Teaching Tool Transparency 9 (Hundred Chart), cubes, counters, or other small objects (50–60 each of 3 types per group), small bowls or plastic bags (10 per group)

Strand Connection patterns

	Before Lesson	During Lesson	After Lesson
Daily Math			
p. 150A Problem of the Day			
p. 150A Math Routines			
p. 150A Mental Math			
Teaching Options			
p. 150B Facilitating and Assessing…			
Options for Reaching All Learners			
p. 150B Inclusion			
p. 150B Language Development			
Technology Options			
p. 150 Interactive CD-ROM Lesson 4			
Subject Connections			
p. 150A Literature Connection			
Assessment Options			
p. 150 Talk About It			
p. 151 Error Intervention			
p. 151 Performance Assessment			
Resources			
4-2 Practice			
4-2 Reteaching			
4-2 Enrichment			
4-2 Problem Solving			
4-2 Daily Transparency			

Problem of the Day

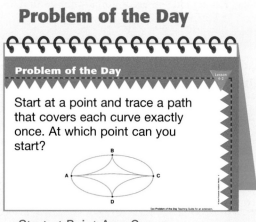

Start at a point and trace a path that covers each curve exactly once. At which point can you start?

Start at Point A or C.

Math Routines

Patterns Have students name multiplication facts from the 9s table. Ask them what pattern they see in the tens digits. Always 1 less than the factor multiplied by 9.

Time Choose a time some number of minutes after an hour, such as 11:20. Have students count from that time by 2s, 5s, and 9s as far into the hour as possible.

Mental Math

Find each sum. Explain your thinking.

7 + 6 13   70 + 60 130   700 + 600 1,300

8 + 9 17   80 + 90 170   800 + 900 1,700

Literature Connection

In *Henry and the Boy Who Thought Numbers Were Fleas* by Marjorie Kaplan, the dog Henry helps Sam with his multiplication facts by wagging his tail to show the products.

- Ask students how many times Henry would have to wag his tail to show the product of 9 and 6. 54

Facilitating and Assessing **Explore** Lesson 4-2

Use with pages 150 and 151.

Get Started Demonstrate to students how they can use a calculator to skip count. For example, entering ⊞ ② [CONS] or ⊞ ② establishes 2 as a constant, or a number that stays the same. Have students try these key sequences to skip count by 2:

[ON/AC] ⊞ ② [CONS] [CONS] [CONS] ...

[ON/AC] ⊞ ② ⊟ ⊟ ⊟ ...

You may want to assign the roles of calculator operator, recorder, and reporter. Have students alternate roles for each set of multiples. Also assign the group skill Explain and Summarize, which students can practice as they work.

Observe Be alert for students who are confused when they have to shade some squares more than once. You may have them circle the numbers with colored pencils.

Students who are having difficulty recognizing number patterns in the multiples may find it helpful to list the numbers that are shaded each color.

Discuss Encourage students to focus on number patterns (rather than patterns of color or positions in the chart), as these will be most helpful when students are trying to recall the product of an isolated, basic multiplication fact.

Assess Use the rubric to assess students' work. See sample for Practice Exercise 4.

4 Full Accomplishment
$$2 \times 8 = 16$$

Assessment Rubric

4 Full Accomplishment
- finds products and describes how number patterns and multiplication properties can help find products

3 Substantial Accomplishment
- finds most products and describes, with prompting, how number patterns and multiplication properties can help find products

2 Partial Accomplishment
- finds some products and partially describes use of a number pattern and a multiplication property

1 Little Accomplishment
- does not find products or describe use of number patterns and multiplication properties

Options for Reaching All Learners

Inclusion

Marking Multiples
Use small objects to mark multiples on a hundred chart.

Materials Teaching Tool Transparency 9 (Hundred Chart), cubes, counters, or other small objects (50–60 of 3 types per group)

Learning Style Kinesthetic, Visual

- Enlarge a hundred chart from $8\frac{1}{2} \times 11$ paper to 11×17 paper to make 1-inch squares. Distribute three sets of different small objects and the enlarged chart to each group.

- As students skip count, have them put one type of small object on each number they find: a cube on each multiple of 2, another type on each multiple of 5, and yet another type on each multiple of 9. Common multiples will have stacks of two or three items.

Language Development

Model Properties
Use counters to strengthen understanding of multiplication properties.

Materials Counters (50 per group), small bowls or plastic bags (10 per group)

Learning Style Kinesthetic, Verbal

- Have one student in each group put 4 counters into each of 6 bowls or bags. Have another student put 6 counters into each of 4 bowls or bags. Have a third student tell which of the properties listed on page 151 is being shown. Have students write the multiplication sentence and discuss how it represents that property. Order Property; $6 \times 4 = 4 \times 6$

- Encourage students to model and discuss the One Property and the Zero Property using the same system.

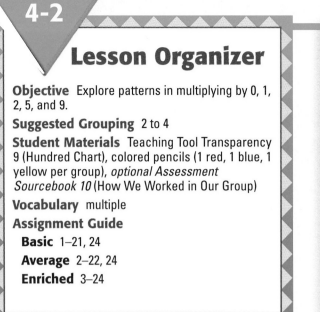

4-2

Lesson Organizer

Objective Explore patterns in multiplying by 0, 1, 2, 5, and 9.

Suggested Grouping 2 to 4

Student Materials Teaching Tool Transparency 9 (Hundred Chart), colored pencils (1 red, 1 blue, 1 yellow per group), *optional Assessment Sourcebook 10* (How We Worked in Our Group)

Vocabulary multiple

Assignment Guide

Basic 1–21, 24

Average 2–22, 24

Enriched 3–24

1 Introduce

Review

Skip count by each number to 30.

1. by 2s 2, 4, 6, ... 30
2. by 5s 5, 10, 15, 20, 25, 30
3. by 9s 9, 18, 27

Build on Prior Knowledge

After students review multiples of 2, 5, and 9, ask how skip counting is related to the total number in arrays. Possible answer: The numbers said are the total numbers in 1, 2, 3, ... rows in arrays.

2 Teach

See Facilitating and Assessing...on page 150B.

Interactive CD-ROM Lesson 4 includes content in this lesson.

Explore

As students work together, you may want to ask questions such as:

- Why did you shade that number blue?
- Why didn't you shade that number?

Answers for Work Together

1a-c, 2 See pages D1–D4.

Talk About It **Ongoing Assessment**

Listen for an understanding of multiples and the phrase "in common."

Answers for Talk About It

3, 4 See pages D1–D4.

Chapter 4 Lesson 2

Exploring Patterns in Multiplying by 0, 1, 2, 5, and 9

Problem Solving Connection
Look for a Pattern

Materials
- hundred chart
- yellow, blue, and red pencils

Vocabulary
multiple
the product of a given whole number and any other whole number

Explore

Patterns can help you remember multiplication facts.

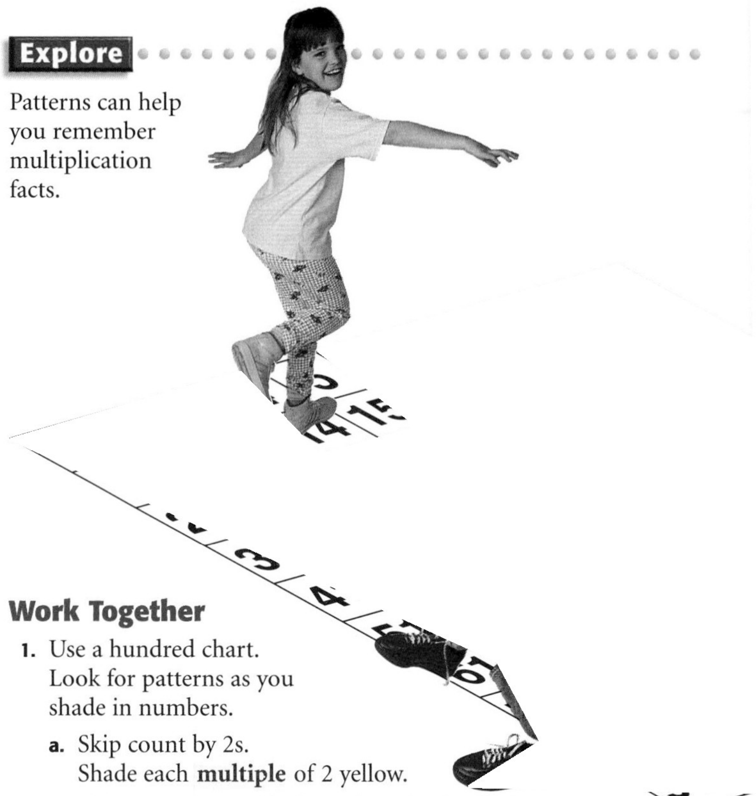

Math Tip
Look for patterns to help you find the multiples more quickly!

Work Together

1. Use a hundred chart. Look for patterns as you shade in numbers.
   a. Skip count by 2s. Shade each **multiple** of 2 yellow.
   b. Skip count by 5s. Shade each multiple of 5 blue.
   c. Skip count by 9s. Shade each multiple of 9 red.
2. What patterns do you see in the multiples of 2? Of 5? Of 9?

Talk About It

3. Which multiples do 2 and 5 have in common on the hundred chart?
4. Which multiples do 5 and 9 have in common on the hundred chart?

Practice 4-2

Name ______________ Practice 4-2

Exploring Patterns in Multiplying by 0, 1, 2, 5, and 9

Complete.

1. Multiples of 2 end in 0, 2, 4, 6, or 8.
2. Multiples of 5 end in 0 or 5.
3. Describe the pattern that multiples of 9 follow.
   Possible answers: The sum of the digits is always 9. The tens digit is 1 less than the other factor.
4. Does 3 × 5 = 5 × 3? Explain.
   Yes; The Order Property states that two numbers can be multiplied in any order.

Find each product.

5. 2 × 3 = 6	6. 5 × 4 = 20	7. 5 × 6 = 30
8. 9 × 4 = 36	9. 7 × 5 = 35	10. 5 × 3 = 15
11. 9 × 7 = 63	12. 2 × 4 = 8	13. 0 × 6 = 0
14. 6 × 1 = 6	15. 9 × 8 = 72	16. 4 × 5 = 20
17. 2 × 7 = 14	18. 1 × 4 = 4	19. 6 × 9 = 54
20. 5 × 9 = 45	21. 8 × 0 = 0	22. 9 × 2 = 18
23. 2 × 0 = 0	24. 9 × 6 = 54	25. 5 × 2 = 10
26. 7 × 1 = 7	27. 6 × 5 = 30	28. 9 × 9 = 81

29. Find the product of 5 and 8. 40
30. Find the product of 3 and 9. 27
31. Which is greater, 4 × 5 or 3 × 6? Explain.
    4 × 5; 4 × 5 = 20, 3 × 6 = 18
32. Which is less, 7 × 8 or 6 × 9? Explain.
    6 × 9; 6 × 9 = 54, 7 × 8 = 56

Reteaching 4-2

Name ______________ Another Look 4-2

Exploring Patterns in Multiplying by 0, 1, 2, 5, and 9

In your book you used a hundred chart to find multiplication patterns. Here is another way to explore patterns in multiplying by 0, 1, 2, 5, and 9.

You can use counters and patterns to help you multiply.

Skip counting by 2s with counters can help you multiply by 2.
Find 6 × 2.

Skip count by 2s until you have counted 6 groups of 2. 6 × 2 = 12

Skip counting by 5s with counters can help you multiply by 5.
Find 4 × 5.

Skip count by 5s until you have counted 4 groups of 5. 4 × 5 = 20

Find each product. Use counters or draw pictures to help.

1. 
   4 × 2 = 8
2. 
   3 × 5 = 15
3. 9 × 1 = 9
4. 5 × 4 = 20
5. 2 × 8 = 16
6. 9 × 5 = 45
7. 1 × 7 = 7
8. 0 × 6 = 0

Look for patterns to help you remember multiples of 2, 5, and 9.

Multiples of 2	Multiples of 5	Multiples of 9
$2 \times 0 = 0$	$5 \times 0 = 0$	$9 \times 0 = 0$
$2 \times 1 = 2$	$5 \times 1 = 5$	$9 \times 1 = 9$
$2 \times 2 = 4$	$5 \times 2 = 10$	$9 \times 2 = 18$
$2 \times 3 = 6$	$5 \times 3 = 15$	$9 \times 3 = 27$
$2 \times 4 = 8$	$5 \times 4 = 20$	$9 \times 4 = 36$
$2 \times 5 = 10$	$5 \times 5 = 25$	$9 \times 5 = 45$
$2 \times 6 = 12$	$5 \times 6 = 30$	$9 \times 6 = 54$
$2 \times 7 = 14$	$5 \times 7 = 35$	$9 \times 7 = 63$
$2 \times 8 = 16$	$5 \times 8 = 40$	$9 \times 8 = 72$
$2 \times 9 = 18$	$5 \times 9 = 45$	$9 \times 9 = 81$
Multiples of 2 end in 0, 2, 4, 6, 8.	Multiples of 5 end in 0 or 5.	Multiples of 9: The tens digit is 1 less than the other factor. The sum of the digits is 9.

Learning multiplication properties can also help you remember basic facts.

Order Property
Two numbers can be multiplied in any order.
$5 \times 4 = 4 \times 5$

One Property
The product of a number and 1 is that number.
$5 \times 1 = 5$

Zero Property
The product of a number and 0 is 0.
$5 \times 0 = 0$

Practice ·

Find each product.

1. 2×6 12 **2.** 2×9 18 **3.** 9×1 9 **4.** 2×8 16 **5.** 9×6 54

6. 3×9 27 **7.** 5×5 25 **8.** 9×8 72 **9.** 2×5 10 **10.** 0×2 0

11. 5×9 45 **12.** 2×7 14 **13.** 5×8 40 **14.** 9×0 0 **15.** 1×2 2

16. 5×7 35 **17.** 9×9 81 **18.** 2×3 6 **19.** 5×4 20 **20.** 9×4 36

21. Find the product of 9 and 7. **63** **22.** Find the product of 2 and 4. **8**

23. **Critical Thinking** 10 is a multiple of 2 and 5. Is the product of any number and 10 also a multiple of 2 and 5? Explain.

24. **Journal** Describe the number patterns that could help you remember multiples of 2, 5, and 9.

Connect ·

After reviewing the number patterns and the multiplication properties, have students talk about how the patterns and properties could help them find products.

Error Intervention Ongoing Assessment

Observation Students write incorrect products.

How to Help Have students circle 2, 5, 9, 0, or 1 if any is a factor in a multiplication expression. Then have them think of the patterns for multiples of 2, 5, or 9 or the properties of 1 and 0.

Practice ·

Exercise 23 Students may find it helpful to list several multiples of 10 and then check whether they fit the patterns for multiples of 2 and 5.

For Early Finishers Challenge early finishers to choose five exercises from Exercises 1–15 and tell what pattern or multiplication property could be used to help find each product.

③ Close and Assess

Performance Assessment

Find each product. Explain how a number pattern or multiplication property can be used to help.

1. 5×6 30; Multiples of 5 end in 0 or 5

2. 7×0 0; The product of a number and 0 is 0.

Assess using the rubric on page 150B.

ANSWERS

23 Yes; Possible answers: All multiples of 10 end in 0, and numbers ending in 0 are multiples of 2 and 5. Since 10 is a multiple of 2 and 5, any multiple of 10 is also a multiple of 2 and 5.

24 Possible answer: Multiples of 2 end in 2, 4, 6, 8, or 0; multiples of 5 end in 0 or 5; the digits in multiples of 9 add to 9.

Enrichment 4-2	Problem Solving 4-2

Multiplying with 3 and 4 as Factors

At-A-Glance Planning

Lesson Planning Checklist

Objective Multiply with 3 or 4 as a factor.

Student Book Lesson Materials *Optional* counters (28)

Materials for pages 152A and 152B Counters (80 per group), colored markers

Subject Connections health—roller skating, history—invention of roller skates

Strand Connections time, algebra readiness, mental math

	Before Lesson	During Lesson	After Lesson
Daily Math			
p. 152A Problem of the Day			
p. 152A Math Routines			
p. 152A Mental Math			
Teaching Options			
p. 152 Student Book Lesson			
p. 152B Another Way to Learn…			
Options for Reaching All Learners			
p. 152B Reading Assist			
p. 152B Cultural Connection			
Technology Options			
p. 152 Interactive CD-ROM Lesson 4			
Subject Connections			
p. 152A Physical Education Connection			
Assessment Options			
p. 152 Talk About It			
p. 153 Error Intervention			
p. 153 Interview			
p. 153 Quick Check			
Resources			
4-3 Practice			
4-3 Reteaching			
4-3 Enrichment			
4-3 Problem Solving			
4-3 Daily Transparency			

Problem of the Day

Problem of the Day

Complete this puzzle so that the numbers along each line have a sum of 34.

For solution art, see pages D1–D4.

Math Routines

Measurement Use your hands to show the length of 1 ft. Ask students to name objects that are 3 and 4 ft long.

Money Tell students to suppose you are going to deposit $100 in the bank, which will give you $2 in interest every 3 months. Ask how much money you would have at the end of the year. $108

Mental Math

Tell which sum is greater. Explain.

50 + 50 or 80 + 30 80 + 30

40 + 70 or 20 + 80 40 + 70

70 + 70 or 60 + 90 60 + 90

30 + 70 or 50 + 40 30 + 70

Physical Education Connection

In a speed-skating relay race, each team member skates the same number of laps, or times around the track. The team with the fastest combined times wins.

• Have students find how many laps make up the race if 4 skaters each go 5 laps. 20 laps

Another Way to [**Learn**] Lesson 4-3

Use as an alternative or in addition to pages 152 and 153.

Materials Counters (80 per group)

Learning Style Kinesthetic

- Have groups use counters to build arrays and find the products of 2 × 8 and 1 × 8. Have them record the products and then find the sum of the two arrays. 16; 8; 24

- Have groups build an array to find the product of 3 × 8. 24

- Have groups compare the total of the 2-by-8 and 1-by-8 arrays with the total of the 3-by-8 array and talk about why they are the same. 2 rows of 8 + 1 row of 8 = 3 rows of 8

- Demonstrate the connection among these three arrays on the overhead and write multiplication facts and addition sentences to show the symbolic notation.

    ● ● ● ● ● ● ● ●
    ● ● ● ● ● ● ● ●   2 × 8 = 16
                                      16 + 8 = 24
    ● ● ● ● ● ● ● ●   1 × 8 = 8

- Repeat for products of 2 × 8, 2 × 8, and 4 × 8.

- Have groups write other multiplication expressions with 3 or 4 as the first factor and a 1-digit number as the second factor. Have them draw an array with 2 rows and an array with 1 row, or two arrays with 2 rows each, and write the corresponding multiplication and addition sentences to find the multiples of 3 or 4.

- Assign Check and Practice on Student Book page 153 or *Practice Master 4-3*.

- Assess using the following rubric.

Assessment Rubric

4 Full Accomplishment
- finds multiples of 3 or 4

3 Substantial Accomplishment
- with prompting, finds multiples of 3 or 4

2 Partial Accomplishment
- struggles to find multiples of 3 or 4

1 Little Accomplishment
- does not find multiples of 3 or 4

Options for Reaching All Learners

Reading Assist

Understand Organizational Devices
Use colored markers to develop understanding of the use of special typefaces.

Materials Colored markers

Learning Style Visual

- Point out to students the use of red type on page 152. Talk about why the numbers appear in red. To make it easier to focus on these numbers and recognize partial products and the product.

- Have students write the 2s and/or 1s facts and the addition sentences for several Check or Practice exercises in colored pencil. Then have them add.

Cultural Connection

Three and Four by Other Names
Use prefixes to practice multiplying by 3 and 4.

Learning Style Verbal/Auditory, Visual

- Invite students who speak Spanish, French, or Italian to share the word names for three and four in these languages: Spanish, *tres, cuatro*; French *trois, quatre*; Italian: *tre, quattro*.

- Write the prefixes *tri-* and *quadr-* on the chalkboard. Ask students if they know what these prefixes mean. Emphasize the similarity in pronunciation between the word names for three and four and these Latin-based prefixes.

- Brainstorm with students a list of words that use the prefixes *tri-* and *quadr-* that are related to three and four. triangle, triathlon, quadrilateral, quadruplet

Lesson Organizer

Objective Multiply with 3 or 4 as a factor.
Student Materials None
Teacher Materials *Optional* counters (28)
Assignment Guide
  Basic 7–28, 31, 35–40
  Average 9–31, 35–40
  Enriched 12–40

1 Introduce

Review

Find each product.
1. 2 × 4 8   **2.** 2 × 5 10
3. 2 × 7 14   **4.** 2 × 9 18

Build on Prior Knowledge

After students review 2s facts, have them use what they know about the relationship of 2 and 4 to tell how the product 4 × 6 compares to the product 2 × 6 and explain why. Possible answers: The product 4 × 6 is greater because 4 > 2; The product 4 × 6 is twice as great because 4 is twice as great as 2.

2 Teach

See Another Way to Learn...on page 152B.

Interactive CD-ROM Lesson 4 includes content in this lesson.

Learn ○ ○ ○ ○ ○ ○ ○ ○ ○ ○ ○ ○ ○ ○ ○ ○ ○

As students look at the examples, ask:

- How many groups of 6 does the first example ask about? How many groups of 7 are in the second example? 3; 4

- How many groups are shown by the first array and by the second array in each example? 2 and 1; 2 and 2

You may want to use counters to demonstrate on the overhead.

Talk About It) Ongoing Assessment

Listen for students to recognize that 3 equal groups contain as many as 2 equal groups and 1 more group of equal size.

Answers for Talk About It

Find 2 × 9 = 18, then add 1 × 9 = 9 to get 3 × 9 = 27.

Multiplying with 3 and 4 as Factors

You Will Learn
how to use known facts to multiply with 3 or 4 as a factor

Math Tip
4 × 7 is the same as 2 × 7 plus 2 × 7. It's a "double double."

Learn ● ● ● ● ● ●

Watch out for Dylan! He's speedy on his inline skates. He often plays roller hockey with friends in his neighborhood.

Dylan lives in Cooper City, Florida. He gets a lot of exercise by inline skating.

Example 1
Suppose Dylan plays 6 games of roller hockey each week for 3 weeks. How many games will he play? Use 2s facts to find 3 × 6.

● ● ● ● ● ●
● ● ● ● ● ●   2 × 6 = 12

● ● ● ● ● ●   1 × 6 = 6

                  12 + 6 = 18
3 × 6 = 18
So, Dylan will play 18 games.

Example 2
Suppose 7 friends each wore 4 guards— 2 wrist guards and 2 knee guards. How many guards were worn in all? Use 2s facts to find 4 × 7.

● ● ● ● ● ● ●
● ● ● ● ● ● ●   2 × 7 = 14

● ● ● ● ● ● ●
● ● ● ● ● ● ●   2 × 7 = 14

                  14 + 14 = 28
4 × 7 = 28
So, there were 28 wrist and knee guards.

Talk About It

How can you use 2 × 9 to find 3 × 9?

152   Chapter 4 • Multiplication and Division Concepts and Facts

---

Practice 4-3

Name _____   Practice 4-3

Multiplying with 3 and 4 as Factors
Find each product.

1. 3 × 6 = 18	**2.** 4 × 7 = 28	**3.** 5 × 3 = 15	**4.** 2 × 6 = 12
5. 9 × 3 = 27	**6.** 7 × 4 = 28	**7.** 4 × 5 = 20	**8.** 8 × 4 = 32
9. 2 × 3 = 6	**10.** 5 × 4 = 20	**11.** 3 × 4 = 12	**12.** 3 × 7 = 21
13. 4 × 4 = 16	**14.** 3 × 5 = 15	**15.** 4 × 9 = 36	**16.** 6 × 3 = 18
17. 3 × 9 = 27	**18.** 4 × 6 = 24	**19.** 4 × 8 = 32	**20.** 3 × 8 = 24

21. 4 × 3 = 12   **22.** 6 × 4 = 24   **23.** 7 × 3 = 21
24. 5 × 7 = 35   **25.** 0 × 4 = 0   **26.** 8 × 4 = 32

27. Find the product of 3 and 8. 24
28. Find the product of 4 and 7. 28
29. Find the product of 3 and 9. 27
30. Find the product of 4 and 5. 20
31. To multiply 6 by 3 you can find the product of 2 and 6 and the product of 1 and 6 and _add_ them.
32. To multiply 4 by 9 you can find the product of 5 and 9 and the product of 1 and 9 and _subtract_ them

---

Reteaching 4-3

Name _____   Another Look 4-3

Multiplying with 3 and 4 as Factors
You can use triangles and squares to help you multiply by 3 and 4.

Find 7 × 3.

Draw 7 triangles. Each triangle has 3 sides. Count the number of sides in all the triangles. The total number of sides will equal the product of 3 and 7.

△ △ △ △ △ △ △

3 + 3 + 3 + 3 + 3 + 3 + 3 = 21.

7 × 3 = 21

Find 8 × 4.

Draw 8 squares. Each square has 4 sides. Count the number of sides in all the squares. The total number of sides will equal the product of 4 and 8.

□ □ □ □ □ □ □ □

4 + 4 + 4 + 4 + 4 + 4 + 4 + 4 = 8 × 4 = 32
8 × 4 = 32

Find each product. Draw triangles and squares to help you.

1. 6 × 3   **2.** 7 × 4

△ △ △   □ □ □ □
△ △ △   □ □ □

3. 6 × 3 = 18   **4.** 7 × 4 = 28
3. 3 × 8 = 24   **4.** 3 × 9 = 27
5. 4 × 9 = 36   **6.** 4 × 3 = 12

Check

Find each product.

1. 3×5 **15**   2. 4×9 **36**   3. 4×8 **32**   4. 3×7 **21**   5. 3×9 **27**

6. **Reasoning** How can you use 2×6 to find 4×6?
Find $2 \times 6 = 12$, then double it to get $4 \times 6 = 24$.

Practice

Skills and Reasoning

Find each product.

7.	8.	9.	10.	11.
2	5	3	2	3
$\times 3$	$\times 4$	$\times 4$	$\times 5$	$\times 8$
6	**20**	**12**	**10**	**24**

12.	13.	14.	15.	16.
4	3	4	9	8
$\times 4$	$\times 3$	$\times 3$	$\times 4$	$\times 3$
16	**9**	**12**	**36**	**24**

17. 3×7 **21**   18. 5×5 **25**   19. 0×8 **0**   20. 4×7 **28**   21. 4×2 **8**

22. 2×9 **18**   23. 5×6 **30**   24. 4×5 **20**   25. 3×6 **18**   26. 5×7 **35**

27. Find the product of 4 and 6. **24**   28. Find the product of 3 and 7. **21**

29. To multiply 7 by 3 you can find the product of 2 and 7 and the product of 1 and 7 and _____ them. **Add**

Problem Solving and Applications

30. **Health** You can burn about 285 calories during a 30-minute skate. If you skate for an hour, about how many calories will you burn? **About 570 calories**

31. **History** J. L. Plimpton invented a four-wheel roller-skate design in 1863. How many wheels did he need to make the first four pairs of skates? **32 wheels**

Algebra Readiness Copy and complete.

32. Find 4×6.
$\blacksquare \times 6 = 12$ **2**
$12 + 12 = \blacksquare$ **24**

33. Find 3×5.
$\blacksquare \times 5 = 10$ **2**
$10 + 5 = \blacksquare$ **15**

34. Find 4×9.
$\blacksquare \times 9 = 18$ **2**
$18 + 18 = \blacksquare$ **36**

Mixed Review and Test Prep

Mental Math Use mental math to find each answer.

35. $22 + 23$ **45**   36. $29 - 7$ **22**   37. $33 + 35$ **68**   38. $55 - 25$ **30**   39. $95 - 20$ **75**

40. Which of the following shows the Order Property for addition? **B**
Ⓐ $5 + 0 = 5$ Ⓑ $5 + 4 = 4 + 5$ Ⓒ $0 + 3 = 3$ Ⓓ $0 \times 1 = 0 \times 1$

Skills Practice Bank, page 562, Set 1   Lesson 4-3   **153**

Enrichment 4-3

Name _____   **Extend Your Thinking 4-3**

Decision Making
You are having a party for 24 people. You have $60 to spend on supplies. You can choose between two stores for supplies.

Store A is 3 miles away
• Forks: set of 4 for $1.00
• Plates: set of 6 for $3.00
• Cups: set of 3 for $2.00

Store B is 2 miles away
• Forks: set of 6 for $3.00
• Plates: set of 8 for $5.00
• Cups: set of 6 for $3.00

1. Suppose you buy all your supplies at Store A.
   a. How many sets of each item would you have to buy?
   forks **6 sets**   plates **4 sets**   cups **8 sets**
   b. How much would each item cost?
   forks **$6.00**   plates **$12.00**   cups **$16.00**
   c. How much would you pay all together? **$34.00**

2. Suppose you buy all your supplies at Store B.
   a. How many sets of each item would you have to buy?
   forks **4 sets**   plates **3 sets**   cups **4 sets**
   b. How much would each item cost?
   forks **$12.00**   plates **$15.00**   cups **$12.00**
   c. How much would you pay all together? **$39.00**

3. Suppose you buy the least expensive items from Store A and Store B.
   a. How much money would each item cost?
   forks **$6.00**   plates **$12.00**   cups **$12.00**
   b. How much money would you pay all together? **$30.00**

4. Would you choose to buy all your supplies at one store, or go to both stores to get the least expensive supplies? Explain.
Possible answer: I would just go to Store A because it isn't worth going to two stores to save $4.00.

Problem Solving 4-3

Name _____   **Problem Solving 4-3**

Multiplying with 3 and 4 as Factors

History Presidential elections happen every 4 years. This 4-year cycle is called a term.

1. Franklin D. Roosevelt served a little more than 3 full terms as president. About how long was he president?   **About 12 years**

2. In 1944, Roosevelt was elected to serve a 4th term, which he never completed. How many years would Roosevelt have been in office if he had completed a 4th term?   **16 years**

3. Because Roosevelt won so many elections, Congress passed a law. It states that presidents can only serve 2 terms. How many years can a president remain in office today?   **8 years**

4. Adrienne and Derrick each bought 4 comic books.
   a. How many comic books did they buy in all?   **8 comic books**
   b. Each comic book they bought cost $3. How much did they spend in all?   **$24**

5. Aaron practices the piano 7 days a week. How many days does he practice in 4 weeks?   **28 days**

6. Joel made 3 roundtrips to the next town. The roundtrip is a total of 6 miles. How many miles did he travel?   **18 miles**

7. Keith went swimming 3 days a week during his summer vacation. His summer vacation was 9 weeks long. How many days did he go swimming?   **27 days**

8. It takes Alan 4 minutes to complete a puzzle. How long will it take him to complete 5 puzzles?   **20 minutes**

Check

Exercises 1–5 Before students begin, ask them for which exercise they can use a 2s fact plus a 1s fact and for which exercise they can double a 2s fact. Exercises 1, 4, or 5; Exercises 2 or 3

Error Intervention Ongoing Assessment

Observation Students may write the product of a 2s fact and forget to double it or add the product of a 1s fact.

How to Help Have students stack their facts and use underlining to help them remember to add.

$2 \times 5 = 10$ $2 \times 9 = 18$
$1 \times 5 = 5$ $2 \times 9 = 18$
$3 \times 5 = 15$ $4 \times 9 = 36$

Practice

Exercises 7–26 Encourage students to use the Order, One, and Zero Properties they learned in Lesson 4-2 to help them solve some of these exercises.

Exercise 31 Help students recognize that 4 pairs equal 8 skates or that 1 pair equals 8 wheels.

For Early Finishers Challenge early finishers to choose Exercise 11 or 20 and, keeping the first factor the same, rewrite and solve it three times with three different 1-digit numbers as the second factor.

③ Close and Assess

Interview

Ask students to write or draw pictures to show you how they could use 2s facts to find the product of 3 and another 1-digit number and the product of 4 and another 1-digit number. Explanations or pictures should show adding the products of 2s and 1s facts for problems with 3 as a factor, or two 2s facts for problems with 4 as a factor.

Quick Check

Number Sense Without multiplying, tell which Skill exercise has the least product. Explain. Exercise 4; both factors, 3 and 4, are less than the factors in the other exercises.

Skill Find each product.

1. 3×9 **27**   2. 4×5 **20**
3. 4×8 **32**   4. 3×4 **12**

Chapter 4 • Lesson 4-3   **153**

Multiplying with 6, 7, and 8 as Factors

At-A-Glance Planning

Lesson Planning Checklist

Objective Multiply with 6, 7, or 8 as a factor.

Vocabulary square number

Student Book Lesson Materials *Optional* 64 counters, Teaching Tool Transparency 8 (Geoboard Dot Paper)

Materials for pages 154A and 154B Counters (80 per group); Teaching Tool Transparency 7 ($\frac{1}{4}$-Inch Grid Paper); crayons or colored pencils; two number cubes per group

Subject Connections physical education—swimming, history—Matthew Webb, social studies—cricket

Strand Connections algebra readiness, money, time, patterns

	Before Lesson	During Lesson	After Lesson
Daily Math			
p. 154A Problem of the Day			
p. 154A Math Routines			
p. 154A Mental Math			
Teaching Options			
p. 154 Student Book Lesson			
p. 154B Another Way to Learn...			
Options for Reaching All Learners			
p. 154B Language Development			
p. 154B Gifted & Talented			
Technology Options			
p. 154A *Math Workshop*			
p. 154 Interactive CD-ROM Lesson 4			
Assessment Options			
p. 155 Talk About It			
p. 155 Error Intervention			
p. 157 Observation			
p. 157 Quick Check			
Resources			
4-4 Practice			
4-4 Reteaching			
4-4 Enrichment			
4-4 Problem Solving			
4-4 Daily Transparency			

Problem of the Day

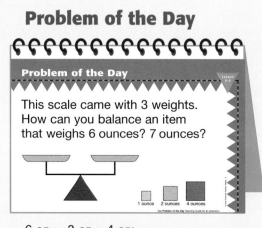

This scale came with 3 weights. How can you balance an item that weighs 6 ounces? 7 ounces?

1 ounce   2 ounces   4 ounces

6 oz = 2 oz + 4 oz;
7 oz = 1 oz + 2 oz + 4 oz

Math Routines

Measurement Have students measure across their desks, using the width of their hands as the unit of measure. Then ask them to estimate the width of their desks in inches, assuming that their hands are about 4 inches wide.

Calendar Ask students how many days are in 8 full weeks. Ask them whether this number of days is ever exactly 2 full consecutive months. 56 days; No

Mental Math

Tell which sum is greater. Explain.

400 + 800 or 100 + 900 400 + 800

500 + 500 or 300 + 600 500 + 500

800 + 500 or 900 + 300 800 + 500

Math Workshop

Have students play *Bowling for Numbers*. Students who answer ten multiplication questions correctly earn a strike. Students can track their progress in the Hall of Fame and print out certificates of achievement to keep in their portfolios.

Another Way to **Learn** Lesson 4-4

Use as an alternative or in addition to pages 154–157.

Materials Counters (80 per group)

Learning Style Kinesthetic

- Have groups use counters to build arrays and find the products 3 × 8 and 3 × 8. Have them record the products and then find the sum. 24; 24; 48

- Then have groups build arrays to find the product 6 × 8. Have them compare the total of the two 3-by-8 arrays with the total of the 6-by-8 array and talk about why they are the same. 3 rows of 8 + 3 rows of 8 = 6 rows of 8

- Repeat for products 5 × 6, 2 × 6, and 7 × 6 and for products 4 × 7, 4 × 7, and 8 × 7.

- Demonstrate the connection among the arrays and write multiplication facts and addition sentences for each set.

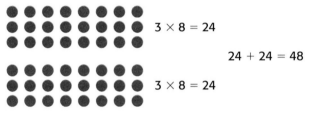

3 × 8 = 24

24 + 24 = 48

3 × 8 = 24

- Have groups build arrays for other multiplication expressions having 6, 7, or 8 as the first factor and a 1-digit number as the second factor.

- Assign Check and Practice on Student Book pages 155–157 or *Practice Master 4-4*.

- Assess using the following rubric.

Assessment Rubric

4 Full Accomplishment
- finds multiples of 6, 7, and 8

3 Substantial Accomplishment
- with prompting, finds multiples of 6, 7, and 8

2 Partial Accomplishment
- struggles to find multiples of 6, 7, and 8

1 Little Accomplishment
- does not find multiples of 6, 7, or 8

Options for Reaching All Learners

Language Development

Be Square!
Use grid paper to strengthen understanding of **square numbers.**

Materials Teaching Tool Transparency 7 ($\frac{1}{4}$-Inch Grid Paper), crayons or colored pencils

Learning Style Visual, Verbal

- Have students identify square shapes in the classroom and talk about why they are square.

- Have students color rows of squares on grid paper to make arrays that represent 6 × 6. Have them write the multiplication sentence and identify the shape they created. 6 × 6 = 36; A square

- Have students find the first 10 square numbers by repeating the previous step for 1 × 1, 2 × 2, 3 × 3, …, 10 × 10.

- Have students talk about why these products are called square numbers.

Gifted & Talented

The Helpful Fact Game
Use a game to strengthen ability to multiply greater numbers.

Materials Two number cubes per group, one labeled 0, 1, 2, 6, 7, 8, the other labeled 3–8

Learning Style Social, Logical

- Have students form two teams and take turns tossing the two cubes.

- Team members should record the two numbers tossed, write a basic multiplication fact, and find the product. For each correct product greater than 36, the team gets two points. For each correct product less than 36, the team gets one point.

- The first team to get 25 points wins.

Lesson Organizer

Objective Multiply with 6, 7, or 8 as a factor.

Student Materials None

Teacher Materials *Optional* counters (64), Teaching Tool Transparency 8 (Geoboard Dot Paper)

Vocabulary square number

Assignment Guide

Basic 23–57, 66, 68–69, 72–83

Average 28–57, 63, 67–69, 72–83

Enriched 33–42, 53–83

1 Introduce

Review

Find each product.

1. 2 × 7 14   **2.** 5 × 8 40

3. 4 × 9 36   **4.** 3 × 6 18

Build on Prior Knowledge

After reviewing 2s, 3s, 4s, and 5s facts, ask students which of these facts could help them multiply by 6. Have them explain why. Possible answers: 3s facts, because 3 + 3 = 6; 5s facts, because 5 + 1 = 6; 2s and 4s facts, because 2 + 4 = 6

2 Teach

See Another Way to Learn...on page 154B.

Interactive CD-ROM Lesson 4 includes content in this lesson.

Learn • • • • • • • • • • • • • • • • • • •

As students look at the examples, ask:

- How many groups of 7 does the first example ask about? How many groups of 8 are in the second example? How many groups of 8 are in the third example? 6; 7; 8

- How many arrays are shown in each example? What facts do the arrays show? 2 arrays each; Show 3s and 3s; 5s and 2s; and 4s and 4s facts

You may want to use counters to demonstrate Examples 1–3 on the overhead as well as to make an 8-by-8 array to illustrate why 64 is a square number.

Multiplying with 6, 7, and 8 as Factors

You Will Learn
how to use known facts to multiply with 6, 7, or 8 as a factor

Vocabulary
square number
the product when both factors are the same

Learn •

Allie and her friends swim on a team. They practice 5 days a week and go to swim meets on weekends. Allie sets the same goal for every race—to go faster than in her previous race.

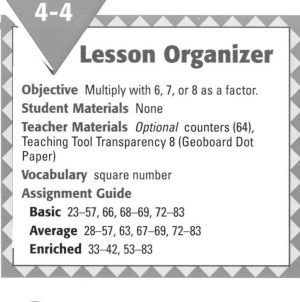

Allie, from Salt Lake City, Utah, was one of five American finalists for an Arete Award. This award is given to athletes who overcome difficult challenges.

Math Tip
You can double a 3s fact to find a 6s fact.

Example 1

Suppose Allie swims 7 laps, then rests. She does this 6 times. How many laps will she swim in all? Use 3s facts to find 6 × 7.

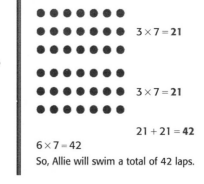

3 × 7 = **21**

3 × 7 = **21**

21 + 21 = **42**

6 × 7 = 42

So, Allie will swim a total of 42 laps.

Managing Time

You may want to spend one-third of the class time introducing the lesson and examples, one-third on Talk About It and Check, and have students use the remaining class time to begin their homework assignment.

Example 2

Suppose Allie takes 8 breaths in each lap across the pool. If she swims 7 laps, how many breaths will she take?

Use 5s and 2s facts to find 7×8.

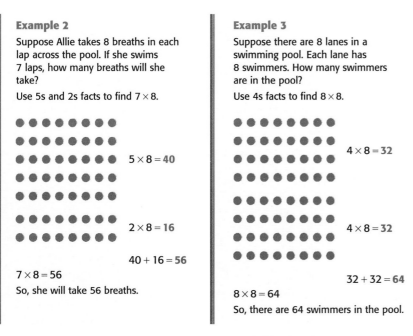

$5 \times 8 = 40$

$2 \times 8 = 16$

$40 + 16 = 56$

$7 \times 8 = 56$

So, she will take 56 breaths.

Example 3

Suppose there are 8 lanes in a swimming pool. Each lane has 8 swimmers. How many swimmers are in the pool?

Use 4s facts to find 8×8.

$4 \times 8 = 32$

$4 \times 8 = 32$

$32 + 32 = 64$

$8 \times 8 = 64$

So, there are 64 swimmers in the pool.

The product when both factors are the same is a **square number**. The product of 8×8 is a square number. So, 64 is a square number.

Talk About It

1. What is another way you could use facts you know to find 6×7?

2. How can you use doubling to find 8×5?

Check

Find each product.

1. 8×6 48 2. 6×9 54 3. 6×6 36 4. 7×9 63 5. 7×7 49

6. 6×4 24 7. 8×2 16 8. 7×6 42 9. 8×5 40 10. 7×3 21

11. 4×8 32 12. 9×9 81 13. 6×5 30 14. 8×7 56 15. 7×2 14

16. 6×2 12 17. 7×4 28 18. 3×6 18 19. 7×5 35 20. 8×3 24

21. **Reasoning** How could you use the product of 3×4 to find 6×4? Possible answer: Find $3 \times 4 = 12$, then double it to get $6 \times 4 = 24$.

22. **Reasoning** Seven multiplied by a number is a square number. What are the two factors? What is the square number? 7 and 7; 49

Lesson 4-4   155

Listen for students to recognize that any two multiplication facts can be helpful in finding a product if the sum of the factors in these facts is a factor in the original fact.

Answers for Talk About It

1 Possible answer: Find $5 \times 7 = 35$, then add $1 \times 7 = 7$ to get $6 \times 7 = 42$.

2 Possible answer: Find $4 \times 5 = 20$, then double it to get $8 \times 5 = 40$.

Check

Exercises 1–20 Before students begin work, have them identify at least one product they can find by doubling a 3s fact, by doubling a 4s fact, and by using a 2s and 5s fact. Exercises 1–3, 6, 8, 13, 16, or 18; Exercises 1, 7, 9, 11, 14, or 20; Exercises 4, 5, 8, 10, 14, 15, 17, or 19

Then have them identify the products that will be square numbers. Exercises 3, 5, and 12

Error Intervention Ongoing Assessment

Observation Students write incorrect products.

How to Help Encourage students to check their work by applying the Order Property and reversing factors and multiplying again. For example, to check that $7 \times 3 = 21$, students may find the product 3×7 by multiplying 2×7 and 1×7 and adding.

Meeting Individual Needs

Learning Style	Teaching Approach
Visual	Have students circle arrays of dots on geoboard dot paper to show the two arrays that can represent multiplying by 6, 7, or 8. Have them record the multiplication sentence represented by each array and the addition sentence represented by both arrays.
Logical	Have students list the first ten square numbers in order. Then have them look for a pattern. Each number is 3, 5, 7,…, 19 greater than the one before it.

Practice

Exercise 64 Encourage students to name the multiplication property that Jair uses.

Exercise 65 Students may find it helpful to start with a number of counters equal to the product and build arrays that meet the other criteria given.

Exercise 68 Students must recognize that the second rule listed concerns batting with bounces, as the third rule mentions batting without a bounce.

For Early Finishers Challenge early finishers to use a different multiplication rule to make an In/Out table similar to the tables in Exercises 81 and 82. Students may exchange and complete each other's tables.

Practice

Skills and Reasoning

Find each product.

23. 8×3 24 **24.** 6×9 54 **25.** 5×6 30 **26.** 7×8 56 **27.** 6×7 42

28. 6×3 18 **29.** 2×8 16 **30.** 7×4 28 **31.** 3×8 24 **32.** 8×4 32

33. 8×9 72 **34.** 6×2 12 **35.** 7×5 35 **36.** 6×6 36 **37.** 9×7 63

38. 2×5 10 **39.** 3×3 9 **40.** 4×7 28 **41.** 3×6 18 **42.** 5×8 40

43.	44.	45.	46.	47.
8 ×8 = 64	7 ×6 = 42	9 ×8 = 72	1 ×8 = 8	7 ×5 = 35

48.	49.	50.	51.	52.
7 ×7 = 49	6 ×4 = 24	6 ×8 = 48	5 ×3 = 15	4 ×4 = 16

53.	54.	55.	56.	57.
4 ×5 = 20	9 ×3 = 27	7 ×2 = 14	7 ×8 = 56	9 ×4 = 36

58.	59.	60.	61.	62.
5 ×0 = 0	3 ×7 = 21	4 ×3 = 12	8 ×9 = 72	9 ×6 = 54

63. Draw an array for $5 \times 5 = 25$. Explain why it makes sense to call 25 a square number. **The array is a square, 5 × 5.**

64. Jair says that after he multiplied 7×9, he knew the answer to 9×7 as well. What does he mean? **The Order Property states that 7 × 9 = 9 × 7.**

Problem Solving and Applications

65. Algebra Readiness Ramon multiplied two numbers. The product was 24. One factor was 6. What was the other factor? **4**

66. Money Tickets to the fair cost $6 each. How much money would you need to buy 8 tickets? **$48; $6 × 8 = $48**

67. History In 1875, Matthew Webb became the first person to swim the English Channel. His time was 21 hours and 45 minutes. In 1994, Chad Hundeby swam the English Channel in 7 hours and 17 minutes.

   a. What is the difference in swimming times between the two records?

   b. How many years were there between the two records? **119 years**

   67a. 14 hours and 28 minutes

Practice 4-4

Name _____

Practice 4-4

Multiplying with 6, 7, and 8 as Factors

Find each product.

1. $6 \times 4 =$ **24** **2.** $8 \times 6 =$ **48** **3.** $7 \times 3 =$ **21**

4. $8 \times 8 =$ **64** **5.** $6 \times 7 =$ **42** **6.** $7 \times 2 =$ **14**

7. $7 \times 7 =$ **49** **8.** $6 \times 8 =$ **48** **9.** $8 \times 9 =$ **72**

10. $8 \times 7 =$ **56** **11.** $4 \times 1 =$ **4** **12.** $6 \times 3 =$ **18**

13. $8 \times 3 =$ **24** **14.** $9 \times 7 =$ **63** **15.** $6 \times 9 =$ **54**

16. $4 \times 2 =$ **8** **17.** $5 \times 6 =$ **30** **18.** $6 \times 6 =$ **36**

19.	20.	21.	22.
4 ×6 = 24	7 ×4 = 28	4 ×8 = 32	6 ×3 = 18

23.	24.	25.	26.
5 ×7 = 35	3 ×8 = 24	8 ×6 = 48	6 ×7 = 42

27.	28.	29.	30.
2 ×6 = 12	4 ×7 = 28	8 ×5 = 40	7 ×8 = 56

31.	32.	33.	34.
3 ×6 = 18	8 ×3 = 24	8 ×4 = 32	2 ×7 = 14

35. Draw an array for $6 \times 6 = 36$. Explain why it makes sense to call 36 a square number. **Check students' drawings.**

The array is a square; 6 × 6

Reteaching 4-4

Name _____

Another Look 4-4

Multiplying with 6, 7, and 8 as Factors

You can use 5s to help you multiply by 6s, 7s, and 8s.

Find 6×4.

Find 5×4 and add 1 more 4.

$5 \times 4 = 20$ $20 + 4 = 24$

$6 \times 4 = 24$

$$\begin{array}{r} 4 \\ \times 5 \\ \hline 20 \\ +4 \\ \hline 24 \end{array}$$

Find 7×6.

Find 5×6 and add 2 more 6s.

$5 \times 6 = 30$ $30 + 6 = 36$ $36 + 6 = 42$

$7 \times 6 = 42$

$$\begin{array}{r} 6 \\ \times 5 \\ \hline 30 \\ +6 \\ \hline 36 \\ +6 \\ \hline 42 \end{array}$$

Find 8×9.

Find 5×9 and add 3 more 9s.

$5 \times 9 = 45$ $45 + 9 = 54$

$54 + 9 = 63$ $63 + 9 = 72$

$8 \times 9 = 72$

$$\begin{array}{r} 9 \\ \times 5 \\ \hline 45 \\ +9 \\ \hline 54 \\ +9 \\ \hline 63 \\ +9 \\ \hline 72 \end{array}$$

Find each product. You may use counters or draw pictures to help.

1. Find 6×9.

$5 \times 9 =$ **45** **45** $+ 9 =$ **54** $6 \times 9 =$ **54**

2. Find 7×4.

$5 \times 4 =$ **20** **20** $+ 4 =$ **24** **24** $+ 4 =$ **28** $7 \times 4 =$ **28**

Problem Solving and SOCIAL STUDIES

Children and adults in Barbados, a Caribbean Island, play a game from England called cricket. Cricket matches can last as long as 5 days!

Cricket Rules

- A batter must run to a marker called a "wicket" to score a run.
- If a ball is hit to the boundary, it scores 4 runs.
- If a ball is hit to the boundary without a bounce, it scores 6 runs.

68. If 5 balls are batted to the boundary with bounces, how many runs are scored? **20 runs**

69. If 5 balls are batted to the boundary without bounces, how many runs are scored? **30 runs**

70. If there are 10 fielders, 1 bowler, 2 batters, and 2 umpires on the cricket field, how many people are on the field? **15 people**

71. Write Your Own Problem Use multiplication facts to write a problem about a cricket game. **Answers will vary.**

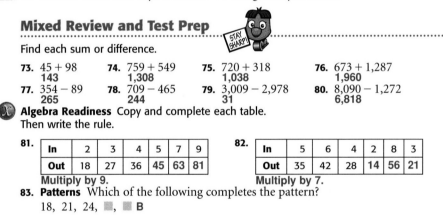

In cricket, teams take turn to bat and field. There are two batters on the field at one time.

72. Journal Write two ways to solve 9×6 using facts you know.

Mixed Review and Test Prep

Find each sum or difference.

73. $45 + 98$
143

74. $759 + 549$
1,308

75. $720 + 318$
1,038

76. $673 + 1,287$
1,960

77. $354 - 89$
265

78. $709 - 465$
244

79. $3,009 - 2,978$
31

80. $8,090 - 1,272$
6,818

Algebra Readiness Copy and complete each table. Then write the rule.

81.

In	2	3	4	5	7	9
Out	18	27	36	45	63	81

Multiply by 9.

82.

In	5	6	4	2	8	3
Out	35	42	28	14	56	21

Multiply by 7.

83. Patterns Which of the following completes the pattern?

18, 21, 24, ▦, ▦ **B**

Ⓐ 25, 26   Ⓑ 27, 30   Ⓒ 26, 28   Ⓓ 34, 44

Enrichment 4-4

Problem Solving 4-4

Cultural Note

Cricket was first played in England in the early 1300s and became a major sport in that country during the 1700s. Cricket is still very popular in England and in countries such as Barbados that were once British colonies.

A cricket game consists of one or two periods, or *innings*. An inning ends for a team when 10 of its 11 players have been *dismissed*, or put out. A batter may be dismissed in numerous ways. A teammate replaces a dismissed batter. Because 20 players are dismissed during just one inning, it is quite possible for teams to score hundreds of runs.

③ Close and Assess

Observation

Have students select three exercises that have a 6, 7, or 8 as a factor from Exercises 23–62 and show what other multiplication facts they could use to find the product.

Quick Check

Number Sense Which products in the Skill exercises could you find by doubling? Explain. Exercises 1 and 2: Use a 3s fact and double it because 6 is a factor; Exercises 2 and 4: Use a 4s fact and double it because 8 is a factor.

Skill Find each product.

1. 6×5 30   **2.** 8×6 48

3. 7×9 63   **4.** 7×8 56

Resources

Technology Master 11

ANSWERS

72 Possible answer: **1** 9×6 is 6×9. Find $3 \times 9 = 27$ and double it. $9 \times 6 = 54$. **2** Use 6×9. Find $5 \times 9 = 45$, add $1 \times 9 = 9$ to get $6 \times 9 = 54$.

Exploring Patterns in Multiples of 10, 11, and 12

At-A-Glance Planning

Objective Explore patterns in multiples of 10, 11 and 12.

Student Book Lesson Materials Teaching Tool Transparency 10 (Addition/Multiplication Fact Table), *optional* calculators (1 per group), *Assessment Sourcebook 10* (How We Worked in Our Group), *Reading Strategies for Math* Chart 29 (Number Machine)

Materials for pages 158A and 158B Colored pencils or markers

Strand Connections patterns, measurement, using data

	Before Lesson	During Lesson	After Lesson
Daily Math			
p. 158A Problem of the Day			
p. 158A Math Routines			
p. 158A Mental Math			
Teaching Options			
p. 158B Facilitating and Assessing…			
Options for Reaching All Learners			
p. 158B Inclusion			
p. 158B Cultural Connection			
Subject Connections			
p. 158A Science Connection			
Assessment Options			
p. 158 Talk About It			
p. 159 Error Intervention			
p. 159 Performance Assessment			
Resources			
4-5 Practice			
4-5 Reteaching			
4-5 Enrichment			
4-5 Problem Solving			
4-5 Daily Transparency			

Problem of the Day

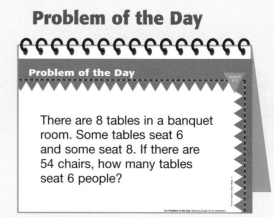

Problem of the Day

There are 8 tables in a banquet room. Some tables seat 6 and some seat 8. If there are 54 chairs, how many tables seat 6 people?

5 tables

Math Routines

Calendar Ask students to name the number of months old they were on their last birthday and the number of months as of today.

Patterns Ask students to continue the pattern through 9 ft, then describe it.

1 ft = 11 in. + 1 in. = 12 in.

2 ft = 22 in. + 2 in. = 24 in.

3 ft = 33 in. + 3 in. = 36 in.

Multiply feet by 11 and add a number of inches equal to number of feet.

Mental Math

Find each difference. Explain.

800 − 500 300   600 − 400 200   900 − 100 800

Science Connection

• Queen Alexandra's birdwing butterflies of New Guinea have wingspans of about 11 inches. How long a line would 7 of these butterflies wing-to-wing make? a 77-inch line

• Adult male Komodo dragons are about 10 feet in length. How long a line would 6 of these lizards head-to-tail make? 60 ft

Facilitating and Assessing **Explore** Lesson 4-5

Use with pages 158 and 159.

Get Started Have group members alternate completing each row or column of the table and skip counting aloud. You may want to allow students to use calculators to help skip count. Assign the roles of recorder and reporter and the group skill Explain and Summarize, which students can practice as they look for and share patterns they find in the table.

Observe Notice whether students are having difficulty completing the table or are using shortcuts. Because of the Order Property, there are pairs of matching columns and rows.

Discuss As students discuss the patterns they find in multiples of 10, 11, and 12, they may be satisfied to identify one pattern for each and stop. Encourage them to find more by looking at how the tens and ones digits may change and how the ones and tens digits may be related to each other and to the numbers heading the columns or rows.

Although students are to focus on multiples of 10, 11, and 12, they may recognize other patterns in the table. Encourage them to discuss these also.

Assess Use the rubric to assess students' work. See sample for Practice Exercise 1.

> **4 Full Accomplishment**
> $12 \times 8 = 96$

Assessment Rubric

4 Full Accomplishment
- finds products; describes patterns for multiples of 10, 11, and 12

3 Substantial Accomplishment
- finds most products; with prompting, describes patterns for multiples of 10, 11, and 12

2 Partial Accomplishment
- finds some products; describes one pattern for multiples of 10, 11, or 12

1 Little Accomplishment
- does not find products or describe patterns for multiples of 10, 11, and 12

Options for Reaching All Learners

Inclusion

Finding Patterns
Use colors to help find patterns.

Materials Colored pencils or markers

Learning Style Visual

Students may have difficulty focusing on tens digits and ones digits in order to find patterns in multiples of 10, 11, and 12.

- As students record the multiples of 10, 11, and 12, have them write all tens digits in one color and all ones digits in another color.

- Guide students to look for patterns using directions such as: Look at the red tens digits. What do you notice?

Cultural Connection

A 12 is a 12 is a 12
Use different ways of writing 12 to increase awareness of other cultures' numeration systems.

Learning Style Logical, Visual

- Show students ways of writing 12 in different ancient systems of numeration.

Egyptian hieroglyphics	∩‖
Babylonian cuneiform	⟨YY
Roman numerals	X‖
Attic numerals (early Greek)	ΔII
Maya numerals	⸚

- Have students identify which parts of each numeral they think represent 10 and 2. For the Maya system, tell them that — represents 5.

- Have students make a list of things that are usually found in 12s, using different ways of writing 12.

Lesson Organizer

Objective Explore patterns in multiples of 10, 11, and 12.

Suggested Grouping 2 to 4

Student Materials Teaching Tool Transparency 10 (Addition/Multiplication Fact Table), *optional* calculators (1 per group), *Assessment Sourcebook 10* (How We Worked in Our Group), *Reading Strategies for Math* Chart 29 (Number Machine)

Assignment Guide
  Basic 1–15, 24
  Average 6–22, 24
  Enriched 11–24

1 Introduce

Review

Name the first six multiples of each number.

1. 4 0, 4, 8, 12, 16, 20

2. 6 0, 6, 12, 18, 24, 30

3. 7 0, 7, 14, 21, 28, 35

Build on Prior Knowledge

After students review multiples of 4, 6, and 7, ask how they could find multiples of 10, 11, or 12. Possible answers: Skip count; Repeatedly add 10, 11, or 12; Use the calculator's constant feature

2 Teach

See Facilitating and Assessing…on page 158B.

Explore ● ○ ○ ○ ○ ○ ○ ○ ○ ○ ○ ○ ○ ○ ○ ○ ○ ○ ○ ○

As students work together, ask questions such as:

• What does each row or column of the table represent? Multiples of the first number in the row or column

You may want to use Teaching Tool Transparency 10 (Addition/Multiplication Fact Table) for demonstration.

Talk About It **Ongoing Assessment**

Listen for recognition of patterns and the use of the term *common multiples*.

Answers for Talk About It

1 Possible answers: 10s: The ones digit is always 0. 11s: The ones and tens digits both increase by 1 each time.

2 0, 60, 120

Exploring Patterns in Multiples of 10, 11, and 12

Problem Solving Connection
■ Look for a Pattern
■ Make a Table

Materials
fact table

Explore ● ○

You can use patterns to fill in a multiplication table.

Work Together

Copy and complete the table.

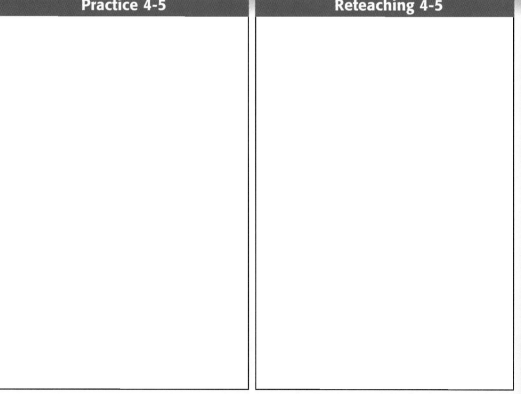

Remember
A multiple is the product of a whole number and any whole number.

Talk About It

1. What patterns can you find in the table?

2. Which numbers on the chart are multiples of both 10 and 12?

158 Chapter 4 • Multiplication and Division Concepts and Facts

Practice 4-5	Reteaching 4-5

Connect

Here are some patterns in the multiples of 10, 11, and 12.

Multiples of 10	Multiples of 11	Multiples of 12
$10 \times 0 = 0$	$11 \times 0 = 0$	$12 \times 0 = 0$
$10 \times 1 = 10$	$11 \times 1 = 11$	$12 \times 1 = 12$
$10 \times 2 = 20$	$11 \times 2 = 22$	$12 \times 2 = 24$
$10 \times 3 = 30$	$11 \times 3 = 33$	$12 \times 3 = 36$
$10 \times 4 = 40$	$11 \times 4 = 44$	$12 \times 4 = 48$
$10 \times 5 = 50$	$11 \times 5 = 55$	$12 \times 5 = 60$
$10 \times 6 = 60$	$11 \times 6 = 66$	$12 \times 6 = 72$
$10 \times 7 = 70$	$11 \times 7 = 77$	$12 \times 7 = 84$
$10 \times 8 = 80$	$11 \times 8 = 88$	$12 \times 8 = 96$
$10 \times 9 = 90$	$11 \times 9 = 99$	$12 \times 9 = 108$
$10 \times 10 = 100$	$11 \times 10 = 110$	$12 \times 10 = 120$
$10 \times 11 = 110$	$11 \times 11 = 121$	$12 \times 11 = 132$
$10 \times 12 = 120$	$11 \times 12 = 132$	$12 \times 12 = 144$
Zero is in the ones place.	Ones digit increases by 1 each time.	Ones digit increases by 2 each time.

Practice

Find each product.

1. 12×8 **96** 2. 11×9 **99** 3. 7×10 **70** 4. 6×12 **72** 5. 11×5 **55**

6. 4×12 **48** 7. 12×9 **108** 8. 10×8 **80** 9. 3×11 **33** 10. 12×5 **60**

11. 10×6 **60** 12. 7×11 **77** 13. 12×2 **24** 14. 10×10 **100** 15. 12×12 **144**

16. 11×6 **66** 17. 10×12 **120** 18. 11×11 **121** 19. 5×10 **50** 20. 3×12 **36**

21. How can you use the fact $5 \times 12 = 60$ to solve 7×12?
Possible answer: Find $2 \times 12 = 24$, then add $5 \times 12 = 60$ to get $7 \times 12 = 84$.

22. **Measurement** The recipe for the world's largest pancake calls for 7 cartons of eggs. Each carton contains 1 dozen eggs. How many eggs does the recipe call for in all? $7 \times 12 = 84$ eggs

23. **Using Data** Use the Data File on page 144. Write a multiplication sentence using the number 11 and the number of glasses that Ashrita Furman balanced on his chin. $5 \times 11 = 55$ glasses

24. **Journal** Describe patterns for multiples of 10, 11, and 12.

Skills Practice Bank, page 562, Set 3   Lesson 4-5   **159**

Enrichment 4-5

Name _____

Extend Your Thinking 4-5

Patterns in Numbers
Complete each pattern. Then write the rule used for each pattern.

1. 8, 16, 24, __32__, __40__, __48__
   Rule: __Add 8.__

2. 4, 8, 12, __16__, __20__, __24__
   Rule: __Add 4.__

3. 5, 10, 15, __20__, __25__, __30__
   Rule: __Add 5.__

4. 0, 24, 48, 72, __96__, __120__, __144__
   Rule: __Add 24.__

Look at **1–4** again. Describe each pattern in terms of multiples.

5. **1** shows multiples of __8__

6. **2** shows multiples of __4__

7. **3** shows multiples of __5__

8. **4** shows multiples of __24__

9. Write your own patterns of multiples. Describe each pattern using multiples and then by an addition rule. **Check students' answers.**

Pattern: _____
Multiples of: _____
Rule: _____
Pattern: _____
Multiples of: _____
Rule: _____

Problem Solving 4-5

Name _____

Problem Solving 4-5

Exploring Patterns in Multiples of 10, 11, and 12
Use a hundred chart to help you answer each question.

1. List the multiples of 10 in order.
   0, 10, 20, 30, 40, 50, 60, 70, 80, 90, 100

2. Write a rule using addition for the multiples of 10.
   Add 10.

3. List the multiples of 11 in order.
   0, 11, 22, 33, 44, 55, 66, 77, 88, 99

4. Write a rule using addition for the multiples of 11.
   Add 11.

5. List the multiples of 12 in order.
   0, 12, 24, 36, 48, 60, 72, 84, 96

6. Write a rule using addition for the multiples of 12.
   Add 12.

7. Write a rule using addition to find the multiples of any number.
   Add the number to each previous multiple.

8. What other patterns do you see on a hundred chart?
   Possible answers: Rows increase by 10, all numbers in a column have the same ones digit.

9. What patterns can you find in the sums of digits in a column?
   They increase by 1.

10. What patterns do you notice in the diagonal from 1 to 100?
   Numbers increase by 11.

Connect

Have students compare the patterns they found as they worked together to the patterns described on page 159.

For each set of multiples, also talk about how the tens digit relates to the second factor.

Error Intervention Ongoing Assessment

Observation Students write incorrect products of 10s, 11s, and 12s facts.

How to Help Encourage students to recall patterns in multiples of a particular number by writing the problems and then circling the factor 10, 11, or 12. If 10, 11, or 12 is not the first factor in a multiplication sentence, suggest that students use the Order Property to rewrite the expression. Students can also use the Number Machine Chart to practice their 10s, 11s, and 12s facts.

Practice

Exercise 22 If necessary, review the meaning of *dozen*.

For Early Finishers Challenge early finishers to choose one exercise from Exercises 1–5 and explain how they could use 2s, 3s, 4s, or 5s facts to solve it.

3 Close and Assess

Performance Assessment

Find each product. Explain how you could use a number pattern to help.

1. 10×3 30; The tens digit is the same as the second factor, and the product ends in 0.

2. 11×9 99; The ones and tens digits are the same as the second factor.

3. 12×6 72; The tens digit increased by one 6 times, skipping the sixth digit, and the ones digit is a multiple of 2.

Assess using the rubric on page 158B.

Resources

Technology Master 12

ANSWERS

24 As multiples of 10 increase, the tens digit increases by 1. As multiples of 11 increase, both digits increase by 1. As multiples of 12 increase, the ones digit increases by 2 and the tens digit increases by 1, skipping every sixth digit.

Chapter 4 • Lesson 4-5   **159**

Chapter 4
Stop and Practice

Students will practice skills taught in Lessons 1 through 5.

Find Each Product

Remind students to think of patterns in multiples; the Zero, One, and Order Properties; and how to use multiplication facts they know to complete other facts.

Error Search

ANSWERS

51 Incorrect; Possible answer: 40 is a multiple of 8. Divided or multiplied wrong

52 Incorrect; The product of 6 and 0 is 0.

53 Correct

54 Incorrect; 11 multiplied by 2 is 22. Multiplied by 3 instead of 2

55 Incorrect; The product of 9 and 1 is 9. Multiplied wrong

56 Correct

STOP and Practice

Find each product.

1. $\begin{array}{r} 3 \\ \times 4 \\ \hline 12 \end{array}$	**2.** $\begin{array}{r} 7 \\ \times 0 \\ \hline 0 \end{array}$	**3.** $\begin{array}{r} 6 \\ \times 4 \\ \hline 24 \end{array}$	**4.** $\begin{array}{r} 2 \\ \times 8 \\ \hline 16 \end{array}$	**5.** $\begin{array}{r} 7 \\ \times 3 \\ \hline 21 \end{array}$
6. $\begin{array}{r} 7 \\ \times 4 \\ \hline 28 \end{array}$	**7.** $\begin{array}{r} 5 \\ \times 6 \\ \hline 30 \end{array}$	**8.** $\begin{array}{r} 3 \\ \times 8 \\ \hline 24 \end{array}$	**9.** $\begin{array}{r} 5 \\ \times 7 \\ \hline 35 \end{array}$	**10.** $\begin{array}{r} 9 \\ \times 3 \\ \hline 27 \end{array}$
11. $\begin{array}{r} 8 \\ \times 4 \\ \hline 32 \end{array}$	**12.** $\begin{array}{r} 7 \\ \times 1 \\ \hline 7 \end{array}$	**13.** $\begin{array}{r} 11 \\ \times 8 \\ \hline 88 \end{array}$	**14.** $\begin{array}{r} 6 \\ \times 7 \\ \hline 42 \end{array}$	**15.** $\begin{array}{r} 8 \\ \times 3 \\ \hline 24 \end{array}$
16. $\begin{array}{r} 9 \\ \times 4 \\ \hline 36 \end{array}$	**17.** $\begin{array}{r} 8 \\ \times 5 \\ \hline 40 \end{array}$	**18.** $\begin{array}{r} 6 \\ \times 0 \\ \hline 0 \end{array}$	**19.** $\begin{array}{r} 8 \\ \times 8 \\ \hline 64 \end{array}$	**20.** $\begin{array}{r} 7 \\ \times 7 \\ \hline 49 \end{array}$
21. $\begin{array}{r} 7 \\ \times 10 \\ \hline 70 \end{array}$	**22.** $\begin{array}{r} 6 \\ \times 9 \\ \hline 54 \end{array}$	**23.** $\begin{array}{r} 7 \\ \times 8 \\ \hline 56 \end{array}$	**24.** $\begin{array}{r} 9 \\ \times 8 \\ \hline 72 \end{array}$	**25.** $\begin{array}{r} 9 \\ \times 9 \\ \hline 81 \end{array}$
26. $\begin{array}{r} 11 \\ \times 3 \\ \hline 33 \end{array}$	**27.** $\begin{array}{r} 6 \\ \times 6 \\ \hline 36 \end{array}$	**28.** $\begin{array}{r} 4 \\ \times 9 \\ \hline 36 \end{array}$	**29.** $\begin{array}{r} 9 \\ \times 6 \\ \hline 54 \end{array}$	**30.** $\begin{array}{r} 8 \\ \times 7 \\ \hline 56 \end{array}$

31. $10 \times 5 \ 50$ **32.** $3 \times 3 \ 9$ **33.** $2 \times 12 \ 24$ **34.** $10 \times 8 \ 80$ **35.** $10 \times 2 \ 20$

36. $10 \times 10 \ 100$ **37.** $7 \times 5 \ 35$ **38.** $4 \times 9 \ 36$ **39.** $7 \times 6 \ 42$ **40.** $12 \times 1 \ 12$

41. $10 \times 0 \ 0$ **42.** $2 \times 9 \ 18$ **43.** $0 \times 12 \ 0$ **44.** $10 \times 4 \ 40$ **45.** $8 \times 9 \ 72$

46. $6 \times 8 \ 48$ **47.** $4 \times 7 \ 28$ **48.** $5 \times 11 \ 55$ **49.** $8 \times 6 \ 48$ **50.** $3 \times 9 \ 27$

Error Search

Find each sentence that is not correct. Write it correctly. Explain the error.

51. 42 is a multiple of 8.

52. The product of 6 and 0 is 6.

53. 5×9 equals 9×5. **Correct**

54. 11 multiplied by 2 is 33.

55. The product of 9 and 1 is 1.

56. The product of 8×9 is equal to the product of 4×9 doubled. **Correct**

Underwater Riddle!

What do you call a hockey game that is played on the floor of a swimming pool? Multiply to solve the riddle. Match each letter to its answer in the blank below. Some letters are not used.

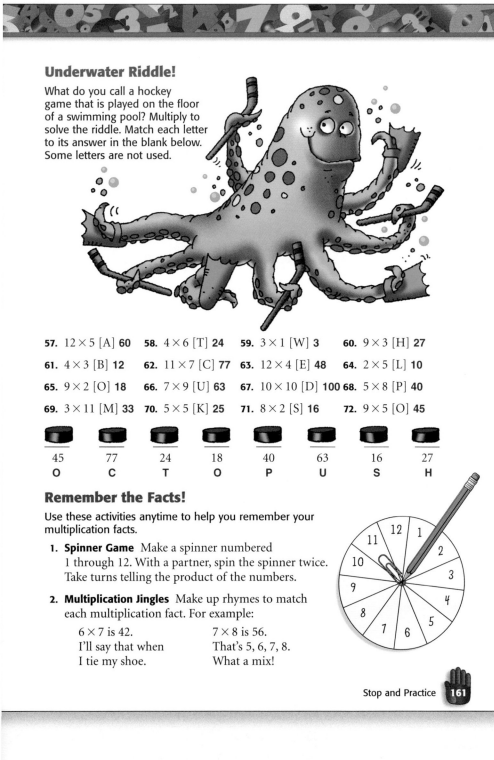

57. 12×5 [A] **60**   **58.** 4×6 [T] **24**   **59.** 3×1 [W] **3**   **60.** 9×3 [H] **27**

61. 4×3 [B] **12**   **62.** 11×7 [C] **77**   **63.** 12×4 [E] **48**   **64.** 2×5 [L] **10**

65. 9×2 [O] **18**   **66.** 7×9 [U] **63**   **67.** 10×10 [D] **100**   **68.** 5×8 [P] **40**

69. 3×11 [M] **33**   **70.** 5×5 [K] **25**   **71.** 8×2 [S] **16**   **72.** 9×5 [O] **45**

45	77	24	18	40	63	16	27
O	C	T	O	P	U	S	H

Remember the Facts!

Use these activities anytime to help you remember your multiplication facts.

1. **Spinner Game** Make a spinner numbered 1 through 12. With a partner, spin the spinner twice. Take turns telling the product of the numbers.

2. **Multiplication Jingles** Make up rhymes to match each multiplication fact. For example:

   6×7 is 42.
   I'll say that when
   I tie my shoe.

   7×8 is 56.
   That's 5, 6, 7, 8.
   What a mix!

Underwater Riddle!

As an extension, suggest that students create their own riddles about their favorite water activity and add them to the class riddle book.

Remember the Facts!

Spinner Game Spinners may be placed in the math center for use at any time.

For Early Finishers Challenge early finishers to choose five exercises from Exercises 1–50, rewrite each pair of factors by increasing one factor by 1 and decreasing the other factor by 1, and find each new product.

Resources

TestWorks: Test and Practice Software

Decision Making: Raising Money for Sneakers

At-A-Glance Planning

Lesson Planning Checklist

Objective Solve problems by making decisions.

Student Book Lesson Materials *Optional Assessment Sourcebook 10* (How We Worked in Our Group), calculators (1 per group), *Reading Strategies for Math* Chart 14 (Venn Diagram—Two Circles), Teaching Tool Transparencies 1, 2 (Guided Problem Solving 1, 2)

Materials for pages 162A and 162B None

Subject Connection social studies—fund-raising

Strand Connections money, time

	Before Lesson	During Lesson	After Lesson
Daily Math			
p. 162A Problem of the Day			
p. 162A Math Routines			
p. 162A Mental Math			
Teaching Options			
p. 162B Facilitating and Assessing…			
Options for Reaching All Learners			
p. 162B Reading Assist			
p. 162B Gifted & Talented			
Technology Options			
p. 162A *Logical Journey of the Zoombinis*			
Assessment Options			
p. 163 Journal			
Resources			
4-6 Practice			
4-6 Reteaching			
4-6 Enrichment			
4-6 Problem Solving			
4-6 Daily Transparency			

Problem of the Day

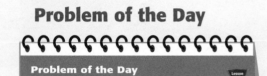

Problem of the Day   Lesson 4-6

An ancient Egyptian water clock kept time by measuring the water dripping out of a container. If 3 cups dripped out between 1 P.M. and 3 P.M., how many cups dripped out in 8 hours?

12 cups of water

Math Routines

Time Ask students to name lengths of time that two activities could take so that the total will be exactly 1 hour.

Calendar Ask students how old they will be in 2005. Then ask them how they can use that information to tell how old they will be in 2025. Add 20 to the first answer.

Mental Math

Name each difference. Explain your thinking.

$1,500 - 700$ 800	$1,400 - 900$ 500
$1,300 - 500$ 800	$1,700 - 1,200$ 500

Logical Journey of the Zoombinis

Every puzzle requires students to make decisions that will help move the Zoombinis over bridges, through caves, over lily pad paths, and so on. The Zoombini Puzzle Log helps strengthen students' decision-making skills. As they record the steps they take to solve a puzzle, they must focus on the thought process they used to develop a solution plan and carry it out.

Facilitating and Assessing Explore Lesson 4-6

Use with pages 162 and 163.

Get Started As students start to work together, you may want to assign these roles to group members: reader, calculator, recorder, and reporter. Encourage group members to practice the group skills Listen to Others and/or Disagree in an Agreeable Way as they work toward making a decision that everyone supports.

Observe For Exercises 6 and 7, some students may use number sense (basic facts and place value) or repeated addition. As needed, allow students to use calculators so they can focus on the decision-making process.

Discuss As groups make their decisions, listen for recognition that raising the money will take a combination of both jobs.

Assess Use the rubric to assess students' work. See sample.

4 Full Accomplishment

Working Wednesdays: $2 \times \$5 = \$10$, $6 \times \$10 = \$60$
Working Saturdays: $2 \times \$4 = \$8$, $5 \times \$8 = \$40$

Day	1st Week	2nd Week	3rd Week	4th Week	5th Week	6th Week	7th Week	8th Week
Wednesday	$60	$60	$60	$60	$60		$60	
Saturday	$40	$40	$40	$40		$40		$40
Wednesday and Saturday	$100	$100	$100	$100	$60	$40	$60	$40

Assessment Rubric

4 Full Accomplishment
- finds solution that meets problem criteria
- explains how a decision was made

3 Substantial Accomplishment
- with prompting, finds solution that meets criteria
- with prompting, explains how a decision was made

2 Partial Accomplishment
- finds solution that meets some criteria
- explains in part how a decision was made

1 Little Accomplishment
- does not find a solution
- does not explain how a decision was made

Options for Reaching All Learners

Reading Assist

Understand Organizational Devices
Use a table to help organize data.

Learning Style Logical, Visual

- To help students determine how many players are free on each day, write the following table on the chalkboard or overhead:

Player	Wednesday	Saturday
Antoine		
Ben		
Chip		

- Have students reread and use the facts and data they are given on page 162 about player availability to complete similar tables, putting checkmarks in the appropriate column(s) for each day a player is available to work.

- Have students count the checkmarks listed for each day.

Gifted & Talented

Decisive Discussion
Use discussion to strengthen understanding of issues involved in fund-raising.

Learning Style Verbal, Logical

- Have groups choose an item they think they would like to have the class raise money to purchase. Provide groups with the cost or have them research it themselves.

- Have groups decide whether they would sell merchandise, tickets for a production, or services to raise the money.

- Have them talk about the considerations that affected their decisions.

- Groups can set prices and figure out how long it might take to raise the money.

Lesson Organizer

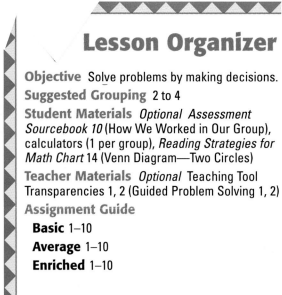

Objective Solve problems by making decisions.

Suggested Grouping 2 to 4

Student Materials *Optional Assessment Sourcebook 10* (How We Worked in Our Group), calculators (1 per group), *Reading Strategies for Math Chart* 14 (Venn Diagram—Two Circles)

Teacher Materials *Optional* Teaching Tool Transparencies 1, 2 (Guided Problem Solving 1, 2)

Assignment Guide

Basic 1–10

Average 1–10

Enriched 1–10

1 Introduce

Review

A student is paid $3 per hour to rake leaves. How much can she earn raking leaves for

1. 2 hours on 1 day? $6

2. 3 hours each day for 2 days? $18

Build on Prior Knowledge

Ask students how they might find out how much 4 students could earn raking leaves for 2 hours each day for 3 days. Possible answers: Find out how much 1 student could earn in 3 days and multiply by 4 or add 4 times; Find out how much 4 students could earn in 1 day and multiply by 3.

2 Teach

See Facilitating and Assessing…on page 162B.

Explore •

Ask students if the team could earn enough money by watering plants only or by cutting grass only. 6 players can earn only $480 for 8 weeks watering plants; 5 players can earn only $320 for 8 weeks of cutting grass.

Reading Assist Find Main Idea with Supporting Details

Have students read page 162 aloud. Then help them find the details they need.

• How much time does the team have to raise money for sneakers? 2 months

• How many players are on the team? 10

• What jobs can team members do to raise money? Water plants and cut grass

---

Problem Solving

Decision Making:
Raising Money for Sneakers

You Will Learn
how to use facts to make a decision

Explore •

"Practice! Practice! Practice! We have two months until our first game," said the coach. The basketball team plans to buy new sneakers before the season starts. Sneakers cost about $60 per pair, so they will need to raise about $600. How can the team raise the money?

There are 5 starting pla[...]
[t]he players' schedules are:

• Antoine, Ben, Chip, and Darryl are not free on Wednesday afternoons.

• Frank, Gary, Hank, Ian, and Jorge are not free on Saturday afternoons.

Elton is free on Wednesdays and Saturdays.

Job	Day	Number of Hours	Pay per Player
Watering plants	Wednesday	2 hours	$5 per hour
Cutting grass	Saturday	2 hours	$4 per hour

Name _____

Decision Making

Robin's class is developing a community garden. There are 15 students in Robin's class. They volunteer to work in a community garden at various times during the school week (Monday to Friday). Robin's teacher says it will take about 3 weeks to complete the project if 3 students work 1 hour each day. Some students can work on more than one day. The following table lists the number of students who can work on various days:

Day	Monday	Tuesday	Wednesday	Thursday	Friday
Number of Students	2	5	3	3	5

1. How many hours would students have to work each week in order to finish the garden on time?

   15 hours

2. Will 3 students be working every day? Explain.

   No; only 2 students can work on Monday

3. On the second week of the project, the whole class is taking a field trip on Friday. How many students will have to work on a different day that week? Explain.

   2; Then the class will still get 15 hours of work done.

4. The students worked for 12 hours a week during the first two weeks.

   a. How many hours will they need to work in the third week in order to complete the garden on time?

   21 hours

   b. How many hours should each student work in the final week in order to complete the garden on time? Explain your reasoning.

   Possible answer: Each student should work about an hour and a half. $15 \times 1\frac{1}{2} = 22\frac{1}{2}$ hr.

Name _____

Decision Making

Andrew wants to buy his mother a gift that costs $24. He has 4 weeks to save for the gift. To earn the money for the gift, Andrew can work the following jobs.

Day	Job	Number of Hours	Pay
Monday	Babysitting	2	$4 per hour
Wednesday	Clipping shrubs	1	$3 per hour

How can Andrew earn the money for the gift in 4 weeks?

How much money will Andrew make babysitting each week? $2 \times \$4 = \$8$

How long will it take to earn $24? $\$24 \div \$8 = 3$ weeks

How much money will Andrew make clipping shrubs each week? $1 \times \$3 = \$3$

How long will it take to earn $24? $\$24 \div \$3 = 8$ weeks

Andrew can babysit for 3 weeks to earn the money he needs to buy the gift.

Monica wants to buy new sneakers for school track meets. The first meet is in 8 weeks. The sneakers cost $48. Monica could work on Tuesdays watering plants for 2 hours for $3 per hour. She could work on Fridays walking a dog for 2 hours for $4 per hour. How can Monica earn $48 in 8 weeks?

1. a. How much would Monica earn in a week watering plants? **$6**

   b. How many weeks will it take to earn $48? **8 weeks**

2. a. How much would Monica earn in a week walking the dog? **$8**

   b. How many weeks will it take to earn $48? **6 weeks**

3. How much would Monica earn in 8 weeks walking the dog each week? **$64**

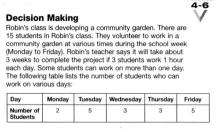

Work Together

▶ **Understand**

1. What do you know?

2. What do you need to find out?

3. What is the main decision you are being asked to make?
How should the team raise $600 in about 8 weeks

▶ **Plan and Solve**

4. 6 players × $5 × 2 hours = $60

5. 5 players × $4 × 2 hours = $40

7a. Possible answers: $100 if Elton works both days; $90 or $92 if he works only one of the days

4. How much money can the team earn in a week watering plants?

5. How much money can the team earn in a week cutting grass?

6. How many weeks will it take to earn $600 watering plants? Cutting grass? **10 weeks; 15 weeks**

7. **a. What If** The players work at both jobs each week. How much can they earn in one week?

   b. About how many weeks would it take to earn $600? **About 6 weeks**

▶ **Make a Decision**

8. How can the team earn the money? **Answers will vary.**

▶ **Present Your Decision**

9. Make a table to show the number of weeks it will take to earn the money. Explain your decision on how to raise $600.

Money Earned			
	1st Week	2nd Week	3rd Week
Wednesday			
Saturday			
Wednesday and Saturday			

10. Find out how schools raise money for sports equipment, or other items they need. Check out **www.mathsurf.com/4/ch4**. Did you get any ideas for your school? **Answers will vary.**

9. Possible answer: If Elton works both days, the team can make $100 in a week.

Week	1	2	3	4	5	6
Money	$100	$200	$300	$400	$500	$600

Skills Practice Bank, page 562, Set 4   Lesson 4-6   **163**

---

3 Close and Assess

Journal

Describe your group's decision-making experience. Include your group's decision, how the plan was made, the most difficult part of your work, and the simplest part. Check students' journals.

ANSWERS

1 Possible answers: Number of players; Possible jobs; Players' free time; Amount of money needed; Time to raise it

2 How much the team can earn each week by watering plants or cutting grass; How long it will take to raise $600

Enrichment 4-6

Name _____ **Extend Your Thinking 4-6**

Visual Thinking
Draw the next figure in each row to continue the pattern.

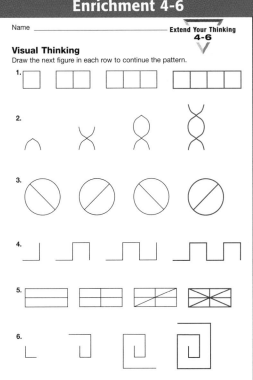

1.
2.
3.
4.
5.
6.

Problem Solving 4-6

Name _____ **Problem Solving 4-6**

Decision Making
The cross country ski club is planning a weekend trip to Manchester, Vermont. They are leaving for the trip in 6 weeks. They need to raise about $40 per person for the trip. There are 12 students in the club, so they need to raise $480 in 6 weeks. How should the club raise money?

Facts and Data
6 students are not free on Tuesdays.
4 students are not free on Thursdays.

Possible jobs:

Day	Job	Number of Hours per Student	Pay
Tuesday	Shoveling Snow	2 hours	$5 per hour
Thursday	Walking Dogs	2 hours	$4 per hour

1. How many students are available to work on Tuesdays? **6 students**
2. How many students are available to work on Thursdays? **8 students**
3. How much can the club earn in a week shoveling snow? **$60**
4. How much can the club earn in a week walking dogs? **$64**
5. How many weeks will it take to earn $480 shoveling snow? walking dogs?
   8 weeks shoveling snow; 7½ weeks walking dogs
6. **a.** If the club members worked at both jobs each week, how much would they earn per week? **$124**
   b. About how many weeks would it take to earn $480? **About 4 or 5 weeks working at both jobs**
7. What do you think the club should do to earn the money they need for the trip? Explain.
   Possible answer: 6 of the students should shovel snow each week and 6 of the students should walk dogs each week, because they will make over $480 in 6 weeks.

Section A
Review and Practice

Use the Skills Checklist

Review the **Skills Checklist** on the page with students. Then ask questions such as the following:

- For which exercises would it be helpful to understand what factors and products are? Exercises 3–25

- Which operation will you use to solve Exercise 24? Why? Possible answer: Multiplication; He drinks the same number of glasses of milk each day.

Assess

You may wish to use this information to assess students' understanding of the lesson objectives.

Item Analysis		
Lesson Objective		**Items**
4-1	Review the meaning of multiplication.	1–6
4-2	Explore patterns in multiplying by 0, 1, 2, 5, and 9.	7–10, 20, 22
4-3	Multiply with 3 or 4 as a factor.	11–13, 16, 17, 21, 23, 24
4-4	Multiply with 6, 7, or 8 as a factor.	14–16, 18, 19, 23, 25
4-5	Explore patterns in multiples of 10, 11, and 12.	2, 17, 19
4-6	Solve problems by making decisions.	24

Resources

Practice Masters

- Practice Chapter 4 Section A

Assessment Sourcebook

- Quiz Chapter 4 Section A

TestWorks: Test and Practice Software

ANSWERS

25 Possible answer: To find 7 × 9, add 9 + 9 + 9 + 9 + 9 + 9 + 9 to get 63.

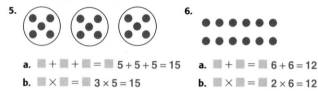

SECTION A
Review and Practice

Vocabulary Match each with its example.

1. array d   **a.** 66
2. multiple of 11 a   **b.** 6 and 7
3. product of 5 × 5 c   **c.** square number
4. factors of 42 b   **d.** ● ● ● ● ● ●

(Lesson 1) Copy and complete each number sentence.

5.

a. ■ + ■ + ■ = ■ 5 + 5 + 5 = 15
b. ■ × ■ = ■ 3 × 5 = 15

6.

a. ■ + ■ = ■ 6 + 6 = 12
b. ■ × ■ = ■ 2 × 6 = 12

(Lesson 2) Copy and complete.

7. The product of 0 and any number is ■. 0

8. 1 × 3 = ■ 3

9. 0, 2, 4, 6, and 8 are the first five multiples of ■. 2

10. 0, 9, 18, 27, and 36 are the first five multiples of ■. 9

(Lessons 3–5) Find each product.

11. 3 × 5 15   12. 3 × 7 21   13. 4 × 4 16

14. 6 × 8 48   15. 7 × 9 63   16. 8 × 4 32

17. 4 × 10 40   18. 8 × 9 72   19. 8 × 11 88

20. 2 × 2 4   21. 3 × 2 6   22. 2 × 5 10

23. **Reasoning** How can you use the product of 4 × 7 to find 8 × 7? Possible answer: Find 4 × 7 = 28, then double it to get 8 × 7 = 56.

(Lesson 6) Solve.

24. **Time** Keith drinks 3 glasses of milk each day. How many glasses of milk does he drink in a week? 21 glasses of milk

25. **Journal** Use words or pictures to find 7 × 9.

164 Chapter 4 • Review and Practice

Skills Checklist
In this section, you have:
☑ Reviewed the Meaning of Multiplication
☑ Explored Patterns in Multiplying by 0, 1, 2, 5, and 9
☑ Multiplied with 3, 4, 6, 7, and 8 as Factors
☑ Explored Patterns in Multiples of 10, 11, and 12
☑ Solved Problems by Making Decisions

REVIEW AND PRACTICE

Practice

Name _____

Practice
Chapter 4
Section A

Review and Practice

Vocabulary Complete each sentence with the correct word from the list.

    factor   product   array   multiple

1. A(n) __array__ is an arrangement of objects in rows and columns.
2. One of the numbers being multiplied is called a(n) __factor__.
3. The __product__ of a number and 1 is that number.

(Lesson 1) Complete each number sentence.

4.

5.

a. 6 + 6 + 6 = 18
b. 3 × 6 = 18

a. 4 + 4 + 4 = 12
b. 3 × 4 = 12

(Lesson 2) Complete.

6. 0, 6, 12, 18, and 24 are the first five multiples of __6__.
7. 0, 1, 2, 3, and 4 are the first five multiples of __1__.
8. 1 × 5 = 5   9. 0 × 5 = 0   10. 2 × 6 = 12

(Lessons 3–5) Find each product.

11. 9 × 6 = __54__   12. 3 × 6 = __18__
13. 6 × 8 = __48__   14. 6 × 0 = __0__
15. 9 × 4 = __36__   16. 10 × 8 = __80__
17. 12 × 8 = __96__   18. 6 × 12 = __72__
19. 10 × 7 = __70__   20. 3 × 7 = __21__
21. 4 × 8 = __32__   22. 5 × 11 = __55__

(Mixed Review) Use mental math to find each answer.

23. 32 + 18 = __50__   24. 38 − 19 = __19__

Understanding Division

In this section, students will use equal groups, arrays, repeated subtraction, and multiplication to review the meaning of division and develop basic facts.

Subskills

The work in this section builds on...

- Using counters to make models

15 in 3 equal groups   15 in 3 equal rows

- Using basic multiplication facts

$5 \times 3 = 15$ $2 \times 9 = 18$

- Subtracting 1-digit numbers from 1- or 2-digit numbers

$15 - 5 = 10$ $10 - 5 = 5$ $5 - 5 = 0$

Use the Section Opener

Forty unicyclists aged 7 to 16 from New Hampshire form the Andover One-Wheelers, the only U.S. precision unicycle team. They stay in formation by holding hands.

Have students discuss how they could use math to divide the team members shown in the picture into equal groups. 1 group of 4; 2 groups of 2; 4 groups of 1

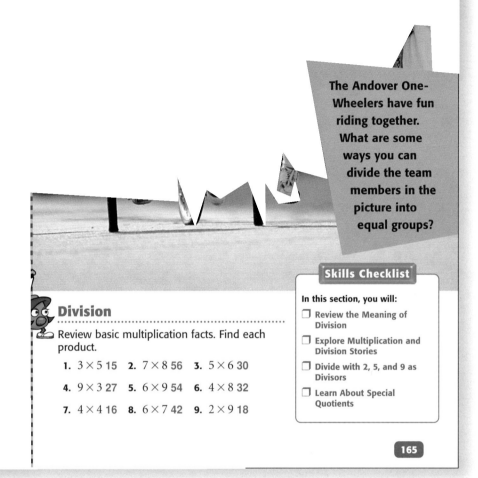

The Andover One-Wheelers have fun riding together. What are some ways you can divide the team members in the picture into equal groups?

Division

Review basic multiplication facts. Find each product.

1. 3×5 15   2. 7×8 56   3. 5×6 30
4. 9×3 27   5. 6×9 54   6. 4×8 32
7. 4×4 16   8. 6×7 42   9. 2×9 18

Skills Checklist

In this section, you will:

☐ Review the Meaning of Division

☐ Explore Multiplication and Division Stories

☐ Divide with 2, 5, and 9 as Divisors

☐ Learn About Special Quotients

165

Skills Trace

(Red numbers indicate pages in this section.)

Lesson and Skill	First Introduced	Grade Four			
		Introduce	Develop	Practice/Apply	Review
4-7 Review the meaning of division.	Grade 3	166, 167	166 191, 193, 561	167, 174, 182, 183, 195, 335	174, 191, 192,
4-8 Explore multiplication and division stories.	Grade 3	168, 169	168, 169	169, 174, 182, 183, 191, 193, 561	174, 191, 192, 195
4-9 Divide with 2, 5, and 9 as divisors.	Grade 3	170, 171	170	171, 174, 182, 183, 191, 193, 561	174, 191, 192, 195, 298, 318, 334, 335, 336, 468, 471, 557
4-10 Divide with 0 and 1.	Grade 3	172, 173	172	173, 174, 182, 183, 191, 193, 561	174, 191, 192, 195

Mixed Review and Test Prep exercises for this chapter occur on pages 149, 153, 157, 167, 171, 173, 177, 179.

Multi-Age Classrooms Use pages 275–298 in Grade 3 or pages 167–192 in Grade 5 to relate to the content of this section.

Reviewing the Meaning of Division

At-A-Glance Planning

Objective Review the meaning of division.

Student Book Lesson Materials *Optional* Overhead counters (24), Lesson Enhancement Transparency 16

Materials for pages 166A and 166B Counters (60 per group), small bowls or plastic bags (6 per group), small self-stick notes (2 per student), magazines or newspapers, scissors, tape

Subject Connection sports—unicycling

Strand Connections patterns, time

	Before Lesson	During Lesson	After Lesson
Daily Math			
p. 166A Problem of the Day			
p. 166A Math Routines			
p. 166A Mental Math			
Teaching Options			
p. 166 Student Book Lesson			
p. 166B Another Way to Learn…			
Options for Reaching All Learners			
p. 166B Inclusion			
p. 166B Language Development			
Subject Connections			
p. 166A Physical Education Connection			
Assessment Options			
p. 166 Talk About It			
p. 167 Error Intervention			
p. 167 Portfolio			
p. 167 Quick Check			
Resources			
4-7 Practice			
4-7 Reteaching			
4-7 Enrichment			
4-7 Problem Solving			
4-7 Daily Transparency			

Problem of the Day

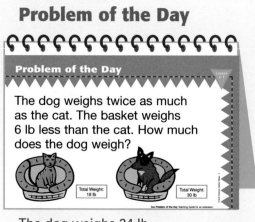

The dog weighs twice as much as the cat. The basket weighs 6 lb less than the cat. How much does the dog weigh?

The dog weighs 24 lb.

Math Routines

Patterns Ask students whether they could share 10, 15, 20, or 30 objects evenly among 2, 3, or 4 people. List their responses on the chalkboard in columns. Invite students to describe any patterns they see. 10: 2 people; 15: 3 people; 20: 2 or 4 people; 30: 2 or 3 people.

Money Name money amounts between $0.25 and $0.50. For each amount, ask students whether the amount could be shared evenly by 2, 3, or 4 people.

Mental Math

Find each difference. Explain your thinking.

$2,400 - 1,100$ 1,300 $4,200 - 3,900$ 300

$3,500 - 2,800$ 700 $5,900 - 5,400$ 500

Physical Education Connection

The longest bicycle ever built measured 72 feet $11\frac{1}{2}$ inches. It carried 4 people.

• If each student wanted to ride the longest bike, how many trips would it take for all to get a turn? Possible answer: for 26 students, 7 trips

Another Way to **Learn** Lesson 4-7

Use as an alternative or in addition to pages 166 and 167.

Materials Counters (60 per group), small bowls or plastic bags (6 per group)

Learning Style Kinesthetic, Verbal

• Have each group find 15 ÷ 3 with counters in three ways:

Put 15 counters in 3 bowls or bags so each has an equal number of counters.

Start with 15 counters and repeatedly take away groups of 3 counters.

Make a 3-row array with 15 counters.

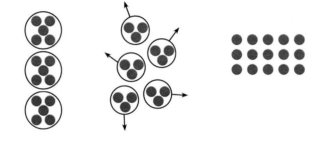

• Have students compare and contrast the models. All three started with the same number and separated counters into equal groups.

• Demonstrate how to draw pictures of the models and write a division sentence to describe each: 15 ÷ 3 = 5.

• Assign Check and Practice on Student Book page 167 or *Practice Master 4-7*.

• Assess using the following rubric.

Assessment Rubric

4 Full Accomplishment
  • finds quotients; demonstrates how to use sharing, repeated subtraction, or multiplication to find quotients

3 Substantial Accomplishment
  • finds most quotients; demonstrates sharing, repeated subtraction, or multiplication to find most quotients

2 Partial Accomplishment
  • finds some quotients but does not demonstrate any method for finding quotients

1 Little Accomplishment
  • does not find quotients

Options for Reaching All Learners

Inclusion

Basic Fact Flip

Use operation signs to connect division and multiplication.

Materials Small self-stick notes (2 per student)

Learning Style Logical

• Ask students to draw a multiplication symbol on one self-stick note and an equals sign on the other. Have them write 12 ÷ 3 = ___ in large symbols on their paper.

• Tell them to cover the equals sign with the multiplication symbol and the division symbol with the equals sign. Have a volunteer read the new fact.

• Ask students to complete the new fact, 12 = 3 × ___ .

• Have students remove the self-stick notes and read both facts. Ask them how the facts are related. Multiplication and division are opposites.

Language Development

Photo Ops

Use pictures to strengthen understanding of the language used for the three meanings of division.

Materials Magazines or newspapers, scissors, tape

Learning Style Visual, Verbal

• Have pairs cut out photos of groups of people, animals, or objects.

• Have students make up scenarios about the photos that involve division, and write the related division sentences.

• Have students give scenarios for sharing, repeated-subtraction and missing-factor meanings of division. Encourage the use of vocabulary such as *share, repeated subtraction*, and *opposite of multiplication* in the scenarios.

Lesson Organizer

Objective Review the meaning of division.

Student Materials None

Teacher Materials *Optional* Overhead counters (24), Lesson Enhancement Transparency 16

Assignment Guide

Basic 12–26, 28, 33–38

Average 13–29, 32–38

Enriched 15–38

1 Introduce

Review

Find each product.

1. 6×4 24 **2.** 6×6 36

3. 7×8 56 **4.** 8×9 72

Build on Prior Knowledge

After reviewing basic multiplication facts, ask students what operation they would use to find how many groups they could make if they had 18 things that they wanted to put into groups of 2. Possible answers: Multiply 2 by a number to get 18. Repeatedly subtract 2 from 18 and count the total number of groups removed. Divide.

2 Teach

See Another Way to Learn…on page 166B.

Learn ● ○ ● ○ ● ○ ● ○ ● ○ ● ○ ● ○ ● ○ ● ○ ● ○

As students focus on the examples, have them talk about what is the same in all three situations. They should recognize that the total number of riders and the number of equal groups or the number in each group are given. Either the number in each group or the number of groups must be found. You may wish to use the transparency of the examples on the overhead during discussion.

You may want to use counters on the overhead to demonstrate each example.

Talk About It) **Ongoing Assessment**

Listen for explanations that indicate understanding of the relationship between multiplication and division.

Answer for Talk About It

$4 \times 9 = 36$

Reviewing the Meaning of Division

You Will Learn

three ways to think about division

Learn ○ ○ ○ ○ ○ ○ ○ ○ ○ ○ ○

Could you ride a bike with no brakes, no handlebars, and only one wheel? The Andover One-Wheelers do it all the time! It's a club for unicycle riders.

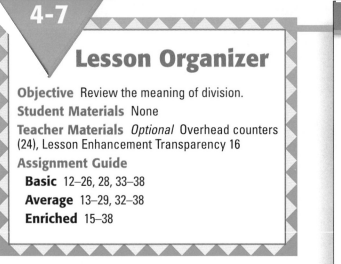

The Andover One-Wheelers are from Andover, New Hampshire.

Example 1

You can think of division as sharing.

Suppose 24 riders form 3 circles. How many riders are in each circle?

Find $24 \div 3$.

8 riders are in each circle.

Example 2

You can think of division as repeated subtraction.

If 24 riders form circles with 6 riders in each circle, how many circles are there?

Find $24 \div 6$.

Subtract 6 from 24 until you have 0. Count how many times you subtracted.

$24 - \mathbf{6} = 18$
$18 - \mathbf{6} = 12$
$12 - \mathbf{6} = 6$
$6 - \mathbf{6} = 0$

$24 \div 6 = 4$
There are 4 circles.

Example 3

You can think of division as the opposite of multiplication.

Suppose 24 riders form 2 rows with an equal number of riders in each row. How many riders are in each row?

$24 \div 2 = ?$
$2 \times ? = 24$
$2 \times 12 = 24$
$24 \div 2 = 12$

So, there are 12 riders in each row.

Talk About It

What multiplication fact can help you find $36 \div 4$?

Practice 4-7	Reteaching 4-7

Divide.

1. $12 \div 3 \, 4$　　2. $10 \div 2 \, 5$　　3. $14 \div 7 \, 2$　　4. $20 \div 4 \, 5$　　5. $72 \div 8 \, 9$

6. $16 \div 4 \, 4$　　7. $15 \div 5 \, 3$　　8. $35 \div 7 \, 5$　　9. $36 \div 9 \, 4$　　10. $36 \div 6 \, 6$

11. **Reasoning** How can you use repeated subtraction to find $54 \div 9$? **Possible answer: Count the number of times you take away groups of 9 until you have 0. The number of groups you take away (6) is the answer to $54 \div 9$.**

Practice

Skills and Reasoning

Divide.

12. $21 \div 3 \, 7$　　13. $24 \div 6 \, 4$　　14. $32 \div 4 \, 8$　　15. $27 \div 3 \, 9$　　16. $4 \div 2 \, 2$

17. $42 \div 7 \, 6$　　18. $48 \div 8 \, 6$　　19. $81 \div 9 \, 9$　　20. $32 \div 4 \, 8$　　21. $56 \div 7 \, 8$

22. $25 \div 5 \, 5$　　23. $30 \div 6 \, 5$　　24. $27 \div 3 \, 9$　　25. $16 \div 2 \, 8$　　26. $30 \div 5 \, 6$

27. By what number do you divide 10 to get 5? **2**

28. What multiplication fact can help you find $56 \div 7$? **$7 \times 8 = 56$**

Problem Solving and Applications

29. Suppose 12 players make 2 teams with an equal number of players on each team. How many players are on each team? **6 players**

30. If 3 players each scored 4 goals, how many goals were scored all together? **12 goals**

31. **Sports** At the end of the first quarter, the basketball team scored 18 points. How many baskets did they make, if each basket was worth 2 points? **9 baskets**

32. **What If** The Andover One-Wheelers practice for 2 hours each week. How many weeks will it take them to practice 10 hours? **5 weeks**

The One-Wheelers have fun playing hockey, tag, and basketball.

Mixed Review and Test Prep

Find each product.

33. $2 \times 3 \, 6$　　34. $5 \times 7 \, 35$　　35. $9 \times 9 \, 81$　　36. $12 \times 0 \, 0$　　37. $7 \times 8 \, 56$

38. Find the sum of 409 and 389. **D**
  Ⓐ 889　　Ⓑ 788　　Ⓒ 898　　Ⓓ 798

Lesson 4-7　**167**

Enrichment 4-7

Name _____　Extend Your Thinking 4-7

Critical Thinking

Answer the riddles using the numbers below.

24　? 20　? 3　? 1　? 9　?11　9　? ?12 ? 1 36 ? ? 3 0 ? 10

1. I am a 2-digit number. I am divisible by 5 and 2. I am less than 20. What number am I?　**10**

2. I am a 1-digit number. I am only divisible by myself. If you multiply a number by me, you get that number. What number am I?　**1**

3. I am a 2-digit number. I am divisible by 1, 2, 3, 4, 6, 9, 12, 18, and 36. What number am I?　**36**

4. I am a 1-digit number. I am a factor of 18, 27, 36, and 45. I am not 1. I am less than 5. What number am I?　**3**

5. I am a 2-digit number. I am divisible by 6 different numbers that include 3, 4, and 6. I am a factor of 12, 24, 36, and 48. What number am I?　**12**

6. I am a 2-digit number. I am a factor of 80, 60, 40, and 20. I am divisible by 6 different numbers that include 4, 5, and 10. What number am I?　**20**

7. I am a 1-digit number. I only have 2 factors. I am a factor of 6, 9, and 12. What number am I?　**3**

8. I am a 1-digit number. If you multiply any number by me, you always get the same product.　**0**

Problem Solving 4-7

Name _____　Problem Solving 4-7

Reviewing the Meaning of Division

Language Arts Books are often divided into sections called chapters. Sometimes chapters are grouped together to form parts. *Gulliver's Travels*, by Jonathan Swift, is divided into 4 parts, and each one of those parts is divided into chapters.

1. Mark is reading Part I (A Voyage to Lilliput) of *Gulliver's Travels*. He has 63 pages to read. If he reads 7 pages each day, how long will it take him to read Part I?　**9 days (nights)**

2. Part I of *Gulliver's Travels* has 8 chapters. If your class spends 16 days studying Part I, how many days will you spend on each chapter?　**2 days**

3. Chapter 1 of Part I is 9 pages long. If you want to read the chapter in 3 days, how many pages should you read each day?　**3 pages**

4. Lila, who is planning on competing in a spelling bee, needs to study the spelling of 72 frequently misspelled words. She has 9 days to get ready. How many words should she study each day?　**8 words**

5. Gary is assigned a role in a play on May 1st. He has 36 lines to memorize. He needs to know all of his lines by heart by May 6th.

  a. If he studies the same number of lines each day, how many should he memorize each day?　**6 lines**

  b. Suppose Gary forgets to study his lines on May 1st and 2nd. How many lines does he need to memorize each of the remaining days?　**9 lines**

6. Graham is backpacking with his family. They have 56 miles to cover in a week. How many miles should they walk in a day?　**8 miles**

Check

Exercise 11 Have students explain how thinking of division as sharing and as the opposite of multiplication could help find $54 \div 9$. Draw 9 large circles and put an equal number of marks in each until you make 54 marks. Think of the missing factor in $9 \times \blacksquare = 54$.

Error Intervention Ongoing Assessment

Observation Students find incorrect quotients.

How to Help Have students check their answers by using division methods other than those in Examples 1–3. For example, if students make mistakes using repeated subtraction, have them check their work by sharing in groups or by multiplying.

Practice

Exercises 12–26 Encourage students who are having difficulty finding answers to draw pictures or use counters.

Exercises 29–32 Remind students that operations other than division can be used to solve some exercises.

For Early Finishers Challenge early finishers to write word problems that could be represented by one of the division expressions in Exercises 12–26.

③ Close and Assess

Portfolio

Have students choose one exercise from Exercises 12–26 and use words and/or pictures to explain how to find the answer by thinking of division as sharing, as repeated subtraction, or as the opposite of multiplication. Have students place their explanations and/or pictures in their portfolios.

Quick Check

Number Sense Which Skill exercises will have answers less than 5? Explain your thinking. Possible answer: Exercise 1; when the product of 5 multiplied by the divisor is greater than the dividend the answer is less than 5.

Skill Divide.

1. $8 \div 2 \, 4$　　2. $42 \div 6 \, 7$

3. $28 \div 4 \, 7$　　4. $18 \div 3 \, 6$

Exploring Multiplication and Division Stories

At-A-Glance Planning

Lesson Planning Checklist

Objective Explore multiplication and division stories.

Vocabulary fact family

Student Book Lesson Materials *Optional Assessment Sourcebook 10* (How We Worked in Our Group)

Materials for pages 168A and 168B Teaching Tool Transparency 6 (Centimeter Grid Paper), scissors, tape or glue

Subject Connection physical education—soccer

Strand Connection algebra readiness

	Before Lesson	During Lesson	After Lesson
Daily Math			
p. 168A Problem of the Day			
p. 168A Math Routines			
p. 168A Mental Math			
Teaching Options			
p. 168B Facilitating and Assessing…			
Options for Reaching All Learners			
p. 168B Inclusion			
p. 168B Language Development			
Subject Connections			
p. 168A Literature Connection			
Assessment Options			
p. 168 Talk About It			
p. 169 Error Intervention			
p. 169 Performance Assessment			
Resources			
4-8 Practice			
4-8 Reteaching			
4-8 Enrichment			
4-8 Problem Solving			
4-8 Daily Transparency			

Problem of the Day

Problem of the Day

Each letter stands for a digit. A different letter is a different digit. What digit does each letter stand for?

$$\begin{array}{r} IT \\ IT \\ + IT \\ \hline HI \end{array}$$

T = 1, I = 3, and H = 9
T = 4, I = 2, and H = 7
T = 7, I = 1, and H = 5

Math Routines

Money Give students the following data: 1 quarter = $0.25 and 4 quarters = $1. Ask them to write all the number sentences they can that include these amounts. $4 \times \$0.25 = \$1$; $\$0.25 \times 4 = \$1$; $\$1 \div 4 = \$0.25$; $\$1 \div \$0.25 = 4$

Time Tell students to suppose that while studying at home, they take a break every 10 minutes. Ask them to name the next 6 break times if the last break was at 6:52. 7:02, 7:12, 7:22, 7:32, 7:42, 7:52

Mental Math

Is each sum greater (>) or less (<) than 200? Explain your thinking.

145 + 65 >   139 + 54 <
127 + 91 >   86 + 138 >

Literature Connection

In *The 329th Friend* by Marjorie Weinman Sharmat, Emery has many guests coming to dinner. They show up in ones, pairs, threes, fours, fives, tens, twenties, and fifties.

• Ask students to find how many pairs of frogs there are if 22 frogs come in by twos. 11

Facilitating and Assessing **Explore** Lesson 4-8

Use with pages 168 and 169.

Get Started While all group members should brainstorm story ideas, you may want to assign alternating roles of recorder, calculator (writes a complete multiplication or division sentence), and checker as well as the group skill Listen to Others.

Observe Watch for groups that are having difficulty developing stories. Encourage them to think of things that may be found in 7s and 5s. Also watch to see that they are using the appropriate operations to answer the questions their stories ask.

Discuss Have students talk about how writing one multiplication or division story can help them write another division or multiplication story involving the same three numbers. For Work Together Exercise 2, their stories for a and c and for b and d may be related.

Assess Use the rubric to assess students' work. See sample for Practice Exercise 1.

4 Full Accomplishment
6, 8, 48
$6 \times 8 = 48$ $48 \div 6 = 8$
$8 \times 6 = 48$ $48 \div 8 = 6$

Assessment Rubric

4 Full Accomplishment
- writes a complete fact family and a multiplication or division story

3 Substantial Accomplishment
- writes a complete fact family; with prompting, writes or tells a multiplication or division story

2 Partial Accomplishment
- writes part of a fact family and part of a multiplication or division story

1 Little Accomplishment
- does not write any part of a fact family or write or tell a multiplication or division story

Options for Reaching All Learners

Inclusion

Understanding Fact Families
Use grids to model a fact family.

Materials Teaching Tool Transparency 6 (Centimeter Grid Paper), scissors, tape or glue

Learning Style Visual

- Have pairs cut four 3-by-5 rectangles from grid paper and attach them to a sheet of paper.
- Have them write multiplication and division sentences. Discuss the fact family represented.

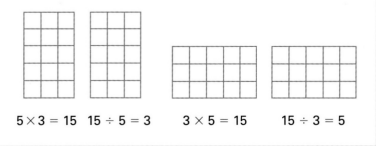

$5 \times 3 = 15$ $15 \div 5 = 3$ $3 \times 5 = 15$ $15 \div 3 = 5$

Language Development

Math Mini-Mysteries
Use brainstorming to support students in their writing of multiplication and division stories.

Learning Style Visual, Verbal

- Help students brainstorm simple topics or situations for their stories, such as a baseball game, a parade, or a trip to the museum.
- Have pairs of students choose story topics and write all the possibilities for numbers they can think of for the story. For example, a parade will include various numbers of clowns, floats, marching bands, and so on.
- Encourage each pair to use its list to write math mini-mysteries for others to solve.

Lesson Organizer

Objective Explore multiplication and division stories.

Suggested Grouping 2 to 4

Student Materials *Optional Assessment Sourcebook 10* (How We Worked in Our Group)

Vocabulary fact family

Assignment Guide

Basic 1–14, 19

Average 2–14, 16, 17, 19

Enriched 5–19

1 Introduce

Review

If there are 5 people on each team, how many people are on

1. 2 teams? 10

2. 5 teams? 25

3. 7 teams? 35

Build on Prior Knowledge

After students review multiplying, ask how many teams there are if 40 people play and there are 5 people on each team. Then ask how this problem is different from the others. 8; This problem uses division.

2 Teach

See Facilitating and Assessing…on page 168B.

Explore

Before students begin to write their stories, have them read the sample stories and discuss the multiplication or division problem they would use to answer the question.

As students work together, you may want to ask why particular stories are multiplication or division stories.

Talk About It Ongoing Assessment

Listen for explanations that show an understanding of the relationship between multiplication and division.

Answer for Talk About It

Possible answer: If you know 8×9 is 72, you know that $72 \div 8$ must equal 9.

Exploring Multiplication and Division Stories

Problem Solving Connection

Work Backward

Vocabulary

fact family
a group of related facts using the same set of numbers

Math Tip
Don't forget to end your story with a question!

Explore

Write multiplication and division stories about yourself.

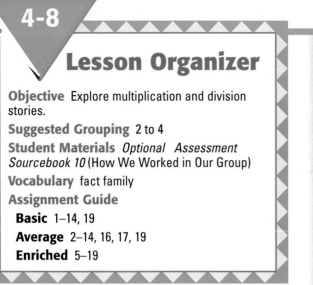

42 ÷ 7
I love soccer! I can't wait for the season to start. We still have 42 days before the first game. I figured out how many weeks that is. Can you?

6 × 7
Our first soccer game is in 6 weeks, against the Raging Rapids team. How many days until we play them?

1. Answers will vary. Possible answer: I practiced the piano 7 hours every week for 6 weeks. How many hours did I practice? $6 \times 7 = 42$; If I practiced 7 hours a week for a total of 42 hours, how many weeks did I practice? $42 \div 7 = 6$; 6 weeks

Work Together

1. Write your own multiplication and division stories for $42 \div 7$ and 6×7. Then solve them.

2. Write multiplication and division stories for each. Solve.
   a. 7×8 **b.** 5×7 **c.** $56 \div 7$ **d.** $35 \div 5$
   Answers will vary.

Talk About It

How does 8×9 help you find $72 \div 8$?

Practice 4-8

Name _____

Practice
4-8

Exploring Multiplication and Division Stories
Complete each fact family.

1. 5, 6, 30
   5 × 6 = 30
   6 × 5 = 30
   30 ÷ 5 = 6
   30 ÷ 6 = 5

2. 6, 7, 42
   6 × 7 = 42
   7 × 6 = 42
   42 ÷ 6 = 7
   42 ÷ 7 = 6

3. 25, 5, 5
   5 × 5 = 25
   25 ÷ 5 = 5

4. 49, 7, 7
   7 × 7 = 49
   49 ÷ 7 = 7

Write a fact family for each set of numbers.

5. 4, 6, 24
   4 × 6 = 24
   6 × 4 = 24
   24 ÷ 6 = 4
   24 ÷ 4 = 6

6. 35, 7, 5
   7 × 5 = 35
   5 × 7 = 35
   35 ÷ 5 = 7
   35 ÷ 7 = 5

7. 81, 9
   9 × 9 = 81
   81 ÷ 9 = 9

Write a question to finish each problem. Then solve each.

8. "I have a collection of 24 candles that I display on 4 shelves."
   Possible answer: How many candles are on each shelf? 6

9. "I have 4 shelves that hold 6 candles each."
   Possible answer: How many candles do I have in all? 24

10. "I have 35 candles packaged in bundles of 7."
   Possible answer: How many candles are in each bundle? 5

Reteaching 4-8

Name _____

Another Look
4-8

Exploring Multiplication and Division Stories
In your book you explored multiplication and division by writing stories. Here is another way to explore division and multiplication. Think about objects in groups.

Lila has 2 packs of baseball cards. There are 8 cards in each pack. Write the fact family for this problem.
$2 \times 8 = 16$
$8 \times 2 = 16$
$16 \div 2 = 8$
$16 \div 8 = 2$

Write the fact families for the pictures below.

1.
   $3 \times 8 = 24$
   $8 \times 3 = 24$
   $24 \div 8 = 3$
   $24 \div 3 = 8$

2.
   $8 \times 4 = 32$
   $4 \times 8 = 32$
   $32 \div 8 = 4$
   $32 \div 4 = 8$

3.
   $6 \times 3 = 18$
   $3 \times 6 = 18$
   $18 \div 6 = 3$
   $18 \div 3 = 6$

Connect

You can think about **fact families** to connect multiplication and division.

Fact Family

Fact Family
$7 \times 8 = 56$ $\quad$ $56 \div 7 = 8$
$8 \times 7 = 56$ $\quad$ $56 \div 8 = 7$

Practice

Copy and complete each fact family.

1. 6, 8, 48
$\blacksquare \times \blacksquare = 48$ **6, 8**
$\blacksquare \times \blacksquare = 48$ **8, 6**
$48 \div \blacksquare = \blacksquare$ **6, 8**
$48 \div \blacksquare = \blacksquare$ **8, 6**

2. 36, 6, 6
$\blacksquare \times \blacksquare = 36$ **6, 6**
$\blacksquare \div \blacksquare = 6$ **36, 6**

3. 3, 27, 9
$\blacksquare \times \blacksquare = 27$ **9, 3**
$27 \div \blacksquare = \blacksquare$ **9, 3**
$\blacksquare \times \blacksquare = 27$ **3, 9**
$27 \div \blacksquare = \blacksquare$ **3, 9**

4. 81, 9, 9
$\blacksquare \times \blacksquare = 81$ **9, 9**
$\blacksquare \div \blacksquare = 9$ **81, 9**

5. 20, 5, 4
$\blacksquare \times \blacksquare = 20$ **4, 5**
$20 \div \blacksquare = \blacksquare$ **4, 5**
$\blacksquare \times \blacksquare = 20$ **5, 4**
$20 \div \blacksquare = \blacksquare$ **5, 4**

6. 32, 8, 4
$\blacksquare \times \blacksquare = 32$ **8, 4**
$\blacksquare \div \blacksquare = 8$ **32, 4**
$\blacksquare \times 8 = \blacksquare$ **4, 32**
$\blacksquare \div \blacksquare = 4$ **32, 8**

7. 28, 7, 4
$\blacksquare \div 7 = \blacksquare$ **28, 4**
$\blacksquare \times \blacksquare = 28$ **7, 4**
$4 \times \blacksquare = \blacksquare$ **7, 28**
$28 \div \blacksquare = \blacksquare$ **4, 7**

8. 8, 2, 16
$2 \times \blacksquare = 16$ **8**
$\blacksquare \div \blacksquare = 8$ **16, 2**
$\blacksquare \times \blacksquare = 16$ **8, 2**
$16 \div \blacksquare = 2$ **8**

Write a fact family for each set of numbers.

9. 54, 6, 9   **10.** 36, 9, 4   **11.** 25, 5, 5

12. 21, 3, 7   **13.** 40, 5, 8   **14.** 72, 9, 8

15. Reasoning The fact family for 49, 7, and 7 has only two number sentences. What is another fact family that has only two sentences?
Possible answer: 36, 6, 6

Write a question to finish **16** and **17**. Then solve each.

16. "I picked 16 daisies and put them into 2 bunches."
Possible answer: How many daisies are in each bunch? 8

17. "I have 2 bunches with 8 daisies in each bunch."
Possible answer: How many daisies do I have in all? 16

18. At soccer practice, Byron saved 7 goals and Jim saved 5 goals. How many goals did they save all together? 12 goals

19. Journal Describe a situation at school or at home where you have used multiplication or division facts.

Lesson 4-8   **169**

Enrichment 4-8

Name _____ Extend Your Thinking
4-8

Visual Thinking
Write the multiplication and division fact families for the following pictures. Order may vary.

1. ◯◯◯◯◯◯◯
◯◯◯◯◯◯◯
◯◯◯◯◯◯◯
◯◯◯◯◯◯◯
◯◯◯◯◯◯◯
◯◯◯◯◯◯◯

$6 \times 7 = 42$
$7 \times 6 = 42$
$42 \div 7 = 6$
$42 \div 6 = 7$

2. ◯◯◯◯

$4 \times 1 = 4$
$1 \times 4 = 4$
$4 \div 4 = 1$
$4 \div 1 = 4$

Write fact families for each set of numbers.
3. 21, 3, 7 $3 \times 7 = 21, 7 \times 3 = 21, 21 \div 7 = 3, 21 \div 3 = 7$
4. 36, 6, 6 $6 \times 6 = 36, 36 \div 6 = 6$
5. 56, 7, 8 $7 \times 8 = 56, 8 \times 7 = 56, 56 \div 7 = 8, 57 \div 8 = 7$

6. Choose one of the fact families from **3–5** and draw a picture for it.
Check students' drawings.

7. Write a story using your own fact family and picture.
Check students' stories.

Problem Solving 4-8

Name _____ Problem Solving
4-8

Exploring Multiplication and Division Stories

1. Suppose you wanted to write a multiplication and division story with the numbers 4, 20, and 5. Write the number sentences you could use.
$4 \times 5 = 20, 20 \div 4 = 5, 5 \times 4 = 20, 20 \div 5 = 4$

2. Some fact families only have 2 number sentences.
a. Write four fact families that have only 2 number sentences.
Possible answers: $1 \times 1 = 1, 1 \div 1 = 1; 2 \times 2 = 4,$
$4 \div 2 = 2; 3 \times 3 = 9, 9 \div 3 = 3; 4 \times 4 = 16; 16 \div 4 = 4$
b. What do the fact families with 2 number sentences have in common? Explain.
Possible answer: Each family includes a number multiplied by itself.

3. Suppose you want to write a multiplication or division story with the number 36. Write all of the possible basic facts (using factors under 10) you could use.
$4 \times 9 = 36, 9 \times 4 = 36, 36 \div 4 = 9, 36 \div 9 = 4;$
$6 \times 6 = 36, 36 \div 6 = 6$

4. Describe a situation with money where you could use multiplication and division facts.
Possible answer: Tan mowed his neighbor's lawn for 2 hours and was paid $4 per hour. How much did Tan make an hour?

5. Write a multiplication or division story using the basic facts 4×3 and $12 \div 3$.
Check students' answers.

Connect

Ask students to describe how the sentences in a fact family are *related*. Use colored markers on the overhead to help them.

Error Intervention Ongoing Assessment

Observation Students do not know how many facts are in a fact family.

How to Help Encourage students to write one multiplication fact, then use the Order Property to write a different multiplication fact, if possible. For each multiplication fact, write the related division fact.

Practice

Exercises 2, 4, and 11 Ask students to explain why these families have only two facts each. Review the term *square number*.

For Early Finishers Challenge early finishers to write complete division and multiplication sentences to answer the question they wrote in Exercises 16 and 17. $16 \div 2 = 8$; $2 \times 8 = 16$

3 Close and Assess

Performance Assessment

Write a fact family for 30, 6, and 5. Then write stories that could be represented by one of the multiplication facts and by one of the division facts. $6 \times 5 = 30, 5 \times 6 = 30, 30 \div 5 = 6, 30 \div 6 = 5$; Possible answer: Each of 6 teams has 5 players. How many players are there all together? There are 5 players on a team. How many teams could be formed with 30 players?

Assess using the rubric on page 168B.

ANSWERS

9 $6 \times 9 = 54, 9 \times 6 = 54, 54 \div 6 = 9, 54 \div 9 = 6$

10 $9 \times 4 = 36, 4 \times 9 = 36, 36 \div 9 = 4, 36 \div 4 = 9$

11 $5 \times 5 = 25, 25 \div 5 = 5$

12 $3 \times 7 = 21, 7 \times 3 = 21, 21 \div 3 = 7, 21 \div 7 = 3$

13 $5 \times 8 = 40, 8 \times 5 = 40, 40 \div 5 = 8, 40 \div 8 = 5$

14 $9 \times 8 = 72, 8 \times 9 = 72, 72 \div 9 = 8, 72 \div 8 = 9$

19 Students might tell of sharing a snack among friends.

Chapter 4 • Lesson 4-8   **169**

Dividing with 2, 5, and 9

At-A-Glance Planning

Lesson Planning Checklist

Objective Divide with 2, 5, and 9 as divisors.

Vocabulary quotient, dividend, divisor

Student Book Lesson Materials None

Materials for pages 170A and 170B Counters (85 per group), small bowls or plastic bags (9 per group), fact-family cards (2 sets per group)

Subject Connections physical education—cycling, science—bones

Strand Connections time, money, using data, mental math

	Before Lesson	During Lesson	After Lesson
Daily Math			
p. 170A Problem of the Day			
p. 170A Math Routines			
p. 170A Mental Math			
Teaching Options			
p. 170 Student Book Lesson			
p. 170B Another Way to Learn…			
Options for Reaching All Learners			
p. 170B Language Development			
p. 170B Reading Assist			
Technology Options			
p. 170A *Math Workshop*			
p. 170 Interactive CD-ROM Lesson 4			
Assessment Options			
p. 170 Talk About It			
p. 171 Error Intervention			
p. 171 Journal			
p. 171 Quick Check			
Resources			
4-9 Practice			
4-9 Reteaching			
4-9 Enrichment			
4-9 Problem Solving			
4-9 Daily Transparency			

Problem of the Day

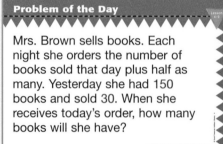

Problem of the Day

Mrs. Brown sells books. Each night she orders the number of books sold that day plus half as many. Yesterday she had 150 books and sold 30. When she receives today's order, how many books will she have?

165 books

Math Routines

Calendar Ask students whether this month can be divided into equal groups of 2, 5, or 9 days with no days left over. 31-day months: no; 30-day months: 2, 5; 28-day month: 2

Patterns Show students a hundred chart. Ask them to tell how they could use number patterns to find all the numbers that could be divided evenly by 9. Possible answer: The sum of the digits must be 9.

Mental Math

Is each sum greater or less than 500? Explain your thinking.

$367 + 120 <$ $255 + 231 <$ $392 + 139 >$

 ## Math Workshop

Students can practice their division facts by playing *Bowling for Numbers.* Ten correct answers to multiple-choice questions earn the player a strike. Students can track their progress in the Hall of Fame. You can adjust the difficulty to match students' abilities. Certificates of achievement can be printed and saved in students' portfolios.

Another Way to [Learn] Lesson 4-9

Use as an alternative or in addition to pages 170 and 171.

Materials Counters (85 per group), small bowls or plastic bags (9 per group)

Learning Style Kinesthetic

- Have students use counters to model 20 ÷ 5 and find the quotient by using bowls or plastic bags to form equal groups. 4
- Model 20 ÷ 5 = 4 on the overhead and write the division sentence in two forms.

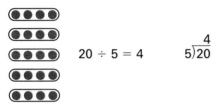

$$20 \div 5 = 4 \qquad 5\overline{)20}$$

- Introduce the terms *dividend, divisor,* and *quotient,* identifying them in both division sentences.
- Have the class read both sentences aloud: 20 divided by 5 equals 4.

- Have groups model the following problems, write the division sentence for each in two ways, and identify the dividend, divisor, and quotient in each sentence.

  14 ÷ 2 7   72 ÷ 9 8
- Assign Check and Practice on Student Book page 171 or *Practice Master 4-9.*
- Assess using the following rubric.

Assessment Rubric
4 Full Accomplishment • finds quotients with divisors of 2, 5, and 9
3 Substantial Accomplishment • finds most quotients with divisors of 2, 5, and 9
2 Partial Accomplishment • finds some quotients with divisors of 2, 5, and 9
1 Little Accomplishment • does not find quotients with divisors of 2, 5, and 9

Options for Reaching All Learners

Language Development

Colorful Expressions

Use colors to strengthen ability to read division sentences.

Materials Fact-family cards (2 sets per group)

Learning Style Visual, Verbal

- Provide each group with 2 color-coded sets of the same dividend, divisor, and quotient cards.

$$\boxed{3} \times \boxed{2} = \boxed{6} \qquad \boxed{6} \div \boxed{3} = \boxed{2}$$
$$\boxed{2} \times \boxed{3} = \boxed{6} \qquad \boxed{6} \div \boxed{2} = \boxed{3}$$

- Have students arrange their cards to show the same fact in two ways.

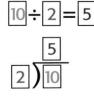

- Have students talk about where the dividend, divisor, and quotient are placed in each sentence.

Reading Assist

Make Predictions

Uses multiplication facts to help find quotients.

Learning Style Logical

- Have students read the instructions for solving the example problem. Ask students to focus on, "Think: 3 times what number equals 15?"
- Ask students how the question relates to the problem. Which number in the question is the dividend and which is the divisor? Multiplication is the opposite of division; 3 is the divisor and 15 is the dividend.
- Ask students what question they could ask to help them divide 27 by 9. Tell students to look back at the question in the example as a guide. Replace 3 and 15 with the divisor and dividend of the new division problem. 9 times what number equals 27?

Lesson Organizer

Objective Divide with 2, 5, and 9 as divisors.
Student Materials None
Vocabulary quotient, dividend, divisor
Assignment Guide
  Basic 12–33, 38–42
  Average 14–35, 38–42
  Enriched 17–42

1 Introduce

Review

Find each product.

1. 2 × 7 14   **2.** 5 × 8 40
3. 8 × 9 72   **4.** 9 × 4 36

Build on Prior Knowledge

After students review 2s, 5s, and 9s multiplication facts, ask which of the multiplication facts in the Review exercises they could use to find 40 ÷ 5. Have them explain. 5 × 8 = 40; It's in the same fact family.

2 Teach

See Another Way to Learn...on page 170B.

Interactive CD-ROM Lesson 4 includes content in this lesson.

Learn ○

Pronunciation Note: Chamear (shah-MEER)

As students look at the two ways of writing a division sentence, ask them to explain what the dividend, divisor, and quotient are. Possible answers: dividend is the whole amount or the number you start with; divisor is the number you divide by; quotient is the answer

Then have them tell to what part of a multiplication sentence each corresponds. Dividend is the product, divisor and quotient are the factors.

Talk About It) **Ongoing Assessment**

Listen for students to mention looking for a 9s fact that has 54 as the product or a fact that is in the same fact family as 54 ÷ 9.

Answers for Talk About It

1 9 × 6 = 54

2 5 × 7 = 35

Dividing with 2, 5, and 9

You Will Learn
how multiplication can help you divide by 2, 5, and 9

Vocabulary
quotient
the answer to a division problem
dividend
the number to be divided in a division number sentence
divisor
the number by which a dividend is divided

Did You Know?
Bicycle racing began in France in 1869.

Learn ○ ○ ○ ○ ○ ○ ○ ○ ○

Chamear likes to exercise regularly. She rode her bike for 15 hours over 3 weeks. If she rode the same number of hours each week, how many hours a week did she ride?

Chamear lives in Charleston, West Virginia. She enjoys riding her bike.

Since you are separating 15 into 3 equal groups, you can divide.

Find 15 ÷ 3.

Think: 3 times what number equals 15?

$3 \times 5 = 15$

So, $15 \div 3 = 5$

Chamear rode her bike for 5 hours each week.

You can write a division number sentence in two ways.

$$\underset{\underset{\text{dividend} \quad \text{divisor}}{\uparrow \quad \uparrow}}{\overset{\overset{\text{quotient}}{\downarrow}}{15 \div 3 = 5}} \qquad \overset{\overset{\text{quotient}}{\downarrow}}{\underset{\underset{\text{divisor}}{\uparrow}}{3\overline{)15} \leftarrow \text{dividend}}}$$

Talk About It

1. What multiplication fact can help you find 54 ÷ 9?
2. What multiplication fact can help you find 35 ÷ 5?

170   Chapter 4 • Multiplication and Division Concepts and Facts

---

Practice 4-9

Name _____

Practice 4-9

Dividing with 2, 5, and 9
Find each quotient.

1. 25 ÷ 5 5   **2.** 81 ÷ 9 9   **3.** 36 ÷ 4 9
4. 45 ÷ 9 5   **5.** 35 ÷ 7 5   **6.** 63 ÷ 9 7
7. 16 ÷ 2 8   **8.** 40 ÷ 5 8   **9.** 14 ÷ 2 7
10. 45 ÷ 5 9   **11.** 30 ÷ 5 6   **12.** 12 ÷ 2 6
13. 54 ÷ 6 9   **14.** 18 ÷ 2 9   **15.** 63 ÷ 7 9
16. 18 ÷ 2 9   **17.** 35 ÷ 5 7   **18.** 72 ÷ 9 8
19. 7 ÷ 7 1   **20.** 9 ÷ 1 9   **21.** 5 ÷ 5 1

22. 4)16 4   **23.** 5)30 6   **24.** 6)30 5   **25.** 9)81 9
26. 9)36 4   **27.** 8)72 9   **28.** 5)20 4   **29.** 2)14 7
30. 9)54 6   **31.** 4)20 5   **32.** 9)63 7   **33.** 5)25 5
34. 3)27 9   **35.** 3)15 5   **36.** 9)18 2   **37.** 5)45 9
38. 9)45 5   **39.** 2)10 5   **40.** 9)72 8   **41.** 5)40 8

42. The divisor is 9; the dividend is 72. What is the quotient? __8__
43. The divisor is 2; the dividend is 12. What is the quotient? __6__
44. The dividend is 25; the divisor is 5. What is the quotient? __5__
45. The dividend is 36; the divisor is 9. What is the quotient? __4__
46. 45 is the dividend; 5 is the divisor. What is the quotient? __9__
47. The dividend is 42; the divisor is 7. What is the quotient? __6__
48. The dividend is 42; the divisor is 6. What is the quotient? __7__
49. The dividend is 9; the divisor is 9. What is the quotient? __1__

Reteaching 4-9

Name _____

Another Look 4-9

Dividing with 2, 5, and 9
You can use counters to help you divide by 2, 5, and 9.

Example 1 Find 18 ÷ 2.
Place 18 counters on your desk.
Divide the counters into 2 equal groups.
How many counters are in each group?
__9__
So, 18 ÷ 2 = __9__.

Example 2 Find 30 ÷ 5.
Place 30 counters on your desk.
Divide the counters into 5 equal groups.
How many counters are in each group?
__6__
So, 30 ÷ 5 = __6__.

Find each quotient. Use counters to help.

1. 27 ÷ 9
  a. How many counters do you need to start with? __27__
  b. Divide the counters into __9__ equal groups.
  c. Draw the groups of counters in the space below.

  d. 27 ÷ 9 = __3__
2. 14 ÷ 2 = __7__   **3.** 25 ÷ 5 = __5__   **4.** 36 ÷ 9 = __4__

Check

Find each quotient.

1. $45 \div 5$ 9
2. $54 \div 6$ 9
3. $14 \div 2$ 7
4. $72 \div 9$ 8
5. $30 \div 5$ 6

6. $2\overline{)12}$ 6
7. $5\overline{)15}$ 3
8. $2\overline{)8}$ 4
9. $9\overline{)81}$ 9
10. $5\overline{)40}$ 8

11. **Reasoning** If $45 \div 9 = 5$, what does $45 \div 5$ equal? Explain.
9; They are number sentences in the same fact family.

Practice

Skills and Reasoning

Find each quotient.

12. $10 \div 2$ 5
13. $27 \div 9$ 3
14. $10 \div 5$ 2
15. $18 \div 9$ 2
16. $45 \div 5$ 9

17. $15 \div 3$ 5
18. $81 \div 9$ 9
19. $36 \div 9$ 4
20. $35 \div 7$ 5
21. $30 \div 5$ 6

22. $2\overline{)18}$ 9
23. $9\overline{)63}$ 7
24. $9\overline{)72}$ 8
25. $5\overline{)45}$ 9
26. $2\overline{)6}$ 3

27. $3\overline{)27}$ 9
28. $5\overline{)20}$ 4
29. $8\overline{)72}$ 9
30. $6\overline{)54}$ 9
31. $2\overline{)16}$ 8

32. 5 is the divisor. 35 is the dividend. What is the quotient? **7**

33. 63 is the dividend. 9 is the divisor. What is the quotient? **7**

Problem Solving and Applications

34. **Time** Kerry rode her bike a total of 35 miles in a week. If she rode the same number of miles each day, how many miles did she ride each day? **5 miles**

35. **Money** If Chamear rents a bike for 2 hours at $11 an hour, how much does she pay? **$22**

36. **Using Data** How many years ago did people begin racing bikes? Use the *Did You Know?* on page 170.
Subtract 1869 from the current year.

37. **Science** There are 3 bones in each finger and 2 bones in each thumb. How many bones are in all your fingers and thumbs? **28 bones**

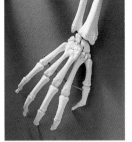

Mixed Review and Test Prep

Mental Math Use mental math to find each sum.

38. $450 + 50$ **500**
39. $825 + 150$ **975**
40. $330 + 160$ **490**
41. $540 + 222$ **762**

42. Find the number that means 5 thousands, 8 tens, 6 ones. **D**
   Ⓐ 586   Ⓑ 5,806   Ⓒ 5,068   Ⓓ 5,086

Skills Practice Bank, page 563, Set 5   Lesson 4-9   **171**

Enrichment 4-9

Problem Solving 4-9

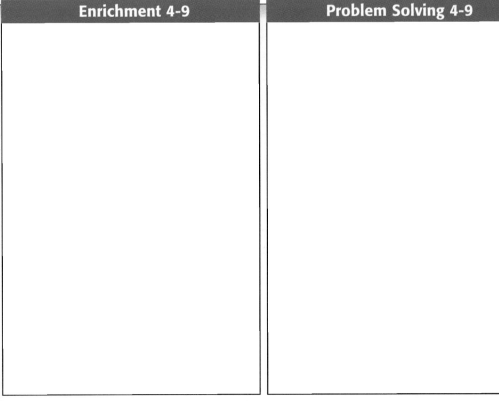

Check

Exercise 11 Be sure that students understand that, in a division fact family, the order of the divisor and quotient can be reversed so $45 \div 9 = 5$ and $45 \div 5 = 9$.

Error Intervention Ongoing Assessment

Observation Students are confused by the fact that the dividend appears first in one form of division sentence and then appears in the other form.

How to Help Have students practice reading both forms of division sentences aloud: *Dividend* divided by *divisor* equals *quotient*.

Practice

Exercises 34–37 Tell students that these exercises may involve operations other than division.

For Early Finishers Challenge early finishers to choose one division exercise from Exercises 12–21 and one from Exercises 22–31 and write each in the other form. Then have them write the multiplication fact(s) and the other division fact, if applicable, that are in the same fact family.

③ Close and Assess

Journal

Have students write the multiplication fact that can help them find $32 \div 4$ and explain why. Then have them write what other division fact, if any, the multiplication fact could help them solve. $4 \times 8 = 32$; $32 \div 8 = 4$

Quick Check

Number Sense For which Skill exercises could you write another related division fact? Explain. Exercise 1: $18 \div 9 = 2$; Exercise 2: $35 \div 7 = 5$; Exercises 3 and 4 are square numbers, so there is only one division fact in each fact family.

Skill Find each quotient.

1. $18 \div 2$ 9
2. $35 \div 5$ 7
3. $9\overline{)81}$ 9
4. $5\overline{)25}$ 5

Special Quotients

At-A-Glance Planning

Objective Divide with 0 and 1.

Student Book Lesson Materials None

Materials for pages 172A and 172B Counters (9 per group), small bowls or plastic bags (9 per group), markers or colored pencils, posterboard or large sheets of paper (1 per student or group)

Subject Connection health—eye blinks

Strand Connections using data, algebra readiness, time

	Before Lesson	During Lesson	After Lesson
Daily Math			
p. 172A Problem of the Day			
p. 172A Math Routines			
p. 172A Mental Math			
Teaching Options			
p. 172 Student Book Lesson			
p. 172B Another Way to Learn…			
Options for Reaching All Learners			
p. 172B Inclusion			
p. 172B Language Development			
Subject Connections			
p. 172A Career Connection			
Assessment Options			
p. 172 Talk About It			
p. 173 Error Intervention			
p. 173 Interview			
p. 173 Quick Check			
Resources			
4-10 Practice			
4-10 Reteaching			
4-10 Enrichment			
4-10 Problem Solving			
4-10 Daily Transparency			

Problem of the Day

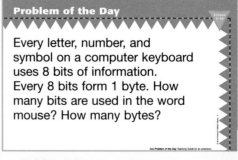

Problem of the Day

Every letter, number, and symbol on a computer keyboard uses 8 bits of information. Every 8 bits form 1 byte. How many bits are used in the word mouse? How many bytes?

40 bits, 5 bytes

Math Routines

Measurement Tell students there are 4 quarts in 1 gallon. If a family drinks a quart of juice a day, how many days does it take them to drink a gallon of juice? Have students write a division sentence to show this quotient. 4 qt ÷ 1 qt per day = 4 days

Patterns Ask students to give the products for 1s facts. Then have them give the related division facts. Discuss any patterns they find.

Mental Math

Find the sums. Explain your thinking.

23 + 47 70	31 + 59 90
38 + 92 130	74 + 26 100

Career Connection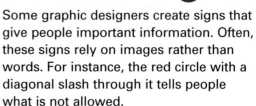

Some graphic designers create signs that give people important information. Often, these signs rely on images rather than words. For instance, the red circle with a diagonal slash through it tells people what is not allowed.

• Have students create their own signs to show that you cannot divide by zero.

Another Way to **Learn** Lesson 4-10

Use as an alternative or in addition to pages 172 and 173.

Materials Counters (9 per group), small bowls or plastic bags (9 per group)

Learning Style Kinesthetic

- Have students try to model 0 ÷ 4, 4 ÷ 0, 4 ÷ 1, and 4 ÷ 4 by dividing the number of counters represented by each dividend into the number of bowls or bags represented by the divisor. 4 bowls with 0 counters in each; can't be done because there are no bowls; 1 bowl with 4 in it; 4 bowls with 1 in each

- Demonstrate by drawing each model on the overhead and writing the division sentence and division rule.

- Have group members take turns modeling one of the division rules with 0 or 1 while the other group members identify the rule modeled.

- Assign Check and Practice on Student Book pages 172 and 173 or *Practice Master 4-10*.

- Assess using the following rubric.

Assessment Rubric
4 **Full Accomplishment** • consistently applies division rules with 0 and 1
3 **Substantial Accomplishment** • usually applies division rules with 0 and 1
2 **Partial Accomplishment** • applies some division rules with 0 and 1
1 **Little Accomplishment** • does not apply division rules with 0 and 1

Options for Reaching All Learners

Inclusion

Dividing with 0 or 1
Use drawings to strengthen understanding of division rules with 0 and 1.

Materials Markers or colored pencils, posterboard or large sheet of paper (1 per student or group)

Learning Style Visual

- Have students work individually or in pairs to select a division rule involving 0 or 1 and create a poster for it.

- Posters should include a drawing of a real-life situation or a model, such as with counters, and a statement of the rule.

- Display posters as reminders to the class.

Language Development

Special Operations
Use numerical examples to strengthen understanding of operations involving 0 and 1.

Learning Style Logical, Verbal

- Have students write several examples in each of these forms:

  ▨ + 0   ▨ − 0   ▨ × 0   ▨ ÷ 0   can't do
  ▨ + 1   ▨ − 1   ▨ × 1   ▨ ÷ 1

- Have students write all sums, differences, products, and quotients that they can.

- Have students talk about the effect of adding 0 and 1, subtracting 0 and 1, multiplying with 0 and 1, and dividing by 1.

- Encourage students to use the terms *quotient, dividend, divisor, factor, product, sum, addend,* and *difference* appropriately in discussion.

Lesson Organizer

Objective Divide with 0 and 1.
Student Materials None
Assignment Guide
Basic 12–35, 42–45
Average 14–37, 40, 42–45
Enriched 17–45

① Introduce

Review

Find each product.

1. $3 \times 0\ 0$ 2. $0 \times 3\ 0$
3. $3 \times 1\ 3$ 4. $1 \times 3\ 3$

Build on Prior Knowledge

After students review multiplication with 0 and 1, ask what they think might be true about division by 1 and have them explain. Possible answer: If you divide a number by 1, you get that number, because if you multiply a number by 1 you get that number.

② Teach

See Another Way to Learn…on page 172B.

Learn ● ● ● ● ● ● ● ● ● ● ● ● ● ● ● ● ● ●

As students focus on the examples of the division rules with 0 and 1, have them suggest division stories to represent each example. For instance, $0 \div 2$ could represent sharing 0 objects equally among 2 people. Each person receives 0. $2 \div 0$ would then represent sharing 2 objects among 0 people. If there are no people, no attempt at sharing the 2 could even occur.

Talk About It **Ongoing Assessment**

Listen for fact families that include all multiplication and division sentences.

Answer for Talk About It

$5 \times 1 = 5, 1 \times 5 = 5, 5 \div 1 = 5, 5 \div 5 = 1$

Check ● ● ● ● ● ● ● ● ● ● ● ● ● ● ● ● ● ●

Exercise 11 Encourage students to refer to the division rules with 0 in their explanations.

Special Quotients

You Will Learn
how to divide with 0 and 1

Learn ● ● ● ● ● ● ● ● ●

Look what happened to the calculator display when Jeremy tried to divide 2 by 0. Division rules with 0 and 1 can help you divide.

Example 1
Division rules with 0.

$0 \div 2 = n$
Think: $2 \times 0 = 0$
Divide. $0 \div 2 = 0$
0 divided by any number (except 0) is 0.

$2 \div 0 = n$
Think: $0 \times \blacksquare = 2$
No numbers work.
You cannot divide by 0.

Here are rules to remember when you divide by 1.

Example 2
Division rules with 1.

$6 \div 1 = n$
Think: $1 \times 6 = 6$
Divide. $6 \div 1 = 6$
Any number divided by 1 is that number.

$6 \div 6 = n$
Think: $6 \times 1 = 6$
Divide. $6 \div 6 = 1$
Any number divided by itself (except 0) is 1.

Talk About It

What is the fact family for 5, 5, and 1?

Remember
Think about multiplication to help you divide.

Check ●

Find each quotient.

1. $8 \div 1\ 8$ 2. $0 \div 7\ 0$ 3. $0 \div 8\ 0$ 4. $9 \div 3\ 3$ 5. $9 \div 9\ 1$
6. $4 \div 4\ 1$ 7. $3\overline{)0}\ 0$ 8. $4 \div 1\ 4$ 9. $2\overline{)12}\ 6$ 10. $1\overline{)3}\ 3$

11. **Reasoning** Can you divide 0 by 0? Explain.
No; You cannot divide any number by 0.

Practice 4-10

Name _____

Special Quotients
Find each quotient.

1. $9 \div 9 = $ __1__   2. $10 \div 1 = $ __10__   3. $0 \div 8 = $ __0__
4. $4 \div 1 = $ __4__   5. $16 \div 4 = $ __4__   6. $0 \div 4 = $ __0__
7. $28 \div 7 = $ __4__   8. $45 \div 9 = $ __5__   9. $42 \div 6 = $ __7__
10. $21 \div 21 = $ __1__   11. $1 \div 1 = $ __1__   12. $27 \div 3 = $ __9__

13. $1\overline{)8}$ __8__   14. $6\overline{)0}$ __0__   15. $6\overline{)36}$ __6__   16. $4\overline{)24}$ __6__
17. $1\overline{)16}$ __16__   18. $7\overline{)7}$ __1__   19. $3\overline{)27}$ __9__   20. $6\overline{)6}$ __1__
21. $1\overline{)10}$ __10__   22. $12\overline{)0}$ __0__   23. $1\overline{)7}$ __7__   24. $8\overline{)8}$ __1__

25. Find the quotient of 5 divided by 5. __1__
26. Find the quotient of 0 divided by 8. __0__
27. Find the quotient of 3 divided by 1. __3__
28. Divide 2 by 1. __2__
29. Divide 0 by 10. __0__
30. Divide 6 by 6. __1__

31. Explain which rule you would use to help you find $0 \div 64$.
0, divided by any number (except 0) is 0.
32. Explain which rule you would use to help you find $64 \div 1$.
Any number divided by 1 is that number.
33. Write a fact family for this set of numbers: 2, 1, 2.
$2 \times 1 = 2, 1 \times 2 = 2, 2 \div 1 = 2, 2 \div 2 = 1$
04. Write a fact family for this set of numbers: 3, 3, 1.
$3 \times 1 = 3, 1 \times 3 = 3, 3 \div 1 = 3, 3 \div 3 = 1$

Reteaching 4-10

Name _____

Special Quotients

A full pizza has been divided into 8 slices. If each person receives 1 slice, how many people can be fed?

$8 \div 1 = 8$

Any number divided by 1 is that number. So, 8 people can each eat 1 slice.

Everyone wants a second slice, but there is no more pizza left. How many people will receive a second slice?

$0 \div 8 = 0$

0 divided by any number (except 0) equals 0. It doesn't matter how many people want a second slice. There is no more pizza left to be divided.

Use what you know about dividing with 0s and 1s to find each quotient.

1. $7 \div 7 = $ __1__   2. $7 \div 1 = $ __7__
3. $0 \div 4 = $ __0__   4. $9 \div 1 = $ __9__
5. $6 \div 6 = $ __1__   6. $0 \div 1 = $ __0__

7. $4\overline{)4}$ __1__   8. $1\overline{)2}$ __2__   9. $3\overline{)0}$ __0__
10. $1\overline{)7}$ __7__   11. $1\overline{)10}$ __10__   12. $5\overline{)5}$ __1__
13. $6\overline{)0}$ __0__   14. $1\overline{)4}$ __4__   15. $3\overline{)3}$ __1__

Skills and Reasoning

Find each quotient.

12. $12 \div 1$ **12** **13.** $0 \div 3$ **0** **14.** $8 \div 8$ **1** **15.** $9 \div 1$ **9** **16.** $35 \div 5$ **7**

17. $5\overline{)0}$ **0** **18.** $2\overline{)2}$ **1** **19.** $7\overline{)0}$ **0** **20.** $1\overline{)6}$ **6** **21.** $9\overline{)0}$ **0**

22. $18 \div 6$ **3** **23.** $24 \div 6$ **4** **24.** $7 \div 7$ **1** **25.** $12 \div 3$ **4** **26.** $6 \div 6$ **1**

27. $1\overline{)2}$ **2** **28.** $4\overline{)0}$ **0** **29.** $3\overline{)15}$ **5** **30.** $5\overline{)5}$ **1** **31.** $2\overline{)14}$ **7**

32. Find the quotient of 8 divided by 8. **1** **33.** Divide 0 by 5. **0**

34. Explain which rule you would use to help you find $24 \div 24$.
Any number (except 0) divided by itself equals 1.

35. Write a fact family for this set of numbers: 8, 8, 1.
$8 \times 1 = 8, 1 \times 8 = 8, 8 \div 8 = 1, 8 \div 1 = 8$

Problem Solving and Applications

Using Data Use the Data File on page 145 to answer **36** and **37**.

36. In the second period, 4 Spirit players scored goals. How many goals did each player score? **1 goal**

37. In the fourth period, how many more goals did the Crunch score than the Spirit? **4 goals**

Algebra Readiness Copy and complete each table. Then write the rule.

38.

In	8	4	7	2	5
Out	40	20	35	10	25

Multiply by 5.

39.

In	18	36	45	63	81
Out	2	4	5	7	9

Divide by 9.

40. Health A typical eye blinks once every 5 seconds. How many times would a typical eye blink in 30 seconds? **6 times**

41. Critical Thinking If the quotient is 0, what do you know about the dividend? **It is also 0.**

Mixed Review and Test Prep

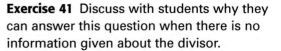

Find each difference.

42. $2,008 - 1,214$ **794** **43.** $3,090 - 2,913$ **177** **44.** $5,004 - 3,883$ **1,121**

45. Time Romunda started her homework at 4:30 P.M. She worked for 35 minutes. Then she took a 15 minute break. It took her another 20 minutes to finish all her homework. What time did she finish? **D**

Ⓐ 6:40 P.M. Ⓑ 5:20 P.M. Ⓒ 5:25 P.M. Ⓓ 5:40 P.M.

Lesson 4-10 **173**

Enrichment 4-10	Problem Solving 4-10

Observation Students say that a problem like Exercise 7 cannot be worked.

How to Help Remind students how to read a division problem written in this form and have them rewrite it $0 \div 3$.

Practice •

Exercise 41 Discuss with students why they can answer this question when there is no information given about the divisor.

For Early Finishers Challenge early finishers to use the same numbers to rewrite each table in Exercises 38 and 39 so that the rules are to use the opposite operations. Students should recognize that this requires reversing the In and Out numbers.

③ Close and Assess

Interview

Ask students to tell you fact families for 7, 0, and 0 and for 7, 7, and 1. Have them tell what rule they used for each fact and, if any family does not have four facts, explain why.
$7 \times 0 = 0, 0 \times 7 = 0, 0 \div 7 = 0, 7 \times 1 = 7,$
$1 \times 7 = 7, 7 \div 7 = 1, 7 \div 1 = 7$; you cannot say $7 \div 0$ because you cannot divide by 0.

Quick Check

Number Sense If you know the quotient is 1, what do you know about the dividend and the divisor? They are the same number.

Skill Find each quotient.

1. $5 \div 5$ **1** **2.** $0 \div 3$ **0**

3. $1\overline{)9}$ **9** **4.** $6\overline{)6}$ **1**

Resources

Technology Master 13

Section B
Review and Practice

Use the Skills Checklist

Review the **Skills Checklist** on the page with students. Then ask such questions as the following:

- For which exercises would thinking of a multiplication fact be helpful? Exercises 1–15, 17–42

- How might you complete Exercise 16 to create a division story problem? Possible answer: Ask how many pieces each person gets.

- Which division rule will you use for Exercise 27? Exercise 28? Any number divided by itself (except 0) is 1. Zero divided by any number (except 0) is 0.

Assess

You may wish to use this information to assess students' understanding of the lesson objectives.

Item Analysis

Lesson Objective		Items
4-7	Review the meaning of division.	1–7, 42
4-8	Explore multiplication and division stories.	8–16
4-9	Divide with 2, 5, and 9 as divisors.	10, 12, 15, 17–26, 31–36, 38, 40
4-10	Divide with 0 and 1.	13, 27–31, 33, 37–39, 42

Resources

Practice Masters
- Practice Chapter 4 Section B

Assessment Sourcebook
- Quiz Chapter 4 Section B

TestWorks: Test and Practice Software

ANSWERS

12–15, 42 See pages D1–D4.

Review and Practice

(Lesson 7) Divide.

1. $20 \div 4$ **5** 2. $12 \div 6$ **2** 3. $32 \div 4$ **8** 4. $18 \div 3$ **6** 5. $15 \div 3$ **5**

6. **Reasoning** Which multiplication fact will help you find $64 \div 8$? $8 \times 8 = 64$

7. There were 48 cyclists in a parade, with 6 cyclists in each row. How many rows were there? **8 rows**

(Lesson 8) Copy and complete each fact family.

8. 42, 7, 6	9. 49, 7, 7	10. 63, 9, 7	11. 16, 4, 4
$6 \times \blacksquare = 42$ **7**	$\blacksquare \times \blacksquare = 49$ **7, 7**	$\blacksquare \times 9 = 63$ **7**	$\blacksquare \div 4 = \blacksquare$ **16, 4**
$\blacksquare \times \blacksquare = 42$ **7, 6**	$\blacksquare \div 7 = \blacksquare$ **49, 7**	$\blacksquare \times 7 = 63$ **9**	$\blacksquare \times \blacksquare = 16$ **4, 4**
$\blacksquare \div 7 = \blacksquare$ **42, 6**		$63 \div \blacksquare = \blacksquare$ **9, 7**	
$\blacksquare \div \blacksquare = 7$ **42, 6**		$\blacksquare \div 7 = \blacksquare$ **63, 9**	

Write a fact family for each set of numbers.

12. 35, 5, 7   13. 8, 1, 8   14. 18, 6, 3   15. 63, 9, 7

16. Write a question to finish the problem. "I have a dozen pieces of licorice. I'll share them equally with my 3 friends." **Possible answer: How many pieces will each friend and I get?**

(Lessons 9 and 10) Find each quotient.

17. $2\overline{)14}$ **7** 18. $5\overline{)35}$ **7** 19. $9\overline{)27}$ **3** 20. $2\overline{)10}$ **5** 21. $9\overline{)63}$ **7**

22. $10 \div 2$ **5** 23. $27 \div 9$ **3** 24. $15 \div 5$ **3** 25. $18 \div 9$ **2** 26. $45 \div 5$ **9**

27. $7 \div 7$ **1** 28. $0 \div 3$ **0** 29. $4 \div 4$ **1** 30. $16 \div 1$ **16** 31. $0 \div 9$ **0**

32. $40 \div 5$ **8** 33. $9 \div 9$ **1** 34. $9\overline{)81}$ **9** 35. $30 \div 5$ **6** 36. $16 \div 2$ **8**

37. $0 \div 4$ **0** 38. $5 \div 5$ **1** 39. $6 \div 1$ **6**

40. **Reasoning** 72 is the dividend. 9 is the divisor. What is the quotient? **8**

41. **Health** The outer skin on the human body is replaced about once a month. How many times is it replaced in a year? **About 12 times**

42. **Journal** Explain how multiplication facts help you divide.

> **Skills Checklist**
>
> In this section, you have:
> - ☑ Reviewed the Meaning of Division
> - ☑ Explored Multiplication and Division Stories
> - ☑ Divided with 2, 5, and 9 as Divisors
> - ☑ Learned About Special Quotients

Practice

Name _____

Practice
Chapter 4
Section B

Review and Practice
(Lesson 7) Divide.

1. $16 \div 8 = $ __2__ 2. $36 \div 6 = $ __6__ 3. $25 \div 5 = $ __5__
4. $56 \div 7 = $ __8__ 5. $12 \div 3 = $ __4__ 6. $14 \div 2 = $ __7__

7. Which multiplication fact will help you find $49 \div 7$? __$7 \times 7 = 49$__
8. Which multiplication fact will help you find $63 \div 9$? __$9 \times 7 = 63$__

(Lesson 8) Complete each fact family.

9. 21, 7, 3
$3 \times \boxed{7} = 21$
$\boxed{7} \times \boxed{3} = 21$
$\boxed{21} \div 7 = \boxed{3}$
$\boxed{21} \div \boxed{3} = 7$

10. 35, 7, 5
$\boxed{7} \times 5 = 35$
$\boxed{5} \times 7 = 35$
$35 \div \boxed{5} = \boxed{7}$
$\boxed{35} \div 7 = \boxed{5}$

11. Write a fact family for this set of numbers: 3, 5, 15.
$3 \times 5 = 15, 5 \times 3 = 15, 15 \div 3 = 5, 15 \div 5 = 3$

(Lessons 9 and 10) Find each quotient.

12. $15 \div 5 = $ __3__ 13. $45 \div 9 = $ __5__ 14. $36 \div 9 = $ __4__
15. $8 \div 8 = $ __1__ 16. $40 \div 5 = $ __8__ 17. $63 \div 9 = $ __7__
18. $0 \div 7 = $ __0__ 19. $2 \div 1 = $ __2__ 20. $12 \div 3 = $ __4__
21. $42 \div 6 = $ __7__ 22. $27 \div 3 = $ __9__ 23. $16 \div 4 = $ __4__

24. $5\overline{)30}$ **6** 25. $9\overline{)81}$ **9** 26. $9\overline{)72}$ **8** 27. $2\overline{)16}$ **8**
28. $2\overline{)8}$ **4** 29. $9\overline{)27}$ **3** 30. $5\overline{)25}$ **5** 31. $2\overline{)14}$ **7**

(Mixed Review) Find each product.

32. $8 \times 8 = $ __64__ 33. $4 \times 7 = $ __28__ 34. $6 \times 8 = $ __48__
35. $6 \times 6 = $ __36__ 36. $7 \times 8 = $ __56__ 37. $3 \times 7 = $ __21__

Extending Multiplication and Division

In this section, students will learn more basic division facts and explore even and odd numbers and factors. They will also learn to compare strategies and solve problems with too much or too little information.

Subskills

The work in this section builds on…

- Understanding multiplication

  2 groups of 6

  2 rows of 6

- Understanding the meaning of division

  dividing 12 into equal groups of 2

  repeatedly subtracting groups of 2

  the opposite of $6 \times 2 = 12$

- Using basic multiplication facts

  $6 \times 4 = 24$ $7 \times 6 = 42$

Use the Section Opener

Brittany is an honor student and enjoys dance, cheerleading, singing, and softball. Ask how many hours Brittany and her classmates skate during a 9-month school year. 18 hours

Once a month, Brittany and her classmates go to skating nights from 6:00 P.M. to 8:00 P.M. During the school year, how many total hours do they skate on these nights?

Extending Multiplication and Division

Review basic facts. Find each product.

1. 7×9 63   **2.** 8×4 32   **3.** 6×8 48

4. 7×4 28   **5.** 9×3 27   **6.** 8×8 64

7. 6×5 30   **8.** 2×7 14   **9.** 3×5 15

Skills Checklist

In this section, you will:

☐ Divide with 3, 4, 6, 7, and 8 as Divisors

☐ Explore Even and Odd Numbers

☐ Explore Factors

☐ Solve Problems with Too Much or Too Little Information

☐ Solve Problems by Comparing Strategies: Guess and Check/Draw a Picture

175

Skills Trace

(Red numbers indicate pages in this section.)

Lesson and Skill	First Introduced	Grade Four			
		Introduce	Develop	Practice/Apply	Review
4-11 Divide with 3 and 4 as divisors.	Grade 3	176, 177	176	177, 182, 183, 190, 191, 193, 561	190, 192, 195, 295, 336, 339, 381, 412
4-12 Divide with 6, 7, and 8 as divisors.	Grade 3	178, 179	178	179, 182, 183, 190, 191, 193, 561	190, 192, 195, 298, 336, 339, 471, 523
4-13 Explore even and odd numbers.	Grade 3	180, 181	180, 181	181, 182, 183, 190, 194, 561	190, 192, 195, 334
4-14 Explore factors.	Grade 4	184, 185	184, 185	185, 190, 194, 561	190, 192, 195
4-15 Solve problems with too much or too little information.	Grade 4	186, 187	186, 187	187, 190, 561	190, 192, 195
4-16 Solve problems by comparing strategies.	Grade 3	188, 189	188, 189	189, 190, 561	190, 192, 195

Mixed Review and Test Prep exercises for this chapter occur on pages 149, 153, 157, 167, 171, 173, 177, 179.

Multi-Age Classrooms Use pages 283–312 in Grade 3 or pages 175–192 in Grade 5 to relate to the content of this section.

Dividing with 3 and 4

At-A-Glance Planning

Lesson Planning Checklist

Objective Divide with 3 and 4 as divisors.

Student Book Lesson Materials None

Materials for pages 176A and 176B Counters, Teaching Tool Transparency 5 (Number Lines), number cube labeled 3, 3, 3, 4, 4, 4 (1 per group)

Subject Connections physical education—baseball, history—baseball, science—bones

Strand Connections measurement, algebra readiness, money

	Before Lesson	During Lesson	After Lesson
Daily Math			
p. 176A Problem of the Day			
p. 176A Math Routines			
p. 176A Mental Math			
Teaching Options			
p. 176 Student Book Lesson			
p. 176B Another Way to Learn…			
Options for Reaching All Learners			
p. 176B Inclusion			
p. 176B Gifted & Talented			
Technology Options			
p. 176 Interactive CD-ROM Lesson 4			
Subject Connections			
p. 176A Literature Connection			
Assessment Options			
p. 176 Talk About It			
p. 177 Error Intervention			
p. 177 Observation			
p. 177 Quick Check			
Resources			
4-11 Practice			
4-11 Reteaching			
4-11 Enrichment			
4-11 Problem Solving			
4-11 Daily Transparency			

Problem of the Day

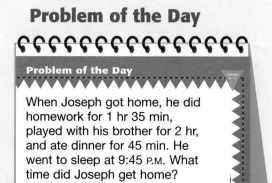

Problem of the Day

When Joseph got home, he did homework for 1 hr 35 min, played with his brother for 2 hr, and ate dinner for 45 min. He went to sleep at 9:45 P.M. What time did Joseph get home?

5:25 P.M.

Math Routines

Patterns Ask students to describe the rule and complete the table. Divide by 9

In	54	45	36	27	18	9
Out	6	5	4	3	2	1

Measurement There are 64 ounces in a half-gallon. Ask students to find the number of ounces in 4 equal containers totaling 64 ounces. 16

Mental Math

Find each sum. Explain your thinking.

189 + 211 400   308 + 192 500
579 + 321 900   804 + 196 1,000

Literature Connection

In *Jim and the Beanstalk* by Raymond Briggs, Jim cuts down the beanstalk so that the Giant cannot chase him home.

• Suppose the beanstalk is 24 miles tall and Jim cuts it into 3 equal pieces. How many miles long is each piece?
8 mi

Another Way to [Learn] Lesson 4-11

Use as an alternative or in addition to pages 176 and 177.

Materials Counters (30 per group)

Learning Style Kinesthetic

- Have students use counters to model 18 ÷ 3 and find the quotient. 6

- Have students talk about how they decided how many rows to make and how many counters to put in each row. Have them tell what multiplication fact their model also represents. 3 × 6 = 18

- Demonstrate modeling 18 ÷ 3 = 6 on the overhead and write the division and multiplication facts represented by the model.

18 ÷ 3 = 6
3 × 6 = 18

- Have groups model the following problems and write the division fact and multiplication fact represented by each model.

    21 ÷ 3 7   28 ÷ 4 7   12 ÷ 3 4   12 ÷ 4 3

- Have students discuss how thinking of a multiplication fact can help them complete a division fact.

- Assign Check and Practice on Student Book pages 176 and 177 or *Practice Master 4-11.*

- Assess using the following rubric.

Assessment Rubric

4 **Full Accomplishment**
- finds quotients with divisors of 3 and 4

3 **Substantial Accomplishment**
- find most quotients with divisors of 3 and 4

2 **Partial Accomplishment**
- finds some quotients with divisors of 3 and 4

1 **Little Accomplishment**
- does not find quotients with divisors of 3 and 4

Options for Reaching All Learners

Inclusion

Number Line Division

Use number lines to strengthen understanding of dividing with 3 and 4 as divisors.

Materials Teaching Tool Transparency 5 (Number Lines)

Learning Style Visual, Verbal

- Have students make number lines from 0 to 40.

- Have students show 28 ÷ 4 by starting at 0 and making jumps of 4 until they reach 28. Have them count the jumps to find the quotient.

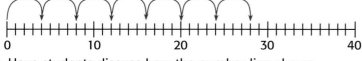

- Have students discuss how the number line shows 28 ÷ 4 = 7 and how it shows the other facts in the same family: 28 ÷ 7 = 4; 4 × 7 = 28, and 7 × 4 = 28.

- Repeat for other division facts with divisors of 3 and 4.

Gifted & Talented

Three in a Row

Use a game format to strengthen knowledge of 3s and 4s division facts.

Materials Number cube labeled 3, 3, 3, 4, 4, 4 (1 per group), counters (9 per student)

Learning Style Logical, Social

- Have each player draw a 3-by-3 gameboard and write a different multiple of 3 less than 30 or multiple of 4 less than 40 in each square.

- Players take turns tossing the number cube. For each toss, the player chooses an uncovered square with a number that is a multiple of the number on the cube. If the player correctly names the quotient of the number on the gameboard and the number on the cube, he or she covers the number on the gameboard.

- The first player to cover three numbers across, down, or diagonally wins.

Lesson Organizer

Objective Divide with 3 and 4 as divisors.

Student Materials None

Assignment Guide

Basic 7–34, 40–43

Average 9–35, 37, 38, 40–43

Enriched 12–43

1 Introduce

Review

Find each product.

1. 3 × 7 21 **2.** 4 × 8 32

3. 3 × 6 18 **4.** 4 × 7 28

Build on Prior Knowledge

After students review multiplying with 3s and 4s, ask which division fact they could complete by thinking of 4 × 7. Have them explain. 28 ÷ 4 = 7 or 28 ÷ 7 = 4 because they are in the same fact family

2 Teach

See Another Way to Learn…on page 176B.

Interactive CD-ROM Lesson 4 includes content in this lesson.

Learn

As students look at both examples, have them explain why division is used to solve each problem and why each multiplication fact shown is helpful.

Talk About It Ongoing Assessment

Listen for students to name a multiplication fact in the same fact family.

Answer for Talk About It

3 × 7 = 21

Check

Exercise 6 Review which parts of a division fact correspond to parts of a multiplication fact.

Dividing with 3 and 4

You Will Learn
how multiplication can help you divide with 3 and 4

Learn

In 1994, Krissy was voted best baseball player in the Little League World Series. She was the only girl playing!

Krissy, from Brooklyn Center, Minnesota, is a star player on more than one sports team.

Example 1

Suppose the pitcher on Krissy's team pitched 27 balls at practice. He pitched 3 balls to each batter. How many batters were there?

Find 27 ÷ 3.

Think: 3 times what number equals 27?

3 × 9 = 27

$$27 \div 3 = 9 \qquad 3\overline{)27}^{\,9}$$

So, there were 9 batters.

Example 2

Krissy also plays tennis. In doubles tennis, 4 players play on a court. If 32 players are in a tournament, how many courts are needed for all players to play at one time?

Find 32 ÷ 4.

Think: 4 times what number equals 32?

4 × 8 = 32

$$32 \div 4 = 8 \qquad 4\overline{)32}^{\,8}$$

So, 8 courts are needed.

Talk About It

Remember
Think about multiplication to divide!

What multiplication fact can you use to find 21 ÷ 3?

Check

Find each quotient.

1. 24 ÷ 3 8 **2.** 16 ÷ 4 4 **3.** 15 ÷ 3 5 **4.** 28 ÷ 4 7 **5.** 18 ÷ 3 6

6. Reasoning How do multiplication facts of 3 and 4 help you divide by 3 and 4? Multiplication facts of 3 and 4 belong to the same fact family as division facts of 3 and 4.

176 Chapter 4 • Multiplication and Division Concepts and Facts

---

Practice 4-11

Name _____

Dividing with 3 and 4

Find each quotient.

1. 8 ÷ 4 = __2__ **2.** 12 ÷ 3 = __4__ **3.** 18 ÷ 3 = __6__

4. 0 ÷ 3 = __0__ **5.** 20 ÷ 4 = __5__ **6.** 28 ÷ 4 = __7__

7. 12 ÷ 4 = __3__ **8.** 21 ÷ 3 = __7__ **9.** 3 ÷ 3 = __1__

10. 0 ÷ 4 = __0__ **11.** 9 ÷ 3 = __3__ **12.** 27 ÷ 3 = __9__

13. 16 ÷ 4 = __4__ **14.** 32 ÷ 4 = __8__ **15.** 24 ÷ 3 = __8__

16. 9)27̄ ³ **17.** 4)16̄ ⁴ **18.** 9)45̄ ⁵ **19.** 7)28̄ ⁴

20. 8)8̄ ¹ **21.** 7)0̄ ⁰ **22.** 3)27̄ ⁹ **23.** 9)36̄ ⁴

24. 3)15̄ ⁵ **25.** 4)4̄ ¹ **26.** 3)6̄ ² **27.** 4)24̄ ⁶

28. 4)36̄ ⁹ **29.** 8)32̄ ⁴ **30.** 7)21̄ ³ **31.** 3)24̄ ⁸

32. 5)20̄ ⁴ **33.** 8)24̄ ³ **34.** 1)3̄ ³ **35.** 2)6̄ ³

36. Divide 15 by 3. __5__ **37.** Divide 28 by 4. __7__

38. Divide 32 by 4. __8__ **39.** Divide 27 by 3. __9__

40. What multiplication fact can help you find 18 ÷ 3? __3 × 6 = 18__

41. What multiplication fact can help you find 28 ÷ 4?

Reteaching 4-11

Name _____

Dividing with 3 and 4

It's easier to divide by 3 or 4 if you know your multiplication facts.

3 × 1 = 3	4 × 1 = 4
3 × 2 = 6	4 × 2 = 8
⟨3 × 3 = 9⟩	4 × 3 = 12
3 × 4 = 12	4 × 4 = 16
3 × 5 = 15	4 × 5 = 20
3 × 6 = 18	4 × 6 = 24
3 × 7 = 21	4 × 7 = 28
3 × 8 = 24	4 × 8 = 36
	4 × 9 = 36
3 × 10 = 30	4 × 10 = 40

To solve 9 ÷ 3, find a multiplication fact that has a product of 9 and a factor of 3.

Since 3 × ③ = 9, 9 ÷ 3 = __3__.

Complete each statement.

1. Since 3 × ④ = 12, 12 ÷ 3 = ④.

2. Since 4 × ③ = 12, 12 ÷ 4 = ③.

3. Since __4 × 8 = 32__, 32 ÷ 4 = ⑧.

4. Since __3 × 9 = 27__, 27 ÷ 3 = ⑨.

5. Since __3 × 6 = 18__, 18 ÷ 3 = ⑥.

6. Since __4 × 6 = 24__, 24 ÷ 4 = ⑥.

7. Since __3 × 8 = 24__, 24 ÷ 3 = ⑧.

8. Since __4 × 2 = 8__, 8 ÷ 4 = ②.

9. Since __4 × 5 = 20__, 20 ÷ 4 = ⑤.

10. Since __3 × 7 = 21__, 21 ÷ 3 = ⑦.

11. Since __9 × 4 = 36__, 36 ÷ 4 = ⑨.

12. Since __4 × 7 = 28__, 28 ÷ 4 = ⑦.

13. Since __4 × 4 = 16__, 16 ÷ 4 = ④.

14. Since __3 × 5 = 15__, 15 ÷ 3 = ⑤.

Skills and Reasoning

Find each quotient.

7. $3\overline{)18}$ **6**   8. $9\overline{)36}$ **4**   9. $4\overline{)20}$ **5**   10. $3\overline{)27}$ **9**   11. $3\overline{)6}$ **2**

12. $28 \div 4$ **7**   13. $27 \div 9$ **3**   14. $12 \div 3$ **4**   15. $15 \div 3$ **5**   16. $32 \div 8$ **4**

17. $9 \div 3$ **3**   18. $24 \div 3$ **8**   19. $0 \div 5$ **0**   20. $21 \div 3$ **7**   21. $16 \div 4$ **4**

22. $4\overline{)36}$ **9**   23. $3\overline{)3}$ **1**   24. $4\overline{)32}$ **8**   25. $4\overline{)24}$ **6**   26. $3\overline{)0}$ **0**

27. $12 \div 4$ **3**   28. $4 \div 4$ **1**   29. $15 \div 5$ **3**   30. $8 \div 4$ **2**   31. $0 \div 4$ **0**

32. Divide 36 by 4. **9**   33. Divide 21 by 3. **7**

34. What multiplication fact can help you find $24 \div 3$? $3 \times 8 = 24$

Problem Solving and Applications

35. Krissy played 24 innings in 3 baseball games.
    a. If she played the same number of innings in each game, how many innings did she play in each? **8 innings**
    b. If each game had 9 innings, for how many innings was Krissy on the bench? **3 innings**

36. **Measurement** Wooden baseball bats usually weigh 2 or 3 ounces less than the number of inches in their length. If a wooden bat is 28 inches long, how much will it weigh? **25 or 26 ounces**

37. **History** Baseball gloves were not used until 1875. That was 25 years after baseball was invented. When was baseball invented? **1850**

Algebra Readiness Copy and complete the table. Then write the rule.

38.

In	12	21	27	18	9
Out	4	7	9	6	3

Divide by 3.

39.

In	16	20	36	24	8
Out	4	5	9	6	2

Divide by 4.

Mixed Review and Test Prep

Find each sum or difference.

40. $297 + $189 **$486**
41. $507 - $312 **$195**
42. $1,251 + $912 **$2,163**

43. **Science** A newborn baby's body has 350 bones. An adult's body has 206 bones. How many more bones does a newborn have? **C**
    Ⓐ 556   Ⓑ 146   Ⓒ 144   Ⓓ not here

Lesson 4-11 **177**

Enrichment 4-11	**Problem Solving 4-11**

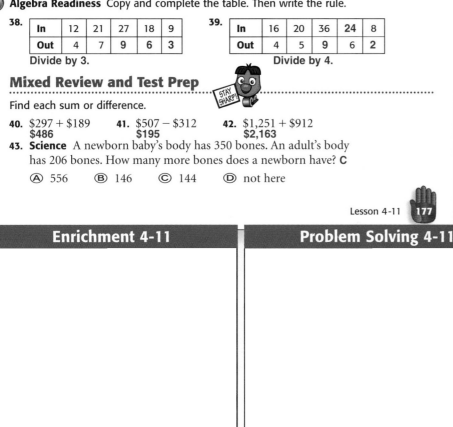

Error Intervention Ongoing Assessment

Observation Students write incorrect quotients because they don't know their multiplication facts.

How to Help Review ways to help find products: skip count, think of patterns in multiples, double products of 2s facts to find products of 4s facts.

Practice •

Exercise 35 Tell students that they can use the solution to Part a to solve Part b.

Exercise 38 and 39 Tell students to use basic facts to help them complete the table.

For Early Finishers Challenge early finishers to choose three exercises from Exercises 7–31, think about fact families, and tell what other quotients they can find because they have completed these division facts.

③ Close and Assess

Observation

Observe the extent to which students are relying on multiplication facts to find quotients and whether they are starting to learn division facts.

Quick Check

Number Sense Without dividing, tell which quotient will be greater: $2\overline{)12}$ or $12 \div 3$; $15 \div 3$ or $12 \div 3$? Explain. $2\overline{)12}$, When you divide the same number into fewer groups, there will be more in each group; $15 \div 3$, When you divide a greater number by the same number, the quotient will be greater.

Skill Find each quotient.

1. $3\overline{)12}$ **4**   2. $3\overline{)24}$ **8**
3. $32 \div 4$ **8**   4. $24 \div 4$ **6**

Dividing with 6, 7, and 8

At-A-Glance Planning

Lesson Planning Checklist

Objective Divide with 6, 7, and 8 as divisors.

Student Book Lesson Materials *Optional* Lesson Enhancement Transparency 15

Materials for pages 178A and 178B Counters, index cards, plastic 6-pack rings, color cubes (60), old calendars cut apart into weekly strips, boxes of 8 crayons or markers, piano or picture of keyboard

Subject Connections sports—ice skating, history—Jane Torvill and Christopher Dean

Strand Connections time, using data, money

	Before Lesson	During Lesson	After Lesson
Daily Math			
p. 178A Problem of the Day			
p. 178A Math Routines			
p. 178A Mental Math			
Teaching Options			
p. 178 Student Book Lesson			
p. 178B Another Way to Learn…			
Options for Reaching All Learners			
p. 178B Inclusion			
p. 176B Cultural Connection			
Technology Options			
p. 178A *Math Workshop*			
p. 178 Interactive CD-ROM Lesson 4			
Assessment Options			
p. 178 Talk About It			
p. 179 Error Intervention			
p. 179 Journal			
p. 179 Quick Check			
Resources			
4-12 Practice			
4-12 Reteaching			
4-12 Enrichment			
4-12 Problem Solving			
4-12 Daily Transparency			

Problem of the Day

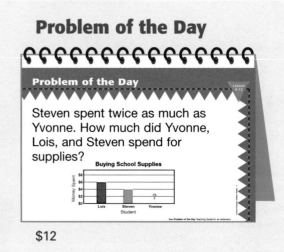

Steven spent twice as much as Yvonne. How much did Yvonne, Lois, and Steven spend for supplies?

$12

Math Routines

Time Ask students whether an hour can be evenly divided into periods of 6 minutes without any minutes left over. Then ask the same for 7 and 8 minutes. Discuss how the relationship between 6 and 60 is different from the one between 7 or 8 and 60. 60 is a multiple of 6.

Calendar Ask students how many weeks are in 49, 56, and 42 days. 7, 8, and 6 weeks

Mental Math

Find each difference. Explain your thinking.

47 − 30 17   59 − 21 38

63 − 30 33   81 − 31 50

Math Workshop

As students gain confidence in their division skills, encourage them to adjust the difficulty level of *Bowling for Numbers* themselves. Have them check their progress in the Hall of Fame and print out certificates of achievement to add to their portfolios.

Another Way to [Learn] Lesson 4-12

Use as an alternative or in addition to pages 178 and 179.

Materials Counters (50 per group)

Learning Style Kinesthetic

- Demonstrate modeling $42 \div 6 = 7$ on the overhead and write the division and multiplication facts represented by the model.

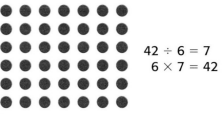

$$42 \div 6 = 7$$
$$6 \times 7 = 42$$

- Have students use counters to model $42 \div 7$ and find the quotient. 6

- Have students talk about how they decided how many rows to make and how many counters to put in each row. Have them tell what multiplication fact their model also represents. $7 \times 6 = 42$

- Have groups model the following and write the division fact and multiplication fact represented by each model.

  $49 \div 7 \ 7$ $32 \div 8 \ 4$ $28 \div 7 \ 4$ $40 \div 8 \ 5$

- Have students discuss how thinking of a multiplication fact can help them complete a division fact.

- Assign Check and Practice on Student Book pages 178 and 179 or *Practice Master 4-12.*

- Assess using the following rubric.

Assessment Rubric
4 **Full Accomplishment** • finds quotients with divisors of 6, 7, and 8
3 **Substantial Accomplishment** • finds most quotients with divisors of 6, 7, and 8
2 **Partial Accomplishment** • finds some quotients with divisors of 6, 7, and 8
1 **Little Accomplishment** • does not find quotients with divisors of 6, 7, and 8

Options for Reaching All Learners

Inclusion

Real 6s, 7s, and 8s

Use real situations to strengthen dividing with 6, 7, and 8 as divisors.

Materials Index cards, plastic 6-pack rings, color cubes (60), old calendars cut apart into weekly strips, counters (70), boxes of 8 crayons or markers

Learning Style Kinesthetic

- Place rings and cubes on one table, calendar strips and counters on another, and crayons or markers along with the empty boxes on another. Write division sentences with 6, 7, and 8 as divisors on index cards and place them on the appropriate tables.

- Have students choose a fact card and count out the number of cubes, counters, or crayons as the quotient. Have them place the cubes in rings, the counters on days of the week, or crayons in the boxes and count the rings, strips, or boxes to find the dividend.

Cultural Connection

How Many in an Octave?

Use the divisor 8 to explore musical scales.

Materials Piano or picture of a keyboard

Learning Style Musical

Tell students that in Western music, there are 8 notes in a scale. Demonstrate by playing a C-major scale on the piano, or showing it to students on a picture of a keyboard. Point out that there are eight white keys from C to C, and that the interval of sound between these two notes is called an octave. Scales in keys other than C major include both black and white piano keys, but all scales have eight notes.

- Have students find out how many keys, both black and white, are on a piano keyboard. 88

- Have students use 8 and 88 to write musical division stories.

Lesson Organizer

Objective Divide with 6, 7, and 8 as divisors.

Student Materials None

Teacher Materials *Optional* Lesson Enhancement Transparency 15

Assignment Guide

Basic 7–28, 35–39

Average 9–31, 35–39

Enriched 12–39

1 Introduce

Review

Find each product.

1. 6 × 9 54   **2.** 8 × 8 64

3. 7 × 4 28   **4.** 8 × 9 72

Build on Prior Knowledge

After students review 6s, 7s, and 8s multiplication facts, ask which division fact they could complete by thinking of 8 × 9. Have them explain. 72 ÷ 8 = 9 or 72 ÷ 9 = 8 because they are in the same fact family

2 Teach

See Another Way to Learn…on page 178B.

 Interactive CD-ROM Lesson 4 includes content in this lesson.

Learn

As students look at the first example, have them explain why division is used to solve the problem. As they look at the other examples, have them suggest division stories that could be represented by the division facts. For each example, have them explain why the multiplication fact is helpful.

Talk About It **Ongoing Assessment**

Listen for students to name a multiplication fact in the same fact family.

Answer for Talk About It

7 × 6 = 42

Check

Exercise 6 Encourage students to think about and explain the answer before dividing. Then suggest that they divide and compare quotients to check their explanation.

178 *Chapter 4 • Lesson 4-12*

Chapter 4 Lesson 12

Dividing with 6, 7, and 8

You Will Learn how multiplication can help you divide with 6, 7, and 8

Learn

"All skaters! Please turn around and skate in the opposite direction now. Remember to stay in your groups!"

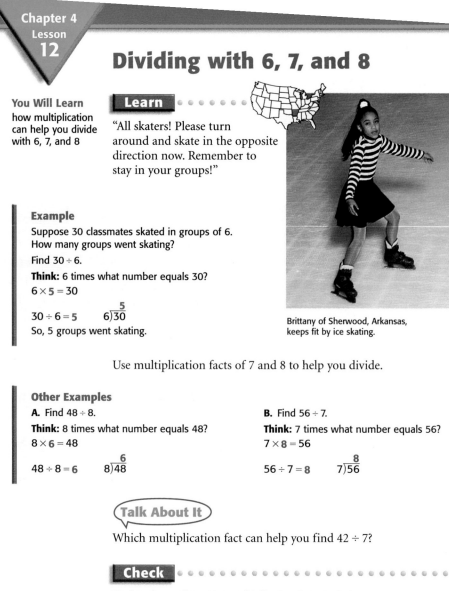

Brittany of Sherwood, Arkansas, keeps fit by ice skating.

Example

Suppose 30 classmates skated in groups of 6. How many groups went skating?

Find 30 ÷ 6.

Think: 6 times what number equals 30?

6 × 5 = 30

30 ÷ 6 = 5   6)30 = 5

So, 5 groups went skating.

Use multiplication facts of 7 and 8 to help you divide.

Other Examples

A. Find 48 ÷ 8.

Think: 8 times what number equals 48?

8 × 6 = 48

48 ÷ 8 = 6   8)48 = 6

B. Find 56 ÷ 7.

Think: 7 times what number equals 56?

7 × 8 = 56

56 ÷ 7 = 8   7)56 = 8

Talk About It

Which multiplication fact can help you find 42 ÷ 7?

Check

Find each quotient. Use multiplication facts to help.

1. 18 ÷ 6 3   **2.** 24 ÷ 8 3   **3.** 7)14 2   **4.** 54 ÷ 6 9   **5.** 7)28 4

6. Reasoning Is the quotient of 63 ÷ 7 greater than or less than the quotient of 64 ÷ 8? Explain. Greater than; 63 ÷ 7 = 9 > 64 ÷ 8 = 8

178 Chapter 4 • Multiplication and Division Concepts and Facts

---

Practice 4-12

Name _____

Practice 4-12

Dividing with 6, 7 and 8

Find each quotient.

1. 18 ÷ 6 = 3   **2.** 24 ÷ 8 = 3   **3.** 14 ÷ 7 = 2

4. 6 ÷ 6 = 1   **5.** 0 ÷ 8 = 0   **6.** 35 ÷ 7 = 5

7. 36 ÷ 6 = 6   **8.** 48 ÷ 8 = 6   **9.** 12 ÷ 6 = 2

10. 56 ÷ 7 = 8   **11.** 54 ÷ 6 = 9   **12.** 56 ÷ 8 = 7

13. 28 ÷ 7 = 4   **14.** 24 ÷ 6 = 4   **15.** 30 ÷ 6 = 5

16. 7)49 7   **17.** 8)72 9   **18.** 7)21 3   **19.** 6)42 7

20. 7)0 0   **21.** 7)63 9   **22.** 8)64 8   **23.** 6)48 8

24. 7)42 6   **25.** 8)40 5   **26.** 8)32 4   **27.** 8)16 2

28. 7)7 1   **29.** 9)72 8   **30.** 5)40 8   **31.** 3)24 8

32. 9)54 6   **33.** 4)28 7   **34.** 2)16 8   **35.** 9)63 7

36. Divide 64 by 8. 8   **37.** Divide 48 by 6. 8

38. Divide 42 by 7. 6   **39.** Divide 32 by 8. 4

40. Divide 56 by 7. 8   **41.** Divide 63 by 7. 9

42. What multiplication fact can help you find 40 ÷ 8?

43. What multiplication fact can help you find 63 ÷ 7?

Reteaching 4-12

Name _____

Another Look 4-12

Dividing with 6, 7 and 8

You can use multiplication facts to help you divide by 6, 7, or 8.

To find 18 ÷ 6, think 6 times what number equals 18.

6 × □ = 18   ○ ○ ○ ○ ○ ○   6 × 1 = 6

∞∞ ∞∞ ∞∞ ∞∞   6 × 2 = 12

∞∞∞ ∞∞∞ ∞∞∞   6 × 3 = 18

To solve 18 ÷ 6, find a multiplication fact that has a product of 18 and a factor of 6.

Since 6 × 3 = 18, 18 ÷ 6 = 3 .

Complete each statement.

1. Since 6 × 4 = 24,   24 ÷ 6 = 4 .

2. Since 8 × 3 = 24,   24 ÷ 8 = 3 .

3. Since 7 × 3 = 21,   21 ÷ 7 = 3 .

4. Since 6 × 8 = 48,   48 ÷ 6 = 8 .

5. Since 7 × 5 = 35,   35 ÷ 7 = 5 .

6. Since 8 × 8 = 64,   64 ÷ 8 = 8 .

7. Since 6 × 2 = 12,   12 ÷ 6 = 2 .

8. Since 7 × 4 = 28,   28 ÷ 7 = 4 .

9. Since 8 × 7 = 56,   56 ÷ 8 = 7 .

10. Since 6 × 9 = 54,   54 ÷ 6 = 9 .

11. Since 5 × 8 = 40,   40 ÷ 8 = 5 .

12. Since 7 × 7 = 49,   49 ÷ 7 = 7 .

13. Since 6 × 6 = 36,   36 ÷ 6 = 6 .

Practice

Skills and Reasoning

Find each quotient.

7. 64 ÷ 8 **8**   **8.** 7 ÷ 7 **1**   **9.** 40 ÷ 8 **5**   **10.** 42 ÷ 7 **6**   **11.** 32 ÷ 8 **4**

12. 30 ÷ 6 **5**   **13.** 28 ÷ 7 **4**   **14.** 32 ÷ 4 **8**   **15.** 35 ÷ 7 **5**   **16.** 49 ÷ 7 **7**

17. 6)‾42‾ **7**   **18.** 7)‾21‾ **3**   **19.** 8)‾56‾ **7**   **20.** 8)‾72‾ **9**   **21.** 6)‾36‾ **6**

22. 8)‾16‾ **2**   **23.** 7)‾56‾ **8**   **24.** 7)‾63‾ **9**   **25.** 8)‾8‾ **1**   **26.** 6)‾48‾ **8**

27. Divide 0 by 8. **0**   **28.** Divide 42 by 6. **7**

29. If you divide a number by 4, will the quotient be greater than
or less than the quotient of the same number divided by 8?
Explain. **Greater than; 16 ÷ 4 = 4, but 16 ÷ 8 = 2; Dividing
by a lesser number gives a greater quotient.**

Problem Solving and Applications

30. Time Corie practices ice skating 14 hours a week. If she practices
the same number of hours each day, how many hours does she
practice a day? **2 hours**

31. In an ice show, 24 skaters entered the
ice rink in equal rows. If there were
8 skaters in each row, how many rows
were there? **3 rows**

32. Sports In the 1984 Olympics, Jane
Torvill and Christopher Dean were
the first skaters to score nine perfect
sixes. What was their total score? **54**

Jane Torvill and Christopher Dean

Using Data Use the Data File on page 145 to solve **33** and **34**.

33. If there are 72 baseball players,
how many official teams can be
formed? **8 teams**

34. How many field hockey players do
you need to make 4 teams?
44 players

Mixed Review and Test Prep

Find each difference.

35. 270 − 49   **36.** 103 − 58   **37.** 4,039 − 322   **38.** 4,007 − 399
221   **45**   **3,717**   **3,608**

39. Money If you buy a ticket to an ice-skating rink for $2.79 and pay
with a $5 bill, how much change will you get? **D**
Ⓐ $7.79   Ⓑ $3.21   Ⓒ $3.20   Ⓓ $2.21

Skills Practice Bank, page 563, Set 6   Lesson 4-12   **179**

Name _____   Problem Solving
                                4-12

Dividing with 6, 7 and 8

Science Don't call a spider an insect! A spider is an
arachnid. Insects have 6 legs while arachnids have 8 legs.
   Some insects: flies, beetles, mosquitoes, ants
   Some arachnids: spiders, scorpions, mites, aphids

1. A very careful scientist was studying photographs of
   her ant farm. In one picture, she counted 54 individual
   ant legs. How many ants were in the picture?   **9**

2. The same scientist came across some bug tracks in the
   sand. She decided the tracks were made by a scorpion.
   If there were 56 individual footprints in the sand, how
   many times did each of the scorpion's legs touch
   the ground?   **7**

3. Eight scientists on the project agreed to share the
   research time equally. If 40 hours are needed, how many
   hours is each scientist responsible for?   **5**

4. It takes 14 days for a canary egg to incubate (get ready
   to hatch). How many weeks is this?   **2**

5. Find the incubation period for each bird:
   a. Chickens: 21 days or __**3**__ weeks
   b. Turkeys: __**28**__ days or 4 weeks

6. It takes 28 days for a squirrel to gestate (get ready to be
   born). How many weeks is this?   **4**

7. Find the gestation period for each animal:
   a. Dog: 63 days or __**9**__ weeks
   b. Cat: __**56**__ days or 8 weeks

Error Intervention Ongoing Assessment

Observation Students write incorrect
quotients because they don't know their
multiplication facts.

How to Help Review ways to help find
products of 6s, 7s, and 8s: doubling 3s
and 4s facts and adding the products of
2s and 5s facts.

Practice

Exercise 29 Encourage students having
difficulty to try some examples and then
make a generalization.

Exercise 32 Be sure students realize that the
pair of skaters, not each skater, received nine
perfect sixes.

Exercises 33 and 34 You can use Lesson
Enhancement Transparency 15 to illustrate
the Data File.

For Early Finishers Challenge early finishers
to find the other formations in which the
skaters in Exercise 31 could enter the rink in
equal rows. **24 rows of 1, 12 rows of 2, 8
rows of 3, 6 rows of 4, 4 rows of 6, 2 rows of
12, 1 row of 24**

③ Close and Assess

Journal

Have students write three division facts that
are difficult for them to remember. For each,
have them explain what they do to help find
the quotient.

Quick Check

Number Sense Without dividing, tell which
quotient in the Skill exercises will be greater
than 6. Explain your thinking. Exercise 2: 6 ×
6 = 36 and 48 > 36. Exercise 3: 8 × 6 = 48
and 72 > 48.

Skill Find each quotient.

1. 21 ÷ 7 **3**   **2.** 48 ÷ 6 **8**
3. 8)‾72‾ **9**   **4.** 7)‾42‾ **6**

Chapter 4 • Lesson 4-12   **179**

Exploring Even and Odd Numbers

At-A-Glance Planning

Lesson Planning Checklist

Objective Explore even and odd numbers.

Vocabulary even number, odd number

Student Book Lesson Materials Counters (60 per group), *optional Assessment Sourcebook 10* (How We Worked in Our Group)

Materials for pages 180A and 180B Small self-sticking notes (3 each of two colors per student or group), Teaching Tool Transparency 6 (Centimeter Grid Paper), scissors

Strand Connections patterns, collecting data

	Before Lesson	During Lesson	After Lesson
Daily Math			
p. 180A Problem of the Day			
p. 180A Math Routines			
p. 180A Mental Math			
Teaching Options			
p. 180B Facilitating and Assessing…			
Options for Reaching All Learners			
p. 180B Language Development			
p. 180B Inclusion			
Subject Connections			
p. 180A Physical Education Connection			
Assessment Options			
p. 180 Talk About It			
p. 181 Error Intervention			
p. 181 Performance Assessment			
Resources			
4-13 Practice			
4-13 Reteaching			
4-13 Enrichment			
4-13 Problem Solving			
4-13 Daily Transparency			

Problem of the Day

Problem of the Day

If you spin the spinner 20 times, about how many times do you think it will land on red?

10 times

Math Routines

Measurement Have students name two lengths whose sum is a number with a ones digit of 0, 2, 4, 6, or 8. Discuss any pattern they see. Either two odd or two even measurements

Money Ask students to name two amounts between $0.10 and $0.20. Have them add the two and tell whether the total could be evenly divided between 2 people. If both numbers are even or odd, yes; If not, no.

Mental Math

Find each difference. Explain.

402 − 100 302   398 − 190 208

215 − 105 110   565 − 355 210

Physical Education Connection

In football, a team earns 6 points for a touchdown, 1 for a kick after a touchdown, 2 for a pass or a run into the opponent's end zone after a touchdown, 3 for a field goal, and 2 for a safety.

• Ask students for which events a team can earn an odd number of points. Kick after touchdown, field goal

Facilitating and Assessing Explore Lesson 4-13

Use with pages 180 and 181.

Get Started You may want to assign the role of recorder to one student in each group. However, all students should have an opportunity to build models or draw pictures of even and odd numbers. You may want to assign the group skill Disagree in an Agreeable Way, which students can practice as they work, especially on Exercise 2.

Observe Watch for groups that quickly discover a pattern in even and odd numbers and do not build models or draw pictures. This is acceptable as long as all group members are able to explain how they know a number is even or odd.

For Exercise 2, some groups may give examples with sums or products greater than 18. If they are not sure whether these larger numbers are even or odd, have them build models or draw pictures of these numbers as well.

Discuss As students model each number and identify it as even or odd, listen to their reasoning and notice whether they recognize any patterns. As students identify sums or products as odd or even, some may give examples and draw a generalization. Others may use number sense and reasoning.

Assess Use the rubric to assess students' work. See sample for Practice Exercise 9.

4 Full Accomplishment

19 is an odd number.

Assessment Rubric

4 Full Accomplishment
- identifies even and odd numbers; explains or demonstrates why a number is even or odd

3 Substantial Accomplishment
- identifies most even and odd numbers; with prompting, explains or demonstrates why a number is even or odd

2 Partial Accomplishment
- identifies most even and odd numbers; does not explain or demonstrate why a number is even or odd

1 Little Accomplishment
- does not identify even and odd numbers or explain or demonstrate why a number is even or odd

Options for Reaching All Learners

Language Development

The Hunt for Evens and Odds
Use everyday examples to strengthen understanding of even and odd numbers.

Materials Small self-sticking notes (3 each of two colors per student or group)

Learning Style Visual, Verbal

- Point out an even group of classroom objects and an odd group. Have students talk about why the number in each group is even or odd.

- Provide each student or group with self-stick notes. Have them write *even* and their initials on one color and *odd* and their initials on the other color.

- Have students find even and odd groups of objects and tag them. Encourage them to explain how they know the number of objects is even or odd.

Inclusion

Sums of Evens and Odds
Use grid paper to explore sums of even and odd numbers.

Materials Teaching Tool Transparency 6 (Centimeter Grid Paper), scissors

Learning Style Visual, Kinesthetic

- Guide students to draw and cut out models of the even and odd numbers for 1–18 formed with two rows of squares.

- Have students use their models to explore sums in Practice Exercise 14 on page 181 by trying to put three models together to form two equal rows.

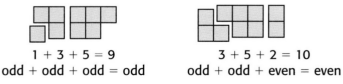

| $1 + 3 + 5 = 9$ | $3 + 5 + 2 = 10$ |
| odd + odd + odd = odd | odd + odd + even = even |

Lesson Organizer

Objective Explore even and odd numbers.

Suggested Grouping 2 to 4

Student Materials Counters (60 per group), *optional* Assessment Sourcebook 10 (How We Worked in Our Group)

Vocabulary even number, odd number

Assignment Guide

Basic 1–13, 18

Average 1, 3–16, 18

Enriched 1, 4–18

1 Introduce

Review

Find each quotient.

1. 10 ÷ 2   **2.** 14 ÷ 2

3. 18 ÷ 2   **4.** 12 ÷ 2

Build on Prior Knowledge

After students review dividing with 2 as a divisor, ask them to use what they know about division to explain what would happen if they tried to divide 7 counters into 2 equal groups. You could put 3 counters into each group, but 1 counter would be left over.

2 Teach

See Facilitating and Assessing...on page 180B.

Explore ● ● ● ● ● ● ● ● ● ● ● ● ● ● ● ● ● ● ●

As students work together, you may want to ask questions such as these.

• How do you know that a number, sum, or product is an even number?

• How do you know that a number, sum, or product is an odd number?

Have groups share their findings for Exercise 2 and discuss any differences in their answers.

Talk About It **Ongoing Assessment**

Listen for explanations that indicate an understanding of what makes a number even or odd.

Answer for Talk About It

No; If a number can be divided into two equal groups, it is even. If it cannot, it is odd.

Exploring Even and Odd Numbers

Problem Solving Connection

■ Use Objects/ Act It Out

■ Look for a Pattern

Materials

counters

Vocabulary

even number
a whole number that has 0, 2, 4, 6, or 8 in the ones place

odd number
a whole number that has 1, 3, 5, 7, or 9 in the ones place

Problem Solving Hint

Look for a pattern in the digits in the ones place.

Explore

You can divide to decide if a number is even or odd.

An **even number** can be divided into two equal groups.

An **odd number** has one left over when it is divided into two equal groups.

Work Together

Use counters or draw pictures.

1. Try to divide each number from 2 through 18 into two equal groups.

   1a. 2, 4, 6, 8, 10, 12, 14, 16, 18

   a. Which numbers can be divided into two equal groups?

   b. Which numbers have one left over? 3, 5, 7, 9, 11, 13, 15, 17

   c. Which of the numbers are even numbers? Which are odd numbers? 2, 4, 6, 8, 10, 12, 14, 16, 18; 3, 5, 7, 9, 11, 13, 15, 17

2. Copy and complete the table. Write if each sum or product will be even or odd. Give four examples for each case. **Examples will vary.**

Numbers	Sum	Product
2 even numbers	even	even
2 odd numbers	even	odd
1 even number, 1 odd number	odd	even

Talk About It

Can a number be both even and odd? Explain.

Practice 4-13

Name _____

Exploring Even and Odd Numbers

1. What digits do even numbers have in the ones place?
0, 2, 4, 6, or 8

2. What digits do odd numbers have in the ones place?
1, 3, 5, 7, or 9

Write *odd* or *even* for each. You may use counters or draw pictures.

3. ○○○○○○○   **4.** ○○○○
○○○○○○○   ○○○○
Odd   **Even**

5. ○○○○○○○○○   **6.** ○○○○
○○○○○○○○○   ○○○○○
Even   **Odd**

7. 67 **Odd**   **8.** 77 **Odd**

9. 38 **Even**   **10.** 92 **Even**

11. 26 **Even** **12.** 35 **Odd**

13. Start with 21 and name the next 4 odd numbers. Explain how you know which numbers are odd.
23, 25, 27, 29; Not evenly divisible by 2

14. If you add 2 odd numbers, will the sum be odd or even? **Even**

15. If you add 4 odd numbers, will the sum be odd or even? **Even**

16. If you add 5 even numbers, will the sum be odd or even? **Even**

Complete the pattern. Then write *odd* or *even* for each group.

17. 419, 417, 415, **413** ; **411** ; **409** ; **Odd**

18. 1,092; 1,094; 1,096; **1,098** ; **1,100** ; **1,102** ; **Even**

19. 516; 518; 520; **522** ; **524** ; **526** ; **Even**

Reteaching 4-13

Name _____

Exploring Even and Odd Numbers

In your book you used counters to explore even and odd numbers. Here is another way to explore even and odd.

Is 17 odd or even?

Below are 17 stars. Draw a ring around each pair of stars. If there are no stars left over, 17 is even. If there is one star left over, 17 is odd.

17 is an **odd** number.

1. Is 8 even or odd? **Even**

2. Is 9 even or odd? **Odd**

3. Is 11 even or odd? **Odd**

4. Is 16 even or odd? **Even**

Connect

An even number can be divided by 2 with no leftovers. An odd number has one left over when it is divided by 2.

You can find patterns in even and odd numbers.

Even numbers have a 0, 2, 4, 6, or 8 in the ones place.

Odd numbers have a 1, 3, 5, 7, or 9 in the ones place.

1	2	3	4	5	6	7	8	9	10
11	12	13	14	15	16	17	18	19	20
21	22	23	24	25	26	27	28	29	30
31	32	33	34	35	36	37	38	39	40
41	42	43	44	45	46	47	48	49	50
51	52	53	54	55	56	57	58	59	60
61	62	63	64	65	66	67	68	69	70
71	72	73	74	75	76	77	78	79	80
81	82	83	84	85	86	87	88	89	90
91	92	93	94	95	96	97	98	99	100

Practice

Write *odd* or *even* for each. You may use counters or draw pictures.

1. ●●●●●●● ●●●●●●● **Even**
2. ●●●●●●● ●●●●●●● **Odd**

3. 33 **Odd**
4. 66 **Even**
5. 35 **Odd**
6. 71 **Odd**
7. 24 **Even**
8. 60 **Even**
9. 19 **Odd**
10. 25 **Odd**
11. 100 **Even**
12. 289 **Odd**

13. Start with 12 and name the next 4 even numbers. Explain how you know which numbers are even.
14, 16, 18, 20; Divisible by 2

14. **Reasoning** Choose at least two questions to answer. Give three examples to explain your answers. **Answers should include 3 examples.**

   a. If you add three odd numbers, will the sum be odd or even? **Odd**

   b. If you add three even numbers, will the sum be odd or even? **Even**

   c. If you add two even numbers and an odd number, will the sum be odd or even? **Odd**

   d. If you add two odd numbers and an even number, will the sum be odd or even? **Even**

Patterns Copy and complete the pattern. Then write *odd* or *even* for each group of numbers.

15. 234, 236, 238, ▮, ▮, ▮
240, 242, 244; Even
16. 2,555, 2,553, 2,551, ▮, ▮, ▮
2,449, 2,447, 2,445; Odd

17. **Collecting Data** Find at least five numbers in the sports section of a newspaper or magazine. Copy the numbers and write if each is even or odd. **Answers will vary.**

18. **Journal** Describe the patterns you see in even numbers. Describe the patterns you see in odd numbers.

Lesson 4-13 **181**

Enrichment 4-13

Name _____ **Extend Your Thinking 4-13**

Patterns in Numbers
Write what comes next in each pattern. Then write the rule used for each pattern.

1. 11, 13, 15, 17, __19__, __21__, __23__
   Rule: **Add 2.**

2. 48, 41, 34, 27, __20__, __13__, __6__
   Rule: **Subtract 7.**

3. 3, 7, 12, 18, __25__, __33__, __42__
   Rule: **Add 4, 5, 6, and so on.**

4. 3, 9, 27, __81__, __243__, __729__
   Rule: **Multiply by 3.**

5. 12, 13, 15, 16, 17, 19, 20, __21__, __23__, __24__
   Rule: **Add 1, add 2, add 1, and repeat.**

6. 1, 2, 6, 24, __120__, __720__, __5,040__
   Rule: **Multiply by 2, 3, 4, and so on.**

7. 1; 10; 101; 1,010; __10,101__; __101,010__; __1,010,101__
   Rule: **Alternate placing 1 or 0 to the right of the previous number.**

8. Write your own number pattern. Write its rule.
   Pattern: **Check students' answers.**
   Rule: _____

Problem Solving 4-13

Name _____ **Problem Solving 4-13**

Exploring Even and Odd Numbers
1. How many odd numbers are there between 5 and 25 (not including 5 or 25)?
   9
   List them:
   7, 9, 11, 13, 15, 17, 19, 21, 23

2. How many even numbers are there between 0 and 30 (not including 0 or 30)?
   14
   List them:
   2, 4, 6, 8, 10, 12, 14, 16, 18, 20, 22, 24, 26, 28

   Possible answers:
3. What two even numbers can be added together to get a sum of 62? **30 + 32**

4. What two odd numbers can be added together to get a sum of 62? **31 + 31**

5. What kind of numbers can be added together to get a sum of 47? (Circle all correct answers.)
   a. two even numbers
   b. two odd numbers
   (c.) one even number and one odd number

6. What kind of numbers can be added together to get a sum of 26? (Circle all correct answers.)
   (a.) two even numbers
   (b.) two odd numbers
   c. one even number and one odd number

Connect

Students should recognize that the numbers they listed as even as they worked together are multiples of 2.

Error Intervention Ongoing Assessment

Observation Students look at the digit in the tens place or at the leading digit to decide whether a number is even or odd.

How to Help Have students use counters or draw pictures to show attempts to divide each pair of numbers into two equal groups: 24 and 34, 17 and 27, 25 and 26, 31 and 32. Compare even and odd differences in the digits and in the models or pictures.

Practice

Exercise 14 Some students may make generalizations based on their examples. Others may think about what kind of number the sum of the first two addends is and what kind of number that sum plus the third addend is.

Exercises 15 and 16 Guide students to realize that, regardless of the number of digits in a number, it is the digit in the ones place that makes the number even or odd.

For Early Finishers Challenge early finishers to change *add* and *sum* in Exercise 14 to *multiply* and *product* and answer at least two questions. 14a: Odd; 14b: Even; 14c: Even; 14d: Even

3 Close and Assess

Performance Assessment

Write *odd* or *even*. Explain your thinking in words, with models, or with pictures.

1. 47 Odd; Has 1 left over when divided into two equal groups and the ones digit is 7

2. 56 Even; Can be divided into two equal groups with no leftovers and the ones digit is 6

Assess using the rubric on page 180B.

Resources

Technology Master 14

ANSWERS

18 Even numbers have 0, 2, 4, 6, or 8 in the ones place. Odd numbers have 1, 3, 5, 7, or 9 in the ones place.

Chapter 4 • Lesson 4-13 **181**

Chapter 4
Stop and Practice

Students will practice skills taught in Lessons 1 through 13.

Find Each Product

Remind students to think of patterns in multiples; the Zero, One, and Order Properties; and how to use multiplication facts they know to complete other multiplication and division facts.

Error Search

ANSWERS

51 Incorrect; Possible answer: 54 is a multiple of 9. Divided or multiplied wrong

52 Incorrect; The quotient of 0 divided by 4 is 0. Added instead of divided

53 Correct

54 Incorrect; The quotient of 9 ÷ 9 is 1. Divided wrong

55 Incorrect; The quotient of 12 ÷ 6 is less than the quotient of 12 ÷ 4. Divided or compared wrong

56 Correct

---

 and Practice

Find each product.

1. $\begin{array}{r} 6 \\ \times 2 \\ \hline 12 \end{array}$	**2.** $\begin{array}{r} 5 \\ \times 0 \\ \hline 0 \end{array}$	**3.** $\begin{array}{r} 6 \\ \times 4 \\ \hline 24 \end{array}$	**4.** $\begin{array}{r} 2 \\ \times 8 \\ \hline 16 \end{array}$	**5.** $\begin{array}{r} 7 \\ \times 3 \\ \hline 21 \end{array}$
6. $\begin{array}{r} 3 \\ \times 5 \\ \hline 15 \end{array}$	**7.** $\begin{array}{r} 8 \\ \times 9 \\ \hline 72 \end{array}$	**8.** $\begin{array}{r} 4 \\ \times 4 \\ \hline 16 \end{array}$	**9.** $\begin{array}{r} 3 \\ \times 9 \\ \hline 27 \end{array}$	**10.** $\begin{array}{r} 4 \\ \times 9 \\ \hline 36 \end{array}$

11. 6×8 48 **12.** 7×9 63 **13.** 8×4 32 **14.** 9×5 45 **15.** 7×7 49

16. 4×10 40 **17.** 12×9 108 **18.** 9×11 99 **19.** 12×8 96 **20.** 11×6 66

21. 6×1 6 **22.** 7×8 56 **23.** 11×4 44 **24.** 9×0 0 **25.** 7×10 70

Find each quotient.

26. $14 \div 2$ 7 **27.** $27 \div 9$ 3 **28.** $15 \div 5$ 3 **29.** $18 \div 2$ 9 **30.** $45 \div 5$ 9

31. $4\overline{)20}$ 5 **32.** $6\overline{)42}$ 7 **33.** $3\overline{)24}$ 8 **34.** $3\overline{)9}$ 3 **35.** $9\overline{)9}$ 1

36. $20 \div 5$ 4 **37.** $0 \div 3$ 0 **38.** $2 \div 2$ 1 **39.** $28 \div 4$ 7 **40.** $64 \div 8$ 8

41. $2\overline{)16}$ 8 **42.** $5\overline{)35}$ 7 **43.** $9\overline{)81}$ 9 **44.** $2\overline{)10}$ 5 **45.** $9\overline{)72}$ 8

46. $8\overline{)48}$ 6 **47.** $6\overline{)54}$ 9 **48.** $9\overline{)36}$ 4 **49.** $8\overline{)72}$ 9 **50.** $9\overline{)63}$ 7

Error Search

Find each sentence that is not correct. Write it correctly and explain the error.

51. 56 is a multiple of 9.

52. The quotient of 0 divided by 4 is 4.

53. $45 \div 9$ equals $35 \div 7$.

54. The quotient of $9 \div 9$ is 0.

55. The quotient of $12 \div 6$ is greater than $12 \div 4$.

56. 100 is a multiple of 10.

Goal!

The world's largest soccer stadium is in Rio de Janeiro, Brazil. It holds 165,000 people. What is its name? Multiply or divide to find the answer. Match each letter to its answer in the blank. Some letters are not used.

57. $81 \div 9$ [A] 9   **58.** $56 \div 7$ [I] 8   **59.** $8 \div 8$ [A] 1   **60.** $18 \div 9$ [A] 2

61. 3×7 [N] 21   **62.** 8×8 [W] 64   **63.** 11×5 [R] 55   **64.** 5×7 [B] 35

65. $42 \div 6$ [D] 7   **66.** $40 \div 8$ [G] 5   **67.** $0 \div 6$ [V] 0   **68.** $15 \div 5$ [T] 3

69. 4×8 [M] 32   **70.** 9×7 [S] 63   **71.** 4×6 [A] 24   **72.** 7×8 [E] 56

73. $24 \div 4$ [A] 6   **74.** 5×8 [F] 40   **75.** $16 \div 4$ [O] 4   **76.** 8×9 [C] 72

56	63	3	9	7	8	4	
E	S	T	A	D	I	O	

32	6	55	1	72	2	21	24
M	A	R	A	C	A	N	A

Remember the Facts!

Use this activity any time to help you remember your multiplication and division facts.

Be a Writer! Make your own multiplication and division book. Choose 10 difficult facts you want to remember. Draw a picture and write a number sentence for each.

Goal!

As an extension, suggest that students create their own riddles about their favorite team sport and add them to the class riddle book.

Remember the Facts!

Fact books may be placed in the math center for use at any time. Have students share their books with a third-grade class.

For Early Finishers Challenge early finishers to choose five exercises from Exercises 1–25 and two from Exercises 26–50 and write the other multiplication and division facts in the same fact families.

Resources

TestWorks: Test and Practice Software

Exploring Factors

At-A-Glance Planning

Objective Explore factors.

Vocabulary prime number, composite number

Student Book Lesson Materials Teaching Tool Transparency 6 (Centimeter Grid Paper), *optional Assessment Sourcebook 10* (How We Worked in Our Group)

Materials for pages 184A and 184B Color cubes (40 per group)

Strand Connection patterns, algebra readiness

	Before Lesson	During Lesson	After Lesson
Daily Math			
p. 184A Problem of the Day			
p. 184A Math Routines			
p. 184A Mental Math			
Teaching Options			
p. 184B Facilitating and Assessing…			
Options for Reaching All Learners			
p. 184B Language Development			
p. 184B Gifted & Talented			
Subject Connections			
p. 184A Art Connection			
Assessment Options			
p. 184 Talk About It			
p. 185 Error Intervention			
p. 185 Performance Assessment			
Resources			
4-14 Practice			
4-14 Reteaching			
4-14 Enrichment			
4-14 Problem Solving			
4-14 Daily Transparency			

Problem of the Day

Problem of the Day

Stacy did three times as many homework problems as Lani. They each did an even number of problems. Between them, they did more than 20 but fewer than 30 problems. How many did each girl do?

Stacy did 18, Lani did 6.

Math Routines

Measurement Tell students there are 16 ounces in 1 pint. Ask them to describe the various ways a pint of water could be shared equally. 2 people get 8 oz; 4 people get 4 oz; 8 people get 2 oz; 16 people get 1 oz

Calendar Ask students to name the factors of a 30-day month. 1, 2, 3, 5, 6, 10, 15, 30.

Mental Math

Find each sum. Explain your thinking.

$1.55 + $1.35 $2.90 $2.23 + $0.57 $2.80

$2.68 + $1.02 $3.70 $0.89 + $1.01 $1.90

Art Connection

The weight times the length of the rod on one side of a mobile equals the weight times the length of the rod on the other side.

• Ask students what other rod lengths and weights could be used on the right side. 1 in., 20 oz; 4 in., 5 oz; 5 in., 4 oz; 10 in., 2 oz; 20 in., 1 oz

4 in. | **2 in.**

5 oz   **10 oz**

Facilitating and Assessing **Explore** Lesson 4-14

Use with pages 184 and 185.

Get Started You may want to assign the role of factor recorder to one student in each group. Each group member, however, should try to draw as many different rectangles as possible and write the multiplication sentences for 24, 36, and 11. You may also want to assign the group skill Check for Understanding, which students can practice as they work.

Observe Watch for groups that list the same factors twice because they draw the same size rectangle turned in two different ways. Guide them to see that both rectangles help find the same two factors, so only one rectangle is needed.

Discuss Have students talk about the strategies they used to draw all rectangles for a number. Then have them talk about how they might be able to find the factors of a number without drawing rectangles.

Assess Use the rubric to assess students' work. See sample for Practice Exercise 1.

Assessment Rubric
4 Full Accomplishment • identifies prime and composite numbers; explains why a number is prime or composite
3 Substantial Accomplishment • identifies most prime and composite numbers; with prompting, explains why a number is prime or composite
2 Partial Accomplishment • identifies all factors of most numbers; does not explain why a number is prime or composite
1 Little Accomplishment • identifies some factors of most numbers; does not explain why a number is prime or composite

4 Full Accomplishment

$1 \times 9 = 9$

$3 \times 3 = 9$

Factors of 9: 1, 3, 9

Options for Reaching All Learners

Language Development

Organized Rectangles

Use color cubes to develop the language of factors.

Materials Color cubes (40 per group)

Learning Style Kinesthetic, Verbal

Students may have difficulty finding all the factors of a number because they don't consider all possible rectangles.

• Have small groups of students try making rectangles with 36 cubes. Have them identify each row and column, saying, "1 row of 36, 2 rows of 18, 3 rows of 12," and so on. Have them write the multiplication sentence for each rectangle identifying each factor and product aloud.

• When finding factors of 36, have students discuss what happens at 9 rows. The rectangle is the same as for 4 rows, only rows and columns are rotated.

Gifted & Talented

Prime Times

Use a game to strengthen identification of prime and composite numbers.

Learning Style Social

• Have players stand in a circle.

• Beginning with 2, each player says the next consecutive number. If the number is prime, the player then says *prime*. If the number is composite, the player then must name one factor of the number other than 1 and the number itself.

• A player who incorrectly identifies a number as prime or composite sits down.

• Play continues until only one player remains standing or until players are unable to use mental math to find factors.

Lesson Organizer

Objective Explore factors.

Suggested Grouping 2 to 4

Student Materials Teaching Tool Transparency 6 (Centimeter Grid Paper), *optional Assessment Sourcebook 10* (How We Worked in Our Group)

Teacher Materials Teaching Tool Transparency 6 (Centimeter Grid Paper)

Vocabulary prime number, composite number

Assignment Guide

Basic 1–18, 24

Average 2–19, 22, 24

Enriched 3–24

1 Introduce

Review

Find each product.

1. 4 × 5 20 **2.** 7 × 7 49

3. 6 × 3 18 **4.** 6 × 6 36

Build on Prior Knowledge

After students review basic multiplication facts, ask them how they could write another multiplication sentence whose product is 20. Think of two numbers that, when multiplied, equal 20, such as 2 × 10.

2 Teach

See Facilitating and Assessing…on page 184B.

Explore ● ● ● ● ● ● ● ● ● ● ● ● ● ● ● ● ● ● ●

Before students begin working together, have them look at the example of how to use rectangles to find factors of 12. Use Teaching Tool Transparency 6 (Centimeter Grid Paper) to demonstrate if necessary.

Answers for Work Together

1a, 1b, 2a, 2b, 3 See pages D1–D4.

Talk About It) Ongoing Assessment

Listen for responses that indicate understanding of how to find all the factors of a number and the common factors of two or more numbers.

Answers for Talk About It

4 1, 2, 3, 4, 6, 8, 12, 24; 1, 2, 3, 4, 6, 9, 12, 18, 36

5 1, 2, 3, 4, 6, 12

184 *Chapter 4 • Lesson 4-14*

Exploring Factors

Problem Solving Connection

■ Use Objects/ Act It Out

■ Make an Organized List

Materials

grid paper

Vocabulary

prime number a whole number greater than 1 that has only two factors, itself and 1

composite number a whole number greater than 1 with more than two factors

Remember A square is also a rectangle.

Explore ●

You can use rectangles to find factors. These rectangles show the factors of 12.

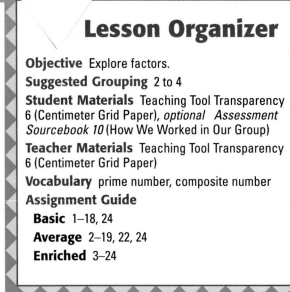

$3 \times 4 = 12$

factor factor product

$1 \times 12 = 12$

$2 \times 6 = 12$

Factors of 12: 1, 2, 3, 4, 6, 12

Work Together

Use grid paper to find different factors of a number.

1. a. Draw rectangles that have a total of 24 squares.

b. For each rectangle write a multiplication sentence: ■ × ■ = 24.

2. a. Draw rectangles that have a total of 36 squares.

b. For each rectangle write a multiplication sentence: ■ × ■ = 36.

3. Use rectangles to find all the factors of 11. List all the factors.

Talk About It

4. What are all of the factors of 24? Of 36?

5. What factors do 24 and 36 have in common?

184 Chapter 4 • Multiplication and Division Concepts and Facts

---

Name _____

Practice 4-14

Exploring Factors

Write a definition for each term.

1. prime _A prime number has only 2 factors, itself and 1._

2. composite _A composite number has more than 2 factors._

3. factor _A factor is a number that divides another number evenly._

Complete. Then list all the factors for each number.

4. [1] × [4] = 4   **5.** [1] × [6] = 6   **6.** [1] × [10] = 10
  [2] × [2] = 4   [2] × [3] = 6   [2] × [5] = 10
  1, 2, 4   1, 2, 3, 6   1, 2, 5, 10

List all the factors for each number. You may draw rectangles on grid paper to help you.

7. 16: 1, 2, 4, 8, 16

8. 36: 1, 2, 3, 4, 6, 9, 12, 18, 36

9. 43: 1, 43

10. 24: 1, 2, 3, 4, 6, 8, 12, 24

Write whether each number is prime or composite.

11. 13 ___Prime___   **12.** 31 ___Prime___   **13.** 15 ___Composite___

14. 51 ___Composite___   **15.** 18 ___Composite___   **16.** 81 ___Composite___

17. 18 ___Composite___   **18.** 23 ___Prime___   **19.** 66 ___Composite___

Complete each list of prime numbers.

20. 7, 11, 13, ___17___, ___19___   **21.** 19, 23, 29, ___31___, ___37___

22. 29, 31, 37, ___41___, ___43___   **23.** 5, 7, 11, ___13___, ___17___

Complete each list of composite numbers.

24. 30, 36, 39, ___40___, ___42___   **25.** 42, 44, 45, ___46___, ___48___

26. 2, 4, 6, ___8___, ___9___   **27.** 14, 15, 16, ___18___, ___20___

Name _____

Another Look 4-14

Exploring Factors

In your book you used rectangles to find factors. Here is another way to explore factors.

To find *all* the factors for a number, make an organized list of multiplication sentences. Write sentences until your factors start to repeat. (Ignore any sentences that won't work.) Then list the factors.

Find all the factors of 48.

48 = 1 × 48
  2 × 24
  3 × 16
  4 × 12
  5 × ―
  6 × 8
  7 × ―
  8 × 6 (← STOP! Repeat of 6 × 8).

The factors of 48 are 1, 2, 3, 4, 6, 8, 12, 16, 24 and 48.

The factors of 48 are 1, 2, 3, 4, 6, 8, 12, 16, 24, and 48.

1. Find all the factors of 15.   **2.** Find all the factors of 24.

15 = 1 × [15]

  2 × ―

  3 × [5]

  4 × ―

  5 × [3]

1, 3, 5, 15   1, 2, 3, 4, 6, 8, 12, 24

3. Find all the factors of 56.   **4.** Find all factors of 32.

1, 2, 4, 7, 8, 14, 28, 56   1, 2, 4, 8, 16, 32

Connect

A **prime number** has exactly two factors, 1 and itself.

You can draw only one rectangle to show a prime number.

Factors of 7: 1, 7

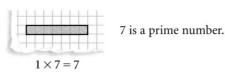

7 is a prime number.

$1 \times 7 = 7$

A **composite number** has more than two factors.

You can draw more than one rectangle to show a composite number.

Factors of 8: 1, 2, 4, 8

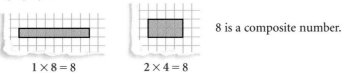

8 is a composite number.

$1 \times 8 = 8$ $2 \times 4 = 8$

The number 1 is neither prime nor composite.

Practice

Copy and complete. Then list all the factors for each number.

1. $1 \times \blacksquare = 9$ 9   **2.** $\blacksquare \times \blacksquare = 5$ 1, 5   **3.** $1 \times \blacksquare = 15$ 15   **4.** $\blacksquare \times \blacksquare = 13$ 1, 13
    $\blacksquare \times 3 = 9$ 3   1, 5 $\blacksquare \times 5 = 15$ 3   1, 13
    1, 3, 9   1, 3, 5, 15

List the factors for each number. You may draw rectangles to help you.

5. 20   **6.** 14   **7.** 17   **8.** 12   **9.** 19   **10.** 3   **11.** 22
         1, 2, 7, 14   1, 17   1, 19   1, 3   1, 2, 11, 22

Write whether each number is prime or composite.

12. 18   **13.** 11   **14.** 15   **15.** 3   **16.** 10   **17.** 4   **18.** 17
Composite   Prime   Composite   Prime   Composite   Composite   Prime

Copy and complete each list of prime numbers.

19. 3, 5, 7, ■, ■ 11, 13   **20.** 13, 17, 19, ■, ■ 23, 29   **5.** 1, 2, 4, 5, 10, 20
                                                  8. 1, 2, 3, 4, 6, 12

Copy and complete each list of composite numbers.

21. 12, 14, 15, ■, ■   **22.** 24, 25, 26, ■, ■
     16, 18   27, 28

23. Reasoning What is the only even prime number? Explain.

24. Journal How do you decide if a number is prime or composite?

Lesson 4-14   **185**

Connect

After reviewing prime and composite numbers, have students identify each number they worked with on page 184 (24, 36, and 11) as prime or composite. 24: Composite; 36: Composite; 11: Prime

Guide students to understand that 1 is neither prime nor composite because it has only one factor.

Error Intervention Ongoing Assessment

Observation Students identify a composite number as a prime number.

How to Help Encourage students to check a number in a systematic way by asking themselves: Is there a 2s fact that has this number as a product? Is there a 3s fact? A 4s fact?…

Practice

Exercises 19–22 Remind students to look for subsequent prime or composite numbers and not computation patterns to complete each exercise.

For Early Finishers Challenge early finishers to find three prime numbers between 40 and 50. 41, 43, 47

3 Close and Assess

Performance Assessment

Tell whether each number is prime or composite. Explain.

1. 2 Prime; 2 has only two factors: 1 and 2.

2. 32 Composite; 32 has more than two factors, 1, 2, 4, 8, 16, and 32.

3. 37 Prime; 37 has only two factors: 1 and 37.

Assess using the rubric on page 184B.

ANSWERS

23 2; 2 has only two factors, 1 and 2. All other even numbers have at least three factors, 1, 2, and the number.

24 Possible answers: Determine if the number has more than two factors. Use grid paper to find out if it can be drawn as a rectangle in more than one way.

Enrichment 4-14

Name _____ Extend Your Thinking
                                      4-14

Critical Thinking

Suppose you are an ancient Egyptian stone worker. The Queen has hired you to make a pyramid sculpture for her garden.

"I will give you 140 blocks of stone," she said. "Do not waste them."

The Queen showed you a model using 14 blocks. The model is 3 blocks high. The top layer has 1 block, the 2nd layer has 4 blocks, and the 3rd layer has 9 blocks.

A mathematician whispered to you, "You will be able to use all the blocks if you follow the Queen's model. Just look for the pattern."

After a while, the pattern becomes clear. You build the pyramid, using all the blocks, and are richly rewarded by the Queen.

1. How many layers did your finished pyramid have? 7

2. How many blocks did you use for each layer?
(In order:) 1, 4, 9, 16, 25, 36, and 49

3. Describe the pattern the mathematician was talking about.
The number of blocks per layer is determined by the next largest square number. (Or, layer 1 has 1 × 1 blocks, layer 2 has 2 × 2 or 4 blocks, layer 3 has 3 × 3 or 9 blocks, and so on.)

4. Could you make another pyramid with 200 blocks following the same pattern? Explain.
No, to continue the pattern, the next layer should have 64 blocks. 140 + 64 = 204

5. How many blocks of stone would you need to follow the same pattern and make a pyramid:
a. 8 blocks high? 204
b. 9 blocks high? 285
c. 10 blocks high? 385

Problem Solving 4-14

Name _____ Problem Solving
                                        4-14

Exploring Factors

1. a. List the factors of 12 and 24.
12: 1, 2, 3, 4, 6, 12
24: 1, 2, 3, 4, 6, 8, 12, 24

b. What factors do 12 and 24 have in common?
1, 2, 3, 4, 6, 12

2. a. List the factors of 48, 50, and 63.
48: 1, 2, 3, 4, 6, 8, 12, 16, 24, 48
50: 1, 2, 5, 10, 25, 50
63: 1, 3, 7, 9, 21, 63

b. Which has the greatest number of factors? 48

c. What factors do they all have in common? 1

3. Do any prime numbers end in 4? Explain.
No, if a number ends in 4, it is an even number. The only even prime number is 2.

4. How can a number have only 3 factors? Give examples of 3 numbers with only 3 factors.
Possible answer: When a number is a square number, it could have only 3 factors: 4, 9, 25

5. List the dimensions of all the rectangles you could draw to show 60.
1 by 60, 2 by 30, 3 by 20, 4 by 15, 5 by 12, 6 by 10

At-A-Glance Planning

Lesson Planning Checklist

Objective Solve problems with too much or too little information.

Student Book Lesson Materials None

Materials for pages 186A and 186B Teaching Tool Transparencies 1, 2 (Guided Problem Solving 1, 2), photocopies of page 187

Subject Connections physical education—sports equipment, social studies—population, health—sleep

Strand Connections money, using data, time

	Before Lesson	During Lesson	After Lesson
Daily Math			
p. 186A Problem of the Day			
p. 186A Math Routines			
p. 186A Mental Math			
Teaching Options			
p. 186 Student Book Lesson			
p. 186B Another Way to Learn...			
Options for Reaching All Learners			
p. 186B Reading Assist			
p. 186B Inclusion			
Subject Connections			
p. 186A Social Studies Connection			
Assessment Options			
p. 186 Talk About It			
p. 187 Quick Check			
Resources			
4-15 Practice			
4-15 Reteaching			
4-15 Enrichment			
4-15 Problem Solving			
4-15 Daily Transparency			

Problem of the Day

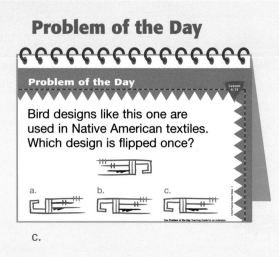

Problem of the Day

Bird designs like this one are used in Native American textiles. Which design is flipped once?

a.   b.   c.

c.

Math Routines

Time Ask students to list all the ways they could break up 6 hours into 2 whole numbers of hours. 4 ways

Money Ask students to list all the ways they could pay for a 75-cent item with quarters and nickels. 3 quarters; 2 quarters, 5 nickels; 1 quarter 10 nickels; 15 nickels

Mental Math

Name the amount of change for each. Explain your thinking.

Cost $0.29 Paid $1.00 $0.71

Cost $0.55 Paid $1.00 $0.45

Cost $0.83 Paid $1.00 $0.17

Social Studies Connection

Basketball was invented in 1891. Peach baskets were attached to a balcony railing 10 ft above the floor. A soccer ball was used. Today, baskets are still 10 ft above the floor, and basketballs 30 in. and 29 in. around are used.

- How long ago was basketball invented? Subtract 1891 from the current year.

- How much larger is a basketball than a soccer ball? Can't be answered because the size of a soccer ball is not given

Another Way to [Learn] Lesson 4-15

Use as an alternative or in addition to pages 186 and 187.

Materials Teaching Tool Transparencies 1, 2 (Guided Problem Solving 1, 2)

Learning Style Logical, Social

- Present this information to students.

  In their first game of the season, the Wolves scored 57 points and beat the Panthers, who had 18 turnovers, by 15 points. In their second game, the Wolves beat the Panthers by only 9 points.

- Have students use any strategy they can to find the total points scored in each game. First game: 99 points; Second Game: Can't be found because you need to know how many points were scored by at least one team, and that is not given

- Use the Guided Problem Solving transparencies on the overhead to demonstrate trying to find the points scored in each game. Have students identify extra information given for the first game and what information is needed for the second game.

- Tell students that the Wolves scored 3 more points in the second game than in the first and have them try to find the total points scored in the second game. 111 points

- Assign Check and Practice on Student Book page 187 or *Practice Master 4-15.*

- Assess using the following rubric.

Assessment Rubric

4 Full Accomplishment
- identifies if problems have too much or too little information; solves word problems

3 Substantial Accomplishment
- with prompting, identifies if problems have too much or too little information; solves most problems

2 Partial Accomplishment
- does not consistently identify if problems have too much or too little information; solves some problems

1 Little Accomplishment
- does not identify if problems have too much or too little information; does not solve word problems

Options for Reaching All Learners

Reading Assist

Find Main Idea with Supporting Details
Use different markings to identify information needed to solve problems.

Materials Photocopies of page 187

Learning Style Visual

- Have students mark up each problem as follows:

  Underline what you are asked to find.

  Circle the information given that you need to solve the problem.

  Cross out any information given that you do not need to solve the problem.

- If a problem has too little information, have students write a brief description of what is needed below the problem and circle that description.

Inclusion

Picture This
Use pictures to strengthen understanding of too much or too little information.

Learning Style Visual, Logical

- Copy the images onto the chalkboard to display the information given at the top of page 186. Use the information to draw price tags on items.

- Have students refer to the images as they work through the problem solving process on page 186. Focus on the blank price tags representing too little information.

Lesson Organizer

Objective Solve problems with too much or too little information.

Suggested Grouping 2 to 4

Student Materials None

Assignment Guide

Basic 3, 5, 7, 8

Average 3, 5–7, 9

Enriched 3–6, 9

1 Introduce

Review

Tickets to a baseball game are $7 for adults and $5 for students. What is the total cost of

1. 3 student tickets? $15

2. 2 adult tickets and 1 student ticket? $19

Build on Prior Knowledge

Ask students to find the cost of 1 adult ticket and 1 student ticket to a football game and explain their thinking. It can't be found because the cost of football game tickets are not given.

2 Teach

See Another Way to Learn...on page 186B.

Learn ● ● ● ● ● ● ● ● ● ● ● ● ● ● ● ● ● ●

Reading Assist **Find Main Idea with Supporting Details**

Pair fluent and less-fluent readers to read the problem together, paraphrase it, and talk about each step of the problem solving process. As part of the Look Back, have students suppose that the bat cost $14, then try to carry out their plans.

Talk About It **Ongoing Assessment**

Listen for the ability to distinguish between necessary and unnecessary information.

Answers for Talk About It

Possible answers: Too little: Only if you can find necessary information elsewhere. Too much: Yes; You can ignore the extra information.

Problem Solving

Analyze Word Problems:
Too Much or Too Little Information

You Will Learn
how to solve problems with too much or too little information

Learn ●

Sometimes when you solve problems, you may have more information than you need. Or, you may not have enough.

Jared's coach bought a baseball and a bat. He also bought a $10 football and a $25 football helmet. He spent $57. How much did the baseball cost?

Work Together

▶ **Understand**
❶ How much the football and helmet cost, and the total he spent

What do you know? ❶

What do you need to find out? How much the baseball cost

▶ **Plan**
To find the cost of the baseball, add the cost of all the items except the baseball. Then subtract that total from $57.

Item	Cost
Football	$10
Helmet	$25
Bat	?

▶ **Solve**
Add the cost of the football, helmet, and bat.

You cannot add in the cost of the bat because it is not known.

▶ **Look Back**
Can you get an answer? Explain. No; You need more information. You cannot solve the problem without knowing the cost of the bat.

Talk About It

Can you solve problems with too little information? Too much? Explain.

Name _____

Practice 4-15

Analyze Word Problems:
Too Much or Too Little Information
Decide if the problem has too much or too little information. Then solve, if possible.

1. Find the cost of dessert if the whole meal—soup, salad, lasagna, 3 glasses of milk, and dessert—costs $14. The milk costs $0.75 a glass, the lasagna costs $5, and the salad costs $2.50. — **Too little**

2. Find the cost of dessert if the whole meal—salad, spaghetti, 2 glasses of milk, and dessert—costs $9.75. The milk costs $0.75 a glass, the spaghetti costs $4.50, the salad costs $2 and juice costs $1.00. — **Too much; $1.75**

3. Tony, his brother, and his uncle played a game of basketball. Tony scored 3 baskets, his brother scored 9 baskets, and his uncle scored 5 baskets. How many baskets did Tony and his brother score together? — **Too much; 12**

4. Joselyn and Deidre played soccer against Angela and Becka. Joselyn and Deidre won the game with 12 goals; Angela and Becka made 8 goals. Joselyn made 8 goals by herself. How many goals did Becka make? — **Too little**

5. The bus had 1 passenger get on at the first stop, 3 at the second and 4 at the third. How many passengers were on the bus at the fifth stop? — **Too little**

Name _____

Another Look 4-15

Analyze Word Problems: Too Much or Too Little Information
To solve a word problem, look carefully at the information. Does it give you enough information to find the answer?

Example Julie bought milk, cereal, and juice today. How much did she spend if the milk cost $1.85 and the cereal cost $4.25.

a. What does the problem tell you? _the cost of the milk and cereal_
What does it leave out? _the total cost; the cost of the juice_

b. Can you figure out the answer? Explain. _No. I don't know how much the juice cost so I can't figure the total cost._

1. Central Middle School has 450 students in 7th, 8th, and 9th grade. There are 185 students in the 7th grade and 115 students in the 8th grade. How many students are in the 9th grade?

a. What does the problem tell you? _The total number of students, the number of students in 7th grade, the number of students in 8th grade_
What does it leave out? _The number of students in 9th grade_

b. Can you figure out the answer? Explain. _Yes; I can subtract the number of students in 7th and 8th grade from the total number to find the number of students in 9th grade._

2. Central High School has 215 students in 10th grade and 158 students in 11th grade. How many students are in 10th, 11th, and 12th grade?

a. What does the problem tell you? _The number of students in 10th grade, the number of students in 11th grade_
What does it leave out? _The number of students in 12th grade, the total number of students_

b. Can you figure out the answer? Explain. _No; I need to know how many students are in the 12th grade._

Decide if the problem has too much or too little information.
Then solve, if possible.

Problem
Solving
Understand
Plan
Solve
Look Back

1. Find the cost of a soccer ball if the total cost of a ball, shin guards, and soccer shirt is $37. The soccer shirt costs $12, the shin guards cost $10, and the socks cost $8. **Too much information; $15**

2. Find the cost of two soccer balls, shin guards, socks, and a shirt. The two soccer balls cost $40, and the shirt costs $12.
   Too little information to solve

Problem Solving
Practice •

Decide if the problem has too much or too little information.
Then solve, if possible.

3. In a soccer game, Jon scored 1 goal and Jason scored 3 goals. If Ron also scored 1 goal, how many goals did Azzam score? **Too little information to solve**

GPS 4. Sue, Leanne, and Ash made a total of 10 goals. Sue made 4 goals and Leanne made 2. Ash made twice as many goals as Leanne. How many goals did Ash make? **Too much information; 4 goals**

5. **Social Studies** In Missouri, about 15,000 people live in Warrensburg. About 140,000 people live in Springfield, and about 430,000 live in Kansas City. About how many more people live in Kansas City than in Springfield? **Too much information; About 290,000 people**

6. David's father works for a baseball team. He gave David some $5 tickets to a game to give to 6 of his friends. Each friend got 2 tickets. How many tickets did David's father give him? **Too much information; 12 tickets**

Problem Solving Strategies

- Use Objects/Act It Out
- Draw a Picture
- Look for a Pattern
- Guess and Check
- Use Logical Reasoning
- Make an Organized List
- Make a Table
- Solve a Simpler Problem
- Work Backward

Choose a Tool

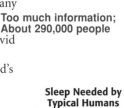

Using Data Use the bar graph to answer **7–9**.

7. About how many more hours of sleep per day does a 40 year old need than a 70 year old? **About 3 hours**

8. About how many more hours of sleep does a newborn baby need than a 4 year old? **About 9 hours**

9. Kim is 10 years old. If she went to sleep at 8:15 P.M. and woke up at about 7:30 A.M., did she get enough sleep? Explain. **Yes; About 11 hours**

Sleep Needed by Typical Humans

Age
- More than 60 years
- 40 years
- 10 years
- 4 years
- Newborn

Hours (per day)
0   5   10   15   20   25

PROBLEM SOLVING PRACTICE

Check •

Have students discuss how they know Exercises 1 and 2 have too much or too little information.

Practice •

Exercises 7–9 Students must estimate answers, when possible, because of the graph scale.

For Early Finishers Challenge early finishers to make up reasonable information for one or more of those problems they decided did not have enough information and solve the problems.

3 Close and Assess

Have students share their problem solving plans and solutions, and how they determined whether the problems had too much or too little information.

Quick Check

1. In what step of the problem solving process are you most likely to realize that a problem has too much or too little information? Explain. Possible answer: As you try to complete the Solve step, you will find that all the information you need is not given or that there is some information you do not need.

2. What can you do to solve a real-life problem if you find that you are given too little information? Possible answer: Try to find the information you need in another place.

Enrichment 4-15

Name _____   **Extend Your Thinking 4-15**

Decision Making
The Math Club has raised $450 for this year's trip. They've decided to go to New York City. Today, all 8 members will vote on what to do when they get there. They must choose from among the following choices:

A. Go to a Broadway play.
  • Each matinee ticket costs $28.
  • A play lasts for 2 or 3 hours.
  • There is 1 matinee a day, usually at 2:00 P.M.

B. See a show at Radio City Music Hall.
  • Each ticket costs $12.
  • A show lasts about 90 minutes.
  • There are 5 shows a day, starting at 9:00 A.M.

C. Go to the Museum of Natural History.
  • Each ticket costs $5.
  • The museum is free to the public on Wednesdays.
  • The museum is across the street from Central Park.

D. Go to the Statue of Liberty.
  • Each ticket costs $11.
  • The statue is in New York Harbor.
  • The ferry ride to the statue takes about 20 minutes.

The train ride to New York takes 1 hour and costs $12 each way. Lunch costs about $10 per person, unless you bring your own.

If you were in the Math Club, how would you vote to spend the day? Explain.

Accept any answer, as long as student accommodates the
$56.25 allotted per club member. Student may choose to
augment this with pocket money from each member.
Possible answer: Go on a Wednesday. Go to Radio City in the
morning, then to the Museum, have lunch in a restaurant,
then visit the Statue of Liberty in the afternoon. Cost: (train)
$24, (Radio City) $12, (Museum) free, (lunch) $10 (Statue)
$11, for a total of $57. Everyone has to bring at least one
dollar of their own.

Problem Solving 4-15

Name _____   **Guided Problem Solving 4-15**

GPS PROBLEM 4, STUDENT PAGE 187

Sue, Leanne, and Ash made a total of 10 goals. Sue made 4 goals and Leanne made 2. Ash made twice as many goals as Leanne. How many goals did Ash make?

— **Understand** —
1. Underline the question you need to answer.
2. Circle the sentence that tells you how to find the answer.
3. Look at the rest of the problem. What information do you need to find the answer? Draw a box around it.

— **Plan** —
4. How will you find your answer? What operation will you use?
   Multiply Leanne's goals by 2; Multiplication

— **Solve** —
5. Write a number sentence and solve the problem.
   $2 \times 2 = 4$; Ash made 4 goals.

— **Look Back** —
6. Did it help to know how many goals Sue made or how many total goals were made?   **No**

7. How can you check your answer?
   Possible answer: Divide my answer by 2. The result should be the number of goals Leanne made.

SOLVE ANOTHER PROBLEM

Daniel slept 8 hours on Mon., 6 hours Tues., 7 hours Thurs., 8 hours Fri., 9 hours Sat., and 9 hours Sun. What is the *median* number of hours Daniel slept this week?
Too little information; don't know the number of hours Daniel slept on Wed.

Compare Strategies:
Guess and Check/Draw a Picture

At-A-Glance Planning

Objective Solve problems by comparing strategies.

Student Book Lesson Materials None

Materials for pages 188A and 188B Teaching Tool Transparencies 1, 2 (Guided Problem Solving 1, 2); assorted manipulatives such as counters, color cubes, and Power Polygons

Subject Connections physical education—field hockey, health—teeth

Strand Connections using data, money

	Before Lesson	During Lesson	After Lesson
Daily Math			
p. 188A Problem of the Day			
p. 188A Math Routines			
p. 188A Mental Math			
Teaching Options			
p. 188 Student Book Lesson			
p. 188B Another Way to Learn…			
Options for Reaching All Learners			
p. 188B Inclusion			
p. 188B Reading Assist			
Technology Options			
p. 188A *Logical Journey of the Zoombinis*			
Assessment Options			
p. 188 Talk About It			
p. 189 Quick Check			
Resources			
4-16 Practice			
4-16 Reteaching			
4-16 Enrichment			
4-16 Problem Solving			
4-16 Daily Transparency			

Problem of the Day

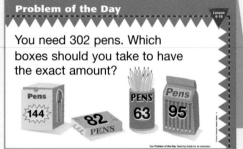

You need 302 pens. Which boxes should you take to have the exact amount?

Take the boxes of 144, 63, and 95 pens.

Math Routines

Calendar Ask students to find the number of days until the end of the year, then discuss the strategies they used. Possible answer: Find the number of days remaining in the current month and each remaining month. Add the days.

Money Tell students you have five coins totaling $0.51. Ask them to name the coins. 1 quarter, 2 dimes, 1 nickel, 1 penny

Mental Math

Name the amount of change for each.

Cost $1.99 Paid $5.00 $3.01

Cost $2.59 Paid $5.00 $2.41

Cost $3.35 Paid $10.00 $6.65

Logical Journey of the Zoombinis

To provide opportunities to compare problem solving strategies, have several students choose and solve the same puzzle, recording their thinking in the Zoombini Puzzle Log. They can use their logs to compare strategies and thinking.

Another Way to **Learn** Lesson 4-16

Use as an alternative or in addition to pages 188 and 189.

Materials Teaching Tool Transparencies 1, 2 (Guided Problem Solving 1, 2)

Learning Style Logical, Social

- Present this problem and these strategies to students:

  Derek and Alicia are standing at opposite sides of a field that is 200 ft wide. They each toss a softball toward each other. Derek tosses a softball 30 ft. It lands 120 ft from Alicia's softball. How far did Alicia toss her softball?

Guess and Check

Guess 40 ft.: 30 + 120 + 40 = 190. Too few.

Guess 50 ft.: 30 + 120 + 50 = 200. That checks!

Draw a Picture

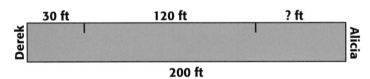

30 + 120 = 150; 200 − 150 = 50

Alicia tossed the ball 50 ft.

- Have students talk about when it is helpful to use Guess and Check and when it is helpful to use Draw a Picture.
- Assign Check and Practice on page 189 or *Practice Master 4-16.*
- Assess using the following rubric.

Assessment Rubric
4 Full Accomplishment • solves problems • applies strategies appropriately
3 Substantial Accomplishment • solves most problems • usually applies strategies appropriately
2 Partial Accomplishment • solves some problems • sometimes applies strategies appropriately
1 Little Accomplishment • solves few, if any, problems • does not apply strategies appropriately

Options for Reaching All Learners

Inclusion

Make a Model

Use manipulatives to strengthen understanding of the Draw a Picture strategy.

Materials Assorted manipulatives such as counters, color cubes, and Power Polygons

Learning Style Kinesthetic

- Have students use manipulatives to model the problem situations in this lesson. Possibilities include:

  Use red and yellow counters to represent Warren's oranges and Toby's oranges.

  For Exercise 2, use hexagons and triangles to represent whole and half oranges.

  For Exercise 4, use stacks of 2 and 3 cubes to represent bicycles and tricycles.

Reading Assist

Word Meaning

Use explanations to strengthen understanding of number information given in words.

Learning Style Verbal

- Have students read Exercise 4 on page 189 and tell what information is needed to solve the problem. Total number of cycles; Number of wheels on a tricycle; Number of wheels on a bicycle
- Ask students how they know the number of wheels on each type of cycle. *Tri-* and *bi-* at the beginning of the cycle names indicate 3 and 2 wheels.
- Have students scan their math books to create a list of words that appear in problems as number clues. Possible answers: *Dozen, decade, century, couple, triplet, quartet*

Lesson Organizer

Objective Solve problems by comparing strategies.

Student Materials None

Assignment Guide

Basic 3, 5–7

Average 2, 3, 5–7

Enriched 2–5, 8

1 Introduce

Review

Name three different strategies you could use to solve word problems. **Possible answers: Guess and Check, Draw a Picture, Make an Organized List**

Build on Prior Knowledge

Review the problem solving strategies students name. Then ask students how they decide what strategy to use when they read a problem. **Possible answer: If the problem is complicated, I think about drawing a picture to try to make it easier to see how to solve it.**

2 Teach

See Another Way to Learn...on page 188B.

Learn ●

Reading Assist Recognize Sequence

As students work together, have them paraphrase the sequence of steps followed in each of the two strategies.

Point out that, as part of the Look Back step, students may use a different strategy and check whether they get the same solution.

⟨Talk About It⟩ Ongoing Assessment

Listen for explanations that show an understanding of how to use Guess and Check and Draw a Picture. Students can be encouraged to think of strategies other than these, as well.

Answer for Talk About It

Possible answer: Guess and Check; I could change the numbers until I found the ones that fit.

188 *Chapter 4 • Lesson 4-16*

Problem Solving

Compare Strategies: Guess and Check/Draw a Picture

You Will Learn
how to solve problems using Guess and Check and Draw a Picture

Learn ●

Together, Toby and Warren brought 16 oranges for their field hockey team to eat at halftime. Toby brought 2 more oranges than Warren did. How many did they each bring?

Here are two ways to solve the problem.

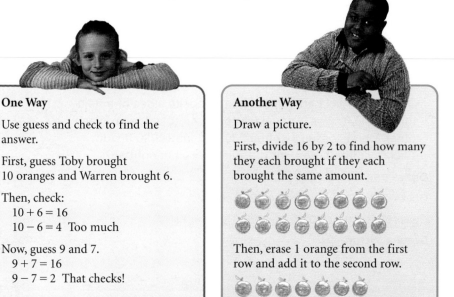

One Way

Use guess and check to find the answer.

First, guess Toby brought 10 oranges and Warren brought 6.

Then, check:
$10 + 6 = 16$
$10 - 6 = 4$ Too much

Now, guess 9 and 7.
$9 + 7 = 16$
$9 - 7 = 2$ That checks!

Another Way

Draw a picture.

First, divide 16 by 2 to find how many they each brought if they each brought the same amount.

Then, erase 1 orange from the first row and add it to the second row.

So, Toby brought 9 oranges. Warren brought 7.

⟨Talk About It⟩

Which strategy would you use to solve this problem? Explain.

188 Chapter 4 • Multiplication and Division Concepts and Facts

---

Practice 4-16

Reteaching 4-16

Name _____

Another Look
4-16

Compare Strategies: Guess and Check/Draw a Picture

Together, Janie and Howard brought 15 fruit tarts to a party. If Howard brought 3 more tarts than Janie, how many fruit tarts did they each bring?

| JANIE | HOWARD |

You can solve the problem by drawing a picture. First write the names "Janie" and "Howard". Draw 1 tart under "Janie" and 4 tarts under "Howard." Howard has 3 more tarts than Janie, but the picture doesn't show 15 tarts.

| JANIE | HOWARD |

Now add one tart to Janie's and one tart to Howard's until you have 15 tarts in all.

This drawing shows that Janie brought 6 tarts and Howard brought 9.

Marla and Ahmed brought 18 beach shells to show and tell. If Marla brought 4 more shells than Ahmed, how many did they each bring?

1. What do you need to find out?
How many shells Ahmed and Marla each brought

2. Draw a picture to show the number of shells each person brought to show. **Check students' drawings.**

3. How many shells did Ahmed bring? **7 shells**

4. How many shells did Marla bring? **11 shells**

Use Guess and Check, Draw a Picture, or any other strategy to solve the problem.

Problem Solving
Understand
Plan
Solve
Look Back

1. Sam has eight loose sports socks in a drawer. Four of them have green stripes and four have red stripes. He wants a matching pair of socks, but it is too dark to see. What is the least number of socks he can take out to be sure of having a matching pair? Explain.

Problem Solving Practice •

Use any strategy to solve each problem.

2. The field hockey coach asked Mariel's mom to bring oranges for the 11 players to eat at halftime. Each player needs $1\frac{1}{2}$ oranges. How many oranges should Mariel's mom bring? **17 oranges**

3. The coach wants to bring string cheese sticks for the team. He needs 12 sticks. How many bags should he buy, if each bag contains 4 sticks? **3 bags**

4. The Taneytown Cyclers put on a show. They used tricycles and bicycles. There were 12 tricycles and bicycles with a total of 27 wheels in the show. How many bicycles were there? **9 bicycles**

5. **Health** A typical young child has these teeth in each jaw: 4 incisors, 2 canines, and 4 molars.

   a. How many teeth are in both jaws of a typical young child? **20 teeth**

   b. A typical adult has 32 permanent teeth. Typically, how many more teeth does an adult have than a young child? **12 more**

Using Data Use the table to answer 6–8.

6. How much will two mouth guards cost? **$5.90**

7. What is the difference in price between a hockey stick and a hockey ball? **$31.75**

8. How many shin guards can you buy with $45? **2**

Problem Solving Strategies

- Use Objects/Act It Out
- Draw a Picture
- Look for a Pattern
- Guess and Check
- Use Logical Reasoning
- Make an Organized List
- Make a Table
- Solve a Simpler Problem
- Work Backward

Choose a Tool

Field Hockey Equipment	
Hockey stick	$37.50
Shin guard	$15.25
Mouth guard	$2.95
Hockey ball	$5.75

PROBLEM SOLVING PRACTICE

Check •

Encourage students to solve this problem using at least two different strategies. Then have students share their solutions and strategies.

Practice •

Exercise 2 Some students may find that drawing a picture of parts of oranges is helpful. Others may think about 1 orange being needed to give 2 players $\frac{1}{2}$ each.

For Early Finishers Challenge early finishers to check one of the exercises they have already solved by using a different strategy.

③ Close and Assess

Have students share the different strategies they used to solve each problem. Encourage them to explain why they chose to use particular strategies.

Quick Check

Suppose a problem contains confusing information. You realize that using Guess and Check or Draw a Picture could help you solve it. How would you decide which strategy to use? Possible answer: I'd use Guess and Check if I could make a good guess about the solution. I'd use Draw a Picture if I was having difficulty figuring out how information related or if the numbers were difficult to work with, like fractions.

ANSWERS

1 3 socks; If Sam chooses only 2 socks, he could get a green and a red. If he chooses 3 socks, he could get 2 greens and a red, 2 reds and a green, 3 greens, or 3 reds. In any case, with 3 socks he always has a matching pair.

Name _____   **Guided Problem Solving 4-16**

GPS PROBLEM 4, STUDENT PAGE 189

The Taneytown Cyclers put on a show. They used tricycles and bicycles. There were 12 tricycles and bicycles with a total of 27 wheels in the show. How many bicycles were there?

— **Understand** —
1. What do you know? The number of tricycles and bicycles together and the total number of wheels

2. What do you need to find out? The number of bicycles

— **Plan** —
3. Name one number that would be too high of a guess of the number of bicycles. Name another number that would be too low. Explain.
   Possible answers: 12 bicycles would be too many because there would be no tricycles. 3 bicycles would be too few because there would be over 27 wheels.

— **Solve** —
4. Check a guess of 6 bicycles. Are there too many or too few wheels?   Too many

5. How many bicycles were in the show?   9

— **Check** —
6. Describe another strategy you could use to check your work.
   Possible answer: Draw a Picture.

SOLVE ANOTHER PROBLEM

Martha and Enrique brought 24 oranges to a picnic. Enrique brought 6 more oranges than Martha. How many oranges did they each bring?
Enrique—15, Martha—9

Section C
Review and Practice

Use the Skills Checklist

Review the **Skills Checklist** on the page with students. Then ask questions such as the following:

- How could you find the quotients in Exercises 5–24 if you can't remember the division facts? Possible answer: Think of a multiplication fact in the same fact family.

- How can you decide whether the numbers in Exercises 25–34 are even or odd? Look at the ones digit.

- How can you decide whether the numbers in Exercises 38–41 are prime or composite? Figure out whether they have more than two factors.

Assess

You may wish to use this information to assess students' understanding of the lesson objectives.

Item Analysis

Lesson Objective	Items
4-11 Divide with 3 and 4 as divisors.	5, 6, 13, 14, 16, 19
4-12 Divide with 6, 7, and 8 as divisors.	8–12, 15, 17, 22–24, 43
4-13 Explore even and odd numbers.	3, 4, 25–34
4-14 Explore factors.	1, 2, 35–41
4-15 Solve problems with too much or too little information.	42
4-16 Solve problems by comparing strategies.	

Resources

Practice Masters

- Practice Chapter 4 Section C

Assessment Sourcebook

- Quiz Chapter 4 Section C

TestWorks: Test and Practice Software

ANSWERS

43 $7 \times 9 = 63$; Use members of the same fact family.

Vocabulary Match each word with its meaning.

1. composite number **b**
2. prime number **a**
3. even **d**
4. odd **c**

 a. a number that has only two factors, itself and 1
 b. a number that has more than two factors
 c. a number that cannot be divided into two equal groups
 d. a number that can be divided into two equal groups

(Lessons 11 and 12) Find each quotient.

5. $4\overline{)24}$ 6   6. $3\overline{)12}$ 4   7. $9\overline{)27}$ 3   8. $6\overline{)18}$ 3   9. $7\overline{)63}$ 9

10. $8\overline{)24}$ 3   11. $7\overline{)35}$ 5   12. $6\overline{)36}$ 6   13. $4\overline{)32}$ 8   14. $3\overline{)21}$ 7

15. $12 \div 6$ 2   16. $28 \div 4$ 7   17. $0 \div 6$ 0   18. $81 \div 9$ 9   19. $24 \div 4$ 6

20. $45 \div 5$ 9   21. $54 \div 9$ 6   22. $14 \div 7$ 2   23. $72 \div 8$ 9   24. $48 \div 6$ 8

(Lesson 13) Write *even* or *odd* for each.

25. 32 Even   26. 19 Odd   27. 15 Odd   28. 16 Even   29. 57 Odd
30. 159 Odd   31. 400 Even   32. 921 Odd   33. 1,024 Even   34. 1,185 Odd

(Lesson 14) Copy and complete. Then list all the factors of each number.

35. $1 \times \blacksquare = 12$ 12   36. $1 \times \blacksquare = 18$ 18   37. $\blacksquare \times \blacksquare = 11$ 1, 11
 $2 \times \blacksquare = 12$ 6 $2 \times \blacksquare = 18$ 9   1, 11
 $3 \times \blacksquare = 12$ 4 $3 \times \blacksquare = 18$ 6
 1, 2, 3, 4, 6, 12   1, 2, 3, 6, 9, 18

Write whether each number is prime or composite.

38. 7 Prime   39. 28 Composite   40. 17 Prime   41. 39 Composite

(Lesson 15) Use any strategy to solve.

42. **History** In the 1940s, soccer shoes weighed about 1 lb each. Today soccer shoes weigh about 8 oz each and have 6 studs on the soles. Today, what is the weight of a pair of soccer shoes? **16 oz or 1 lb**

43. **Journal** What multiplication fact would you use to find $63 \div 7$? Explain.

REVIEW AND PRACTICE

Skills Checklist

In this section, you have:

- ☑ Divided with 3, 4, 6, 7, and 8 as Divisors
- ☑ Explored Even and Odd Numbers
- ☑ Explored Factors
- ☑ Solved Problems with Too Much or Too Little Information
- ☑ Solved Problems by Comparing Strategies: Guess and Check/Draw a Picture

190 Chapter 4 • Review and Practice

Practice

Name _____

Practice
Chapter 4
Section C

Review and Practice
Vocabulary Write true or false for each statement.

1. A number that has more than two factors is a composite number.   true
2. An even number can be divided into 2 equal groups.   true
3. A prime number has only two factors, itself and 0.   false

(Lessons 11 and 12) Find each quotient.

4. $8\overline{)0}$ 0   5. $6\overline{)30}$ 5   6. $3\overline{)24}$ 8   7. $2\overline{)18}$ 9
8. $16 \div 4 =$ 4   9. $36 \div 6 =$ 6   10. $25 \div 5 =$ 5
11. $56 \div 7 =$ 8   12. $49 \div 7 =$ 7   13. $42 \div 6 =$ 7

(Lesson 13) Write *even* or *odd* for each.
14. 45 __odd__   15. 18 __even__   16. 24 __even__

(Lesson 14) Complete. Then list all the factors of each number.
17. $1 \times 20 = 20$ 18. $1 \times 14 = 14$
 $2 \times 10 = 20$ $2 \times 7 = 14$
 $4 \times 5 = 20$ 1, 2, 7, 14
 1, 2, 4, 5, 10, 20

Write whether each number is prime or composite.
19. 21 __Composite__   20. 42 __Composite__   21. 47 __Prime__

(Lesson 15) Use any strategy to solve.
22. Merle began the 3 mile walk to the library at 12:30 P.M. Justin walked 1 mile to his bus stop and rode 6 more miles. They both arrived at the library at 2:00 P.M. How long did it take Merle to walk to the library?   **An hour and a half**

(Mixed Review) Use mental math to find each sum.
23. $350 + 50 =$ 400   24. $640 + 333 =$ 973
25. $266 + 24 =$ 290   26. $533 + 216 =$ 749

YOUR CHOICE

Choose at least one. Use what you have learned in this chapter.

1 Let the Good Times Roll

Think of a favorite song. Rewrite it using words about multiplying or dividing. Make it silly, dramatic, or serious! When you are done, share it with your classmates.

2 The Daily Times

At Home Work with a family member or friend. Think about shopping, traveling, or cooking. Find at least three ways you use multiplication. Write multiplication stories and number sentences for these ways.

Possible answers: 3 cereals at $2 each = $6; 5 miles × 2 trips = 10 miles; $2 per week for newspapers = $8 per month

3 Follow the Map

Complete each fact. Then add the answers to find the shortest way from home to the park.
Home to pool to tree to park

9
9 ÷ 1

Home

3 × 6
18

36
3 × 12

36
6 × 6

Park

6 × 5
30

32
4 × 8

18 ÷ 6
3

5 × 3
15

6 × 4
24

3 × 7
21

4 Beans on the Table

Share jelly beans with 3 friends. Make a table that shows how many jelly beans you will each get from 1 dozen jelly beans, 2 dozen jelly beans, 3 dozen jelly beans, and 4 dozen jelly beans. You can use a calculator to help you.

	Number of Jelly Beans	Each Person's Share
1 dozen	12	3
2 dozen	24	6
3 dozen	36	9
4 dozen	48	12

REVIEW AND PRACTICE

Calculator Connection

For Beans on the Table, suggest that students work out the answers with paper and pencils or use mental math. They can use their calculators to check their work.

Home-School Connection

For The Daily Times, as students work with family members to identify situations in which multiplication is used, encourage them also to find out how adult family members may use multiplication at work.

Parents can use the Web site at **www.parent.mathsurf.com**.

Your Choice

Students will review the skills and concepts of the chapter using learning style strengths.

This page of activities is a good opportunity for portfolio assessment.

1 Let the Good Times Roll

Learning Style Musical

If available, provide students with rhythm instruments to use during their presentations to the class.

2 The Daily Times

Learning Style Social

Possible answers: 3 cereals at $2 each = $6; 5 miles × 2 trips = 10 miles; $2 per week for newspapers = $8 per month

3 Follow the Map

Learning Style Visual

Home to pool to tree to park

4 Beans on the Table

Learning Style Logical

	Number of Jelly Beans	Each Person's Share
1 dozen	12	3
2 dozen	24	6
3 dozen	36	9
4 dozen	48	12

Chapter 4 Review/Test

This page may be used to review or assess students' knowledge of Chapter 4.

Item Analysis		
Lesson	Objective	Items
4-1	Review the meaning of multiplication.	3
4-2	Explore patterns in multiplying by 0, 1, 2, 5, and 9.	1, 11, 12, 13, 16
4-3	Multiply with 3 or 4 as a factor.	7, 8, 14, 15, 19
4-4	Multiply with 6, 7, or 8 as a factor.	8–10, 12 14, 15, 17
4-5	Explore patterns in multiples of 10, 11, and 12.	9, 11, 13
4-6	Solve problems by making decisions.	
4-7	Review the meaning of division.	21–30
4-8	Explore multiplication and division stories.	6, 17–20
4-9	Divide with 2, 5, and 9 as divisors.	2, 4, 5, 22 25, 26, 30
4-10	Divide with 0 and 1.	25, 26
4-11	Divide with 3 and 4 as divisors.	21, 23
4-12	Divide with 6, 7, and 8 as divisors.	24, 27–29
4-13	Explore even and odd numbers.	
4-14	Explore factors.	
4-15	Solve problems with too much or too little information.	31, 33
4-16	Solve problems by comparing strategies.	32

Resources

Reading Strategies for Math
Chart 6 (Preparing for a Test)

Assessment Sourcebook
Chapter 4 Tests
- Forms A and B (free response)
- Form C (multiple choice)
- Form E (mixed response)
- Form F (cumulative chapter test)

TestWorks: Test and Practice Software

Home and Community Connections
- Letter Home for Chapter 4 in English and Spanish

Review/Test

Vocabulary Complete each sentence with the correct word.

Word List
product
fact family
multiple
divisor
dividend
quotient

1. 28 is a _____ of 2. **multiple**
2. The _____ is the answer to a division problem. **quotient**
3. The _____ is the answer to a multiplication problem. **product**
4. The number by which another number is to be divided is the _____. **divisor**
5. The number that is to be divided is the _____. **dividend**
6. $9 \times 5 = 45$ and $45 \div 9 = 5$ are in the same _____. **fact family**

(Lessons 1–5) Find each product.

7. 3×3 **9**   8. 6×4 **24**   9. 12×7 **84**   10. 7×6 **42**   11. 0×11 **0**

12. 6×9 **54**   13. 5×11 **55**   14. 7×4 **28**   15. 4×8 **32**   16. 1×9 **9**

(Lesson 8) Write a story for each number sentence. Stories will vary for 17–20.

17. $6 \times 8 = 48$ 18. $21 \div 3 = 7$ 19. $5 \times 4 = 20$ 20. $36 \div 9 = 4$

(Lessons 7, 9–12) Find each quotient.

21. $18 \div 3$ **6**   22. $81 \div 9$ **9**   23. $24 \div 4$ **6**   24. $48 \div 8$ **6**   25. $0 \div 5$ **0**

26. $9\overline{)9}$ **1**   27. $7\overline{)63}$ **9**   28. $8\overline{)72}$ **9**   29. $6\overline{)36}$ **6**   30. $2\overline{)14}$ **7**

(Lessons 15 and 16) Solve. Use any strategy.

31. Becky ran 5 miles every day after school. How many miles did she run in all? **Too little information to solve**

32. Jonah and Robyn scored 24 runs together during the baseball season. Jonah scored 4 runs fewer than Robyn. How many runs did Robyn score? **14 runs**

33. Sometimes Anna takes a bus to school. It costs 25¢ and the ride takes 4 minutes. How long does it take Anna to go to school and back home again? **8 minutes**

Assessment

Performance Assessment

After the first month of the Little League baseball season, the Huntsville Tigers compared their hitting records. Here's how they looked:

Name	Singles	Extra Base Hits
Michelle	11	6
Elise	8	8
Ty	10	7
Kathy	10	4
Paul	12	6
Chandrika	9	8
Jim	12	4
Tomas	9	9
Pat	8	7

Match the name of the player with the position he or she plays. Use the facts to help.

- The sum of the pitcher's hits is 15 and the product is 56. **Pat**
- The sum of the catcher's hits is 16 and the quotient is 3. **Jim**
- The sum of the shortstop's hits is 16 and the quotient is 1. **Elise**
- The sum of the first baseman's hits is 14 and the product is 40. **Kathy**
- The sum of the center fielder's hits is 17 and the product is 70. **Ty**
- The sum of the left fielder's hits is 17 and the product is 72. **Chandrika**

1. **Decision Making** Decide how your group will match six of the players with the position he or she plays. **Answers will vary.**

2. **Recording Data** Make a list or table to show your solution.

3. **Critical Thinking** Write your own riddles to match the remaining players with these positions: right field, third base, and second base.

4. **Explain Your Thinking** How did your group divide the work? How did you figure out each player's position? How can you change the lineup by using different sum, product, and quotient riddles? **Answers will vary.**

REVIEW/TEST

Assessment

Your class is going to work in 4 small groups to make bead jewelry for a craft fair. Each group will be given one of the boxes of beads below.

Box A	Box B	Box C	Box D
25 strings	18 strings	42 strings	24 strings
45 round beads	72 round beads	49 round beads	36 round beads
40 square beads	81 square beads	63 square beads	48 square beads

a. **Making Decisions** Each group will have a different number of students. In each group students share the materials equally, with no materials left over. Decide how many will be in each group. (Hint: Think about basic facts of multiplication. There is only one possible answer for each box of beads.)

b. **Recording Data** Make and complete a table like tne one below.

Group	Number of students	Box	Strings for each student	Round beads for each student	Square beads for each student
A		A			
B		B			
C		C			
D		D			

c. **Analyzing Data** Use the answers in the table.

In which group did each member get the most string?

In which group did each member get the least string?

In which group did each member get the most round beads?

d. **Making Decisions** Suppose you wanted to sell the jewelry at a craft fair. How would you decide what to charge? You want to make a profit.

Chapter 4 Performance Assessment

Students will apply addition, multiplication, and division skills as they solve a series of problems about a baseball team.

Introduce the Task

Review the riddles given about each player to be sure students understand that both the sum and the product or quotient must be correct for each position.

Review Exercises 1–4 to be sure students understand the directions. Share Level 4 of the rubric with students before they begin.

Facilitate and Assess

Before students work, you may wish to ask questions such as the following:

- What is the sum of Michelle's hits? the product? 17, 66
- What do you think is a good way to solve this problem?

Assessment Rubric

4 Full Accomplishment
- finds solutions and explains or demonstrates the process clearly

3 Substantial Accomplishment
- finds most solutions, explains or demonstrates the process with prompting

2 Partial Accomplishment
- finds some solutions with prompting, but does not explain or demonstrate the process

1 Little Accomplishment
- does not find solutions or explain the process

Resources

Assessment Sourcebook

Chapter 4 Test

- Form D (performance assessment)

ANSWERS

3 Possible answers: Paul: The sum of the right fielder's hits is 18 and the quotient is 2. Michelle: The sum of the third baseman's hits is 17 and the product is 66. Tomas: The sum of the second baseman's hits is 18 and the product is 81.

Math Magazine

Students will use the sieve of Eratosthenes to find prime numbers.

Student Materials Teaching Tool Transparency 9 (Hundred Chart, 1 copy per student), calculators (1 per student)

Historical Note

Eratosthenes was a Greek mathematician who lived approximately during 276–195 B.C. Using his observations of shadows and knowledge of geometry, he calculated the circumference of the earth through the poles to be between 28,000 and 29,000 miles. The actual circumference is 24,860 miles.

Cultural Link

To help students understand why the sieve of Eratosthenes is an appropriate name for a tool that retains only prime numbers, demonstrate using a sieve to separate stones from dirt or sand. Invite students to share any experiences they may have had with sieves.

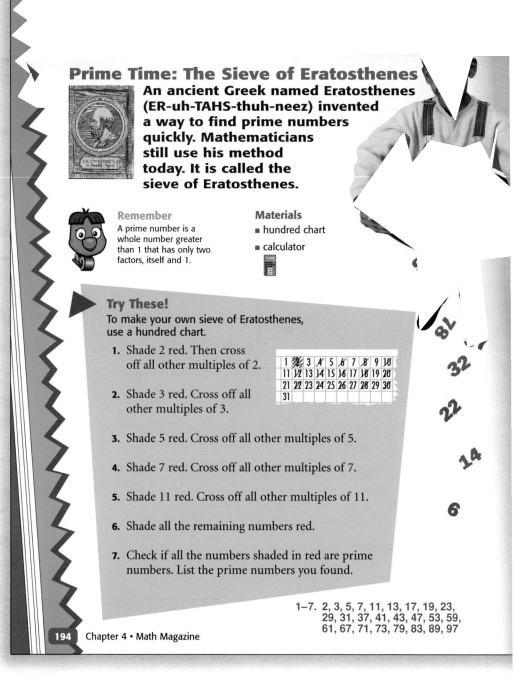

Prime Time: The Sieve of Eratosthenes

An ancient Greek named Eratosthenes (ER-uh-TAHS-thuh-neez) invented a way to find prime numbers quickly. Mathematicians still use his method today. It is called the sieve of Eratosthenes.

Remember
A prime number is a whole number greater than 1 that has only two factors, itself and 1.

Materials
- hundred chart
- calculator

Try These!
To make your own sieve of Eratosthenes, use a hundred chart.

1. Shade 2 red. Then cross off all other multiples of 2.

2. Shade 3 red. Cross off all other multiples of 3.

3. Shade 5 red. Cross off all other multiples of 5.

4. Shade 7 red. Cross off all other multiples of 7.

5. Shade 11 red. Cross off all other multiples of 11.

6. Shade all the remaining numbers red.

7. Check if all the numbers shaded in red are prime numbers. List the prime numbers you found.

1–7. 2, 3, 5, 7, 11, 13, 17, 19, 23, 29, 31, 37, 41, 43, 47, 53, 59, 61, 67, 71, 73, 79, 83, 89, 97

Additional Resources for the Teacher

Mathematics: A Way of Thinking, Robert Barrata-Lorton. Menlo Park: CA: Addison-Wesley Publishing Co.

Making Numbers Make Sense, Ron Ritchart. Menlo Park, CA: Dale Seymour Publications.

Discovery in Mathematics, Robert B. Davis. Menlo Park, CA: Dale Seymour Publications.

Cumulative Review

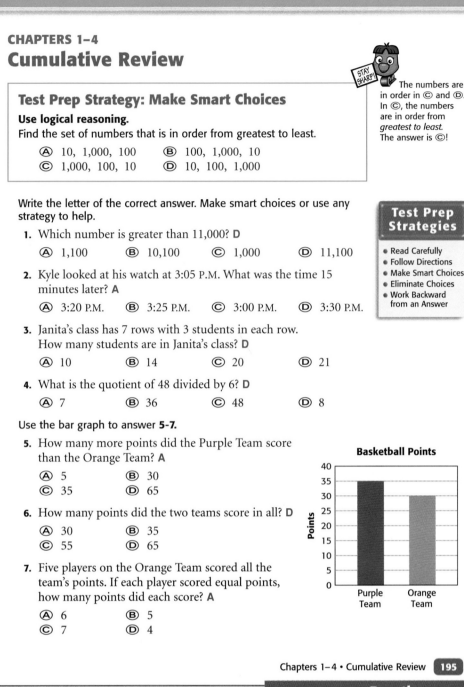

Test Prep Strategy: Make Smart Choices

Use logical reasoning.
Find the set of numbers that is in order from greatest to least.

Ⓐ 10, 1,000, 100   Ⓑ 100, 1,000, 10
Ⓒ 1,000, 100, 10   Ⓓ 10, 100, 1,000

The numbers are in order in Ⓒ and Ⓓ. In Ⓒ, the numbers are in order from *greatest to least*. The answer is Ⓒ!

Write the letter of the correct answer. Make smart choices or use any strategy to help.

1. Which number is greater than 11,000? **D**
   Ⓐ 1,100   Ⓑ 10,100   Ⓒ 1,000   Ⓓ 11,100

2. Kyle looked at his watch at 3:05 P.M. What was the time 15 minutes later? **A**
   Ⓐ 3:20 P.M.   Ⓑ 3:25 P.M.   Ⓒ 3:00 P.M.   Ⓓ 3:30 P.M.

3. Janita's class has 7 rows with 3 students in each row. How many students are in Janita's class? **D**
   Ⓐ 10   Ⓑ 14   Ⓒ 20   Ⓓ 21

4. What is the quotient of 48 divided by 6? **D**
   Ⓐ 7   Ⓑ 36   Ⓒ 48   Ⓓ 8

Use the bar graph to answer 5-7.

5. How many more points did the Purple Team score than the Orange Team? **A**
   Ⓐ 5   Ⓑ 30
   Ⓒ 35   Ⓓ 65

6. How many points did the two teams score in all? **D**
   Ⓐ 30   Ⓑ 35
   Ⓒ 55   Ⓓ 65

7. Five players on the Orange Team scored all the team's points. If each player scored equal points, how many points did each score? **A**
   Ⓐ 6   Ⓑ 5
   Ⓒ 7   Ⓓ 4

Basketball Points

Test Prep Strategies
- Read Carefully
- Follow Directions
- Make Smart Choices
- Eliminate Choices
- Work Backward from an Answer

REVIEW AND PRACTICE

Chapters 1–4 • Cumulative Review **195**

Practice

Name _____   Practice Chapters 1–4

Cumulative Review

(Chapter 2 Lesson 10) Find each elapsed time.
1. 6:08 P.M. to 11:30 P.M. __5 hr 22 min__
2. 7:15 A.M. to 1:33 P.M. __6 hr 18 min__
3. 9:47 P.M. to 10:30 P.M. __43 min__
4. 10:20 P.M. to 7:42 A.M. __9 hr 22 min__
5. Harold sat down to read a book at 6:25 P.M. He got up to get a snack 2 hours 25 minutes later. What time was it when he went to get a snack? __8:50 P.M.__

(Chapter 3 Lessons 8 and 13) Add or subtract.
6.	7.	8.	9.
600 − 467 = 133	703 − 289 = 414	2,083 − 1,487 = 596	3,001 − 176 = 2,825
10. $1.92 − 1.19 = $0.73	11. $4.08 + 1.68 = $5.76	12. $8.54 − 3.49 = $5.05	13. $9.01 + 9.26 = $18.27

(Chapter 4 Lessons 4 and 5) Find each product.
14. 3 × 8 = __24__   15. 7 × 9 = __63__   16. 8 × 5 = __40__
17. 11 × 5 = __55__   18. 12 × 6 = __72__   19. 11 × 10 = __110__
20. 4 × 10 = __40__   21. 2 × 11 = __22__   22. 3 × 12 = __36__
23. 7 × 8 = __56__   24. 6 × 9 = __54__   25. 12 × 11 = __132__
26. 2 × 7 = __14__   27. 12 × 9 = __108__   28. 8 × 4 = __32__

(Chapter 4 Lesson 16) Use any strategy to solve.
29. Tim and Bobby Jo have been asked to give out worksheets to the class. Tim gives out 5 more worksheets than Bobby Jo. There are 25 students in the class. How many worksheets did each give out?
__Tim—15; Bobby Jo—10__

Chapters 1–4 Cumulative Review

Students review and maintain skills and concepts taught in Chapters 1–4 and practice test-taking strategies. Special attention is given here to the Test Prep Strategy, Make Smart Choices: Use Logical Reasoning.

Introduce the Test Prep Strategy

Make Smart Choices: Use Logical Reasoning
Read and discuss the Test Prep Strategy note. After students work through the example, present the following problem:
What is the difference of 24 and 6? B
Ⓐ 30 Ⓑ 18 Ⓒ 8 Ⓓ 4

Encourage students to find other problems on this page where Make Smart Choices: Use Logical Reasoning might be a helpful strategy.

Some students may prefer another strategy for some of the identified items. Have them tell which strategy they would use and explain why.

Review and Assess

Item Analysis	
Item	Lesson
1	2-5
2	2-10
3	4-4
4	4-12
5	1-1
6	1-1
7	4-9

Resources

Practice Masters
- Cumulative Review Chapters 1–4

Section	Pacing		Lessons			Your Test	Materials	
	Day	Lesson/Page	Objective			Correlation	Student Book	Another Way to Learn
 **Multiplication Number Sense** Students multiply tens, hundreds, and thousands; estimate products; and use arrays to find partial products. **Problem Solving Connection** *Look for a Pattern* *Use Objects/Act It Out* *Solve a Simpler Problem*	Day 1	5-1	200–201	Multiply by multiples of ten.				Place-value blocks, 9-Digit Place-Value Chart
	Day 2	5-2	202–203	Explore multiplication patterns.				Calculators
	Day 3	5-3	204–205	Estimate products.				Place-value blocks
	Day 4	5-4	206–207	Explore multiplication with arrays.			Place-value blocks	
B **Multiplying** Students multiply 2-, 3-, and 4-digit numbers by 1-digit numbers with and without regrouping. **Problem Solving Connection** *Decision Making*	Day 5	5-5	210–213	Multiply 2-digit numbers.				Place-value blocks
	Day 6	5-6	214–215	Multiply 3-digit numbers.				Place-value blocks
	Day 7	5-7	216–217	**Problem Solving** Solve problems by making decisions about cooking.				
	Day 8	5-8	218–219	Multiply using different methods.				Calculators
C **Extending Multiplication** Students multiply three factors and apply their multiplication skills to solve money problems and multiple-step problems. **Problem Solving Skill** *Multiple-Step Problems* **Problem Solving Strategy** *Make a Table*	Day 9	5-9	224–225	Multiply amounts of money.				Play money
	Day 10	5-10	228–229	Use mental math to multiply.				Place-value blocks
	Day 11	5-11	230–231	Multiply when you have three factors.			Calculators	Counters
	Day 12	5-12	232–233	**Problem Solving** Solve multiple-step problems.			Calculators (optional)	Classroom objects
	Day 13	5-13	234–237	**Problem Solving** Solve problems by making a table.				
Chapter Assessment	Day 14		242–243	Assess student understanding and skills for Chapter 5.				

Also in this Chapter Data File, pp. 196–197, **Projects/Extensions,** pp. 198, 244

Chapter 5
Key Math Idea

Patterns, arrays, and basic facts can be used to help multiply greater numbers. The multiplication algorithm involves regrouping across places.

Connections		Section Resources	
Strand	**Subject**	**Technology**	**Review and Assessment**
	Recreation, Science, Language	**Performance Math: Multiplication** 💿 **World Wide Web** 🌐 www.mathsurf.com/4/ch5 Chapter Opener, p. 197	**Review** Section A Opener, p. 199 Mixed Review and Test Prep, pp. 201, 205 Section A Review and Practice, p. 208 Skills Practice Bank, p. 564
Mental Math	Physical Education, Language	**Math Workshop** 💿 Multiplying Tens, p. 200A **Calculator** 🖩 Exploring Multiplication Patterns, p. 202	**Ongoing Assessment** *Teacher's Edition,* all lessons *Assessment Sourcebook,* Quiz Chapter 5 Section A
Money, Using Data, Algebra Readiness	Art, Careers	**Interactive CD-ROM Journal** 💿 Exploring Multiplication Patterns, p. 203 Exploring Multiplication with Arrays, p. 207	
Using Data	Science, Literature, Language	**Interactive CD-ROM Lesson 5** 💿 Exploring Multiplication with Arrays, p. 206	
Estimation, Time, Using Data, Collecting Data, Algebra Readiness	Science, Geography, Culture	**Performance Math: Multiplication** 💿 **Interactive CD-ROM Lesson 5** 💿 Multiplying 2-Digit Numbers, p. 210	**Review** Section B Opener, p. 209 Mixed Review and Test Prep, pp. 213, 215, 219 Practice Game, pp. 220–221
Using Data, Patterns	Science, Literature, Reading	**Interactive CD-ROM Journal** 💿 Multiplying 2-Digit Numbers, p. 212	Section B Review and Practice, p. 222 Skills Practice Bank, p. 564
	Careers, Reading, Language	**Logical Journey of the Zoombinis** 💿 Decision Making, p. 216A **World Wide Web** 🌐 www.mathsurf.com/4/ch5	**Ongoing Assessment** *Teacher's Edition,* all lessons *Assessment Sourcebook,* Quiz Chapter 5
Mental Math, Estimation, Using Data	Health, Science, Culture	Decision Making, p. 217	Section B
Logic, Using Data, Patterns	Physical Education, Literature, Language	**Performance Math: Multiplication** 💿 **Calculator** 🖩 Multiple-Step Problems, p. 232	**Review** Section C Opener, p. 223 Mixed Review and Test Prep, pp. 225, 229, 231, 237
Mental Math, Money, Algebra Readiness, Collecting Data	Technology, Science, Language	**Logical Journey of the Zoombinis** 💿 Analyze Strategies, p. 234A	Stop and Practice, pp. 226–227 Section C Review and Practice, p. 240
Geometry Readiness, Logic, Patterns	Music, Social Studies, Language	**Interactive CD-ROM Journal** 💿 Analyze Strategies, p. 236 **DataWonder!** 💾	Your Choice, p. 241 Skills Practice Bank, p. 565
	Music, Science, Language, Reading	Technology, pp. 238–239	**Ongoing Assessment** *Teacher's Edition,* all lessons *Assessment Sourcebook,* Quiz Chapter 5 Section C
Patterns, Using Data	Art, Language		
		TestWorks 💿	Chapter Review/Test, p. 242 Performance Assessment, p. 243 Cumulative Review, p. 245

Manipulatives

Using the Manipulatives

Place-Value Blocks (Base 10 Blocks)
Students use place-value blocks to model the multiplication algorithm. They build understanding of the concept of regrouping as they combine ten ones to make one ten, ten tens to make one hundred, and so on.

1 ten = 10 ones

Play Money Students reinforce their understanding of regrouping by physically manipulating coins and bills to solve problems in Lesson 9. The concrete models help show regrouping when multiplying money amounts.

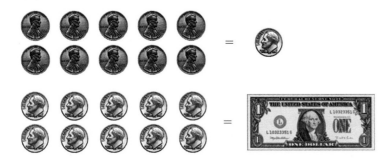

Suggested Materials	Alternatives
Place-value blocks	Grid paper
Play coins	Different-colored counters
Number cards	Cardboard squares with handwritten numbers
Number cubes	———
Play bills	Cardboard strips with dollar markings
2-color counters	Buttons, beans
Power Polygons	Cardboard shapes

Literature

The King's Commissioners

Aileen Friedman. New York: Scholastic, 1994.

Use with Lesson 5-4 A king asks for a count of all of his commissioners. The princess shows the king how to use arrays and multiplication to count quickly.

An Octopus is Amazing

Patricia Lauber. New York: Thomas Y. Crowell, 1990.

Use with Lesson 5-6 The number of suction cups on a tentacle and other interesting numerical data about these sea creatures provide opportunities to multiply.

The Story of Money

Betsy Maestro. New York: Clarion Books, 1993.

Use with Lesson 5-9 The process of printing money for the United States Treasury shows the use of arrays in real-life situations.

Additional Resources

Investigations in Number, Data, and Space: Arrays and Shares (Multiplication and Division), Karen Economopoulos, et al. Menlo Park, CA: Dale Seymour Publications.

Quest 2000: Exploring Mathematics, Grade 4, Randall Charles, et al. Menlo Park, CA: Addison-Wesley Publishing Company. *Unit 4.*

Number SENSE: Simple Effective Number Sense Experiences, Grade 3–4; Number SENSE: Simple Effective Number Sense Experiences, Grades 4–6, Alistair McIntosh, et al. Menlo Park, CA: Dale Seymour Publications.

ScottForesman ESL: Accelerating English Language Learning, Grade 4, Anna Uhl Chamot, et al. Glenview, IL: ScottForesman. *pp. 62–63.*

For the Teacher

 ### Teacher's Resource Planner CD-ROM

The Teacher's Resource Planner CD-ROM allows you to create customized lesson plans tailored to your own class's needs. It also allows you to preview any supplement page, edit if you wish, and print it.

 ### World Wide Web

Visit **www.teacher.mathsurf.com** for additional activities, links to lesson plans from teachers and other professionals, NCTM information, and other useful sites.

TestWorks Test and Practice Software

A database of questions allows you to generate personalized practice worksheets and tests.

For the Student

 ### Interactive CD-ROM

Use with Lessons 5-4 and 5-5 Students can use the Journal Tool in conjunction with the Place-Value Blocks Tool to illustrate examples of multiplication with arrays and 2-digit factors.

 ### World Wide Web

Use with Chapter Opener Have students go online at **www.mathsurf.com/4/ch5** to report on favorite sports activities.

 ### DataWonder!

Use with Technology: Comparing Costs Students use spreadsheet and calculation commands to record, graph, and figure the total cost of eyeball props for a drama club's play.

 ### Performance Math

Use daily throughout Chapter 5 Students can practice daily to increase their familiarity with basic multiplication facts.

Logical Journey of the Zoombinis

Use with Lessons 5-7 and 5-13 Students apply logical reasoning and analyze patterns as they play *Stone Rise* and *Pizza Pass.*

 ### Math Workshop

Use with Lesson 5-1 Students develop their multiplication skills by playing *Bowling for Numbers.*

 Calendar Time Kit

Calendar

One of the concepts in this chapter is multiplying 2-digit numbers. You may use the Calendar Time Kit to reinforce this concept with the following activity:

Use calendar dates to multiply by 1-digit factors.

- Each day, roll a number cube with the digits 1 through 6.
- If the calendar date is a 1-digit number, make it a multiple of 10 and then multiply it by the digit on the number cube. If the calendar date is already a 2-digit number, multiply it by the digit on the number cube.
- Discuss strategies and shortcuts for multiplying by different factors.
- Record the multiplication sentence for each day on the calendar. Ask students which products are possible for each date and whether the same products appear more than once. Have students explain any patterns they see.

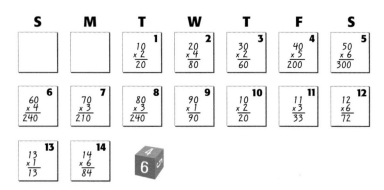

Technology Centers

Technology Helpers

Sometimes the best available technology resources are sitting right in your classroom.

- Choose a few technology-proficient students to be weekly "Technology Helpers." Group them with students who have less experience with computers. Make certain the helpers understand the difference between helping classmates and doing the work for them.
- In this chapter, students have an opportunity to use the Interactive CD-ROM Spreadsheet/Grapher Tool to create double-bar graphs of data they collect. Invite students to share any experiences they have had or graphs they have made using graphing software.

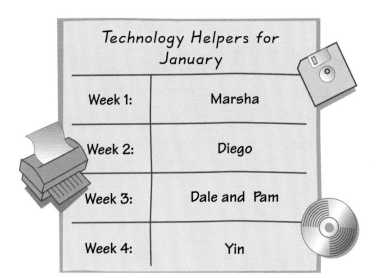

Bulletin Board

Objective Students multiply money and time to plan the costs and schedule for an after-school talent show.

Materials Colored paper, markers, poster board

- Organize students into four groups: schedule, props, publicity, tickets.
- Discuss how students can use multiplication to plan a talent show.
- Each group should create an example of their work to display: a schedule with individual and total running times, a prop list with projected costs, a flyer with photocopying costs, and a ticket with projected sales.

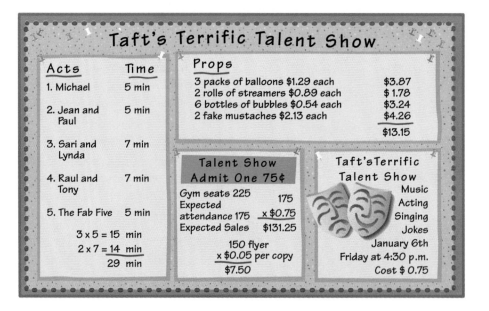

Traditional Assessment	
Review and Practice	Student Edition: pages 208, 222, 240
Cumulative Review	Student Edition: page 245; Assessment Sourcebook, Form F
Section Quizzes	Assessment Sourcebook: Section Quizzes A, B, C
Chapter Tests **Free Response** **Multiple Choice** **Mixed Response**	Student Edition: page 242; Assessment Sourcebook: Forms A and B Assessment Sourcebook: Form C Assessment Sourcebook: Form E

Alternative Assessment	
Ongoing Assessment	Teacher's Edition: every core lesson; Assessment Sourcebook: pages 11–13, 16–19, 21
Portfolio	Teacher's Edition: page 215; Assessment Sourcebook: pages 9, 13, 14, 16, 23
Interview and Observation	Teacher's Edition: pages 201, 205, 213, 219, 225, 229; Assessment Sourcebook: pages 18, 20
Journal	Student Edition: pages 201, 203, 207, 208, 213, 222, 229, 237, 240; Teacher's Edition: pages 217, 231; Assessment Sourcebook: pages 8–11, 15
Performance Assessment	Student Edition: page 243; Teacher's Edition: pages 203, 207; Assessment Sourcebook: Form D

NCTM Assessment Standards

Focus on Mathematics

Projects Assessment should reflect key and important mathematics. Projects and problem situations that have clear mathematical focus and direction are excellent tools for assessing understanding of important mathematics. The Chapter 5 Team Project appears on page 198.

Test Prep

- The Test Prep Strategy **Eliminate Choices: Estimate** is introduced and practiced in the Cumulative Review on page 245.
- Mixed Review and Test Prep occurs throughout this chapter.

TestWorks

TestWorks can create personalized multiple-choice tests, free-response tests, and practice worksheets.

Standardized-Test Correlation		ITBS	CTBS	CAT	SAT	MAT
Lesson/Objective		Form M	4th Ed.	5th Ed.	7th Ed.	9th Ed.
5-1	Multiply by multiples of ten.	●	●	●	●	●
5-2	Explore multiplication patterns.	●	●	●	●	●
5-3	Estimate products.	●	●	●	●	●
5-4	Explore multiplication with arrays.				●	
5-5	Multiply 2-digit numbers.	●	●	●	●	●
5-6	Multiply 3-digit numbers.	●	●	●	●	●
5-7	Solve problems by making decisions about cooking.	●	●	●	●	●
5-8	Multiply using different methods.	●	●	●	●	●
5-9	Multiply amounts of money.	●		●	●	●
5-10	Use mental math to multiply.					
5-11	Multiply when you have three factors.					
5-12	Solve multiple-step problems.	●	●	●	●	●
5-13	Solve problems by making a table.					

Key
ITBS Iowa Test of Basic Skills   **CTBS** Comprehensive Test of Basic Skills   **CAT** California Achievement Test
SAT Stanford Achievement Test   **MAT** Metropolitan Achievement Test

The Multiplication Solution Web

Task Students develop, apply, and describe strategies for solving multiplication problems.

Objective Explore how to multiply greater numbers by 1-digit factors.

Parallel Student Book Lessons Lessons 5-1 through 5-6, 5-10

Materials

butcher paper

colored markers

place-value blocks

counters or other small manipulatives

calculators

Teaching Tool Transparencies 5, 6, 9 (Number Lines, Centimeter Grid Paper, Hundred Chart)

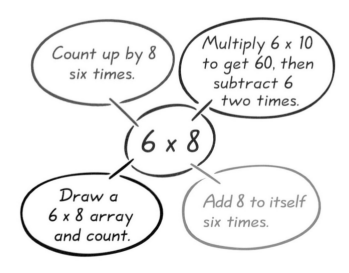

1 Introduce the Investigation

Conduct this investigation over a one- or two-week period. You may wish to have students solve and discuss problems as described below on a daily basis. Proceed to the Close and Assess activity when students are comfortable with various ways of multiplying greater numbers by 1-digit factors.

Find Multiplication Facts

1. Write 6×8 or a similar multiplication fact that most students haven't memorized on the chalkboard. Ask: What is the product? Wait until most hands are raised, then record the answers offered.

Share Multiplication Strategies

2. Ask: Who would like to explain his or her method? Encourage everyone to contribute to the discussion. If necessary, assure students that there is more than one way to multiply.

3. Create a word web outline of the explanations on the chalkboard as students speak. As each new idea arises, ask questions such as: Who thought of it the same way? Who has another way of thinking about 6×8? Continue until many methods have been represented on the chalkboard.

4. Repeat on subsequent days with other multiplication facts that most students haven't memorized. Encourage students having difficulty to try one of the methods described by their classmates.

② Investigate

Define the Task

5. Write 54×6 on the chalkboard. Ask students to solve it by any method they choose. Make manipulatives, calculators, and transparencies available to students.

Facilitate Discussion

6. Have students share their methods. Encourage students to question their classmates when they don't understand or agree with the method used. Be sure that one way of thinking is not valued over another.

Repeat with 3-Digit Factors; Mental Math

7. On subsequent days, you may wish to have students multiply 3-digit numbers by 1-digit factors or solve problems using mental math strategies.

Extend the Investigation

8. Present multiplication stories to the class. Have students work in small groups to discuss and find solutions.

Error Intervention Ongoing Assessment
Observation Students make calculations mistakes.
How to Help Remind students to check their answers by estimating the products.

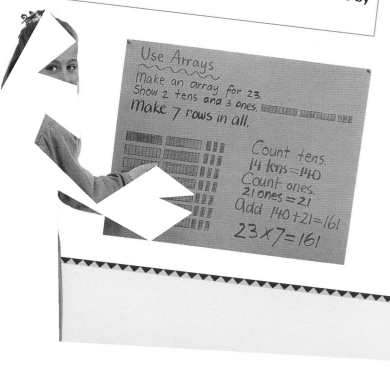

Use Arrays
Make an array for 23.
Show 2 tens and 3 ones.
Make 7 rows in all.

Count tens.
14 tens = 140
Count ones.
21 ones = 21
Add 140 + 21 = 161
$23 \times 7 = 161$

③ Close and Assess

Conclude the investigation and assess student learning with this poster activity:

Assign the class a problem such as 23×7. Have students discuss the various methods by which the problem could be solved. Tell students they will make a word web poster for the classroom. Each group can illustrate and explain one method that has been discussed during the course of the investigation. Encourage groups to make rough drafts before adding their contributions to the wall poster.

Ask questions such as the following as you observe students at work.

• Does your part of the web clearly show the multiplication method?

• Could a person look at your part of the web, follow the instructions given, and be sure that the answer is correct?

• Look at all the methods shown on the poster. Are there any more that should be included?

Assessment Rubric
4 Full Accomplishment • develops and applies strategies to solve multiplication problems • describes and shows strategies used in a clear and organized way
3 Substantial Accomplishment • applies strategies to solve multiplication problems • describes and shows strategies used
2 Partial Accomplishment • applies strategies to solve most multiplication problems • has some difficulty describing and showing strategies used
1 Little Accomplishment • does not apply strategies to solve multiplication problems • does not describe or show multiplication strategies

Multiplying by 1-Digit Factors

Theme: Time Out from School

Teacher Materials: *Optional* Lesson Enhancement Transparency 17

Introduce the Chapter

After-school activities offer meaningful contexts for multiplication. Chapter 5 begins by building multiplication sense through patterns. After learning the multiplication algorithm, students apply multiplication skills to solve money problems and multiple-step problems. Problem solving continues to be an emphasis, now focusing on the use of data presented in tables.

Activate Prior Knowledge

Brainstorm a list of students' favorite after-school activities.

- Is there a class favorite? Discuss ways that you might show that information.

Use the Data File

You may wish to use Lesson Enhancement Transparency 17 along with the following questions to discuss the Data File.

- How is the data represented? Double-bar graph, table, list

- Use the graph to name countries that shipped beads to Ghana in the 1970s. Italy, Czechoslovakia, France, Germany, African countries, and other European countries

- Tell whether 10 minutes of jumping rope is as healthy as 10 minutes of jogging or 30 minutes spent skiing. Ratings are the same, so all activities are equally healthy.

- Use the recipe for Meatless Pemmican to figure out how many people could be served with 3 times the recipe amounts. 36

Chapter 5
Multiplying by 1-Digit Factors

SECTION A

TIME OUT FROM School

Multiplication Number Sense

Stringing beads is a colorful pastime. It was so popular in Ghana that tons of beads were imported there until the 1970s! Just where did all the beads come from? Take a look.

Shipments of Beads to Ghana, West Africa

(bar graph, Country or Region vs. metric tons 0–35)
Italy, Czechoslovakia, France, Germany, African Countries, Other European Countries

■ 1931 Metric Tons
■ 1936 Metric Tons

Extensions

⬤ Career Connection

Have students discuss favorite recipes that they can make themselves. Conduct a class survey to find the class's five favorite snacks. Make a bar graph of the results in which each segment represents a snack. Have students use skip counting or multiplication facts to describe the results.

Then ask students what kind of mathematics chefs and other food workers would need to use.

⬤ Performance Math: Multiplication

To help students prepare to multiply with greater numbers, have them review basic multiplication facts daily throughout the chapter using *Performance Math*. Each session lasts about 10 minutes. If possible, set up a classroom computer work station that students can use throughout the day.

Multiplying 209

Is jumping rope for 10 minutes as good for you as jogging for 10 minutes or skiing for 30 minutes? Explain.

Surfing the World Wide Web!

Do you have a favorite sports activity? Find out how your choice compares with those of other students around the country. Walk, jog, swim, or ski over to **www.mathsurf.com/4/ch5.**

SECTION
C

Use the data you find to report the top three sports activities preferred by other students in your grade.

Extending Multiplication 223

Some students cook up a storm when school gets out. Here's a recipe for a high-energy snack. How many friends could you serve if you made 3 times the recipe amount?

Meatless Pemmican
(Serves 12)

8 tbsp raisins 8 tbsp dried apples 8 tbsp dry cornmeal
8 tbsp peanuts 8 tbsp dried pumpkin 6 tbsp honey
8 tbsp hickory nuts

Chop up the raisins, nuts, dried apples, and dried pumpkin. Combine all of these ingredients in a bowl. Stir in the cornmeal. Add the honey, and blend completely. Press a large spoonful of the mixture to form a small cake. Repeat until you have used all of the mixture.

Preview the Sections

A Multiplication Number Sense

Students will identify patterns in multiplying multiples of 10, 100, and 1,000 and use them to estimate products. They will also use arrays to show multiplication.

B Multiplying

Students will learn the algorithm for multiplying by a 1-digit number and choose appropriate methods for multiplying.

C Extending Multiplication

Students will learn mental math strategies, multiply 3 factors, and apply multiplication skills to money problems and multiple-step problems.

Math in the Community

School-Community Connection

Create an After-School Club Have students create after-school clubs based on their interests. Group students by interest to research community locations and resources.

Students can use multiplication skills to report information such as cost per club member for dues, cost of club supplies, and so on.

Community Project The Chapter 5 community project is available in *Home and Community Connections.*

Home-School Connection

Master Those Multiples Ask students to find examples of multiples at home. Practice by searching the classroom for multiples such as:

- the array of desks in rows
- days and weeks on the calendar

Ask them for examples of multiples they might find at home, for example:

- arrangements of floor tiles
- shelves of dishes in the kitchen
- stairs leading to the top floor

Parents can use the Web site at **www.parent.mathsurf.com**.

At the end of this chapter, you may wish to distribute the Letter Home from *Home and Community Connections.*

Pinwheel Energy

Students will create a pinwheel and determine ways to calculate the revolutions per minute (RPMs).

Student Materials 10-inch paper squares, scissors, rulers, markers or crayons, clocks or watches with second hands, unsharpened pencils, thumbtacks, *optional Assessment Sourcebook 10* (How We Worked in Our Group)

Vocabulary RPMs (revolutions per minute)

Introduce the Project

Have students describe what they know about windmills. Windmills may have originated in Iran as early as A.D. 600. Picturesque windmills in the Netherlands were used to grind wheat and even crush stone. Today similar windmills are used to produce electricity in California and other states. Point out that a pinwheel is a model of the wheel portion of a windmill.

Preview the self-assessment checklist below. Invite students to help set the standard for their work.

Self-Assessment Checklist

__ Construct a working pinwheel

__ Accurately collect and record data

__ Clearly and accurately report the process and results

Complete the Project

Discuss the class data. Have students average the group results to find a class RPM number.

ANSWERS

Possible Answers for Talk About It

• It's hard to blow steadily. It's impossible to blow continuously for 1 minute.

• Practice blowing steadily; Measure for 10 sec and multiply by 6.

Possible Answers for Present the Project

• A range of 42 to 48 RPMs is reasonable.

• Used measurement to make pinwheel. Used counting to find number of turns.

• Multiplied to find the number of turns per minute.

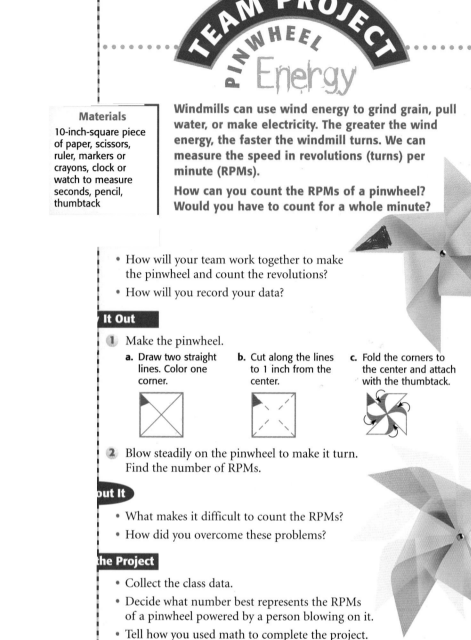

TEAM PROJECT — PINWHEEL Energy

Materials
10-inch-square piece of paper, scissors, ruler, markers or crayons, clock or watch to measure seconds, pencil, thumbtack

Windmills can use wind energy to grind grain, pull water, or make electricity. The greater the wind energy, the faster the windmill turns. We can measure the speed in revolutions (turns) per minute (RPMs).

How can you count the RPMs of a pinwheel? Would you have to count for a whole minute?

• How will your team work together to make the pinwheel and count the revolutions?
• How will you record your data?

Try It Out

1. Make the pinwheel.

   a. Draw two straight lines. Color one corner.

   b. Cut along the lines to 1 inch from the center.

   c. Fold the corners to the center and attach with the thumbtack.

2. Blow steadily on the pinwheel to make it turn. Find the number of RPMs.

Talk About It

• What makes it difficult to count the RPMs?
• How did you overcome these problems?

Present the Project

• Collect the class data.
• Decide what number best represents the RPMs of a pinwheel powered by a person blowing on it.
• Tell how you used math to complete the project.

Science Connection

While wind continues to be used as an energy source, the design of windmills has changed. One type of modern windmill, or wind turbine, has two long blades that look like propellers on a helicopter. It can produce 2 megawatts of electricity in a moderate wind.

• Have students work in small groups to find out more information on two types of windmills, one historical and one modern. Ask them to find the average number of revolutions per minute for each type of windmill.

Cooperative Learning

Suggest that team members take the following roles as they work:

• draftsperson—draws and colors
• engineer/timekeeper—assembles pinwheel, watches time
• recorder—counts revolutions, records results
• reporter—reports results

Distribute *Assessment Sourcebook 10* (How We Worked in Our Group) and have students fill it out for the skill Encourage and Respect Others. Review the characteristics of this skill. Invite students to judge themselves on the skill as they work together.

Multiplication Number Sense

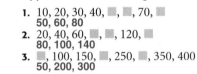

Using Patterns to Multiply

 Review multiples of 10. Look for patterns. Copy and write the missing numbers.

1. 10, 20, 30, 40, ■, ■, 70, ■
   50, 60, 80
2. 20, 40, 60, ■, ■, 120, ■
   80, 100, 140
3. ■, 100, 150, ■, 250, ■, 350, 400
   50, 200, 300

Skills Checklist

In this section, you will:
- ☐ Multiply Tens
- ☐ Explore Multiplication Patterns
- ☐ Estimate Products
- ☐ Explore Multiplication with Arrays

199

Multiplication Number Sense

In this section, students will multiply by tens, hundreds, and thousands; estimate products; and use arrays to learn the partial-product algorithm.

Subskills

The work in this section builds on…
- Using multiplication facts
- Place-value patterns
  40, 400, 4,000
- Rounding to the nearest 10 and 100

Use the Section Opener

When Davida was in seventh grade, she began producing a fashion line at her home in Philadelphia, Pennsylvania. The hat she created has 4,000 sequins.

Encourage students to discuss how they might use patterns, addition, estimation, and multiplication to count the sequins on Davida's jacket. Possible answer: Use estimation. Find out how many sequins are in a small section, estimate total number of sections, and find out how many are in all the sections.

Skills Trace

(Red numbers indicate pages in this section.)

Lesson and Skill	First Introduced	Grade Four			
		Introduce	Develop	Practice/Apply	Review
5-1 Multiply by multiples of ten.	Grade 3	200, 201	200	201, 208, 241, 242	208, 241, 242
5-2 Explore multiplication patterns.	Grade 3	202, 203	202, 203	203, 208, 241, 242	208, 241, 242
5-3 Estimate products.	Grade 3	204, 205	204	205, 208, 226–227, 241, 242	208, 241, 242, 245
5-4 Explore multiplication with arrays.	Grade 3	206, 207	206, 207	207, 208, 241, 242	208, 241, 242

Mixed Review and Test Prep exercises for this chapter occur on pages 201, 205, 213, 215, 219, 225, 229, 231, 237.

Multi-Age Classrooms Use pages 356–371 in Grade 3 or pages 111–132 in Grade 5 to relate to the content of this section.

At-A-Glance Planning

Lesson Planning Checklist

Objective Multiply by multiples of ten.

Student Book Lesson Materials *Optional* Teaching Tool Transparency 3 (9-Digit Place-Value Chart)

Materials for pages 200A and 200B Place-value blocks (40 tens, 40 ones per group) Teaching Tool Transparencies 3, 7 (9-Digit Place-Value Chart, $\frac{1}{4}$-Inch Grid Paper), play money (10 dimes and 100 pennies per pair), number cards 1–9 (1 set per pair)

Subject Connections recreation—cricket, science—tadpoles

Strand Connection time

	Before Lesson	During Lesson	After Lesson
Daily Math			
p. 200A Problem of the Day			
p. 200A Math Routines			
p. 200A Mental Math			
Teaching Options			
p. 200 Student Book Lesson			
p. 200B Another Way to Learn…			
Options for Reaching All Learners			
p. 200B Inclusion			
p. 200B Language Development			
Technology Options			
p. 200A *Math Workshop*			
Assessment Options			
p. 200 Talk About It			
p. 201 Error Intervention			
p. 201 Interview			
p. 201 Quick Check			
Resources			
5-1 Practice			
5-1 Reteaching			
5-1 Enrichment			
5-1 Problem Solving			
5-1 Daily Transparency			

Problem of the Day

Problem of the Day

It takes a lumberjack six minutes to cut a log into 3 pieces. How long will it take to cut a log into 4 pieces? Explain.

9 minutes. To cut a log into 3 pieces, 2 cuts are made; $6 \div 2 = 3$. Each cut takes 3 minutes; $3 \times 3 = 9$.

Math Routines

Time Have students tell how many minutes are in 1 hour, 10 hours, 100 hours. 60 min, 600 min, 6,000 min

Money Have students count

a. by 10-cent intervals to $1.00.

b. by 10-cent intervals from $1.50 to $2.50.

Mental Math

Find each sum. Explain your thinking.

30 + 60 90	70 + 110 180
200 + 600 800	800 + 400 1,200

 ## Math Workshop

Students can play *Bowling for Numbers* to develop their multiplication skills. Students answer multiple-choice questions based on multiplication. Ten correct answers earn each student a strike. Players can track their progress at the Hall of Fame and print out certificates of their achievements.

Another Way to **Learn** Lesson 5-1

Use as an alternative or in addition to pages 200 and 201.

Materials Place-value blocks (40 tens, 40 ones per group), Teaching Tool Transparency 3 (9-digit Place-Value Chart)

Learning Style Kinesthetic

- Share Level 4 of the Assessment Rubric with students before they begin their work.

- Have groups use place-value blocks to show 3 equal groups of 6 and 3 equal groups of 60 and find how many in all for each set of groups. 18; 180

- Have students compare and contrast the models.

- Use the overhead place-value chart to model the problems. Draw models of the blocks and write a multiplication sentence for each model.

$3 \times 6 = 18$ $3 \times 60 = 180$

- Have groups draw pictures and write multiplication sentences for the following:
  3 equal groups of 9 $3 \times 9 = 27$
  2 equal groups of 5 $2 \times 5 = 10$
  3 equal groups of 90 $3 \times 90 = 270$
  2 equal groups of 50 $2 \times 50 = 100$

- Assign Check and Practice on Student Book page 201 or *Practice Master 5-1.*

- Assess using the following rubric.

Assessment Rubric
4 **Full Accomplishment** • multiplies by multiples of 10 correctly
3 **Substantial Accomplishment** • multiplies by most multiples of 10 correctly
2 **Partial Accomplishment** • multiplies by some multiples of 10 correctly
1 **Little Accomplishment** • does not multiply by multiples of 10 correctly

Options for Reaching All Learners

Inclusion

Multiple Coins

Use play money and role-play to strengthen understanding of multiplying multiples of 10.

Materials Play money (10 dimes and 100 pennies per pair), number cards 1–9 (1 set per pair)

Learning Style Kinesthetic, Visual

- Have pairs of students role-play dimes and pennies. Have the "dime" choose two number cards, such as 5 and 2. The "dime" displays 5 groups of 2 dimes and says "5 groups of 2 dimes." The "penny" displays 5 groups of 20 pennies and says: "5 groups of 20 pennies."

- Together they display and say: "5 groups of 2 dimes equals 5 groups of 20 pennies"; "10 dimes equal 100 pennies; 10 tens equal 100 ones."

Language Development

Multiple Multiples

Use 1-by-10 strips of grid paper to strengthen language related to multiplying multiples of 10.

Materials Teaching Tool Transparency 7 ($\frac{1}{4}$-Inch Grid Paper)

Learning Style Visual

- Cut grid paper into 1-by-10 strips.

- Model 20 ones as 2 groups of 10. Encourage students to describe the model in a variety of ways: 20 is a *multiple* of 10, 20 *ones* equal 2 *tens.*

- Then model 5 groups of 2 tens. Encourage students to describe the model in a variety of ways: a *multiple* of 10, 5 *groups* of 2 *tens,* 5 *groups* of 20, and, finally, 100.

- Have groups use grid paper to model first a multiple of 10 and then a number of groups of that multiple.

Lesson Organizer

Objective Multiply by multiples of ten.

Student Materials None

Teacher Materials *Optional* Teaching Tool Transparency 3 (9-Digit Place-Value Chart)

Assignment Guide

Basic 5–17, 22–33

Average 7–18, 20, 22–33

Enriched 7, 10–33

1 Introduce

Review

Find each product.

1. 6 × 1 6 **2.** 2 × 3 6

3. 5 × 7 35 **4.** 8 × 9 72

Build on Prior Knowledge

After students review some basic multiplication facts, ask how 2 × 30 is different from 2 × 3. Possible answer: 2 × 30 is 2 × 3 tens, instead of 2 × 3 ones.

2 Teach

See Another Way to Learn...on page 200B.

Learn ◦

Have students explain how the multiplication sentence in the example is related to the labels and tens blocks pictured. There are 5 equal groups of 20.

Use Teaching Tool Transparency 3 (9-Digit Place-Value Chart) for demonstration, if desired.

Talk About It **Ongoing Assessment**

Encourage students to think of situations in which they put things into equal groups of multiples of 10 to find the total amount.

Answer for Talk About It

It is easier and quicker to count by 20.

You Will Learn
how to multiply by multiples of ten

Remember
10, 20, 30, 40, and 50 are multiples of ten.

Multiplying Tens

Learn ◦

The principal announced, "If the school collects enough labels for a new computer, I'll kiss a frog!"

Julie and some friends formed a team to collect soup labels. How many labels did her team collect?

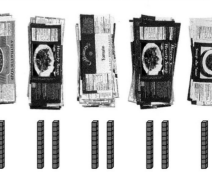

Here is one way Julie can count the labels her team collected.

Julie stacks her labels in 5 groups of 20.

She counts: 20 40 60 80 100

5 groups of 20 labels
5×2 tens = 10 tens
$5 \times 20 = 100$

So, Julie's team has collected 100 labels.

Talk About It

Why is it helpful to put things into equal groups of 20?

Practice 5-1	Reteaching 5-1

Check

Use a multiplication fact to help you find each product.

1. 4×2 tens = ■ tens
   $4 \times 20 =$ ■
   8 tens; 80

2. 5×3 tens = ■ tens
   $5 \times 30 =$ ■
   15 tens; 150

3. 5×4 tens = ■ tens
   $5 \times 40 =$ ■
   20 tens; 200

4. **Reasoning** How are your answers to **1–3** alike?
   All end in zero; They are multiples of 10.

Practice

Skills and Reasoning

Use a multiplication fact to help you find each product.

5. 3×1 ten = ■ tens
   $3 \times 10 =$ ■
   3 tens; 30

6. 3×5 tens = ■ tens
   $3 \times 50 =$ ■
   15 tens; 150

7. 4×9 tens = ■ tens
   $4 \times 90 =$ ■
   36 tens; 360

8. 2×30 **60**   9. 7×10 **70**   10. 4×80 **320**   11. 7×50 **350**   12. 5×60 **300**

13. 5×20 **100**   14. 8×20 **160**   15. 6×60 **360**   16. 9×50 **450**   17. 4×70 **280**

18. Can you use the same multiplication fact to find 6×40 and 4×60? Explain. **Yes; 6×4 is the same as 4×6.**

Problem Solving and Applications

19. One team collected 4 stacks of 10 labels each. Another team collected 8 stacks of 50 labels each. Julie's team collected 120 labels. In all, how many labels did these three teams collect? **560 labels**

20. **Recreation** Cricket is a popular ball game in England. If Eric's team scored 60 runs on each day of a 3-day cricket match, how many runs did his team score in all? **180 runs**

21. **Science** Tadpoles hatch from frogs' eggs. It takes a tadpole about 12 weeks to become a frog and leave the water. About how many days does it take for the tadpole to become a frog? **About 84 days**

22. **Journal** Explain why 10 is a multiple of 10.

Mixed Review and Test Prep

STAY SHARP!

Find each sum or difference.

23. $52 + 14$ **66**   24. $67 + 39$ **106**   25. $131 + 92$ **223**   26. $209 + 71$ **280**   27. $1,423 + 384$ **1,807**

28. $37 - 19$ **18**   29. $58 - 39$ **19**   30. $112 - 23$ **89**   31. $75 - 48$ **27**   32. $317 - 154$ **163**

33. Find $7,008 - 4,319$. **D**
   Ⓐ 2,391   Ⓑ 11,327   Ⓒ 3,317   Ⓓ not here

Lesson 5-1   **201**

Check

Exercise 3 Be sure students understand why there are two zeros in the product of 5×40.

Error Intervention Ongoing Assessment

Observation Students may not write the correct numbers of zeros in the products.

How to Help Have students use colored pencils to circle the digits in the multiplication facts. Students should circle all multiplication facts with the same color.

③ × ⑤0 = ⑮0   ⑥ × ⑤0 = ③00

Practice

Exercise 19 Students must find two products and then add three amounts.

Exercise 22 If students have difficulty, have them list the factors of 10 (1, 2, 5, 10).

For Early Finishers Challenge early finishers to look at Exercise 19 and write a number sentence to describe a way Julie could have put her 120 labels into equal groups of a multiple of 10. Possible answers: $12 \times 10 = 120$; $6 \times 20 = 120$; $3 \times 40 = 120$

③ Close and Assess

Interview

Have students choose one problem from Exercises 8–12 and explain or demonstrate how they solved it. Answers should include use of a basic multiplication fact to help multiply a multiple of 10.

Quick Check

Number Sense Decide which Skill exercises below have products less than 100. Explain. Exercises 1 and 3, because the related multiplication fact has a product less than 10

Skill Find each product.

1. 8×10 **80**   2. 6×50 **300**

3. 3×30 **90**   4. 7×60 **420**

ANSWERS

22 Possible answer: $1 \times 10 = 10$

Enrichment 5-1

Name _____   Extend Your Thinking 5-1

Critical Thinking

Mr. Jones had 10 chickens on his farm. Each chicken lays an average of 1 egg a day.

1. Finish the table recording the number of eggs laid in a week on Mr. Jones' farm.

Days	1	2	3	4	5	6	7
Eggs	10	20	30	40	50	60	70

Answer the questions using your data.

2. How many eggs did Mr. Jones collect after 4 days? __**40 eggs**__

3. Estimate the number of eggs Mr. Jones will collect in two weeks. Explain your reasoning.
   140 eggs; He collected 10 eggs a day. 14 tens is 140.

4. If he sells half the eggs each day, how many eggs would he have left on the third day? Explain.
   15 eggs; Half of 30 is 15. 5 eggs × 3 days = 15 eggs

5. Suppose Mr. Jones adds 10 more chickens to his flock.
   a. How many eggs will he collect in a week? Explain.
   140 eggs. 20 eggs × 7 days = 140 eggs

   b. Why is the number of eggs collected in one week the same as the answer to 3?
   Possible answer: 10 chickens lay the same number of eggs in 14 days as 20 chickens lay in 7 days.
   $10 \times 14 = 140$; $20 \times 7 = 140$

Problem Solving 5-1

Name _____   Problem Solving 5-1

Multiplying Tens

Careers Professional photographers take many pictures of events. Then they select the best pictures to sell.

1. Karen used 7 rolls of film to photograph the school's sports events. Each roll has 40 exposures. How many pictures did she take?
   280 pictures

2. Karen can develop 6 pictures an hour. If she works 40 hours a week, how many pictures can she develop?
   $6 \times 40 = 240$

3. The best pictures will go in the school's photo album. The album has 20 pages. Each page in the album holds 8 pictures. How many pictures will the album hold in all?
   $8 \times 20 = 160$ pictures

4. We drove to the Olympic games in 4 hours. Our speed averaged 60 miles per hour. We traveled another 3 hours at the same speed to visit a Civil War site.
   a. How many miles did we travel to the Olympic games? **240 miles**
   b. How many miles did we travel from there to the Civil War site? **180 miles**
   c. We drove home from the Civil War site in 5 hours at 60 miles per hour. How many miles did we travel on the entire trip?
   $300 + 240 + 180 = 720$ miles
   d. Our car gets 20 miles to the gallon. If we bought 20 gallons twice on our journey, would we have enough for the whole trip?
   Yes; $(20 \times 2) \times 20 = 800$

Chapter 5 • Lesson 5-1   **201**

Exploring Multiplication Patterns

At-A-Glance Planning

Lesson Planning Checklist

Objective Explore multiplication patterns.

Student Book Lesson Materials Calculators, *optional Assessment Sourcebook 10* (How We Worked in Our Group), place-value blocks (12 hundreds, 12 tens, 12 ones)

Materials for pages 202A and 202B Place-value blocks (10 hundreds, 10 tens, 10 ones per group)

Strand Connections patterns, algebra readiness, mental math

	Before Lesson	During Lesson	After Lesson
Daily Math			
p. 202A Problem of the Day			
p. 202A Math Routines			
p. 202A Mental Math			
Teaching Options			
p. 202B Facilitating and Assessing…			
Options for Reaching All Learners			
p. 202B Inclusion			
p. 202B Language Development			
Technology Options			
p. 203 Interactive CD-ROM Journal			
Subject Connections			
p. 202A Physical Education Connection			
Assessment Options			
p. 202 Talk About It			
p. 203 Error Intervention			
p. 203 Performance Assessment			
Resources			
5-2 Practice			
5-2 Reteaching			
5-2 Enrichment			
5-2 Problem Solving			
5-2 Daily Transparency			

Problem of the Day

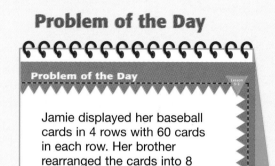

Problem of the Day

Jamie displayed her baseball cards in 4 rows with 60 cards in each row. Her brother rearranged the cards into 8 equal rows. How many cards are in each row?

30 cards

Math Routines

Patterns Tell students that a tadpole has a mass of 4 grams. Ask what would be the mass of 10 tadpoles, 100 tadpoles, and 1,000 tadpoles. 40 g; 400 g; 4,000 g

Money Ask students to name $1.20, $1.50, $2.50, and $3.50 as numbers of dimes. 12 dimes, 15 dimes, 25 dimes, 35 dimes

Mental Math

Find each sum. Explain your thinking.

20 + 20 + 20 + 20 + 20 100

50 + 50 + 50 150

200 + 200 + 200 600

Physical Education Connection

Some sports events are relays. Four people on a team each run or swim the same distance. Have students find the total distance of each event given these individual distances.

- track relay: 100 m 400 m
- track relay: 400 m 1,600 m
- freestyle swimming relay: 200 m 800 m

Facilitating and Assessing Explore Lesson 5-2

Use with pages 202 and 203.

Get Started You may wish to assign students the roles of reader, calculator user, and recorder, as well as the group skill Check for Understanding for students to practice.

Observe Students may want to use a calculator to complete all the multiplication sentences. At this exploration stage, you may prefer that they use calculators only to complete Work Together Exercise 1.

For later exercises, have students look for a pattern in the number sentences, try using the pattern, and finally use a calculator to check whether they correctly identified and applied the pattern.

Discuss As students discuss the patterns in related multiplication sentences, direct their focus to patterns that will help them complete similar sentences.

Some students may recognize that each product in a set of sentences has one more zero than the previous product. This alone is not helpful for completing a multiplication sentence. The relationship between factors and the product must also be recognized.

Assess Use the rubric to assess students' work. See sample for Practice Exercise 1.

---

4 Full Accomplishment

$$4 \times 7 = 28$$
$$4 \times 70 = 280$$
$$4 \times 700 = 2,800$$

Assessment Rubric

4 Full Accomplishment
- uses mental math to find multiplication patterns

3 Substantial Accomplishment
- with prompting, uses mental math to find most multiplication patterns

2 Partial Accomplishment
- uses mental math to find some multiplication patterns

1 Little Accomplishment
- does not use mental math to find multiplication patterns

Options for Reaching All Learners

Inclusion

Recognizing Patterns
Use place-value blocks to identify patterns.

Materials Place-value blocks (10 hundreds, 10 tens, 10 ones per group)

Learning Style Kinesthetic

- Have students use place-value blocks to model 3×2, 3×20, and 3×200. For each model, have students record the multiplication sentence.

- Have students talk about what is the same for all three models and all three sentences and what is different. Make sure students recognize the importance of place value in their sentences. They should note that the product is ones, tens, or hundreds, according to the factors in the sentence.

- Have students repeat for other sets of related multiplication expressions.

Language Development

5-Step Relays
Use a flow chart to reinforce language used for multiplying.

Learning Style Visual, Logical

- Draw the flow chart shown and group students into teams of 5.

- Write several multiplication expressions on the chalkboard (one per team). Call out each step and have a team member perform it at the chalkboard.

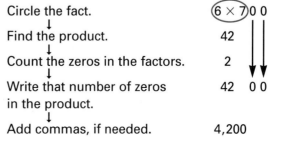

Circle the fact.	6×700
Find the product.	42
Count the zeros in the factors.	2
Write that number of zeros in the product.	42 0 0
Add commas, if needed.	4,200

Lesson Organizer

Objective Explore multiplication patterns.

Suggested Grouping 2 to 4

Student Materials Calculators, *optional* Assessment Sourcebook 10 (How We Worked in Our Group)

Teacher Materials Place-value blocks (12 hundreds, 12 tens, 12 ones)

Assignment Guide
Basic 1–9, 15–17, 20, 22
Average 1–4, 15–22
Enriched 1, 10–22

1 Introduce

Review 📠

Find each product.

1. 1 × 90 90   **2.** 3 × 70 210

3. 7 × 40 280   **4.** 6 × 90 540

Build on Prior Knowledge

After students review multiplying a multiple of 10, ask how they could find 6 × 900.
Multiply 6 × 9 hundreds. Accept all reasonable answers.

2 Teach

See Facilitating and Assessing…on page 202B.

Explore •

Be sure students understand that the products in Exercises 2a and 2b have one more zero than the factors because the multiplication facts have a zero in them.

Talk About It ⟩ Ongoing Assessment

Listen for students' explanations to focus on using multiplication facts and the relationship between the place values and zeros in one factor and the product.

Answers for Talk About It

3 The product has the same number of zeros as the number of zeros in the factor with zeros and the basic fact product.

4 Find 5 × 4 and put 2 zeros at the end.
5 × 400 = 2,000

5 Find 7 × 6 and put 3 zeros at the end.
7 × 6,000 = 42,000

Exploring Multiplication Patterns

Problem Solving Connection
Look for a Pattern

Explore •

Place value and patterns can help you multiply.

Materials
calculator

Math Tip
Think about using basic facts.

Work Together

1. Use a calculator to find each product. Look for patterns.

   a. 6 × 40 = n 240   **b.** 5 × 30 = n 150   **c.** 2 × 70 = n 140
   6 × 400 = n 2,400   5 × 300 = n 1,500   2 × 700 = n 1,400
   6 × 4,000 = n 24,000   5 × 3,000 = n 15,000   2 × 7,000 = n 14,000

2. Use patterns to find each product. Then check your answers with a calculator.

   a. 5 × 60 = n 300   **b.** 2 × 50 = n 100   **c.** 8 × 700 = n 5,600
   5 × 600 = n 3,000   2 × 500 = n 1,000   8 × 7,000 = n 56,000
   5 × 6,000 = n 30,000   2 × 5,000 = n 10,000   8 × 70,000 = n 560,00

   d. 4 × 80 = n 320   **e.** 7 × 60 = n 420   **f.** 3 × 90 = n 270
   4 × 800 = n 3,200   7 × 600 = n 4,200   3 × 900 = n 2,700
   4 × 8,000 = n 32,000; 7 × 6,000 = n 42,000   3 × 9,000 = n 27,000
   4 × 80,000 = n 320,0007 × 60,000 = n 420,0003 × 90,000 = n 270,00

Talk About It

3. Describe the patterns you found.

4. Explain how you can find 5 × 400 mentally.

5. If you know the product of 7 × 6, how can you find the product of 7 and 6,000?

Practice 5-2

Name _____   **Practice 5-2** ∇

Exploring Multiplication Patterns
Use patterns to find each product.

1. 2 × 3 ones = __6__ ones or __6__

2. 2 × 3 tens = __6__ tens or __60__

3. 2 × 3 hundreds = __6__ hundreds or __600__

4. 2 × 3 thousands = __6__ thousands or __6,000__

5. 3 × 6 = __18__
   3 × __60__ = 180
   __3__ × 600 = 1,800

6. 7 × 4 = __28__
   __7__ × 40 = 280
   7 × __400__ = 2,800

7. 4 × 9 = __36__
   4 × __90__ = 360
   __4__ × 900 = 3,600

8. 5 × 6 = __30__
   __5__ × 60 = 300
   5 × __600__ = 3,000

Find each product.

9. 6 × 50 = __300__

10. 7 × 4,000 = __28,000__

11. 9 × 300 = __2,700__

12. 2 × 3,000 = __6,000__

13. 3 × 800 = __2,400__

14. 8 × 80 = __640__

15. 5 × 700 = __3,500__

16. 4 × 60 = __240__

17. 6 × 7,000 = __42,000__

18. 5 × 70 = __350__

19. If you know that the product of 8 and 90 is 720 how can you find the product of 8 and 9,000? Explain.

   Possible answer: Add two more zeros to the right of 720;
   8 × 9,000 = 72,000.

20. Explain why you get 3 zeros when you multiply 8 × 9,000 and 4 zeros when you multiply 8 × 5,000.

   Possible answer: The basic fact 8 × 5 = 40 has a zero
   in the product.

Reteaching 5-2

Name _____   **Another Look 5-2** ∇

Exploring Multiplication Patterns
In your book you multiplied using patterns. Here is another way to multiply.

4 × 4 ones = 4 × 4 = 16   4 × 4 tens = 4 × 40 = 160

So, 4 × 4 hundreds = 4 × 400 = 1,600

Complete each multiplication sentence. Think of place-value blocks and look for patterns.

1. 5 × 5 = 25
   5 × 5 tens = __250__
   5 × 5 hundreds = 2,500

2. 4 × 3 = __12__
   4 × 3 tens = 120
   4 × 3 hundreds = 1,200

Use patterns to complete each multiplication sentence.

3. 4 × 80 = __320__
   __4__ × 800 = 3,200
   4 × __8,000__ = 32,000
   4 × __80,000__ = 320,000

4. 3 × __50__ = 150
   3 × 500 = __1,500__
   3 × __5,000__ = 15,000
   3 × __50,000__ = 150,000

Find each product.

5. 6 × 400 = __2,400__

6. 3 × 200 = __600__

7. 5 × 700 = __3,500__

8. 8 × 2,000 = __16,000__

9. 4 × 3,000 = __12,000__

10. 6 × 5,000 = __30,000__

Connect

Place-value patterns and mental math can help you find $3 \times 4,000$.

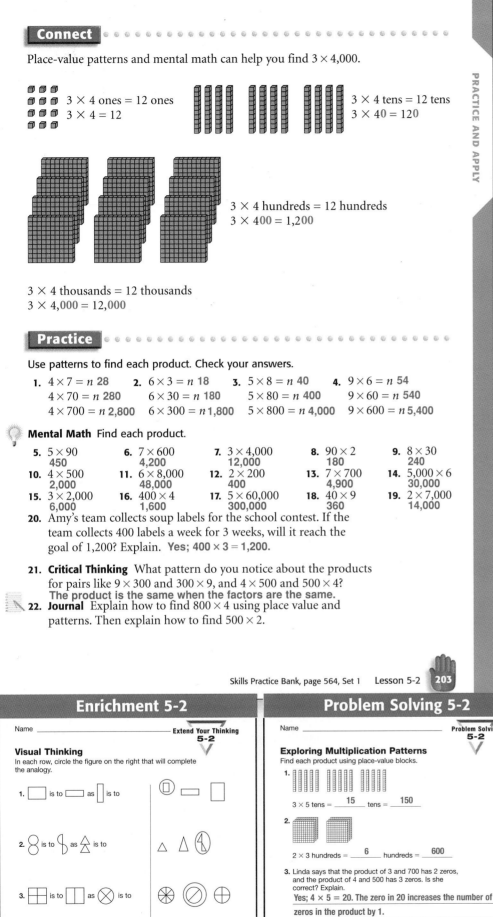

3×4 ones $= 12$ ones
$3 \times 4 = 12$

3×4 tens $= 12$ tens
$3 \times 40 = 120$

3×4 hundreds $= 12$ hundreds
$3 \times 400 = 1,200$

3×4 thousands $= 12$ thousands
$3 \times 4,000 = 12,000$

Practice

Use patterns to find each product. Check your answers.

1. $4 \times 7 = n$ 28
   $4 \times 70 = n$ 280
   $4 \times 700 = n$ 2,800

2. $6 \times 3 = n$ 18
   $6 \times 30 = n$ 180
   $6 \times 300 = n$ 1,800

3. $5 \times 8 = n$ 40
   $5 \times 80 = n$ 400
   $5 \times 800 = n$ 4,000

4. $9 \times 6 = n$ 54
   $9 \times 60 = n$ 540
   $9 \times 600 = n$ 5,400

Mental Math Find each product.

5. 5×90
   450

6. 7×600
   4,200

7. $3 \times 4,000$
   12,000

8. 90×2
   180

9. 8×30
   240

10. 4×500
    2,000

11. $6 \times 8,000$
    48,000

12. 2×200
    400

13. 7×700
    4,900

14. $5,000 \times 6$
    30,000

15. $3 \times 2,000$
    6,000

16. 400×4
    1,600

17. $5 \times 60,000$
    300,000

18. 40×9
    360

19. $2 \times 7,000$
    14,000

20. Amy's team collects soup labels for the school contest. If the team collects 400 labels a week for 3 weeks, will it reach the goal of 1,200? Explain. **Yes; $400 \times 3 = 1,200$.**

21. **Critical Thinking** What pattern do you notice about the products for pairs like 9×300 and 300×9, and 4×500 and 500×4? **The product is the same when the factors are the same.**

22. **Journal** Explain how to find 800×4 using place value and patterns. Then explain how to find 500×2.

Skills Practice Bank, page 564, Set 1   Lesson 5-2   **203**

Connect

Use place-value blocks on the overhead to model 3×4, 3×40, and 3×400.

Error Intervention Ongoing Assessment

Observation Students may have difficulty recognizing the connection between the zeros in the factor and the zeros in the product.

How to Help Have students find the basic multiplication product first. Then have them find the number of zeros needed in the product and write the same number of zeros to the right of the basic fact product. Check their understanding by asking them how writing zeros to the right of the product affects the place value of the product.

Practice

Exercise 21 These pairs are examples of the Commutative Property.

Interactive CD-ROM Journal Students can use the Journal Tool for Exercise 22. They can also use the Place-Value Block Tool to create examples for their explanations.

For Early Finishers Challenge early finishers to redo Exercises 10–14, but with an extra zero written to the right of each factor that is a multiple of 10. 20,000; 480,000; 4,000; 49,000; 300,000

3 Close and Assess

Performance Assessment

Find the product of 7×8, then complete each sentence. Explain your thinking.

$7 \times 800 = $ ▇ 5,600 $7 \times $ ▇ $= 56,000$ 8,000

Possible answer: $7 \times 8 = 56$; Use that basic fact to complete other sentences.

Assess using the rubric on page 202B.

Resources

Technology Master 15

ANSWERS

22 Find 8×4 and put 2 zeros at the end, $800 \times 4 = 3,200$. This applies to 500×2, also, $500 \times 2 = 1,000$.

Enrichment 5-2

Name _____   Extend Your Thinking 5-2

Visual Thinking
In each row, circle the figure on the right that will complete the analogy.

1. ☐ is to ▭ as ▯ is to   ⬭ ▭ ☐

2. 8 is to ৪ as △ is to   △ △ Ⓐ

3. ⊞ is to □ as ⊗ is to   ⊛ ⊘ ⊕

4. ⊞ is to ⊟ as ⊞ is to   ⊞ ⬭ ⊞

5. ✳ is to ✳ as ▦ is to   ▦ ▦ ▦

6. △ is to △ as ∴ is to   ∴ ∴ ∵

Problem Solving 5-2

Name _____   Problem Solving 5-2

Exploring Multiplication Patterns
Find each product using place-value blocks.

1.
   3×5 tens $= $ 15 tens $= $ 150

2.
   2×3 hundreds $= $ 6 hundreds $= $ 600

3. Linda says that the product of 3 and 700 has 2 zeros, and the product of 4 and 500 has 3 zeros. Is she correct? Explain. **Yes; $4 \times 5 = 20$. The zero in 20 increases the number of zeros in the product by 1.**

Tell how many zeros will be in each product. Use place-value patterns to find each.

4. 4×700 2; 2,800

5. $9 \times 3,000$ 3; 27,000

6. $8 \times 4,000$ 3; 32,000

7. $7 \times 50,000$ 4; 350,000

8. 3×30 1; 90

9. 6×70 1; 420

10. 5×200 3; 1,000

11. 8×50 2; 400

12. How are **10** and **11** different from **4–9**? **The basic facts used to solve 10 and 11 have zeros. This adds 1 more zero to the product.**

Solve using patterns.

13. A ream of paper is 500 sheets of paper. A case of paper has 2 stacks of 5 reams. How many sheets of paper are in a case of paper? **5,000 sheets of paper**

Chapter 5 • Lesson 5-2   **203**

Estimating Products

At-A-Glance Planning

Objective Estimate products.

Student Book Lesson Materials *Optional* Lesson Enhancement Transparency 17

Materials for pages 204A and 204B Craft catalogs, place-value blocks (10 hundreds, 35 tens, 35 ones per group), number cubes (3 cubes per pair, labeled 1–6, 3–8, and 4–9)

Subject Connection art—clothing design

Strand Connections estimation, money, probability, using data, algebra readiness

	Before Lesson	During Lesson	After Lesson
Daily Math			
p. 204A Problem of the Day			
p. 204A Math Routines			
p. 204A Mental Math			
Teaching Options			
p. 204 Student Book Lesson			
p. 204B Another Way to Learn…			
Options for Reaching All Learners			
p. 204B Inclusion			
p. 204B Gifted & Talented			
Subject Connections			
p. 204A Career Connection			
Assessment Options			
p. 204 Talk About It			
p. 205 Error Intervention			
p. 205 Interview			
p. 205 Quick Check			
Resources			
5-3 Practice			
5-3 Reteaching			
5-3 Enrichment			
5-3 Problem Solving			
5-3 Daily Transparency			

Problem of the Day

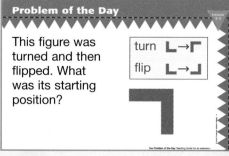

Problem of the Day

This figure was turned and then flipped. What was its starting position?

turn L→Γ
flip L→⅃

Math Routines

Measurement An adult's stride is about 3 feet. Ask students to estimate the length of 18, 31, and 49 strides. About 60 ft, 90 ft, 150 ft

Calendar Have students name three pairs of dates for this month that have products close to, but not exactly, 60. Possible answer: 4×16, 5×13, 8×7

Mental Math

Is each product less than or greater than the estimate given? Explain.

8×34 is about 240
Greater

6×49 is about 300
Less

Career Connection

Many countries have large industries that depend on handicrafts. Explain that some craftspeople determine the selling price of an item by doubling the cost of the materials used to make it.

• Provide craft catalogs.

• Have small groups choose a craft item, figure out the cost of materials for one item, then determine the selling price.

Another Way to **Learn** Lesson 5-3

Use as an alternative or in addition to pages 204 and 205.

Materials Place-value blocks (10 hundreds, 35 tens, 35 ones per group)

Learning Style Kinesthetic

• Have groups use place-value blocks to model 3 × 47. Then have them model an estimate using tens. About 150

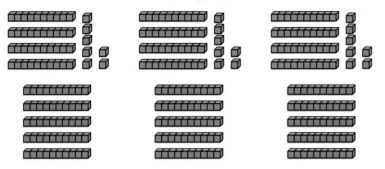

• Review the steps in the estimation process: round a 2-digit factor to a multiple of 10; round a 3-digit factor to a multiple of 100; use multiplication facts and place value to estimate the product. Then have groups try these:

6 × 23 About 120   2 × 351 About 800

• Assign Check and Practice on Student Book pages 204 and 205 or *Practice Master 5-3.*

• Assess using the following rubric.

Assessment Rubric
4 Full Accomplishment • estimates products accurately • clearly explains how to use rounding to estimate products
3 Substantial Accomplishment • estimates most products accurately • clearly explains how to use rounding to estimate products
2 Partial Accomplishment • estimates products but may make some errors in rounding • struggles with explaining how to use rounding to estimate products
1 Little Accomplishment • has difficulty estimating most products • does not explain how to use rounding to estimate products

Options for Reaching All Learners

Inclusion

Rounding
Use number lines to strengthen skill in rounding.

Learning Style Visual

• Draw a number line from 0 to 100 on the chalkboard. Label all tens. Label all ones between 30 and 40.

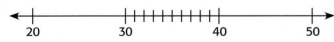

• Have students identify all numbers between 30 and 40 that are closer to 30. Explain that these round to 30. Repeat for numbers closer to 40. Explain that 35 is equally close to 30 and 40, but mathematicians have agreed to round it to 40.

• Name other 2-digit numbers. Have students mark them on a number line and tell the ten they round to.

• Repeat for 3-digit numbers on a number line.

Gifted & Talented

Range Game
Use a game to strengthen estimation skills.

Materials Number cubes (3 cubes per pair, labeled 1–6, 3–8, 4–9)

Learning Style Social

• Have each player draw a 4-by-4 square gameboard and write a range of 50 in each square in any order: 1–50, 51–100, 101–150, and so on.

• Have players take turns rolling the number cubes, using the three digits rolled to write two factors, estimating their product, and marking the game square with the product's range. For example, roll 1, 5, and 3; write 3 × 51; estimate the product, 150; mark square 101–150.

• The first player to mark four boxes across, down, or diagonally wins.

Lesson Organizer

Objective Estimate products.

Student Materials None

Teacher Materials *Optional* Lesson Enhancement Transparency 17

Assignment Guide

Basic 12–26, 31, 35–43

Average 17–29, 31, 33–43

Enriched 19–43

1 Introduce

Review

Find each product.

1. 5 × 700 3,500   **2.** 5 × 80 400

3. 5 × 70 350   **4.** 6 × 700 4,200

Build on Prior Knowledge

After students review using mental math to multiply multiples of 10 and 100, ask them which Review exercises have products close to 500. Which have products close to 4,000? Exercises 2, 3; Exercises 1, 4

2 Teach

See Another Way to Learn…on page 204B.

Learn ● ● ● ● ● ● ● ● ● ● ● ● ● ● ● ● ●

When focusing on Examples 1 and 2, ask students why they have to multiply after they rounded the total number of beads or sequins in one scoop or one bag. Without multiplying, you do not have products to compare to the actual beads or sequins needed to complete a jacket or hat.

Talk About It **Ongoing Assessment**

Listen for students to recognize when an estimated product is sufficient. Encourage students to think of examples in which an exact product is needed and examples in which it is not necessary.

Answer for Talk About It

No; An approximate number is good enough for estimating.

Check ● ● ● ● ● ● ● ● ● ● ● ● ● ● ● ● ●

Exercises 2, 3, 4, 7, and 10 Be sure students understand that they estimate the same way when the 2- or 3-digit factor appears first.

Estimating Products

You Will Learn
how to estimate products

Learn ● ● ● ● ● ● ● ● ● ● ● ● ● ● ● ● ●

Davida had a sparkling idea! Instead of paying for decorated clothes, she decided to make them herself. Now Davida sells her creations and saves the money for college.

Davida is a young fashion designer in Philadelphia, Pennsylvania.

Example 1

Davida needs about 600 beads to decorate a jacket. She takes 8 scoops. Each scoop holds about 78 beads. Will she have enough beads for the jacket?

Number of scoops
    | Number of beads in one scoop
    |

8 × 78

   Round 78 to the nearest 10.

8 × 80 = 640

There are about 640 beads in 8 scoops. So, Davida will have enough beads.

Math Tip
When you don't need an exact amount, an estimate is good enough.

Example 2

A bag holds 625 sequins. Will 7 bags be enough for Davida to decorate a hat with about 4,000 sequins?

Number of bags
  | Number of sequins in one bag
  |

7 × 625

   Round 625 to the nearest 100.

7 × 600 = 4,200

Davida will have about 4,200 sequins. So, 7 bags will be enough.

Talk About It

Does Davida need to know the exact number of beads in a scoop? Explain.

Check ●

Estimate each product.

1. 5 × 81   **2.** 54 × 3   **3.** 98 × 3   **4.** 43 × 6   **5.** 7 × 79
   400   150   300   240   560

6. 5 × 224   **7.** 557 × 4   **8.** 2 × 312   **9.** 3 × 697   **10.** 493 × 8
   1,000   2,400   600   2,100   4,000

11. **Reasoning** Estimate to decide how many digits are in the product of 2 and 62. **3 digits; 2 × 60 = 120.**

Practice 5-3

Name _____

Estimating Products

Estimate each product. **Possible estimates given.**

1. 5 × 25 = **150**   **2.** 6 × 173 = **1,200**   **3.** 8 × 42 = **320**

4. 4 × 525 = **2,000**   **5.** 3 × 87 = **270**   **6.** 47 × 5 = **250**

7. 7 × 284 = **2,100**   **8.** 4 × 714 = **2,800**   **9.** 26 × 8 = **240**

10. 48 × 8 = **400**   **11.** 388 × 4 = **1,600**   **12.** 284 × 5 = **1,500**

13. 69 × 2 = **140**   **14.** 53 × 8 = **400**   **15.** 34 × 9 = **270**

16. 468 × 3 = **1,500**   **17.** 403 × 3 = **1,200**   **18.** 786 × 2 = **1,600**

19. Estimate the product of 7 and 87. **630**

20. Estimate the product of 5 and 524. **2,500**

21. Estimate to decide if the product of 7 and 68 will be less than or greater than 490. **Less than**

22. Estimate to decide if the product of 7 and 532 will be less than or greater than 3,500. **Greater than**

23. Estimate to decide which is greater: 6 × 42 or 3 × 87.
3 × 87

24. Circle each of the exercises below whose product you estimate to be greater than 1,000.

(375 × 4)   (716 × 2)   232 × 4

78 × 5   (274 × 5)   (417 × 3)

(354 × 3)   110 × 9   340 × 2

Reteaching 5-3

Name _____

Estimating Products

Estimate.

Example 1 3 × 12

Round 12 to nearest multiple of 10.

Think of the multiples of 10.

0, 10, 20, 30, 40, 50, 60, 70, 80, …
     ↑
    12

Which number is nearest to 12?

Replace 12 in the problem with 10.

3 × 1̶2̶
   ↓
3 × 10 = 30

Example 2 4 × 570

Round 570 to nearest multiple of 100.

570 is closer to 600.

Replace 570 with 600.

4 × 5̶7̶0
   ↓
4 × 600 = 2,400

Write the nearest multiple of ten for each number.

1. 83 **80**   **2.** 46 **50**   **3.** 57 **60**   **4.** 48 **50**

Write the nearest multiple of 100 for each number.

5. 120 **100**   **6.** 280 **300**   **7.** 940 **900**   **8.** 350 **400**

Estimate each product by rounding each two-digit number to the nearest multiple of 10. Round each three-digit number to the nearest multiple of 100.

9. 2 × 93   **10.** 37 × 7   **11.** 6 × 49
  2 × **90** = **180**   **40** × 7 = **280**   6 × **50** = **300**

12. 5 × 14   **13.** 42 × 5   **14.** 85 × 4
   50   **200**   **360**

15. 47 × 8   **16.** 26 × 9   **17.** 7 × 81
   400   **270**   **560**

Practice

Skills and Reasoning

Estimate each product.

12. 6×34
180

13. 7×284
2,100

14. 9×53
450

15. 5×636
3,000

16. 2×76
160

17. 36×4
160

18. 8×395
3,200

19. 3×825
2,400

20. 7×79
560

21. 37×9
360

22. 5×299
1,500

23. 9×889
8,100

24. 58×3
180

25. 42×7
280

26. 23×8
160

27. Estimate the product of 6 and 98.
600

28. Estimate the product of 4 and 613.
2,400

29. Estimate to decide if the product of 6 and 79 will be less than or greater than 480. Explain.
Less than; 79 was rounded up.

30. Estimate to decide if the product of 6 and 435 will be less than or greater than 2,400. Explain.
Greater than; 435 was rounded down

Problem Solving and Applications

31. Money Each Bike-a-Thon rider who earns at least $30 will win a T-shirt decorated by Davida. Geri earns $2 for each mile she rides. If she rides for 19 miles, will she win a T-shirt? Explain.
Yes; $2 × 20 = $40.

32. Probability One in ten bicyclists at the Bike-a-Thon is likely to earn at least $30. If there are 78 riders, about how many of them might earn $30? **About 8 bicyclists**

Using Data Use the Data File on page 196 to solve **33** and **34**.

33. Which country shipped more beads to Ghana in 1936 than in 1931? **Czechoslovakia**

34. Which regions shipped at least twice as many beads to Ghana in 1931 than in 1936? **Germany and African countries**

AFRICA

Ghana

Mixed Review and Test Prep

Find each sum or difference.

35.
$$\begin{array}{r} 518 \\ + 397 \\ \hline 915 \end{array}$$

36.
$$\begin{array}{r} 407 \\ - 169 \\ \hline 238 \end{array}$$

37.
$$\begin{array}{r} 1,548 \\ + 9,252 \\ \hline 10,800 \end{array}$$

38.
$$\begin{array}{r} 2,004 \\ - 1,653 \\ \hline 351 \end{array}$$

39.
$$\begin{array}{r} 4,081 \\ - 3,294 \\ \hline 787 \end{array}$$

Algebra Readiness Find each missing number.

40. $407 + n = 943$ 536

41. $n + 127 = 682$ 555

42. $554 + n = 813$ 259

43. Find the difference between $6.02 and $0.69. **B**

ⓐ $6.08   ⓑ $5.33   ⓒ $12.92   ⓓ not here

Enrichment 5-3

Name _____ Extend Your Thinking 5-3

Decision Making

The student council at Greenway Elementary needs to choose an event to raise money for their school. Here are three possible choices:

A. Rent-a-Student. Costs involved in the Rent-a-Student program total $100. The Council estimates that 27 students are available for 8 hours each. The cost to rent a student is $1 an hour.

B. Ticket Raffle. The students raffle two tickets to a professional basketball game. Each ticket to the game costs $74. Each raffle ticket will sell for $2. The students should be able to sell 378 tickets in a week.

C. Juice Sale. The students sell juice at the school carnival. They think they can sell 6 cases of juice at $18 a case. The booth is open for 6 hours. The juice costs $12 for 1 case.

1. Estimate the cost of each choice.
Choice A __$100__ Choice B __$140__ Choice C __$60__

2. About how much money will each choice earn?
Choice A __$240__ Choice B __$800__ Choice C __$120__

3. About how much profit does the school earn from each choice?
Choice A __$140__ Choice B __$660__ Choice C __$60__

4. Besides profit, what other factors should the student council consider before making their decision?
Possible answers: Number of volunteers each event requires;
The amount of time and hard work needed to set up and
complete each event

5. Which event would be the best choice? Explain.
Possible answer: B is the easiest to arrange and earns the
greatest profit.

Problem Solving 5-3

Name _____ Problem Solving 5-3

Estimating Products

Science It takes 24 hours (one full day) for the earth to make one complete turn. The earth makes 365 complete turns every year.

1. Estimate the number of hours it takes the earth to make 8 complete turns.
160 hours

2. Estimate the number of times the earth turns in 5 years.
2,000

3. Does the earth turn more or less than 2,700 times in 9 years? Explain.
More; 9 × 300 = 2,700, so 9 × 365 must be greater
than 2,700.

4. Which is the closest estimate for the number of hours it takes the earth to turn 7 times?
A. 210 hours   B. 280 hours   C. 140 hours   D. 100 hours
C

Jake rented a video game system for 5 days. The system cost $18 for a 1-day rental. He also rented 2 games. Each game cost $12.00 for a 5-day period.

5. About how much did Jake pay to rent the system and the games for 5 days? About $120

6. Estimate the total cost of renting the video game system only for 6 days. About $120

7. About how much would it cost to rent the system only for 3 days? About $60

Error Intervention Ongoing Assessment

Observation Students may incorrectly round the 2- or 3-digit factor.

How to Help Review rounding with students. Have them circle the leading digit. Have them underline the digit to the circled digit's right and use this digit to decide whether to leave the circled digit as it is or to add 1.

Practice

Exercise 31 Some students may estimate the product of 19 × $2, while others may count by 2s to find that 15 × $2 = $30.

Exercises 33 and 34 Students must compare the lengths of the bars in the graph but do not need to determine actual amounts represented by the bars. You may wish to use Lesson Enhancement Transparency 17, which reproduces the bar graph.

For Early Finishers Challenge early finishers to determine whether the actual products in Exercises 12–21 would be greater than or less than the estimated products.

3 Close and Assess

Interview

Ask students to estimate 7 × 563 and explain how they did it. Explanations should include rounding 563 to the nearest hundred (600) and using mental math to multiply 7 × 600 to get 4,200.

Quick Check

Number Sense Use number sense to decide which estimated products for the Skill exercises below are greater than the actual products would be. Explain. Exercises 1, 3, 4; Because the multiple of 10 or 100 that was multiplied is greater than the actual factor

Skill Estimate each product.

1. 3×87
About 270

2. 24×4
About 80

3. 6×293
About 1,800

4. 9×572
About 5,400

Exploring Multiplication with Arrays

At-A-Glance Planning

Objective Explore multiplication with arrays.

Vocabulary array

Student Book Lesson Materials Place-value blocks (7 tens, 56 ones per group) *optional* Teaching Tool Transparency 6 (Centimeter Grid Paper), Lesson Enhancement Transparency 18

Materials for pages 206A and 206B Examples of arrays (stickers, postage stamps, and so on)

Subject Connection science—egg production

Strand Connection using data

	Before Lesson	During Lesson	After Lesson
Daily Math			
p. 206A Problem of the Day			
p. 206A Math Routines			
p. 206A Mental Math			
Teaching Options			
p. 206B Facilitating and Assessing…			
Options for Reaching All Learners			
p. 206B Language Development			
p. 206B Inclusion			
Technology Options			
p. 206 Interactive CD-ROM Lesson 5			
p. 207 Interactive CD-ROM Journal			
Subject Connections			
p. 206A Literature Connection			
Assessment Options			
p. 206 Talk About It			
p. 207 Error Intervention			
p. 207 Performance Assessment			
Resources			
5-4 Practice			
5-4 Reteaching			
5-4 Enrichment			
5-4 Problem Solving			
5-4 Daily Transparency			

Problem of the Day

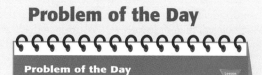

Problem of the Day

When Jason emptied his pockets, he found 5 more nickels than dimes. If he had 45¢ in nickels, how much money did he have in all?

85¢

Math Routines

Money Ask students how they would arrange quarters to count the total dollar amount easily. Stack the quarters by 4s.

Calendar Have students look at this month's calendar. Ask: What is the least number of rows possible in a month with 28 days? With 31 days? 4 rows; 5 rows

Mental Math

In each pair, which has the greater product? Explain your thinking.

3 × 80	or	8 × 50 8 × 50
7 × 600	or	4 × 800 7 × 600

Literature Connection

In Aileen Friedman's *The King's Commissioners*, the king has appointed so many commissioners that he has lost track of how many there are in all. The king's daughter organized the commissioners into 4 rows of 10 with 7 left over.

• Ask students to draw a picture to show this array. Ask students why this method of counting is convenient. Possible answer: Because it is easy to count groups of 10

Facilitating and Assessing **Explore** Lesson 5-4

Use with pages 206 and 207.

Get Started You may wish to assign the roles of reader, array builder, and recorder. Have students alternate roles.

Observe Students may find different ways to arrange their arrays and multiply, while still arriving at the same answer. Especially at this exploration stage, such variations in approach should be encouraged. Any array of tens and ones that gives the correct product is acceptable. As students draw their arrays, some may sketch tens and ones. Others may prefer to outline or color rows of 10 squares and 2 squares on grid paper.

Discuss Focus discussion on finding the totals in the parts of the array and adding these totals.

Assess Use the rubric to assess students' work. See sample for Practice Exercise 8.

4 Full Accomplishment

$5 \times 20 = 100$

$5 \times 3 = 15$

$100 + 15 = 115$

Assessment Rubric

4 Full Accomplishment
- draws arrays and solves multiplication problems
- explains the array/product relationship

3 Substantial Accomplishment
- draws most arrays and solves most multiplication problems
- explains most of the array/product relationship

2 Partial Accomplishment
- draws some arrays and solves some multiplication problems
- does not fully explain the array/product relationship

1 Little Accomplishment
- does not draw arrays or solve multiplication problems
- does not explain or demonstrate the array/product relationship

Options for Reaching All Learners

Language Development

Arrays! Hooray!
Use common objects to introduce the term **array**.

Materials Examples of arrays (rows of stickers, postage stamps, and so on)

Learning Style Visual

- Use this activity at the beginning of the lesson to make sure students understand the term *array*.
- Show common arrays such as rows of stickers, postage stamps, and desks.
- Have students discuss what is the same about these arrays, then introduce the term *array*. In an array, the objects are arranged in rows and columns.
- Challenge students to name examples of other arrays and explain why each qualifies as an array. Encourage them to use the word *array* in their explanations.

Inclusion

Regrouping
Draw pictures to show regrouping and equivalency.

Learning Style Visual, Verbal

- Reinforce the concept of regrouping ones as tens and ones by having students draw pictures, label groups, and write the number sentences.

  10 ones   =   1 ten

  14 ones   =   1 ten 4 ones

- Invite students to count aloud the blocks shown in their drawings.
- Emphasize the equivalency of the paired groups.

Lesson Organizer

Objective Explore multiplication with arrays.

Suggested Grouping 2 to 4

Student Materials Place-value blocks (7 tens, 56 ones per group), *optional* Teaching Tool Transparency 6 (Centimeter Grid Paper)

Teacher Materials *Optional* Lesson Enhancement Transparency 18

Vocabulary array

Assignment Guide
Basic 1–12, 16
Average 2–14, 16
Enriched 3–16

1 Introduce

Review

Find each product.

1. 6
   × 5
   ——
   30

2. 60
   × 5
   ——
   300

3.   4
   × 7
   ——
   28

4. 40
   × 7
   ——
   280

Build on Prior Knowledge

After students review how to multiply with multiples of 10, ask them to add the answers to Review Exercises 1 and 2. 330; 308

2 Teach

See Facilitating and Assessing…on page 206B.

Interactive CD-ROM Lesson 5 includes content in this lesson.

Explore ·

You may wish to ask questions such as the following as you observe students at work.

• How did you decide how many of each kind of place-value block belonged in one row? 16 = 1 ten 6 ones; 13 = 1 ten 3 ones

Additional Examples

3 × 18 54   2 × 16 32   4 × 15 60

Talk About It **Ongoing Assessment**

Look for students to focus on the products that are the results of multiplying ones and tens.

Answers for Talk About It

3 3 rows of 10 and 3 rows of 6

4 Multiply the tens and multiply the ones, then add the products.

Exploring Multiplication with Arrays

Problem Solving Connection
■ Use Objects/ Act It Out
■ Solve a Simpler Problem

Materials
place-value blocks

Vocabulary
array
data arranged in rows and columns

Did You Know?
A typical chicken lays about 18 eggs a month.

Explore · · · · · · · · · ·

School's out! Where's Caleb? He's on another egg hunt! Caleb raises Rhode Island Red chickens. Every day he collects eggs to sell to his neighbors and friends.

Two of Caleb's cartons hold 5 rows of 12 eggs each. How many eggs are in Caleb's cartons?

Work Together

1. Use place-value blocks to show an **array**. Find 5×12.

   a. Show 1 ten and 2 ones in a row. This shows 1×12.

   b. Make 4 more rows of 12. Now this shows 5×12.

   c. How many tens are there? How many ones? 5 tens; 10 ones

   d. What is the product for 5×12? 60

2. Use the place-value blocks to show 3×16 and 4×13. Draw pictures to show what you did with the place-value blocks. Write the product for each. **Drawings should show a 3-by-16 array and a 4-by-13 array. $3 \times 16 = 48$. $4 \times 13 = 52$.**

Talk About It

3. Describe the array you made to show 3×16.

4. Explain how multiplying with place-value blocks is like solving two simpler problems.

Practice 5-4	Reteaching 5-4

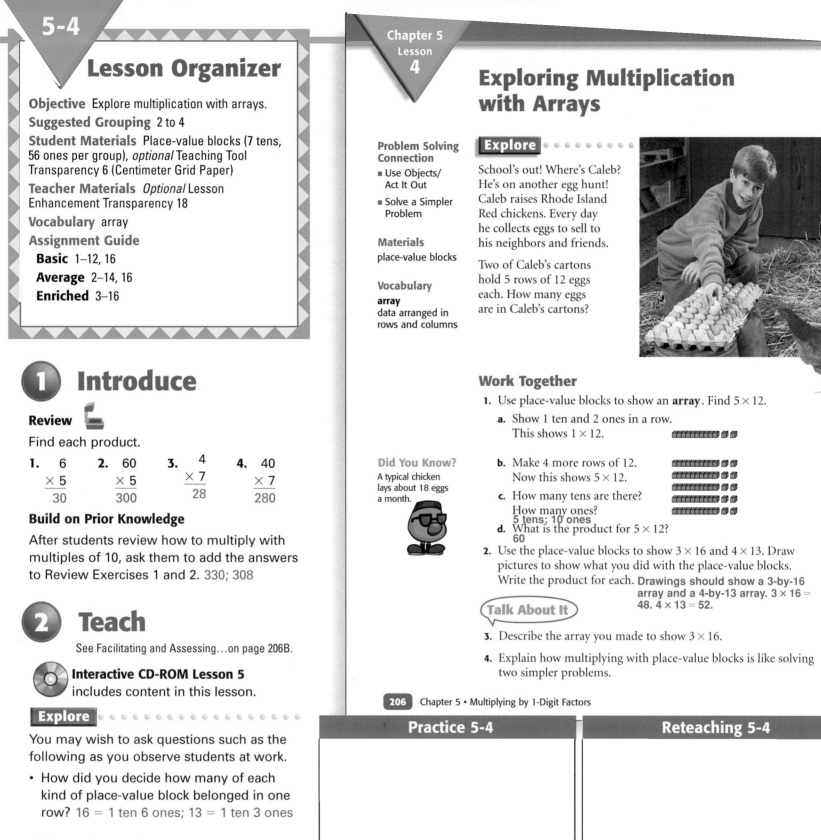

Connect

You can use what you know about arrays to multiply. Find 4×13.

What You See

$4 \times 10 = 40$ $4 \times 3 = 12$

$40 + 12 = 52$

What You Write

$$\begin{array}{r} 13 \\ \times\ 4 \\ \hline 12 \\ + 40 \\ \hline 52 \end{array}$$
4×3 ones
4×1 ten

PRACTICE AND APPLY

Practice

Copy and complete to find each product. You may use place-value blocks to help.

1.
$$\begin{array}{r} 2\ 4 \\ \times\ \ 3 \\ \hline 1\ 2 \\ 6\ 0 \\ \hline 72 \end{array}$$
$3 \times 20 = 60$ $3 \times 4 = 12$

2.
$$\begin{array}{r} 1\ 8 \\ \times\ \ 7 \\ \hline 5\ 6 \\ \\ \hline 70 \\ 126 \end{array}$$
$7 \times 10 = n$ $7 \times 8 = 56$

Find each product. Draw pictures to help.

3.
$$\begin{array}{r} 3\ 7 \\ \times\ \ 4 \\ \hline 2\ 8 \\ 1\ 2\ 0 \\ \hline 148 \end{array}$$

4. $\begin{array}{r} 6\ 2 \\ \times\ 7 \\ \hline \end{array}$ 14; 420; 434

5. $\begin{array}{r} 7\ 2 \\ \times\ 8 \\ \hline \end{array}$ 16; 560; 576

6. $\begin{array}{r} 4\ 9 \\ \times\ 5 \\ \hline \end{array}$ 45; 200; 245

7. $\begin{array}{r} 5\ 8 \\ \times\ 6 \\ \hline \end{array}$ 48; 300; 348

8. $\begin{array}{r} 23 \\ \times\ 5 \\ \hline 115 \end{array}$

9. $\begin{array}{r} 45 \\ \times\ 2 \\ \hline 90 \end{array}$

10. $\begin{array}{r} 34 \\ \times\ 3 \\ \hline 102 \end{array}$

11. $\begin{array}{r} 28 \\ \times\ 8 \\ \hline 224 \end{array}$

12. $\begin{array}{r} 39 \\ \times\ 4 \\ \hline 156 \end{array}$

13. Is 3×28 the same as 3×8 plus 3×20? Explain.
Yes; 28 is 2 tens and 8 ones.

14. **Critical Thinking** A typical large egg has a mass of 56 grams. The egg that has the greatest mass on record is 8 times as much as that of a typical egg. How many grams is that? **448 grams**

15. **Using Data** Caleb has 8 chickens. About how many eggs will Caleb collect each month? Use the fact from *Did You Know?* on page 206 to help answer the question. **144 eggs**

16. **Journal** Explain how to find 5×18 by breaking it into two simpler problems.

Lesson 5-4   **207**

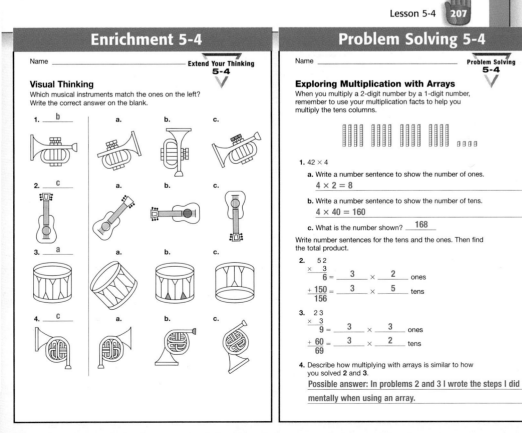

Enrichment 5-4

Extend Your Thinking 5-4

Visual Thinking
Which musical instruments match the ones on the left? Write the correct answer on the blank.

1. **b**   a.   b.   c.

2. **c**   a.   b.   c.

3. **a**   a.   b.   c.

4. **c**   a.   b.   c.

Problem Solving 5-4

Problem Solving 5-4

Exploring Multiplication with Arrays
When you multiply a 2-digit number by a 1-digit number, remember to use your multiplication facts to help you multiply the tens columns.

1. 42×4

a. Write a number sentence to show the number of ones.
$4 \times 2 = 8$

b. Write a number sentence to show the number of tens.
$4 \times 40 = 160$

c. What is the number shown? _**168**_

Write number sentences for the tens and the ones. Then find the total product.

2.
$$\begin{array}{r} 5\ 2 \\ \times\ \ 3 \\ \hline 6 \\ + 150 \\ \hline 156 \end{array}$$
$= \underline{3} \times \underline{2}$ ones
$= \underline{3} \times \underline{5}$ tens

3.
$$\begin{array}{r} 2\ 3 \\ \times\ \ 3 \\ \hline 9 \\ + 60 \\ \hline 69 \end{array}$$
$= \underline{3} \times \underline{3}$ ones
$= \underline{3} \times \underline{2}$ tens

4. Describe how multiplying with arrays is similar to how you solved **2** and **3**.
Possible answer: In problems 2 and 3 I wrote the steps I did mentally when using an array.

Connect

You may wish to use Lesson Enhancement Transparency 18, which reproduces the Connect material. Have students use place-value blocks to demonstrate the steps to find products.

Error Intervention Ongoing Assessment

Observation Students may have difficulty understanding the connection between the array and the algorithm.

How to Help Have students make an array with place-value blocks, cover the tens with paper, and compare the array of ones to the products of ones. Repeat for tens.

Practice

Exercise 14 Discuss the meaning of the terms *mass* and *gram*.

 **Interactive CD-ROM Journal**
Students can use the Journal Tool for Exercise 16. They may wish to use the Place-Value Block Tool to illustrate their explanations.

For Early Finishers Challenge early finishers to repeat Exercise 15 to find out how many eggs Caleb will collect in 3, 6, and 9 months. 432; 864; 1,296

3 Close and Assess

Performance Assessment

Draw an array to show 4×26, then find the product.

$$\begin{array}{r} 26 \\ \times\ 4 \\ \hline 24 \\ 80 \\ \hline 104 \end{array}$$
4×6 ones
4×2 tens

Assess using the rubric on page 206B.

ANSWERS

16 5×8 plus 5×10

Section A
Review and Practice

Use the Skills Checklist

Review the **Skills Checklist** on the page with students. Then ask questions such as the following:

- In which problems can you use basic multiplication facts? Exercises 1–26
- Where can you use patterns of 10s, 100s, or 1,000s? Exercises 6–8
- Where will you use rounding to estimate? Exercises 16–25
- In which problems do you need to think about place value? Exercises 1–26

Assess

You may wish to use this information to assess students' understanding of the lesson objectives.

Item Analysis	
Lesson Objective	Items
5-1 Multiply by multiples of ten.	1–8
5-2 Explore multiplication patterns.	9–13
5-3 Estimate products.	16–25
5-4 Explore multiplication with arrays.	26, 27

Resources

Practice Masters

- Practice Chapter 5 Section A

Assessment Sourcebook

- Quiz Chapter 5 Section A

TestWorks: Test and Practice Software

ANSWERS

27 Answer should include that numbers multiplied together are called factors and the result is called a product; that multiples are products that have a common factor; that an array is a way to picture a number.

Review and Practice

(Lesson 1) Use a multiplication fact to help you find each product.

1. 4×30 **120** **2.** 2×70 **140** **3.** 7×50 **350** **4.** 8×60 **480** **5.** 5×80 **400**

(Lesson 2) Use patterns to find each product.

6. $7 \times 9 = n$ **63**   **7.** $8 \times 3 = n$ **24**   **8.** $4 \times 7 = n$ **28**

$7 \times 90 = n$ **630** $8 \times 30 = n$ **240** $4 \times 70 = n$ **280**

$7 \times 900 = n$ **6,300** $8 \times 300 = n$ **2,400** $4 \times 700 = n$ **2,800**

💡 **Mental Math** Find each product.

9. 8×400 **3,200** **10.** $6 \times 3,000$ **18,000** **11.** 5×60 **300**   **12.** $6 \times 2,000$ **12,000**

13. A sheet of baseball cards has 100 cards. How many cards are there in 5 sheets?

Using Data Use the pictograph for **14** and **15.**

14. How many people will fit in the Tampa Thunderdome? **28,000 people**

15. How many people will fit in the Calgary Saddledome? **20,000 people**

Capacity of Hockey Stadiums	
Madison Square Garden	🏒🏒🏒🏒🏒
Tampa Thunderdome	🏒🏒🏒🏒🏒🏒🏒
Calgary Olympic Saddledome	🏒🏒🏒🏒🏒

🏒 = 4,000 people

(Lesson 3) Estimate each product.

16. 6×64 **360** **17.** 5×914 **4,500** **18.** 8×47 **400** **19.** 7×23 **140** **20.** 5×91 **450**
21. 9×58 **540** **22.** 4×573 **2,400** **23.** 3×285 **900** **24.** 5×143 **500** **25.** 9×362 **3,600**

(Lesson 4) Find the product. Use the array to help.

26.
$\begin{array}{r} 17 \\ \times\ 6 \\ \hline 102 \end{array}$

$6 \times 10 = n$ $6 \times 7 = 42$

27. Journal Explain what you have learned about multiplication. Use any of the following words: multiple, array, factor, or product.

> **Skills Checklist**
>
> **In this section, you have:**
> - ☑ Multiplied Tens
> - ☑ Explored Multiplication Patterns
> - ☑ Estimated Products
> - ☑ Explored Multiplication with Arrays

REVIEW AND PRACTICE

Practice

Name _____

Practice
Chapter 5
Section A

Review and Practice

(Lesson 1) Use a multiplication fact to help you find each product.

1. $50 \times 3 =$ __150__   **2.** $4 \times 20 =$ __80__

3. $6 \times 30 =$ __180__   **4.** $70 \times 8 =$ __560__

(Lesson 2) Use patterns to find each product.

5. $5 \times 7 =$ __35__   **6.** $8 \times 9 =$ __72__

$5 \times 70 =$ __350__ $8 \times 90 =$ __720__

$5 \times 700 =$ __3,500__ $8 \times 900 =$ __7,200__

Find each product.

7. $7 \times 50 =$ __350__   **8.** $4 \times 5,000 =$ __20,000__   **9.** $6 \times 300 =$ __1,800__

Use the pictograph for **10** and **11.**

10. How many people live in Blairstown? __25,000__

11. How many people live in Middletown? __35,000__

Population	
Blairstown	●●●●●
Middletown	●●●●●●●
Centerville	●●●●

● = 5,000 people

(Lesson 3) Estimate each product.

12. 9×456 __4,500__   **13.** 331×7 __2,100__

14. 3×899 __2,700__   **15.** 711×4 __2,800__

(Lesson 4) Find the product. Use the array to help.

16. $\begin{array}{r} 13 \\ \times\ 5 \\ \hline 65 \end{array}$

$5 \times 10 = n$ $5 \times 3 = 15$

(Mixed Review) Add or subtract.

17. $\begin{array}{r} 3,612 \\ +\ 839 \\ \hline 4,451 \end{array}$ **18.** $\begin{array}{r} 3,048 \\ -1,479 \\ \hline 1,569 \end{array}$ **19.** $\begin{array}{r} 9,177 \\ -5,791 \\ \hline 3,386 \end{array}$ **20.** $\begin{array}{r} 608 \\ +\ 55 \\ \hline 663 \end{array}$

When the Happy Hoppers of Dayton, Ohio, compete, the team scores high. Each jump scores a specific number of points. How do you think the team keeps track of its scores?

GET READY!

Multiplying Greater Numbers

Review multiplication facts. Find each product.

1. 4 × 6 24	**2.** 5 × 8 40	**3.** 3 × 4 12
4. 7 × 2 14	**5.** 9 × 4 36	**6.** 5 × 7 35
7. 3 × 9 27	**8.** 6 × 6 36	**9.** 8 × 7 56
10. 4 × 4 16	**11.** 9 × 5 45	**12.** 8 × 8 64

Skills Checklist

In this section, you will:
- ☐ Multiply 2-Digit Numbers
- ☐ Multiply 3-Digit Numbers
- ☐ Solve Problems by Making Decisions
- ☐ Choose a Calculation Method

209

Multiplying

In this section, students will multiply a 2-, 3-, or 4-digit number by a 1-digit factor using an algorithm.

Subskills

The work in this section builds on…
- Using multiplication facts
  $2 \times 6 = 12$
- Finding the product of a 1-digit number and a multiple of 10
  $2 \times 80 = 160$
- Breaking apart a number using place value
  $86 = 8$ tens 6 ones, or $80 + 6$

Use the Section Opener

Jumping rope is both fun and good exercise. Young people around the country compete in a variety of tournaments. Some jumpers have mastered difficult jumping skills used in Double-Dutch, or two-rope jumping, such as handsprings and 360s (turns in midair).

Encourage students to discuss tournaments they have watched or in which they have competed. Ask how the Happy Hoppers might keep track of the team's score.
Possible answer: Use a table, list or chart.

Skills Trace

(Red numbers indicate pages in this section.)

Lesson and Skill	First Introduced	Grade Four			
		Introduce	Develop	Practice/Apply	Review
5-5 Multiply 2-digit numbers.	Grade 3	212, 213	212	213, 221, 222, 226, 229, 231, 240, 241, 562	222, 240, 242
5-6 Multiply 3-digit numbers.	Grade 3	214, 215	214	215, 221, 222, 226, 229, 242, 562	222, 240, 242
5-7 Solve problems by making decisions about cooking.	Grade 4	216, 217	216, 217	217, 222, 236, 241, 562	222, 240, 242
5-8 Multiply using different methods.	Grade 4	218, 219	218	219, 221, 222, 227, 233, 239, 240, 241, 242, 562	222, 240, 242

Mixed Review and Test Prep exercises for this chapter occur on pages 201, 205, 213, 215, 219, 225, 229, 231, 237.

👫 **Multi-Age Classrooms** Use pages 211–230 in Grade 3 or pages 116–127 in Grade 5 to relate to the content of this section.

Multiplying 2-Digit Numbers

At-A-Glance Planning

Lesson Planning Checklist

Objective Multiply 2-digit numbers.

Student Book Lesson Materials *Optional Reading Strategies for Math* Chart 23 (Making a Bar Graph)

Materials for pages 210A and 210B Place-value blocks (1 hundred, 13 tens, 35 ones per group), *optional* beads (2 kinds of colors)

Subject Connections science—pandas, geography—mountains

Strand Connections estimation, time, using data, collecting data

	Before Lesson	During Lesson	After Lesson
Daily Math			
p. 210A Problem of the Day			
p. 210A Math Routines			
p. 210A Mental Math			
Teaching Options			
p. 210 Student Book Lesson			
p. 210B Another Way to Learn…			
Options for Reaching All Learners			
p. 210B Inclusion			
p. 210B Cultural Connection			
Technology Options			
p. 210 Interactive CD-ROM Lesson 5			
p. 212 Interactive CD-ROM Journal			
Subject Connections			
p. 210A Science Connection			
Assessment Options			
p. 211 Talk About It			
p. 211 Error Intervention			
p. 213 Interview			
p. 213 Quick Check			
Resources			
5-5 Practice			
5-5 Reteaching			
5-5 Enrichment			
5-5 Problem Solving			
5-5 Daily Transparency			

Problem of the Day

Problem of the Day

This petroglyph, a picture carved on rock, was found in Hawaii. What shapes are in the drawing? How many of each shape are there?

9 triangles, 1 circle, 1 rectangle

Math Routines

Time Remind students that $\frac{1}{4}$ hour is 15 minutes. Have them tell how many minutes are in $\frac{1}{2}$ hour, $\frac{3}{4}$ hour, 1 hour, $1\frac{1}{2}$ hours. 30 min, 45 min, 60 min, 90 min

Calendar Ask students how many days of the year are in months that have 31 days. 217 days

Mental Math

Solve mentally. Solve the problem in the parentheses first.

$(8 \times 2) - 8$ 8 $(32 - 2) \div 5$ 6

$(7 \times 4) + 1$ 29 $(4 \times 5) + 6$ 26

Science Connection

To keep pets healthy, pet owners must feed them appropriate, nutritious food in proper amounts.

- A medium-sized dog eats 3 c of dry food each day. Have students find how much food the dog eats in 1 week and in 1 month (4 weeks). 21 c; 84 c

- Have students choose another pet and find out how much food it should eat each day. Then have them figure out how much food the pet would eat in 1 week and in 1 month.

Another Way to `Learn` Lesson 5-5

Use as an alternative or in addition to pages 210–213.

Materials Place-value blocks (1 hundred, 13 tens, 35 ones per group)

Learning Style Kinesthetic

- Have groups use place-value blocks to find 6 × 23. Have them show 6 rows of 2 tens and 3 ones, find how many ones, and regroup the 18 ones for 1 ten 8 ones. Have them find how many tens and regroup the 13 tens for 1 hundred 3 tens. Then they name the product. 138

- Use the overhead projector to model the problem, drawing a picture, and writing the algorithm. As each partial product is found and blocks are regrouped, write the appropriate step in the multiplication algorithm. Model how to draw the blocks in the array and the product.

- Have groups draw pictures of blocks and record the steps symbolically for additional exercises.

- Assign Check and Practice on Student Book pages 211–213 or *Practice Master 5-5*.

- Assess using the following rubric.

Assessment Rubric
4 Full Accomplishment • multiplies 2-digit numbers by 1-digit numbers • connects place value and multiplication
3 Substantial Accomplishment • multiplies most 2-digit numbers by 1-digit numbers • connects place value and multiplication
2 Partial Accomplishment • multiplies some 2-digit numbers by 1-digit numbers • struggles to connect place value and multiplication
1 Little Accomplishment • does not multiply 2-digit numbers by 1-digit numbers • does not connect place value and multiplication

Options for Reaching All Learners

Inclusion

Regrouping
Use visual reminders to add regrouped tens.

Learning Style Visual

- As students write a multiplication problem, have them draw a small box with an addition sign at the top of the tens column.

- After students multiply ones, have them write any regrouped tens in the box.

- After students have added the tens, have them cross out the box.

- When students multiply 3- and 4-digit numbers in Lessons 5-6 and 5-8, they can continue using this reminder for thousands or hundreds columns.

Cultural Connection

Baubles, Bangles, and Beads
Use other counting systems to reinforce understanding of 2-digit numbers.

Materials *Optional* Beads (2 kinds or colors per pair)

Learning Style Linguistic, Visual, Kinesthetic

In Central Africa, beads were once used as a currency form.

- Write the following on the chalkboard or overhead.

  5 beads = 1 unit

  5 units = 25 beads = 1 *M unit**

  2 *M units* = 50 beads = 1 *L unit**

  3 *L units* = 150 beads = 1 *MT unit**

- Using drawings or beads, model how to express 53 using the bead currency system. 1 *L unit* and 3 beads

- Have pairs model other 2-digit numbers.

  **M, L,* and *MT units* are used to represent African words.

Lesson Organizer

Objective Multiply 2-digit numbers.
Suggested Grouping 2 to 4
Student Materials None
Teacher Materials *Optional Reading Strategies for Math* Chart 23 (Making a Bar Graph)
Vocabulary regroup
Assignment Guide
  Basic 25–46, 48, 50, 56, 57, 61–70
  Average 29–48, 50–52, 55, 58, 61–70
  Enriched 32–49, 51–70

① Introduce

Review

Tell how many ones, how many tens, then how many there are all together.

1. 16	**2.** 28	**3.** 54
× 4	× 3	× 5
24 ones;	24 ones	20 ones;
4 tens;	6 tens	25 tens;
64 in all	84 in all	270 in all

Build on Prior Knowledge

After students review how to use partial products to multiply, ask them to describe how they could use mental math to find 4 × 16. Possible answers: Remember 4 × 6 (24) and 4 × 10 (40), and add mentally to get 64.

② Teach

See Another Way to Learn...on page 210B.

Interactive CD-ROM Lesson 5 includes content in this lesson.

Learn ○ ○ ○ ○ ○ ○ ○ ○ ○ ○ ○ ○ ○ ○ ○ ○ ○ ○ ○

Have students work in small groups to compare Pam and Jerry's methods. How are they alike? How are they different? Possible answer: Both use place value and multiplication, and both get the same product. Jerry writes the products for the ones and the tens and then adds. Pam uses regrouping and writes only the end product.

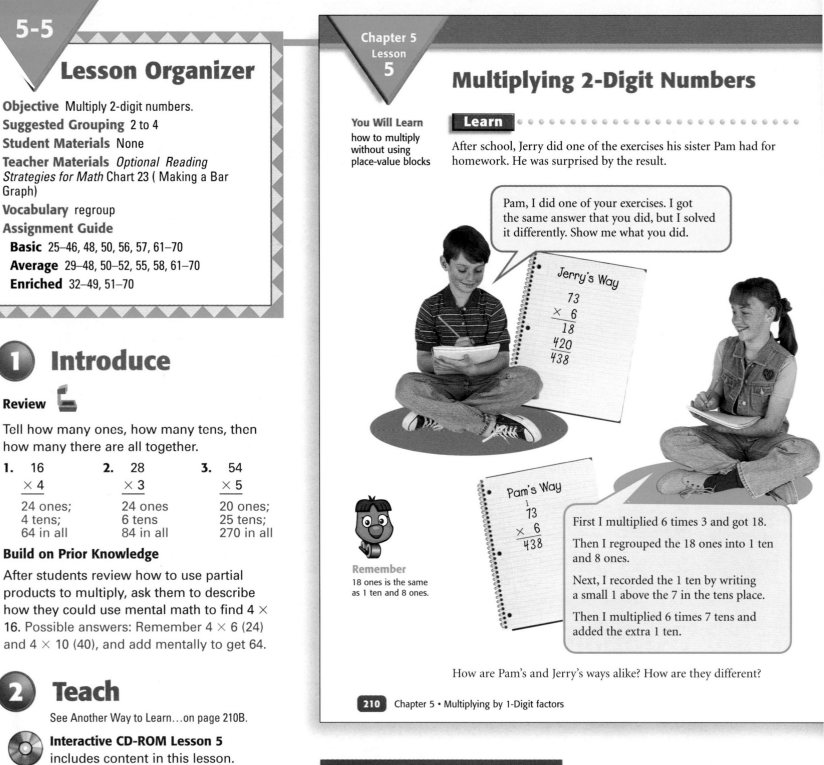

Multiplying 2-Digit Numbers

You Will Learn how to multiply without using place-value blocks

Learn ●

After school, Jerry did one of the exercises his sister Pam had for homework. He was surprised by the result.

Pam, I did one of your exercises. I got the same answer that you did, but I solved it differently. Show me what you did.

Jerry's Way

73
× 6
18
420
438

Pam's Way

1
73
× 6
438

First I multiplied 6 times 3 and got 18.

Then I regrouped the 18 ones into 1 ten and 8 ones.

Next, I recorded the 1 ten by writing a small 1 above the 7 in the tens place.

Then I multiplied 6 times 7 tens and added the extra 1 ten.

Remember
18 ones is the same as 1 ten and 8 ones.

How are Pam's and Jerry's ways alike? How are they different?

Managing Time

Have students complete the Check exercises as soon as they have completed the Learn portion of this lesson. The Practice exercises can be done as homework.

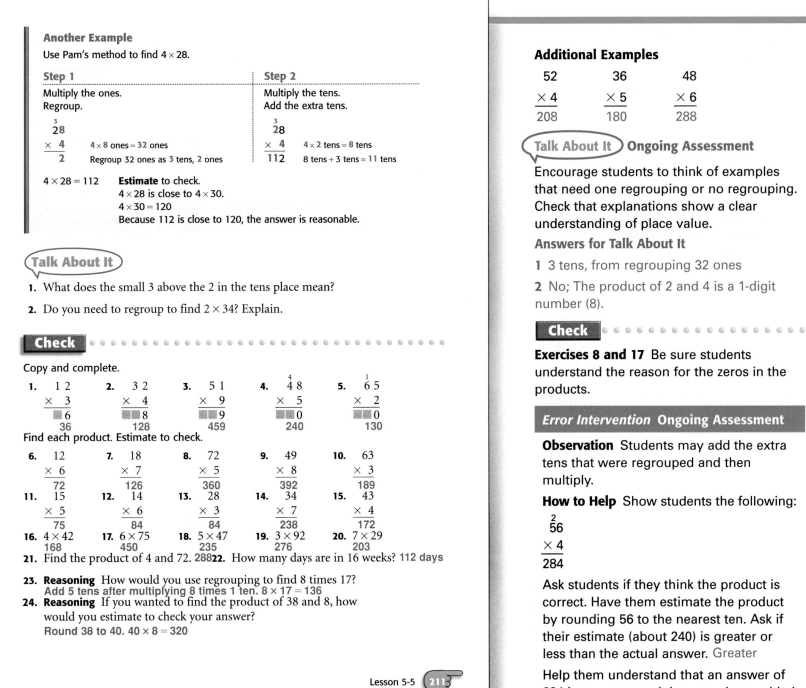

Another Example

Use Pam's method to find 4×28.

Step 1	Step 2
Multiply the ones. Regroup.	Multiply the tens. Add the extra tens.

Step 1:
$$\begin{array}{r} \overset{3}{28} \\ \times\ 4 \\ \hline 2 \end{array}$$
4×8 ones $= 32$ ones
Regroup 32 ones as 3 tens, 2 ones

Step 2:
$$\begin{array}{r} \overset{3}{28} \\ \times\ 4 \\ \hline 112 \end{array}$$
4×2 tens $= 8$ tens
8 tens $+ 3$ tens $= 11$ tens

$4 \times 28 = 112$ **Estimate** to check.
4×28 is close to 4×30.
$4 \times 30 = 120$
Because 112 is close to 120, the answer is reasonable.

Talk About It

1. What does the small 3 above the 2 in the tens place mean?

2. Do you need to regroup to find 2×34? Explain.

Check

Copy and complete.

1. $\begin{array}{r} 1\,2 \\ \times\ 3 \\ \hline \blacksquare 6 \\ 36 \end{array}$
2. $\begin{array}{r} 3\,2 \\ \times\ 4 \\ \hline \blacksquare\blacksquare 8 \\ 128 \end{array}$
3. $\begin{array}{r} 5\,1 \\ \times\ 9 \\ \hline \blacksquare\blacksquare 9 \\ 459 \end{array}$
4. $\begin{array}{r} \overset{4}{4\,8} \\ \times\ 5 \\ \hline \blacksquare\blacksquare 0 \\ 240 \end{array}$
5. $\begin{array}{r} \overset{1}{6\,5} \\ \times\ 2 \\ \hline \blacksquare\blacksquare 0 \\ 130 \end{array}$

Find each product. Estimate to check.

6. $\begin{array}{r} 12 \\ \times\ 6 \\ \hline 72 \end{array}$
7. $\begin{array}{r} 18 \\ \times\ 7 \\ \hline 126 \end{array}$
8. $\begin{array}{r} 72 \\ \times\ 5 \\ \hline 360 \end{array}$
9. $\begin{array}{r} 49 \\ \times\ 8 \\ \hline 392 \end{array}$
10. $\begin{array}{r} 63 \\ \times\ 3 \\ \hline 189 \end{array}$
11. $\begin{array}{r} 15 \\ \times\ 5 \\ \hline 75 \end{array}$
12. $\begin{array}{r} 14 \\ \times\ 6 \\ \hline 84 \end{array}$
13. $\begin{array}{r} 28 \\ \times\ 3 \\ \hline 84 \end{array}$
14. $\begin{array}{r} 34 \\ \times\ 7 \\ \hline 238 \end{array}$
15. $\begin{array}{r} 43 \\ \times\ 4 \\ \hline 172 \end{array}$

16. 4×42 168
17. 6×75 450
18. 5×47 235
19. 3×92 276
20. 7×29 203

21. Find the product of 4 and 72. 288
22. How many days are in 16 weeks? 112 days

23. **Reasoning** How would you use regrouping to find 8 times 17?
Add 5 tens after multiplying 8 times 1 ten. $8 \times 17 = 136$
24. **Reasoning** If you wanted to find the product of 38 and 8, how would you estimate to check your answer?
Round 38 to 40. $40 \times 8 = 320$

Lesson 5-5   211

Additional Examples

52	36	48
$\times\ 4$	$\times\ 5$	$\times\ 6$
208	180	288

Talk About It Ongoing Assessment

Encourage students to think of examples that need one regrouping or no regrouping. Check that explanations show a clear understanding of place value.

Answers for Talk About It

1 3 tens, from regrouping 32 ones

2 No; The product of 2 and 4 is a 1-digit number (8).

Check

Exercises 8 and 17 Be sure students understand the reason for the zeros in the products.

Error Intervention Ongoing Assessment

Observation Students may add the extra tens that were regrouped and then multiply.

How to Help Show students the following:

$$\begin{array}{r} \overset{2}{56} \\ \times\ 4 \\ \hline 284 \end{array}$$

Ask students if they think the product is correct. Have them estimate the product by rounding 56 to the nearest ten. Ask if their estimate (about 240) is greater or less than the actual answer. Greater

Help them understand that an answer of 284 is too great and they may have added before multiplying. (The correct product is 224.)

Meeting Individual Needs

Learning Styles	Teaching Approach
Verbal	Have students work Check and Practice exercises in pairs, explaining to each other the steps and regrouping they do.
Social	Have students work in groups of three. For each exercise, one student multiplies the ones and records, another multiplies and adds the tens and records, and the third uses estimation to check the product.

Practice •••••••••••••••••••••

Exercises 53 and 59 Have students trade the questions they write or save them for use at another time.

Exercise 54 You may wish to have students use *Reading Strategies for Math* Chart 23, (Making a Bar Graph).

Interactive CD-ROM Journal
Students can use the Journal Tool for Exercise 61. They can also use the Place-Value Block Tool to illustrate their explanations.

For Early Finishers Challenge early finishers to choose one exercise from Exercises 25–44 and write a word problem using those numbers.

Practice •••••••••••••••••••••••••••••••••

Skills and Reasoning

Find each product. Estimate to check.

25.	26.	27.	28.	29.
26	71	48	33	91
× 5	× 8	× 9	× 6	× 7
130	568	432	198	637

30.	31.	32.	33.	34.
96	74	59	65	88
× 4	× 7	× 8	× 3	× 6
384	518	472	195	528

35.	36.	37.	38.	39.
27	93	52	47	46
× 8	× 4	× 5	× 8	× 3
216	372	260	376	138

40. 9×24 **216** **41.** 5×43 **215** **42.** 7×55 **385** **43.** 4×61 **244** **44.** 7×68 **476**

45. Find the product of 3 and 42. **126** **46.** Find the product of 67 and 9. **603**

47. How would you use regrouping to find the product of 23 and 9?
Add 2 tens after multiplying 9 times 2 tens. $23 \times 9 = 207$

48. Estimation Use estimation to find the greater product: 906×3 or 806×4?
906×3 is about $900 \times 3 = 2,700$.
806×4 is about $800 \times 4 = 3,200$.
$806 \times 4 > 906 \times 3$

Problem Solving and Applications

49. Time Jerry has to read a book that has 157 pages. If he reads 15 pages a night, will he finish the book in a week? Explain.
No; 15 pages times 7 days is only 105 pages in a week.

Using Data Use the double-bar graph for **50–53**.

50. On which day did Jerry spend more time doing homework than Pam? **Wednesday**

51. About how many hours did Jerry spend doing homework that week? **About 2 hours**

52. How much more time did Pam spend than Jerry doing homework that week? **135 minutes**

53. Write Your Own Problem Write a question that can be answered using the bar graph. Ask a friend to solve it. **Answers will vary.**

54. Collecting Data Work with a partner to keep track of the time you spend doing homework each day for a week. Make a double-bar graph of your data. **Answers will vary.**

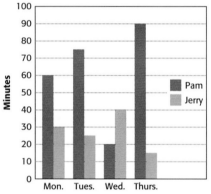
Time Spent Doing Homework

Practice 5-5

Reteaching 5-5

Problem Solving and SCIENCE

China is the home of the giant panda. Its Chinese name, Xiong Mao (shee-ung mow), means "giant cat bear." A giant panda eats about 32 pounds of bamboo leaves and stems each day. Giant pandas grow to 5 ft tall and weigh about 330 pounds.

55. About how many pounds of bamboo leaves and stems does a giant panda eat in a week? **224 pounds**

56. A giant panda spends about 14 hours each day eating. How many hours in a week does a panda spend eating? **98 hours**

57. A giant panda eats about 84 pounds of bamboo shoots each day. About how many pounds does it eat in 5 days? **420 pounds**

58. A zoo needs to transport 2 pandas to another zoo. The zoo has a medium-size truck that can hold 1,000 pounds. Will the truck be able to hold both pandas at the same time? Explain.
Yes; 2 × 330 pounds = 660 pounds, 660 < 1,000

59. **Write Your Own Problem** Use the data about pandas. Write a question that can be answered using multiplication. **Answers will vary.**

60. **Geography** The world's tallest mountain peak, Mt. Everest, is on the border of China and Nepal. It is almost 9,000 ft taller than Mt. McKinley. At 20,320 ft, Mt. McKinley is the tallest U.S. mountain. About how tall is Mt. Everest? **about 29,000 ft**

61. **Journal** How do you use place value to help you find 3×34?

Mixed Review and Test Prep

Algebra Readiness Find each missing number.

62. $4 \times n = 2,400$ **600**
63. $n \times 30 = 90$ **3**
64. $n \times 700 = 5,600$ **8**
65. $5 \times 200 = n$ **1,000**
66. $6 \times n = 36$ **6**
67. $n \times 4 = 36$ **9**
68. $18 \div n = 9$ **2**
69. $n \div 3 = 6$ **18**

70. **Estimation** A package of cookies contains 18 cookies. About how many cookies are in 4 packages? **C**

Ⓐ 40 cookies   Ⓑ 50 cookies   Ⓒ 80 cookies   Ⓓ not here

Skills Practice Bank, page 564, Set 2   Lesson 5-5   **213**

Enrichment 5-5

Problem Solving 5-5

PRACTICE AND APPLY

Science Note

In the early 1990s, fewer than 1,000 giant pandas were surviving in the wild. A large portion of the panda's natural habitat has been lost in China due to the cutting of forests for wood and farmland.

In an attempt to protect the panda, the Chinese government has established 13 reserves containing an abundance of bamboo. Large bamboo reserves are needed because, every 15 to 20 years, bamboo plants flower, produce seeds, and die. In the several years that it takes for seeds to grow into food-providing plants, many pandas might die of starvation.

3 Close and Assess

Interview

Have students choose one exercise from Check or Practice and explain how they solved it and how they knew the answer was reasonable. The explanation should include multiplying ones and tens, regrouping if necessary, and estimating the product to check for reasonableness.

Quick Check

Number Sense Estimate to order the products in the Skill exercises below from least to greatest. Exercises 4, 1, 3, 2

Skill Find each product.

1. 3×72 216

2. 6×87 522

3. 9×45 405

4. 5×38 190

ANSWERS

61 Possible answer: Multiply 3×4 ones and regroup the product as 1 ten and 2 ones. Multiply 3×3 tens and add 1 ten. $3 \times 34 = 102$

Chapter 5 • Lesson 5-5   **213**

At-A-Glance Planning

Lesson Planning Checklist

Objective Multiply 3-digit numbers.

Student Book Lesson Materials None

Materials for pages 214A and 214B Place-value blocks (5 hundreds, 13 tens, 15 ones per group), Teaching Tool Transparency 6 (Centimeter Grid Paper)

Subject Connection science—worms

Strand Connections using data, patterns

	Before Lesson	During Lesson	After Lesson
Daily Math			
p. 214A Problem of the Day			
p. 214A Math Routines			
p. 214A Mental Math			
Teaching Options			
p. 214 Student Book Lesson			
p. 214B Another Way to Learn…			
Options for Reaching All Learners			
p. 214B Inclusion			
p. 214B Reading Assist			
Subject Connections			
p. 214A Literature Connection			
Assessment Options			
p. 214 Talk About It			
p. 215 Error Intervention			
p. 215 Portfolio			
p. 215 Quick Check			
Resources			
5-6 Practice			
5-6 Reteaching			
5-6 Enrichment			
5-6 Problem Solving			
5-6 Daily Transparency			

Problem of the Day

Problem of the Day

Copy the array. Cross out pairs of numbers having a product of: 46, 72, 210, or 222. What number is left?

2	18	3
37	4	42
5	23	6

3

Math Routines

Time Ask students how many minutes long a 2-hour movie is. Then ask how many hours and minutes long a 90-minute movie is. 120 minutes; 1 hour and 30 minutes.

Patterns Have students multiply 3 × 100, 3 × 200, and 3 × 300 and look for a pattern. 300, 600, 900; Product increases by 300 each time.

Mental Math

Add 10. Explain your thinking.

73 83   97 107

198 208   992 1,002

Literature Connection

Patricia Lauber's *An Octopus Is Amazing* provides science facts and numerical data about these sea creatures.

- Explain that an octopus has 8 tentacles, or arms, and that each tentacle has about 240 small suction cups on it. Ask students to write a multiplication sentence that shows about how many suction cups an octopus has in all. 8 × 240 = 1,920

Another Way to ▮ Learn ▮ Lesson 5-6

Use as an alternative or in addition to pages 214 and 215.

Materials Place-value blocks (5 hundreds, 13 tens, 15 ones per group)

Learning Style Kinesthetic

• Have groups use place-value blocks to find 3 × 145. 435

• Review steps in the multiplication process. Then have groups try these.

  3 × 134 402   2 × 206 412   4 × 130 520

• Model on the overhead the connection of the manipulatives to symbolic recording. Emphasize regrouping. Model how to draw pictures of blocks.

• Have groups draw pictures of blocks and record the steps symbolically for the following exercises.

  4 × 214 856   3 × 306 918   3 × 167 501

• Have students talk about how they regroup.

• Assign Check and Practice on Student Book page 215 or *Practice Master* 5-6.

• Assess using the following rubric.

Options for Reaching All Learners

Inclusion

Regrouping

Use grid paper to align and add regrouped numbers.

Materials Teaching Tool Transparency 6 (Centimeter Grid Paper)

Learning Style Visual

• Some students may misalign regrouped numbers or forget to add them after multiplying. Use grid paper to help students position the numbers.

• Marking the regrouped number with a colored pen may help students remember to add it.

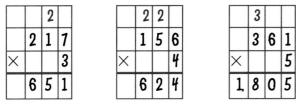

Reading Assist

Recognize Sequence

Use transparencies to reinforce the algorithms sequence.

Learning Style Visual, Verbal/Auditory

Students may have trouble following the sequence of steps for multiplying a 3-digit number by a 1-digit number.

• Copy Example 1 on page 214 on a transparency. Add place-value heads to guide students.

• Invite a volunteer to read aloud Step 1, pausing after each sentence. Ask students which numbers should be multiplied. Trace over these numbers in red. 6, 5

• Ask students to give the product for the ones and tell where the product should be written. Repeat for Steps 2 and 3.

Lesson Organizer

Objective Multiply 3-digit numbers.

Student Materials None

Assignment Guide

Basic 7–17, 21, 23, 24, 26–30

Average 7–11, 17–23, 25–30

Enriched 12–30

1 Introduce

Review

Find each product.

1. 60	**2.** 57	**3.** 34
× 7	× 2	× 3
420	114	102

Build on Prior Knowledge

After students review how to find 3 × 34, ask how they could use what they know about multiplication to find 3 × 334. Multiply the hundreds by repeating the steps used for ones and tens. Accept all reasonable answers.

2 Teach

See Another Way to Learn…on page 214B.

Learn ● ● ● ● ● ● ● ● ● ● ● ● ● ● ● ● ● ●

When focusing on the question in Example 1, ask why multiplication is used for the solution. Multiplication helps combine equal groups.

Additional Examples

412	719	307
× 9	× 8	× 4
3,708	5,752	1,228

Talk About It **Ongoing Assessment**

Encourage students to think of examples requiring that they regroup once, twice, or not at all. Check that students' explanations show a clear understanding of place value.

Answer for Talk About It

Round 125 to 100. 100 × 6 = 600;
Round 208 to 200. 200 × 8 = 1,600

Multiplying 3-Digit Numbers

You Will Learn

how to multiply a 3-digit number by a 1-digit number

Learn ● ● ● ● ● ● ● ● ● ● ● ● ● ● ● ● ● ●

Taz cares for worms that recycle garbage into rich soil. A start-up worm kit has 125 red worms.

Example 1

How many red worms are needed for 6 kits? Find 6 × 125.

Step 1	**Step 2**	**Step 3**
Multiply the ones. Regroup as needed.	Multiply the tens. Add any extra tens. Regroup as needed.	Multiply the hundreds. Add any extra hundreds.
3 125 × 6 0	1 3 125 × 6 50	1 3 125 × 6 750

6 × 125 = 750 So, 750 worms are needed for 6 kits.

Here's how to multiply when there's a zero in a 3-digit number.

Example 2

Find 8 × 208.

Step 1	**Step 2**	**Step 3**
Multiply the ones. Regroup as needed.	Multiply the tens. Add any extra tens. Regroup as needed.	Multiply the hundreds. Add any extra hundreds.
6 208 × 8 4	6 208 × 8 64	6 208 × 8 1,664

8 × 208 = 1,664

Remember

You can multiply this way, too.

208
× 8
64
0
1,600
1,664

Talk About It

How can you estimate each product in the Examples?

Name _____

Practice 5-6

Multiplying 3-Digit Numbers

Multiply.

1. 402 × 9 3,618	**2.** 524 × 7 3,668	**3.** 509 × 4 2,036	**4.** 457 × 6 2,742
5. 707 × 7 4,949	**6.** 512 × 3 1,536	**7.** 305 × 9 2,745	**8.** 758 × 5 3,790
9. 403 × 8 3,224	**10.** 705 × 8 5,640	**11.** 315 × 4 1,260	**12.** 607 × 9 5,463
13. 568 × 6 3,408	**14.** 804 × 4 3,216	**15.** 423 × 8 3,384	**16.** 618 × 7 4,326
17. 233 × 4 932	**18.** 724 × 9 6,516	**19.** 365 × 6 2,190	**20.** 424 × 5 2,120
21. 630 × 7 4,410	**22.** 197 × 3 591	**23.** 872 × 2 1,744	**24.** 550 × 8 4,400

25. 894 × 8 = _7,152_

26. 7 × 664 = _4,648_

27. 6 × 752 = _4,512_

28. 4 × 953 = _3,812_

29. Find the product of 8 and 307. _2,456_

30. Find the product of 4 and 209. _836_

31. Multiply 6 and 273. _1,638_

32. Multiply 8 and 743. _5,944_

Name _____

Another Look 5-6

Multiplying 3-Digit Numbers

Breaking numbers apart can make them easier to multiply.

Find the product of 547 and 4.

You can break 547 into hundreds, tens, and ones.

Step 1 547 = 500 + 40 + 7

Step 2 Multiply each part by 4.

4 × 7 = 28

4 × 40 = 160

4 × 500 = 2,000

Step 3 Add. 2,188

Find each product. Break numbers apart to help you.

1. 566 = 500 + 60 + 6
× 4

4 × 6 = _24_
4 × 60 = _240_
4 × 500 = _2,000_
_2,264_

2. 601 = 600 + 1
× 5

5 × 1 = _5_
5 × 600 = _3,000_
_3,005_

3. 789 = 700 + 80 + 9
× 3

3 × 9 = _27_
3 × 80 = _240_
3 × 700 = _2,100_
_2,367_

4. 342 = 300 + 40 + 2
× 8

8 × 2 = _16_
8 × 40 = _320_
8 × 300 = _2,400_
_2,736_

Check

Multiply. Estimate to check.

1.	234	2.	903	3.	829	4.	706	5.	617
	× 3		× 5		× 6		× 4		× 8
	702		4,515		4,974		2,824		4,936

6. **Reasoning** How could you use the product of 104 and 6 to find the product of 208 and 6? **Multiply the product of 104 and 6 by 2.**

Practice

Skills and Reasoning

Multiply. Estimate to check.

7.	301	8.	562	9.	408	10.	346	11.	608
	× 8		× 6		× 3		× 5		× 7
	2,408		3,372		1,224		1,730		4,256
12.	613	13.	204	14.	647	15.	302	16.	404
	× 4		× 8		× 4		× 7		× 9
	2,452		1,632		2,588		2,114		3,636

17. 783 × 9 **7,047** 18. 7 × 553 **3,871** 19. 5 × 641 **3,205** 20. 3 × 842 **2,526**

21. Find the product of 9 and 206. **1,854**   22. Multiply 3 and 108. **324**

Problem Solving and Applications

Using Data Taz measured some red worms. Use the table to answer **23** and **24**.

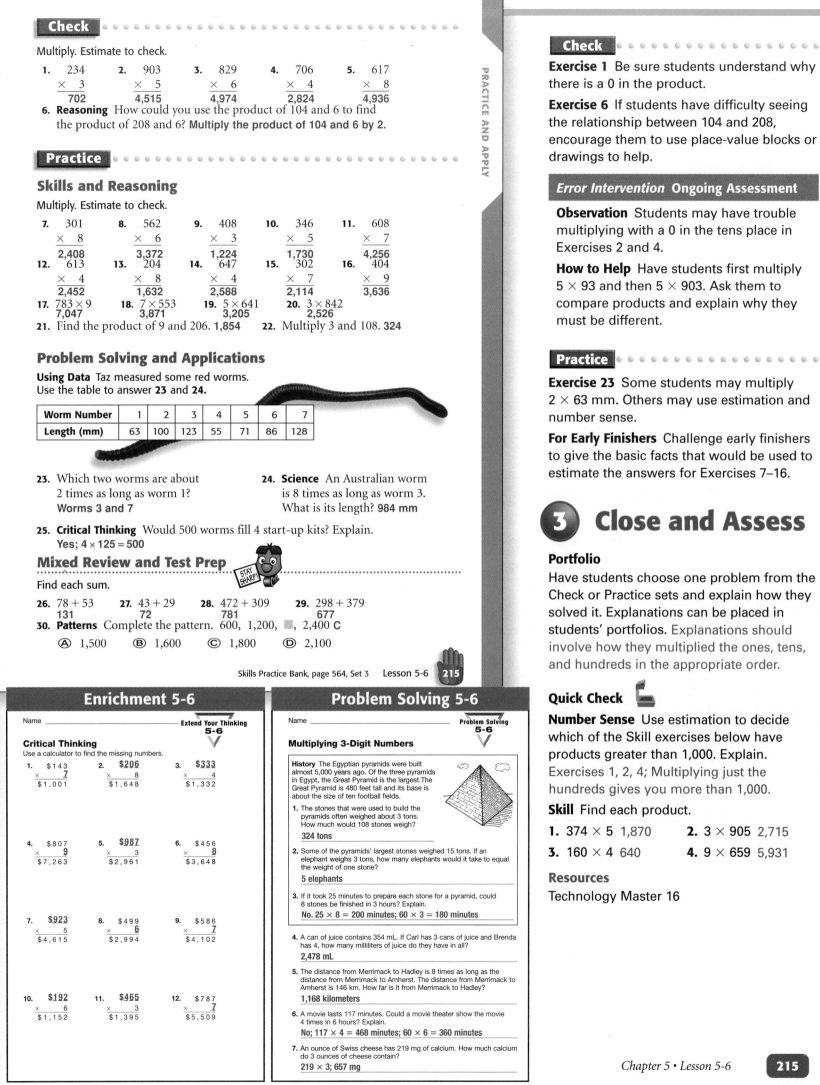

Worm Number	1	2	3	4	5	6	7
Length (mm)	63	100	123	55	71	86	128

23. Which two worms are about 2 times as long as worm 1? **Worms 3 and 7**

24. **Science** An Australian worm is 8 times as long as worm 3. What is its length? **984 mm**

25. **Critical Thinking** Would 500 worms fill 4 start-up kits? Explain. **Yes; 4 × 125 = 500**

Mixed Review and Test Prep

Find each sum.

26. 78 + 53 **131**   27. 43 + 29 **72**   28. 472 + 309 **781**   29. 298 + 379 **677**

30. **Patterns** Complete the pattern. 600, 1,200, ■, 2,400 **C**

ⓐ 1,500   ⓑ 1,600   ⓒ 1,800   ⓓ 2,100

Skills Practice Bank, page 564, Set 3   Lesson 5-6   **215**

Enrichment 5-6

Name _____ **Extend Your Thinking 5-6**

Critical Thinking
Use a calculator to find the missing numbers.

1.	$143	2.	$206	3.	$333
	× 7		× 8		× 4
	$1,001		$1,648		$1,332

4.	$807	5.	$987	6.	$456
	× 9		× 3		× 8
	$7,263		$2,961		$3,648

7.	$923	8.	$499	9.	$586
	× 5		× 6		× 7
	$4,615		$2,994		$4,102

10.	$192	11.	$465	12.	$787
	× 6		× 3		× 7
	$1,152		$1,395		$5,509

Problem Solving 5-6

Name _____ **Problem Solving 5-6**

Multiplying 3-Digit Numbers

History The Egyptian pyramids were built almost 5,000 years ago. Of the three pyramids in Egypt, the Great Pyramid is the largest. The Great Pyramid is 480 feet tall and its base is about the size of ten football fields.

1. The stones that were used to build the pyramids often weighed about 3 tons. How much would 108 stones weigh?

   324 tons

2. Some of the pyramids' largest stones weighed 15 tons. If an elephant weighs 3 tons, how many elephants would it take to equal the weight of one stone?

   5 elephants

3. If it took 25 minutes to prepare each stone for a pyramid, could 8 stones be finished in 3 hours? Explain.

   No. 25 × 8 = 200 minutes; 60 × 3 = 180 minutes

4. A can of juice contains 354 mL. If Carl has 3 cans of juice and Brenda has 4, how many milliliters of juice do they have in all?

   2,478 mL

5. The distance from Merrimack to Hadley is 8 times as long as the distance from Merrimack to Amherst. The distance from Merrimack to Amherst is 146 km. How far is it from Merrimack to Hadley?

   1,168 kilometers

6. A movie lasts 117 minutes. Could a movie theater show the movie 4 times in 6 hours? Explain.

   No; 117 × 4 = 468 minutes; 60 × 6 = 360 minutes

7. An ounce of Swiss cheese has 219 mg of calcium. How much calcium do 3 ounces of cheese contain?

   219 × 3; 657 mg

Check

Exercise 1 Be sure students understand why there is a 0 in the product.

Exercise 6 If students have difficulty seeing the relationship between 104 and 208, encourage them to use place-value blocks or drawings to help.

Error Intervention Ongoing Assessment

Observation Students may have trouble multiplying with a 0 in the tens place in Exercises 2 and 4.

How to Help Have students first multiply 5 × 93 and then 5 × 903. Ask them to compare products and explain why they must be different.

Practice

Exercise 23 Some students may multiply 2 × 63 mm. Others may use estimation and number sense.

For Early Finishers Challenge early finishers to give the basic facts that would be used to estimate the answers for Exercises 7–16.

③ Close and Assess

Portfolio

Have students choose one problem from the Check or Practice sets and explain how they solved it. Explanations can be placed in students' portfolios. Explanations should involve how they multiplied the ones, tens, and hundreds in the appropriate order.

Quick Check

Number Sense Use estimation to decide which of the Skill exercises below have products greater than 1,000. Explain.
Exercises 1, 2, 4; Multiplying just the hundreds gives you more than 1,000.

Skill Find each product.

1. 374 × 5 **1,870**   2. 3 × 905 **2,715**

3. 160 × 4 **640**   4. 9 × 659 **5,931**

Resources

Technology Master 16

Chapter 5 • Lesson 5-6   **215**

Decision Making: What's Cooking?

At-A-Glance Planning

Objective Solve problems by making decisions about cooking.
Student Book Lesson Materials None
Materials for pages 216A and 216B None
Subject Connection career–baking
Strand Connections time, using data

	Before Lesson	During Lesson	After Lesson
Daily Math			
p. 216A Problem of the Day			
p. 216A Math Routines			
p. 216A Mental Math			
Teaching Options			
p. 216B Facilitating and Assessing…			
Options for Reaching All Learners			
p. 216B Reading Assist			
p. 216B Language Development			
Technology Options			
p. 216A *Logical Journey of the Zoombinis*			
Assessment Options			
p. 217 Journal			
Resources			
5-7 Practice			
5-7 Reteaching			
5-7 Enrichment			
5-7 Problem Solving			
5-7 Daily Transparency			

Problem of the Day

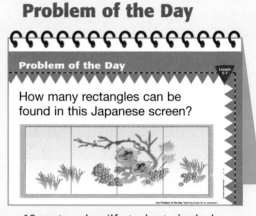

Problem of the Day

How many rectangles can be found in this Japanese screen?

10 rectangles (If students include the gold border, 11 rectangles.)

Math Routines

Calendar Ask students whether it is possible to find three consecutive months in the same year that have a total of exactly 90 days. In non–leap years, Jan, Feb, Mar: 31 + 28 + 31

Money Which is worth more: 9 dimes or the sum of $0.60 + $0.20? 9 dimes

Mental Math

Name the number that is 20 less. Explain your thinking.

62 42	102 82
314 294	1,410 1,390

 Logical Journey of the Zoombinis

The games found in the *Logical Journey of the Zoombinis* help develop students' problem solving skills. Each game requires students to make decisions to move the Zoombini characters along.

• Have students play the Very Hard and Very, Very Hard levels of *Stone Rise* to create networks with the shortest number of connections.

Facilitating and Assessing **Explore** Lesson 5-7

Use with pages 216 and 217.

Getting Started You may want to assign these roles to group members: reader, calculator, recorder, and reporter.

Observe Encourage students to pay attention to the baking temperatures. Students may not know that some cookies require different temperatures and cannot be baked at the same time.

Discuss Encourage students to think about baking time and number of cookies on a sheet.

Assess Use the rubric to assess students' work. See sample.

4 Full Accomplishment

Kind of Cookie	Quantity	Baking Time
Cinnamon	4 dozen	12 min
Sugar	4 dozen	20 min
Peanut butter	12 dozen	45 min
Total	20 dozen	1 hour 17 min

Assessment Rubric

4 Full Accomplishment
- uses data to make decisions and solve problems
- explains how the plan was made

3 Substantial Accomplishment
- uses data to make decisions and solve most problems
- explains how the plan was made

2 Partial Accomplishment
- uses data to make some decisions and solve some problems
- partially explains how the plan was made

1 Little Accomplishment
- does not use data to make decisions or solve problems
- does not explain how to make a plan

Options for Reaching All Learners

Reading Assist

Read Tables
Use questions to strengthen reading skills.

Learning Style Verbal, Kinesthetic

- Have students alternate asking each other questions based on the table on page 216, such as:

  a. At what temperature do you bake almond cookies?
  350°F

  b. Which kind of cookie must bake for 20 minutes?
  Chocolate chip

- Have students who answer questions show on the table the rows and columns in which they looked. **a.** Row: Almond; Column: Temperature; **b.** Row: Chocolate chip; Column: Baking Time

- Challenge students to ask other questions about information in the table.

Language Development

A Cooking Timetable
Use a discussion about information in a table to strengthen communication skills.

Learning Style Visual

- Write the following table outline on the overhead.

Start Time	End Time	Kind of Cookie	Quality

- Have groups discuss and complete this schedule, based on the plans they develop for baking cookies. As students talk, you can rephrase and elaborate on ideas they present, using simple, standard English.

Lesson Organizer

Objective Solve problems by making decisions about cooking.

Suggested Grouping 2 to 4

Student Materials None

Assignment Guide

Basic 1–16

Average 1–16

Enriched 1–16

1 Introduce

Review

Multiply to find how many in each amount.

1. 1 dozen 12   **2.** 2 dozen 24

3. 3 dozen 36   **4.** 5 dozen 60

Build on Prior Knowledge

After students have reviewed the meaning of the word *dozen* and practiced finding the number in several dozen, ask how they might solve the following problem: If a cookie sheet holds 16 cookies, how many sheets do you need for 3 dozen cookies? Multiply 16 by 2 and by 3 and compare the products to 36.

2 Teach

See Facilitating and Assessing...on page 216B.

Explore ● ● ● ● ● ● ● ● ● ● ● ● ● ● ● ● ●

You may wish to ask questions such as the following as you observe students at work.

• How did you find out how many cookies the rack would hold? $3 \times 16 = 48$

Reading Assist Find the Main Idea

Make sure students understand what they are to do. Have students tell in their own words what they think their task is. You can rephrase and elaborate on their ideas without correcting them. Be sure students understand that there may be different plans that fit the situation.

Problem Solving
Decision Making: What's Cooking?

You Will Learn how to solve problems by making decisions

Explore ●

Louise and Lizzie invented a rack that holds 3 cookie sheets. Each cookie sheet holds 16 cookies. Your group has offered to bake cookies for Family Night at school. Plan to use one of Louise and Lizzie's racks. What kinds of cookies will you make? How many cookies will you make of each kind?

Louise and Lizzie are from St. Paul, Minnesota. The cookie rack they invented is now sold in stores and catalogs.

Facts and Data

You need to make at least 20 dozen cookies for Family Night.

You want to make at least three different kinds of cookies.

You have only two hours to bake the cookies.

The baking times and temperatures of some kinds of cookies are different.

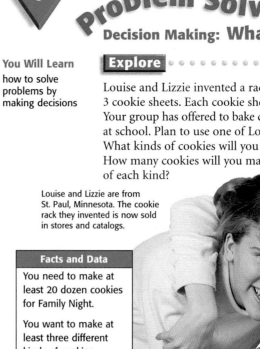

Kind of Cookie	Quantity in Recipe	Number per Cookie Sheet	Baking Time	Temperature
Chocolate chip	3 dozen	12 cookies	20 min	350°F
Peanut butter	6 dozen	16 cookies	15 min	375°F
Almond	5 dozen	16 cookies	12 min	350°F
Gingersnaps	5 dozen	16 cookies	10 min	350°F
Cinnamon	4 dozen	16 cookies	12 min	375°F
Sugar	4 dozen	12 cookies	10 min	375°F

216   Chapter 5 • Multiplying by 1-Digit Factors

Practice 5-7

Name _____

Practice 5-7

Decision Making

Scientists say dinosaurs hatched from eggs just like alligators do today. Dinosaur eggs have been found in sizes ranging from 3 inches to over 18 inches long. A nest of these eggs is called a clutch. In science class, Tomás drew 24 clutches with 5 eggs each and Mary Jane drew 18 clutches with 8 eggs each. Who drew the greater number of eggs?

1. What are you asked to find?
Who drew the greater number of eggs

2. Circle the numbers needed to answer the question.
Circle 24, 5, 18, 8.

3. What operation will you use? __Multiplication__

Write number sentences.

4. __24__ × __5__ = __120__ (total number of eggs Tomás drew)

5. __18__ × __8__ = __144__ (total number of eggs Mary Jane drew)

6. Who drew the greater number of eggs? __Mary Jane__

7. How could you check your answer?
Possible answer: By drawing an array

8. What if Tomás drew 24 clutches with 6 eggs each? Who would have drawn the greater number of eggs?
24 × 6 = 144; Both would have drawn the same number.

Reteaching 5-7

Name _____

Another Look 5-7

Decision Making

A group of sea otters is called a raft. Several rafts of sea otters live off the coast of California. Scientists who study sea otters often tag a few otters of different ages in each raft. They often tag 1 of 10 otters in each raft. They make conclusions based on what they notice about the tagged otters.

65 otters
× 7 rafts
455

Seven rafts had 65 sea otters each.

How many otters are there all together? __455__

How many tens are there in 455? __45__ tens

How many sea otters will be tagged? __45__

1. In another area, there are 8 rafts with 82 sea otters in each raft.

a. How many otters are there all together? __656__

b. How many tens are there? __65__ tens

c. How many sea otters will be tagged? __65__

2. By one island, there are 6 rafts of 72 sea otters.

a. How many otters are there all together? __432__

b. How many tens are there? __43__ tens

c. How many sea otters will be tagged? __43__

3. How many otters will be tagged in each of the following:

a. 5 rafts of 42 __21__

b. 4 rafts of 53? __21__

c. 7 rafts of 25? __17__

Work Together

▶ **Understand**

1. What do you know?

2. What are you asked to do? **Bake 20 dozen cookies in 2 hours.**

3. What is the main decision you have to make? **Decide what kinds of cookies to make, and how many of each kind to make.**

▶ **Plan and Solve**

4. Which cookie recipe provides the greatest quantities? **Peanut butter**

5. Which kinds of cookies let you bake the most on a cookie sheet at one time? **Peanut butter, almond, gingersnaps, cinnamon**

6. Which cookies bake at the same temperature?

7. Which cookies do you want to make? **Answers will vary.**

8. Find out how many of each kind of cookie you can bake at one time. **3 dozen chocolate chip; 4 dozen of any other kind of cookies**

Problem Solving Tip
Estimate to help you make decisions.

▶ **Make a Decision**

9. Write a list of the cookies that you plan to make. **Answers will vary.**

10. How many cookies of each kind will you make? **Answers will vary but should include 20 dozen all together.**

11. What is the total amount of time you will spend baking cookies? **Answers will vary but should be ≤ 2 hrs**

▶ **Present Your Decision**

12. Tell how you arrived at your plan. **Answers will vary.**

13. What activities related to making cookies does the table on page 216 not include? **Cost, time preparing dough, buying ingredients**

14. Do you think you would still be able to make at least 20 dozen cookies within 2 hours? **No, not if you have to make dough.**

15. Multiply the number of cookies you can bake at one time

15. How did you use multiplication to make decisions?

16. Check out **www.mathsurf.com/4/ch5** to look for cookie recipes. Then try a recipe to bake cookies for your friends.

PROBLEM SOLVING PRACTICE

Reading Assist **Find Supporting Details**

After students understand what they are to do, ask them where they can find supporting details that will be helpful in implementing their decision. Then ask questions such as the following:

• How many cookies are in a dozen? 12

• How many cookies do you need to bake? At least 240

• How many cookies can you bake on the rack? 48

Exercise 4–8 will help students to identify supporting ideas.

For Early Finishers Challenge early finishers to plan which kinds of cookies and how many of each kind they would make if they needed to make at least 30 dozen in 3 hours.

③ Close and Assess

Journal

Summarize your plan. Explain how you decided which cookies to make. Students should include explanations of how they arrived at their plans, as well as a list of cookies, the number of each kind of cookie, and how long the baking will last.

Assess using the rubric on page 216B.

ANSWERS

1 Number of cookies in a recipe, number of cookies that fit on a cookie sheet, baking time, baking temperatures

6 Chocolate chip, almond, and gingersnaps; peanut butter, cinnamon, and sugar

---

Enrichment 5-7

Name _____   **Extend Your Thinking 5-7**

Decision Making

Approximately 220 dinosaur egg sites have been found around the world in Asia, North America, Europe, South America, and Africa.

Professor Jenkins and her assistant are planning a scientific research trip to visit a dinosaur egg site. These 3 trips are available. Which destination should they choose?

Destination	Number of Days	Cost per Person	Other Information
Asia	8	$1,750	Asia has the greatest number of dinosaur egg sites.
North America	10	$979	There is only one dinosaur egg site in North America.
Europe	7	$1,549 (meals not included)	Europe has two dinosaur egg sites.

1. Which trip could Professor Jenkins and her assistant take for less than $3,000? Explain.
   North America; 2 × $979 is less than $3,000.

2. If meals in Europe cost an additional $175 per person, how much would a trip to Europe for 2 cost? **$3,448**

3. On which trip(s) will Professor Jenkins and her assistant be able to see at least 2 dinosaur egg sites?
   Europe and Asia

4. What additional information could you use to help Professor Jenkins and her assistant make their decision?
   Possible answers: What are the additional expenses? How many days would they like to travel? How close to each other are the dinosaur egg sites in Asia?

5. Which trip should they choose? Explain how you made your decision.
   Check students' reasoning.

Problem Solving 5-7

Name _____   **Problem Solving 5-7**

Decision Making

Suppose you and 7 friends went to a pizza parlor. Each wanted 3 slices of pizza. A large pizza has 20 slices, a medium has 8 slices, and a small has 6 slices. Two friends wanted pepperoni, one wanted sausage, three wanted only cheese, and two wanted ham. What pizzas would you order?

1. What are you asked to do?
   Decide what pizzas to order.

2. How many slices of pizza do you need altogether?
   8 × 3 = 24 slices

3. What size pizzas would you order? Describe two different orders that would provide enough slices of pizza.
   Possible answers: 1 large and 1 small; 3 medium; 1 medium and 3 small; 4 small

4. What strategy can you use to help you determine the toppings for each pizza?
   Possible answers: Draw a picture.

5. What additional information would help you make your decision?
   Possible answers: cost of pizzas; will those who want single toppings want to eat pizza with more than one topping?

6. Make a list of the pizzas you would order. List sizes and toppings.
   Answers will vary. Possible answer: 5 small, 1 with pepperoni, 1 with ham, 1 with sausage, 2 with cheese

7. Describe how you made your decision.
   Answers will vary. Possible answer: This way everyone can have the topping they want.

Choosing a Calculation Method

At-A-Glance Planning

Objective Multiply using different methods.

Student Book Lesson Materials None

Materials for pages 218A and 218B Calculators (1 per group); abacus or box, string, and beads

Subject Connections health—jumping rope, science —giant redwood seeds

Strand Connections mental math, estimation, using data, money

	Before Lesson	During Lesson	After Lesson
Daily Math			
p. 218A Problem of the Day			
p. 218A Math Routines			
p. 218A Mental Math			
Teaching Options			
p. 218 Student Book Lesson			
p. 218B Another Way to Learn…			
Options for Reaching All Learners			
p. 218B Gifted & Talented			
p. 218B Cultural Connection			
Subject Connections			
p. 218A Science Connection			
Assessment Options			
p. 218 Talk About it			
p. 219 Error Intervention			
p. 219 Observation			
p. 219 Quick Check			
Resources			
5-8 Practice			
5-8 Reteaching			
5-8 Enrichment			
5-8 Problem Solving			
5-8 Daily Transparency			

Problem of the Day

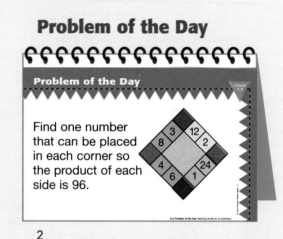

Find one number that can be placed in each corner so the product of each side is 96.

2

Math Routines

Money Ask students to find the value of 17 nickels. $0.85 Some students may skip count by 5s. Some may find the value of 20 nickels and count backward.

Calendar Have students find the greatest number of Saturdays that could be in a month of 31 days. Then have them find the least number. 5; 4

Mental Math

Find each sum. Explain your thinking.

60 + 60 + 60	70 + 70 + 70 + 70
180	280
400 + 400 + 400	200 + 200 + 900
1,200	1,300

Science Connection

The largest giant redwood tree in the U.S. is 365 feet tall and 638 inches around.

• Have students estimate their heights to the nearest foot and use a calculator to find how many times taller the giant redwood tree is than they are.

• Have students measure their arm spans to the nearest inch, then find how many students it would take to encircle the tree.

Another Way to **Learn** Lesson 5-8

Use as an alternative or in addition to pages 218 and 219.

Materials Calculators (1 per group)

Learning Style Logical

- On the chalkboard, list methods students can use to multiply: paper and pencil, calculator, mental math, repeated addition.

- Have each group member choose one of these methods to multiply 3 × 1,247. 3,741

- Have group members compare their work.

- Review the steps in multiplying a 4-digit number by a 1-digit number using each method.

- Have groups find these products. Have each member use a different method, alternating for each exercise.

  5 × 3,000 15,000   6 × 2,508 15,048

  7 × 2,010 14,070   3 × 8,615 25,845

- Have students talk about which methods worked best for different kinds of factors. Students are likely to prefer mental math for problems that don't involve regrouping or include multiples of 10, and paper and pencil or calculator for more difficult numbers.

- Assign Check and Practice on Student Book pages 218 and 219 or *Practice Master 5-8.*

- Assess using the following rubric.

Assessment Rubric

4 Full Accomplishment
- chooses appropriate methods for multiplying
- multiplies a 4-digit number by a 1-digit number

3 Substantial Accomplishment
- with prompting, chooses appropriate methods for multiplying
- multiplies a 4-digit number by a 1-digit number

2 Partial Accomplishment
- has difficulty choosing appropriate methods for multiplying
- multiplies some 4-digit numbers by a 1-digit number

1 Little Accomplishment
- does not choose appropriate methods for multiplying
- has difficulty multiplying a 4-digit number by a 1-digit number

Options for Reaching All Learners

Gifted & Talented

Multiply Mentally by 5

Use mental math to develop a shortcut for multiplying by 5.

Learning Style Logical

- Have students use mental math to follow these steps as you say them one at a time:

  To multiply 42 × 5, divide 42 by 2.

  Multiply the number you get by 10.

- Have students record their answers, use paper and pencil to multiply 5 × 42, and compare.

  42 ÷ 2 = 21   10 × 21 = 210   5 × 42 = 210

- Ask students to explain why the shortcut works. Have them choose other numbers and use the shortcut to multiply by 5. Multiplying a number by 5 is the same as multiplying half of that number by 10 because 10 ÷ 2 = 5.

Cultural Connection

Abacus Multiplication

Strengthen understanding of calculation tools.

Materials Abacus or box, string, and beads

Learning Style Kinesthetic

The abacus is used in Japan as widely as calculators are used in the United States. Demonstrate 3 × 1,223 on a real or home-made abacus. To show 3 × 3 ones, push down 3 sets of 3 ones beads each on the ones string. Continue in this way for 3 × 2 tens, 3 × 2 hundreds, and 3 × 1 thousand.

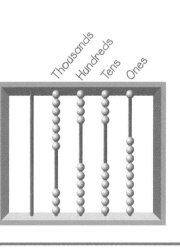

Lesson Organizer

Objective Multiply using different methods.

Student Materials None

Assignment Guide

Basic 6–15, 22, 24–25, 27–32

Average 11–20, 22–25, 27–32

Enriched 14–32

1 Introduce

Review

Find each product.

1. 375	**2.** 500	**3.** 208
× 4	× 7	× 9
1,500	3,500	1,872

Build on Prior Knowledge

After students review ways to multiply a 3-digit number, ask which Review exercises can be solved mentally and which require paper and pencil to solve. Accept all reasonable answers.

2 Teach

See Another Way to Learn...on page 218B.

Learn

Have students compare John, Shauna, and Albert's ways to the ways students have used to multiply a 3-digit number by a 1-digit number.

Additional Examples

1,276	3,007	4,000
× 5	× 6	× 8
6,380	18,042	32,000

Talk About It Ongoing Assessment

Listen for students to recognize that multiples of 10 lend themselves to mental calculation, while problems that require regroupings are often easier to solve with pencil and paper or a calculator.

Answer for Talk About It

When multiplying with greater numbers that require regrouping

Check

Have students using different methods for the same exercise and compare products.

Chapter 5
Lesson
8

Choosing a Calculation Method

You Will Learn
how to multiply using different methods

Learn

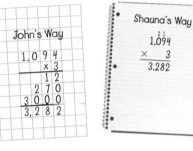

Jumping rope is no longer just a backyard sport. In one contest, the Happy Hoppers jump-rope team earned 3 points for each jump. How many points did the Happy Hoppers earn if the team jumped a total of 1,094 times?

The Happy Hoppers, from Dayton, Ohio, compete in jump-rope contests.

Did You Know?
In 1988, 90 teenagers in Japan used a single jump rope to make 163 jumps in a row—all together.

John, Shauna, and Albert used different ways to find $3 \times 1,094$.

The Happy Hoppers earned 3,282 points.

Talk About It

When might using a calculator be a good method for multiplying?

Check

Multiply.

1. 3,041	**2.** 1,907	**3.** 2,930	**4.** 4,221
× 6	× 6	× 4	× 5
18,246	11,442	11,720	21,105

5. Reasoning How would you find $3 \times 4,000$? Explain. Possible answer: Mental math; 3×4 is a basic fact.

Practice 5-8	Reteaching 5-8

Practice

Skills and Reasoning

Choose a tool

Multiply.

6. 2,567 $\times$ 4 = 10,268	**7.** 4,623 $\times$ 6 = 27,738	**8.** 8,061 $\times$ 5 = 40,305	**9.** 6,000 $\times$ 3 = 18,000	**10.** 8,513 $\times$ 8 = 68,104
11. 4,010 $\times$ 3 = 12,030	**12.** 3,728 $\times$ 4 = 14,912	**13.** 5,000 $\times$ 3 = 15,000	**14.** 7,842 $\times$ 9 = 70,578	**15.** 4,874 $\times$ 7 = 34,118
16. 8,009 $\times$ 4 = 32,036	**17.** 9,000 $\times$ 6 = 54,000	**18.** 9,726 $\times$ 9 = 87,534	**19.** 6,736 $\times$ 8 = 53,888	**20.** 7,309 $\times$ 7 = 51,163

21. Mental Math How would you use mental math to find $3,100 \times 2$?
Multiply 2×3 thousands and 2×1 hundreds to get 6,200.

22. Find the product of 8 and 7,009. 56,072 **23.** Multiply 6 and 5,437. 32,622

24. Estimation Is $4 \times 3,918$ greater than 15,000? Explain. Yes; Round 3,918 to 4,000; $4 \times 4000 = 16,000$, which is greater than 15,000.

Problem Solving and Applications

25. In the game of "Bounce Off," you get 9 points if you jump rope and bounce a ball at the same time. The Happy Hoppers made 1,043 jumps and bounces. How many points did they get?
9,387 points

26. Science There are about 7,688 giant redwood seeds in 1 oz of seeds. About how many seeds are there in half a pound?
61,504 seeds

Remember
16 ounces (oz) = 1 pound (lb)

27. Using Data Use the Data File on page 197. Which activities have the same health rating as jumping rope? Jogging and skiing

Mixed Review and Test Prep

Find each quotient.

28. $18 \div 9$ 2 **29.** $54 \div 6$ 9 **30.** $63 \div 9$ 7 **31.** $21 \div 3$ 7

32. Using Data Use the table to answer. Ms. Owens ordered eight 10-ft jump ropes, eight 8-ft jump ropes, and two 16-ft jump ropes for her P.E. class. How much did the order cost? **B**

Length (ft)	7	8	10	16
Price	$4	$5	$6	$9

Ⓐ $176   Ⓑ $106

Ⓒ $84   Ⓓ $66

Lesson 5-8 **219**

Enrichment 5-8

Name _____ **Extend Your Thinking 5-8**

Critical Thinking
Joe Smith is an all-star running back for his football team. This card shows his record for five years.

Year	Total Yards	Touchdowns	Carries
1990	1,220	9	210
1991	1,340	7	264
1992	1,220	6	190
1993	1,640	9	283
1994	1,084	8	186

1. a. Estimate the total number of yards Joe ran from 1990 to 1994. Should you use a calculator? Explain.
About 6,000; You can round the numbers and add mentally to estimate.

b. Explain how you used multiplication to estimate the total number of yards.
The total number of yards for 4 years rounds to 1,000, so you can find the estimate by multiplying 4 by 1,000 and adding the final 2,000.

2. Estimate the total number of carries Joe made. Can you use multiplication? Explain.
About 1,200; you could use multiplication with grouping.
$(200 \times 3) + (300 \times 2)$

3. Would you estimate to find the total number of touchdowns Joe made? How many did he make?
No; 39

Problem Solving 5-8

Name _____ **Problem Solving 5-8**

Choosing a Calculation Method

Geography Charles lives in Boston. He often has to travel to other cities on business. He earns one frequent flier point for each mile he travels.

1. How many round trips between Boston and St. Louis would Charles need to take to earn 15,000 points? 8

2. a. How many fewer round trips to San Antonio would Charles need to take to earn 15,000 points? 3

b. Explain how you found your answer.
Possible answer: I found the number of round trips Charles would have to take to San Antonio to earn 15,000 points. Then I subtracted from 8.

3. Describe one combination of round trips Charles could take to St. Louis and to San Antonio to earn 15,000 points.
Possible answer: 2 trips to San Antonio and 4 trips to St. Louis

4. Maria, Jack, Cindy, and Ron each have jump ropes 187 centimeters long. If they lay their jump ropes end to end, how many centimeters in all will their jump ropes measure?
748 centimeters

5. Maria uses her jump rope to jump 328 times. If each of the other students jumps half that number of times, how many jumps are made in all?
820 jumps

Error Intervention Ongoing Assessment

Observation Students may assume all products on calculators are correct.

How to Help Discuss the types of errors that can be made when using a calculator. Encourage students to estimate to check the reasonableness of answers.

Practice

Exercise 24 Extend this by having students estimate how much less than 16,000 the product is.

For Early Finishers Challenge early finishers to change a number in a Check or Practice exercise for which they used a calculator so that mental math would be the best method and vice versa.

③ Close and Assess

Observation

Observe whether students are able to use mental math, paper and pencil, and a calculator to multiply appropriately.

Possible choices for mental math: Exercises 9, 11, 13, 16, 17; For partial products: Exercises 11, 16; For paper and pencil or calculator: Exercises 6, 7, 8, 10, 12, 14, 15, 18, 19, 20

Quick Check

Number Sense Use estimation to decide which of the Skill exercises below have products greater than 30,000. Explain.
Exercises 2 and 3; After rounding the 4-digit factor to thousands, the multiplication fact has a product greater than 30.

Skill Find each product. For each, explain your choice of method.

1. $3 \times 6,040$ 18,120; Possible answers: Paper and pencil or calculator or mental math

2. $6,789 \times 5$ 33,945; Possible answers: Paper and pencil or calculator

3. $8,000 \times 9$ 72,000; Possible answer: Mental math

4. $7 \times 4,026$ 28,182; Possible answers: Paper and pencil or calculator

Chapter 5
Practice Game

Students will strengthen number sense and multiplication skills as they play the practice game.

Learning Style Logical

Student Materials Digit cards 0–9 for each group, *optional Assessment Sourcebook 10* (How We Worked in Our Group)

Preparation

Make a set of digit cards for each pair or group of students.

How to Play

Distribute the digit cards and explain the goal of The Greatest Product Game.

Review the steps of the game with the students or play a demonstration game as a class.

The Greatest Product Game

Players
2 or more

Materials
set of digit cards

Object
The object of the game is to make a multiplication problem with the greatest product.

How to Play

1. Each player draws a multiplication grid like the one below. Shuffle the cards and lay them face down.

2. One player turns over a card. Each player writes that number in any box on his or her multiplication grid.

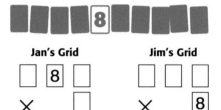

Jan's Grid   Jim's Grid

Math Center Option

As an alternative, set up this game in a math center for students to play independently or in pairs. Post a recording sheet or a journal prompt question for students to record their greatest products and the strategies they used.

③ A player continues turning over cards until players have placed numbers in all of the boxes on the grid.

④ Multiply. The player with the greatest product wins.

⑤ Play five or more games. Look for winning strategies.

Talk About It

1. What strategies did you use to get the greatest product?

2. Which card did you least like to turn over? Why?

More Ways to Play

■ Play again. Use a grid like this.

■ Play another game. Use either grid. This time the winner is the player with the least product.

■ Play the game using this grid.

The winner is the player who gets closest to 3,000 or any number players choose.

Reasoning

1. Suppose an 8 were turned over and you could put it in any box on this grid. What strategy would you use if you were playing the Greatest Product Game?

☐ ☐ ☐
× ☐ 9

2. Suppose you turned over a 9 to put on this grid. What strategy would you use if you were playing the Greatest Product Game?

4 ☐ ☐
× ☐

3. Suppose your grid looks like this in the Least Product Game. What number do you hope to pick next so that you get the least product? Explain why it is the best number.

7 3
× ☐

4. **What If** You are playing a game called Closest to 3,000. How can you arrange the digits in this grid to get closest to 3,000?

4 5 6
× 1

The Greatest Product Game **221**

Cooperative Learning

Distribute *Assessment Sourcebook 10* (How We Worked in Our Group) and have students fill it out for the skill Encourage and Respect Others. Review the characteristics of this skill. Invite students to judge themselves on the skill as they work together.

Section B
Review and Practice

Use the Skills Checklist

Review the **Skills Checklist** on the page with students. Then ask questions such as the following:

- In which exercises will you not have to regroup ones? Exercises 8, 11, 18
- In which exercises will you have to regroup two times at the most? 4 times? Exercises 3–14; Exercises 26–32
- Where will you use rounding to check? Exercises 3–14
- What decision must you make in Exercises 24 and 25? What operation to use
- Is a calculator a good method to use for the multiplication in Exercise 32? Explain. Yes; A lot of regrouping is needed.

Assess

You may wish to use this information to assess students' understanding of the lesson objectives.

Item Analysis		
Lesson Objectives		Items
5-5	Multiply 2-digit numbers.	3–14, 24
5-6	Multiply 3-digit numbers.	15–23
5-7	Solve problems by making decisions about cooking.	1, 2, 24, 25
5-8	Multiply using different methods.	26–33

Resources

Practice Masters
- Practice Chapter 5 Section B

Assessment Sourcebook
- Quiz Chapter 5 Section B

TestWorks: Test and Practice Software

ANSWERS

33 Possible answer: Multiply the ones, then the tens, then the hundreds, then the thousands, regrouping as needed.

Review and Practice

Vocabulary Choose the word that best completes each sentence.

1. Addition, subtraction, multiplication, and division are _____. **C**
   Ⓐ estimates Ⓑ products Ⓒ operations Ⓓ factors

2. You can _____ 32 ones as 3 tens and 2 ones. **C**
   Ⓐ multiply Ⓑ estimate Ⓒ regroup Ⓓ add

(Lesson 5) Find each product. Estimate to check.

3. 37
   × 4
   148

4. 18
   × 9
   162

5. 29
   × 6
   174

6. 86
   × 7
   602

7. 34
   × 8
   272

8. 2 × 53 **106**   9. 64 × 5 **320**   10. 76 × 4 **304**   11. 3 × 92 **276**   12. 6 × 47 **282**

13. Find the product of 58 and 6. **348**   14. Find the product of 8 and 46. **368**

(Lesson 6) Multiply.

15. 236
   × 3
   708

16. 756
   × 2
   1,512

17. 709
   × 6
   4,254

18. 450
   × 3
   1,350

19. 805
   × 5
   4,025

20. 347 × 4 **1,388**   21. 406 × 6 **2,436**   22. 812 × 6 **4,872**   23. Find the product of 805 and 5. **4,025**

(Lesson 7) Solve each problem.

24. Four students baked 16 muffins each. How many muffins did they bake in all? **64 muffins**

25. Joel ate 4 carrots and had 16 left. How many carrots did he start with? **20 carrots**

(Lesson 8) Multiply.

26. 1,347
   × 7
   9,429

27. 6,058
   × 8
   48,464

28. 5,608
   × 4
   22,432

29. 5,079
   × 8
   40,632

30. 2,489
   × 2
   4,978

31. 1,235
   × 6
   7,410

32. **Critical Thinking** Suppose you used a calculator to find 8,562 × 7 and got 5,992. How could you tell that this is not the right answer?

33. **Journal** Describe each step you would follow to find 4,539 × 6.

32. Possible answer: Estimate; Round 8,562 to 9,000; 9,000 × 7 would be 63,000.

Skills Checklist

In this section, you have:
- ☑ Multiplied 2-Digit Numbers
- ☑ Multiplied 3-Digit Numbers
- ☑ Solved Problems by Making Decisions
- ☑ Learned to Choose a Calculation Method

REVIEW AND PRACTICE

Practice

Name _____

Practice
Chapter 5
Section B

Review and Practice
Vocabulary Write true or false for each statement.

1. The product of 6 and 8 is 14. __False__
2. You can regroup 14 ones as 1 hundred and 4 tens. __False__
3. The operation used to find a sum is addition. __True__

(Lessons 5 and 6) Find each product. Estimate to check.

4. 5 4
   × 7
   378

5. 1 8
   × 3
   54

6. 9 2
   × 5
   460

7. 6 5
   × 4
   260

8. 3 1 8
   × 9
   2,862

9. 6 1 5
   × 5
   3,075

10. 9 8 2
   × 2
   1,964

11. 5 1 7
   × 7
   3,619

12. 39 × 8 = __312__   13. 427 × 7 = __2,989__

14. Find the product of 6 and 49. __294__

(Lesson 7) Solve each problem.

15. a. Five students each baked 3 dozen cookies for a class bake sale. How many cookies were made in all? __180__

   b. Six dozen cookies were sold in the first lunch period. How many were left? __108__

(Lesson 8) Multiply.

16. 3,4 5 1
   × 5
   17,255

17. 8,0 0 0
   × 3
   24,000

18. 4,9 6 0
   × 7
   34,720

19. 5,0 0 7
   × 9
   45,063

(Mixed Review) Divide.

20. 64 ÷ 8 = __8__   21. 18 ÷ 9 = __2__
22. 49 ÷ 7 = __7__   23. 35 ÷ 7 = __5__

Extending Multiplication

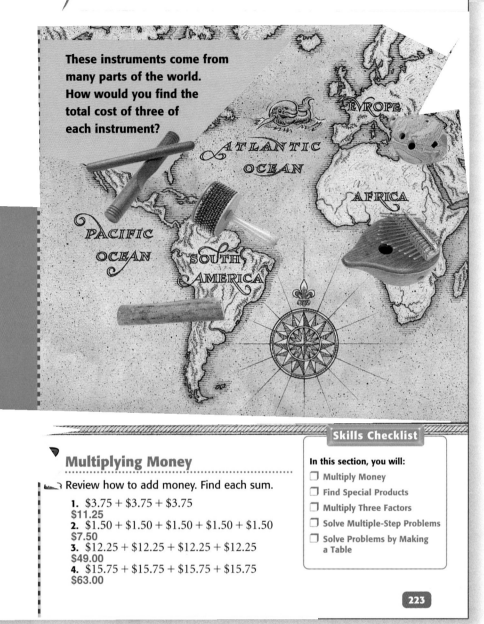

These instruments come from many parts of the world. How would you find the total cost of three of each instrument?

Multiplying Money

Review how to add money. Find each sum.

1. $3.75 + $3.75 + $3.75
$11.25
2. $1.50 + $1.50 + $1.50 + $1.50 + $1.50
$7.50
3. $12.25 + $12.25 + $12.25 + $12.25
$49.00
4. $15.75 + $15.75 + $15.75 + $15.75
$63.00

Skills Checklist

In this section, you will:
- ☐ Multiply Money
- ☐ Find Special Products
- ☐ Multiply Three Factors
- ☐ Solve Multiple-Step Problems
- ☐ Solve Problems by Making a Table

223

Extending Multiplication

In this section students will apply multiplication by a 1-digit number to problem solving situations.

Subskills

The work in this section builds on...
- Using the multiplication algorithm
- Writing money amounts as dollars and cents
- Breaking numbers apart using place value
- Naming numbers in alternative ways
- Basic multiplication facts
- Grouping three factors in different ways

Use the Section Opener

The instruments shown here (from top to bottom on left: claves, cabaça, rainstick; on right: kalimba) are just a few of the many percussion instruments that have developed all over the world.

Ask students which instruments they would include in a band and how they would find the cost of three of each. Costs will vary. Listen for students who suggest finding the cost of each instrument and multiplying (or adding) to find the total cost.

Skills Trace

(Red numbers indicate pages in this section.)

Lesson and Skill	First Introduced	Grade Four			
		Introduce	Develop	Practice/Apply	Review
5-9 Multiply amounts of money.	Grade 3	224, 225	224	225, 226, 233, 238, 239, **243**, 562	240, 242, 245
5-10 Use mental math to multiply.	Grade 3	228, 229	228	229, 240, 562	240, 242
5-11 Multiply when you have three factors.	Grade 4	230, 231	230	231, 237, 240, 562	240, 242
5-12 Solve multiple-step problems.	Grade 3	118, 119	118, 232	233, 237, 238, 239, 240, 562	240, 241, 242
5-13 Solve problems by making a table.	Grade 3	234–237	234, 235	236, 237, 240, 562	240, 241, 242, 462, 463

Mixed Review and Test Prep exercises for this chapter occur on pages 201, 205, 213, 215, 219, 225, 229, 231, 237.

Multi-Age Classrooms Use pages 258, 259, and 380–383 in Grade 3 or pages 133–142 in Grade 5 to relate to the content of this section.

Multiplying Money

At-A-Glance Planning

Objective Multiply amounts of money.

Student Book Lesson Materials None

Materials for pages 224A and 224B Play money (12 dimes, 12 pennies, 2 $10 bills, 12 $1 bills per group), calculators (1 per student)

Subject Connection physical education—swimming

Strand Connections money, logic, using data, patterns

	Before Lesson	During Lesson	After Lesson
Daily Math			
p. 224A Problem of the Day			
p. 224A Math Routines			
p. 224A Mental Math			
Teaching Options			
p. 224 Student Book Lesson			
p. 224B Another Way to Learn…			
Options for Reaching All Learners			
p. 224B Language Development			
p. 224B Gifted & Talented			
Subject Connections			
p. 224A Literature Connection			
Assessment Options			
p. 224 Talk About It			
p. 225 Error Intervention			
p. 225 Interview			
p. 225 Quick Check			
Resources			
5-9 Practice			
5-9 Reteaching			
5-9 Enrichment			
5-9 Problem Solving			
5-9 Daily Transparency			

Problem of the Day

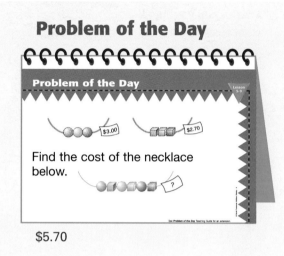

$5.70

Math Routines

Patterns Ask students to find the price for each number of 35-cent apples for 4 to 8 apples. $1.40, $1.75, $2.10, $2.45, $2.80

Money Have students choose a number between 5 and 9. Ask them to find the cost of that number of quarts of orange juice if each quart costs $1.59. 6 qt: $9.54, 7 qt: $11.13, 8 qt: $12.72

Mental Math

Write the amount that is $0.50 less. Explain your thinking.

$2.65 $2.15 $5.70 $5.20

$9.80 $9.30 $10.75 $10.25

Literature Connection

In *The Story of Money*, Betsy Maestro describes how bills are printed. 32 bills can be printed on a single sheet.

• Ask students to find the value of a single sheet of $1, $10, and $100 bills. $32, $320, $3,200

• Ask students how many sheets of paper would equal $3,200. 1 sheet of $100 bills; 10 sheets of $10 bills; 100 sheets of $1 bills

Another Way to Learn   **Learn**   Lesson 5-9

Use as an alternative or in addition to pages 224 and 225.

Materials Play money (12 dimes, 12 pennies, 2 $10 bills, 12 $1 bills per group)

Learning Style Kinesthetic

- Have groups use play money to find 3 × $1.44. $4.32
- Review the multiplication process, including regrouping. Then have groups try these.

  5 × $0.40 $2.00   2 × $14.06 $28.12

- Use play money to model the problems on the overhead. Emphasize writing the dollar sign and decimal point in the answer.

  $1.44   + $1.44   + $1.44   = $4.32

- Have groups use play money or draw pictures of money and record the steps symbolically for additional exercises.

- Have students talk about how they regroup and how they write the answer to show dollars and cents.
- Assign Check and Practice on Student Book page 225 or *Practice Master 5-9*.
- Assess using the following rubric.

Assessment Rubric
4 **Full Accomplishment** • multiplies money amounts by 1-digit numbers accurately
3 **Substantial Accomplishment** • multiplies most money amounts by 1-digit numbers
2 **Partial Accomplishment** • multiplies some money amounts by 1-digit numbers
1 **Little Accomplishment** • does not multiply money amounts by 1-digit numbers

Options for Reaching All Learners

Language Development

Writing Dollars and Cents
Use a writing activity to strengthen the connection between words and symbols related to money amounts.

Learning Style Visual

- Write a series of money amounts such as four dollars and twenty-five cents on the chalkboard.
- Have partners work together to write these amounts using numbers, dollar signs, and decimal points.
- Discuss students' answers as a class. Elicit from students that $ stands for *dollars*, that a decimal point replaces the word *and*, and that amounts less than one dollar are written to the right of the decimal point.
- Have each student write a few money amounts in numbers and symbols. Have partners exchange lists and write the amounts in words. They can check one another's work.

Gifted & Talented

Mental Math with Money
Use a mental math strategy to multiply money amounts.

Materials Calculators (1 per student)

Learning Style Logical

- Point out to students that items in stores often have prices that end in 95 cents or 99 cents.
- Demonstrate the following method for multiplying mentally 3 × $1.99.

Round to the nearest dollar.	$1.99 → $2.00
Multiply.	3 × $2 = $6
Remember.	$1.99 = $2.00 − $0.01
	3 × $0.01 = $0.03
Subtract to find the actual price.	$6 − $0.03 = $5.97

- Have students use this method to find similar products. They can check their answers with a calculator.

Lesson Organizer

Objective Multiply amounts of money.

Student Materials None

Assignment Guide

Basic 6–18, 24–27

Average 8–20, 22, 24–27

Enriched 10–27

1 Introduce

Review

Find each product.

1.	125	**2.**	409	**3.**	799
	× 7		× 4		× 3
	875		1,636		2,397

Build on Prior Knowledge

After students review how to multiply 3 × 799, ask how they could use what they know about multiplication to find 3 × $7.99. Possible answer: Multiply as with whole numbers and then write a dollar sign and decimal point in the product.

2 Teach

See Another Way to Learn…on page 224B.

Learn ● ● ● ● ● ● ● ● ● ● ● ● ● ● ● ● ● ● ●

When focusing on writing the answer in the example, ask why the decimal point was placed before 05. Possible answers: The decimal point separates dollars from cents. There are 22 dollars and 5 cents.

Explain that 5 cents, or 5¢, is $\frac{5}{100}$, or 0.05 (five hundredths), of a dollar.

Additional Examples

$6.08	$0.72	$3.06
× 4	× 7	× 5
$24.32	$5.04	$15.30

Talk About It **Ongoing Assessment**

Listen for explanations that focus on place value.

Answer for Talk About It

No; The place value of the digits would be different.

Multiplying Money

You Will Learn
how to multiply amounts of money

Learn ● ● ● ● ● ● ● ● ● ● ● ●

"Swimmers, take your marks," the starter shouts. BANG! The swimmers spring into action and dive into the pool. The Seahawks Swim Team sells T-shirts and other items to raise money to travel to its swim meets.

Multiplying amounts of money is like multiplying whole numbers.

T-shirt	$7.35
Sweatshirt	$12.40
Towel	$15.45
Goggles	$4.85

Math Tip
2205 is not the same as $22.05.

Example

Rob wants to buy 3 T-shirts. How much money does he need?

To find the cost of 3 T-shirts, multiply $7.35 by 3.

Step 1	Step 2
$\overset{1\ 1}{\$7.35}$	$\overset{1\ 1}{\$7.35}$
× 3 Multiply the same way as	× 3
2 2 0 5 with whole numbers.	$22.05 Write the answer in dollars and cents.

Rob needs $22.05 to buy 3 T-shirts.

Talk About It

Suppose you forgot to write the answer in dollars and cents. Would your answer make sense? Explain.

Practice 5-9	Reteaching 5-9

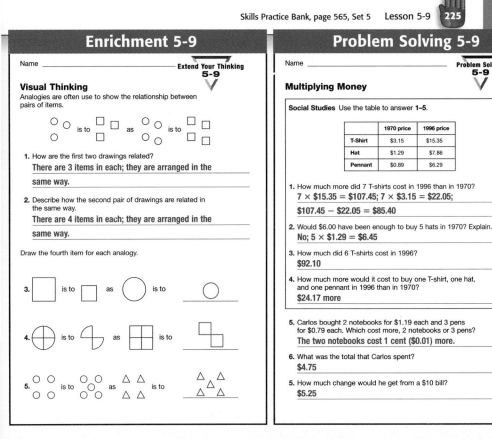

Check

$1.25 each

The Seahawks

Find each cost.

1. 3 pins	2. 8 pins	3. 5 pins	4. 6 pins
$3.75	$10.00	$6.25	$7.50

5. **Reasoning** Is $8.00 enough to buy 7 pins? Explain.
No; 7 × $1.25 = $8.75

Practice

Skills and Reasoning

Find each product.

6. $1.37	7. $2.70	8. $34.75	9. $20.04	10. $14.99
× 7	× 4	× 5	× 6	× 8
$9.59	$10.80	$173.75	$120.24	$119.92

11. 5 × $32.75	12. 9 × $2.21	13. 3 × $4.75	14. 4 × $51.25
$163.75	$19.89	$14.25	$205.00

Find each cost.

$2.39 each

$2.75 each

15. 2 fish magnets	16. 4 fish magnets
$4.78	$9.56
17. 9 bird magnets	18. 7 bird magnets
$24.75	$19.25

19. Is $12.00 enough to buy 5 fish magnets?
Yes; 5 × $2.39 = $11.95

Problem Solving and Applications

20. How much would 5 sweatshirts cost? Use the data on page 224. $62.00

21. **Logic** Who was last to swim in the relay race? Raúl swam after Jamal. Toby started the race. Nick was not the fourth swimmer. **Raúl**

Using Data Use the table to answer 22 and 23.

22. How much more did 6 energy bars cost in 1996 than in 1991? $4.20

23. Would $5.00 have bought 4 comic books and a hamburger in 1991? Explain. **Yes; 4 × $0.75 = $3.00; $3.00 + $1.45 = $4.45**

	1991 Price	1996 Price
Comic Book	$0.75	$1.45
Hamburger	$1.45	$1.65
Energy Bar	$0.99	$1.69

Mixed Review and Test Prep

STAY SHARP!

Patterns Copy and complete.

24. 12, 36, 108, ■, ■, ■
324; 972; 2,916

25. 10, 40, 160, ■, ■, ■
640; 2,560; 10,240

26. 4, 20, 100, ■, ■, ■
500; 2,500; 12,500

27. Find the number that means 3 thousands, 8 tens, 7 ones. **D**

Ⓐ 18   Ⓑ 315   Ⓒ 387   Ⓓ not here

Check

Exercise 5 Some students may multiply 7 × $1.25. Others may recognize that 7 × $1 = $7 and 7 × $0.25 is more than $1.

Error Intervention Ongoing Assessment

Observation Students may not find the correct factors for each exercise.

How to Help Have students look at the picture to help identify each pair of factors before multiplying.

Practice

Exercise 21 Students may find it helpful to use the strategy Make an Organized List, writing names as they work out the relationships given in the clue.

For Early Finishers Challenge early finishers to write the products for Exercises 12–14 in words. Nineteen dollars and eighty-nine cents; Fourteen dollars and twenty-five cents; Two hundred five dollars

3 Close and Assess

Interview

Have students choose either Exercise 15 or 16 and explain how they identified the factors, estimated the product, and solved the problem. Explanations should involve how they multiplied and how they wrote the product using a decimal point and dollar sign.

Quick Check

Number Sense Tell students that one factor in a multiplication sentence is 5 and that the product is less than $10. Ask for the greatest possible second factor. $1.99

Skill Find each product.

1. 3 × $4.25 $12.75

2. 5 × $7.50 $37.50

3. 4 × $0.89 $3.56

4. 7 × $12.09 $84.63

Resources

Technology Master 17

Enrichment 5-9

Name _____ Extend Your Thinking 5-9

Visual Thinking

Analogies are often use to show the relationship between pairs of items.

○ ○ ○ □ □ ○ ○ ○ □ □
○ is to □ □ as ○ ○ is to □ □
        □   □ □

1. How are the first two drawings related?
There are 3 items in each; they are arranged in the same way.

2. Describe how the second pair of drawings are related in the same way.
There are 4 items in each; they are arranged in the same way.

Draw the fourth item for each analogy.

3. ☐ is to ☐ as ○ is to ○

4. ⊕ is to ◷ as ▦ is to ▨

5. ○ ○ is to ○ ○ ○ as △ △ is to △ △ △
   ○ ○   ○ ○   △ △   △ △

Problem Solving 5-9

Name _____ Problem Solving 5-9

Multiplying Money

Social Studies Use the table to answer 1–5.

	1970 price	1996 price
T-Shirt	$3.15	$15.35
Hat	$1.29	$7.86
Pennant	$0.89	$6.29

1. How much more did 7 T-shirts cost in 1996 than in 1970?
7 × $15.35 = $107.45; 7 × $3.15 = $22.05;
$107.45 − $22.05 = $85.40

2. Would $6.00 have been enough to buy 5 hats in 1970? Explain.
No; 5 × $1.29 = $6.45

3. How much did 6 T-shirts cost in 1996?
$92.10

4. How much more would it cost to buy one T-shirt, one hat, and one pennant in 1996 than in 1970?
$24.17 more

5. Carlos bought 2 notebooks for $1.19 each and 3 pens for $0.79 each. Which cost more, 2 notebooks or 3 pens?
The two notebooks cost 1 cent ($0.01) more.

6. What was the total that Carlos spent?
$4.75

5. How much change would he get from a $10 bill?
$5.25

Chapter 5
Stop and Practice

Students will practice skills taught in Lessons 1 through 9.

Find Each Product

Exercises 11–20, 32–34, 37–42, 48, 50
Remind students to use a comma to separate the thousands from the hundreds in their answers.

Exercises 21–30, 43–47 Review the idea that multiplying money uses the algorithm for multiplying whole numbers. Remind students to write products as dollars and cents and to place the decimal point correctly.

Error Search

ANSWERS

51 2,106; Didn't add the extra tens and hundreds

52 Correct

53 $19.80; The decimal is in the wrong place.

54 $263.20; Didn't add the extra tens and hundreds

55 Correct

 STOP and Practice

Find each product. Estimate to check.

1. 63 $\times$ 4 = 252	2. 43 $\times$ 8 = 344	3. 98 $\times$ 3 = 294	4. 46 $\times$ 5 = 230	5. 68 $\times$ 7 = 476
6. 58 $\times$ 5 = 290	7. 93 $\times$ 3 = 279	8. 59 $\times$ 7 = 413	9. 83 $\times$ 6 = 498	10. 39 $\times$ 5 = 195
11. 712 $\times$ 6 = 4,272	12. 204 $\times$ 8 = 1,632	13. 647 $\times$ 4 = 2,588	14. 408 $\times$ 8 = 3,264	15. 534 $\times$ 9 = 4,806
16. 1,879 $\times$ 6 = 11,274	17. 2,302 $\times$ 7 = 16,114	18. 3,604 $\times$ 7 = 25,228	19. 4,523 $\times$ 5 = 22,615	20. 7,968 $\times$ 6 = 47,808
21. $8.79 $\times$ 6 = $52.74	22. $2.02 $\times$ 7 = $14.14	23. $6.04 $\times$ 4 = $24.16	24. $5.20 $\times$ 9 = $46.80	25. $7.08 $\times$ 8 = $56.64
26. $18.79 $\times$ 6 = $112.74	27. $24.02 $\times$ 7 = $72.06	28. $65.04 $\times$ 7 = $455.28	29. $25.20 $\times$ 5 = $126.00	30. $70.08 $\times$ 8 = $560.64

31. 68×4 272	32. 6×932 5,592	33. 893×9 8,037	34. 8×592 4,736	35. 219×3 657
36. 403×2 806	37. 806×4 3,224	38. $6 \times 2,932$ 17,592	39. $8,893 \times 9$ 80,037	40. 409×8 3,272
41. $8 \times 5,092$ 40,736	42. $4,803 \times 3$ 14,409	43. $8 \times \$3.92$ $31.36	44. $\$9.03 \times 5$ $45.15	45. $7 \times \$21.99$ $153.93
46. $6 \times \$46.32$ $277.92	47. $\$59.03 \times 7$ $413.21	48. $2,124 \times 3$ 6,372	49. 6×78 468	50. 8×555 4,440

Error Search

Find each product that is not correct. Write it correctly and explain the error.

51. 234 $\times$ 9 = 1,876	52. 1,207 $\times$ 6 = 7,242	53. $3.96 $\times$ 5 = $1,980.00	54. $32.90 $\times$ 8 = $246.20	55. 880 $\times$ 3 = 2,640

Something Fishy!

Multiply to solve the riddle. Match each letter to its answer in the blank below. Some letters are not used.

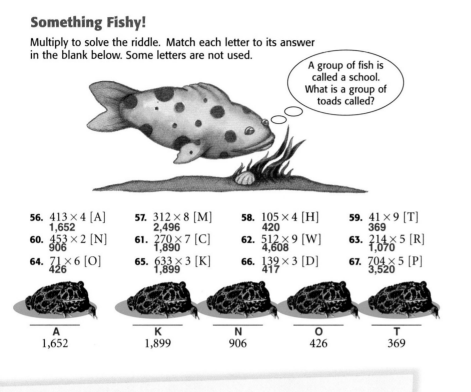

A group of fish is called a school. What is a group of toads called?

56. 413×4 [A]
1,652
57. 312×8 [M]
2,496
58. 105×4 [H]
420
59. 41×9 [T]
369
60. 453×2 [N]
906
61. 270×7 [C]
1,890
62. 512×9 [W]
4,608
63. 214×5 [R]
1,070
64. 71×6 [O]
426
65. 633×3 [K]
1,899
66. 139×3 [D]
417
67. 704×5 [P]
3,520

A	K	N	O	T
1,652	1,899	906	426	369

Number Sense Estimation and Reasoning

Write whether each statement is true or false. Explain your answer.

68. The product of 4 and 22 is greater than 100. **F: 4 × 22 = 88**

69. The product of 7 and 800 is less than 5,000. **F: 7 × 800 = 5,600**

70. The product of 5 and 400 is greater than 1,500. **T: 5 × 400 = 2,000**

71. The product of 3 and 52 is 6 more than 150. **T: 3 × 52 = 156**

72. The product of 6 and 73 is closer to 420 than 430. **F: 6 × 73 = 438**

73. The product of 8 and 600 is 800 more than 4,800. **F: 8 × 600 = 4,800**

74. The product of 2 and 301 is greater than the product of 3 and 201.
F: 2 × 301 = 602; 3 × 201 = 603

Something Fishy!

Some students may be able to use estimation to solve this riddle.

As an extension, suggest that students create their own riddles to compile into a class riddle book.

Number Sense

Remind students to use estimation to answer the questions. Discuss the strategies students used, for example, basic facts, multiply tens.

For Early Finishers Challenge early finishers to write examples like the ones in Exercises 68–74 for classmates to answer.

Resources

TestWorks: Test and Practice Software

Mental Math: Special Products

At-A-Glance Planning

Lesson Planning Checklist

Objective Use mental math to multiply.

Student Book Lesson Materials None

Materials for pages 228A and 228B Place-value blocks (15 tens, 30 ones per group), Teaching Tool Transparency 6 (Centimeter Grid Paper)

Subject Connections technology—CD-ROM; science—insects

Strand Connections mental math, money, algebra readiness, collecting data

	Before Lesson	During Lesson	After Lesson
Daily Math			
p. 228A Problem of the Day			
p. 228A Math Routines			
p. 228A Mental Math			
Teaching Options			
p. 228 Student Book Lesson			
p. 228B Another Way to Learn…			
Options for Reaching All Learners			
p. 228B Inclusion			
p. 228B Language Development			
Subject Connections			
p. 228A Science Connection			
Assessment Options			
p. 228 Talk About It			
p. 229 Error Intervention			
p. 229 Interview			
p. 229 Quick Check			
Resources			
5-10 Practice			
5-10 Reteaching			
5-10 Enrichment			
5-10 Problem Solving			
5-10 Daily Transparency			

Problem of the Day

Problem of the Day

Roger watched a movie lasting 2 hr 25 min. Then he watched a documentary lasting 103 min. If he finished watching both at 5:15 P.M., at what time did he start?

1:07 P.M.

Math Routines

Patterns Ask students to name the operations that were used on the three numbers to get each result.

3, 2, 1	7	2, 2, 5	9
1, 2, 3	5	4, 5, 3	23

Multiply the first two; add the third.

Measurement Tell students that the length of a shoe is 8 inches. Ask them how long 4 of these shoes in a line are. 32 inches

Mental Math

Solve mentally. Explain your thinking.

$10 + 40 + 20 + 20$ 90

$30 + 40 - 10 + 20$ 80

$60 + 30 - 30 + 40$ 100

Science Connection

All insects have six legs and most also have wings. Explain that spiders are arachnids, not insects. Spiders have eight legs and no wings.

• Have students find pictures of insects and arachnids. Have them compare the numbers of legs and wings on the animals in the pictures.

Another Way to **Learn** Lesson 5-10

Use as an alternative or in addition to pages 228 and 229.

Materials Place-value blocks (15 tens, 30 ones per group)

Learning Style Kinesthetic

- Have groups use place-value blocks to find 2×32. Have students talk about whether it made a difference first to find the total ones or the total tens. 64; made no difference

- Use the place-value blocks on the overhead to show that 30×2 and $2 \times 2 = 32 \times 2$.

$$(2 \times 30) + (2 \times 2) = 60 + 4 = 64$$

- Then have groups use place-value blocks to find 3×40. Have students talk about how they would have to change their models to show 3×39. 120; Take a 1 away from each group.

- For each strategy, have students talk about what parts of the work they were able to do mentally.

- Assign Check and Practice on Student Book pages 228 and 229 or *Practice Master 5-10*.

- Assess using the following rubric.

Assessment Rubric

4 Full Accomplishment
- uses mental math to multiply 2-digit numbers
- clearly explains the connection between mental math strategies and factors

3 Substantial Accomplishment
- uses mental math to multiply most 2-digit numbers
- explains the connection between mental math strategies and factors

2 Partial Accomplishment
- uses mental math to multiply some 2-digit numbers
- struggles to explain the connection between mental math strategies and factors

1 Little Accomplishment
- does not use mental math to multiply 2-digit numbers
- does not explain the connection between mental math strategies and factors

Options for Reaching All Learners

Inclusion

Breaking Apart
Use grid paper to model broken-apart factors.

Learning Style Visual

Materials Teaching Tool Transparency 6 (Centimeter Grid Paper)

- Reinforce the equivalency of broken-apart factors by using grid paper. For 3×32, students shade 3 rows of 10 squares plus 2 squares, three times. For 3×49, students shade 4 rows of 10 squares plus 9 squares, three times.

- Have students model the broken-apart factors in the Check exercises before doing the exercises mentally. For Exercises 1–5, have students model 41 as $40 + 1$, 52 as $50 + 2$, 63 as $60 + 3$, 81 as $80 + 1$, and 92 as $90 + 2$.

- Encourage students to explain their models.

Language Development

Breaking Up
Use student discussion to further understanding of the break-apart strategy for multiplication.

Learning Style Verbal/Auditory

- Group students acquiring English with fluent speakers.

- Have each group discuss how to break the special factors in the Check exercises into tens and ones that are easy to multiply.

- Have each group say each statement of equivalency, then write it.

"forty-one is forty plus one"	$41 = 40 + 1$
"thirty-nine is forty minus one"	$39 = 40 - 1$

Lesson Organizer

Objective Use mental math to multiply.
Student Materials None
Assignment Guide
 Basic 12–33, 40–45
 Average 15–36, 40–45
 Enriched 18–45

1 Introduce

Review

Find each product.

1. 4 × 3 12
2. 4 × 30 120
3. 4 × 4 16
4. 4 × 40 160

Build on Prior Knowledge

After students review multiplying 1-digit numbers and multiples of 10 by a 1-digit number, ask them to round the following numbers to the nearest ten.

43 40   32 30   44 40   49 50

2 Teach

 See Another Way to Learn…on page 228B.

Learn ●

Ask students why Adam's method involves addition and Patti's method uses subtraction. Adam multiplied tens that are less than the actual 2-digit number, so the product will be greater. Patti multiplied tens that were greater, so the product will be less.

Additional Examples

74 × 4 296   28 × 2 56

Talk About It **Ongoing Assessment**

Listen for students to recognize that both Adam and Patti rounded to the nearest 10 and then looked at the differences from that nearest 10.

Answer for Talk About It

Each method breaks down the problem to use numbers that are easy to work with.

Check ● ● ● ● ● ● ● ● ● ● ● ● ● ● ● ● ● ● ●

Exercise 11 Students are not directed to use a particular method.

Mental Math: Special Products

You Will Learn
two different methods of using mental math to multiply

Learn ●

Adam and Patti play the computer game "Insect Power." Each insect they collect scores 3 points.

Adam collected 32 insects. To find his score, he multiplies 32 and 3.

Patti collected 49 insects. To find her score, she multiplies 49 and 3.

I think of 32 as 30 + 2.
30 × 3 is 90.
2 × 3 is 6.
90 + 6 = 96. So, 32 × 3 = 96.
My score is 96.

I think of 49 as almost 50.
50 × 3 is 150.
Subtract 1 group of 3.
150 − 3 = 147.
So, 49 × 3 = 147.
My score is 147.

Did You Know?
One of the first popular video games was Pong, which was developed in the 1970s. A winning score was 21.

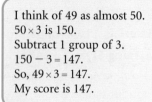

What do you think?

Talk About It

How do these methods make it easier to multiply mentally?

Check ●

Use Adam's method to find each product.

1. 41 × 6   246
2. 8 × 52   416
3. 63 × 2   126
4. 81 × 4   324
5. 4 × 92   368

Use Patti's method to find each product.

6. 3 × 39   117
7. 28 × 5   140
8. 4 × 79   316
9. 58 × 3   174
10. 8 × 59   472

11. Reasoning Which method would you use to find 48 × 6? Explain.

228   Chapter 5 • Multiplying by 1-Digit Factors

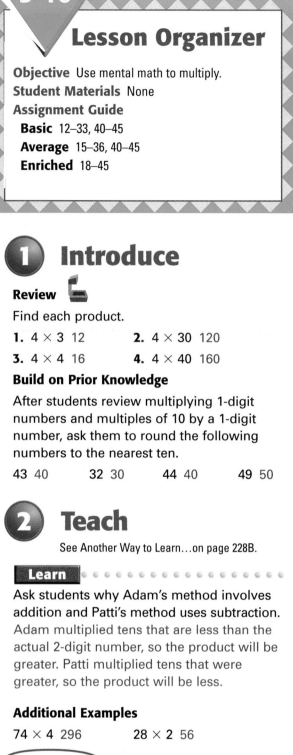

Practice 5-10

Name _____

Practice 5-10

Mental Math: Special Products
Use mental math to find each product.

1. 21 × 5   105
2. 6 × 18   108
3. 9 × 14   126
4. 68 × 4   272
5. 8 × 71   568
6. 61 × 6   366
7. 88 × 9   792
8. 4 × 63   252
9. 23 × 4   92
10. 7 × 39   273
11. 41 × 4   164
12. 59 × 7   413
13. 33 × 5   165
14. 4 × 81   324
15. 99 × 3   297
16. 6 × 49   294
17. 22 × 7   154
18. 5 × 93   465
19. 2 × 77   154
20. 74 × 3   222
21. 6 × 30   180
22. 5 × 17   85
23. 45 × 6   270
24. 3 × 52   156
25. 14 × 9   126
26. 36 × 4   144
27. 9 × 99   891
28. 43 × 5   215

29. Find the product of 53 and 6 mentally.   318

30. Find the product of 98 and 7 mentally.   686

31. Multiply 5 and 49 mentally.   245

32. Describe how you would find the product of 37 and 7 mentally.
 Possible answer: 37 is almost 40. 40 × 7 = 280.
 Subtract 3 groups of 7.   280 − 21 = 259. So 37 × 7 = 259.

Reteaching 5-10

Name _____

Another Look 5-10

Mental Math: Special Products
Here is a way to solve problems mentally when one number is even. Cutting an even number in half and doubling the other number can help you do mental math.

6 × 15 =

Half of 6 is: 3
Double 15 is: 30

3 × 30 = 90

If one number is still too large, you can keep cutting it in half to make it easier, but don't forget to double your other number! Try 13 × 16.

Double		Half
26	×	8
52	×	4
104	×	2 = 208

Use mental math to solve these problems. If necessary, cut one number in half and double the other.

1. 4 × 18   72
2. 6 × 35   210
3. 8 × 42   336
4. 45 × 4   180
5. 25 × 6   150
6. 49 × 4   196
7. 22 × 8   176
8. 44 × 6   264
9. 4 × 36   144
10. 55 × 8   440
11. 6 × 27   162
12. 4 × 29   116
13. 32 × 4   128
14. 54 × 8   432
15. 43 × 6   258
16. 34 × 4   136

Skills and Reasoning

Mental Math Find each product.

12. 32×6 192
13. 7×19 133
14. 8×61 488
15. 59×5 295
16. 9×81 729

17. 51×6 306
18. 99×8 792
19. 3×72 216
20. 32×5 160
21. 5×29 145

22. 51×2 102
23. 49×6 294
24. 22×6 132
25. 6×71 426
26. 88×3 264

27. 7×39 273
28. 59×3 177
29. 38×6 228
30. 2×91 182
31. 9×21 189

32. Find the product of 42 and 5 mentally. **210** **33.** Multiply 6 and 39 mentally. **234**

34. Would you use addition or subtraction to find 26×8 mentally? Explain.
Possible answer: Addition; $20 \times 8 = 160$, $6 \times 8 = 48$, $160 + 48 = 208$.

Problem Solving and Applications

35. Money A computer game costs $19. Use mental math to find how much it will cost for 8 computer games. **$152**

36. Technology In 1990, a CD-ROM could transfer data at about 150 kilobytes per second. By 1996, CD-ROMs could transfer data about 8 times as fast. Estimate the speed of a 1996 CD-ROM. **1,200 kilobytes per second**

Dragonfly

37. Algebra Readiness A CD rack holds 12 CDs. How many racks would you need to hold 84 CDs? **7 racks**

38. Science There are about 6,500 kinds of dragonflies and 2,000 kinds of praying mantis. How many more kinds of dragonflies are there than praying mantis?
4,500 kinds

39. Collecting Data Make a list of 5 video games. Ask your classmates to name their favorites. Then make a bar graph to show the class data.

40. Journal Explain how you would use the mental math strategies in this lesson to find 59×4 and 71×6.

Praying mantis

Mixed Review and Test Prep

Find each sum or difference.

41. $2,500 - 375$ 2,125
42. $906 + 48$ 954
43. $735 - 217$ 518
44. $13,195 + 504$ 13,699

45. Which has a greater product than 18×7? **B**

   Ⓐ 23×4 Ⓑ 16×8 Ⓒ 27×3 Ⓓ 15×8

Lesson 5-10 **229**

Enrichment 5-10	Problem Solving 5-10

Error Intervention Ongoing Assessment

Observation Students may add or subtract incorrect partial products.

How to Help Have students record each partial product before mentally adding or subtracting it. Then use estimation to check the reasonableness of the answer.

Practice · · · · · · · · · · · · · · · · · ·

Exercises 12–33 You may wish to have students identify exercises for which the addition or subtraction methods are preferable.

For Early Finishers Challenge students to change one digit in Exercises 12–16 so that it would be more appropriate to use the other mental math strategy.

③ Close and Assess

Interview

Ask students which mental math strategy they used for a particular exercise and why. The explanation should indicate a choice based on the ones digit in the 2-digit factor.

Quick Check

Number Sense For which Skill exercises below will you use multiplication and addition? Multiplication and subtraction? Explain. Addition: 2 and 3, because the 2-digit factor is a little more than a multiple of 10; Subtraction: 1 and 4, because the 2-digit factor is a little less than a multiple of 10

Skill Use mental math to find each product.

1. 3×38 114   **2.** 64×2 128

3. 83×6 498   **4.** 8×47 376

ANSWERS

11 Either, but it might be easier to use Patti's method; $50 \times 6 = 300$, $2 \times 6 = 12$, $300 - 12 = 288$.

39 Bar graph should show 5 bars to represent the video games, a scale for the number of students, and a title.

40 Possible answer: Multiply 60×4 and subtract one group of 4 to get 236; Multiply 70×6 and add one more group of 6 to get 426.

Multiplying 3 Factors

At-A-Glance Planning

Lesson Planning Checklist

Objective Multiply when you have three factors.
Vocabulary grouping property
Student Book Lesson Materials None
Materials for pages 230A and 230B Counters
(75 per group), index cards (1 per group)
Subject Connection music—dancing
Strand Connections geometry readiness, logic, patterns, time

	Before Lesson	During Lesson	After Lesson
Daily Math			
p. 230A Problem of the Day			
p. 230A Math Routines			
p. 230A Mental Math			
Teaching Options			
p. 230 Student Book Lesson			
p. 230B Another Way to Learn…			
Options for Reaching All Learners			
p. 230B Language Development			
p. 230B Inclusion			
Subject Connections			
p. 230A Social Studies Connection			
Assessment Options			
p. 230 Talk About It			
p. 231 Error Intervention			
p. 231 Journal			
p. 231 Quick Check			
Resources			
5-11 Practice			
5-11 Reteaching			
5-11 Enrichment			
5-11 Problem Solving			
5-11 Daily Transparency			

Problem of the Day

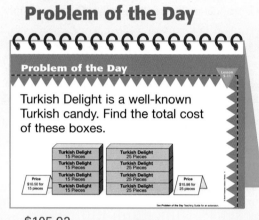

Turkish Delight is a well-known Turkish candy. Find the total cost of these boxes.

$105.92

Math Routines

Patterns Have students find each product, then continue the pattern through 10.

$1 \times 1 \times 1$ $2 \times 2 \times 2$ $3 \times 3 \times 3$

1, 8, 27; 64, 125, 216, 343, 512, 729, 1,000

Calendar Ask students: A club meets on the third Wednesday of every month. On what date will they meet next month?

Mental Math

Find each product. Explain your thinking.

1×7 10×7 100×7 7, 70, 700

8×300 8×30 8×3 2,400, 240, 24

Social Studies Connection

At international festivals, people enjoy food, entertainment, and crafts from many countries. One festival might offer:

Food: Mexican, Italian, Middle Eastern, Asian

Dancing: Greek, Chinese, Caribbean

Storytelling: Danish, Native American

• Ask how many different combinations students can make if they combine one of each category. 24

Another Way to **Learn** Lesson 5-11

Use as an alternative or in addition to pages 230 and 231.

Materials Counters (75 per group)

Learning Style Kinesthetic

- Have groups use counters to show the following.

three 2-by-4 arrays   two 4-by-3 arrays   four 2-by-3 arrays

- Have group members compare arrays. different arrangements, same total

- Model each array and connect it to the symbolic recording.

X X X X   X X X X   X X X X
X X X X   X X X X   X X X X $(2 \times 4) \times 3 = 8 \times 3 = 24$

X X X   X X X
X X X   X X X
X X X   X X X $2 \times (4 \times 3) = 2 \times 12 = 24$
X X X   X X X

X X X   X X X   X X X   X X X
X X X   X X X   X X X   X X X $2 \times 4 \times 3 = 6 \times 4 = 24$

- Have students group the following factors in three different ways, draw pictures to show the groupings, and find the products. $2 \times 5 \times 6$ 60 $5 \times 4 \times 2$ 40 Students' drawings should be similar to model above.

- Assign Check and Practice on Student Book pages 230 and 231 or *Practice Master 5-11.*

- Assess using the following rubric.

Assessment Rubric

4 Full Accomplishment
- multiplies three factors correctly
- clearly demonstrates the grouping property

3 Substantial Accomplishment
- multiplies most groups of three factors
- with prompting, demonstrates the grouping property

2 Partial Accomplishment
- multiplies some groups of three factors
- struggles to demonstrate the grouping property

1 Little Accomplishment
- has difficulty multiplying three factors
- does not demonstrate the grouping property

Options for Reaching All Learners

Language Development

Grouping Factors
Use acting out to strengthen understanding of the grouping property.

Learning Style Kinesthetic

- Choose 2 groups of 4 to stand at the front of the class and 2 more groups of 4 to stand at the back. Point to the front, say "two teams of four," and write 2×4. Repeat for the back.

- Write $2 \times (2 \times 4)$ as you say *"two times* two groups of four." Ask students to find the product. 16

- Now have the groups split up to form 2 groups of 2 on all sides of the classroom. For each side of the room, point and say "two groups of two." Each time, write 2×2. Then write $(2 \times 2) \times 4$ as you say "two groups of two *four times!"* Again find the product. 16

Inclusion

It's in Line
Use counters to understand the grouping property.

Materials Counters (75 per group), 6 index cards

Learning Style Kinesthetic

- Divide students into 6 groups and give each group one index card with one of the following equations on each side:

$(2 \times 3) \times 4$	$(2 \times 4) \times 3$	$2 \times (3 \times 4)$	$2 \times (4 \times 3)$
$(3 \times 4) \times 2$	$(3 \times 2) \times 4$	$3 \times (4 \times 2)$	$3 \times (2 \times 4)$
$(4 \times 3) \times 2$	$(4 \times 2) \times 3$	$4 \times (3 \times 2)$	$4 \times (2 \times 3)$

- Have students use counters to model the two equations on their card.

- Have groups compare and share their groupings. Emphasize that although numbers are grouped differently, the products are the same.

Lesson Organizer

Objective Multiply when you have three factors.
Student Materials None
Vocabulary grouping property
Assignment Guide
Basic 6–21, 29–33
Average 10–24, 27–33
Enriched 12–33

1 Introduce

Review

Copy and complete.

1. $7 \times 8 = \blacksquare \times 7\,8$ **2.** $6 \times 9 = 9 \times \blacksquare\,6$
3. $4 \times \blacksquare = 7 \times 4\,7$ **4.** $\blacksquare \times 8 = 8 \times 5\,5$

Build on Prior Knowledge

After students have reviewed the order property (Commutative Property), ask them to predict whether it would make a difference which two factors they multiplied first in $8 \times 5 \times 2$. No; accept all reasonable explanations.

2 Teach

See Another Way to Learn...on page 230B.

Learn

You or your students may be more familiar with the grouping property as the Associative Property. Point out that when there are no parentheses, you can multiply any two factors first. Have students talk about how they could choose these factors.

Talk About It Ongoing Assessment

Check that students' explanations indicate a clear understanding that changing the grouping of factors does not change the product.

Answer for Talk About It

They both get the same answer. They multiply a different pair of factors first.

Check

Exercise 5 Students should look for compatible numbers. Students who multiply the first two factors first will have two 2-digit factors to multiply, a skill they have not yet learned.

You Will Learn
how to multiply when you have three factors

Vocabulary
grouping property
when the grouping of factors is changed, the product remains the same

Did You Know?
There are about 3,000 official tartan plaids. A tartan plaid is a kind of woven cloth with different color patterns.

Multiplying 3 Factors

Learn

Ashley spends a lot of her free time dancing. She competes in Scottish Highland dance and has won many championships.

The Highland fling can have 6 steps. Each step takes up 8 bars of music. And each bar has 4 counts. How many counts are in the fling?

Ashley lives in Shelby Township, Michigan.

Find $6 \times 8 \times 4$.

Here are some ways you can find the product when there are 3 factors. The parentheses tell which factors to multiply first.

Example 1	**Example 2**	**Example 3**
Multiply these first.	Multiply these first.	Pick any two. Try these.
↓ ↓	↓ ↓	↓ ↓
$(6 \times 8) \times 4$	$6 \times (8 \times 4)$	$6 \times 8 \times 4$
$48 \times 4 = 192$	$6 \times 32 = 192$	$24 \times 8 = 192$

There are 192 counts in this Highland Fling.

The examples show the **grouping property**. Changing the grouping of the factors does not change the product.

Talk About It

In what way are $(3 \times 2) \times 7$ and $3 \times (2 \times 7)$ the same? Different?

Check

Find each product.

1. $4 \times 7 \times 5$ **2.** $3 \times 2 \times 5$ **3.** $4 \times 9 \times 8$ **4.** $6 \times 7 \times 3$
  140   30   288   126
5. Reasoning What is an easy way to multiply $4 \times 8 \times 25$? Explain.

Practice 5-11

Name _____

Multiplying 3 Factors
Find each product.

1. $(3 \times 9) \times 4 =$ __108__   **2.** $6 \times (7 \times 8) =$ __336__
3. $(12 \times 3) \times 7 =$ __252__   **4.** $4 \times (8 \times 6) =$ __192__
5. $7 \times (26 \times 4) =$ __728__   **6.** $(13 \times 5) \times 2 =$ __130__
7. $9 \times (7 \times 6) =$ __378__   **8.** $4 \times (71 \times 3) =$ __852__
9. $(25 \times 5) \times 3 =$ __375__   **10.** $(7 \times 3) \times 9 =$ __189__

Find each product.

11. $13 \times 4 \times 7$ **12.** $9 \times 8 \times 12$ **13.** $4 \times 9 \times 7$
    364   864   252
14. $5 \times 14 \times 3$ **15.** $21 \times 2 \times 6$ **16.** $8 \times 6 \times 7$
    210   252   336

17. Write $7 \times 4 \times 6$ in three different ways.
Possible answers: $(7 \times 4) \times 6$, or $7 \times (4 \times 6)$, or $(7 \times 6) \times 4$

18. Write $11 \times 5 \times 8$ in three different ways.
$(11 \times 5) \times 8$, or $(8 \times 11) \times 5$, or $11 \times (5 \times 8)$

19. Explain how you would find the product of $(3 \times 5) \times 8 \times (9 \times 2) \times 0 \times 6$.
When one of the factors is zero, the product is zero.

20. Explain how you would find the product of $17 \times 4 \times 25$.
$17 \times (4 \times 25) = 17 \times 100 = 1,700$

21. Write three factors. Find their product.
Answers will vary.

Reteaching 5-11

Name _____

Multiplying 3 Factors
Here is a way you can find the product when there are 3 factors. Multiply the least numbers or use the easy facts first. Use parentheses to show what to multiply first.

$5 \times 9 \times 3 = (5 \times 3) \times 9$
              ↓
          $15 \times 9 = 135$

Write each product. Multiply the least numbers first and use parentheses.

1. $6 \times 2 \times 8$
  $(2 \times 6) \times 8 = 12 \times 8 = 96$
2. $5 \times 7 \times 3$
  $(3 \times 5) \times 7 = 15 \times 7 = 105$
3. $4 \times 9 \times 2$
  $(2 \times 4) \times 9 = 8 \times 9 = 72$
4. $3 \times 6 \times 4$
  $(3 \times 4) \times 6 = 12 \times 6 = 72$
5. $9 \times 5 \times 7$
  $(5 \times 7) \times 9 = 35 \times 9 = 315$
6. $4 \times 1 \times 8$
  $(1 \times 4) \times 8 = 4 \times 8 = 32$
7. $3 \times 7 \times 2$
  $(2 \times 3) \times 7 = 6 \times 7 = 42$
8. $5 \times 2 \times 6$
  $(2 \times 5) \times 6 = 10 \times 6 = 60$

Practice

Skills and Reasoning

Find each product.

6. $(2 \times 14) \times 6$ **168**   **7.** $4 \times (9 \times 7)$ **252**   **8.** $(11 \times 5) \times 2$ **110**   **9.** $8 \times (7 \times 6)$ **336**

10. $3 \times (5 \times 4)$ **60**   **11.** $(2 \times 5) \times 8$ **80**   **12.** $(25 \times 3) \times 3$ **225**   **13.** $7 \times (16 \times 5)$ **560**

14. $(81 \times 2) \times 4$ **648**   **15.** $(3 \times 8) \times 9$ **216**   **16.** $(5 \times 6) \times 7$ **210**   **17.** $6 \times (2 \times 7)$ **84**

Find each product.

18. $12 \times 8 \times 5$ **480**   **19.** $6 \times 9 \times 11$ **594**   **20.** $4 \times 4 \times 7$ **112**   **21.** $5 \times 7 \times 6$ **210**

22. Write $5 \times 6 \times 8$ in three different ways. $(5 \times 6) \times 8$ or $5 \times (6 \times 8)$ or $(5 \times 8) \times 6$; Product is 240

23. Write $6 \times 9 \times 0$ in three different ways. Then solve. $(6 \times 9) \times 0$ or $6 \times (9 \times 0)$ or $(6 \times 0) \times 9$; Product is zero.

Problem Solving and Applications

24. Music One version of the Strathspey reel has 2 steps. Each step has 16 bars of music. Each bar has 4 counts. What's the total number of counts? **128 counts**

Use the diagram to answer **25** and **26.**

25. Geometry Readiness Each letter shows a dancer's starting position. Follow the arrows. How many times will dancer A change places to come back to where he or she started? **6 times**

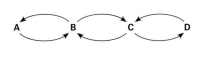

26. Logic When dancers A and B pass each other, which shoulder (right or left) will be nearest the other dancer? **Left shoulder**

27. Patterns If green is next in this tartan plaid, what color comes after that? **Red**

28. Calculator After 23 hours and 44 minutes, Roy Castle stopped tap dancing. How many minutes was that in all? **1,424 min**

Mixed Review and Test Prep

Find each answer.

29. $491 + 837$ **1,328**   **30.** $2,006 - 1,924$ **82**   **31.** $1,433 + 297$ **1,730**   **32.** $3,051 - 2,834$ **217**

33. Which number sentence is in the same family of facts as $16 - 9 = 7$? **C**

  Ⓐ $16 + 7 = 23$ Ⓑ $16 \times 9 = 144$ Ⓒ $9 + 7 = 16$ Ⓓ $16 + 9 = 25$

Skills Practice Bank, page 565, Set 6   Lesson 5-11   **231**

Enrichment 5-11	Problem Solving 5-11

Error Intervention Ongoing Assessment

Observation Students may forget to multiply by the third factor.

How to Help Until students can consistently multiply three factors accurately, encourage them to write all the steps. To check, have them group the factors in a different way and multiply again.

Practice

Exercise 23 Use this opportunity to review the zero property.

Exercise 28 This is a two-step problem.

For Early Finishers Challenge early finishers to choose one multiplication expression from Exercises 6–21 and write a word problem that could be represented by it.

③ Close and Assess

Journal

Have students explain in their journals what the grouping property is and how it can be used to multiply three factors. Encourage them to include examples. The explanation and examples should involve getting the same product while grouping the factors in different ways.

Quick Check

Number Sense Which products in the Skill exercises below could you find by using mental math? Explain. Possible answer: Exercises 2–4; Two of the factors have a product that is a multiple of 10 and the third factor is a 1-digit number.

Skill Find each product.

1. $(3 \times 8) \times 7$ 168   **2.** $2 \times (4 \times 15)$ 120

3. $5 \times 4 \times 9$ 180   **4.** $25 \times 6 \times 2$ 300

ANSWERS

5 Possible answer: Group 4×25, which equals 100, and then multiply by 8; the product is 800.

At-A-Glance Planning

Problem of the Day

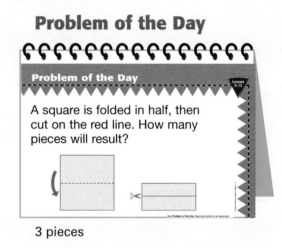

Problem of the Day

A square is folded in half, then cut on the red line. How many pieces will result?

3 pieces

Math Routines

Patterns Have students continue the pattern through the sixth step and then describe the pattern. Start with 10. Add 3. Subtract 1. Add 5. Subtract 2. 13; 12; 17; 15; 22; 19. Add 2 more than the last addition, then subtract 1 more than the last subtraction.

Time Ask students how long a one-hour TV show really is if there are 4 sets of commercials and each set is 4 minutes long. 44 minutes

Mental Math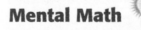

Solve mentally. Explain your thinking.
Begin with 60. Multiply by 2. Add 10. 130
Begin with 90. Subtract 40. Add 50. 100

Science Connection

The amount of energy your body gains from food is measured in calories. A person burns an average of 8 calories per minute while cycling and 6 calories per minute while swimming.

• How many more calories can be burned in half an hour of cycling than in half an hour of swimming? 60

Another Way to **Learn** Lesson 5-12

Use as an alternative or in addition to pages 232 and 233.

Materials Assortment of small classroom objects, such as pencils, markers, erasers, and so on

Learning Style Visual

- Set up a small classroom store by labeling objects with prices such as $0.10 or $0.25.

- Have students talk about how to solve a simple multiple-step problem such as: What is the total cost of 3 pencils and 2 erasers?

- Make the connection to the symbolic by writing the two steps of the solution on the overhead.

Multiply.	Add.
$3 \times \$0.10 = \$0.30$	$\$0.30 + \$0.50 = \$0.80$
$2 \times \$0.25 = \$0.50$	

- Have groups create other problems based on the classroom store and solve them, showing all work.

- Assign Check and Problem Solving Practice on Student Book page 233 or *Practice Master 5-12*.

- Assess using the following rubric.

Assessment Rubric

4 Full Accomplishment
- makes a plan for solving a multiple-step problem
- follows a plan and solves a multiple-step problem

3 Substantial Accomplishment
- with prompting, makes a plan for solving most multiple-step problems
- with prompting, follows a plan and solves most multiple-step problems

2 Partial Accomplishment
- makes a plan for solving some multiple-step problems
- follows a plan and solves some multiple-step problems

1 Little Accomplishment
- does not make a plan for solving a multiple-step problem
- does not follow a plan and solve a multiple-step problem

Options for Reaching All Learners

Language Development

Do the Two-Step
Use same-language pairing to develop an understanding of two-step problems.

Learning Style Verbal, Logical

- Pair students who speak the same language to work on the Check exercises.

- Have one student identify Step 1 of the problem, indicate the operation needed with a symbol, and write the calculations needed to do this step.

- Have the second student do the actual computation.

- Partners switch roles for Step 2.

- Repeat, changing roles for other problems.

- Pairs can describe their work to the class. Students who are less fluent in English may demonstrate while you explain.

Reading Assist

Read Illustrations
Use newspapers to strengthen ability to interpret information from advertisements and illustrations.

Materials Grocery store ads (1 page of ads per group)

Learning Style Logical

- Have each group study a grocery store ad to find out which foods are advertised and in what quantities the foods are available.

- Lead a discussion with the following questions: What do the ads tell you? How do you know which price goes with which item? How do you know the quantities in which the foods are available? Which words can you ignore when you are looking only for prices and quantities?

Objective Solve multiple-step problems.
Suggested Grouping 2 to 4
Student Materials Calculators
Assignment Guide
  Basic 4–11
  Average 4–11
  Enriched 4–11

1 Introduce

Review

Find each product.

1. 3 × $2.50 $7.50   **2.** 4 × $3.75 $15.00
3. 6 × $12.20 $73.20   **4.** 2 × $1.60 $3.20

Build on Prior Knowledge

After students review multiplying money amounts, ask how they could find the total cost of the ocarinas that Joy must order.
Possible answer: Multiply $9.20 by 8.

2 Teach

See Another Way to Learn…on page 232B.

Learn ● ● ● ● ● ● ● ● ● ● ● ● ● ● ● ● ●

Reading Assist Find Main Idea and Supporting Details

Have students read the problem at the top of page 232 and rephrase the question being asked. This is the main idea of the problem. The information given about musical instruments and prices tells the supporting details. Students can use the Understand step as a guide for organizing what they know about the main idea and supporting details.

(Talk About It) **Ongoing Assessment**

Look for students to realize that finding the cost of any one group of instruments does not complete the answer.

Answer for Talk About It

It uses two different operations.

Problem Solving

Analyze Word Problems: Multiple-Step Problems

You Will Learn
how to solve problems that have more than one step

Learn ●

The World Beat band plays instruments from around the world. Joy must order 8 ocarinas, 6 rainsticks, and 2 cabaças (kuh BAS ahs) for the next performance. How much money will she need?

Claves, Haiti $6.90

Kalimba, Uganda $18.50

Ocarina, Italy $9.20

Cabaça, South America $9.50

Rainstick, Chile $8.75

❶ Joy needs: 8 ocarinas at $9.20 each, 6 rainsticks at $8.75 each, 2 cabaças at $9.50 each.

Work Together

▶ **Understand**   What do you know? ❶
                    What do you need to find out?
                    The total cost of all instruments.

▶ **Plan**   How can you begin?   Multiply to find the cost of each instrument.
                    What's the next step? Add to find the total cost.

▶ **Solve**   Step 1: Multiply.

Ocarinas	Rainsticks	Cabaças
$9.20	$8.75	$9.50
× 8	× 6	× 2
$73.60	$52.50	$19.00

                    Step 2: Add. $73.60 + $52.50 + $19.00 = $145.10
                    What's the answer?   Joy needs $145.10 to buy the instruments.

▶ **Look Back**   How can you check if your answer makes sense?

(Talk About It)   Estimate. There are 16 instruments at about $10 each. 16 × $10 = $160. The answer is reasonable.

                    Why does it take two steps to solve this problem?

232   Chapter 5 • Multiplying by 1-Digit Factors

Practice 5-12

Name _____

Practice 5-12

Analyze Word Problems: Multiple-Step Problems

$4.49 $8.69 $15.99 $3.25 $9.79

Use the prices of the athletic equipment above for 1–5.

1. Suppose Alden wanted 4 jump ropes and 2 soccer balls.

  a. How much money would he need for the jump ropes? for the soccer balls? $13.00; $19.50

  b. How much money would he need for 4 jump ropes and 2 soccer balls? $32.50

2. How much would it cost to buy 3 flying discs, 8 jump ropes, and 2 softball mitts? $71.45

3. Alden has $100. If he bought 6 softball mitts, how much money would he have left? $4.06

4. How much money do you need for 6 softball bats, 9 flying discs, and 3 soccer balls? $121.80

5. Jane has $50. She bought 5 soccer balls. What is her change? $1.25

Reteaching 5-12

Check

Use the prices shown on page 232 to solve **1–3**.

1. Suppose Joy wanted 6 ocarinas and 5 cabaças.

   a. How much money would she need for each type of instrument? **$55.20 for ocarinas, $47.50 for cabaças**

   b. How much money would she need in all? **$102.70**

2. How much would it cost to buy 4 ocarinas, 8 kalimbas, and 2 rainsticks? **$202.30**

3. Joy has $100. If she bought 9 sets of claves, how much money would she have left? **$37.90**

Problem Solving Practice

Use the prices shown on page 232 to solve **4–7**.

4. How much money do you need for 7 ocarinas, 9 rainsticks, and 1 kalimba? **$161.65**

5. Joy's aunt pays her $1.50 to walk her dog. Could Joy afford a cabaça if she walked the dog 6 times? Explain. **No; $1.50 × 6 = $9.00**

GPS 6. Joy has $50. She ordered 5 rainsticks. What is her change? **$6.25**

7. How much more would you pay for 8 cabaças than for 8 rainsticks? **$6.00**

8. **Music** American folk music typically has about 120 beats per minute. Akadinda music played in western Africa can reach about 10 beats *per second*. How many more beats per minute are played in akadinda than in American folk music? **480 beats**

9. In the World Beat band, 3 rows of students wear red T-shirts, 2 rows wear blue T-shirts, and 1 row wears green T-shirts. If there are 12 students in each row, how many students are in the band? What strategy did you use? **72 students**

10. To raise money for the band, Patti sold 5 boxes of dried fruit. Eddie sold 7 boxes of granola bars. If a box of dried fruit costs $3.20 and a box of granola bars costs $2.75, how much did Patti and Eddie collect? **$35.25**

11. **Time** Craig went to the band practice at 7:30 P.M. Practice had started 45 minutes earlier. What time did the practice start? **6:45 P.M.**

Problem Solving Strategies

- Use Objects/Act It Out
- Draw a Picture
- Look for a Pattern
- Guess and Check
- Use Logical Reasoning
- Make an Organized List
- Make a Table
- Solve a Simpler Problem
- Work Backward

Choose a Tool

Check

Exercise 3 Be sure students use subtraction rather than addition for the second step.

Practice

Exercises 8 and 10 These are multiple-step problems.

Exercise 9 Ask students how the colors of the t-shirts affect their attempts to solve the problem in Exercise 9. Guide them to see that this is unnecessary information.

For Early Finishers Challenge early finishers to write a problem with more than one step based on the data given on page 232. Have students exchange problems and solve.

3 Close and Assess

Invite students to share their strategies and solutions for the Check and Practice problems. In particular, encourage students who used different strategies for the same problem to share their thinking.

Quick Check

1. **How do you solve a problem that has more than one step?** Make a plan; solve one step at a time; look back to check that the solution makes sense.

2. **How do you know that a problem has more than one step?** The plan shows that it uses more than one operation or that it uses one operation more than one time.

Resources

Technology Master 18

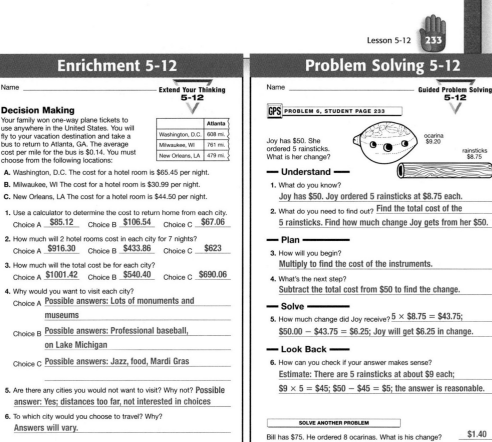

Enrichment 5-12

Name _____

Extend Your Thinking 5-12

Decision Making

Your family won one-way plane tickets to use anywhere in the United States. You will fly to your vacation destination and take a bus to return to Atlanta, GA. The average cost per mile for the bus is $0.14. You must choose from the following locations:

	Atlanta
Washington, D.C.	608 mi.
Milwaukee, WI	761 mi.
New Orleans, LA	479 mi.

A. Washington, D.C. The cost for a hotel room is $65.45 per night.

B. Milwaukee, WI The cost for a hotel room is $30.99 per night.

C. New Orleans, LA The cost for a hotel room is $44.50 per night.

1. Use a calculator to determine the cost to return home from each city.
   Choice A __$85.12__ Choice B __$106.54__ Choice C __$67.06__

2. How much will 2 hotel rooms cost in each city for 7 nights?
   Choice A __$916.30__ Choice B __$433.86__ Choice C __$623__

3. How much will the total cost be for each city?
   Choice A __$1001.42__ Choice B __$540.40__ Choice C __$690.06__

4. Why would you want to visit each city?
   Choice A __Possible answers: Lots of monuments and museums__
   Choice B __Possible answers: Professional baseball, on Lake Michigan__
   Choice C __Possible answers: Jazz, food, Mardi Gras__

5. Are there any cities you would not want to visit? Why not? __Possible answer: Yes; distances too far, not interested in choices__

6. To which city would you choose to travel? Why? __Answers will vary.__

Problem Solving 5-12

Name _____

Guided Problem Solving 5-12

GPS PROBLEM 6, STUDENT PAGE 233

Joy has $50. She ordered 5 rainsticks. What is her change?

ocarina $9.20

rainsticks $8.75

— **Understand** —

1. What do you know?
   Joy has $50. Joy ordered 5 rainsticks at $8.75 each.

2. What do you need to find out? Find the total cost of the 5 rainsticks. Find how much change Joy gets from her $50.

— **Plan** —

3. How will you begin?
   Multiply to find the cost of the instruments.

4. What's the next step?
   Subtract the total cost from $50 to find the change.

— **Solve** —

5. How much change did Joy receive? 5 × $8.75 = $43.75; $50.00 − $43.75 = $6.25; Joy will get $6.25 in change.

— **Look Back** —

6. How can you check if your answer makes sense?
   Estimate: There are 5 rainsticks at about $9 each; $9 × 5 = $45; $50 − $45 = $5; the answer is reasonable.

SOLVE ANOTHER PROBLEM

Bill has $75. He ordered 8 ocarinas. What is his change? __$1.40__

At-A-Glance Planning

Objective Solve problems by making a table.

Student Book Lesson Materials *Optional* Lesson Enhancement Transparencies 19–21, Power Polygons

Materials for pages 234A and 234B Common examples of patterns (wallpaper border, necklace with bead pattern, and so on), Teaching Tool Transparency 9 (Hundred Chart), construction paper strips, scissors, sample gameboards

Subject Connection art—design patterns, rug weaving

Strand Connections patterns, using data

	Before Lesson	During Lesson	After Lesson
Daily Math			
p. 234A Problem of the Day			
p. 234A Math Routines			
p. 234A Mental Math			
Teaching Options			
p. 234 Student Book Lesson			
p. 234B Another Way to Learn…			
Options for Reaching All Learners			
p. 234B Language Development			
p. 234B Gifted and Talented			
Technology Options			
p. 234A *Logical Journey of the Zoombinis*			
p. 236 Interactive CD-ROM Journal			
Assessment Options			
p. 235 Talk About It			
p. 237 Quick Check			
Resources			
5-13 Practice			
5-13 Reteaching			
5-13 Enrichment			
5-13 Problem Solving			
5-13 Daily Transparency			

Problem of the Day

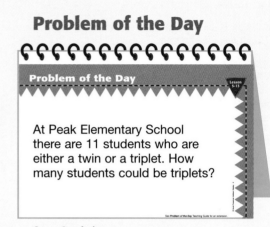

Problem of the Day

At Peak Elementary School there are 11 students who are either a twin or a triplet. How many students could be triplets?

3 or 9 triplets

Math Routines

Patterns Ask students what happens when they move down a hundred chart. Then ask what happens when they move to the right. Number increases by 10 for each square down; Number increases by 1 for each square to the right

Calendar Ask students to think of the calendar as a chart. Starting on the first Wednesday of the month, ask students for the date:

• 2 rows down and 2 columns to the right

• 1 row down and 3 columns to the right

Mental Math

Solve mentally. Explain your thinking.

$(20 \times 3) - 10$ 50 $(30 \times 4) + 20$ 140

$(60 \times 2) + 80$ 200 $(3 \times 50) - 30$ 120

Logical Journey of the Zoombinis

To provide opportunities for making tables, have students use the Evidence sheets for *Pizza Pass*. They can create a table of Arno's favorite toppings and then feed him the perfect pizza.

Another Way to **Learn** Lesson 5-13

Use as an alternative or in addition to pages 234–237.

Learning Style Social, Visual, Kinesthetic

- Tell students that making a table helps to show the relationship among data.
- Have students act out the following for four rounds:

  Round 1: One student stands with arms outstretched.

  Round 2: Two students stand, and each holds one of the first student's hands and stretches out his or her other arm.

- Repeat Round 2 for Rounds 3 and 4.
- Make a table on the overhead.
- Have students compare the numbers in the second column of the table two at a time and record the relationship.

Number of Rounds	Number of Students
1	1
2	3
3	5
4	7

- Have students work in pairs to complete the table to find how many students will be holding hands after 8 rounds. 15 students
- Have students talk about how the table helped them solve the problem.
- Assign Check and Problem Solving Practice on Student Book pages 235–237 or *Practice Master 5-13*.
- Assess using the following rubric.

Assessment Rubric

4 Full Accomplishment
- uses a table to organize data to solve problems

3 Substantial Accomplishment
- uses a table to organize data to solve most problems

2 Partial Accomplishment
- with prompting, uses a table to organize data to solve some problems

1 Little Accomplishment
- does not use a table to organize data to solve problems

Options for Reaching All Learners

Language Development

Pattern Patter

Use common objects to develop understanding of patterns.

Materials Common examples of patterns (wallpaper border, necklace with bead pattern, and so on)

Learning Style Visual

- Show common examples of patterns and use the word *pattern* when describing each one.
- Demonstrate common numerical patterns, such as skip counting, multiples of 10, and so on.
- Together, discuss the qualities of all patterns and formulate a definition. In a pattern, steps or elements are repeated in a predictable manner.
- Then, using the term *pattern*, have students name examples of other tangible or numerical patterns.
- As students share their examples, have them explain why each qualifies as a pattern.

Gifted and Talented

Multiple Patterns

Use a hundred chart to create patterns and compare with patterns on gameboards.

Materials Teaching Tool Transparency 9 (Hundred Chart), construction paper strips, scissors, sample gameboards

Learning Style Visual, Kinesthetic

Board games such as checkers, chess, and backgammon involve moving counters and pieces on patterned boards.

- Have students choose a number from 2 through 9. Have them cut and paste a color square on each square of the hundreds chart containing a multiple of their number.
- Have students compare patterns for multiples of different numbers.
- Finally, have students look at gameboards and identify patterns.

Lesson Organizer

Objective Solve problems by making a table.

Suggested Grouping 2 to 4

Student Materials None

Teacher Materials *Optional* Lesson Enhancement Transparencies 19–21, Power Polygons

Assignment Guide
Basic 4–6, 11–26
Average 4–7, 9–26
Enriched 5–26

1 Introduce

Review

Give the next number in each pattern.

1. 2, 4, 6, 8, ■ 10

2. 5, 10, 15, 20, ■ 25

3. 18, 15, 12, 9, ■ 6

Build on Prior Knowledge

After students review finding the next number in a pattern, ask them how they can use what they know about patterns to find the eighth number in this pattern: 2, 5, 8, 11. Add 3 four more times; 23

2 Teach

See Another Way to Learn...on page 234B.

Learn

Use Lesson Enhancement Transparencies 19 and 20 to show the patterns used in this lesson. As students work together on the example on page 234, ask them why there are 6 pieces for 1 star but 14 pieces for 2 stars. There are 6 pieces for every star, and stars are linked by 2 pieces.

While students can use Power Polygons or drawings to help them see a pattern, watch for students who continue to use Power Polygons or drawings rather than using a pattern.

Problem Solving

Analyze Strategies: Make a Table

You Will Learn
how to solve problems by making a table

Learn

Put on your creative hat! How many pattern pieces do you need to make a headband with 7 stars? One star has 6 pattern pieces. Two pattern pieces link the stars.

1 star   2 stars   3 stars

Ojibwa (oh JIB wah) headband

❶ How many pieces are in 1 star and the number of linking pieces

Work Together

▶ **Understand**
What do you know? ❶
What do you need to find out? How many pieces are in 7 stars and the pieces linking them

▶ **Plan**
Think how you might organize the data in a table. Decide what it will show.

Label a column *Number of Stars.* Label another column called *Number of Pieces.*

▶ **Solve**
Make the table. Fill in what you know.
Keep filling in the table.
Use the table to complete the pattern.

Number of Stars	Number of Pieces
1	6
2	14
3	22
4	30
5	38
6	46
7	54

Problem Solving Hint
You can use Power Polygons or draw a picture to help you see a pattern.

What is the answer? With 7 stars, there are 54 pieces in all.

▶ **Look Back**
How can you check your answer? Continue the pattern and count the pieces.

234 Chapter 5 • Multiplying by 1-Digit Factors

Managing Time

Have student groups complete the Learn, Check, and Problem Solving Practice Exercises 4–11 in class. They can finish Exercises 12–26 as homework.

Another Example

If you continue this pattern until there are 5 stars, how many pieces will you need? Make a table.

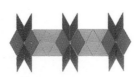

What You See

a. A star is made up of 6 pieces.

b. A star is linked to another star by 6 green triangles.

c. Continue the pattern until there are 5 stars.

What You Do

Number of Stars	Number of Pieces
1	6
2	18
3	30
4	42
5	?

When this pattern has 5 stars, there will be 54 pieces in all.

Talk About It

1. How do the tables help you solve the problems?

2. What patterns did you find in the second table?

Check

Copy and complete the table. Use Power Polygons or draw a picture to help you see a pattern.

Problem Solving
Understand
Plan
Solve
Look Back

1. If your pattern has 4 blue rectangles, how many pieces will it have in all? **19 pieces**

2. If you use 5 blue rectangles, how many pieces will you have? **23 pieces**

3. **Reasoning** How could you make a table that shows how the number of squares changes with the growing pattern? Label the first column "number of squares" and record data for this shape.

Number of Blue Rectangles	Number of Pieces
1	7
2	11
3	15
4	
5	

Meeting Individual Needs

Learning Styles	Teaching Approach
Musical	Clap rhythm patterns such as 3 long and 2 short beats. Have students use a table to find how many beats in all or how many long or short beats are in a given number of clapping sets.
Kinesthetic	Use sets of beads of different shapes to make patterns such as 4 round and 2 rectangular shapes. Have students make a table to find how many beads in all or how many beads of different kinds are in strings of beads of different lengths.

Practice ⬡ ◦ ◦ ◦ ◦ ◦ ◦ ◦ ◦ ◦ ◦ ◦ ◦ ◦ ◦

Exercise 8 Some students may make a table, while others may use logical reasoning.

Exercise 9 Students may find it helpful to organize their work in a table with columns for ingredients, original amounts, and increased amounts.

Interactive CD-ROM Journal
Students can use the Journal Tool to record their favorite recipes. They can use the Spreadsheet/Grapher Tool to make tables of adjusted measurements and amounts. You might collect the recipes and make a class cookbook.

For Early Finishers Challenge students to solve Exercises 4–6 for different numbers of squares and rectangles.

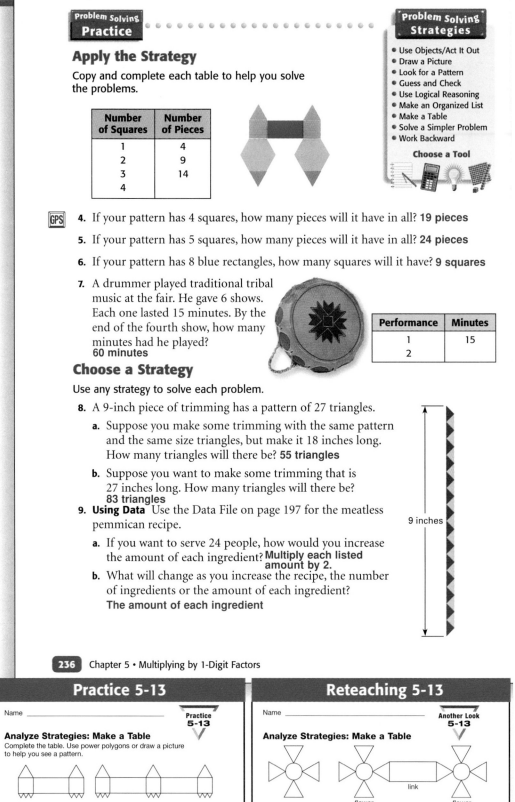

Problem Solving Practice ◦

Apply the Strategy

Copy and complete each table to help you solve the problems.

Number of Squares	Number of Pieces
1	4
2	9
3	14
4	

Problem Solving Strategies
- Use Objects/Act It Out
- Draw a Picture
- Look for a Pattern
- Guess and Check
- Use Logical Reasoning
- Make an Organized List
- Make a Table
- Solve a Simpler Problem
- Work Backward

Choose a Tool

GPS **4.** If your pattern has 4 squares, how many pieces will it have in all? **19 pieces**

5. If your pattern has 5 squares, how many pieces will it have in all? **24 pieces**

6. If your pattern has 8 blue rectangles, how many squares will it have? **9 squares**

7. A drummer played traditional tribal music at the fair. He gave 6 shows. Each one lasted 15 minutes. By the end of the fourth show, how many minutes had he played?
60 minutes

Performance	Minutes
1	15
2	

Choose a Strategy

Use any strategy to solve each problem.

8. A 9-inch piece of trimming has a pattern of 27 triangles.

a. Suppose you make some trimming with the same pattern and the same size triangles, but make it 18 inches long. How many triangles will there be? **55 triangles**

b. Suppose you want to make some trimming that is 27 inches long. How many triangles will there be?
83 triangles

9. Using Data Use the Data File on page 197 for the meatless pemmican recipe.

a. If you want to serve 24 people, how would you increase the amount of each ingredient? **Multiply each listed amount by 2.**

b. What will change as you increase the recipe, the number of ingredients or the amount of each ingredient?
The amount of each ingredient

9 inches

Practice 5-13

Name _____

Practice 5-13

Analyze Strategies: Make a Table
Complete the table. Use power polygons or draw a picture to help you see a pattern.

Number of Rectangles (that are not squares)	Number of Pieces in All
1	11
2	17
3	23
4	29
5	35
6	41

1. If your pattern has 7 rectangles, how many pieces will it have in all? **47**

2. If your pattern has 8 rectangles, how many pieces will you have? **53**

3. If your pattern has 10 rectangles, how many pieces will you have? **65**

4. How did the table help you solve the problems above?
Possible answer: The table helped to see the pattern.

5. Suppose a percussionist plays the maracas for 6 beats and then plays a triangle for 2 beats. If she continues this pattern, what instrument will she be playing on the 25th beat? **The maracas**

6. What will she be playing on the 47th beat? **The triangle**

Reteaching 5-13

Name _____

Another Look 5-13

Analyze Strategies: Make a Table

1 flower   2 flower bracelet   flower   link   flower

How many pattern pieces do you need to make a bracelet with 3 flowers?

Understand What do you know?
There are _5_ pieces in a flower.
There are _11_ pieces in a 2-flower bracelet.

What do you need to find out? How many pieces are there in a 3-flower bracelet?

Plan Make a table to organize the data.

Solve Fill in the table. You can use power polygons or draw a picture to help you see a pattern. Complete the table to find the pattern.

Number of Flowers	Number of Pieces
1	5
2	11
3	17

When there are 3 flowers, there are _17_ pieces in all.

Look Back How can you check your answer?
Possible answer: Draw a picture.

Use the pattern above to answer the questions.

1. If you continue the pattern until you have a 4-flower bracelet, how many pieces will you need? **23**

2. If your bracelet has 6 flowers, how many pieces will it have in all? **35**

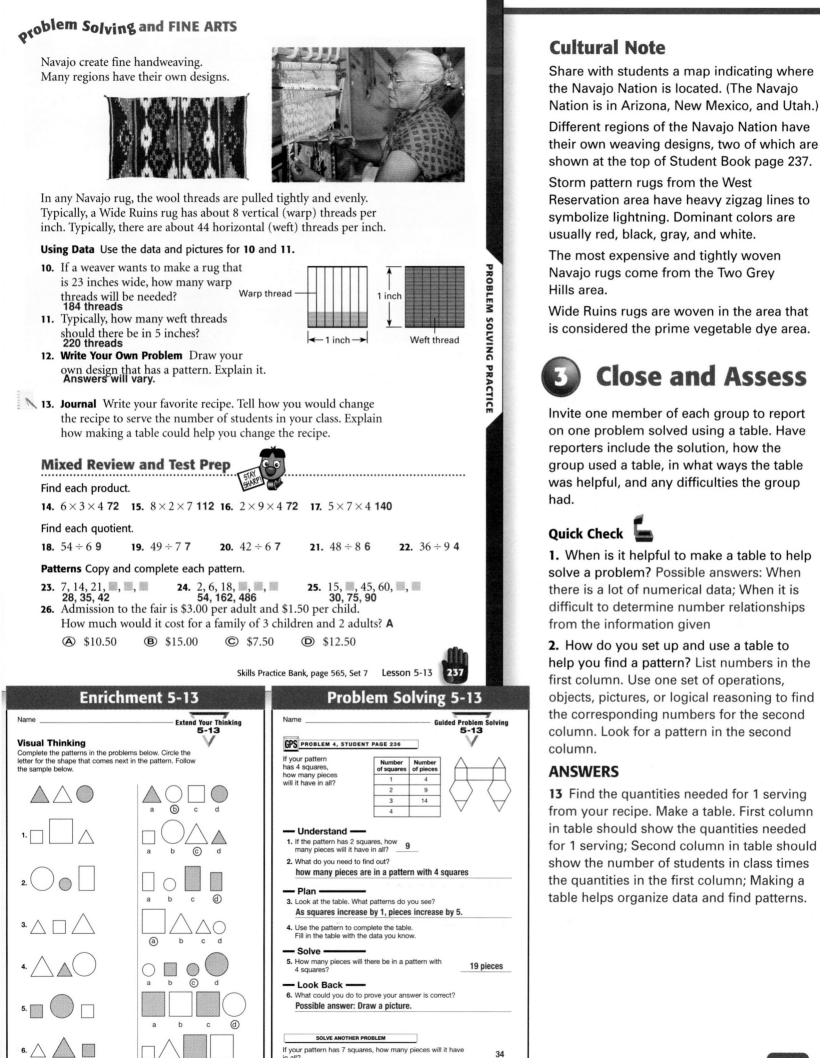

Problem Solving and FINE ARTS

Navajo create fine handweaving.
Many regions have their own designs.

In any Navajo rug, the wool threads are pulled tightly and evenly. Typically, a Wide Ruins rug has about 8 vertical (warp) threads per inch. Typically, there are about 44 horizontal (weft) threads per inch.

Using Data Use the data and pictures for **10** and **11**.

10. If a weaver wants to make a rug that is 23 inches wide, how many warp threads will be needed?
184 threads

Warp thread — 1 inch
←— 1 inch —→ Weft thread

11. Typically, how many weft threads should there be in 5 inches?
220 threads

12. **Write Your Own Problem** Draw your own design that has a pattern. Explain it.
Answers will vary.

13. **Journal** Write your favorite recipe. Tell how you would change the recipe to serve the number of students in your class. Explain how making a table could help you change the recipe.

Mixed Review and Test Prep

Find each product.

14. $6 \times 3 \times 4$ **72** 15. $8 \times 2 \times 7$ **112** 16. $2 \times 9 \times 4$ **72** 17. $5 \times 7 \times 4$ **140**

Find each quotient.

18. $54 \div 6$ **9** 19. $49 \div 7$ **7** 20. $42 \div 6$ **7** 21. $48 \div 8$ **6** 22. $36 \div 9$ **4**

Patterns Copy and complete each pattern.

23. 7, 14, 21, ▦, ▦, ▦
28, 35, 42
24. 2, 6, 18, ▦, ▦, ▦
54, 162, 486
25. 15, ▦, 45, 60, ▦, ▦
30, 75, 90

26. Admission to the fair is $3.00 per adult and $1.50 per child. How much would it cost for a family of 3 children and 2 adults? **A**

Ⓐ $10.50 Ⓑ $15.00 Ⓒ $7.50 Ⓓ $12.50

Skills Practice Bank, page 565, Set 7   Lesson 5-13   **237**

Cultural Note

Share with students a map indicating where the Navajo Nation is located. (The Navajo Nation is in Arizona, New Mexico, and Utah.)

Different regions of the Navajo Nation have their own weaving designs, two of which are shown at the top of Student Book page 237.

Storm pattern rugs from the West Reservation area have heavy zigzag lines to symbolize lightning. Dominant colors are usually red, black, gray, and white.

The most expensive and tightly woven Navajo rugs come from the Two Grey Hills area.

Wide Ruins rugs are woven in the area that is considered the prime vegetable dye area.

③ Close and Assess

Invite one member of each group to report on one problem solved using a table. Have reporters include the solution, how the group used a table, in what ways the table was helpful, and any difficulties the group had.

Quick Check

1. When is it helpful to make a table to help solve a problem? Possible answers: When there is a lot of numerical data; When it is difficult to determine number relationships from the information given

2. How do you set up and use a table to help you find a pattern? List numbers in the first column. Use one set of operations, objects, pictures, or logical reasoning to find the corresponding numbers for the second column. Look for a pattern in the second column.

ANSWERS

13 Find the quantities needed for 1 serving from your recipe. Make a table. First column in table should show the quantities needed for 1 serving; Second column in table should show the number of students in class times the quantities in the first column; Making a table helps organize data and find patterns.

Enrichment 5-13

Name _____ **Extend Your Thinking 5-13**

Visual Thinking
Complete the patterns in the problems below. Circle the letter for the shape that comes next in the pattern. Follow the sample below.

1.
2.
3.
4.
5.
6.

Problem Solving 5-13

Name _____ **Guided Problem Solving 5-13**

GPS PROBLEM 4, STUDENT PAGE 236

If your pattern has 4 squares, how many pieces will it have in all?

Number of squares	Number of pieces
1	4
2	9
3	14
4	

— **Understand** —
1. If the pattern has 2 squares, how many pieces will it have in all? **9**
2. What do you need to find out?
how many pieces are in a pattern with 4 squares

— **Plan** —
3. Look at the table. What patterns do you see?
As squares increase by 1, pieces increase by 5.
4. Use the pattern to complete the table. Fill in the table with the data you know.

— **Solve** —
5. How many pieces will there be in a pattern with 4 squares? **19 pieces**

— **Look Back** —
6. What could you do to prove your answer is correct?
Possible answer: Draw a picture.

SOLVE ANOTHER PROBLEM

If your pattern has 7 squares, how many pieces will it have in all? **34**

Chapter 5: Technology

Students will use graphing software to make a table, calculate, and graph data.

Student Materials *DataWonder!* or other graphing software

Preparation

To gain familiarity with the tools and tasks required, you may wish to work through this lesson before using it with your class. This lesson was written for the Macintosh version of *DataWonder!* If your students are using the Windows version of *DataWonder!* (which differs slightly in certain respects), or software other than *DataWonder!* you may wish to modify some of the lesson steps to fit its features. Check your user's manual or online helper for assistance, if needed.

Introduce the Task

Have students open *DataWonder!* and select the Full Data Table. Practice:

- pulling down the menu options
- entering data in cells
- changing the width of a column (not available in Windows)
- navigating across the rows with the tab key
- moving down the columns with the return key (students using the Windows version can use the arrow keys)
- reducing the size of the table
- selecting more than one cell

Technology

Comparing Costs

When the curtain lifts, all you'll see are eyes! That's the effect the Drama Club wants for the opening scene of "Eyes on You." The club plans to order plastic eyeballs.

The Drama Club needs to order:

> 3 Glow-in-the-Dark Eyeballs
> 9 Eyeballs with Veins
> 3 Cat's Eyeballs
> 7 Extra-Large Eyeballs

How much will each order cost?

Materials
DataWonder! or other graphing software

Work Together

Use your graphing software to calculate and graph data.

1. Open a **Full Data Table**. Copy the data table shown here. Remember, you can change the width of the columns.

2. Find the item totals. For each item:
   - From the **Calculate** menu, choose **Multiply.**
   - Select the cells of the Cost and the Number Ordered, then press Return.
   - Click on the cell in the Total column to enter the product on the form.
   - Find the total cost.

Cooperative Learning

If you have only one computer station in your classroom, you may assign the following cooperative roles for groups of students to work together:

- reader/reporter—reads the task and the data to input; writes the report for the group
- data processor—enters data
- calculator—uses *DataWonder!* to perform calculation tasks required
- grapher—uses *DataWonder!* to create graph of totals

③ Graph the item totals.

- From the **Graph** menu, choose **Show Graph**.

- Select the four products.

- Drag the selected products onto the Graph window.

- Make a bar graph.

④ Insert the table and graph into the Report window.

Graph	
Show Graph	⌘ G
Choose Scale	⌘ H
Vertical Bar . . .	
Line Graph	
Pictograph	
Histogram	
Scattergram	
Circle Graph	
Horizontal Bar	
Stem and Leaf	
Box Plot	

Exercises

Answer **1–3** in the Report window. **Print Report** when you are finished.

1. What was the total cost for all the orders? **$281.90**

2. Which orders cost about the same amount? **Glow-in-the-Dark Eyeballs and Eyeball with Veins**

3. The Drama Club has $70 to spend on special props for "Eyes on You." About how many times as much is the cost of the eyeballs? **4 times; 4 × 70 = 280**

Extensions

Using Data Answer **4** and **5** using the table at the right and the prices in the table on page 238. **Print Report** when you are finished.

4. If the summer school actors sell 60 tickets at $7 each for their play, will they have enough money to buy the eyeballs and spend $120 on other props and costumes? Explain.

Item Ordered	Number
Glow-in-the-Dark Eyeball	4
Eyeball with Vein	8
Cat's Eyeball	2
Extra-Large Eyeball	2

5. Reasoning If you used a calculator, what numbers could you leave off the data tables and still make the same bar graphs? **cost, number sold**

Copy and complete the table below. How many of each item were sold?

	Item	Cost ($)	Number Sold	Item Total ($)
6.	Fluorescent Green Eyeball	34.95	6	209.70
7.	Orange Eyeball	18.95	5	94.75
8.	Silver Eyeball	24.95	8	199.60
9.	Gold Eyeball	29.95	3	89.85

Chapter 5 • Technology **239**

Work Together

Guide students through the activity. Before they do the graphing step, remind them to reduce the size of the table so that it shows only the area containing the data.

When opened, the graph will display the information from the whole table. If you want only the products to appear, create a new file using only the desired data. Open a new data table and copy the column into it. (Note that the Macintosh version's copy-by-dragging feature is unavailable in the Windows version; use Control-C to copy instead.) The graph for this new file will display only the information you have copied.

Exercises

Exercise 3 Help students see that they will need to compare the cost of the special props with the total cost of the eyeballs. Students can solve this by dividing 280 by 70.

Extensions

Exercises 6–9 Students can use the Divide function in the Calculate menu of *DataWonder!* to solve these exercises.

Resources

Technology Master 19

ANSWERS

4 Yes; Ticket money is $420 and cost of eyeballs is $219.20; $219.20 + $120.00 = $339.20, an amount less than the ticket money.

Section C
Review and Practice

Use the Skills Checklist

Review the **Skills Checklist** on the page with students. Then ask questions such as the following:

- For which exercises will you need to show the answer as dollars and cents? Exercises 1–6, 20

- Which exercises can you solve mentally using multiplication and addition? Using multiplication and subtraction? Add: Exercises 7, 9, 11, 12; Subtract: Exercises 8, 10

- What can you do to make solving Exercises 13–17 easier? Reorder the factors or change the grouping using parentheses.

- Which exercises might you need to solve using a table? Exercises 22–23

Assess

You may wish to use this information to assess students' understanding of the lesson objectives.

Item Analysis

Lesson Objective		Items
5-9	Multiply amounts of money.	1–6, 20, 24
5-10	Use mental math to multiply.	7–12
5-11	Multiply when you have three factors.	13–19
5-12	Solve multiple-step problems.	20, 21
5-13	Solve problems by making a table.	22, 23

Resources

Practice Masters
- Practice Chapter 5 Section C

Assessment Sourcebook
- Quiz Chapter 5 Section C

TestWorks: Test and Practice Software

ANSWERS

24 Answers should describe the process for multiplying whole numbers and writing decimal point and dollar sign.

SECTION C
Review and Practice

(Lesson 9) Find each product.

1.	2.	3.	4.	5.
$5.26 × 8	$3.48 × 5	$27.39 × 4	$46.52 × 7	$31.95 × 3
$42.08	$17.40	$109.56	$325.64	$95.85

6. **Reasoning** Would $35.00 be more than or less than enough to buy 9 books at $4.25 each? Explain. **less than, $4.25 × 9 = $38.25**

(Lesson 10) **Mental Math** Find each product.

7. 41×3 **123** 8. 6×19 **114** 9. 4×71 **284** 10. 3×99 **297** 11. 7×21 **147**

12. Explain how you would find 3×72 mentally. **Possible answer: Find 3×70, and then add 3 groups of 2 to make 216.**

(Lesson 11) Find each product.

13. $6 \times 6 \times 3$ **108** 14. $4 \times 11 \times 3$ **132** 15. $5 \times 9 \times 4$ **180** 16. $2 \times 5 \times 4$ **40** 17. $6 \times 8 \times 5$ **240**

18. Write $4 \times 8 \times 6$ three different ways. Solve. **$(4 \times 8) \times 6$, or $4 \times (8 \times 6)$, or $(4 \times 6) \times 8$; product is 192**

19. Write $3 \times 9 \times 3$ three different ways. Solve. **$(3 \times 9) \times 3$; or $3 \times (9 \times 3)$; or $(3 \times 3) \times 9$; product is 81**

(Lesson 12) Solve each problem.

20. Monica had $45. She bought 8 harmonicas for $3.50 each. How much money did she have left? **$17**

21. At a cook-out, 7 students ate hamburger meals, 8 ate hot dog meals, and 5 ate chicken meals. If each student had 3 cookies with his or her meal, how many cookies were eaten? **60 cookies**

(Lesson 13) Make a table or use any strategy to help you solve.

Tosh is making a fruit shake for an after-school party.

22. How many scoops of ice cream does Tosh need if he uses 8 cans of fruit juice? **24 scoops**

23. How many cups of water will he need for 8 cans of fruit juice? **16 cups**

24. **Journal** Explain how multiplying money is like multiplying whole numbers. How is it different?

Fruit Shake – Serves 6
2 cans frozen juice
4 cups water
1 liter bottle soda
6 scoops of ice cream

Skills Checklist

In this section, you have:
- ☑ Multiplied Money
- ☑ Found Special Products
- ☑ Multiplied Three Factors
- ☑ Solved Multiple-Step Problems
- ☑ Solved Problems by Making a Table

REVIEW AND PRACTICE

Practice

Name _____

Practice
Chapter 5
Section C

Review and Practice
(Lesson 9) Find each product.

1.	2.	3.	4.
$5.43 × 7	$18.68 × 3	$5.02 × 5	$2.65 × 4
$38.01	$56.04	$25.10	$10.60

5.	6.	7.	8.
$12.16 × 8	$62.90 × 2	$3.07 × 9	$10.22 × 6
$97.28	$125.80	$27.63	$61.32

(Lesson 10) Use mental math to find each product.

9. $31 \times 5 =$ **155** 10. $6 \times 92 =$ **552**
11. $9 \times 79 =$ **711** 12. $52 \times 7 =$ **364**
13. $88 \times 9 =$ **792** 14. $23 \times 4 =$ **92**

15. An atlas of the world costs $27. How much would it cost to purchase 6 of them? **$162**

(Lesson 11) Find each product.

16. $3 \times 8 \times 9$
$3 \times (8 \times 9)$; $3 \times 72 = 216$

17. $9 \times 11 \times 8$
$(9 \times 11) \times 8$; $99 \times 8 = 792$

18. $31 \times 5 \times 2$
$31 \times (5 \times 2)$; $31 \times 10 = 310$

19. $25 \times 4 \times 2$
$(25 \times 4) \times 2$; $100 \times 2 = 200$

(Lessons 12 and 13) Solve each problem.

20. Angela had $52. She bought 4 crystal bud vases for $9.25 each. How much money did she have left? **$15**

21. Each square on Frank's quilt has 13 pieces. The quilt has 9 squares. How many pieces does it have in all? **117**

(Mixed Review) Complete each pattern.

22. 1, 3, 9, 27, **81** , **243** , **729**
23. 10, **15** , 20, 25, **30** , **35** , **40**

YOUR CHOICE

Choose at least one. Use what you have learned in the chapter.

1 Clean Up!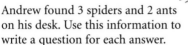

Andrew found 3 spiders and 2 ants on his desk. Use this information to write a question for each answer.

a. 24 b. 12 c. 36 d. 38 e. 6

Go to **www.mathsurf.com/4/ch5** to find information about spiders and ants. Write your own questions and answers.

2 A Trunkful

Mimi has a 28-gallon trunk and Bobo has a 29-gallon trunk. About how many trips will they take to fill a 200-gallon tank? Explain.

3 Multiplication Collage

At Home Use magazines or newspapers to find photos that show multiplication. Cut out the photos and make a collage. Write the multiplication number sentence for each photo. Ask a friend or family member, to see if they can match the multiplication sentence with the photo.

4 Number Detective

Find the rule and write the missing numbers. Then make an In–Out table of your own. Ask a classmate to find the rule. **Multiply by 5.**

In	20	30	70	60	40
Out	100	150	350	300	200

5 Texas Trail

The average pencil can draw a line 35 miles long! Could 7 pencils draw the distance from San Antonio to Dallas? Explain.

No; 7 × 35 miles = 245 miles

Chapter 5 • Your Choice **241**

REVIEW AND PRACTICE

 World Wide Web

For Clean Up!, students can go to **www.mathsurf.com/4/ch5** to begin their search for information about spiders and ants. Encourage them to use words found in various sites as additional key words to further their search.

Home-School Connection

To extend Multiplication Collage, have students ask friends or family members to write a multiplication sentence for a situation at home that shows multiplication. Students can then identify the situation.

Parents can use the Web site **www.parent.mathsurf.com**.

Your Choice

Students will review the skills and concepts of the chapter using learning style strengths.

This page of activities is a good opportunity for portfolio assessment.

1 Clean Up!

Learning Style Verbal, Logical

Help students see that spiders have 8 legs and ants have 6 legs.

Possible answers:

a. How many legs are on 3 spiders?

b. How many legs are on 2 ants?

c. What is the total number of legs on 3 spiders and 2 ants?

d. What is the total number of legs including Andrew's legs?

e. What is the total number of body sections of 2 ants?

2 A Trunkful

Learning Style Visual

The word *about* should indicate to students that they can use estimation.

It takes 4 trips if they fill it together. If each fills the tank alone, Mimi takes 8 trips, Bobo takes 7 trips.

3 Multiplication Collage

Learning Style Visual, Kinesthetic

Answers should include photos with arrays and equal groups, as well as appropriate multiplication sentences to match photos.

4 Number Detective

Learning Style Logical

Students can begin by identifying relationships between the two numbers in the first column. They can then find the rule by testing these relationships on the numbers in the third column.

5 Texas Trail

Learning Style Visual

Help students read the data on the map and confirm that the distance from San Antonio to Dallas is 280 miles.

No; 7 × 35 miles = 245 miles

Chapter 5 **241**

Chapter 5
Review/Test

This page may be used to review or assess students' knowledge of Chapter 5.

Item Analysis

Lesson	Objective	Items
5-1	Multiply by multiples of ten.	2–4, 6–15
5-2	Explore multiplication patterns.	6–15
5-3	Estimate products.	16–20
5-4	Explore multiplication with arrays.	1, 5
5-5	Multiply 2-digit numbers.	16, 17, 20–22
5-6	Multiply 3-digit numbers.	18, 19, 23, 25
5-7	Solve problems by making decisions about cooking.	
5-8	Multiply using different methods.	26–28, 30
5-9	Multiply amounts of money.	24, 29, 33
5-10	Use mental math to multiply.	31
5-11	Multiply when you have three factors.	32
5-12	Solve multiple-step problems.	33
5-13	Solve problems by making a table.	33

Resources

Reading Strategies for Math

Chart 6 (Preparing for a Test)

Assessment Sourcebook

Chapter 5 Tests
- Form A and B (free response)
- Form C (multiple choice)
- Form E (mixed response)
- Form F (cumulative chapter test)

TestWorks: Test and Practice Software

Home and Community Connections

- Letter Home for Chapter 5 in English and Spanish

CHAPTER 5
Review/Test

Vocabulary Match each word with its meaning.

1. array **d**   a. numbers being multiplied
2. factors **a**   b. the answer in multiplication
3. multiples **e**   c. to name a number in a different way
4. product **b**   d. data arranged in rows and columns
5. regroup **c**   e. products of a given number and a whole number

(Lessons 1, 2) Mental Math Find each product using mental math.

6. 9×90 **810**
7. 4×500 **2,000**
8. 2×80 **160**
9. $4 \times 6,000$ **24,000**
10. 8×10 **80**
11. 3×300 **900**
12. 9×600 **5,400**
13. $7 \times 2,000$ **14,000**
14. 5×900 **4,500**
15. 8×600 **4,800**

(Lesson 3) Estimate each product.

16. 6×81 **480**
17. 52×3 **150**
18. 6×503 **3,000**
19. 2×402 **800**
20. 2×27 **60**

(Lessons 4–6, 8, 9) Find each product.

21. 26×8 **208**
22. 31×9 **279**
23. 605×2 **1,210**
24. $\$7.61 \times 8$ **$60.88**
25. 714×5 **3,570**
26. $3,007 \times 6$ **18,042**
27. $2,521 \times 9$ **22,689**
28. $3,506 \times 8$ **28,048**
29. $\$75.00 \times 3$ **$225.00**
30. $8,552 \times 7$ **59,864**

(Lesson 10) Mental Math Answer the question.

31. Explain how would you find 4×52 mentally.
    Possible answer: 4 × 50 is 200, add 4 groups of 2 to make 208.

(Lesson 11) Answer the question.

32. Write $9 \times 3 \times 4$ in three different ways. Then solve.
    (9 × 3) × 4 or 9 × (3 × 4) or (9 × 4) × 3; Product is 108.

(Lessons 12-13) Solve.

33. Six tickets to the play cost $4.50. How much would it cost to buy tickets for a class of 36 students and a class of 30 students? **$49.50**

Number of Tickets	6	12	18
Price	$4.50	$9.00	$13.50

REVIEW/TEST

Assessment

Name _____
Date _____ Score _____

Chapter 5 Test
Form
A

Vocabulary: In 1–3, match each with its meaning.

1. product   a. data arranged in rows and columns   1. ___**b**___
2. array   b. multiplication answer   2. ___**a**___
3. factor   c. number being multiplied   3. ___**c**___

In 4-5, use a multiplication fact to help you find each product.

4. 8×20 4. ___**160**___
5. 9×70 5. ___**630**___

In 6–7, use patterns to find each product.

6. $7 \times 3 =$ __**21**__ $7 \times 30 =$ __**210**__ $7 \times 300 =$ __**2,100**__
7. $5 \times 6 =$ __**30**__ $5 \times 60 =$ __**300**__ $5 \times 600 =$ __**3,000**__

In 8–10, estimate each product.

8. 4×91 8. ___**360**___
9. 48×6 9. ___**300**___
10. 3×76 10. ___**240**___

11. Use the array to help you find the product.   11. ___**68**___

    17×4

In 12–14, find each product. Estimate to check.

12. 5×22 12. ___**110**___
13. 67×3 13. ___**201**___
14. 8×51 14. ___**408**___

In 15–20, multiply.

15. 417×9 15. ___**3,753**___
16. 307×6 16. ___**1,842**___
17. $8,005 \times 3$ 17. ___**24,015**___
18. $8,208 \times 3$ 18. ___**24,624**___
19. $\$3.75 \times 5$ 19. ___**$18.75**___
20. $\$16.41 \times 6$ 20. ___**$98.46**___

In 21-22, use mental math to multiply.

21. 5×52 21. ___**260**___
22. 65×3 22. ___**195**___

23. Write $4 \times 7 \times 5$ in three different ways. Then solve.
    (4 × 7) × 5; 4 × (7 × 5); (4 × 5) × 7; 140

24. Brenda and three friends went bowling. It cost each person $1.25 to rent shoes and $1.75 to play a game. They each bowled 2 games. How much did it cost the group altogether?   24. ___**$19.00**___

25. Alice needs 48 plates. Plates come in packs of 8. Complete the table to find how many packs she needs.   25. ___**6 packs**___

Number of packs	1	2	3	4	5	6
Number of plates	8	16	24	32	40	48

26. **Explain Your Thinking** Explain how multiplying money amounts is like multiplying whole numbers.
    First multiply as though both were whole numbers. Then place the decimal point in the answer.

Performance Assessment

Suppose at the end of the year your art club has $100 to spend on craft supplies. How would you spend the $100?

Craft Supplies

Poster board	$3 per box	Fabric paints	$4 per bottle
Clay	$12 per bag	Paint markers	$2 per marker
Papier mâché	$18 per bottle	Beads	$11 per box
Colored sand	$6 per bag	Colored markers	$5 per box

1. **Decision Making** Decide which items you will buy. Decide how many of each item.

2. **Recording Data** Copy and fill out the table below. Remember that your total can be close to $100, but cannot go over.

Description of Item	How Many	Price of One	Total Price
Total Price of All Items			

3. **Explain Your Thinking** How did you decide which items to buy? How did you decide how many of each item?

4. **Critical Thinking** Find another combination of items that gives you a total closer to $100. **Possible answer: 4 bags clay, 2 bottles papier mache, 2 boxes colored markers, and 1 bag sand is $100.**

Assessment

Name _____

Date _____ Score _____

Chapter 5 Test
Form
D

These groups will represent your school on Community Appreciation Day: 4 first graders, 5 second graders, 6 third graders, 7 fourth graders, and 8 fifth graders. You have been asked to schedule each group to visit one of the places listed below. Each group will visit a different place.

Place	Entrance Fee
City Hall	No cost
History Museum	$2 per student
Library	No cost
Art Museum	$3 per student
Planetarium	$10 per group

During the visit, each student is to choose 7 postcards costing $0.25 each to take back to class for a display. Lunch will cost $2.58 per student.

a. **Making Decisions** What would be a good way to select the students that will represent the school? Decide which group will visit each location.

b. **Recording Data** Copy and complete a table like the one below.

Grade	Number of Students	Place Visited	Cost of Postcards	Cost of Lunch	Total Cost of Visit

c. **Analyzing Data** How many postcards did the first graders and second graders buy in all? How many were bought by all 5 groups?

Which group spent the most money on its visit? The least money? What is the median cost per group?

d. **Critical Thinking** Suppose you want to spend the least amount of money possible. How would you decide which of the groups should be sent to each of the locations?

e. **Making Decisions** Suppose you only have $150 to spend. Could your entire class attend the event you chose for the fourth-grade group? If not, what could you do to make the trip happen for all fourth graders?

Chapter 5 Performance Assessment

Students will show their understanding of multiplying whole numbers and money as they create an art supplies budget.

Introduce the Task

Review Exercises 1–4 with students to be sure they understand the work they are to do. Share Level 4 of the rubric with students before they begin.

Facilitate and Assess

Before students work, you may wish to ask questions such as the following:

- What do you think is a good way to solve this problem?
- How do you plan to organize your work?
- How will you keep track of your work?

Assessment Rubric

4 Full Accomplishment
- makes a logical plan for spending $100 on multiple numbers of items and records it accurately

3 Substantial Accomplishment
- makes a plan for spending $100 on multiple numbers of items and records it with few errors

2 Partial Accomplishment
- makes a partial plan for spending $100 on multiple numbers of items and records most of it

1 Little Accomplishment
- does not make a plan for spending $100 on multiple numbers of items

Resources

Assessment Sourcebook

Chapter 5 Test

- Form D (performance assessment)

Math Magazine

Students will explore an alternative method for multiplying by 2-digit numbers.

Student Materials Teaching Tool Transparency 6 (Centimeter Grid Paper, 1 copy per student)

Teacher Materials Teaching Tool Transparency 6 (Centimeter Grid Paper), *optional* Lesson Enhancement Transparency 22

Note: You may wish to predraw lattice lines on the grid paper before duplicating it. Lesson Enhancement Transparency 22 reproduces the material on page 244.

Historical Note

Lattice multiplication got its name because numbers were arranged to look like the medieval grating or lattice placed at windows of houses. This method first appeared in India around the tenth century, later spread into Arab mathematics, and soon spread to Italy.

Cultural Link

Invite students to share other ways they know to multiply from various cultures. Help students compare what is the same and what is different about the various approaches.

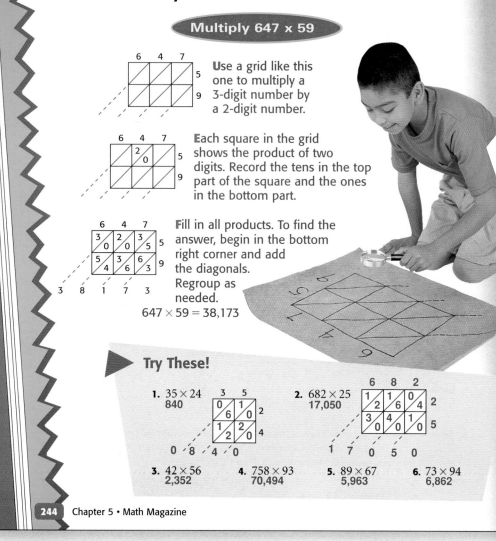

Grid Lock Unlock the secret to solving tough multiplication problems the way people in ancient India did. The key is using a special grid. Here's how they did it.

Multiply 647 × 59

Use a grid like this one to multiply a 3-digit number by a 2-digit number.

Each square in the grid shows the product of two digits. Record the tens in the top part of the square and the ones in the bottom part.

Fill in all products. To find the answer, begin in the bottom right corner and add the diagonals. Regroup as needed.

647 × 59 = 38,173

Try These!

1. 35 × 24
   840

2. 682 × 25
   17,050

3. 42 × 56
   2,352

4. 758 × 93
   70,494

5. 89 × 67
   5,963

6. 73 × 94
   6,862

Additional Resources for the Teacher

Investigations in Numbers, Data, and Space: Arrays and Shares (Multiplication and Division), Karen Economopoulos, et al. Menlo Park, CA: Dale Seymour Publications

Test Prep Strategy: Eliminate Choices!

Estimate.
What is the product of 7 and 307?

(A) 214 (B) 2,149 (C) 21,490 (D) 314

STAY SHARP! 307 is close to 300.

$7 \times 300 = 2,100$.

214 and 314 are too low. 21,490 is too great. The answer is (B) 2,149.

Write the letter of the correct answer. You may estimate or use any strategy to help.

1. For her club meeting, Teresa bought 6 boxes of cookies. If each box held 19 cookies, how many cookies did she bring? **C**

   (A) 25 (B) 13 (C) 114 (D) 240

2. The gym at Emerson school holds 3,123 people. The gym at King school holds 1,521 people. How many people can both gyms hold? **A**

   (A) 4,644 (B) 1,602 (C) 13,644 (D) 644

3. What is the product of 5 and 689? **D**

   (A) 345 (B) 694 (C) 1,445 (D) 3,445

4. The members of the drama club each paid $7 to go to a play. If there are 49 members, how much money did they spend? **C**

   (A) $56 (B) $713 (C) $343 (D) $127

5. Rodrigo put 9 baseball cards on each page of an album. If there are 29 pages in the album, how many cards does he have? **C**

   (A) 38 (B) 162 (C) 261 (D) 181

6. While playing jump rope, Inez jumped 492 times and Alison jumped 611 times. How many more times did Alison jump than Inez? **A**

   (A) 119 (B) 1,103 (C) 321 (D) 27

7. If a concert starts at 8:00 and it takes 55 minutes to get to the concert hall, what time should you leave? **B**

   (A) 6:00 (B) 7:05 (C) 7:15 (D) 7:25

Test Prep Strategies

- Read Carefully
- Follow Directions
- Make Smart Choices
- Eliminate Choices
- Work Backward from an Answer

REVIEW AND PRACTICE

Practice

Name _____

Practice
Chapters 1–5

Cumulative Review
(Chapter 1 Lesson 5) Use the stem-and-leaf plot to answer each question.

Heights (in inches) of Mrs. McKinley's students

| 4 | 6 6 7 7 8 8 8 8 8 9 9 |
| 5 | 0 0 0 1 1 2 2 3 3 4 5 |

1. How tall is the tallest student? __55 inches__
2. What is the most common height in the class? __48 inches__
3. How many students are 51 inches tall? __2__
4. How many students are in Mrs. McKinley's class? __22__

(Chapter 3 Lesson 6) Add.

5.	4 8	6.	6 3 9	7.	7,1 7 3	8.	5,9 2 1
	9 3		5 8 2		6,9 2 0		4 7 7
	+ 5 7		+ 9 2 4		+ 2,8 1 7		+ 4,6 1 8
	198		2,145		16,910		11,016

(Chapter 4 Lessons 9 and 12) Divide.

9. $27 \div 9 =$ __3__ 10. $45 \div 5 =$ __9__ 11. $81 \div 9 =$ __9__

12. $14 \div 2 =$ __7__ 13. $48 \div 6 =$ __8__ 14. $56 \div 7 =$ __8__

15. $72 \div 8 =$ __9__ 16. $25 \div 5 =$ __5__ 17. $35 \div 7 =$ __5__

(Chapter 5 Lessons 6 and 9) Multiply.

18.	1 3 8	19.	6 2 9	20.	7 5 1	21.	3 7 7
	× 3		× 4		× 8		× 6
	414		2,516		6,008		2,262

22.	$6.8 8	23.	$1 4.2 3	24.	$3.1 1	25.	$4.5 0
	× 9		× 4		× 6		× 3
	$61.92		$56.92		$18.66		$13.50

Chapters 1–5
Cumulative Review

Students review and maintain skills and concepts taught in Chapters 1–5 and practice test-taking strategies. Special attention is given here to the Test Prep Strategy, Eliminate Choices: Estimate.

Introduce the Test Prep Strategy

Eliminate Choices: Estimate Read and discuss the Test Prep Strategy note. After students work through the example, present the following problem:

There are 364 children in the Christa McAuliffe School. About one-fifth of these students are in grade 4. How many are in grade 4? C

(A) 7 (B) 35 (C) 73 (D) 82

Encourage students to find other problems on this page where Eliminate Choices: Estimate might be a helpful strategy.

Some students may prefer another strategy for some of the identified items. Have them tell which strategy they would use and explain why.

Review and Assess

Item Analysis	
Item	Lesson
1	5-5
2	3-5
3	5-6
4	5-9
5	5-5
6	3-7
7	2-10

Resources

Practice Masters

• Cumulative Review Chapters 1–5

Section	Pacing	Lessons		Your Test	Materials	
	Day	**Lesson/Page**	**Objective**	**Correlation**	**Student Book**	**Another Way to Learn**
A						
Multiplication Number Sense	Day 1	6-1 250–251	Explore multiplication patterns.		Calculators	
Students use basic facts, estimation, and place value to understand multiplication.	Day 2	6-2 252–253	Estimate products of 2-digit factors.			PV* blocks
Problem Solving Connection	Day 3	6-3 254–255	Multiply by multiples of 10.			PV blocks
Look for a Pattern Use Objects/Act It Out Draw a Picture	Day 4	6-4 256–257	Explore multiplying with 2-digit factors.		PV blocks	
B	Day 5	6-5 260–263	Multiply with 2-digit factors.		Centimeter Grid Paper	PV blocks
Multiplying						
Students develop the algorithm by multiplying with 2-digit factors.	Day 6	6-6 264–265	Estimate greater products.			Calculators
Problem Solving Connection	Day 7	6-7 266–267	Multiply numbers in the thousands.		Calculators (optional)	Calculators
Decision Making	Day 8	6-8 270–271	**Problem Solving** Solve problems by making decisions after analyzing data.			
C	Day 9	6-9 274–275	Multiply amounts of money.			Play money, calculators (optional)
Extending Multiplication						
Multiplication with 2-digit factors is extended to money amounts.	Day 10	6-10 278–279	**Problem Solving** Solve problems needing overestimates or underestimates.		Calculators (optional)	Play money
Problem Solving Skill *Overestimating and Underestimating* **Problem Solving Strategy** *Draw a Picture*	Day 11	6-11 280–281	**Problem Solving** Solve problems by drawing a picture.		Centimeter Grid Paper (optional)	Centimeter Grid Paper
Chapter Assessment	Day 12	284–285	Assess student understanding and skills for Chapter 6.			

Also in this Chapter **Data File,** pp. 246–247, **Projects/Extensions,** pp. 248, 286

* PV = Place Value

Chapter 6
Key Math Idea

Multiplication with 2-digit factors involves multiplying by a 1-digit factor and by a multiple of ten, and then adding to find the product.

Connections		Section Resources	
Strand	**Subject**	**Technology**	**Review and Assessment**
Mental Math, Time, Money, Geometry	Careers, Social Studies, Literature, Language	**Performance Math: Multiplication** 💿 **World Wide Web** 🌐 www.mathsurf.com/4/ch6 Chapter Opener, p. 246 **Calculator** 🖩 Exploring Multiplication Patterns, pp. 250–251 **Interactive CD-ROM Lesson 6** 💿 Exploring Multiplying with 2-Digit Factors, p. 256	**Review** Section A Opener, p. 249 Mixed Review and Test Prep, pp. 253, 255 Section A Review and Practice, p. 258 Skills Practice Bank, p. 566 **Ongoing Assessment** *Teacher's Edition,* all lessons *Assessment Sourcebook,* Quiz Chapter 6 Section A
Time, Using Data, Algebra Readiness	Social Studies, Careers, Reading		
Measurement, Time	History, Literature		
	Language		
Geometry Readiness, Using Data	Geography, History, Math History, Literature, Language, Culture	**Performance Math: Multiplication** 💿 **Logical Journey of the Zoombinis** 💿 Decision Making, p. 270A **World Wide Web** 🌐 www.mathsurf.com/4/ch6 Problem Solving, pp. 270–271	**Review** Section B Opener, p. 259 Mixed Review and Test Prep, pp. 263, 265, 267 Stop and Practice, pp. 268–269 Section B Review and Practice, p. 272 Skills Practice Bank, p. 566 **Ongoing Assessment** *Teacher's Edition,* all lessons *Assessment Sourcebook,* Quiz Chapter 6 Section B
Money, Probability, Using Data	Social Studies, Literature		
Mental Math, Time, Measurement, Money	Social Studies, Geography, Science, Language		
	Social Studies, Language, Reading		
Using Data, Time, Algebra Readiness	Physical Education, Literature, Culture	**Performance Math: Multiplication** 💿 **Logical Journey of the Zoombinis** 💿 Analyze Strategies, p. 280A **World Wide Web** 🌐 www.mathsurf.com/4/ch6 Your Choice, p. 283	**Review** Section C Opener, p. 273 Mixed Review and Test Prep, pp. 275 Practice Game, pp. 276–277 Section C Review and Practice, p. 282 Your Choice, p. 283 Skills Practice Bank, p. 566 **Ongoing Assessment** *Teacher's Edition,* all lessons *Assessment Sourcebook,* Quiz Chapter 6 Section C
Money	Science, Physical Education, Social Studies, Reading, Language		
	Physical Education, Reading		
		TestWorks 💿	Chapter Review/Test, p. 284 Performance Assessment, p. 285 Cumulative Review, p. 287

Manipulatives

Using the Manipulatives

Place-Value Blocks (Base 10 Blocks) Students use place-value blocks to model multiplication arrays and to reinforce their understanding of multiplication patterns.

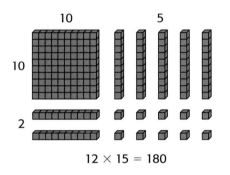

$$12 \times 15 = 180$$

Suggested Materials	Alternatives
Calculators	———
Place-value blocks	Grid paper
Play money	Index cards with values marked

Play Money Play money is used in Lessons 6-9 and 6-10 to model problems involving money amounts. Students increase their familiarity with money by exchanging denominations.

Literature

Melisande

E. Nesbit. New York: Harcourt Brace Jovanovich, 1989.

Use with Lesson 6-1 The King offers his daughter Melisande a wish that he had never used. Upon instruction from the Queen, Melisande wishes for her hair to grow an inch every day and twice as fast every time it is cut.

Much Ado About Aldo

Johanna Hurwitz. New York: Puffin, 1989.

Use with Lesson 6-3 Elaine, Karen, and Aldo search their apartment building for a lost cat by asking door to door.

Cloudy with A Chance of Meatballs

Judi Barrett. New York: Simon & Schuster, 1978.

Use with Lesson 6-5 The residents of Chewandswallow live on food that falls from the sky. One day a storm brings 15-inch drifts of cream cheese and jelly sandwiches.

Henry and Beezus

Beverly Cleary. New York: Morrow, 1952.

Use with Lesson 6-6 Henry Huggins comes across a pile of 49 boxes of gumballs in the bushes.

Orp

Suzy Kline. New York: Putnam Group, 1989.

Use with Lesson 6-9 Orp starts the I HATE MY NAME Club and pays Chloe to type advertising cards.

Additional Resources

Quest 2000: Exploring Mathematics, Grade 4, Randall Charles, et al. Menlo Park, CA: Addison-Wesley Publishing Company. *Unit 4.*

Investigations in Number, Data, and Space: Arrays and Shares (Multiplication and Division), Karen Economopoulos, et al.; **Investigations in Number, Data, and Space: Packages and Groups (Multiplication and Division),** Karen Economopoulos, et al. Menlo Park, CA: Dale Seymour Publications.

Nimble With Numbers, Leigh Childs and Laura Choate. Menlo Park, CA: Dale Seymour Publications.

Mental Math in the Middle Grades, Jack A. Hope, et al. Menlo Park, CA: Dale Seymour Publications.

Cluebusters, Jean E. Haack. Menlo Park, CA: Dale Seymour Publications.

For the Teacher

 ### Teacher's Resource Planner CD-ROM

The Teacher's Resource Planner CD-ROM allows you to create customized lesson plans tailored to your own class's needs. It also allows you to preview any supplement page, edit if you wish, and print it.

 ### World Wide Web

Visit **www.teacher.mathsurf.com** for additional activities, links to lesson plans from teachers and other professionals, NCTM information, and other useful sites.

TestWorks Test and Practice Software

A database of questions allows you to generate personalized practice worksheets and tests.

For the Student

 ### Interactive CD-ROM

Use with Lessons 6-4 and 6-5 Students use the Place-Value Blocks Tool to model multiplying with 2-digit numbers and enhance their understanding of regrouping.

 ### World Wide Web

Use with Chapter Opener, Lesson 6-8, and Your Choice Have students go online at **www.mathsurf.com/4/ch6** to find out about ways that people stay on the move and to learn about roller coasters. To complete the Your Choice activity, students can find information regarding price of different kinds of public transportation.

Performance Math

Use daily throughout Chapter 6 Students can practice daily to increase their familiarity with basic multiplication facts.

Logical Journey of the Zoombinis

Use with Lessons 6-8 and 6-11 *Allegic Cliffs* is a "guess my hidden rule" puzzle for which students must discover the attribute which will allow their Zoombini to cross the bridge. The Zoombini Puzzle Log will help students keep track of their elimination process. Likewise, students must sort and eliminate attributes when they play *Fleens!*

Calendar Time Kit

Calendar

One of the concepts in this chapter is multiplying with 2-digit factors. You may use the Calendar Time Kit to reinforce this concept with the following activity:

Multiply using number cubes and the calendar.

- Each day, roll two number cubes of contrasting colors to obtain a 2-digit number. Designate one color as the ones digit and the other as the tens digit.
- Next, have students multiply the date by that number. If the date is a 1-digit number, multiply it by 10.
- Record results on the calendar.
- Then have students reverse the digits in the number rolled and multiply again. Compare results. *Are the products different? Which product is greater? By about how much? Explain.*

M	T	W	T	F
1 $\begin{array}{r} 10 \\ \times 45 \\ \hline 450 \end{array}$	**2** $\begin{array}{r} 20 \\ \times 32 \\ \hline 640 \end{array}$	**3** $\begin{array}{r} 30 \\ \times 16 \\ \hline 480 \end{array}$	**4** $\begin{array}{r} 40 \\ \times 44 \\ \hline 1{,}760 \end{array}$	**5** $\begin{array}{r} 50 \\ \times 14 \\ \hline 700 \end{array}$
8 $\begin{array}{r} 80 \\ \times 21 \\ \hline 1{,}680 \end{array}$	**9** $\begin{array}{r} 90 \\ \times 52 \\ \hline 4{,}680 \end{array}$	**10** $\begin{array}{r} 10 \\ \times 35 \\ \hline 350 \end{array}$	**11** $\begin{array}{r} 11 \\ \times 61 \\ \hline 671 \end{array}$	**12** $\begin{array}{r} 12 \\ \times 36 \\ \hline 432 \end{array}$

Bulletin Board

Objective Use multiplication to find the distance traveled.

Materials Map of the U.S., index cards, tacks, markers, yarn

- Display a small map of the U.S. on the bulletin board as shown.
- Write the numbers 1–9 each on a separate index card. Each day, have a volunteer select two cards to create a 2-digit number. This number is the number of hours a train has traveled in a week.
- Tell students that the train is moving at 64 mph.
- Have the volunteer write and post the problem and solution on an index card.
- Students can use yarn to show the route of the train for each distance.

Technology Centers

Observation Tips

Observe common software-use problems so you can review their solutions with students.

- In Chapter 6, there are opportunities to observe students as they use problem-solving strategies in the *Logical Journey of the Zoombinis* puzzles *Allergic Cliffs* and *Fleens!*
- Watch for common problems students experience working with the software. For example, if several students are having difficulty clicking on and dragging a Zoombini to a highlighted spot, you may wish to teach a mini-lesson to review this.

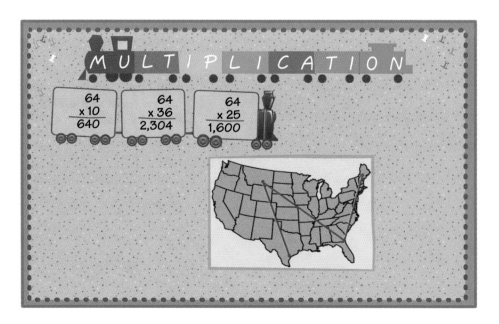

Traditional Assessment	
Review and Practice	Student Edition: pages 258, 272, 282
Cumulative Review	Student Edition: page 287; Assessment Sourcebook: Form F, Quarterly Test Chapters 1–6
Section Quizzes	Assessment Sourcebook: Section Quizzes A, B, C

Chapter Tests
  Free Response
  Multiple Choice
  Mixed Response
	Student Edition: page 284; Assessment Sourcebook: Forms A and B
	Assessment Sourcebook: Form C
	Assessment Sourcebook: Form E

Alternative Assessment	
Ongoing Assessment	Teacher's Edition: every core lesson; Assessment Sourcebook: pages 11–13, 16–19, 21
Portfolio	Teacher's Edition: page 267; Assessment Sourcebook: pages 9, 13, 14, 16, 23
Interview and Observation	Teacher's Edition: pages 255, 263; Assessment Sourcebook: pages 18, 20
Journal	Student Edition: pages 251, 255, 257, 258, 263, 267, 272, 279, 282; Teacher's Edition: pages 253, 265, 271, 275; Assessment Sourcebook: pages 8–11, 15
Performance Assessment	Student Edition: page 285; Teacher's Edition: pages 251, 257; Assessment Sourcebook: Form D

NCTM Assessment Standards

Focus on Inferences

Journals Traditional tests only partially reveal the depth of students' understanding of mathematics. Regular journal entries help students think through mathematical processes and reflect on progress. Journal writing opportunities in Chapter 6 appear on pages 253, 271, and 275.

Test Prep

- The Test Prep Strategy **Eliminate Choices: Estimate** is introduced and practiced in the Cumulative Review on page 287.
- Mixed Review and Test Prep occurs throughout the chapter.

TestWorks

TestWorks can create personalized multiple-choice tests, free-response tests, and practice worksheets.

Standardized-Test Correlation		ITBS	CTBS	CAT	SAT	MAT
Lesson/Objective		**Form M**	**4th Ed.**	**5th Ed.**	**9th Ed.**	**7th Ed.**
6-1	Explore multiplication patterns.	●	●	●	●	●
6-2	Estimate products of 2-digit factors.	●	●	●	●	●
6-3	Multiply by multiples of 10.	●	●	●	●	●
6-4	Explore multiplying with 2-digit factors.	●	●	●	●	●
6-5	Multiply with 2-digit factors.	●	●	●	●	●
6-6	Estimate greater products.	●	●	●	●	●
6-7	Multiply numbers in the thousands.	●				
6-8	Solve problems by making decisions after analyzing data.	●	●	●	●	●
6-9	Multiply amounts of money.	●		●	●	●
6-10	Solve problems needing overestimates or underestimates.	●	●	●	●	●
6-11	Solve problems by drawing a picture.					

Key   **ITBS** Iowa Test of Basic Skills   **CTBS** Comprehensive Test of Basic Skills   **CAT** California Achievement Test
SAT Stanford Achievement Test   **MAT** Metropolitan Achievement Test

Multiplying by 2-Digit Factors

Theme: On the Move!

Teacher Materials *Optional* Lesson Enhancement Transparency 23

Introduce the Chapter

Different modes of transportation offer a context for exploration of multiplication by 2-digit factors. Students extend their multiplication sense to Problem Solving Lessons, which include using data, drawing pictures, and estimation strategies.

Activate Prior Knowledge

Make a class list of forms of transportation students have used. Then ask students which they think is the most interesting.

Use the Data File

You may wish to use Lesson Enhancement Transparency 23 along with the following questions to discuss the data file.

- How is the data represented? Bar graphs, line graph
- Use the bar graph to find which city has the greatest number of people using public transportation. Moscow
- Use the bar graph to find the fastest and slowest forms of transportation. Jumbo jet airplane; Walking
- How does the line graph show the change in subway fares? The rising line shows that fares have increased.

Chapter 6
Multiplying by 2-Digit Factors

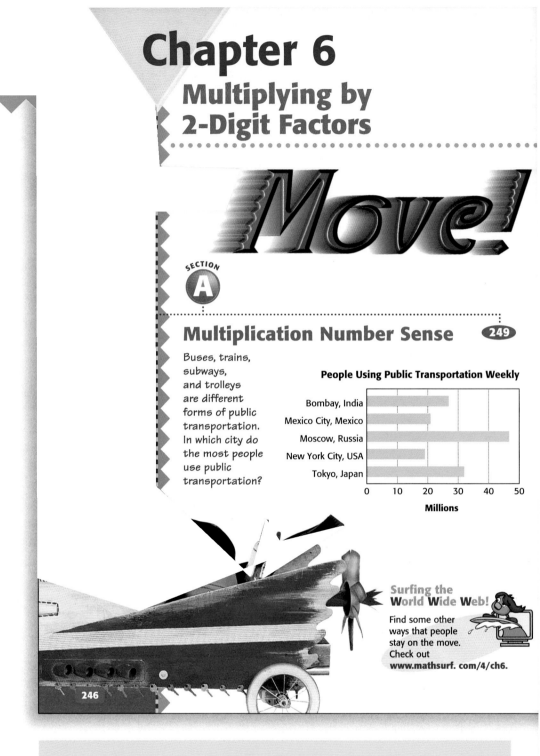

SECTION A

Multiplication Number Sense 249

Buses, trains, subways, and trolleys are different forms of public transportation. In which city do the most people use public transportation?

People Using Public Transportation Weekly

Bombay, India
Mexico City, Mexico
Moscow, Russia
New York City, USA
Tokyo, Japan

0   10   20   30   40   50
Millions

246

Surfing the World Wide Web!
Find some other ways that people stay on the move. Check out www.mathsurf.com/4/ch6.

Extensions

● Social Studies Connection

Provide students with the speed limits set by your state for driving in unmarked residential areas, on rural roads, and on interstate highways. This information is usually available from your local Department of Transportation or a Driver's Education brochure. Have students multiply to find how far they could travel in 3 hours at each speed.

◉ Performance Math: Multiplication

For students still needing to build their knowledge of multiplication facts, provide 10 minutes per day of practice with *Performance Math* throughout the chapter. Have them track their own progress by periodically checking the progress reports. These reports may be added to their portfolios.

Multiplying

259

Sometimes the form of transportation you use depends on how quickly you want to get where you are going. Which form of transportation is fastest? Which is slowest?

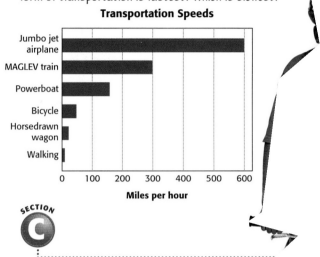

Transportation Speeds

Extending Multiplication

The New York subway began operating in the late 1800s. In 1904, it cost just five cents to ride the subway. How have fares changed since then?

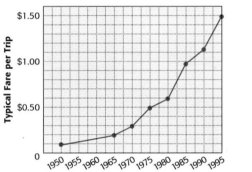

New York City Subway Fares

Preview the Sections

A Multiplication Number Sense

Students will identify patterns in multiples of 10, then use that knowledge to estimate products and to multiply 2-digit numbers. They will also use arrays to explore multiplying 2-digit numbers.

B Multiplying

Students will use the multiplication algorithm and estimation to multiply with 2-digit factors and choose appropriate methods for multiplying. They will also solve problems by analyzing data and making decisions.

C Extending Multiplication

Students will multiply money amounts and apply multiplication skills to problem solving situations involving overestimating and underestimating, as well as the Draw a Picture strategy.

Math in the Community

School-Community Connection

Public Transport Report Group students to research various forms of public transportation used in your community. Sources of information include tourist centers and transportation departments. Students can use multiplication skills to report such things as capacity and mileage.

Community Project The Chapter 6 Community Project is available in *Home and Community Connections.*

Home-School Connection

Transportation Multiplication Have students interview family members or other adults to learn about when they use multiplication to solve problems related to transportation. Possible uses might include:

- estimating the cost of filling the gas tank of a car

- finding the cost of round-trip bus fare for two people

- estimating the time it takes to walk to work and back

Parents can use the Web site at **www.parent.mathsurf.com**.

At the end of this chapter, you may wish to distribute the Letter Home from *Home and Community Connections.*

Inchworm Traveler

Students will create a map and find the distances shown in inches.

Student Materials Rulers, yardsticks, *optional Assessment Sourcebook 10* (How We Worked in Our Group)

Introduce the Project

Point out that a map is a model, or a smaller copy, of an actual area. Have students describe different types of maps they have seen or used.

Review the steps in the project, discuss the questions, and preview the self-assessment checklist below.

Self-Assessment Checklist

___ Measure distances in feet or yards

___ Draw a clear and accurate map showing distances

___ Accurately find each distance in inches

Complete the Project

Have students share their maps and discuss the strategies they used to measure, draw the map, and find distances in inches.

ANSWERS

Possible Answers for Talk About It

- Multiplied the number of feet times 12 (or yards times 36)

- They help you find your way and show distances between towns or landmarks

---

TEAM PROJECT
Inchworm Traveler

Early explorers drew landmarks such as mountains and lakes on maps. This helped them find their way.

Think of a tiny inchworm traveling across your classroom. To move forward, an inchworm stretches out its body, then scrunches itself end-to-end. With each "step" forward, it moves about 1 inch.

Make a map of your classroom for your inchworm traveler. Show at least three landmarks.

a Plan

- Where will the inchworm start and end its trip?
- Choose landmarks your inchworm might see.
- Place the landmarks about where they would be along the inchworm's path.

It Out

1. Measure distances between the landmarks in feet or yards, using whole numbers only.
2. Draw the map showing the distances.
3. Find how many inch-long "steps" your inchworm will take from place to place.

bout It

- How did you find the distances in inches?
- How are maps helpful?

he Project

- Show your map to the class.
- Talk about different routes your inchworm could have taken.

Science Connection

Create a life-size model of a worm common to your area. Have students trace the model, cut it out, and measure it to the nearest inch. Then have students find distances on their maps in "worm lengths."

Cooperative Learning

Suggest that team members take the following roles as they work :

- surveyor—measures distances
- recorder—records distances
- draftsperson—draws map
- reporter—reports routes

All team members should help change distances to inches.

Distribute *Assessment Sourcebook 10* (How We Worked in Our Group) and have students fill it out for the skill Listen to Others. Review the characteristics of this skill. Invite students to judge themselves on the skill as they work together.

Multiplication Number Sense

It isn't a dragon, or even an engine, that powers a dragon boat. It's 20 people paddling about 80 strokes per minute. How would you find the number of strokes a rower paddles during a race?

Jane and her dragon boat team

Multiplying Greater Numbers

Review multiples of 10 and 100. Copy and write each missing number.

1. 10, ▇, 30, 40, ▇, 60, ▇
   20, 50, 70
2. 140, 150, ▇, 170, ▇, 190, ▇
   160, 180, 200
3. 100, 200, 300, ▇, ▇, 600, ▇
   400, 500, 700

Skills Checklist

In this section, you will:

☐ **Explore Multiplication Patterns**

☐ **Estimate Products**

☐ **Multiply by Multiples of 10**

☐ **Explore Multiplying with 2-Digit Factors**

249

Multiplication Number Sense

In this section, students will find patterns in multiples of 10, estimate products, and multiply 2-digit numbers.

Subskills

The work on this section builds on...

- Using basic multiplication facts
  $2 \times 3 = 6$
- Identifying multiples of 10
  10, 20, 30, 40, 50
- Multiplying by 1-digit numbers
  $32 \times 3 = 96$

Use the Section Opener

Dragon boat races began in China during the fourth century B.C. Today, dragon boat teams consist of 22 members—20 rowers, a drummer, and a steerer. Recently, the fastest recorded time for a 500 meter race was slightly under 3 minutes.

Encourage students to explain how to find the number of strokes a dragon boat rower paddles. Multiply the number of minutes in the race by 80 strokes per minute.

Skills Trace

(Red numbers indicate pages in this section.)

Lesson and Skill	First Introduced	Grade Four			
		Introduce	Develop	Practice/Apply	Review
6-1 Explore multiplication patterns.	Grade 3	250, 251	250, 251	251, 258, 286	258, 284, 287
6-2 Estimate products of 2-digit factors.	Grade 4	252, 253	252	253, 258	258, 284, 287
6-3 Multiply by multiples of 10.	Grade 3	254, 255	254	255, 258, 269, 283, 285, 286	258, 283, 284, 287
6-4 Explore multiplying with 2-digit factors.	Grade 3	256, 257	256, 257	257, 258, 268, 269, 276, 277	258, 284, 287

Mixed Review and Test Prep exercises for this chapter occur on pages 253, 255, 263, 265, 267, 275.

Multi-Age Classrooms Use pages 359–388 in Grade 3 or pages 111–132 in Grade 5 to relate to the content of this section.

Exploring Multiplication Patterns

At-A-Glance Planning

Objective Explore multiplication patterns.

Vocabulary multiple, product, factors

Student Book Lesson Materials Calculators (1 per group), *optional* overhead place-value blocks (10 hundreds, 10 tens), *Assesment Sourcebook 10* (How We Worked in Our Group), Lesson Enhancement Transparency 24

Materials for pages 250A and 250B Index cards (25 per group)

Subject Connections career—travel agent, social studies—dhow sailboats

Strand Connections patterns, mental math, time, money, geometry readiness

	Before Lesson	During Lesson	After Lesson
Daily Math			
p. 250A Problem of the Day			
p. 250A Math Routines			
p. 250A Mental Math			
Teaching Options			
p. 250B Facilitating and Assessing…			
Options for Reaching All Learners			
p. 250B Inclusion			
p. 250B Language Development			
Subject Connections			
p. 250A Literature Connection			
Assessment Options			
p. 250 Talk About It			
p. 251 Error Intervention			
p. 251 Performance Assessment			
Resources			
6-1 Practice			
6-1 Reteaching			
6-1 Enrichment			
6-1 Problem Solving			
6-1 Daily Transparency			

Problem of the Day

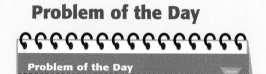

Problem of the Day

Find two numbers whose product is 36 and whose difference is 9.

3 and 12

Math Routines

Money Ask students to name the fewest coins they could exchange for 75 pennies, 95 pennies, and 115 pennies. 1 half dollar, 1 quarter; 1 half dollar, 1 quarter, 2 dimes; 2 half dollars, 1 dime, 1 nickel

Measurement Explain that there are 4 cups in a quart. Ask students how many cups are needed to fill 2 quarts, 3 quarts, and 4 quarts. 8 c, 12 c, 16 c

Mental Math

Tell whether the sum will be even or odd, then add to check. Explain.

23 + 46   81 + 19   72 + 53   68 + 38

Odd, 69; Even, 100; Odd, 125; Even, 106

Literature Connection

In E. Nesbit's *Melisande*, Melisande is granted her wish for hair that grows an inch every day and twice as fast every time it is cut.

• How much would Melisande's hair grow every day if she cut it once? Twice? Three times? 2 in./day; 4 in./day; 8 in./day

Facilitating and Assessing [Explore] Lesson 6-1

Use with pages 250 and 251.

Get Started You may wish to assign the roles of reader, calculator operator, and recorder, as well as the group skill Check for Understanding that students can practice. Share Level 4 of the Assessment Rubric with students before they begin their work.

Observe Watch that students are using the calculator correctly. Some students may need to review the steps needed to multiply numbers. To encourage the use of mental math and pattern recognition, you might suggest that students keep track of the problems they correctly solved without using the calculator.

Discuss As students discuss the patterns in related multiplication sentences, direct their focus to patterns that will help them complete similar sentences. For Exercises 1b and 2c, ask students to distinguish between the role of the basic fact part of the factors and the role of the zeros in the factors.

Assess Use the rubric to assess students' work. See sample for Practice Exercise 1.

4 Full Accomplishment
$20 \times 2 = 40$
$20 \times 20 = 400$
$20 \times 200 = 4,000$
$20 \times 2,000 = 40,000$

Assessment Rubric

4 Full Accomplishment
- uses basic facts and mental math to find multiples of 10, 100, or 1,000

3 Substantial Accomplishment
- uses basic facts and mental math to find most multiples of 10, 100, or 1,000

2 Partial Accomplishment
- uses basic facts and mental math to find some multiples of 10, 100, or 1,000

1 Little Accomplishment
- does not use basic facts and mental math to find multiples of 10, 100, or 1,000

Options for Reaching All Learners

Inclusion

Product Cards
Use number cards to reinforce multiplication patterns.

Materials Index cards (25 per group)

Learning Style Kinesthetic

- Make number cards from index cards. Provide each group with at least two of each number 1 through 9 and seven or eight zeros.

- Demonstrate how to use number cards to show multiplication problems where one factor is a multiple of 10 and the other is a multiple of 10, 100, or 1,000.

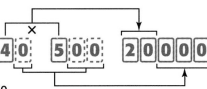

- Have students find the product by showing the basic fact and adding the correct number of zero cards.

Language Development

Word Table
Use a table to strengthen vocabulary skills.

Learning Style Kinesthetic

- Pair fluent English speakers with less-fluent students.

- Put the following table on the board and have pairs copy it. Then have students complete the table.

Factors	20×3	20×30	20×300
Product	60	600	6,000

- Have students discuss the table and any patterns they see. Encourage them to use the terms *multiple*, *product*, and *factors* in their descriptions.

- Have students repeat the activity for other sets of related multiplication expressions.

Lesson Organizer

Objective Explore multiplication patterns.

Suggested Grouping 2 to 4

Student Materials Calculators (1 per group), *optional Assessment Sourcebook 10* (How We Worked in Our Group)

Teacher Materials *Optional* Overhead place-value blocks (10 hundreds, 10 tens), Lesson Enhancement Transparency 24

Vocabulary multiple, product, factors

Assignment Guide

Basic 1–13, 16

Average 2–14, 16

Enriched 3–16

1 Introduce

Review

Find each product.

1. 2×7 14   **2.** 3×4 12

3. 6×5 30   **4.** 4×6 24

Build on Prior Knowledge

After students review basic facts, ask them how they might find 20×7. Possible answer: 20 is a multiple of 10, so the product of 20×7 is 10 times the product of 2×7.

2 Teach

See Facilitating and Assessing...on page 250B.

Explore •

As students work, you might ask questions such as the following:

• How did you know how many zeros to write?

Talk About It **Ongoing Assessment**

Listen for students' recognition of the relationship between the zeros in both factors and the product.

Answers for Talk About It

3 Possible answer: The product has as many zeros as the total number of zeros in the factors plus any additional zeros in the basic fact product.

4 The product (20) for the basic fact 4×5 has a zero.

Chapter 6 Lesson 1

Exploring Multiplication Patterns

Problem Solving Connection

Look for a Pattern

Materials

calculator

Vocabulary

multiple
the product of a given whole number and any other whole number

product
the number obtained after multiplying

factors
numbers that are multiplied together to obtain a product

Explore •

You can use basic facts and multiples of 10 to explore multiplication patterns.

$$20 \times 30 = 600$$

Work Together

1. Use a calculator to find each product. Look for patterns.

   a. $20 \times 3 = n$ 60   **b.** $40 \times 5 = n$ 200   **c.** $30 \times 1 = n$ 30

     $20 \times 30 = n$ 600 $40 \times 50 = n$ 2,000 $30 \times 10 = n$ 300

     $20 \times 300 = n$ 6,000 $40 \times 500 = n$ 20,000 $30 \times 100 = n$ 3,000

     $20 \times 3,000 = n$ 60,000 $40 \times 5,000 = n$ 200,000 $30 \times 1,000 = n$ 30,000

Remember

The numbers 10, 20, 30, 40, … are multiples of 10.

2. Look for patterns to help you find each product. Use a calculator to check your answers.

   a. $40 \times 2 = n$ 80   **b.** $30 \times 3 = n$ 90   **c.** $50 \times 2 = n$ 100

     $40 \times 20 = n$ 800 $30 \times 30 = n$ 900 $50 \times 20 = n$ 1,000

     $40 \times 200 = n$ 8,000 $30 \times 300 = n$ 9,000 $50 \times 200 = n$ 10,000

     $40 \times 2,000 = n$ 80,000 $30 \times 3,000 = n$ 90,000 $50 \times 2,000 = n$ 100,000

Talk About It

3. What patterns did you notice?

4. Why does the product of 40×50 have three zeros instead of two?

Practice 6-1

Name _____

Practice 6-1

Exploring Multiplication Patterns

1. Multiply 70×40.

   a. Find the product of 7 and 4. ___28___

   b. How many zeros are in the two factors? ___2___

   c. Write the product of 70 and 40. ___2,800___

2. Multiply 80×900.

   a. Find the product of 8 and 9. ___72___

   b. How many zeros are in the two factors? ___3___

   c. Write the product of 80 and 900. ___72,000___

Look for patterns to help you find each product. Use a calculator to check your answers.

3. $30 \times 2 =$ ___60___   **4.** $60 \times 4 =$ ___240___

   $30 \times 20 =$ ___600___ $60 \times 40 =$ ___2,400___

   $30 \times 200 =$ ___6,000___ $60 \times 400 =$ ___24,000___

   $30 \times 2,000 =$ ___60,000___ $60 \times 4,000 =$ ___240,000___

5. $50 \times 4 =$ ___200___   **6.** $60 \times 5 =$ ___300___

   $50 \times 40 =$ ___2,000___ $60 \times 50 =$ ___3,000___

   $50 \times 400 =$ ___20,000___ $60 \times 500 =$ ___30,000___

   $50 \times 4,000 =$ ___200,000___ $60 \times 5,000 =$ ___300,000___

Find each product. Use mental math.

7. $80 \times 40 =$ ___3,200___   **8.** $30 \times 900 =$ ___27,000___

9. $70 \times 9,000 =$ ___630,000___   **10.** $400 \times 7,000 =$ ___2,800,000___

11. Tonya rode a bicycle 5 times. Each trip took 30 minutes. How long did she spend on a bike? ___150 min___

12. Benjamin traveled by train 4 times. Each trip was 40 miles. How many miles did he travel by train? ___160 miles___

Reteaching 6-1

Name _____

Another Look 6-1

Exploring Multiplication Patterns

In your book you used a calculator to explore patterns. Here is another way to find patterns. Basic fact and place-value patterns can help you multiply by multiples of 10; 100; or 1,000.

Example 1 70×50

   Basic Fact: $7 \times 5 = \underline{35}$

   Total number of zeros in factors: 2

   Therefore, $70 \times 50 = 3,500$

   basic 2
   fact zeros

Example 2 700×500

   Basic Fact: $7 \times 5 = \underline{35}$

   Total number of zeros in factors: 4

   Therefore, $700 \times 500 = 350,000$

   basic 4
   fact zeros

Use patterns to find each product.

1. 30×70

   a. Find the product of the basic fact: $3 \times 7 =$ ___21___

   b. Count the number of zeros in the factors. ___2___

   c. Write the final product. ___2,100___

2. 600×500

   a. Find the product of the basic fact: $6 \times 5 =$ ___30___

   b. Count the number of zeros in the factors. ___4___

   c. Write the final product. ___300,000___

3. $80 \times 30 =$ ___2,400___   **4.** $900 \times 300 =$ ___270,000___

5. $40 \times 500 =$ ___20,000___   **6.** $800 \times 500 =$ ___400,000___

7. $20 \times 700 =$ ___14,000___   **8.** $300 \times 600 =$ ___180,000___

9. $400 \times 400 =$ ___160,000___   **10.** $200 \times 800 =$ ___160,000___

Connect

You can use basic facts, mental math, and place value to help you multiply by multiples of 10, 100, and 1,000.

	Multiple of 10	Multiple of 100	Multiple of 1,000
Find	60×80	60×800	$60 \times 8,000$
Basic fact	Think: $6 \times 8 = 48$	Think: $6 \times 8 = 48$	Think $6 \times 8 = 48$
Zeros in factors	2	3	4
Product	$60 \times 80 = 4,800$	$60 \times 800 = 48,000$	$60 \times 8,000 = 480,000$

Practice

Look for patterns to help you find each product. Use a calculator to check your answers.

1. $20 \times 2 = n$ **40**
$20 \times 20 = n$ **400**
$20 \times 200 = n$ **4,000**
$20 \times 2,000 = n$ **40,000**

2. $80 \times 4 = n$ **320**
$80 \times 40 = n$ **3,200**
$80 \times 400 = n$ **32,000**
$80 \times 4,000 = n$ **320,000**

3. $50 \times 6 = n$ **300**
$50 \times 60 = n$ **3,000**
$50 \times 600 = n$ **30,000**
$50 \times 6,000 = n$ **300,000**

Mental Math Find each product. Use mental math.

4. 30×10 **300** 5. 50×20 **1,000** 6. 40×70 **2,800** 7. 100×90 **9,000**

8. 60×30
1,800

9. 60×200
12,000

10. $30 \times 8,000$
240,000

11. $500 \times 3,000$
1,500,000

12. **Time** Joshua rode a bus 6 times. Each trip took 10 minutes. How long did he spend on the bus? **60 minutes, or 1 hour**

13. **Careers** Suppose a travel agent earns $50 for each trip that is planned for a customer. How much would the travel agent earn for 20 trips? **$1,000**

14. **Money** Mark got 8 twenty-dollar bills from the bank machine. Write the total amount of money using a dollar sign. **$160**

15. **Geometry Readiness** A square piece of cloth is wide enough and tall enough for the sail on this dhow (DOW), a boat used in Africa and Asia. How many sails could you cut from the cloth? **2 sails**

16. **Journal** Describe how you can find the product of 20 and 400 using basic facts and mental math.

Lesson 6-1 **251**

Enrichment 6-1	Problem Solving 6-1

Connect

Lesson Enhancement Transparency 24 illustrates the table.

Use mental math or overhead place-value blocks to review place-value concepts and how they relate to zeros in products: 10 tens = 100; 10 hundreds = 1,000.

Error Intervention Ongoing Assessment

Observation Students have difficulty recognizing the connection between the zeros in the factors and the zeros in the product.

How to Help For each pair of factors, have students tell whether they are multiplying tens, hundreds, and/or thousands. Ask how many placeholder zeros are written for these numbers. Point out the number of zeros in the factors and the total in the product.

Practice

Exercise 15 Some students may find it helpful to draw a picture.

For Early Finishers Challenge early finishers to solve Exercise 13 for a total of 300 trips planned. $15,000

3 Close and Assess

Performance Assessment

Find the product of 9×7, then complete the following multiplication sentences. Explain your thinking.

$90 \times 7 = n$

$90 \times 70 = n$

$90 \times 700 = n$

$90 \times 7,000 = n$

630; 6,300; 63,000; 630,000; Each product is 10 times greater than the previous product.

Assess using the rubric on page 250B.

ANSWERS

16 Possible answer: Find the basic fact $2 \times 4 = 8$. Find the number of zeros in the two factors. $20 \times 400 = 8,000$

Estimating Products

At-A-Glance Planning

Objective Estimate products of 2-digit factors.

Student Book Lesson Materials *Optional* Lesson Enhancement Transparency 23

Materials for pages 252A and 252B Place-value blocks (10 hundreds, 50 tens, 10 ones per group), number cubes labeled 1–6, 2–7, 3–8, and 4–9 (1 set per group), overhead place-value blocks

Subject Connection social studies—urban transportation

Strand Connections time, using data, algebra readiness, estimation

	Before Lesson	During Lesson	After Lesson
Daily Math			
p. 252A Problem of the Day			
p. 252A Math Routines			
p. 252A Mental Math			
Teaching Options			
p. 252 Student Book Lesson			
p. 252B Another Way to Learn…			
Options for Reaching All Learners			
p. 252B Reading Assist			
p. 252B Gifted & Talented			
Subject Connections			
p. 252A Career Connection			
Assessment Options			
p. 252 Talk About It			
p. 253 Error Intervention			
p. 253 Journal			
p. 253 Quick Check			
Resources			
6-2 Practice			
6-2 Reteaching			
6-2 Enrichment			
6-2 Problem Solving			
6-2 Daily Transparency			

Problem of the Day

Problem of the Day

Draw the next shape in the sequence.

Math Routines

Time Ask students to estimate how many minutes they spend each day traveling to and from school. Each week?

Calendar Ask students to name the month that is 10 months, 15 months, 20 months following November. September; February; July

Mental Math

Tell whether each difference will be odd or even. Then find the differences to check your answers. Explain.

53 – 22   68 – 42   91 – 57   84 – 75

Odd, 31; Even, 26; Even, 34; Odd, 9

Career Connection

One job of the school transportation coordinator is to make sure that there are enough school buses and bus routes.

- Have students find out on how many school buses your district has, what the seating capacity is, and how many runs to school each bus makes.

- Have students estimate how many students could be transported to school by bus each day.

Another Way to [Learn] Lesson 6-2

Use as an alternative or in addition to pages 252 and 253.

Materials Place-value blocks (10 hundreds, 50 tens, 10 ones per group), overhead place-value blocks

Learning Style Kinesthetic

- Have groups use place-value blocks to model the factors 23 and 19. Then have them round each factor to the nearest multiple of 10. Next, have them use only tens blocks to model the product of 20 × 20. Finally, have them exchange tens for hundreds blocks to find the total shown. Repeat the activity for 12 × 34. 400; 300

- Model the connection of the manipulatives to the pictorial and symbolic recording on the overhead, using the problems above. Demonstrate 27 × 41 using only the symbolic recording method.

- Review the steps in the estimation process. Then have groups try these problems, using only the symbolic recording method.

17 × 21	33 × 18	24 × 25
400	600	600

- Assign Check and Practice on Student Book pages 252 and 253 or *Practice Master 6–2.*
- Assess using the following rubric.

Assessment Rubric
4 **Full Accomplishment** • estimates products of 2-digit factors
3 **Substantial Accomplishment** • estimates most products of 2-digit factors
2 **Partial Accomplishment** • with prompting, estimates some products of 2-digit factors
1 **Little Accomplishment** • does not estimate products of 2-digit factors

Options for Reaching All Learners

Reading Assist

Make Inferences
Use other examples to improve recognition of estimation vocabulary.

Learning Style Verbal

- Have students identify vocabulary and contexts in the introductory problem on page 252 and Practice Exercises 32 and 35 that indicates an estimated answer is appropriate or a rounded number is used. Possible answers: A key word suggesting estimation is appropriate is *about*. The zeros at the end of the number indicate rounding.

- Challenge students to look through previous lessons on estimating to identify other examples of vocabulary indicating estimation and/or rounded numbers.

- Have students share their findings and explain their thinking.

Gifted & Talented

Target Products
Use a game to practice estimating products.

Materials Number cubes labeled 1–6, 2–7, 3–8, 4–9; (1 set per group)

Learning Style Social

- Have each player label a 4-by-4 square gameboard with the following ranges in any order:

100–500	2,001–2,500	4,001–4,500	6,001–6,500
501–1,000	2,501–3,000	4,501–5,000	6,501–7,000
1,001–1,500	3,001–3,500	5,001–5,500	7,001–7,500
1,501–2,000	3,501–4,000	5,501–6,000	7,501–8,000

- Have players take turns tossing the number cubes, using four digits to write two factors, estimating their product, and marking the box that contains the product.

- The first to mark four boxes across or down wins.

Lesson Organizer

Objective Estimate products of 2-digit factors.

Student Materials None

Teacher Materials *Optional* Lesson Enhancement Transparency 23

Assignment Guide

Basic 7–28, 36–39

Average 10–28, 32–39

Enriched 14–39

1 Introduce

Review

Find each product.

1. 40 × 50 2,000 **2.** 30 × 60 1,800

3. 40 × 60 2,400 **4.** 30 × 50 1,500

Build on Prior Knowledge

After students review multiplying multiples of 10, ask which Review exercise they could use to estimate the product of 34 × 57 and why. Exercise 2; 34 rounds to 30 and 57 rounds to 60

2 Teach

See Another Way to Learn…on page 252B.

Learn

When focusing on the example, ask why estimating a product is appropriate in this situation. The word *about* indicates that estimation is appropriate.

Then have students explain the rounding and mental multiplication that were done. Review rules of rounding, as needed.

Talk About It Ongoing Assessment

Listen for understanding of the relationship between the factor and the product—decreasing the value of a factor decreases the product.

Answers for Talk About It

1 It's greater. Both factors were rounded to lesser numbers.

2 1,400; 65 rounds to 70.

Check

Exercise 6 Be sure students understand why the product has four digits.

Estimating Products

You Will Learn
how to estimate products of 2-digit factors

Learn

In Dayton, Ohio, electric trolleys help people on the move. A trolley can carry 64 people at one time. Between 2:30 P.M. and 6:30 P.M., trolleys travel along Salem Avenue 23 times. About how many people can be transported during that time?

Tammy Maxwell drives trolleys in Dayton, Ohio.

Did You Know?
Electric trolleys can be found in only five U.S. cities: Boston, Dayton, Philadelphia, San Francisco, and Seattle.

You can estimate the product to find about how many people can be transported.

Example

Estimate 23 × 64.

Round each factor to the nearest multiple of 10.

Number of people **23** × **64** Number of trips
↓ ↓
20 × **60** = 1,200

About 1,200 people can be transported in 23 trolley trips.

Talk About It

1. Without computing, do you think the exact answer is greater or less than the estimate? How can you decide?

2. What would be your estimate if a trolley carried 65 people? Why?

Check

Estimate each product.

1. 26 × 31
900
2. 45 × 23
1,000
3. 87 × 49
4,500
4. 56 × 53
3,000
5. 73 × 97
7,000
6. Reasoning How can you estimate to find the number of digits in the product of 53 and 66? **Find 50 × 70 = 3,500, so 4 digits.**

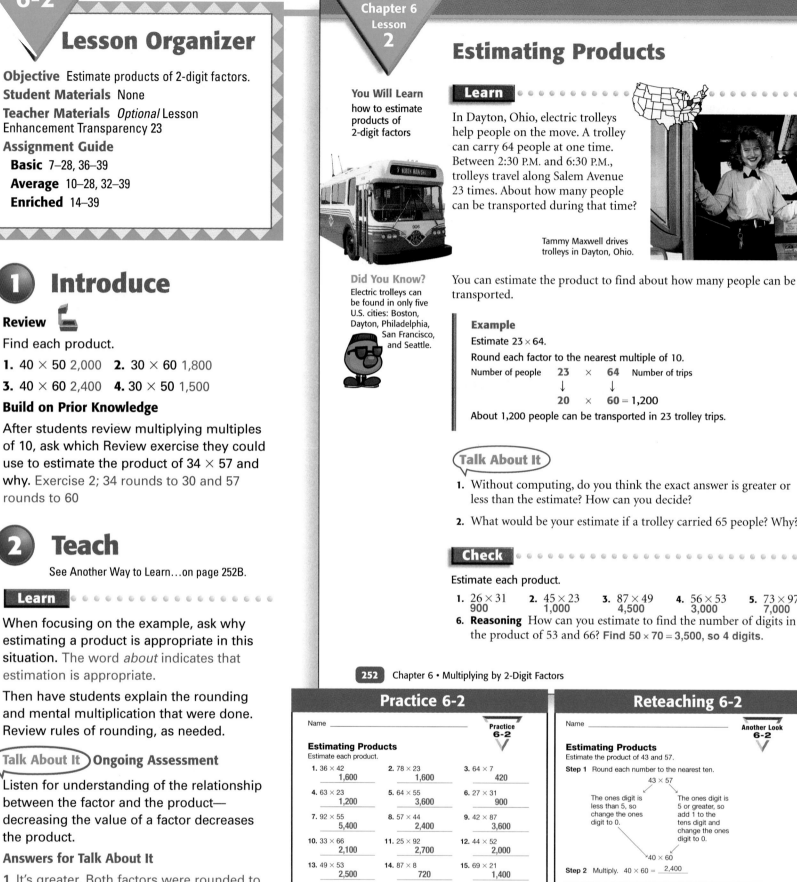

Practice 6-2

Name _____

Practice 6-2

Estimating Products
Estimate each product.

1. 36 × 42 1,600
2. 78 × 23 1,600
3. 64 × 7 420
4. 63 × 23 1,200
5. 64 × 55 3,600
6. 27 × 31 900
7. 92 × 55 5,400
8. 57 × 44 2,400
9. 42 × 87 3,600
10. 33 × 66 2,100
11. 25 × 92 2,700
12. 44 × 52 2,000
13. 49 × 53 2,500
14. 87 × 8 720
15. 69 × 21 1,400
16. 67 × 47 3,500
17. 35 × 29 1,200
18. 82 × 4 320
19. 44 × 54 2,000
20. 78 × 39 3,200
21. 38 × 25 1,200
22. Estimate 11 × 23. 200
23. Estimate 44 × 55. 2,400
24. Estimate the product of 87 and 42. 3,600
25. Would an estimate for the product of 34 and 53 be greater or less than the exact answer? Explain.
Less; both rounded factors are less than the actual factors.
26. Would an estimate for 46 × 56 be greater or less than the exact answer? Explain.
Greater; both rounded factors are greater than the actual factors.

Reteaching 6-2

Name _____

Another Look 6-2

Estimating Products
Estimate the product of 43 and 57.

Step 1 Round each number to the nearest ten.

43 × 57

The ones digit is less than 5, so change the ones digit to 0.

The ones digit is 5 or greater, so add 1 to the tens digit and change the ones digit to 0.

40 × 60

Step 2 Multiply. 40 × 60 = 2,400

Estimate the product.

1. 36 × 82
↓ ↓
40 × 80 = 3,200
2. 68 × 32
↓ ↓
70 × 30 = 2,100
3. 93 × 75
90 × 80 = 7,200
4. 36 × 57
40 × 60 = 2,400
5. 34 × 65
30 × 70 = 2,100
6. 66 × 42
70 × 40 = 2,800
7. 38 × 67
40 × 70 = 2,800
8. 78 × 23
80 × 20 = 1,600
9. 48 × 58
50 × 60 = 3,000
10. 14 × 18
10 × 20 = 200
11. 93 × 26
90 × 30 = 2,700
12. 77 × 44
80 × 40 = 3,200

Skills and Reasoning

Estimate each product.

7. 21×31 **600**	**8.** 48×45 **2,500**	**9.** 16×11 **200**	**10.** 9×39 **400**	**11.** 75×55 **4,800**
12. 33×35 **1,200**	**13.** 77×83 **6,400**	**14.** 44×97 **4,000**	**15.** 19×29 **600**	**16.** 23×94 **1,800**
17. 74×65 **4,900**	**18.** 59×26 **1,800**	**19.** 38×27 **1,200**	**20.** 85×84 **7,200**	**21.** 49×62 **3,000**
22. 41×15 **800**	**23.** 67×22 **1,400**	**24.** 92×47 **4,500**	**25.** 54×42 **2,000**	**26.** 81×36 **3,200**

27. Estimate 9×45. **500** **28.** Estimate the product of 86 and 34. **2,700**

29. Would an estimate for the product of 35 and 47 be greater or less than the exact answer? Explain. **Greater; Both factors round up**

30. Would an estimate for 23×41 be greater or less than the exact answer? Explain. **Less; Both factors round down**

Problem Solving and Applications

31. Although 64 people can fit on each Dayton trolley, only 46 people can be seated at one time. Estimate how many passengers in all of the 23 trolleys would get to sit down. **About 1,000 people**

32. About 4,600 people ride the Route 7 trolley each day in Dayton. About 5,200 people ride the Route 8 trolley. In all, how many people ride these two trolley routes each day? **About 9,100 people**

33. **Time** If it costs Cliff $48 a month to travel on public transportation, about how much will it cost in a year? **About $500**

Using Data Use the Data File on page 246 for **34** and **35.**

34. Which city has fewer than 20 million people using public transportation each week? **New York City**

35. About how many more people in Moscow use public transportation than people in Bombay? **About 20 million**

The Metro in Moscow, Russia

Mixed Review and Test Prep

Algebra Readiness Find each missing number.

36. $67 - n = 20$ **47**   **37.** $526 + n = 750$ **224**   **38.** $n + 621 = 1,000$ **379**

39. **Time** Which is the seventh month of the year? **D**
Ⓐ June   Ⓑ November   Ⓒ August   Ⓓ July

Lesson 6-2   **253**

Error Intervention Ongoing Assessment

Observation Students find an unreasonable estimated product.

How to Help Have students explain their thinking to determine whether their error was made in rounding, multiplying multiples of 10, or using a basic fact. Provide remediation on that specific subskill.

Practice •

Exercises 34 and 35 You can use Lesson Enhancement Transparency 23 to provide the data for these problems.

For Early Finishers Challenge early finishers to determine whether the actual products in Exercises 17–26 would be greater than or less than the estimated products. Greater: 21, 23, 25; Less: 17, 18, 19, 20, 22, 24, 26

③ Close and Assess

Journal

Ask students to estimate 27×85 and explain how they did it. Round 27 and 85 to the next ten. Use mental math to multiply 30×90 to get 2,700.

Quick Check

Number Sense Decide which estimated product below is greater than the actual product. Explain. Exercise 4; Because both multiples of 10 that are used to estimate are greater than the actual factors.

Skill Estimate each product.

1. 43×53 2,000

2. 92×71 6,300

3. 22×64 1,200

4. 39×87 3,600

Enrichment 6-2

Name _____   Extend Your Thinking **6-2** ▽

Visual Thinking

A	B	C
D	E	F
G	H	I

Match each puzzle piece below to the letter in the completed puzzle above.

(puzzle pieces numbered 9, 8, 6, 2, 4, 7, 3, 1, 5)

1. **F**	2. **H**	3. **D**
4. **A**	5. **E**	6. **G**
7. **C**	8. **I**	9. **B**

Problem Solving 6-2

Name _____   Problem Solving **6-2** ▽

Estimating Products

History In 1873, Andrew Hallidge introduced the cable car system to San Francisco. At its peak just before 1900, there were over 600 cable cars and 100 miles of track. The great earthquake in 1906 caused extensive damage to the cars and cable lines. Today, there are 39 cars operating over a 10-mile network.

1. A round trip cable car ride is about 10 miles. A cable car makes about 27 round trips a day. Estimate how many miles the cable car travels each day. **About 300 miles**

2. If one cable car holds 48 people, estimate how many people 39 cable cars will hold. **About 2,000 people**

3. Each cable car has a brake assembly made up of many small pieces. If each brake assembly costs about $600, is $24,500 enough to buy brake assemblies for 39 cars? **Yes;**
$40 \times \$600 = \$24,000$

4. Each cable car is hand built by one skilled craftsperson. It takes about 18 months of work to build a cable car. About how many months of work would it take to build 39 cars? **About 800 months**

5. Mr. Benson works an average of 42 hours a week. If he works for 48 weeks, about how many hours does he work? **About 2,000 hours**

6. Suppose Mr. Benson works an average of 48 hours a week, about how many more hours would he work in 48 weeks? **About 500 hours more**

Chapter 6 • Lesson 6-2   **253**

Multiplying by Multiples of 10

At-A-Glance Planning

Lesson Planning Checklist

Objective Multiply by multiples of 10.

Student Book Lesson Materials None

Materials for pages 254A and 254B Place-value blocks (10 hundreds, 50 tens, 60 ones per group), overhead place-value blocks (4 hundreds, 50 tens, 50 ones)

Subject Connection history—dragon boat racing

Strand Connections measurement, time

	Before Lesson	During Lesson	After Lesson
Daily Math			
p. 254A Problem of the Day			
p. 254A Math Routines			
p. 254A Mental Math			
Teaching Options			
p. 254 Student Book Lesson			
p. 254B Another Way to Learn…			
Options for Reaching All Learners			
p. 254B Inclusion			
p. 254B Gifted & Talented			
Subject Connections			
p. 254A Literature Connection			
Assessment Options			
p. 254 Talk About It			
p. 255 Error Intervention			
p. 255 Interview			
p. 255 Quick Check			
Resources			
6-3 Practice			
6-3 Reteaching			
6-3 Enrichment			
6-3 Problem Solving			
6-3 Daily Transparency			

Problem of the Day

Problem of the Day Lesson 6-3

Use estimation to place digits 2, 3, 4, and 5 in the boxes below to make a true sentence. Use each digit once.

▢▢ x ▢▢ rounds to 1,500.

See Problem of the Day Teaching Guide for an extension.

$25 \times 45, 32 \times 45, 34 \times 52$

Math Routines

Patterns Have students tell what time it is now. Ask what time it will be 2, then 14, hours from now. Repeat for 3 and 15, 6 and 18. Ask students how they found the correct times. Possible answers: Added first number to the present time, then changed A.M. to P.M. (or reverse).

Money Tell students they have 3 piggy banks, each containing $12.99. About how many $20 bills are their savings worth? 2

Mental Math

Find each sum. Explain your thinking.

$20 + 120$	$30 + 270$	$50 + 150$	$40 + 210$
140	300	200	250

Literature Connection

In *Much Ado About Aldo* by Johanna Hurwitz, Elaine, Karen, and Aldo search their 14-floor apartment building for a cat. There are 10 apartments on each floor.

• Ask students to find the total number of apartments in the building. 140

• Ask them to find the total number of apartments if there were 20 apartments on each floor. 280

Another Way to Learn Lesson 6-3

Use as an alternative or in addition to pages 254 and 255.

Materials Place-value blocks (10 hundreds, 50 tens, 60 ones per group), overhead place-value blocks (4 hundreds, 50 tens, 50 ones)

Learning Style Kinesthetic

- Have groups use place-value blocks to model 24 × 2 and 24 × 20 and find the products. Then discuss how the models are the same and different. 48; 480

- Use overhead place-value blocks to review steps in the process. Then have groups try these:

  23 × 2 and 23 × 20 46; 460

  16 × 3 and 16 × 30 48; 480

- Model how to draw pictures of the blocks and write the symbols in vertical form.

- Have groups draw pictures of blocks and use symbols to find these products.

  32 × 3 and 32 × 30 96; 960

  26 × 4 and 26 × 40 104; 1,040

  17 × 5 and 17 × 50 85; 850

- Have students talk about how the recordings are the same and different for each pair.

- Assign Check and Practice on Student Book pages 254 and 255 or *Practice Master 6-3*.

Assess using the following rubric.

Assessment Rubric
4 **Full Accomplishment**   • finds products of 2-digit numbers and multiples of 10
3 **Substantial Accomplishment**   • finds most products of 2-digit numbers and multiples of 10
2 **Partial Accomplishment**   • with prompting, finds some products of 2-digit numbers and multiples of 10
1 **Little Accomplishment**   • does not find products of 2-digit numbers and multiples of 10

Options for Reaching All Learners

Inclusion

Wordy Multiplication

Use numbers and words to strengthen skill in multiplying by a multiple of 10.

Learning Style Verbal, Visual

- If students have difficulty multiplying by a multiple of 10, demonstrate on the chalkboard how to rewrite a multiplication problem using the word form of the multiple of 10. Then rewrite the product in standard form:

$$
\begin{array}{ccc}
& & \overset{1}{} \\
22 & & 22 \\
\times 60 & \rightarrow & \times 6 \text{ tens} \\
\hline
& & 132 \text{ tens} \rightarrow 1,320
\end{array}
$$

- Have students rewrite and solve the multiplication problem 31 × 50 using the word form.

Gifted & Talented

Applied Grouping

Use the grouping property to strengthen understanding of multiplying by multiples of 10.

Learning Style Logical

- Use three 1-digit factors to review the grouping property.

  $(2 \times 5) \times 6 = n$ $\qquad$ $2 \times (5 \times 6) = n$

  $10 \times 6 = 60$ $\qquad$ $2 \times 30 = 60$

- Demonstrate how the grouping property can be used to multiply by a multiple of 10.

  $22 \times 60 = 22 \times (6 \times 10) = (22 \times 6) \times 10$

  $132 \times 10 = 1,320$

- Have students use this method to solve several Check and Practice exercises.

Lesson Organizer

Objective Multiply by multiples of 10.
Student Materials None
Assignment Guide
Basic 7–23, 25–26, 30–35
Average 9–26, 29–35
Enriched 10–35

1 Introduce

Review

Find each product.

1. 24 × 2 48   **2.** 37 × 4 148
3. 56 × 3 168   **4.** 48 × 6 288

Build on Prior Knowledge

Ask students to tell how they used their knowledge of basic multiplication facts to solve the problems. Possible answer: Each step of the multiplication process uses a basic multiplication fact.

2 Teach

See Another Way to Learn…on page 254B.

Learn

When focusing on the example, you may wish to ask these questions.

• In Step 1, why is a zero written in the product? It tells that 22 multiplied by 0 equals 0.

• In Step 2, why is the small 1 written at the top of the tens column? Because 6 × 2 is 12 ones. You must regroup 12 ones as 1 ten and 2 ones.

Talk About It) Ongoing Assessment

Listen for recognition of the role of place value in vertical multiplication.

Answer for Talk About It

It stands for 132 tens, so it goes to the left of the ones place.

Check

Exercises 1 and 3 Encourage students to use mental math instead of paper and pencil for these exercises.

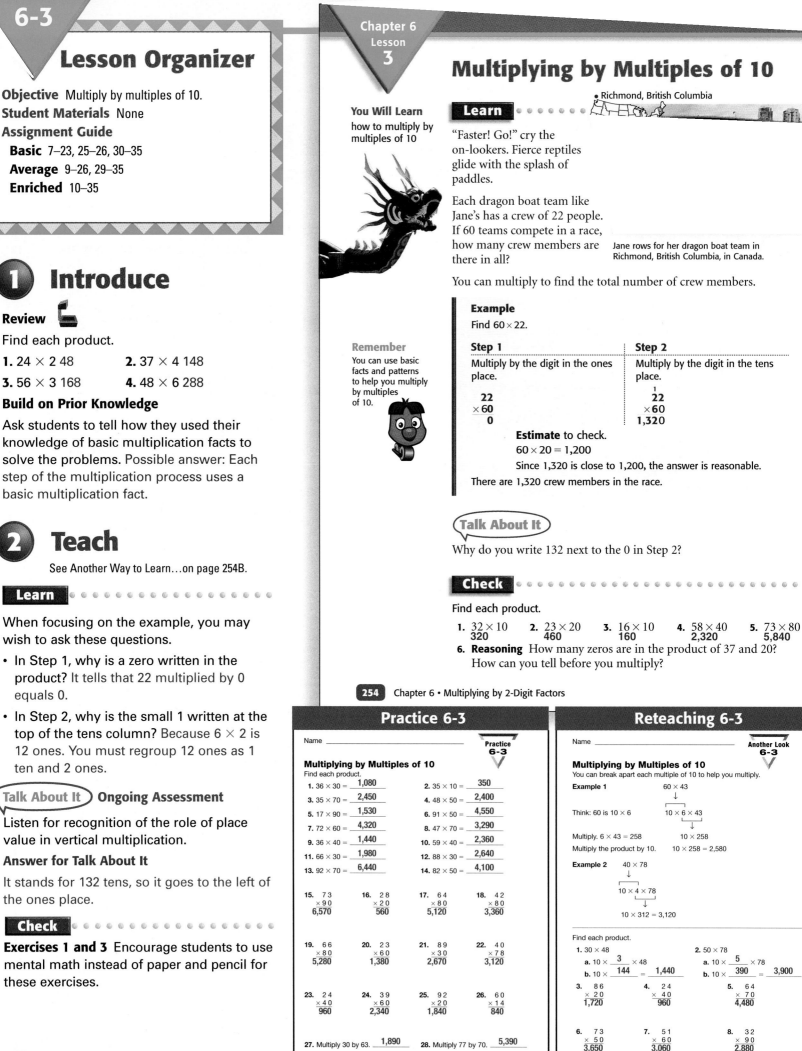

Chapter 6 Lesson 3

Multiplying by Multiples of 10

• Richmond, British Columbia

You Will Learn how to multiply by multiples of 10

Learn

"Faster! Go!" cry the on-lookers. Fierce reptiles glide with the splash of paddles.

Each dragon boat team like Jane's has a crew of 22 people. If 60 teams compete in a race, how many crew members are there in all?

Jane rows for her dragon boat team in Richmond, British Columbia, in Canada.

You can multiply to find the total number of crew members.

Remember
You can use basic facts and patterns to help you multiply by multiples of 10.

Example
Find 60 × 22.

Step 1	Step 2
Multiply by the digit in the ones place.	Multiply by the digit in the tens place.
22 × 60 0	¹22 × 60 1,320

Estimate to check.
60 × 20 = 1,200
Since 1,320 is close to 1,200, the answer is reasonable.
There are 1,320 crew members in the race.

Talk About It
Why do you write 132 next to the 0 in Step 2?

Check

Find each product.

1. 32 × 10
320
2. 23 × 20
460
3. 16 × 10
160
4. 58 × 40
2,320
5. 73 × 80
5,840
6. Reasoning How many zeros are in the product of 37 and 20? How can you tell before you multiply?

254   Chapter 6 • Multiplying by 2-Digit Factors

Practice 6-3

Name _____

Practice 6-3

Multiplying by Multiples of 10
Find each product.

1. 36 × 30 = 1,080   **2.** 35 × 10 = 350
3. 35 × 70 = 2,450   **4.** 48 × 50 = 2,400
5. 17 × 90 = 1,530   **6.** 91 × 50 = 4,550
7. 72 × 60 = 4,320   **8.** 47 × 70 = 3,290
9. 36 × 40 = 1,440   **10.** 59 × 40 = 2,360
11. 66 × 30 = 1,980   **12.** 88 × 30 = 2,640
13. 92 × 70 = 6,440   **14.** 82 × 50 = 4,100

15. 73 × 90 6,570	**16.** 28 × 20 560	**17.** 64 × 80 5,120	**18.** 42 × 80 3,360
19. 66 × 80 5,280	**20.** 23 × 60 1,380	**21.** 89 × 30 2,670	**22.** 40 × 78 3,120
23. 24 × 40 960	**24.** 39 × 60 2,340	**25.** 92 × 20 1,840	**26.** 60 × 14 840

27. Multiply 30 by 63. 1,890   **28.** Multiply 77 by 70. 5,390

29. How many zeros are in the product of 65 and 80? Explain.
2; 8 × 65 = 520, so 65 × 80 = 5,200.

Reteaching 6-3

Name _____

Another Look 6-3

Multiplying by Multiples of 10
You can break apart each multiple of 10 to help you multiply.

Example 1   60 × 43
↓
Think: 60 is 10 × 6   10 × 6 × 43

Multiply. 6 × 43 = 258   10 × 258
Multiply the product by 10.   10 × 258 = 2,580

Example 2   40 × 78
↓
10 × 4 × 78
↓
10 × 312 = 3,120

Find each product.

1. 30 × 48
a. 10 × 3 × 48
b. 10 × 144 = 1,440

2. 50 × 78
a. 10 × 5 × 78
b. 10 × 390 = 3,900

3. 86 × 20 1,720	**4.** 24 × 40 960	**5.** 64 × 70 4,480
6. 73 × 50 3,650	**7.** 51 × 60 3,060	**8.** 32 × 90 2,880

Skills and Reasoning

Find each product.

7. 21×30
630

8. 58×20
1,160

9. 10×49
490

10. 72×90
6,480

11. 85×40
3,400

12. 70×50
3,500

13. 67×80
5,360

14. 54×10
540

15. 90×12
1,080

16. 40×98
3,920

17. 60
$\times 63$
3,780

18. 89
$\times 60$
5,340

19. 30
$\times 99$
2,970

20. 10
$\times 75$
750

21. 46
$\times 50$
2,300

22. Find the product of 20 and 35. **700**

23. Multiply 66 by 80. **5,280**

24. Reasoning How many zeros are in the product of 25 and 40? Explain.
3 zeros; $25 \times 40 = 1,000$

Problem Solving and Applications

25. Forty teams competed at the sixth annual Dragon Boat Festival in New York. With 22 crew members on each boat, how many people competed in all? **880 people**

26. Measurement The course for the Dragon Boat Festival in New York is 640 meters long. If a crew finishes the course, turns around, and paddles back to the starting line, how many meters does it travel? **1,280 meters**

27. Critical Thinking In a dragon boat team, 20 people row, 1 person beats a drum and yells to the rowers, and 1 person steers. If 60 teams compete in a race, how many crew members are not rowing? **120 members**

28. Time A rower paddles 80 strokes per minute. Is this faster than 1 stroke per second? Explain.
Yes; Only 60 sec per min

Dragon boat drum

29. History Dragon boat racing began in China about 24 centuries ago. How many years is that? (Hint: A century is 100 years.)
2,400 years

30. Journal Without finding the exact answer, how do you know the product of 30 and 7,975 will have a zero in the ones place?

Mixed Review and Test Prep

Find each sum or difference.

31. $409 + 38$ **447** **32.** $532 - 485$ **47** **33.** $760 + 67 + 33$ **860** **34.** $300 - 145$ **155**

35. Mental Math What is the sum of 80 and 8 and 800? **B**

Ⓐ 88   Ⓑ 888   Ⓒ 8,880   Ⓓ not here

Skills Practice Bank, page 566, Set 1   Lesson 6-3   **255**

Enrichment 6-3	**Problem Solving 6-3**

Error Intervention Ongoing Assessment

Observation Students forget to write a zero in the ones place of the product.

How to Help Encourage students to estimate to check the reasonableness of their products.

Practice ••••••••••••••••••••••

Exercises 11, 12, 15, 21, 22 These products will have more than one zero. Make sure students understand why these products differ from that of the Example problem.

Exercises 17, 19, 20 Some students will probably find it helpful to rewrite these with the factors in the reverse order.

For Early Finishers Challenge early finishers to change the positions of the non-0 digits in one of the Skill and Reasoning Exercises so the product is greater than the original product. Possible answer: Rewrite Exercise 9 as $10 \times 94 = 940$.

③ Close and Assess

Interview

Ask students to explain how they solved one of the Skills and Reasoning exercises.

Quick Check

Number Sense How many zeros will be in each product below? Explain. One in Exercises 1, 2, and 4; two in Exercise 3 because $5 \times 8 = 40$

Skill Find each product.

1. 21×40 840

2. 46×70 3,220

3. 38×50 1,900

4. 65×90 5,850

ANSWERS

30 30 is a multiple of 10. The product of any number and a multiple of 10 has a zero in the ones place.

Exploring Multiplying with 2-Digit Factors

At-A-Glance Planning

Lesson Planning Checklist

Objective Explore multiplying with 2-digit factors.

Student Book Lesson Materials Place-value blocks (3 hundreds, 12 tens, 20 ones per group), *optional* overhead place-value blocks

Materials for pages 256A and 256B Place-value blocks (10 hundreds, 20 tens, 20 ones per group), Teaching Tool Transparency 6 (Centimeter Grid Paper), colored pencils

Subject Connection history—Pony Express

Strand Connection mental math

	Before Lesson	During Lesson	After Lesson
Daily Math			
p. 256A Problem of the Day			
p. 256A Math Routines			
p. 256A Mental Math			
Teaching Options			
p. 256B Facilitating and Assessing…			
Options for Reaching All Learners			
p. 256B Inclusion			
p. 256B Language Development			
Technology Options			
p. 256A *Math Workshop*			
p. 256 Interactive CD-ROM Lesson 6			
Assessment Options			
p. 256 Talk About It			
p. 257 Error Intervention			
p. 257 Performance Assessment			
Resources			
6-4 Practice			
6-4 Reteaching			
6-4 Enrichment			
6-4 Problem Solving			
6-4 Daily Transparency			

Problem of the Day

Problem of the Day

Four boys are having a race.
Carl is 10 feet ahead of Paul.
Eduardo is 8 feet behind Carl.
Steve is 5 feet ahead of Eduardo.
What is their order in the race?

From first to last: Carl, Steve, Eduardo, Paul

Math Routines

Calendar Ask students to find the month it will be three weeks from today, four weeks from today, 10 weeks from today, and 20 weeks from today.

Measurement Point to a classroom object. Have students name objects that are about 10 times longer.

Mental Math

Find each difference. Explain your thinking.

140 − 40 100   175 − 25 150
65 − 10 55   250 − 100 150

Math Workshop

Have students play *Bowling for Numbers*. Students can practice solving multiplication problems at increasing levels of skill.

Facilitating and Assessing [Explore] Lesson 6-4

Use with pages 256 and 257.

Get Started You may wish to assign the roles of material handlers for hundreds, tens, and ones, and have students alternate roles as they model different problems.

Observe Students may find different ways to arrange their arrays and multiply while still arriving at the same answer. However, students who build their arrays most efficiently using hundreds, ten, and ones will best be able to see partial products modeled.

Some students may recognize that they will have at least 10 tens and will start by using a hundreds block. Encourage others to exchange the 10 tens they build for a hundreds block.

As students draw pictures of arrays, some may sketch the blocks. Others may prefer to use grid paper.

Discuss Direct the discussion first toward the array that represents the problem, then toward how the array can be broken down to show partial products of ones × ones, ones × tens, tens × ones, and ten × tens.

Assess Use the rubric to assess students' work. See sample for Practice Exercise 4.

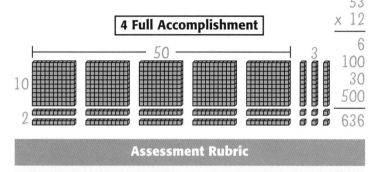

Assessment Rubric

4 Full Accomplishment
- uses place-value blocks and/or drawings to multiply 2-digit factors accurately

3 Substantial Accomplishment
- uses place-value blocks and/or drawings to multiply most 2-digit factors

2 Partial Accomplishment
- uses place-value blocks and/or drawings to multiply some 2-digit factors

1 Little Accomplishment
- does not use place-value blocks and/or drawings to multiply 2-digit factors

Options for Reaching All Learners

Inclusion

Partial Products
Use colors to relate arrays and partial products.

Materials Place-value blocks (10 hundreds, 20 tens, 20 ones per group), Teaching Tool Transparency 6 (Centimeter Grid Paper), colored pencils

Learning Style Visual

- Have groups of students use place-value blocks to build arrays to multiply 32 × 28. Then have each student copy the arrays on Teaching Tool Transparency 6 (Centimeter Grid Paper).
- Have students use one color for grid-paper squares representing ones, another for tens, and a third color for hundreds.
- Guide students to use the corresponding colors to record each step in the partial-product algorithm.

Language Development

Multiplication and Place Value
Use place-value blocks to strengthen verbal skills.

Materials Place-value blocks (10 hundreds, 20 tens, 20 ones per group)

Learning Style Kinesthetic, Verbal

- Group students acquiring English with fluent speakers.
- Have groups model the problem 22 × 34 using place-value blocks and write the steps they used to find the answer. Encourage students to use terms such as *multiples, factors, ones,* and *tens.*
- Ask students to read their descriptions aloud for the rest of the class.
- Ask students to identify parts of their arrays. Encourage the use of complete sentences.

6-4

Lesson Organizer

Objective Explore multiplying with 2-digit factors.

Suggested Grouping 2 to 4

Student Materials Place-value blocks (3 hundreds, 12 tens, 20 ones per group)

Teacher Materials *Optional* Overhead place-value blocks

Assignment Guide

Basic 1–11, 20

Average 4–15, 19–20

Enriched 6–20

---

1 Introduce

Review

Find each product.

1. 42
   × 3
   ―――
   126

2. 42
   × 40
   ―――
   1,680

Build on Prior Knowledge

After students review how to multiply a 2-digit number by a 1-digit number, ask them to predict how they might find 42 × 43. Possible answer: Add the products of 42 × 3 and 42 × 40.

2 Teach

See Facilitating and Assessing...on page 256B.

Interactive CD-ROM Lesson 6 includes content in this lesson.

Explore ● ● ● ● ● ● ● ● ● ● ● ● ● ● ● ● ● ●

You may wish to ask questions such as the following as you observe students at work.

• What multiplication facts did you use to find the hundreds, tens, and ones?

Talk About It Ongoing Assessment

Listen for understanding of the partial products.

Answers for Talk About It

3 No, the array always has 12 blocks along one side and 15 along the other.

4 Possible answer: Made an array with 13 rows and 14 columns to get a total of 1 hundred, 7 tens, and 12 ones or 182.

Chapter 6 Lesson 4

Exploring Multiplying with 2-Digit Factors

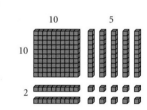

Problem Solving Connection

■ Use Objects/ Act It Out

■ Draw a Picture

Materials

place-value blocks

Remember

An array is data arranged in rows and columns.

Explore ●

For 18 months of 1860 and 1861, the Pony Express delivered mail between St. Joseph, Missouri, and Sacramento, California. Suppose a rider traveled 12 hours a day at a speed of 15 mi/hr. How many miles could the rider travel in a day?

Work Together

1. Use place-value blocks to show 12 × 15 in an array.

a. Show 1 ten and 5 ones in a row.

b. Make 11 more rows of 15. (Hint: You can use a hundred block to show 10 rows of 10.)

c. How many hundreds are there? How many tens? How many ones? **1; 7; 10**

d. How many ones are in the whole array? **180**

e. How many miles could the rider travel in one day? **180 miles a day**

2. Use place-value blocks to show each amount in an array. How many ones are in the whole array?

a. 13 × 14 **182** **b.** 14 × 21 **294** **c.** 11 × 15 **165**

Talk About It

3. Can you show 12 × 15 using 1 hundred block and 8 tens? Explain.

4. Describe how you used place-value blocks to show 13 × 14.

Name _____

Practice 6-4

Exploring Multiplying with 2-Digit Factors

Complete. Draw a picture or use place-value blocks to help.

1. 17
   × 15
   ―――
   3 5 ⟵ 5 × **7**
   5 0 ⟵ 5 × 10
   7 0 ⟵ **10** × 7
   1 0 0 ⟵ 10 × 10
   2 5 5 ⟵ 35 + **5 0** + 70 + **1 0 0**

10 × 10 = 100   10 × 7 = 70
10 × 5 = 50   5 × 7 = 35

2. 6 3
   × 1 2
   ―――
   6 ⟵ 2 × 3
   1 2 0 ⟵ 2 × 60
   3 0 ⟵ 10 × 3
   6 0 0 ⟵ 10 × 60
   7 5 6

3. 3 7
   × 2 4
   ―――
   2 8 ⟵ 4 × 7
   1 2 0 ⟵ 4 × 30
   1 4 0 ⟵ 20 × 7
   6 0 0 ⟵ 20 × 30
   8 8 8

4. 4 5
   × 5 3
   ―――
   1 5
   1 2 0
   2 5 0
   2 0 0 0
   2,3 8 5

5. 3 4
   × 6 2
   ―――
   8
   6 0
   2 4 0
   1 8 0 0
   2,1 0 8

6. 1 7
   × 2 9
   ―――
   6 3
   9 0
   1 4 0
   2 0 0
   4 9 3

7. 7 5
   × 4 3
   ―――
   1 5
   2 1 0
   2 0 0
   2,8 0 0
   3,2 2 5

8. 4 6
   × 3 8
   ―――
   1,748

9. 9 5
   × 2 6
   ―――
   2,470

10. 5 9
   × 5 2
   ―――
   3,068

11. 6 7
   × 1 2
   ―――
   804

Name _____

Another Look 6-4

Exploring Multiplication with 2-Digit Factors

In your book you multiplied using place-value blocks. Here is another way to show multiplication.

Draw rectangles on grid paper to show partial products.

   16
   × 15
   ―――
16 × 5 ⟶ 80
16 × 10 ⟶ 160
16 × 15 ⟶ 240 Add.

16 × 10   16 × 5

1. Draw lines to show the multiplication. Find 11 × 16.

   11
   × 16
   ―――
11 × 6 ⟶ **6 6**
11 × 10 ⟶ **1 1 0**
         1 7 6

11 × 10   11 × 6

2. 18
   × 32
   ―――
18 × 2 ⟶ **3 6**
18 × 30 ⟶ **5 4 0**
         5 7 6

3. 18
   × 43
   ―――
18 × 3 ⟶ **5 4**
18 × 40 ⟶ **7 2 0**
         7 7 4

Find each product.

4. 3 2
   × 1 5
   ―――
   480

5. 7 3
   × 3 2
   ―――
   2,336

6. 4 6
   × 5 5
   ―――
   2,530

Connect

You can use place-value blocks to help find a product.

Find 13×23.

What You See

$10 \times 20 = 200$

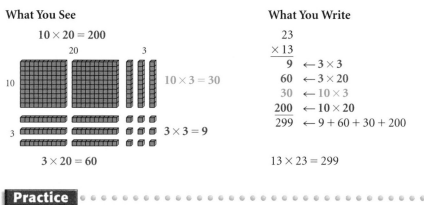

$10 \times 3 = 30$

$3 \times 3 = 9$

$3 \times 20 = 60$

What You Write

$$\begin{array}{r} 23 \\ \times 13 \\ \hline 9 \leftarrow 3 \times 3 \\ 60 \leftarrow 3 \times 20 \\ 30 \leftarrow 10 \times 3 \\ 200 \leftarrow 10 \times 20 \\ \hline 299 \leftarrow 9 + 60 + 30 + 200 \end{array}$$

$13 \times 23 = 299$

Practice

Copy and complete. Draw a picture or use place-value blocks to help.

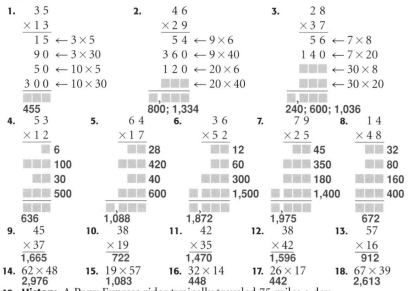

1.
$$\begin{array}{r} 35 \\ \times 13 \\ \hline 15 \leftarrow 3 \times 5 \\ 90 \leftarrow 3 \times 30 \\ 50 \leftarrow 10 \times 5 \\ 300 \leftarrow 10 \times 30 \\ \hline 455 \end{array}$$

2.
$$\begin{array}{r} 46 \\ \times 29 \\ \hline 54 \leftarrow 9 \times 6 \\ 360 \leftarrow 9 \times 40 \\ 120 \leftarrow 20 \times 6 \\ \leftarrow 20 \times 40 \\ \hline 800; 1,334 \end{array}$$

3.
$$\begin{array}{r} 28 \\ \times 37 \\ \hline 56 \leftarrow 7 \times 8 \\ 140 \leftarrow 7 \times 20 \\ \leftarrow 30 \times 8 \\ \leftarrow 30 \times 20 \\ \hline 240; 600; 1,036 \end{array}$$

4.
$$\begin{array}{r} 53 \\ \times 12 \\ \hline 6 \\ 100 \\ 30 \\ 500 \\ \hline 636 \end{array}$$

5.
$$\begin{array}{r} 64 \\ \times 17 \\ \hline 28 \\ 420 \\ 40 \\ 600 \\ \hline 1,088 \end{array}$$

6.
$$\begin{array}{r} 36 \\ \times 52 \\ \hline 12 \\ 60 \\ 300 \\ 1,500 \\ \hline 1,872 \end{array}$$

7.
$$\begin{array}{r} 79 \\ \times 25 \\ \hline 45 \\ 350 \\ 180 \\ 1,400 \\ \hline 1,975 \end{array}$$

8.
$$\begin{array}{r} 14 \\ \times 48 \\ \hline 32 \\ 80 \\ 160 \\ 400 \\ \hline 672 \end{array}$$

9.
$$\begin{array}{r} 45 \\ \times 37 \\ \hline 1,665 \end{array}$$

10.
$$\begin{array}{r} 38 \\ \times 19 \\ \hline 722 \end{array}$$

11.
$$\begin{array}{r} 42 \\ \times 35 \\ \hline 1,470 \end{array}$$

12.
$$\begin{array}{r} 38 \\ \times 42 \\ \hline 1,596 \end{array}$$

13.
$$\begin{array}{r} 57 \\ \times 16 \\ \hline 912 \end{array}$$

14. 62×48
2,976

15. 19×57
1,083

16. 32×14
448

17. 26×17
442

18. 67×39
2,613

19. **History** A Pony Express rider typically traveled 75 miles a day. How many miles could a rider travel in a week? **525 miles**

20. **Journal** Draw a picture to show how to find the product of 14 and 21. Describe each step in multiplying ones and tens.

Lesson 6-4 **257**

Connect

Use overhead place-value blocks to model 13×23. Then match corresponding partial products and parts of the array.

Error Intervention Ongoing Assessment

Observation Students do not write the correct number of zeros in each partial product.

How to Help Have students write the factors in expanded form before finding partial products.

Practice

Exercises 9–18 Assure students that it is acceptable to write the factors for each partial product, as shown in Exercises 1–8, if doing so is helpful.

For Early Finishers Challenge early finishers to estimate the products for Exercises 9–13. They can compare the estimates to the actual products to check the reasonableness of their answers.

3 Close and Assess

Performance Assessment

Draw an array or use place-value blocks to show 13×26. Then find the product.

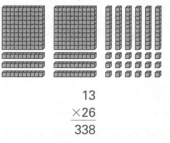

$$\begin{array}{r} 13 \\ \times 26 \\ \hline 338 \end{array}$$

Assess using the rubric on page 256B.

Resources

Technology Master 20

ANSWERS

20 Answers should include: Multiply 1×4, 1×10, 20×4, and 20×10. Add the four products to get 294.

Enrichment 6-4

Name _____ Extend Your Thinking 6-4

Visual Thinking

Shapes' Kitten Picture

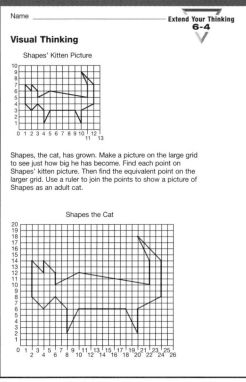

Shapes, the cat, has grown. Make a picture on the large grid to see just how big he has become. Find each point on Shapes' kitten picture. Then find the equivalent point on the larger grid. Use a ruler to join the points to show a picture of Shapes as an adult cat.

Shapes the Cat

Problem Solving 6-4

Name _____ Problem Solving 6-4

Exploring Multiplying with 2-Digit Factors
Complete the multiplication.

1.
$$\begin{array}{r} 32 \\ \times 67 \\ \hline 14 \leftarrow 7 \times 2 \\ 210 \leftarrow 7 \times 30 \\ 120 \leftarrow 60 \times 2 \\ 1800 \leftarrow 60 \times 30 \\ \hline 2,144 \end{array}$$

2.
$$\begin{array}{r} 67 \\ \times 32 \\ \hline 14 \leftarrow 2 \times 7 \\ 120 \leftarrow 2 \times 60 \\ 210 \leftarrow 30 \times 7 \\ 1800 \leftarrow 30 \times 60 \\ \hline 2,144 \end{array}$$

3. Compare **1** and **2**. Explain how they are alike and how they differ?
Possible answers: They have the same products; the factors are in a different order; the second and third partial products are switched.

4. Will 23×76 give the same product as 32×67? Explain.
No; the value of the numbers has changed.

5. Will 47×52 give the same product as 57×42? Draw place-value blocks to show your answer.
No; the value of the numbers has changed.

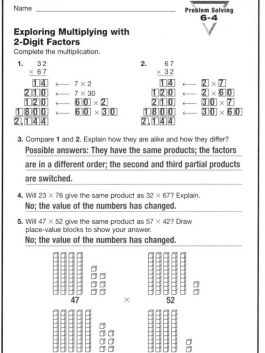

47 $\times$ 52

57 $\times$ 42

Chapter 6 • Lesson 6-4 **257**

Section A
Review and Practice

Use the Skills Checklist

Review the **Skills Checklist** on the page with students. Then ask questions such as the following:

- Where can you use patterns of 10s, 100s, and 1,000s? Exercises 1–5
- Where will you use estimation? Exercises 6–16, 39
- In which exercises will you multiply with 2-digit factors? Exercises 17–36, 38, 39
- In which exercises will you multiply by multiples of 10? Exercises 1–5, 22, 32–36, 38

Assess

You may wish to use this information to assess students' understanding of the lesson objectives.

Item Analysis		
Lesson Objective		**Items**
6-1	Explore multiplication patterns.	1–5
6-2	Estimate products of 2-digit factors.	6–16, 39
6-3	Multiply by multiples of 10.	22, 32–36, 38
6-4	Explore multiplying with 2-digit factors.	17–36, 38, 39

Resources

Practice Masters
- Practice Chapter 6 Section A

Assessment Sourcebook
- Quiz Chapter 6 Section A

TestWorks: Test and Practice Software

ANSWERS

39 Possible answer: Estimate: 2,000; Exact: 1,645; Estimate is greater because both factors were rounded to a greater number.

SECTION A
Review and Practice

(Lesson 1) Patterns Look for patterns to help you find each product.

1. $50 \times 4 = n$ **200**
   $50 \times 40 = n$ **2,000**
   $50 \times 400 = n$ **20,000**
   $50 \times 4,000 = n$ **200,000**

2. $30 \times 7 = n$ **210**
   $30 \times 70 = n$ **2,100**
   $30 \times 700 = n$ **21,000**
   $30 \times 7,000 = n$ **210,000**

3. $80 \times 3 = n$ **240**
   $80 \times 30 = n$ **2,400**
   $80 \times 300 = n$ **24,000**
   $80 \times 3,000 = n$ **240,000**

4. Find the product of 90 and 60. **5,400**

5. Find the product of 30 and 500. **15,000**

(Lesson 2) Estimation Estimate each product.

6. 43×27 **1,200**
7. 18×22 **400**
8. 51×55 **3,000**
9. 28×73 **2,100**
10. 96×34 **3,000**
11. 25×62 **1,800**
12. 86×33 **2,700**
13. 45×29 **1,500**
14. 94×12 **900**
15. 16×38 **800**

16. Tina needs 4 pieces of 28-inch wood to make a picture frame. Estimate the total amount of wood she needs. **About 120 in.**

(Lessons 3 and 4) Find each product.

17. $\begin{array}{r} 18 \\ \times 86 \\ \hline 1,548 \end{array}$	18. $\begin{array}{r} 37 \\ \times 38 \\ \hline 1,406 \end{array}$	19. $\begin{array}{r} 74 \\ \times 15 \\ \hline 1,110 \end{array}$	20. $\begin{array}{r} 19 \\ \times 24 \\ \hline 456 \end{array}$	21. $\begin{array}{r} 62 \\ \times 22 \\ \hline 1,364 \end{array}$
22. $\begin{array}{r} 49 \\ \times 10 \\ \hline 490 \end{array}$	23. $\begin{array}{r} 27 \\ \times 46 \\ \hline 1,242 \end{array}$	24. $\begin{array}{r} 32 \\ \times 13 \\ \hline 416 \end{array}$	25. $\begin{array}{r} 64 \\ \times 12 \\ \hline 768 \end{array}$	26. $\begin{array}{r} 53 \\ \times 57 \\ \hline 3,021 \end{array}$
27. $\begin{array}{r} 57 \\ \times 14 \\ \hline 798 \end{array}$	28. $\begin{array}{r} 88 \\ \times 25 \\ \hline 2,200 \end{array}$	29. $\begin{array}{r} 61 \\ \times 29 \\ \hline 1,769 \end{array}$	30. $\begin{array}{r} 72 \\ \times 44 \\ \hline 3,168 \end{array}$	31. $\begin{array}{r} 96 \\ \times 39 \\ \hline 3,744 \end{array}$

32. 30×72 **2,160**
33. 84×60 **5,040**
34. 50×56 **2,800**
35. 40×78 **3,120**
36. 90×33 **2,970**

37. **History** The *Apollo 11* spacecraft carried the first humans to walk on the moon. Each Apollo flight held 3 astronauts. There were 13 Apollo space flights. How many astronauts were there on the Apollo flights? **39 astronauts**

38. **Money** If a sheet of 20¢ stamps has 4 rows with 5 stamps in each row, how much does the sheet cost? **$4.00**

39. **Journal** Estimate the product of 47 and 35. Then find the exact answer. Explain why your estimate is greater or less than the exact answer.

Skills Checklist

In this section, you have:
- ☑ Explored Multiplication Patterns
- ☑ Estimated Products
- ☑ Multiplied by Multiples of 10
- ☑ Explored Multiplying with 2-Digit Factors

REVIEW AND PRACTICE

Practice

Name _____

Practice
Chapter 6
Section A

Review and Practice

(Lesson 1) Look for patterns to help you find each product.

1. $60 \times 3 =$ **180**
   $60 \times 30 =$ **1,800**
   $60 \times 300 =$ **18,000**
   $60 \times 3,000 =$ **180,000**

2. $70 \times 4 =$ **280**
   $70 \times 40 =$ **2,800**
   $70 \times 400 =$ **28,000**
   $70 \times 4,000 =$ **280,000**

3. Find the product of 50 and 800. **40,000**
4. Find the product of 80 and 7,000. **560,000**

(Lesson 2) Estimate each product.

5. 53×49 **2,500**
6. 16×41 **800**
7. 18×32 **600**
8. 48×48 **2,500**
9. 54×79 **4,000**
10. 27×84 **2,400**

(Lessons 3 and 4) Find each product.

11. $91 \times 20 =$ **1,820**
12. $30 \times 67 =$ **2,010**
13. $60 \times 29 =$ **1,740**
14. $70 \times 18 =$ **1,260**

15. $\begin{array}{r} 16 \\ \times 58 \\ \hline 928 \end{array}$
16. $\begin{array}{r} 36 \\ \times 65 \\ \hline 2,340 \end{array}$
17. $\begin{array}{r} 73 \\ \times 32 \\ \hline 2,336 \end{array}$
18. $\begin{array}{r} 38 \\ \times 79 \\ \hline 3,002 \end{array}$

19. Marly bought a sheet of 32¢ stamps. The sheet had 6 rows of 4 stamps each. How much did the sheet of stamps cost? **$7.68**

20. There were 32 buses at the tollbridge. Each carried 29 passengers. How many passengers were there in total? **928**

(Mixed Review) Add or subtract.

21. $\begin{array}{r} 602 \\ +339 \\ \hline 941 \end{array}$
22. $\begin{array}{r} 900 \\ -479 \\ \hline 421 \end{array}$
23. $\begin{array}{r} 477 \\ -291 \\ \hline 186 \end{array}$
24. $\begin{array}{r} 799 \\ +35 \\ \hline 834 \end{array}$

Multiplying

A ride in the sky can be quiet … except for the engine roar and the hum of the propeller. How can you use multiplication to find out how far you travel?

Liesl is a member of the International Wheelchair Aviators.

GET READY!

Finding Greater Products

Review multiplication by 1-digit factors. Find each product.

1. 28×9 **252** 2. 59×8 **472** 3. 42×5 **210**

4. 46×7 **322** 5. 37×4 **148** 6. 81×3 **243**

7. 16×2 **32** 8. 32×6 **192** 9. 77×8 **616**

Skills Checklist

In this section, you will:

☐ Multiply with 2-Digit Factors

☐ Estimate Greater Products

☐ Choose a Calculation Method

☐ Solve Problems by Making Decisions

259

Multiplying

In this section, students will multiply 2-digit factors, estimate greater products and choose a calculation method to multiply factors in the thousands.

Subskills

The work in this section builds on…

- Using basic facts and multiples of 10 to explore multiplication patterns

  $40 \times 7 = 280 \qquad 40 \times 70 = 2,800$

- Estimating products

  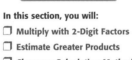

  68×42

  $70 \times 40 = 2,800$

- Using the multiplication algorithm to multiply by ones and by multiples of tens

$$
\begin{array}{cc}
1 & 1 \\
47 & 47 \\
\underline{\times 2} & \underline{\times 20} \\
94 & 940
\end{array}
$$

Use the Section Opener

Encourage students to discuss how Liesl might use multiplication to find how far she travels. Multiply the amount of time by the rate of speed.

Skills Trace

(Red numbers indicate pages in this section.)

Lesson and Skill	First Introduced	Grade Four			
		Introduce	Develop	Practice/Apply	Review
6-5 Multiply with 2-digit factors.	Grade 3	260–263	260, 261	262, 263, 268, 269, 272, 276, 277, 563	272, 284, 287, 427, 523, 538, 557
6-6 Estimate greater products.	Grade 4	264, 265	264	265, 268, 269, 272, 276, 277, 286, 563	272, 284, 287
6-7 Multiply numbers in the thousands.	Grade 4	266, 267	266	267, 268, 269, 272, 276, 277, 283, 286, 563	272, 283, 284, 287
6-8 Solve problems by making decisions after analyzing data.	Grade 3	270, 271	270, 271	271, 272, 285, 563	272, 284, 287

Mixed Review and Test Prep exercises for this chapter occur on pages 263, 265, 267, 275.

Multi-Age Classrooms Use pages 359–388 in Grade 3 or pages 111–132 in Grade 5 to relate to the content of this section.

Multiplying with 2-Digit Factors

At-A-Glance Planning

Lesson Planning Checklist

Objective Multiply with 2-digit factors.

Student Book Lesson Materials *Optional* Lesson Enhancement Transparencies 23, 25, Teaching Tool Transparency 6 (Centimeter Grid Paper)

Materials for pages 260A and 260B Place-value blocks (3 hundreds, 20 tens, 20 ones per group)

Subject Connections geography—flight routes, history—Wright brothers, math history—Inca quipus

Strand Connections estimation, geometry readiness, using data, money

	Before Lesson	During Lesson	After Lesson
Daily Math			
p. 260A Problem of the Day			
p. 260A Math Routines			
p. 260A Mental Math			
Teaching Options			
p. 260 Student Book Lesson			
p. 260B Another Way to Learn…			
Options for Reaching All Learners			
p. 260B Language Development			
p. 260B Cultural Connection			
Technology Options			
p. 260 Interactive CD-ROM Lesson 6			
Subject Connections			
p. 260A Literature Connection			
Assessment Options			
p. 261 Talk About It			
p. 261 Error Intervention			
p. 263 Observation			
p. 263 Quick Check			
Resources			
6-5 Practice			
6-5 Reteaching			
6-5 Enrichment			
6-5 Problem Solving			
6-5 Daily Transparency			

Problem of the Day

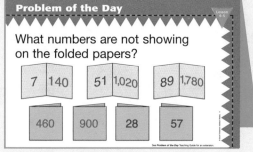

Problem of the Day

What numbers are not showing on the folded papers?

7	140		51	1,020		89	1,780

460	900	28	57

23:460; 45:900; 28:560; 57:1,140

Math Routines

Time Ask students to name the time it will be 90 minutes from now. Ask them to explain how they determined their answer.

Patterns Tell students that it takes 15 minutes to read 6 pages of a certain book. Ask how many pages can be read in 1 hr, $1\frac{1}{2}$ hr, and 2 hr. 24, 36, 48 pages

Mental Math

Find the products. Explain your thinking.

6 × 12 72   7 × 12 84
8 × 12 96   9 × 12 108

Literature Connection

In Judi Barrett's *Cloudy with a Chance of Meatballs*, the residents of the town of Chewandswallow eat food that falls from the sky. One day a storm brings drifts of cream cheese and jelly sandwiches that measure 15 inches high.

• Suppose it snowed sandwiches at the rate of 15 inches per day for 15 days. How high would the drifts be? 225 in.

• What if it snowed 15 inches per day for the whole month of January? 465 in.

Another Way to **Learn** Lesson 6-5

Use as an alternative or in addition to pages 260–263.

Materials Place-value blocks (3 hundreds, 20 tens, 20 ones per group)

Learning Style Kinesthetic

- Have groups use place-value blocks to model 13 × 24. Have them show 3 × 24 using tens and ones, exchanging 10 ones for 1 ten. Then have them show 10 × 24 using hundreds and tens, exchanging 20 tens for 2 hundreds. Have them name the number shown in each part of the array and the total. 72; 240; 312

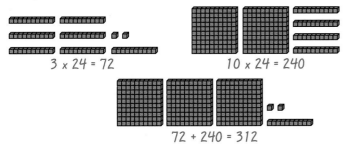

$3 \times 24 = 72$ $10 \times 24 = 240$

$72 + 240 = 312$

- As each partial product is found and blocks are exchanged, write the step in the multiplication algorithm.

- Have groups draw pictures of blocks and record the steps symbolically for the following exercises:

  23 × 36 828   15 × 32 480

- Have students talk about how finding partial products in this lesson is the same as and different from the work they did finding partial products in Lesson 6-4.

- Assign Check and Practice on Student Book pages 261–263 or *Practice Master 6-5.*

- Assess using the following rubric.

Assessment Rubric
4 Full Accomplishment   • finds products with 2-digit factors
3 Substantial Accomplishment   • finds most products with 2-digit factors
2 Partial Accomplishment   • with prompting, finds some products with 2-digit factors
1 Little Accomplishment   • does not find products with 2-digit factors

Options for Reaching All Learners

Language Development

Speaking Multiplication
Use verbal repetition to reinforce algorithm steps.

Learning Style Verbal/Auditory

- Pair students acquiring English with others who speak the same language. As students multiply 2-digit numbers, have them say the multiplication algorithm steps to each other in English and in their native language:

  1. Multiply by ones.

  2. Multiply by tens.

  3. Add the products.

- Students may also record the multiplication algorithm in their own words as numbered steps. Have them read their steps aloud.

Cultural Connection

Egyptian Multiplication
Use Egyptian math strategies to multiply.

Learning Style Logical, Visual

- Ancient Egyptians used repeated doubling to multiply. Demonstrate using 26 × 12.

26	(1 × 26)
+ 26	(1 × 26)
52	(2 × 26)
+ 52	(2 × 26)
104	(4 × 26)
+ 104	(4 × 26)
208	(8 × 26)
208	(8 × 26) $8 + 4 = 12$
+ 104	(4 × 26)
312	(12 × 26)

Lesson Organizer

Objective Multiply with 2-digit factors.
Student Materials *Optional* Teaching Tool Transparency 6 (Centimeter Graph Paper)
Teacher Materials *Optional* Lesson Enhancement Transparencies 23, 25
Assignment Guide
Basic 23–49, 51–53, 57–72
Average 28–45, 48–72
Enriched 28–32, 38–72

1 Introduce

Review

Name the four steps in each multiplication problem. Find the partial and total products.

1. 42
× 17

2. 36
× 43

Multiply ones by ones, ones by tens, tens by ones, tens by tens. **1.** 14; 280; 20; 400; 714 **2.** 18; 90; 240; 1,200; 1,548

Build on Prior Knowledge

After students review using partial products to multiply, ask them to multiply 42 × 7 and 42 × 10. Ask how these products are related to the products in Review Exercise 1. 294; 420; Possible answers: They add up to 714, just as the four partial products do; they are a quicker way to multiply 42 × 17.

2 Teach

See Another Way to Learn…on page 260B.

 Interactive CD-ROM Lesson 6 includes content in this lesson.

Learn ● ● ● ● ● ● ● ● ● ● ● ● ● ● ● ● ●

Pronunciation note: Liesl (LEE-suhl)

Have groups compare Bryan and Arianna's ways. You might ask questions such as the following.

• How did Bryan and Arianna show multiplying 2 × 26?

• How did they show 10 × 26?

Have groups share their comparisons. Both methods multiply by ones and then by tens. Arianna's way shows the combined product for ones on one line and the combined product for tens on one line.

Multiplying with 2-Digit Factors

You Will Learn
how to multiply with 2-digit factors

Did You Know?
The longest regular airline flight is from New York City to Johannesburg, South Africa. It covers a distance of 7,967 miles.

Learn ●

Liesl gets off the ground as often as possible. She's a member of the International Wheelchair Aviators, a group of pilots who fly small airplanes.

Pilots keep logbooks of how many hours they fly. If Liesl flies 26 hours each month, how many hours will she log in one year?

Liesl flies from the airport at Saginaw, Michigan.

Bryan and Arianna solved the problem in different ways.

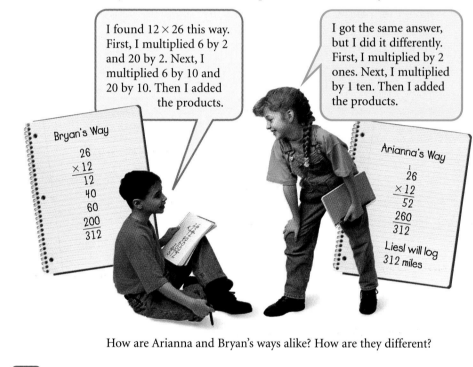

How are Arianna and Bryan's ways alike? How are they different?

Managing Time

Use the first half of the class period for Learn and Check and the second half for the Practice Exercises, Problem Solving and Applications, and Problem Solving and Math History on pages 262 and 263. Assign Mixed Review and Test Prep as homework.

Another Example

Use Arianna's way to find 36×47.

Step 1	Step 2	Step 3
Multiply by ones.	Multiply by tens.	Add the products.
$\begin{array}{r} 4 \\ 47 \\ \times\,36 \\ \hline 282 \end{array}$	$\begin{array}{r} 2 \\ 4 \\ 47 \\ \times\,36 \\ \hline 282 \\ 1410 \end{array}$	$\begin{array}{r} 2 \\ 4 \\ 47 \\ \times\,36 \\ \hline 282 \\ 1410 \\ \hline 1,692 \end{array}$

$36 \times 47 = 1,692$ **Estimate** to check.

36×47 is close to 40×50. $40 \times 50 = 2,000$

Since 1,692 is close to 2,000, the answer is reasonable.

Talk About It

1. In the Example above, what do the small numbers in Step 2 stand for?

2. How would you multiply 60 and 15 mentally?

Check ●

Copy and complete.

1. $\begin{array}{r} 2\,3 \\ \times\,1\,2 \\ \hline \blacksquare\,6 \\ \blacksquare\blacksquare\blacksquare \\ \hline 2\,\blacksquare\,6 \end{array}$
2. $\begin{array}{r} 4\,8 \\ \times\,2\,1 \\ \hline \blacksquare\blacksquare \\ \blacksquare\,6\,\blacksquare \\ \hline 1,\blacksquare\,0\,8 \end{array}$
3. $\begin{array}{r} 3\,6 \\ \times\,1\,7 \\ \hline 2\,5\,\blacksquare \\ 3\,\blacksquare\blacksquare \\ \hline 6\,1\,\blacksquare \end{array}$
4. $\begin{array}{r} 5\,2 \\ \times\,4\,3 \\ \hline \blacksquare\,5\,6 \\ 2\,\blacksquare\blacksquare\blacksquare \\ \hline \blacksquare,2\,3\,6 \end{array}$
5. $\begin{array}{r} 4\,5 \\ \times\,3\,4 \\ \hline 1\,\blacksquare\,0 \\ \blacksquare\blacksquare\blacksquare\blacksquare \\ \hline \blacksquare,\blacksquare\,3\,0 \end{array}$

46; 230; 276   48; 960; 1,008   252; 360; 612   156; 2,080; 2,236   180; 1,350; 1,530

Find each product.

6. $\begin{array}{r} 17 \\ \times\,14 \\ \hline 238 \end{array}$
7. $\begin{array}{r} 39 \\ \times\,22 \\ \hline 858 \end{array}$
8. $\begin{array}{r} 51 \\ \times\,35 \\ \hline 1,785 \end{array}$
9. $\begin{array}{r} 28 \\ \times\,16 \\ \hline 448 \end{array}$
10. $\begin{array}{r} 66 \\ \times\,47 \\ \hline 3,102 \end{array}$

11. $\begin{array}{r} 10 \\ \times\,72 \\ \hline 720 \end{array}$
12. $\begin{array}{r} 43 \\ \times\,56 \\ \hline 2,408 \end{array}$
13. $\begin{array}{r} 69 \\ \times\,40 \\ \hline 2,760 \end{array}$
14. $\begin{array}{r} 86 \\ \times\,19 \\ \hline 1,634 \end{array}$
15. $\begin{array}{r} 75 \\ \times\,70 \\ \hline 5,250 \end{array}$

16. 44×58 17. 28×43 18. 74×39 19. 36×15 20. 55×97
   2,552   1,204   2,886   540   5,335

21. **Reasoning** How can you tell from estimating that the product of 25 and 25 is less than 1,000? **Possible answer:** $30 \times 30 = 900$; $25 < 30$

22. **Reasoning** Write a multiplication sentence that has 4,000 as its product. **Possible answer:** $80 \times 50 = 4,000$

Lesson 6-5   261

Additional Examples

$\begin{array}{r} 41 \\ \times\,13 \\ \hline 533 \end{array}$	$\begin{array}{r} 35 \\ \times\,46 \\ \hline 1,610 \end{array}$

Talk About It Ongoing Assessment

Listen for explanations that show a clear understanding of place value.

Answers for Talk About It

1 2 tens, 4 tens

2 Possible answer: $5 \times 60 = 300$, $10 \times 60 = 600$, $300 + 600 = 900$

Check

Encourage students to estimate to check the reasonableness of their products. When products appear unreasonable, have them check each step of their work.

Error Intervention Ongoing Assessment

Observation Students misalign the digits in the partial products.

How to Help Have students work on lined paper turned sideways. Teaching Tool Transparency 6 (Centimeter Grid Paper) is also helpful.

Meeting Individual Needs

Learning Styles	Teaching Approach
Verbal	Have small groups create a rhythmic chant describing the multiplication algorithm and use it as they work. To help students get started, suggest, "One times ones, regroup, and record. One times tens and add…"
Visual	Have students use different colors to write the digits in the factors. Have them use corresponding colors to record the partial products.
Social	Have students work in groups of four. For each exercise, one student multiplies the ones, another multiplies the tens, another adds the partial products, and a fourth estimates to check.

Practice •

Skills and Reasoning

Find each product. Estimate to check.

23. 44 × 31 **1,364**	24. 32 × 15 **480**	25. 49 × 39 **1,911**	26. 26 × 39 **1,014**	27. 73 × 23 **1,679**
28. 41 × 22 **902**	29. 83 × 13 **1,079**	30. 34 × 83 **2,822**	31. 72 × 11 **792**	32. 53 × 91 **4,823**
33. 32 × 51 **1,632**	34. 61 × 18 **1,098**	35. 45 × 13 **585**	36. 89 × 12 **1,068**	37. 15 × 75 **1,125**

38. 65 × 43   **2,795**
39. 81 × 12   **972**
40. 96 × 27   **2,592**
41. 19 × 19   **361**
42. 78 × 65   **5,070**

43. 38 × 38   **1,444**
44. 21 × 43   **903**
45. 78 × 63   **4,914**
46. 81 × 26   **2,106**
47. 16 × 88   **1,408**

48. Multiply 59 and 29. **1,711**
49. Find the product of 18 and 62. **1,116**

50. How many digits are in the product of 25 and 47? **4 digits; 25 × 47 = 1,175**

Problem Solving and Applications

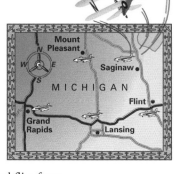

51. **Geography** Liesl flies from Saginaw, Michigan, to Defiance, Ohio—a distance of 196 miles. She also flies to Sheboygan, Wisconsin—a distance of 155 miles. How much farther is the trip to Defiance? **41 miles**

52. Suppose Liesl flies from Saginaw to Mount Pleasant and back once a week for 15 weeks. The round trip distance is 76 miles. How many miles would she fly in all? **1,140 miles**

53. **Geometry Readiness** Use the map. Suppose Liesl flies from Saginaw to Flint, then to Lansing, and then back to Saginaw. What would be the shape of her route? **Triangle**

Using Data Use the Data File on page 247 for **54 and 55.**

54. **History** The plane that Orville and Wilbur Wright built in 1903 flew at 30 miles per hour. Which form of transportation shown on the bar graph is closest to this speed? **Bicycle**

55. The speed of a MAGLEV train is about twice as fast as which form of transportation? **Powerboat**

Practice 6-5

Name _____

Multiplying with 2-Digit Factors
Find each product. Estimate to check.

1. 35 × 42 **1,470**	2. 23 × 51 **1,173**	3. 56 × 85 **4,760**	4. 74 × 32 **2,368**
5. 66 × 33 **2,178**	6. 78 × 27 **2,106**	7. 46 × 84 **3,864**	8. 53 × 68 **3,604**
9. 28 × 46 **1,288**	10. 83 × 16 **1,328**	11. 92 × 25 **2,300**	12. 47 × 76 **3,572**
13. 55 × 76 **4,180**	14. 98 × 26 **2,548**	15. 34 × 54 **1,836**	16. 91 × 71 **6,461**
17. 17 × 37 **629**	18. 83 × 46 **3,818**	19. 29 × 57 **1,653**	20. 53 × 89 **4,717**

21. 64 × 35 = **2,240**
22. 87 × 56 = **4,872**
23. 72 × 39 = **2,808**
24. 45 × 25 = **1,125**
25. 73 × 19 = **1,387**
26. 43 × 75 = **3,225**
27. Multiply 38 and 64. **2,432**
28. Multiply 16 and 54. **864**
29. How many digits are in the product of 24 and 32? **3**

Reteaching 6-5

Name _____

Multiplying with 2-Digit Factors
Multiply 34 × 36.

Step 1 Multiply 6 ones and 34.

   3 4   Regroup.
× 3 6
2 0 4 ←— 6 × 34

Step 2 Multiply 3 tens and 34.

   3 4   Regroup.
× 3 6
2 0 4
1 0 2 0 ←— 30 × 34

Step 3 Add the partial products.

   3 4
× 3 6
 2 0 4
1 0 2 0
1 2 2 4 ←— 204 + 1,020

Step 4 Check by estimating.

34 × 36
↓   ↓
30 × 40 = <u>1,200</u>

Since 1,224 is close to 1,200, the answer is reasonable.

Complete.

1.   2 4
  × 1 7
  1 6 8 ←— 7 × 24
  2 4 0 ←— 10 × 24
  4 0 8

2.   4 2
   × 5 3
   1 2 6 ←— 3 × 42
  2 1 0 0 ←— 50 × 42
  2 2 2 6

3. 76 × 23 **1,748**	4. 63 × 34 **2,142**	5. 45 × 25 **1,125**	6. 56 × 43 **2,408**

The ancient Incas of Peru kept records using knots on strings. The strings were called *quipus*. The knots stood for animals, people, and plots of land. Even through the 1800s, herders in Peru used knotted strings to keep track of their animals. Ancient Greeks and Persians used similar systems of knotted strings to count.

56. Each string stands for a different herd of animals. The first string shows 235 animals in one herd. How many animals are in the herd shown by the second string? **127 animals**

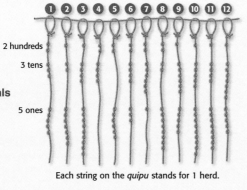

2 hundreds

3 tens

5 ones

57. Which herd has the most animals? How many does it have? **The one shown by the seventh string; 261**

58. How many herds does this *quipu* show? **12 herds**

Each string on the *quipu* stands for 1 herd.

59. Critical Thinking What is the greatest number of knots that could be shown in the tens group? Explain.
9 knots; A tenth knot would be regrouped into the hundreds section.

60. If 14 calves are born in each herd, how many knots would have to be added to the *quipu*? **168 knots**

61. Critical Thinking Why do you think farmers and herders used this system of keeping records?
Possible answer: String could be carried around easily with the farmer or herder.

62. Journal Describe the steps you would follow to find the product of 24 and 12.

Mixed Review and Test Prep

Find each quotient.

63. $8 \div 4$ **2**   **64.** $12 \div 2$ **6**   **65.** $6 \div 3$ **2**   **66.** $14 \div 2$ **7**   **67.** $9 \div 3$ **3**

Find each difference.

68. $\$11.01 - \$9.92$ **$1.09**   **69.** $\$43.20 - \$0.75$ **$42.45**   **70.** $\$14.95 - \$1.24$ **$13.71**   **71.** $\$3.87 - \$2.19$ **$1.68**

72. Which number is a multiple of 9? **B**

Ⓐ 33   Ⓑ 72   Ⓒ 22   Ⓓ 46

Skills Practice Bank, page 566, Set 2   Lesson 6-5   **263**

Enrichment 6-5

Name _____   Extend Your Thinking 6-5

Critical Thinking

Mel has a part-time job at a sandwich shop. He earns $6 per hour. He made a spreadsheet so he could keep track of his earnings. Refer to the spreadsheet to answer the questions.

	A	B	C	D	E
1	Day	Time in	Time out	Hours worked	Amount earned
2	Monday	3:15 P.M.	5:30 P.M.	$2\frac{1}{4}$	$13.50
3	Tuesday	3:30 P.M.	6:30 P.M.	3	$18.00
4	Wednesday	3:00 P.M.	6:15 P.M.	$3\frac{1}{4}$	$19.50
5	Thursday	4:00 P.M.	6:45 P.M.	$2\frac{3}{4}$	$16.50
6	Friday	3:45 P.M.	5:00 P.M.	$1\frac{1}{4}$	$7.50
7	Saturday	10:00 A.M.	2:00 A.M.	4	$24.00
8			Total:	$16\frac{1}{2}$	$99.00

1. How can you figure out what to put in cell **D4**?
Possible answer: Count from 3:00 P.M. to 6:00 P.M. and add on 15 minutes, which is $3\frac{1}{4}$ hours in total.

2. How can you figure out what to put in cell **E7**?
Multiply 4 (hours worked) by 6 (amount per hour).

3. How can you figure out what to put in cells **D8** and **E8**?
Add the numbers on cells **D2–D7**, then the numbers in cells **E2–E7**.

4. Complete the spreadsheet.

5. Suppose Mel gets a raise to $6.25 and keeps the same schedule. What would you put in cell **E8**? Explain. $103.13;
Possible answer: Multiply the amount in cell **D8** by 6.25.

Problem Solving 6-5

Name _____   Problem Solving 6-5

Multiplying with 2-Digit Factors

1. The Mississippi Queen was built in 1976. How many years ago was it built?   **Present year minus 1976**

2. The riverboat travels 55 miles a day up the river. How many miles will it travel in 43 days?   **2,365 miles**

3. The average weight of a suitcase brought on board the riverboat is 27 pounds. How much will 35 suitcases weigh?   **945 pounds**

4. The riverboat has 2 crew members for every 10 passengers. If there are 100 passengers, how many crew members are there?   **20**

5. There are 208 cabins on the riverboat and 78 of them have balconies. How many cabins do not have balconies?   **130 cabins**

6. There are 4 passengers in line at the breakfast buffet. Earl is ahead of Kate. Edward is behind Kate. Earl is behind Tricia. Who is first in line?   **Tricia**

7. Alan says if he reads 11 pages of his book every day for 21 days, he will finish it. How many pages are in his book?   **231 pages**

8. **Choose a Strategy** A spaceship lands in the desert. Creatures exit the spaceship. Some of the creatures have 2 large eyes. Some have 1 very large eye in the middle of their forehead. There are 19 creatures with 29 eyes. How many creatures have 2 eyes? How many creatures have 1 eye?

   • Use Objects/Act It Out
   • Draw a Picture
   • Look for a Pattern
   • Guess and Check
   • Use Logical Reasoning
   • Make an Organized List
   • Make a Table
   • Solve a Simpler Problem
   • Work Backward

   a. What strategy would you use to solve the problem?
   Possible answers: Make an Organized List or Guess and Check

   b. Answer the problem. **2 eyes—10; 1 eye—9**

Historical Note

Lesson Enhancement Transparency 25 illustrates *quipus*.

The Inca Empire, located along the western coast of South America, flourished from about 1438 until it was conquered by the Spanish in 1532. Because the Incas did not develop a system of writing, what we know about them comes from archaeological findings and Spanish writings following the conquest.

The Incas developed mathematical calculations to help in designing terraced fields, roads, and buildings. *Quipus* were used by officials to keep records of various items, each string representing something different.

③ Close and Assess

Observation

Have students choose one problem from the Check or Practice sets and show how they solved it and how they decided their answers were reasonable. Explanations should include multiplying by ones and tens, regrouping if necessary, adding the products, and estimating to check for reasonableness.

Quick Check

Number Sense Use estimation to find two Skill exercises that have the same estimated product. Explain. Exercises 2 and 3; The estimated product of 17×52 is 1,000, and the estimated product of 23×47 is 1,000.

Skill Find each product.

1. 36×41 **1,476**

2. 17×52 **884**

3. 23×47 **1,081**

4. 25×75 **1,875**

Resources

Technology Master 21

ANSWERS

62 Possible answer: Multiply 24 by 2 ones. Multiply 24 by 1 ten. Then add the products to get 288.

Chapter 6 • Lesson 6-5   **263**

Estimating Greater Products

At-A-Glance Planning

Objective Estimate greater products.

Student Book Materials *Optional Reading Strategies for Math* Chart 28 (Steps in a Process)

Materials for pages 264A and 264B Calculators (2 per group), Teaching Tool Transparency 5 (Number Lines), index cards (about 30 per group), paper bags (2 per group)

Subject Connection social studies—subway and bicycle travel

Strand Connections time, estimation, money, probability, using data

	Before Lesson	During Lesson	After Lesson
Daily Math			
p. 264A Problem of the Day			
p. 264A Math Routines			
p. 264A Mental Math			
Teaching Options			
p. 264 Student Book Lesson			
p. 264B Another Way to Learn…			
Options for Reaching All Learners			
p. 264B Inclusion			
p. 264B Gifted & Talented			
Subject Connections			
p. 264A Literature Connection			
Assessment Options			
p. 264 Talk About It			
p. 265 Error Intervention			
p. 265 Journal			
p. 265 Quick Check			
Resources			
6-6 Practice			
6-6 Reteaching			
6-6 Enrichment			
6-6 Problem Solving			
6-6 Daily Transparency			

Problem of the Day

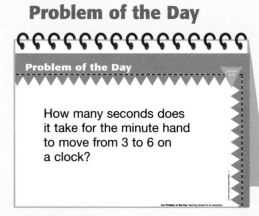

Problem of the Day

How many seconds does it take for the minute hand to move from 3 to 6 on a clock?

900 seconds

Math Routines

Measurement Ask students to order the following objects from lightest to heaviest: sheet of paper, television, apple, dictionary, lunchbox.

Calendar Ask students to estimate the year in which people first rode in a balloon if the first time was about 220 years ago. About 1780.

Mental Math

Estimate each product. Explain your thinking.

1.	**2.**	**3.**	**4.**
34	42	53	27
× 19	× 25	× 44	× 32
600	1,200	2,000	900

Literature Connection

In *Henry and Beezus* by Beverly Cleary, Henry finds 49 boxes of gumballs. Henry estimates that each box contains 300 gumballs.

• Estimate the total number of gumballs. 15,000

• If each box held only 200 gumballs, estimate the total number of gumballs. 10,000

Another Way to [Learn] Lesson 6-6

Use as an alternative or in addition to pages 264 and 265.

Materials Calculators (2 per group)

Learning Style Visual, Kinesthetic

- Briefly review how to enter a multiplication problem into the calculator. Stress that students should be particularly careful when entering several zeros.

- Review the steps for estimating products, then present the problem 34 × 495. Students who think they can predict the number of zeros in the product can share their thinking with the class. Ask groups to estimate the product using the calculator and the method just discussed, then record their results.

- Discuss how the students rounded the factors and found the product. Point out the number of zeros in the product and compare this with students' predictions.

- Ask students to estimate the products of the following problems.

63 × 388	49 × 513	72 × 879
24,000	25,000	63,000

- Assign Check and Practice on Student Book pages 264 and 265 or *Practice Master 6–6.*
- Assess using the following rubric.

Assessment Rubric

4 Full Accomplishment
- estimates greater products accurately

3 Substantial Accomplishment
- estimates most greater products accurately

2 Partial Accomplishment
- estimates some greater products accurately

1 Little Accomplishment
- does not estimate greater products accurately

Options for Reaching All Learners

Inclusion

Rounding on the Number Line
Use number lines to strengthen skill in rounding factors.

Materials Teaching Tool Transparency 5 (Number Lines)

Learning Style Visual

- Provide number lines marked in increments of 10 from 0 to 100 and in increments of 100 from 0 to 1,000.

- For each product students are to estimate, have them show the location of each factor on a number line, identify the nearest ten or hundred, and write the rounded factors.

- Then have them multiply the estimated factors.

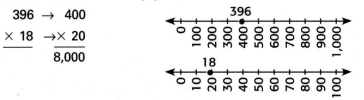

Gifted & Talented

Guess My Zeros
Use a game to strengthen product-estimation skills.

Materials Index cards (about 30 per group), paper bags (2 per group), calculators (1 per group)

Learning Style Logical, Visual

- Make number cards. Half the cards should have 2-digit numbers and half should have 3-digit numbers. These may be random.

- Place the 2-digit cards in one bag and the 3-digit cards in another.

- Students play in teams. The first team draws a number from each bag and predicts how many zeros the estimated product will have. The other team checks the prediction using a calculator.

- Have the teams switch roles and play again.

Lesson Organizer

Objective Estimate greater products.

Student Materials None

Teacher Materials *Optional Reading Strategies for Math* Chart 28 (Steps in a Process)

Assignment Guide

Basic 6–21, 23, 26, 28–33

Average 12–26, 28–33

Enriched 15–33

1 Introduce

Review

Find each product.

1. 30 × 500
15,000

2. 20 × 600
12,000

3. 30 × 600
18,000

4. 20 × 500
10,000

Build on Prior Knowledge

After students review multiplying multiples of 10, ask them which Review exercise has factors that are close to 27 × 563. Exercise 3; 27 rounds to 30 and 563 rounds to 600.

2 Teach

See Another Way to Learn...on page 264B.

Learn

When focusing on the example, ask why estimating a product is appropriate. Then have students explain the rounding and mental multiplication that were done.
Possible answer: The question asks "about how many."Rounded each factor to the nearest 10 or 100, and then used basic facts and place value to find the estimated product

Talk About It) Ongoing Assessment

Listen for an understanding that increasing the value of a factor increases the product.

Answer for Talk About It

Greater; Both factors were rounded to a greater number.

Check

Exercise 5 Have students explain their thinking. Encourage students to make generalizations about the factors.

Estimating Greater Products

You Will Learn
how to estimate greater products

Learn

Kyle and Julian take the subway home from school every day. The train they travel on can seat 396 passengers. If 18 trains travel along their route in an hour, about how many seated passengers can travel during that time?

Kyle and Julian live in Toronto, Ontario, in Canada.

Toronto, Ontario

Math Tip
Estimate to find if your answer is reasonable.

You can estimate the product to find about how many passengers can travel in an hour.

Example
Estimate 18 × 396.

Step 1	**Step 2**
Round each factor.	Multiply the rounded factors.
18 × 396	20 × 400 = 8,000
Round to tens ↓ ↓ Round to hundreds	
20 × 400	

About 8,000 seated passengers can travel in an hour.

Talk About It

Is the estimate greater or less than the exact answer? Explain.

Check

Estimate each product.

1. 126 × 32
3,000

2. 608 × 43
24,000

3. 73 × 564
42,000

4. 36 × 390
16,000

5. Reasoning Name two factors that have an estimated product of 10,000. **Possible answer: 523 and 21**

Practice 6-6	Reteaching 6-6

Practice

Skills and Reasoning

Estimate each product.

6. 185×18	**7.** 525×63	**8.** 149×21	**9.** 542×25
4,000	30,000	2,000	15,000

10. 342	**11.** 417	**12.** 950	**13.** 322	**14.** 661
$\times\ 19$	$\times\ 23$	$\times\ 48$	$\times\ 35$	$\times\ 78$
6,000	8,000	50,000	12,000	56,000

15. 120	**16.** 869	**17.** 981	**18.** 357	**19.** 456
$\times\ 42$	$\times\ 59$	$\times\ 53$	$\times\ 16$	$\times\ 38$
4,000	54,000	8,000	8,000	20,000

20. Estimate the product of 635 and 68.
42,000

21. Estimate 671 by 45.
35,000

22. Write two different sets of factors you could estimate to have a product of about 20,000. **Possible answer:**
501 × 39 and 538 × 43

Problem Solving and Applications

23. About 180 people in each Toronto subway car can stand. Usually there are 6 cars on a train. Estimate how many riders per train might be standing.
About 1,200 riders

24. **Money** If Kyle and Julian's parents spend $34 per week for their childrens' subway tokens, about how much will they spend in a school year of 33 weeks? **About $900**

25. **Probability** Suppose your subway ride takes 9 minutes and the walk from the station to school takes 18 minutes. If you take the 7:36 A.M. train, are you more likely to be late for school or on time? The bell rings at 8:00 A.M. **More likely to be late**

26. **Using Data** Use the Data File on page 247. About how many miles could a bicyclist travel in 6 hours, based on the speed shown? **About 300 miles**

27. **Critical Thinking** What is the greatest whole number factor that you could multiply by 50 to get a product less than 10,000? Explain how you know. **199; 50 × 200 = 10,000. The factor must be 1 less than 200.**

Mixed Review and Test Prep

Find each quotient.

28. $36 \div 6$ **6** **29.** $25 \div 5$ **5** **30.** $20 \div 2$ **10** **31.** $63 \div 9$ **7** **32.** $49 \div 7$ **7**

33. Which number is a factor of 96? **C**

Ⓐ 5 Ⓑ 7 Ⓒ 8 Ⓓ 9

Skills Practice Bank, page 566, Set 3   Lesson 6-6   **265**

Enrichment 6-6

Name _____   **Extend Your Thinking 6-6**

Decision Making

Rodney and his family visit a car factory in Detroit, Michigan.

CAR FACTORY TOUR
OPEN: MONDAY - FRIDAY
HOURS: 9:00 AM — 4:00PM
TOUR: LEAVES EVERY 15 MINUTES
LENGTH OF TOUR: 45 MINUTES
MAXIMUM NUMBER OF PEOPLE PER TOUR: 15
COST: $2.75 EA PERSON

1. How many hours a day is the tour offered?
7 hours

2. What is the maximum number of tours each hour?
4

3. If the tours must be completed by 4:00 P.M., what is the maximum number of tours that can be scheduled from 3:00 P.M. to 4:00 P.M.?
2

4. What is the maximum number of tours that can be offered in one day?
26

5. What is the maximum number of people that can tour the factory each day?
390

6. How much will Rodney's family of 4 spend to take the tour?
$11.00

7. Plan a schedule for a trip to the car factory for you and your family. Assume the travel distance to the factory is one hour.

a. List some things you will have to consider when making your schedule.
Possible answers: Time to leave and return; food and rest stops; wait to buy tickets; wait in line for next tour to begin.

b. Write your schedule with 15-minute intervals.
Answers will vary.

Problem Solving 6-6

Name _____   **Problem Solving 6-6**

Estimating Greater Products

Science The speed a planet travels around the Sun is measured in kilometers per second. The table shows the speed and the number of Earth days it takes a planet to revolve around the Sun.

Planet	Speed around Sun (km/s)	Time to revolve around Sun
Mercury	48	90 Earth days
Venus	35	225 Earth days
Earth	30	365 Earth days
Mars	24	687 Earth days

1. About how many kilometers will Venus travel in 185 seconds?
8,000 km

2. About how many kilometers will Mercury travel in 14 minutes?
30,000 km

3. About how many kilometers will Mars travel
in one minute? **1,200 km**
in one hour? **72,000 km**
in one Earth day? **1,728,000 km**

4. About how many times will Mercury revolve around the Sun in one Earth year? **4–5 times**

5. About how much farther does Mercury travel in 195 seconds than Venus? **about 2,000 km**

6. The Jackson family spends $85 per week on food. Abouthow much will they spend on food in one year?
$4,500 a year

7. A school district has 38 school buses. Each bus seats 48 students. There are 2,300 students enrolled. Estimate to find if the district will have to purchase additional buses. Explain. **38 buses can transport less than 2,000 students. At least ten additional buses would be needed to transport all 2,300 students enrolled.**

Error Intervention Ongoing Assessment

Observation Students find an unreasonable estimated product.

How to Help Have students explain their thinking to determine whether their error was made in rounding, multiplying multiples of 10, or using a basic fact. Focus your assistance on that specific subskill.

Practice

Exercise 25 This is a multistep problem involving addition, elapsed time, and comparing numbers. You might have students use *Reading Strategies for Math* Chart 28 (Steps in a Process) to help them identify the steps.

Exercise 27 Some students may use reasoning, while others may try different numbers and then make a deduction.

For Early Finishers Challenge early finishers to answer Exercise 23 if 280 people stand and there are 8 cars on the train. About 2,400 riders

③ Close and Assess

Journal

Have students explain how to estimate the product of a 2-digit and a 3-digit factor. Have them give an example in which the actual product would be greater than the estimate and one in which it would be less.

Quick Check

Number Sense Which estimated products below are less than the actual products? Explain. Exercises 1 and 4; Because both rounded factors in each are less than the actual factors

Skill Estimate each product.

1. 24×136

2,000

2. 352×76

32,000

3. 17×864

18,000

4. 444×33

12,000

Choosing a Calculation Method

At-A-Glance Planning

Lesson Planning Checklist

Objective Multiply numbers in the thousands.

Student Book Lesson Materials *Optional* Calculators
(1 per student)

Materials for pages 266A and 266B Calculators
(1 per group)

Subject Connections social studies—United States;
geography—Africa

Strand Connections estimation, mental math, time,
measurement, money

	Before Lesson	During Lesson	After Lesson
Daily Math			
p. 266A Problem of the Day			
p. 266A Math Routines			
p. 266A Mental Math			
Teaching Options			
p. 266 Student Book Lesson			
p. 266B Another Way to Learn…			
Options for Reaching All Learners			
p. 266B Inclusion			
p. 266B Language Development			
Subject Connections			
p. 266A Science Connection			
Assessment Options			
p. 266 Talk About It			
p. 267 Error Intervention			
p. 267 Portfolio			
p. 267 Quick Check			
Resources			
6-7 Practice			
6-7 Reteaching			
6-7 Enrichment			
6-7 Problem Solving			
6-7 Daily Transparency			

Problem of the Day

Problem of the Day

Walking briskly uses up about
15 units of energy a minute.
Running uses up about 40 units
a minute. How much more
energy do you use running than
walking briskly for 23 minutes?

575 units of energy

Math Routines

Calendar Tell students to suppose that
they are going on vacation on the 20th of
next month. Ask whether they have fewer
than or more than 4 weeks to wait.

Money Discuss how students know
whether they have received the correct
change from a purchase.

Mental Math

Find each sum. Explain your thinking.

250	500	750	150
+350	+650	+250	+650
600	1,150	1,000	800

Science Connection

Share the following data with the class.

Activity	Calories Burned per Minute
Football	13
Handball	10
Water skiing	14
Baseball	5
Downhill skiing	17

• Have students choose a calculation
method to compare the calories burned
after 3 hours of each activity.

Another Way to **Learn** Lesson 6-7

Use as an alternative or in addition to pages 266 and 267.

Materials Calculators (1 per group)

Learning Style Logical

- Make a class list of methods students can use to multiply. Possible list: Place-value blocks, paper and pencil, calculator, mental math, repeated addition

- Have groups talk about which method would be appropriate to use for multiplying 3- and 4-digit numbers by a 2-digit number. Students will likely say that place-value blocks are too cumbersome for greater numbers, and repeated addition would take too long.

- Have students work individually on the following examples. They can use place-value blocks, mental math, a calculator, paper and pencil, or any other method. For comparison, encourage students to use a different method for each example.

30×601	$48 \times 2,600$	42×653	$51 \times 7,000$
18,030	124,800	27,426	357,000

- Have students talk about which methods worked best for different kinds of factors.

- Assign Check and Practice on Student Book pages 266 and 267 or *Practice Master 6-7*.

- Assess using the following rubric.

Assessment Rubric
4 Full Accomplishment • finds products in the thousands correctly
3 Substantial Accomplishment • finds most products in the thousands correctly
2 Partial Accomplishment • finds some products in the thousands correctly
1 Little Accomplishment • does not find products in the thousands

Options for Reaching All Learners

Inclusion

Calculation Methods

Use positive reinforcement to encourage use of a variety of calculation methods.

Materials Calculators (1 per group)

Learning Style Individual

- Watch for students who consistently use calculators when given their choice of calculation methods.

- Prompt students to use other methods. Then congratulate them for trying a different method, for aligning the partial products correctly, for not making any fact errors, for finding the correct products.

- Have them use calculators to check their work.

- Ask students which method they find easiest to use, and which they find most difficult.

Language Development

So You Say

Use students' definitions to develop vocabulary for multiplication.

Learning Style Verbal/Auditory

- Write several multiplication examples on the chalkboard:

7,003	3,276	1,200
$\times\ \ 40$	$\times\ \ 40$	$\times\ \ 40$
280,120	131,040	48,000

- List the following target words on the chalkboard: *regrouping, factors, tens, ones,* and *products.* Use pictures, models, hand gestures, and symbols such as arrows and circles to describe each term.

- Have students write their own definitions and share them with the class.

Lesson Organizer

Objective Multiply numbers in the thousands.

Student Materials *Optional* Calculators (1 per student)

Assignment Guide

Basic 11–27, 30, 33–39

Average 14–30, 33–39

Enriched 16–39

1 Introduce

Review

Find each product.

1.	300	2.	215	3.	743
	× 60		× 40		× 27
	18,000		8,600		20,061

Build on Prior Knowledge

After students review multiplying 3-digit numbers, ask how 4,215 is different from 215 and 2,743 is different from 743. The first numbers have digits in the thousands place, which means they are greater.

2 Teach

See Another Way to Learn…on page 266B.

Learn ● ● ● ● ● ● ● ● ● ● ● ● ● ● ● ● ● ● ●

Pronunciation note:
Choi Jong-yul (CHEH CHUNG-yōol)

Compare the calculation methods in the example to those students have used to multiply a 3-digit by a 2-digit number.

Talk About It **Ongoing Assessment**

Listen for students to use the same algorithm to multiply 4-digit numbers as for 2- or 3-digit numbers: multiply by ones, then by tens; add the products.

Answer for Talk About It

2 thousands

Check ● ● ● ● ● ● ● ● ● ● ● ● ● ● ● ● ● ●

Exercise 3 Be sure students understand why there appears to be an extra zero in the product.

Exercise 10 Some students may estimate the product while others find the actual product.

Choosing a Calculation Method

You Will Learn
how to multiply numbers in the thousands

Math Tip
When you multiply greater numbers, it's good to know more than one way to find the answer.

Learn ● ● ● ● ● ● ● ● ● ● ● ● ●

Choi Jong-yul was on the move for seven months. His journey took him 4,500 miles across the Sahara Desert in northern Africa. How would it feel to walk that far?

In one mile, you would walk the length of about 15 football fields. How many football-field lengths did Choi Jong-yul walk?

Choi Jong-yul from South Korea likes adventure in the wilderness.

Tanya and Dave used different methods to find $15 \times 4,500$.

Tanya's Way
I multiplied using paper and pencil.

$$\begin{array}{r} \overset{2}{4,500} \\ \times\ 15 \\ \hline 22,500 \\ 45,000 \\ \hline 67,500 \end{array}$$

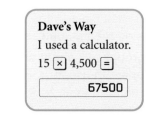

Dave's Way
I used a calculator.
15 × 4,500 =

67500

Choi Jong-yul walked about 67,500 football-field lengths.

Talk About It

What does the small 2 mean in the first method?

Check ●

Find each product.

1.	423	2.	309	3.	5,000	4.	2,966	5.	1,983
	× 26		× 19		× 20		× 33		× 41
	10,998		5,871		100,000		97,878		81,303

6. $3,002 \times 10$ 7. $68 \times 5,172$ 8. $19 \times 7,758$ 9. $40 \times 1,200$
   30,020   351,696   147,402   48,000

10. **Reasoning** How many digits are in the product of 2,999 and 12?
    5 digits; $2,999 \times 12 = 35,988$

Practice 6-7	Reteaching 6-7

Practice

Skills and Reasoning | Choose a tool

Find each product. Estimate to check.

11. 343	12. 118	13. 2,096	14. 6,000	15. 1,789
× 59	× 13	× 21	× 90	× 16
20,237	**1,534**	**44,016**	**540,000**	**28,624**

16. 3,739	17. 3,855	18. 2,021	19. 4,223	20. 1,440
× 12	× 15	× 54	× 18	× 33
44,868	**57,825**	**109,134**	**76,014**	**47,520**

21. $23 \times 3,174$ **73,002**   22. $14 \times 2,000$ **28,000**   23. 320×39 **12,480**   24. $16 \times 3,285$ **52,560**

25. Find the product of 249 and 14. **3,486**   26. Find the product of 3,989 and 12. **47,868**

27. **Mental Math** How would you use mental math to find the product of 4,000 and 12? **Possible answer: Find 12 × 4 and write 3 zeros: 48,000.**

28. How many digits are in the product of 1,111 and 11? **5 digits; 1,111 × 11 = 12,221**

Problem Solving and Applications

29. **Social Studies** Suppose you walked from Washington, D.C., to San Francisco, California, or about 2,922 miles. About how many football-field lengths would you walk, if there are 15 in a mile? **About 45,000 football field lengths**

30. **Geography** The desert across northern Africa grows by about 6 miles a year. About how many miles farther south will it be after 75 years? **About 450 miles**

31. **Time** Choi Jong-yul got to the Red Sea on June 6, 1996, after traveling 7 months. About when did he begin his trip? **Nov. 6, 1995**

32. **Measurement** The temperature in the Sahara can be as low as 5°F in the high mountains or as high as 136°F elsewhere. What is the range of temperature? **131°F**

33. **Journal** Explain which calculation method you would use to find 2,000 × 22.

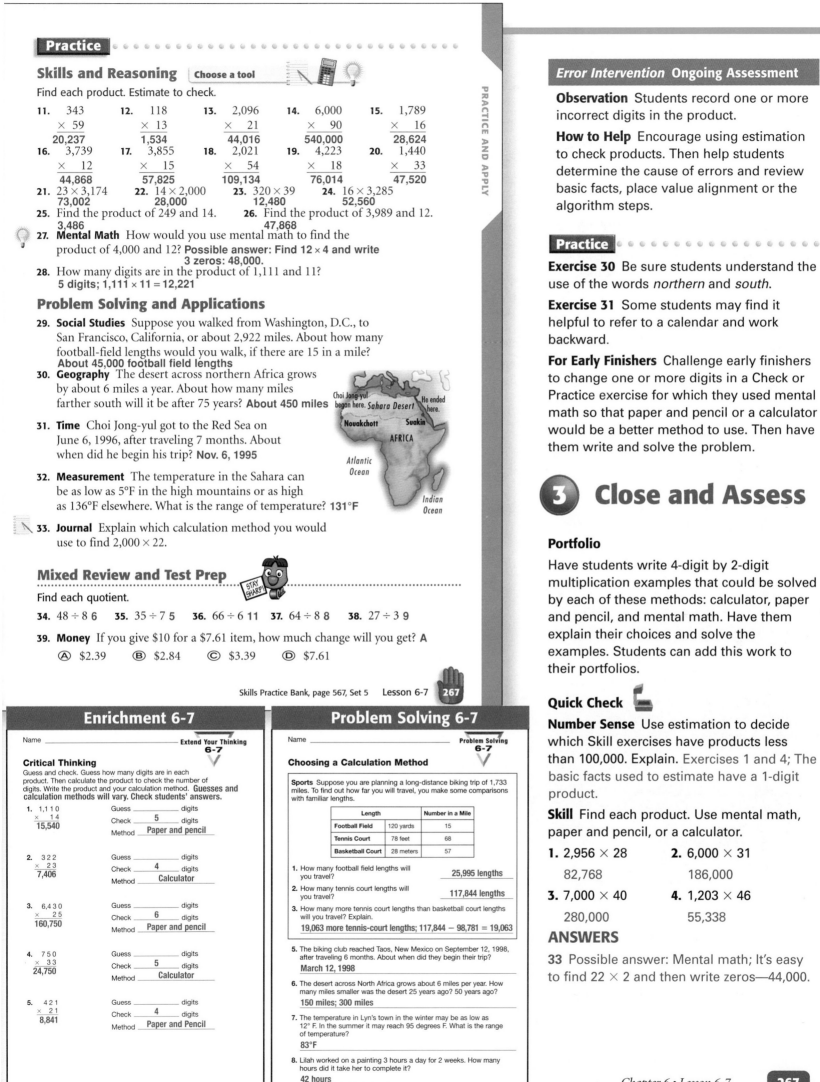

Choi Jong-yul began here. *Sahara Desert* He ended here.
Nouakchott   Suakin
AFRICA
Atlantic Ocean
Indian Ocean

Mixed Review and Test Prep

Find each quotient.

34. $48 \div 8$ **6**   35. $35 \div 7$ **5**   36. $66 \div 6$ **11**   37. $64 \div 8$ **8**   38. $27 \div 3$ **9**

39. **Money** If you give $10 for a $7.61 item, how much change will you get? **A**

Ⓐ $2.39   Ⓑ $2.84   Ⓒ $3.39   Ⓓ $7.61

Skills Practice Bank, page 567, Set 5   Lesson 6-7   **267**

Enrichment 6-7

Name _____   **Extend Your Thinking 6-7**

Critical Thinking

Guess how many digits are in each product. Then calculate the product to check the number of digits. Write the product and your calculation method. **Guesses and calculation methods will vary. Check students' answers.**

1.	1,110	Guess ___ digits
	× 14	Check __5__ digits
	15,540	Method __Paper and pencil__

2.	322	Guess ___ digits
	× 23	Check __4__ digits
	7,406	Method __Calculator__

3.	6,430	Guess ___ digits
	× 25	Check __6__ digits
	160,750	Method __Paper and pencil__

4.	750	Guess ___ digits
	× 33	Check __5__ digits
	24,750	Method __Calculator__

5.	421	Guess ___ digits
	× 21	Check __4__ digits
	8,841	Method __Paper and Pencil__

Problem Solving 6-7

Name _____   **Problem Solving 6-7**

Choosing a Calculation Method

Sports Suppose you are planning a long-distance biking trip of 1,733 miles. To find out how far you will travel, you make some comparisons with familiar lengths.

Length		Number in a Mile
Football Field	120 yards	15
Tennis Court	78 feet	68
Basketball Court	28 meters	57

1. How many football field lengths will you travel? **25,995 lengths**

2. How many tennis court lengths will you travel? **117,844 lengths**

3. How many more tennis court lengths than basketball court lengths will you travel? Explain. **19,063 more tennis-court lengths; 117,844 − 98,781 = 19,063**

5. The biking club reached Taos, New Mexico on September 12, 1998, after traveling 6 months. About when did they begin their trip? **March 12, 1998**

6. The desert across North Africa grows about 6 miles per year. How many miles smaller was the desert 25 years ago? 50 years ago? **150 miles; 300 miles**

7. The temperature in Lyn's town in the winter may be as low as 12° F. In the summer it may reach 95 degrees F. What is the range of temperature? **83°F**

8. Lilah worked on a painting 3 hours a day for 2 weeks. How many hours did it take her to complete it? **42 hours**

Error Intervention Ongoing Assessment

Observation Students record one or more incorrect digits in the product.

How to Help Encourage using estimation to check products. Then help students determine the cause of errors and review basic facts, place value alignment or the algorithm steps.

Practice

Exercise 30 Be sure students understand the use of the words *northern* and *south*.

Exercise 31 Some students may find it helpful to refer to a calendar and work backward.

For Early Finishers Challenge early finishers to change one or more digits in a Check or Practice exercise for which they used mental math so that paper and pencil or a calculator would be a better method to use. Then have them write and solve the problem.

3 Close and Assess

Portfolio

Have students write 4-digit by 2-digit multiplication examples that could be solved by each of these methods: calculator, paper and pencil, and mental math. Have them explain their choices and solve the examples. Students can add this work to their portfolios.

Quick Check

Number Sense Use estimation to decide which Skill exercises have products less than 100,000. Explain. Exercises 1 and 4; The basic facts used to estimate have a 1-digit product.

Skill Find each product. Use mental math, paper and pencil, or a calculator.

1. $2,956 \times 28$ 82,768
2. $6,000 \times 31$ 186,000
3. $7,000 \times 40$ 280,000
4. $1,203 \times 46$ 55,338

ANSWERS

33 Possible answer: Mental math; It's easy to find 22 × 2 and then write zeros—44,000.

Chapter 6 • Lesson 6-7   **267**

Chapter 6
Stop and Practice

Students will practice skills taught in Lessons 6-1 through 6-7.

Find Each Product

Remind students of the algorithm for multiplying by a 2-digit number: multiply by ones, multiply by tens, and add the partial products, regrouping as needed. Encourage students to use estimation to check their answers for reasonableness.

Error Search

ANSWERS

48 Correct

49 The correct answer is 384,240. The digit in the ones place was not multiplied by either the 8 ones or the 4 tens.

50 The correct answer is 71,230. An estimate was given instead of the actual product.

51 The correct answer is 58,496. When adding the products, the regrouped thousand was not added.

52 The correct answer is 21,714. The product of 2 and zero was incorrectly given as 2.

STOP and Practice

Find each product.

1. 72 ×15 = **1,080**	**2.** 74 ×24 = **1,776**	**3.** 42 ×55 = **2,310**	**4.** 81 ×14 = **1,134**	**5.** 60 ×35 = **2,100**
6. 41 ×10 = **410**	**7.** 65 ×85 = **5,525**	**8.** 89 ×27 = **2,403**	**9.** 47 ×34 = **1,598**	**10.** 56 ×18 = **1,008**
11. 419 ×29 = **12,151**	**12.** 245 ×26 = **6,370**	**13.** 153 ×75 = **11,475**	**14.** 463 ×28 = **12,964**	**15.** 218 ×90 = **19,620**
16. 900 ×73 = **65,700**	**17.** 539 ×43 = **23,177**	**18.** 67 ×111 = **7,437**	**19.** 19 ×663 = **12,597**	**20.** 935 ×30 = **28,050**
21. 4,571 ×13 = **59,423**	**22.** 1,776 ×58 = **103,008**	**23.** 6,210 ×61 = **378,810**	**24.** 1,122 ×25 = **28,050**	**25.** 4,506 ×30 = **135,180**
26. 707 ×22 = **15,554**	**27.** 86 ×54 = **4,644**	**28.** 166 ×12 = **1,992**	**29.** 5,284 ×68 = **359,312**	**30.** 3,019 ×77 = **232,463**
31. 31 ×49 = **1,519**	**32.** 460 ×53 = **24,380**	**33.** 588 ×59 = **34,692**	**34.** 2,963 ×44 = **130,372**	**35.** 591 ×98 = **57,918**

36. 82×753 = **61,746**	**37.** $39 \times 3,206$ = **125,034**	**38.** 263×87 = **22,881**	**39.** $66 \times 1,089$ = **71,874**
40. $2,225 \times 71$ = **157,975**	**41.** $3,220 \times 51$ = **164,220**	**42.** $5,432 \times 16$ = **86,912**	**43.** $5,678 \times 36$ = **204,408**
44. 629×33 = **20,757**	**45.** $37 \times 1,834$ = **67,858**	**46.** 57×88 = **5,016**	**47.** $23 \times 5,479$ = **126,017**

Error Search

Find each incorrect product. Write it correctly and explain the error.

48. 5,332 × 50 = **266,600**	**49.** 8,005 × 48 = **384,000**	**50.** 4,190 × 17 = **80,000**	**51.** 1,828 × 32 = **57,496**	**52.** 1,034 × 21 = **23,714**

Find the Ancient Riddler!

Can you name this flying creature from ancient Greek mythology? It has the body of a lion and the head of a person. Sometimes it has wings, but it always speaks in riddles.

Multiply to solve the riddle. Match each letter to its answer in the blank below. Some letters are not used.

53.	419	54.	324	55.	72	56.	421	57.	587
	× 24		× 17		× 12		× 90		× 45
	[H]		[E]		[G]		[I]		[X]
	10,056		5,508		864		37,890		26,415

58.	5,317	59.	628	60.	9,170	61.	691	62.	63
	× 15		× 39		× 29		× 15		× 99
	[O]		[S]		[B]		[N]		[P]
	79,755		24,492		265,930		10,365		6,237

24,492	6,237	10,056	37,890	10,365	26,415
S	p	h	i	n	x

Number Sense Estimation and Reasoning

Copy and complete. Write <, >, or =.

63. 1,200 × 40 ● 4,000 × 30 <
64. 2,000 × 30 ● 700 × 99 <
65. 500 × 33 ● 300 × 55 =
66. 4,000 × 42 ● 997 × 98 >
67. 205 × 80 ● 90 × 195 <
68. 808 × 80 ● 880 × 80 <
69. 5,000 × 20 ● 2,000 × 50 =
70. 600 × 600 ● 6,000 × 60 =

Find the Ancient Riddler!

As an extension, suggest that students read about some mythological characters, create their own riddles about these characters, and compile them into a class riddle book.

Number Sense

ANSWERS

63 <; Think 12 × 4 = 48. 1,200 × 40 = 48,000; Think 4 × 3 = 12. 4,000 × 30 = 120,000

64 <; Think 2 × 3 = 6. 2,000 × 30 = 60,000; Round 99 to 100. 700 × 100 = 70,000

65 =; Use partial products. 500 × 3 = 1,500 and 500 × 30 = 15,000; 300 × 5 = 1,500 and 300 × 50 = 15,000. The answers are the same when the partial products are added. 1,500 + 15,000 = 16,500

66 >; Round 42 to 40. 4,000 × 40 = 160,000; Round 997 to 1,000 and 98 to 100. 1,000 × 100 = 100,000

67 <; Round 205 to 200. 200 × 80 = 16,000. Round 195 to 200. 90 × 200 = 18,000

68 <; Use number sense. Both exercises are multiplied by 80. 808 < 880, so 808 × 80 < 880 × 80.

69 =; Think 5 × 2 = 2 × 5. 5,000 × 20 = 2,000 × 50. Both products equal 100,000.

70 =; Think 6 × 6 = 36. 600 × 600 = 360,000 and 6,000 × 60 = 360,000

For Early Finishers Challenge early finishers to write the products in Exercises 21–25 in order from least to greatest. 28,050; 59,423; 103,008; 135,180; 378,810

Resources

TestWorks: Test and Practice Software

At-A-Glance Planning

Objective Solve problems by making decisions after analyzing data.

Student Book Lesson Materials *Optional* Lesson Enhancement Transparency 26, *Assessment Sourcebook 10* (How We Worked in Our Group)

Materials for pages 270A and 270B None

Subject Connection social studies—recreation

Strand Connections time, using data

	Before Lesson	During Lesson	After Lesson
Daily Math			
p. 270A Problem of the Day			
p. 270A Math Routines			
p. 270A Mental Math			
Teaching Options			
p. 270B Facilitating and Assessing…			
Options for Reaching All Learners			
p. 270B Language Development			
p. 270B Reading Assist			
Technology Options			
p. 270A *Logical Journey of the Zoombinis*			
Assessment Options			
p. 271 Journal			
Resources			
6-8 Practice			
6-8 Reteaching			
6-8 Enrichment			
6-8 Problem Solving			
6-8 Daily Transparency			

Problem of the Day

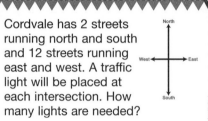

Cordvale has 2 streets running north and south and 12 streets running east and west. A traffic light will be placed at each intersection. How many lights are needed?

24 lights

Math Routines

Money Ask the class how much they would spend if they spent $0.25 per day for the rest of the month starting today.

Time Explain to students that prime time television runs from 8 P.M. to 11 P.M. Ask them how many hour-long shows someone could watch in that time, then how many half-hour shows. 3; 6

Mental Math

Find the products. Explain your thinking.

4	40	400	4,000
× 24	× 24	× 24	× 24
96	960	9,600	96,000

Logical Journey of the Zoombinis

Give students an opportunity to solve the *Allergic Cliffs* puzzle. You may wish to have students work in small groups in order to make the best use of computer time. Afterward, have students complete the Zoombini Puzzle Log to summarize the problem solving process.

Facilitating and Assessing **Explore** Lesson 6-8

Use with pages 270 and 271.

Get Started As students start to work together, you may want to assign the roles of reader, calculator, recorder, and reporter. Encourage students to work on the group skill Listen to Others and discuss different points of view.

Observe Allow students time to plan the method they will use to solve the problem. Plans should include a method of calculating the number of people who will ride in the next 25 minutes and then comparing that number to those already in line.

Discuss As groups make their decisions, have them analyze the various types of data they are given. Students' comments should demonstrate understanding that, while the number of people in line and the ride capacity are needed to find the length of the wait, other aspects of the rides may influence whether they want to wait.

Assess Use the rubric to assess students' work. See sample.

4 Full Accomplishment

Mean Streak $26 \times 25 = 650$.
Only 635 people are in line. The wait will be less than 25 minutes.

Magnum $33 \times 25 = 825$
There are 845 people in line. The wait will be longer than 25 minutes.

I want to ride the tallest and fastest roller coaster, so I'm willing to wait a little longer to ride the Magnum.

Assessment Rubric

4 Full Accomplishment
• analyzes data to make decisions

3 Substantial Accomplishment
• analyzes data to make most decisions

2 Partial Accomplishment
• analyzes data to make some decisions

1 Little Accomplishment
• does not analyze data to make decisions

Options for Reaching All Learners

Language Development

Questions and Answers

Use student-generated questions to strengthen language skills and understanding of data presented in tables.

Learning Style Verbal

• Pair students acquiring English with fluent speakers.

• Have partners ask each other questions based on the table on page 270, such as: How many people can ride the Corkscrew per minute? Which roller coasters have a speed of 60 miles per hour?

• Encourage students to ask questions that require analyzing data in the table, such as: Which roller coasters have a height greater than 150 feet? Are there more people waiting to ride the Mantis or the Gemini?

• Have partners write five of their questions, then trade with another pair to see if they can answer each other's questions.

Reading Assist

Make Inferences

Use data analysis to strengthen understanding.

Learning Style Logical, Visual

• Direct students' attention to the Facts and Data box on page 270.

• Discuss the meaning of the last sentence. Pose questions such as the following:

I have to wait in line 30 minutes to ride the roller coaster I chose. How many other roller coasters will I be able to ride?

I have to wait in line 19 minutes to ride the roller coaster I chose. How many other roller coasters will I be able to ride?

• Discuss some of the things that might make a roller coaster special enough to influence their decision about how long they are willing to wait.

Lesson Organizer

Objective Solve problems by making decisions after analyzing data.

Suggested Grouping 2 to 4

Student Materials *Optional Assessment Sourcebook 10* (How We Worked in Our Group)

Teacher Materials *Optional* Lesson Enhancement Transparency 26

Assignment Guide

Basic 1–12

Average 1–12

Enriched 1–12

---

1 Introduce

Review

Suppose 6 students can go through the cafeteria line in 1 minute. How many students can go through the line in

1. 2 minutes? 12

2. 5 minutes? 30

Build on Prior Knowledge

After students review multiplying, ask how they might find out whether 50 students could go through the line in 7 minutes.
Possible answer: Multiply 6 × 7 and compare the product to 50.

2 Teach

See Facilitating and Assessing...on page 270B.

Explore ● ● ● ● ● ● ● ● ● ● ● ● ● ● ● ● ● ● ●

Lesson Enhancement Transparency 26 illustrates the roller coaster table.

You may wish to ask questions such as the following as students begin work on this activity.

• Will you select the roller coasters you think you want to ride first, or will you find the waiting times first?

• What calculations will you use to find the waiting times?

• What method(s) will you use to find the waiting times?

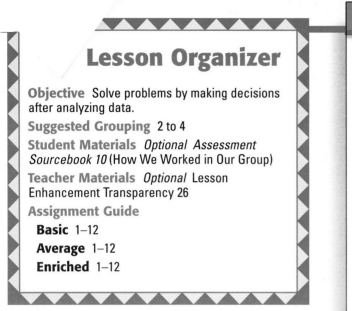

Chapter 6
Lesson 8

Problem Solving

Decision Making: Worth the Wait?

You Will Learn
how to analyze data to make a decision

Explore ● ● ● ● ● ● ● ● ● ● ●

Cedar Point Park has some of the tallest, fastest, and scariest roller coasters in the world. There are 12 roller coasters to choose from!

Your group decides to ride the same roller coasters. There are lots of people in line, so you may have to wait a long time. Which ones will you choose on this busy summer day?

Wild rides at Cedar Point Park in Sandusky, Ohio

You don't want to wait more than 25 minutes for a ride. But you may decide to wait longer for a ride that is special.

You want to ride 3 roller coasters.

If you wait more than 25 minutes in line for any 1 ride, you will be able to ride only 2 roller coasters.

Name _____

Practice 6-8

Decision Making

You and your family are going out to dinner for a special celebration. Your grandmother likes to eat before 7:30 P.M. Your father does not like to eat before 5:30 P.M. Dinner will take about 1 hour and 30 minutes. You call several restaurants in the area to see when they expect to be busy.

• Joe's Family Restaurant has a 20-minute wait between the hours of 5 P.M. and 7 P.M.

• Seth's Healthy Gourmet will have tables open at 6:45 P.M., but not earlier.

• Julianne's Cafe has a 10-minute wait before 5:30 P.M. but a 15-minute wait after 5:30 P.M.

• Kiko's Japanese does not have any tables open until 7:30 P.M.

1. At what time should your family eat dinner?
Possible answers: between 5:30 P.M. and 7:30 P.M.

2. If you need to be home by 8:45 P.M. could you go to Kiko's Japanese? Why?
No; If dinner lasts 1 hour and 30 minutes you would not finish dinner until 9 P.M.

3. Your mother would like to go to Joe's and your uncle would like to go to Seth's. Which do you think is a better choice?
Possible answers: Seth's, because there is no wait; Joe's, because you can eat earlier

4. Which restaurant would you choose? Explain.
Answers will vary.

Name _____

Another Look 6-8

Decision Making

Len is making snacks and drinks for his friends to take to the beach. He only has $\frac{1}{2}$ hour to get the food ready. He wants to take 3 different items. Here is a list of possible choices and the time they take to get ready.

• cheese sandwiches: 10 minutes   • drink mix: 5 minutes
• fruit punch: 10 minutes   • trail mix: 5 minutes
• chips and dip: 10 minutes   • fruit salad: 5 minutes
• tuna sandwiches: 15 minutes   • frosted cake: 15 minutes

Len asked himself the following questions to help him make his decision:

What are my top 6 choices in order?
tuna sandwiches, cake, fruit punch, drink mix, chips and dip, fruit salad

How long will my top 3 choices take to prepare?
40 minutes

Should I take only my top 2 items?
No, drinks are important to have at the beach.

Len decides to bring tuna sandwiches, chips and dip, and drink mix.

1. Which sandwiches are fastest to make? How much time could Len save?
Cheese sandwiches; 5 minutes

2. What drink is the fastest to make? How much time could Len save?
Drink mix; 5 minutes

3. What 3 items could Len bring that would take the least time to make?
Drink mix, trail mix, and fruit salad

4. If you want to take two different kinds of sandwiches, what else would you have time to prepare in the 30 minutes?
Drink mix, trail mix, or fruit salad

---

 270 *Chapter 6 • Lesson 6-8*

Work Together

▶ **Understand**

1. What do you know?

2. What do you need to find out? Which coaster(s) to ride, how many, and which are worth a 25-min wait.

3. What is the main decision you have to make? Which coaster(s) to ride.

▶ **Plan and Solve**

4. Mantis, Raptor, Corkscrew: 750 people; Mean Streak: 650 people; Magnum: 825 people; Gemini: 1,375 people.

5. Mean Streak, Gemini, Corkscrew

6. Magnum; Mantis, Raptor, Corkscrew

4. Find out how many people in line will get on each roller coaster within 25 minutes.

5. Find out which roller coasters you would be able to ride after standing in line for less than 25 minutes.

6. Which roller coaster is fastest? Which coasters have loops?

7. Which roller coasters would you most like to ride?

8. Why might you want to wait in line longer for a certain roller coaster?

7–12. Answers will vary.

Problem Solving Hint

Multiply the number of people per minute by 25 minutes. Compare this with the number of people in line.

▶ **Make a Decision**

9. Write a list of the roller coasters you would like to ride.

10. What is the total amount of time you would spend waiting to ride all of the roller coasters you choose?

▶ **Present Your Decision**

11. Tell how you decided which roller coasters to ride.

12. Check out **www.mathsurf.com/4/ch6** for more information on roller coasters. Compare the data.

PROBLEM SOLVING PRACTICE

271

Reading Assist **Read Tables**

Have pairs of students do a partner reading of Exercise 4. Then have students give an example from the table using one of the roller coasters.

For Early Finishers Challenge early finishers to change their plan and add 40 minutes to their time in the park. They can choose one more roller coaster to ride and explain why they chose it.

3 Close and Assess

Journal

Describe your group's decision-making process. Describe how you chose the roller coasters. What was the most difficult and the simplest part of your work? Answers will vary but should include an evaluation of information given while considering students' own preferences.

Name _____

Problem Solving 6-8

Decision Making

You and a friend go to the local Play-A-Thon. The theater group is putting on 5 plays. You can use the table below to determine how long you must wait to see each show.

You and your friend want to see 2 plays together. You can stay for an hour.

Play	People in Line	Room Capacity	Length of play (minutes)	Reviewer's Scores
Time Travel	37	20	15	good
President	68	30	20	excellent
Campfire	63	35	15	excellent
Big Laugh	49	25	30	good
Cowpokes	72	40	10	fair

1. How long would you have to wait in line to see *President* if there is a 10-minute wait before the next show? **50 minutes**

2. Suppose the next run of each play will be starting in 5 minutes. Which plays would you be able to see without waiting any longer than 30 minutes?
Time Travel, Campfire and Cowpokes

3. Would you wait in line longer than 30 minutes to see any of the plays? Why?
Possible answer: I might wait longer for *President* or Campfire because of their high ratings.

4. Can you see both of the plays that were rated excellent?
Possible answer: No, the two plays lasted 35 minutes and you would have to wait at least 40 minutes to see *President*.

5. Which plays would you choose to see? Explain.
Look for choices based on time and ratings.

Chapter 6 • Lesson 6-8 **271**

Section B
Review and Practice

Use the Skills Checklist

Review the **Skills Checklist** on the page with students. Then ask questions such as the following:

- Which exercises have 2-digit factors only? Exercises 1–10, 23
- Where will you use estimation? Exercises 11–15, 21, 22
- What information do you need to solve Exercise 21? Number of trips per week
- If you had your choice, would you use mental math, paper and pencil, or a calculator for Exercise 15? Why? Possible answer: Paper and pencil; Not much regrouping will be needed.

Assess

You may wish to use this information to assess students' understanding of the lesson objectives.

Item Analysis		
Lesson Objective		Items
6-5	Multiply with 2-digit factors.	1–10, 16–23
6-6	Estimate greater products.	11–15, 21, 22
6-7	Multiply numbers in the thousands.	17–20, 24, 25
6-8	Solve problems by making decisions after analyzing data.	21, 22

Resources

Practice Masters

- Practice Chapter 6 Section B

Assessment Sourcebook

- Quiz Chapter 6 Section B

TestWorks: Test and Practice Software

ANSWERS

25 Possible answer: 2,420 × 18; It involves regrouping and isn't as easy to solve mentally.

272   *Chapter 6*

Review and Practice

(Lesson 5) Find each product.

1. 56 $\times 15$ $\overline{840}$	2. 91 $\times 23$ $\overline{2,093}$	3. 47 $\times 11$ $\overline{517}$	4. 35 $\times 32$ $\overline{1,120}$	5. 76 $\times 18$ $\overline{1,368}$

6. 65×17 7. 82×14 8. 22×31 9. 75×49

10. **Reasoning** Write a multiplication sentence with 2-digit factors that has 5,600 as its product. **Possible answer: 80 × 70 = 5,600**

(Lesson 6) Estimation Estimate each product.

11. 456×19 10,000   12. 946×53 45,000   13. 359×28 12,000   14. 521×33 15,000

15. **Time** Danielle is training for a bike race. If she rides 38 miles each week, about how many miles will she ride in 1 year? **About 2,000 mi**

(Lesson 7) Find each product.   **Choose a tool**

16. 476 $\times\ 44$ $\overline{20,944}$	17. $1,007$ $\times\ 25$ $\overline{25,175}$	18. $4,018$ $\times\ 16$ $\overline{64,288}$	19. $2,603$ $\times\ 69$ $\overline{179,607}$	20. $3,284$ $\times\ 57$ $\overline{187,188}$

Using Data Use the table for **21–23**.

21. If Bus 31 carries about 55 people each trip, how many passengers will it carry in a week? **About 15,455 people**

22. If Bus 15 carries about 46 people each trip, how many passengers will it carry in a week? **About 32,384 people**

Sweetwater City Buses	
Bus Number	**One-Way Trips per Week**
31	281
66	280
15	704
27	477

23. **Write Your Own Problem** Use the data to write a multiplication problem using 2-digit factors. **Answers will vary.**

24. **Reasoning** Which set of factors has the greater product: 1,330 and 22, or 1,311 and 24? $1,330 \times 22 = 29,260$; $1,311 \times 24 = 31,464$

25. **Journal** Suppose you need to find the products for $2,400 \times 10$ and $2,420 \times 18$. If you could use a calculator for only one problem, which would it be? Explain.

Skills Checklist

In this section, you have:

☑ Multiplied with 2-Digit Factors

☑ Estimated Greater Products

☑ Chosen a Calculation Method

☑ Solved Problems by Making Decisions

Practice

Name _____

Practice
Chapter 6
Section B

Review and Practice
(Lesson 5) Find each product.

1. 71 $\times 29$ $\overline{2,059}$	2. 56 $\times 25$ $\overline{1,400}$	3. 82 $\times 43$ $\overline{3,526}$	4. 68 $\times 17$ $\overline{1,156}$

5. $47 \times 62 =$ __2,914__   6. $78 \times 52 =$ __4,056__

(Lesson 6) Estimate each product.
7. 556×18 __12,000__   8. 199×34 __6,000__
9. 417×71 __28,000__   10. 372×97 __40,000__

(Lesson 7) Find each product.

11. 472 $\times 39$ $\overline{18,408}$	12. $2,004$ $\times\ 48$ $\overline{96,192}$	13. $5,078$ $\times\ 56$ $\overline{284,368}$	14. $3,456$ $\times\ 24$ $\overline{82,944}$

15. One commuter plane carries 40 passengers. If the plane makes 8 trips between New York and Boston in one day, how many passengers can it transport each week?   __2,240__

16. Which set of factors has the greater product: 2,127 and 89 or 2,107 and 91?   __2,107 and 91__

(Mixed Review) Find each missing factor.
17. $2 \times$ __7__ $= 14$ 18. $3 \times$ __8__ $= 24$
19. __7__ $\times 8 = 56$ 20. $9 \times$ __0__ $= 0$
21. $5 \times$ __6__ $= 30$ 22. $1 \times$ __9__ $= 9$

Extending Multiplication

Some inline skaters belong to teams that compete in races. If you know how many skaters are on each team and how many teams are in a race, how could you find the number of skaters in a race?

Inline skater, Allen MacDonald

Multiplying Money

Review writing dollars and cents. Write the amount of money in dollars and cents.

1. 3 quarters $0.75

2. 1 dime, 1 nickel, 2 pennies $0.17

3. 2 nickels, 3 pennies, 2 quarters $0.63

Skills Checklist

In this section, you will:

☐ Multiply Money

☐ Solve Problems Needing Overestimates or Underestimates

☐ Solve Problems by Drawing a Picture

273

Extending Multiplication

In this section, students will multiply money amounts, decide when to overestimate and underestimate, and solve problems by drawing a picture.

Subskills

The work in this section builds on...

• Using the multiplication algorithm to multiply 2-digit factors

• Estimating greater products

• Choosing a calculation method to multiply numbers in the thousands

Use the Section Opener

During April of 1996, Allen McDonald skated 6.4 miles in 47 minutes 7 seconds. Allen McDonald was 86 years old at the time, and was cheered on in the races by friends and family, including his grandson.

Encourage students to discuss how they might use multiplication to find out how many skaters are entered in a race. Multiply the number of team members by the number of teams.

Skills Trace

(Red numbers indicate pages in this section.)

			Grade Four		
Lesson and Skill	**First Introduced**	**Introduce**	**Develop**	**Practice/Apply**	**Review**
6-9 Multiply amounts of money.	Grade 3	274, 275	274	275, 282, 283, 285, 286, 563	282, 283, 284, 287, 471
6-10 Solve problems needing overestimates or underestimates.	Grade 4	278, 279	278, 279	279, 282, 283, 285, 286, 563	282, 283, 284, 287
6-11 Solve problems by drawing a picture.	Grade 4	280, 281	280, 281	281, 282, 283, 563	282, 283, 284, 287, 335, 467

Mixed Review and Test Prep exercises for this chapter occur on pages 253, 255, 263, 265, 267, 275.

 Multi-Age Classrooms Use pages 359–388 in Grade 3 or pages 111–132 in Grade 5 to relate to the content of this section.

Multiplying Money

At-A-Glance Planning

Lesson Planning Checklist

Objective Multiply amounts of money.

Student Book Lesson Materials *Optional* Teaching Tool Transparency 4 (Decimal Place-Value Chart)

Materials for pages 274A and 274B Teaching Tool Transparencies 6, 21, 22 (Centimeter Grid Paper, Money—Coins, Bills), *optional* calculator (1 per group)

Subject Connection physical education—skating and sports equipment

Strand Connections money, using data, algebra readiness, time

	Before Lesson	During Lesson	After Lesson
Daily Math			
p. 274A Problem of the Day			
p. 274A Math Routines			
p. 274A Mental Math			
Teaching Options			
p. 274 Student Book Lesson			
p. 274B Another Way to Learn…			
Options for Reaching All Learners			
p. 274B Inclusion			
p. 274B Cultural Connection			
Subject Connections			
p. 274A Literature Connection			
Assessment Options			
p. 274 Talk About It			
p. 275 Error Intervention			
p. 275 Observation			
p. 275 Quick Check			
Resources			
6-9 Practice			
6-9 Reteaching			
6-9 Enrichment			
6-9 Problem Solving			
6-9 Daily Transparency			

Problem of the Day

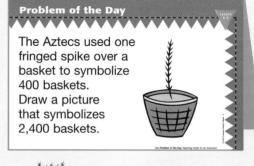

Problem of the Day

The Aztecs used one fringed spike over a basket to symbolize 400 baskets. Draw a picture that symbolizes 2,400 baskets.

Math Routines

Calendar Ask the class to choose an amount of money between $1.00 and $2.00. Ask them to name another amount between $0.10 and $0.35. If they begin with the first amount today and add the second amount each day, on what day will they have more than $4.00?

Patterns Describe this pattern: For every $1 you save, your parents will add double the amount. How much must you save so that you have a total of $21? $7

Mental Math

Find each product.

90	60	300	700
× 40	× 30	× 70	× 50
3,600	1,800	21,000	35,000

Literature Connection

In *Orp* by Suzy Kline, Orp starts the I HATE MY NAME Club. Chloe charges Orp 5¢ per card to type advertising cards.

• Chloe types 25 cards. How much money does she earn? $1.25

• Suppose Chloe types 40 cards. How much money will she earn? $2

Another Way to [**Learn**] Lesson 6-9

Use as an alternative or in addition to pages 274 and 275.

Materials Teaching Tool Transparencies 21, 22 (Money—Coins, Bills), *optional* calculator (1 per group)

Learning Style Logical, Kinesthetic, Verbal

- Ask groups to make predictions about multiplying money amounts. They can tell what they anticipate, what they think might be more difficult, and how they expect it to be the same as and different from multiplying whole numbers.

- Have groups use play money to model 12 × $1.46. Then have them count the total, exchanging coins for bills and coins for larger denominations where appropriate.

- Write the multiplication problem on the overhead. Have students explain what each number represents. Model the multiplication process as students follow.

- Discuss how the process matched students' predictions. Then have groups solve the following problems:

25 × $5.33	27 × $3.85	56 × $6.47
$133.25	$103.95	$362.32

- Allow groups to use a calculator to check their answers. Remind them that they need to place a dollar sign and decimal point in the product.

- Assign Check and Practice on Student Book pages 274 and 275 or *Practice Master 6-9.*

- Assess using the following rubric.

Options for Reaching All Learners

Inclusion

Grid Money
Use grids to strengthen ability to multiply amounts of money.

Materials Teaching Tool Transparency 6 (Centimeter Grid Paper)

Learning Style Visual, Individual

If students have difficulty multiplying money amounts, distribute grids as shown below. Students can use the grids for the Practice exercises as needed.

		$		.				$	1	8	.	9	1
	×							×				1	7
								1	3	2	3	7	
							1	8	9	1	0		
	$			.			$	3	2	1	.	4	7

Cultural Connection

Money in Any Language...
Use currency table to extend understanding of different monetary systems.

Learning Style Verbal, Logical

- Have students discuss similarities and differences in the following currency equivalents.

Country	Standard Units of Currency
United States	1 dollar = 100 cents
France	1 franc = 100 centimes
Egypt	1 pound = 100 piastres
Thailand	1 baht = 100 satangs
Argentina	1 peso = 100 centavos

- Students can translate some of the Practice exercises into a different money system before solving.

Lesson Organizer

Objective Multiply amounts of money.

Student Materials None

Teacher Materials *Optional* Teaching Tool Transparency 4 (Decimal Place-Value Chart)

Assignment Guide

Basic 6–26, 28, 33–38

Average 10–31, 33–38

Enriched 11–38

1 Introduce

Review

Find each product.

1. $1.40	2. $2.99	3. $14.75
× 3	× 6	× 4
$4.20	$17.94	$59.00

Build on Prior Knowledge

After students review multiplying money amounts, ask how multiplying $1.40 × 3 is like multiplying 140 × 3. Multiplying money is like multiplying whole numbers, but you have to write a dollar sign and decimal point in the product.

2 Teach

See Another Way to Learn…on page 274B.

Learn

You might point out that the dollar sign and decimal point are not written in the partial products. They are disregarded until they are written in the final product.

Use Teaching Tool Transparency 4 (Decimal Place-Value Chart) for demonstration, if desired.

Talk About It Ongoing Assessment

Look for students to indicate that two decimal places are used to show cents.

Answer for Talk About It

Starting at the right, count two places to the left and write the decimal point. Then add the dollar sign at the far left.

Check

Exercise 5 Some students may multiply 10 × $9.50. Others may recognize that 10 × $10 = $100, and since $10 is more than $9.50, $100 is enough.

Multiplying Money

You Will Learn
how to multiply amounts of money

Math Tip
Multiplying with money is like multiplying with whole numbers.

Learn

Allen MacDonald is one of the fastest seniors around. He competes as an inline skater. He has competed on his own and as part of a 16-member team.

New brakes for a pair of skates cost $8.99. How much would it cost for Allen's whole team to buy new brakes?

Allen MacDonald lives in Seal Beach, California.

You can multiply to find out.

Example

Find 16 × $8.99.

Step 1	Step 2
5 5	5 5
$8.99	$8.99
× 16 Multiply.	× 16
5394	5394
8990	8990 Write the answer
14384	$143.84 in dollars and cents.

Estimate to check. 16 × $9 = $144

Since $143.84 is close to $144, it is a reasonable answer.

It would cost $143.84 to buy new brakes for the team's skates.

Talk About It

What rule can you think of for writing an answer in dollars and cents?

$9.50

Inline skate wheel

Check

Use the picture to find each cost.

1. 11 wheels $104.50
2. 12 wheels $114.00
3. 24 wheels $228.00
4. 17 wheels $161.50
5. **Reasoning** Is $100 enough to buy 10 skate wheels? Explain.
Yes; 10 × $9.50 = $95.00.

Practice 6-9

Name _____

Practice 6-9

Multiplying Money
Multiply. Estimate to check.

1. 11 × $1.75 = $19.25
2. 15 × $2.49 = $37.35
3. 12 × $3.91 = $46.92
4. 17 × $8.99 = $152.83
5. 22 × $13.67 = $300.74
6. 24 × $15.03 = $360.72

7. $17.50	8. $30.42	9. $13.05	10. $20.44
× 14	× 18	× 23	× 19
$245.00	$547.56	$300.15	$388.36

11. $6.85	12. $5.46	13. $9.03	14. $5.82
× 12	× 16	× 33	× 56
$82.20	$87.36	$297.99	$325.92

15. $3.75	16. $17.99	17. $13.52	18. $16.88
× 45	× 28	× 41	× 27
$168.75	$503.72	$554.32	$455.76

19. Find the product of $12.98 and 13. $168.74

20. Multiply $3.57 by 25. $89.25

21. Could you buy 16 kites at $7.50 each with $105? Explain.
No; 16 × $7.50 = $120.

22. Could you buy 22 kites at $7.50 each with $170? Explain.
Yes; 22 × $7.50 = $165.

Reteaching 6-9

Name _____

Another Look 6-9

Multiplying Money
You can multiply money in the same way you multiply whole numbers.

To multiply $7.89 and 15, multiply the whole numbers 789 and 15.

```
        789
      ×  15
789 × 5 = 3945
789 × 10 = 7890
        11835
```

Place a dollar sign in front of the answer and a decimal point to the left of the tens digit.

$7.89 × 15 = $118.35

Find the product of the whole number amount and place the dollar sign and decimal point.

1. $4.47 × 11

```
        447
      ×  11
      447  ← 447 × 1
     4470  ← 447 × 10
     4917
```

$4.47 × 11 = $49.17

2. $36.19 × 47

```
       3619
      ×  47
     25333  ← 3619 × 7
    144760  ← 3619 × 40
    170093
```

$36.19 × 47 = $1,700.93

3. $6.31	4. $59.80	5. $15.11
× 15	× 4	× 6
$94.65	$239.20	$90.66

Practice

Skills and Reasoning

Multiply. Estimate to check.

| 6. | $5.68 × 19 = $107.92 | 7. | $2.10 × 24 = $50.40 | 8. | $5.68 × 17 = $96.56 | 9. | $7.06 × 23 = $162.38 | 10. | $24.69 × 11 = $271.59 |

6. $5.68
× 19
$107.92

7. $2.10
× 24
$50.40

8. $5.68
× 17
$96.56

9. $7.06
× 23
$162.38

10. $24.69
× 11
$271.59

11. $4.25
× 66
$280.50

12. $12.34
× 21
$259.14

13. $14.08
× 25
$352.00

14. $19.99
× 37
$739.63

15. $16.67
× 51
$850.17

16. $32.13
× 9
$289.17

17. $17.01
× 12
$204.12

18. $20.99
× 20
$419.80

19. $9.78
× 22
$215.16

20. $17.35
× 42
$728.70

21. $2.45 × 10 **$24.50**
22. $1.98 × 14 **$27.72**
23. 13 × $12.50 **$162.50**
24. 16 × $20.98 **$335.68**

25. Find the product of $13.99 and 26. **$363.74**

26. Multiply $2.86 by 15. **$42.90**

27. Could you buy 18 wheels, at $9.50 each, with $165.00? Explain.
No; 18 × $9.50 = $171.00.

Problem Solving and Applications

Using Data Use the prices in the picture and data from page 274 for **28–31**.

28. How much would it cost Allen MacDonald's team to buy racing T-shirts for all team members? **$159.84**

29. How much more does a pair of inline skates cost than a pair of roller skates? **$29.76 more**

30. Which costs more, 2 pairs of inline skates or 20 T-shirts? **20 T-shirts**

31. How much would 3 skateboards cost? **$256.50**

32. **Using Data** Use the Data File on page 247. What was the total fare for 5 people in 1980? In 1995? **$3.00; $7.50**

Mixed Review and Test Prep

Algebra Readiness Find the value of each n.

33. 21 + n = 30 **9**
34. 14 + n = 19 **5**
35. n + 6 = 18 **12**
36. 58 + n = 75 **17**

37. **Time** How many minutes are in 3 hours? **180 minutes**

38. **Time** How many days are in 26 weeks? **C**
   Ⓐ 168 days Ⓑ 172 days Ⓒ 182 days Ⓓ 260 days

Skills Practice Bank, page 567, Set 6   Lesson 6-9 **275**

Enrichment 6-9

Name _____ Extend Your Thinking **6-9**

Decision Making

The table below shows how consumers rated each of 5 brands of mouthwash. Read over the table to decide which is the best buy.

☺ = excellent ☺ = good ☺ = fair ☹ = poor

Brand	Cost	Taste	Freshness	Time it Lasted	Overall
Bright Smile	$2.75	☺	☺	☺	☺
Shine	$3.25	☺	☺	☺	☺
Fresh Breath	$2.00	☺	☺	☺	☺
Winter Mint	$3.30	☺	☺	☺	☺
Mint Wave	$2.10	☺	☹	☹	☹

1. Which mouthwash costs the least? **Fresh Breath**
   How much less is
   a. Fresh Breath than Bright Smile? **$0.75**
   b. Fresh Breath than Shine? **$1.25**
   c. Mint Wave than Winter Mint? **$1.20**
   d. Mint Wave than Shine? **$1.15**

2. Which mouthwash received the highest score for
   a. taste? **Fresh Breath**
   b. freshness? **Winter Mint**
   c. time it lasted? **Shine**

3. Which mouthwash has a combination of low cost and high ratings? **Fresh Breath**

4. Which mouthwash would you choose? Why?
   Possible answer: Fresh Breath. It costs less, tastes best, and is reasonably fresh and long-lasting.

Problem Solving 6-9

Name _____ Problem Solving **6-9**

Multiplying Money

History Life in 1900 was different from the way it is today. There were only 45 states. Women were not yet allowed to vote. Most people traveled by wagon. And prices were much lower. The chart shows the price of some grocery items.

Item	Price in 1900	Price Today
oranges (1 dozen)	$0.10	$2.04
sugar (1 lb)	$0.15	$0.48
turkey (1 lb)	$0.10	$1.59
beef (1 lb)	$0.10	$2.49
bread (1 loaf)	$0.05	$2.49

Compare prices for the shopping list below.

	a. Price in 1900	b. Price Today
1. 4 dozen oranges	$0.40	$8.16
2. 20 lb of sugar	$3.00	$9.60
3. 22 lb of turkey	$2.20	$34.98
4. 12 lb of beef	$1.20	$29.88
5. 3 loaves of bread	$0.15	$7.47

5. The chorus needs red T-shirts for its 24 members. They can buy 2 shirts for $7.92. How much will the T-shirts cost in all? **$95.04**

6. There are 28 students in the Science Club. Each student needs a notebook, which costs $2.59. How much will the notebooks cost in all? **$72.52**

7. An avocado costs $1.19. How much would a crate of 40 avocados cost? **$47.60**

8. One pen costs $1.09. A packet of 8 pens cost $7.79. Which is the better buy? Explain
The packet of 8 pens; $7.79 < $8.72.

Error Intervention Ongoing Assessment

Observation Students forget to write a decimal point in their answers or place it incorrectly.

How to Help Help students remember to place the decimal point by first demonstrating the difference between $38.57 and $385.70 using play money. Some students may benefit from using lined paper turned sideways, grid paper, or formatted worksheets.

Practice

Exercise 28 Students will need to recall from page 274 that there are 16 members on the team.

For Early Finishers Challenge early finishers to rewrite three problems from Lesson 7 Practice Exercises 11–24. They can write the larger number as a money amount, then find the products.

3 Close and Assess

Observation

Have students choose one problem from the Check or Practice sets. Observe how they solve it.

Quick Check

Number Sense Use estimation to decide which exercise below has a product closest to $1,000. Explain. **Exercise 3; Estimating by rounding 53 to 50 and $17.99 to $20 gives $1,000; Other estimates are $60, $60, and $800.**

Skill Find each cost.

1. $3.40 × 21 **$71.40**
2. $6.25 × 14 **$87.50**
3. 53 × $17.99 **$953.47**
4. 36 × $23.07 **$830.52**

Resources

Technology Master 22

Chapter 6 • Lesson 6-9 **275**

Chapter 6
Practice Game

Students will strengthen number sense and multiplication and addition skills as they play the practice game.

Learning Style Kinesthetic, Logical

Student Materials Number cubes labeled 3–8 (2 per group), world map, globe or travel atlas, *optional* calculators, *Assessment Sourcebook 10* (How We Worked in Our Group)

Preparation

Use dot stickers and handwritten numerals to label two blank cubes from 3–8 for each group.

How to Play

Distribute the number cubes and explain the goal of the Around the World Multiplication Game. Use a world map or globe to point out the equator to students.

Review the steps of the game with students or play several demonstration rounds as a class.

Around the World Multiplication Game

Players
2 or more players

Materials
- 2 number cubes, each labeled 3–8
- world map or globe

Object
The object of the game is to find products which, when added together have a sum that is equal to or greater than 25,326—the distance in miles round Earth at the equator.

How to Play

1. Players take turns rolling the two number cubes to make one 2-digit number. Each player chooses which digit will be ones and which will be tens. Repeat to make another 2-digit number.

2. Each player records the two numbers on paper and then multiplies them. The product stands for the number of miles traveled around the earth.

Math Center Option

As an alternative, set up this game in a math center for students to play independently or in pairs. Post a recording sheet or a journal prompt question for students to record their final totals, the number of tries it took, and the strategies they used.

3. Players continue to roll the number cubes, forming 2-digit numbers and multiplying them.

4. Players total their products, trying to get a sum that is equal to or greater than 25,326—the distance in miles around Earth at the equator.

5. Players count how many times they roll the cubes and multiply.

Talk About It

1. How many rolls did it take you to reach the total of 25,326?

2. Do you think it's possible to reach 25,326 without going beyond? Explain.

3. What strategy could you use to reach the total of 25,326 in the fewest tries?

More Ways to Play

■ Play again. This time, subtract your first product from 25,326. Then subtract your next product from the difference. And so on.

■ Play another game. For each product, find a place on a map that is about that distance from your home state. Keep track of the places you "visit."

Reasoning

1. Suppose you get 4 and 3 on the first roll and 3 and 5 on the second roll. How would you arrange your digits if you want to reach the total of 25,326 in the fewest tries? What would be the product?
   Arrange them as 43 and 53; 2,279

2. What is the greatest product possible with the number cubes? How would you get it?
   7,744; Make 88 twice

3. How many rolls of a 5 and 6 will give you a product that is close to the distance around the earth in miles? Explain.
   Twelve rolls; Two rolls will give you 65 × 65 = 4,225. 4,225 × 6 = 25,350.

Around the World Multiplication Game **277**

Teacher to Teacher

Analyze Word Problems:
Overestimating & Underestimating

At-A-Glance Planning

Objective Solve problems needing overestimates or underestimates.

Student Book Lesson Materials *Optional* Calculators (1 per group), *Reading Strategies for Math* Chart 19 (Word Pairs)

Materials for pages 278A and 278B Teaching Tool Transparency 22 (Money—Bills), markers (1 per student)

Subject Connections science—weight limit, physical education—recreation

Strand Connections measurement, money, time

	Before Lesson	During Lesson	After Lesson
Daily Math			
p. 278A Problem of the Day			
p. 278A Math Routines			
p. 278A Mental Math			
Teaching Options			
p. 278 Student Book Lesson			
p. 278B Another Way to Learn…			
Options for Reaching All Learners			
p. 278B Reading Assist			
p. 278B Language Development			
Subject Connections			
p. 278A Social Studies Connection			
Assessment Options			
p. 278 Talk About It			
p. 279 Quick Check			
Resources			
6-10 Practice			
6-10 Reteaching			
6-10 Enrichment			
6-10 Problem Solving			
6-10 Daily Transparency			

Problem of the Day

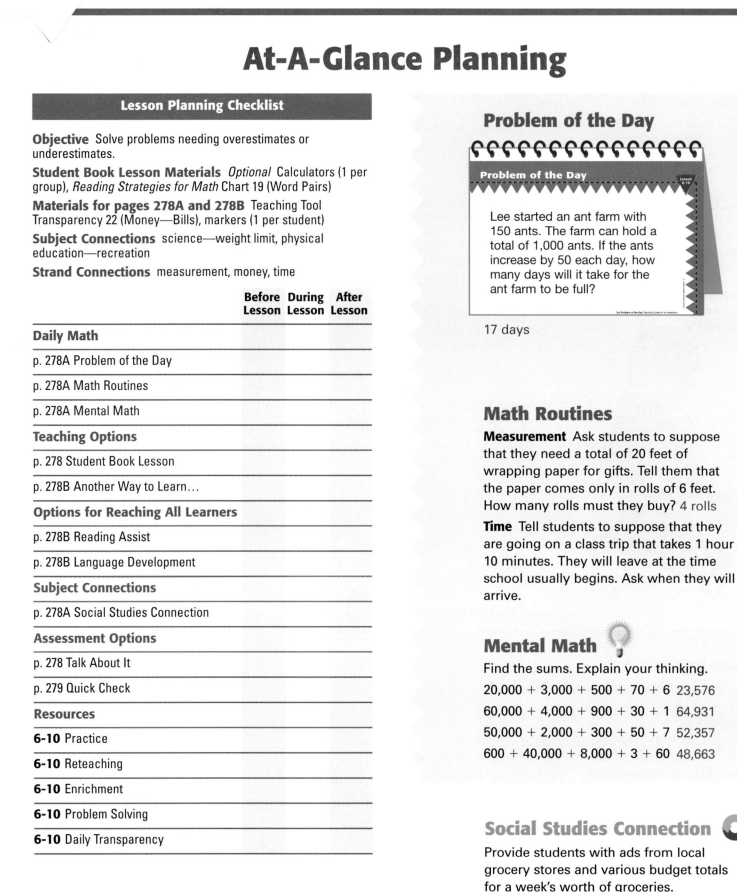

Problem of the Day

Lee started an ant farm with 150 ants. The farm can hold a total of 1,000 ants. If the ants increase by 50 each day, how many days will it take for the ant farm to be full?

17 days

Math Routines

Measurement Ask students to suppose that they need a total of 20 feet of wrapping paper for gifts. Tell them that the paper comes only in rolls of 6 feet. How many rolls must they buy? 4 rolls

Time Tell students to suppose that they are going on a class trip that takes 1 hour 10 minutes. They will leave at the time school usually begins. Ask when they will arrive.

Mental Math

Find the sums. Explain your thinking.

20,000 + 3,000 + 500 + 70 + 6 23,576

60,000 + 4,000 + 900 + 30 + 1 64,931

50,000 + 2,000 + 300 + 50 + 7 52,357

600 + 40,000 + 8,000 + 3 + 60 48,663

Social Studies Connection

Provide students with ads from local grocery stores and various budget totals for a week's worth of groceries.

• Have students use estimation to make grocery lists based on the ads and amounts budgeted for groceries.

Another Way to **Learn** Lesson 6-10

Use as an alternative or in addition to pages 278 and 279.

Materials Teaching Tool Transparency 22 (Money—Bills)

Learning Style Kinesthetic, Visual

- Present this problem to students:

  Three friends want to buy a video game that costs $49.95. Each has saved $15. Have they saved enough to buy it?

- Have groups use play money to act out overestimating the amount saved by rounding $15 to the next-higher multiple of $10, and have 3 students each put that amount together and find the total. Have students talk about whether it appears they have saved enough. 3 × $20 = $60; It appears that they have saved enough.

- Next, have groups act out underestimating the amount saved, following the same steps but rounding to the next-lower multiple of $10. Then have them find the exact amount saved. 3 × $10 = $30; 3 × $15 = $45

- Have students talk about the difference between overestimating and underestimating and which was more appropriate to use for this problem. Then have students

brainstorm a situation involving money in which it would be more appropriate to overestimate.

- Assign Check and Practice on Student Book page 279 or *Practice Master 6-10*.

- Assess using the following rubric.

Assessment Rubric

4 Full Accomplishment
- solves problems using appropriate estimation method

3 Substantial Accomplishment
- solves most problems by using appropriate estimation method

2 Partial Accomplishment
- solves some problems by using appropriate estimation method

1 Little Accomplishment
- does not solve problems by using appropriate estimation method

Options for Reaching All Learners

Reading Assist

Find Main Idea with Supporting Details
Use highlighting to strengthen reading comprehension.

Materials Markers (1 per student)

Learning Style Visual

Provide students with photocopies of page 279.

- As students read each problem, have them use a marker to highlight, underline, or circle the phrases that indicate an overestimate or underestimate is needed, as well as the information needed to make that estimate. An example might be as follows:

- You need about 28 ft of lumber to build a car body for a soapbox derby. Lumber costs $0.85 a foot at your local lumber yard. To make sure you have enough lumber, about how much should you plan to spend? About $28

Language Development

Over and Under
Build vocabulary involving estimation concepts.

Learning Style Verbal, Logical

- Write *overestimate* and *underestimate* on the chalkboard. Ask students to tell what they think the words mean.

- Read a word problem such as the one on page 278 to students. Invite students to revise or add to their understanding of the meanings.

- Highlight or share the following definitions: When you overestimate, you make a good guess that is greater than what you think is the exact answer; when you underestimate, you make a good guess that is less than what you think is the exact answer.

- Discuss situations in which you might want to estimate a smaller number and a larger number than what you think is the exact answer.

Lesson Organizer

Objective Solve problems needing overestimates or underestimates.

Suggested Grouping 2 to 4

Student Book Lesson Materials *Optional* Calculators (1 per group)

Teacher Materials *Optional Reading Strategies for Math* Chart 19 (Word Pairs)

Assignment Guide

Basic 3, 4, 6

Average 3, 5, 6

Enriched 3–6

1 Introduce

Review

Find each product.

1. 20 × $4 $80 **2.** 30 × $3 $90

3. 30 × $4 $120 **4.** 20 × $3 $60

Build on Prior Knowledge

After students review multiplying money amounts by a multiple of 10, ask which pairs of factors in the Review exercises they would multiply to estimate the total cost for a class of 25 students to visit a museum with an admission charge of $4. 30 × $4

2 Teach

See Another Way to Learn…on page 278B.

Learn ● ● ● ● ● ● ● ● ● ● ● ● ● ● ● ● ● ● ●

You might distribute *Reading Strategies for Math* Chart 19 (Word Pairs), using the words *overestimate* and *underestimate* as antonyms.

Reading Assist Word Meaning

Focus on the phrase "how many pounds the merry-go-round can support", which means the most weight the merry-go-round can safely carry.

(Talk About It) Ongoing Assessment

Listen for an understanding of the reasons for overestimating and underestimating.

Answer for Talk About It

It's safer to make sure the total weight of the riders is less than the maximum allowed.

Problem Solving

Analyze Word Problems: Overestimating and Underestimating

You Will Learn how to decide when to overestimate or underestimate

Reading Tip
First read all the information to find the main idea. Then find the facts you need.

Learn ●

Neighbors want to put a merry-go-round in the park. They buy one that holds 14 children.

The neighbors decide to make a sign that tells how many pounds the merry-go-round can support. The typical weight for a child who rides on merry-go-rounds is 75 pounds. Should the sign overestimate or underestimate the weight allowed?

Work Together

▶ **Understand**   What do you know? ❶

What do you need to find out?
Should you overestimate or underestimate the maximum weight for the merry-go-round

▶ **Plan**
❶ How many children the merry-go-round holds; How many pounds an average child weighs

	Decide if you should overestimate or underestimate.	To make sure the merry-go-round can support the weight of 14 children, you should underestimate the weight allowed.

▶ **Solve**   To underestimate, round one or both factors down. Then multiply.

Round 14 to 10.
$10 \times 75 = 750$
The sign should list 750 pounds as the maximum weight allowed.

▶ **Look Back**   How can you check to see if your answer is reasonable?
Compare with the actual answer.
$14 \times 75 = 1,050. \ 750 < 1,050$

(Talk About It)

Why does it make sense to underestimate in this situation?

Name _____

Practice 6-10

Analyze Word Problems: Overestimating and Underestimating

Decide if you should overestimate or underestimate. Solve.

1. Frank is planning a party for 16 friends. He expects to spend about $0.85 per guest on food.

a. Should Frank underestimate or overestimate the total cost of the food? Why?
Possible answer: He should overestimate to be sure he has enough money.

b. Estimate about how much he should plan to spend on food for the party. **$16.00**

Solve each problem.

2. Jenna wants to find out how long it will take to earn enough money to buy a new bicycle. She babysits for $2.50 per hour. She hopes to babysit about 15 hours each month.

a. Should Jenna underestimate or overestimate the amount of money she can expect from babysitting? Why? **Possible answers:**
She should underestimate in case she gets less work than she expects; she may be disappointed if she overestimates.

b. Estimate how much she might earn in a month. **$25.00**

3. Jake can swim out to the diving dock in 5 minutes in calm water. The lifeguards say the waves are higher than usual. Can Jake swim to the diving dock in less than 5 minutes? Explain.
Since the water isn't calm, it will probably take Jake longer to swim to the diving dock.

Name _____

Another Look 6-10

Analyze Word Problems: Overestimating and Underestimating

Asking a series of questions can help you decide when to overestimate and when to underestimate.

Jasmine invites 22 friends to a party. She plans to spend about $0.45 per person on favors. Should she overestimate or underestimate the total cost of favors?

How many people are expected at the party?
22 friends plus Jasmine, 23 people in all

How much does Jasmine plan to spend? **$0.45 per person**

How do you figure the total cost?
Multiply the cost of favors per person by the number of people.

What will happen if she underestimates?
She may not plan for enough money.

What if she overestimates?
She will have money left over.

Should she overestimate or underestimate?
She should overestimate. She can round the cost per favor to a greater amount, $0.50.

$23 \times \$0.50 = \$11.50$

Jasmine will need about $11.50 for favors.

1. The captain is planning a kick-off meeting for her 16-member team. She plans to buy a headband for each person. The headbands cost $0.57 each. Should she overestimate or underestimate the total cost? Explain. How much money should she take when she goes shopping?
Possible answer: She should overestimate to be sure she has enough money; $0.60 × 16 = $9.60.

Decide if you should overestimate or underestimate. Solve.

1. Money You need about 28 ft of lumber to build a car body for a soapbox derby. Lumber costs $0.85 a foot at your local lumber yard. To make sure you have enough lumber, about how much should you plan to spend? Overestimate. Possible answer: $30 \times \$0.90 = \$27.00$

2. You set aside 15 hours to read a book for a book report. You can read about 12 pages an hour. To make sure you have enough time to read the whole book, what is the greatest number of pages the book can have? Underestimate. $10 \times 15 = 150$

Problem Solving
Practice

Solve each problem.

GPS **3.** You want to find how long it will take to earn enough money to buy a skateboard. You earn $3.50 for mowing a lawn. You can mow 12 lawns a month.

a. Should you underestimate or overestimate? Why?

b. Estimate how much you might earn in a month.

4. Most cars need an oil change about every 5,000 miles. Suppose a family drives about 238 miles each week.

a. Will the car need an oil change after 23 weeks? How do you know?

b. Why would you overestimate to find out?

5. Critical Thinking Elheran can walk 30 yd a minute in snowshoes. He wants to make sure he can get to a friend's house before dark. The sun goes down in 65 minutes. Three friends live nearby. To which friend's house should Elheran go? Explain.

Friend	Distance to House
Sebastian	1,900 yd
Andrew	1,750 yd
Janos	2,050 yd

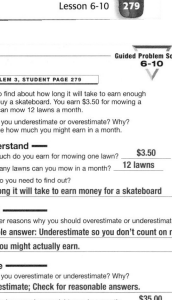

6. Journal Write about a situation in which you overestimated an amount. Explain why it made sense to overestimate. Then tell how you solved the problem.

Lesson 6-10   279

Problem Solving Strategies

- Use Objects/Act It Out
- Draw a Picture
- Look for a Pattern
- Guess and Check
- Use Logical Reasoning
- Make an Organized List
- Make a Table
- Solve a Simpler Problem
- Work Backward

Choose a Tool

PROBLEM SOLVING PRACTICE

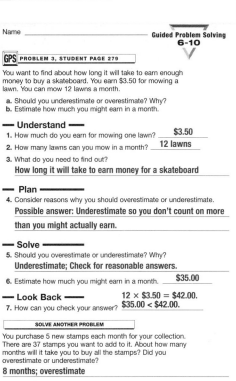

Name _____
Guided Problem Solving
6-10

GPS PROBLEM 3, STUDENT PAGE 279

You want to find about how long it will take to earn enough money to buy a skateboard. You earn $3.50 for mowing a lawn. You can mow 12 lawns a month.

a. Should you underestimate or overestimate? Why?
b. Estimate how much you might earn in a month.

— Understand —
1. How much do you earn for mowing one lawn? **$3.50**
2. How many lawns can you mow in a month? **12 lawns**
3. What do you need to find out?
   How long it will take to earn money for a skateboard

— Plan —
4. Consider reasons why you should overestimate or underestimate.
   Possible answer: Underestimate so you don't count on more than you might actually earn.

— Solve —
5. Should you overestimate or underestimate? Why?
   Underestimate; Check for reasonable answers.
6. Estimate how much you might earn in a month. **$35.00**

— Look Back —
7. How can you check your answer? **12 × $3.50 = $42.00. $35.00 < $42.00.**

SOLVE ANOTHER PROBLEM

You purchase 5 new stamps each month for your collection. There are 37 stamps you want to add to it. About how many months will it take you to buy all the stamps? Did you overestimate or underestimate?
8 months; overestimate

Reading Assist **Find Main Idea with Supporting Details**

Have students read the Check and Practice exercises aloud. Ask volunteers to paraphrase the main ideas and list details.

Practice

Exercises 3 and 4 After students estimate, they can find the actual answers using a calculator.

For Early Finishers Challenge early finishers to solve Exercise 4 for a family that drives about 175 miles each week.

3 Close and Assess

Have students compare their strategies and solutions for one of the Check and Practice problems. Ask them to share whether they overestimated or underestimated and why.

Quick Check

1. What does it mean to overestimate and to underestimate? Estimate to find a value greater than the actual value; Estimate to find a value less than the actual value.

2. For what kinds of problems would you overestimate? Underestimate? Possible answers: To find out if you have enough of something, such as time or money; To find a safe limit, such as weight.

ANSWERS

3a Underestimate. You don't know exactly how many lawns you will mow, so you should get a low estimate.

3b $10 \times \$3.50 = \$35.00$

4a Yes; Estimate 25 weeks $\times$ 250 miles per week $= 6,250$ miles

4b The car may not stay in good shape if the oil isn't changed often enough, so you overestimate to make sure that it is.

5 Andrew's house; Underestimate the amount of time so that Elheran is sure to get there before sunset. $30 \times 60 = 1,800$; Andrew's is the only house within 1,800 yards.

6 Answers will vary.

At-A-Glance Planning

Lesson Planning Checklist

Objective Solve problems by drawing a picture.

Student Book Lesson Materials *Optional* Teaching Tool Transparency 6 (Centimeter Grid Paper)

Materials for pages 280A and 280B Teaching Tool Transparency 6 (Centimeter Grid Paper), markers

Subject Connection physical education—cycling, racing

Strand Connections measurement, time, logic

	Before Lesson	During Lesson	After Lesson
Daily Math			
p. 280A Problem of the Day			
p. 280A Math Routines			
p. 280A Mental Math			
Teaching Options			
p. 280 Student Book Lesson			
p. 280B Another Way to Learn…			
Options for Reaching All Learners			
p. 280B Reading Assist			
p. 280B Inclusion			
Technology Options			
p. 280A *Logical Journey of the Zoombinis*			
Assessment Options			
p. 280 Talk About It			
p. 281 Quick Check			
Resources			
6-11 Practice			
6-11 Reteaching			
6-11 Enrichment			
6-11 Problem Solving			
6-11 Daily Transparency			

Problem of the Day

Problem of the Day *Lesson 6-11*

The Greek alphabet had 2 fewer letters than our alphabet, while the Phoenicians had 4 fewer letters. The Semites had 4 more letters than our alphabet. Make a bar graph to compare the 4 alphabets.

Students' graphs should show: Phoenicians, 22 letters; Greeks, 24 letters; our alphabet, 26 letters; and Semites, 30 letters.

Math Routines

Calendar Have students find the only date that could be both the exact middle of the week and the exact middle of the month. It must be a Wednesday, the 16th of a month with 31 days.

Measurement Tell students that an average person's stride is about 24 inches. Ask how many inches a person would walk in 20 strides. 480 in.

Mental Math

Find each difference. Explain your thinking.

$300 - 50$	$500 - 20$	$600 - 80$	$200 - 70$
250	480	520	130

Logical Journey of the Zoombinis

Students may find Draw a Picture an extremely useful strategy when playing *Fleens!* Students can sketch Zoombini-Fleen combinations to keep a record of corresponding attributes. They can also draw pictures of isolated attribute pairs.

Another Way to **Learn** Lesson 6-11

Use as an alternative or in addition to pages 280 and 281.

Materials Teaching Tool Transparency 6 (Centimeter Grid Paper)

Learning Style Kinesthetic, Visual

- Organize the class into two groups. Arrange groups in different arrays of 4, 5, or 6 rows facing each other. Select one student near the center of each array to raise his or her hand.

- Have half of the class answer these questions about the other half.

  How many are ahead of/behind [student with the raised hand]?

  How many are to the left/right of [that student] and in the same row?

- Use Teaching Tool Transparency 6 (Centimeter Grid Paper) to draw a picture on the overhead of each student array, using Xs, Ys, and Zs to designate the row(s) ahead, the row of, and the row(s) behind the student with the raised hand. Compare the recorded answers to the drawing.

- Have groups draw a picture to solve the following.

  A group of students is seated in 14 rows of 8 each. Marc is in the fifth row. How many students are ahead of him? Behind him? How many students are there in all? 32; 72; 112

- Assign Check and Practice on Student Book page 281 or *Practice Master 6-11.*

- Assess using the following rubric.

Assessment Rubric
4 Full Accomplishment • draws a picture to solve problems
3 Substantial Accomplishment • draws a picture to solve most problems
2 Partial Accomplishment • draws a picture to solve some problems
1 Little Accomplishment • does not draw a picture to solve problems

Options for Reaching All Learners

Reading Assist

Word Meaning

Use paraphrasing to strengthen Draw a Picture skills.

Learning Style Verbal

- On the chalkboard, write the positional words *ahead, behind, right,* and *left.* Review with students the meaning of the words by having them point in the direction indicated as you say each word in random order.

- Before students begin drawing a picture to help solve a problem, have them identify the positional words in the problem. Then have them paraphrase the description of the problem situation and/or the question.

Inclusion

Visualizing Problems

Use grid paper to strengthen ability to visualize problem situations.

Materials Teaching Tool Transparency 6 (Centimeter Grid Paper), markers

Learning Style Visual

- Have students work on grid paper to model problem situations, such as Exercise 4 on page 281.

- Students can use different colors to show the row(s) ahead, the row of, and the row(s) behind a given object.

...esson Organizer

Objective Solve problems by drawing a picture.

Suggested Grouping 2 to 4

Student Materials *Optional* Teaching Tool Transparency 6 (Centimeter Grid Paper)

Assignment Guide

 Basic 3–5

 Average 3–6

 Enriched 3, 5–7

1 Introduce

Review 📖

Answer each question about the rows of letters.

A   B   C   D   E   F

G   H   I   J   K   L

M   N   O   P   Q   R

1. How many letters are in each row? 6

2. How many letters are to the right of N? 4

3. How many letters are to the left of J? 3

Build on Prior Knowledge

After students review directional words, ask how they might describe the position of H. It is the second letter from the left in the second row.

2 Teach

See Another Way to Learn…on page 280B.

Learn ● ● ● ● ● ● ● ● ● ● ● ● ● ● ● ● ● ● ●

Reading Assist Read Illustrations

Have students focus on how each piece of information they are given in the problem is represented in the picture shown for the Solve step.

(**Talk About It**) **Ongoing Assessment**

Listen for recognition that pictures can help to solve problems involving the position of items in relation to one another.

Answer for Talk About It

Possible answer: The picture makes it easier to see the equal groups in each section, then multiply and add.

280 *Chapter 6 • Lesson 6-11*

Problem Solving

Analyze Strategies: Draw a Picture

You Will Learn
how to solve a problem by drawing a picture

Learn ● ● ● ● ● ● ● ● ● ● ●

Suppose you enter a bike race. There are 12 racers in each row. There are 11 rows. You are in the seventh row.

❶ There are 11 rows of 12 racers; You are in row 7.

How many racers start ahead of you? How many racers are there in all?

Work Together

▶ **Understand** What do you know? ❶

What do you need to find out?
The total number of racers;
The number of racers in the rows ahead of you

▶ **Plan** Think of a picture that will help. Decide what it will show.

Write an **A** for each racer ahead of you.
Write a **B** for each racer in your row.
Write a **C** for each racer behind you.

▶ **Solve** Draw the picture. Use labels as needed.

Use the picture to solve the problem.

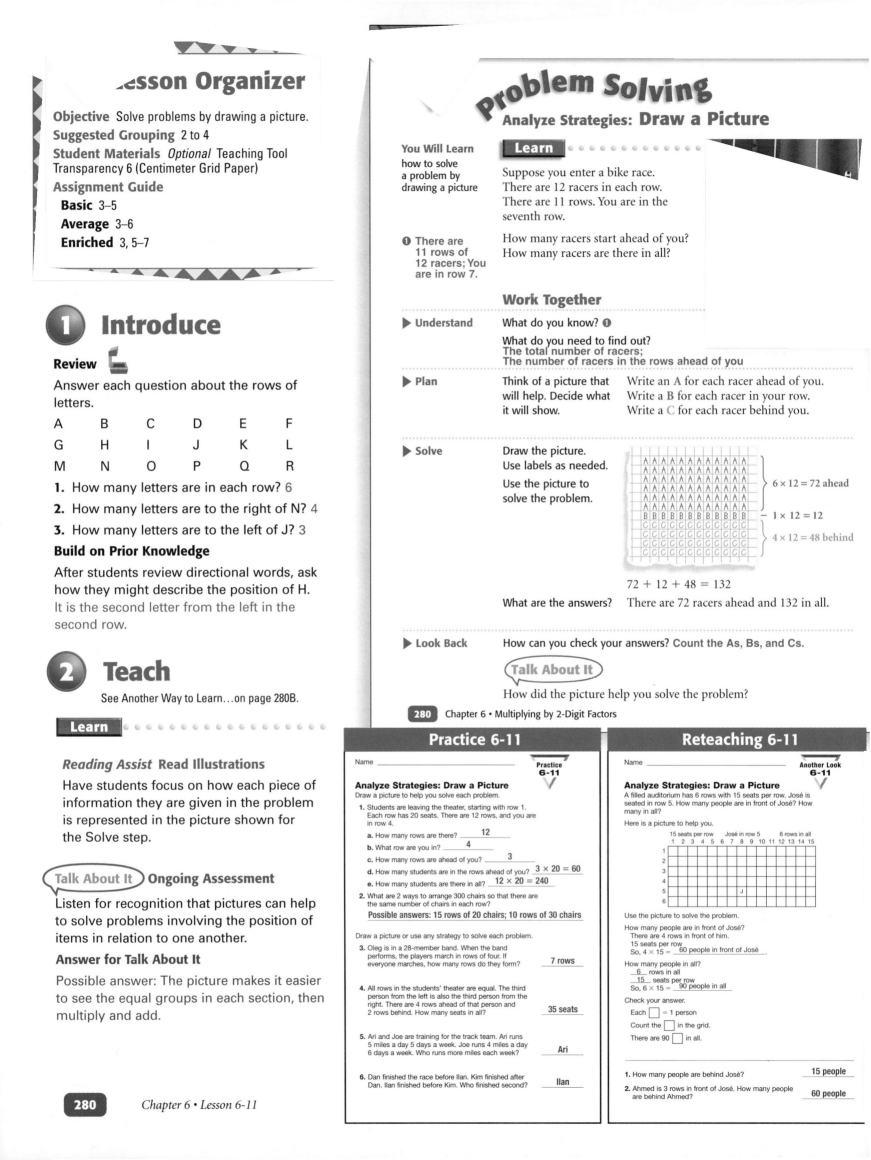

$6 \times 12 = 72$ ahead

$1 \times 12 = 12$

$4 \times 12 = 48$ behind

$72 + 12 + 48 = 132$

What are the answers? There are 72 racers ahead and 132 in all.

▶ **Look Back** How can you check your answers? Count the As, Bs, and Cs.

(**Talk About It**)

How did the picture help you solve the problem?

280 Chapter 6 • Multiplying by 2-Digit Factors

Practice 6-11

Name _____

Analyze Strategies: Draw a Picture

Draw a picture to help you solve each problem.

1. Students are leaving the theater, starting with row 1. Each row has 20 seats. There are 12 rows, and you are in row 4.

 a. How many rows are there? __12__

 b. What row are you in? __4__

 c. How many rows are ahead of you? __3__

 d. How many students are in the rows ahead of you? $3 \times 20 = 60$

 e. How many students are there in all? $12 \times 20 = 240$

2. What are 2 ways to arrange 300 chairs so that there are the same number of chairs in each row?

 Possible answers: 15 rows of 20 chairs; 10 rows of 30 chairs

Draw a picture or use any strategy to solve each problem.

3. Oleg is in a 28-member band. When the band performs, the players march in rows of four. If everyone marches, how many rows do they form? __7 rows__

4. All rows in the students' theater are equal. The third person from the left is also the third person from the right. There are 4 rows ahead of that person and 2 rows behind. How many seats in all? __35 seats__

5. Ari and Joe are training for the track team. Ari runs 5 miles a day 5 days a week. Joe runs 4 miles a day 6 days a week. Who runs more miles each week? __Ari__

6. Dan finished the race before Ilan. Kim finished after Dan. Ilan finished before Kim. Who finished second? __Ilan__

Reteaching 6-11

Name _____

Analyze Strategies: Draw a Picture

A filled auditorium has 6 rows with 15 seats per row. José is seated in row 5. How many people are in front of José? How many in all?

Here is a picture to help you.

15 seats per row   José in row 5   6 rows in all
1 2 3 4 5 6 7 8 9 10 11 12 13 14 15

Use the picture to solve the problem.

How many people are in front of José?
There are 4 rows in front of him.
15 seats per row
So, $4 \times 15 =$ __60__ people in front of José

How many people in all?
__6__ rows in all
__15__ seats per row
So, $6 \times 15 =$ __90__ people in all

Check your answer.

 Each ☐ = 1 person

 Count the ☐ in the grid.

 There are 90 ☐ in all.

1. How many people are behind José? __15 people__

2. Ahmed is 3 rows in front of José. How many people are behind Ahmed? __60 people__

Draw a picture to help you solve each problem.

Problem Solving
Understand
Plan
Solve
Look Back

1. Regina enters a bike race that has 7 rows of racers, with 15 racers in each row.

   a. How many racers are in the race? **105 racers**

   b. If Regina starts in the second row, how many racers will start after her? **75 racers**

   c. If Regina starts in the fifth row, how many racers will start ahead of her? **60 racers**

   d. If 3 racers in each row belong to Speedy Bicycle Club, how many of their club members are in the race? **21 club members**

2. **[GPS]** Max lines up his baseball cards with the same number of cards in each row. The card in the middle of the array has 8 cards to its left, 8 to its right, 8 above, and 8 below.

   a. How many cards are in each row? **17 cards**

   b. How many are there in all? **289 cards**

Problem Solving Practice

Draw a picture or use any strategy to solve each problem.

Problem Solving Strategies
- Use Objects/Act It Out
- Draw a Picture
- Look for a Pattern
- Guess and Check
- Use Logical Reasoning
- Make an Organized List
- Make a Table
- Solve a Simpler Problem
- Work Backward

Choose a Tool

3. If 150 racers enter a race, what are two ways they could line up in rows with the same number of riders in each row? **Possible answer: 10 rows of 15 racers; 25 rows of 6 racers**

4. Roberto is part of a 14-member racing club. When the club members train, they ride in pairs. If the whole club rides together, how many rows do they form? **7 rows**

5. A group of runners is ready to start a race. All rows have the same number of people. The seventh person from the left is also the seventh person from the right. There are six rows of people ahead of that person and six rows behind. How many racers are there in all? **169 racers**

6. Tori and Kim are training for a bike race. Tori rides 12 miles a day, 5 days a week. Kim rides 9 miles a day, 6 days a week. Who rides more miles each week? **Tori**

7. Leda finished ahead of Aris in a bicycle race. Sophie finished behind Leda. Aris finished ahead of Sophie. Who finished in second place? What strategy did you use to solve the problem? **Aris; Possible strategies: Draw a Picture, Use Logical Reasoning**

Skills Practice Bank, page 567, Set 7   Lesson 6-11   **281**

PROBLEM SOLVING PRACTICE

Check

Be sure students are showing correct information in their drawings. They may find it helpful to draw pictures on grid paper, writing one letter or symbol in each box.

Practice

Exercise 3 There are as many solutions to this problem as there are pairs of factors with a product of 150.

Exercise 4 Students must understand that a pair means a row of two.

Exercise 6 To solve this multiple-step problem, most students will multiply twice and compare products.

Exercise 7 Some students may find it helpful to write the names on small pieces of paper that they can move into different positions.

For Early Finishers Challenge early finishers to find the answer to Exercise 2 that has 5 cards to the left and to the right, and 5 cards above and below the card in the middle of the array. 11 cards in each row; 121 cards in all

3 Close and Assess

Ask students what they consider to be the advantages and disadvantages of using the Draw a Picture strategy.

Quick Check

1. How do you use the Draw a Picture strategy to solve a problem? Identify information you are given that is needed to solve the problem. Use the information to draw a picture. Refer to the picture to solve the problem. Check if the solution and the picture agree.

2. For what types of problems is it helpful to draw a picture? Possible answer: Problems that involve arrangements of people or things

---

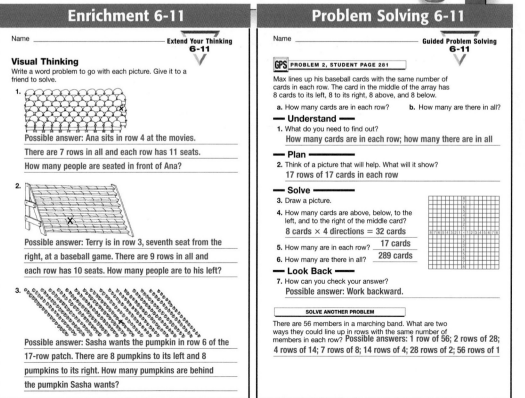

Enrichment 6-11

Name _____

Extend Your Thinking 6-11

Visual Thinking
Write a word problem to go with each picture. Give it to a friend to solve.

1. Possible answer: Ana sits in row 4 at the movies.
   There are 7 rows in all and each row has 11 seats.
   How many people are seated in front of Ana?

2. Possible answer: Terry is in row 3, seventh seat from the right, at a baseball game. There are 9 rows in all and each row has 10 seats. How many people are to his left?

3. Possible answer: Sasha wants the pumpkin in row 6 of the 17-row patch. There are 8 pumpkins to its left and 8 pumpkins to its right. How many pumpkins are behind the pumpkin Sasha wants?

Problem Solving 6-11

Name _____

Guided Problem Solving 6-11

[GPS] PROBLEM 2, STUDENT PAGE 281

Max lines up his baseball cards with the same number of cards in each row. The card in the middle of the array has 8 cards to its left, 8 to its right, 8 above, and 8 below.

a. How many cards are in each row?   b. How many are there in all?

— Understand —
1. What do you need to find out?
   How many cards are in each row; how many there are in all

— Plan —
2. Think of a picture that will help. What will it show?
   17 rows of 17 cards in each row

— Solve —
3. Draw a picture.

4. How many cards are above, below, to the left, and to the right of the middle card?
   8 cards × 4 directions = 32 cards

5. How many are in each row? **17 cards**

6. How many are there in all? **289 cards**

— Look Back —
7. How can you check your answer?
   Possible answer: Work backward.

SOLVE ANOTHER PROBLEM

There are 56 members in a marching band. What are two ways they could line up in rows with the same number of members in each row? Possible answers: 1 row of 56; 2 rows of 28; 4 rows of 14; 7 rows of 8; 14 rows of 4; 28 rows of 2; 56 rows of 1

Section C
Review and Practice
Use the Skills Checklist

Review the **Skills Checklist** on the page with students. Then ask questions such as the following:

- For which problems will you need to show the answers as dollars and cents? Exercises 1–10, 12–14

- How could a wrong choice affect the outcomes of the real-life situations described in Exercises 14 and 15? You could run out of sail cloth or gas.

- How would drawing a picture help you solve Exercise 16? Possible answer: It would help you see how many jars are in each row and how many rows are in the box.

- How might drawing a picture help solve Exercise 18? Possible answer: It would help you see how many blocks you would walk each day.

Assess

You may wish to use this information to assess students' understanding of the lesson objectives.

Item Analysis	
Lesson Objective	Items
6-9 Multiply amounts of money.	1–14
6-10 Solve problems needing overestimates or underestimates.	14, 15
6-11 Solve problems by drawing a picture.	16–18

Resources

Practice Masters
- Practice Chapter 6 Section C

Assessment Sourcebook
- Quiz Chapter 6 Section C

TestWorks: Test and Practice Software
ANSWERS

18 Answers should describe how to multiply 18 blocks by 10 days to get 180 blocks.

SECTION C
Review and Practice

(Lesson 9) Multiply.

1. $6.75
   × 13
   $87.75

2. $1.41
   × 41
   $57.81

3. $3.01
   × 18
   $54.18

4. $5.35
   × 62
   $331.70

5. $2.76
   × 44
   $121.44

6. $19.22
   × 71
   $1,364.62

7. $30.01
   × 12
   $360.12

8. $6.83
   × 15
   $102.45

9. $27.89
   × 31
   $864.59

10. $36.00
    × 29
    $1,044.00

11. **Reasoning** Which could you buy with $20: 12 boxes of crayons for $1.85 each, or 15 rubber spiders for $1.25 each? **15 rubber spiders**

Using Data Use the Data File on page 247.

12. How much would someone have spent for 16 subway rides in 1995? **$24.00**

13. How much would someone have paid for 16 subway rides in 1950? **$1.60**

(Lesson 10) Decide if you should overestimate or underestimate. Solve.

14. **Money** You need about 16 yd of cloth for a sail. The cloth costs $5.79 a yard. To make sure you have enough cloth, about how much should you plan to spend? **Overestimate. Possible answer: $6 × 20 = $120**

15. Suppose a car's gas tank holds 12 gallons of gasoline. The car usually travels about 27 miles per gallon. Estimate the greatest number of miles the driver can go before stopping to get gasoline. **Underestimate. Possible answer: 25 × 10 = 250 miles**

(Lesson 11) Draw a picture to help you solve each problem.

16. Jars of strawberry and plum jam are packed in a box, with the same number of jars in each row. The jar in the middle is the only one that has strawberry jam. There are 5 jars to the left, right, above, and below it. How many jars have plum jam? **120**

17. At the start of a race, there are 14 rows of 12 runners. If Ben is in the ninth row, how many runners are ahead of him? **96 runners**

18. **Journal** If you walked 9 blocks to school every day, each way, how many blocks would you walk in 2 weeks of school days? Explain how you would find the answer.

Skills Checklist
In this section, you have:
☑ Multiplied Money
☑ Solved Problems Needing Overestimates or Underestimates
☑ Solved Problems by Drawing a Picture

REVIEW AND PRACTICE

Practice

Name _____

Practice
Chapter 6
Section C

Review and Practice
(Lesson 9) Multiply.

1. $8.71
   × 39
   $339.69

2. $3.56
   × 22
   $78.32

3. $1.02
   × 63
   $64.26

4. $34.68
   × 47
   $1,629.96

5. $2.39
   × 43
   $102.77

6. $6.24
   × 72
   $449.28

7. $92.01
   × 52
   $4,784.52

8. $10.03
   × 14
   $140.42

9. How much would it cost for a group of 25 people to see a show that costs $7.50 per person? **$187.50**

(Lesson 10) Decide if you would overestimate or underestimate. Solve.

10. You want to buy a remote-controlled car. The one you want is on sale for $65.99. You earn $2.50 each time you deliver flyers, and you now deliver about 12 times a month. How long it will take to earn enough money to buy the car? **underestimate; between 2 and 3 months**

(Lesson 11) Draw a picture to help you solve the problem.

11. Pieces of chocolate candy are packed in a box, with the same number of pieces in each row. The piece in the middle is the only one that has coconut in it. There are 4 pieces to the left, right, above, and below it. How many pieces do not have coconut in them? **80**

(Mixed Review) Complete.

12. 83 – **53** = 30

13. **52** – 42 = 10

14. 723 + **107** = 830

15. **501** + 499 = 1,000

16. What is the fourth month of the year? **April**

Choose at least one. Use what you have learned in this chapter.

① Unlock the Door

To unlock, on which panels should you knock?

a. Knock on 2 panels that have a product of exactly 800. **25 and 32**
b. Knock on 2 panels that have a product greater than 700 and less than 800. **23 and 32**
c. Knock on 2 panels that have a product that is an even number greater than 1,000. **32 and 53**

③ Tour Organizer 🌐

You are the class tour organizer! Check out **www.mathsurf.com/4/ch6** to find prices of different kinds of public transportation. How much will it cost for your class to travel from where you live to a nearby city? Which is the least expensive way to travel? The most expensive?

② Mosaic of Glass

Suppose you buy these figures to make a stained glass window. Use at least 12 figures in your window. Use Power Polygons to make your window, or draw a picture of it. What is the cost of your window?

④ A Case Study

At Home With a family member or friend, find several boxes or cans of food. Make a table. List each item of food, the weight of the item, and the cost of the item. Find out how much a case of 24 of those items would weigh. How much would each case cost?

REVIEW AND PRACTICE

🌐 World Wide Web

If you live in a rural area, have the class select a larger nearby town from which they could begin their travel before visiting **www.mathsurf.com/4/ch6** for Tour Organizer.

Home-School Connection

For A Case Study, have students discuss with a family member or friend why particular brands of food items were selected. Possible reasons include price, size, brand preference, and coupons. Invite students to share their findings with the class.

Parents can use the Web site at **www.parent.mathsurf.com**.

Your Choice

Students will review the skills and concepts of the chapter using learning style strengths.

This page of activities is a good opportunity for portfolio assessment.

① Unlock the Door

Learning Style Logical

Encourage students to use estimation and number sense and then check by actually multiplying. For the third knock, there are three pairs that have a product greater than 1,000. However, students should realize that for a product to be an even number, at least one factor must by even.

a 25 and 32
b 23 and 32
c 32 and 53

② Mosaic of Glass

Materials Power Polygons

Learning Style Kinesthetic, Visual

Encourage students to look at art and architecture books with color plates of stained glass windows. You might also tell them a little about American artist Louis Comfort Tiffany (1848–1933), whose beautiful stained glass works include lamps and ceilings as well as windows. Answers will vary with the number and kind of polygons used.

③ Tour Organizer

Learning Style Visual, Logical

Encourage students to use estimation. Answers will vary with locations and class sizes.

④ A Case Study

Learning Style Visual

Because most food items are bar coded only, without a price stamp or label affixed, it may be necessary for students to visit the grocery store to work this problem. Answers will vary with items chosen.

Chapter 6
Review/Test

This page may be used to review or assess students' knowledge of Chapter 6.

Item Analysis

Lesson Objective		Items
6-1	Explore multiplication patterns.	5–8
6-2	Estimate products of 2-digit factors.	11–13
6-3	Multiply by multiples of 10.	2–9
6-4	Explore multiplying with 2-digit factors.	1, 3, 4, 6, 7, 10, 26
6-5	Multiply with 2-digit factors.	1, 3, 4, 6, 7, 10, 26
6-6	Estimate greater products.	14–16
6-7	Multiply numbers in the thousands.	17–25
6-8	Solve problems by making decisions after analyzing data.	
6-9	Multiply amounts of money.	27–32
6-10	Solve problems needing overestimates or underestimates.	16
6-11	Solve problems by drawing a picture.	33

Resources

Reading Strategies for Math
Chart 6 (Preparing for a Test)

Assessment Sourcebook
Chapter 6 Tests
- Forms A and B (free response)
- Form C (multiple choice)
- Form E (mixed response)
- Form F (cumulative chapter test)

TestWorks: Test and Practice Software

Home and Community Connections
- Letter Home for Chapter 6 in English and Spanish

CHAPTER 6
Review/Test

(Lessons 1, 3, 4, and 5) Find each product.

1. 14×23
322

2. 27×40
1,080

3. 31×34
1,054

4. 15×75
1,125

5. 60×20
1,200

6. 61
$\times 19$
1,159

7. 36
$\times 18$
648

8. 60
$\times 30$
1,800

9. 49
$\times 60$
2,940

10. 19
$\times 18$
342

(Lessons 2, 6, 10) Estimate each product.

11. 43×95
4,000

12. 36×78
3,200

13. 82×74
5,600

14. 198×61
12,000

15. 234×55
12,000

16. Your class of 28 is going on a field trip to the museum. Each ticket costs $2.75. About how much money does your class need? Would you overestimate or underestimate? Explain.
About $90; Overestimate to make sure you have enough money.

(Lesson 7) Find each product.

17. 1,438
$\times\ \ 12$
17,256

18. 100
$\times\ \ 21$
2,100

19. 5,422
$\times\ \ 42$
227,724

20. 3,683
$\times\ \ 14$
51,562

21. 200
$\times\ \ 26$
5,200

22. 291×14
4,074

23. 841×27
22,707

24. $1,100 \times 80$
88,000

25. $2,000 \times 41$
82,000

26. History In 1903, a typical car traveled at 12 miles per hour. Now, the speed limit on many highways is 65 miles per hour.

a. How far would you travel in 12 hours at 12 miles per hour? **144 miles**

b. How far would you travel in 12 hours at 65 miles per hour? **780 miles**

(Lesson 9) Find each product.

27. $\$1.78 \times 32$
$56.96

28. $\$3.21 \times 72$
$231.12

29. $\$2.01 \times 37$
$74.37

30. $\$1.50 \times 29$
$43.50

31. Money In 1889, a meal in a train car cost $0.75. If 23 customers went to dinner one night, how much would they pay all together? **$17.25**

32. Reasoning Which costs more, 2 tickets at $3.50 or 3 tickets at $2.50? **3 tickets at $2.50**

(Lesson 11) Solve.

33. A marching band has 15 rows of 12 members. If you are in the tenth row from the front, how many band members march before you? **108 band members**

Assessment

Name _____

Date _____ Score _____

Chapter 6 Test
Form
A

Vocabulary: In 1–3, match each with its meaning.

1. factors — a. the number obtained after multiplying

2. multiple — b. numbers that are multiplied together to obtain a product

3. product — c. the product of a given whole number and any other whole number

1. b
2. c
3. a

In 4–7, use patterns to find each product.

4. $70 \times 8 = $ **560**
$70 \times 80 = $ **5,600**
$70 \times 800 = $ **56,000**
$70 \times 8,000 = $ **560,000**

6. $40 \times 7 = $ **280**
$40 \times 70 = $ **2,800**
$40 \times 700 = $ **28,000**
$40 \times 7,000 = $ **280,000**

5. $50 \times 4 = $ **200**
$50 \times 40 = $ **2,000**
$50 \times 400 = $ **20,000**
$50 \times 4,000 = $ **200,000**

7. $90 \times 5 = $ **450**
$90 \times 50 = $ **4,500**
$90 \times 500 = $ **45,000**
$90 \times 5,000 = $ **450,000**

In 8–14, estimate each product.

8. 84×23 **8.** 1,600

9. 66×56 **9.** 4,200

10. 29×78 **10.** 2,400

11. 53×67 **11.** 3,500

12. 246×58 **12.** 12,000

13. 709×88 **13.** 63,000

14. 395×31 **14.** 12,000

Name _____

In 15–24, find each product.

15. 72
$\times 30$

16. 53
$\times 80$

17. 41
$\times 28$

18. 57
$\times 43$

19. 95×32

20. 42×39

21. $32 \times 1,247$

22. $2,371 \times 16$

23. $15 \times \$14.95$

24. $12 \times \$24.08$

15. 2,160
16. 4,240
17. 1,148
18. 2,451
19. 3,040
20. 1,638
21. 39,904
22. 37,936
23. $224.25
24. $288.96

In 25, decide if you should overestimate or underestimate. Solve.

25. Marty plans to deposit $4.50 into his bank account each week. Estimate to see if he will have saved $50 to pay for a computer game at the end of 21 weeks.
Underestimate: 4 × 20 = 80; He will have enough money.

In 26, draw a picture to help you solve each problem.

26. Larry is in a bike race. There are 12 bikes in each row. There are 4 rows in front of him and 8 rows behind him. How many racers are there in all?
26. 156 racers

27. Explain Your Thinking Describe the steps you would follow to find the product of 1,258 and 47.
Possible answer: Multiply 1,258 by 7 ones. Then multiply 1,258 by 4 tens. Add the products to get 59,126.

Performance Assessment

Angel's Flight, a funicular (fyoo nik yoo lar), is a cable railway that climbs up steep hills. It runs between Hill Street and a plaza in downtown Los Angeles, 298 feet high.

Angel's Flight Tickets	
1 ticket	$0.25
Book of 10 tickets	$1.00
Book of 40 tickets	$7.50

If you built a funicular to climb a hill, how much would you charge?

1. **Decision Making** Decide what you would call your funicular railway. Then decide on a cost for a single ride and for books of tickets.

2. **Recording Data** Copy and complete the table to show how much you would charge for a single ride, a round-trip ticket, and booklets of 15, 25, and 45 tickets.

Funicular Railway	Ticket Cost
One-way ticket	
Round-trip ticket	
Book of 15 tickets	
Book of 25 tickets	
Book of 45 tickets	

3. **Explain Your Thinking** How did you use multiplication to decide on ticket costs? In what ways could you use estimation to help you?

4. **Critical Thinking** How much does a single ride on Angel's Flight cost if you buy a book of 10 tickets? How can you find out? Why do you think it costs less per ticket if you buy 10 tickets?
$0.10; Divide $1.00 by 10; Possible answer: To encourage people to buy many tickets and use the railway a lot

Angel's Flight is the shortest railway in the world.

3. Possible answer: Multiply the one-way ticket cost by 2, 15, 25, and 45. Use estimation to check answers or decide on a lower price per ticket in the booklets.

Chapter 6 • Performance Assessment **285**

Assessment

Name _____   Chapter 6 Test
                         Form
Date _____ Score _____ **D**

You are helping complete an order for the school store. You will be ordering paper, pencils, and painting supplies.

Pencils
1 Gross

PAINTBRUSHES
6 SETS
5 BRUSHES PER SET

PAPER
1 REAM

TEMPERA
PAINT

1 dozen = 12
1 gross = 12 dozen, or 144
1 ream = 500 sheets

a. **Making Decisions** Think about how many students are in your grade at school. Estimate how many pencils, paintbrushes, sheets of paper, and bottles of tempera paint are needed for the school year. Record your estimates in the first column of the table below.

b. **Recording Data** Copy and complete the order form.

	Estimated number of items needed	Number per box	Number of boxes	Cost per box	Total cost
Pencils				$2.69	
Paintbrushes				$4.00	
Sheets of paper				$24.35	
Tempera paint				$18.27	

c. **Analyzing Data**

How many pencils are in one box?
How many paintbrushes are in one box?
How many sheets of paper are in one box?
What is the total cost of all the items you are ordering?

d. **Explain Your Thinking**

Explain how you decided how many of each item to order.

e. **Making Decisions** Suppose your are ordering items for the entire school. How will you change your order? Explain. Estimate the total cost for the new amounts ordered.

Chapter 6 Performance Assessment

Students will apply multiplication skills in planning how much to charge for a cable railway ride.

Introduce the Task

Review the data given to be sure students understand that different numbers of tickets cost different amounts of money. Then review Exercises 1–4 with students to be sure they understand the directions.

Share Level 4 of the rubric with students before they begin.

Facilitate and Assess

Before students work, you may wish to ask questions such as the following:

- What do you think is a good way to solve this problem?

- How do you plan to organize your work?

- How will you keep track of your work?

Assessment Rubric
4 Full Accomplishment • plans and explains ticket cost for railway • applies multiplication skills correctly
3 Substantial Accomplishment • plans and explains ticket cost, with prompting • applies multiplication skills correctly most of the time
2 Partial Accomplishment • plans but does not explain ticket cost • applies multiplication skills correctly some of the time
1 Little Accomplishment • does not plan or explain ticket cost • does not apply multiplication skills

Resources

Assessment Sourcebook

Chapter 6 Test

• Form D (performance assessment)

Chapter 6   **285**

Math Magazine

Students will explore an early form of monetary system.

Historical Note

The first coins are thought to have been made during the 7th century B.C. in an area that today is part of Turkey. Before that, people used bartering as a system of trade, in which people exchanged goods such as animal skins, cloth, salt, and shells for other goods or services.

Cowries are sea snails that live in warm, shallow ocean water. Their shiny, colorful shells were once used as money in Africa, China, and India. Fiji Island chieftains were also known to wear the shells as badges of office.

Cultural Link

Invite students from other countries to tell about the coins and/or paper money of their countries and what the pictures or symbols on them represent. Students might bring coins or paper money to class.

Answers for Try These!

1 Possible answer: They are the smallest unit of money.

2 Possible answer: *Ogwao*

3 Possible answer: It takes a lot of cowrie shells to buy something.

4 About 6,000 cowrie shells

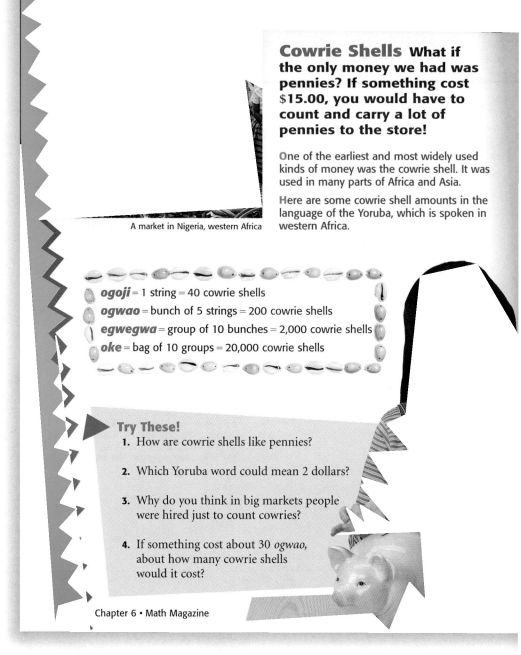

Cowrie Shells What if the only money we had was pennies? If something cost $15.00, you would have to count and carry a lot of pennies to the store!

One of the earliest and most widely used kinds of money was the cowrie shell. It was used in many parts of Africa and Asia.

Here are some cowrie shell amounts in the language of the Yoruba, which is spoken in western Africa.

A market in Nigeria, western Africa

ogoji = 1 string = 40 cowrie shells

ogwao = bunch of 5 strings = 200 cowrie shells

egwegwa = group of 10 bunches = 2,000 cowrie shells

oke = bag of 10 groups = 20,000 cowrie shells

Try These!

1. How are cowrie shells like pennies?

2. Which Yoruba word could mean 2 dollars?

3. Why do you think in big markets people were hired just to count cowries?

4. If something cost about 30 *ogwao*, about how many cowrie shells would it cost?

Chapter 6 • Math Magazine

Additional Resources for the Teacher

Kids Are Consumers, Too! Real-World Mathematics for Today's Classroom, Ian Fair and Mary Melvin. Menlo Park, CA: Dale Seymour Publications.

Test Prep Strategy: Eliminate Choices

Estimate.

What is the product of 57 and 34?

Ⓐ 3,208   Ⓑ 1,938   Ⓒ 18,698   Ⓓ 871

STAY SHARP!

Use your estimate to eliminate unreasonable choices. Estimate 57 × 34. 60 × 30 = 1,800. Ⓐ, Ⓒ, and Ⓓ are not close to 1,800. The answer is Ⓑ.

Write the letter of the correct answer. Eliminate choices or use any other strategy to help.

Using Data Use the graph for **1** and **2**.

1. What is the total number of miles Jennifer trained each week? **D**
   Ⓐ 4 mi   Ⓑ 10 mi
   Ⓒ 70 mi   Ⓓ 160 mi

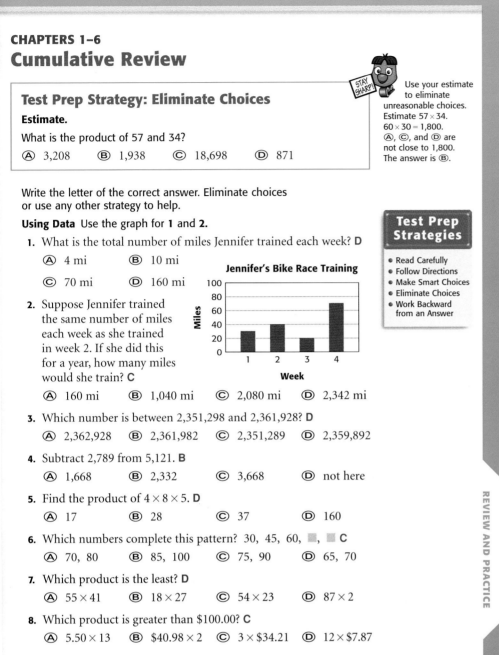

Jennifer's Bike Race Training

2. Suppose Jennifer trained the same number of miles each week as she trained in week 2. If she did this for a year, how many miles would she train? **C**
   Ⓐ 160 mi   Ⓑ 1,040 mi   Ⓒ 2,080 mi   Ⓓ 2,342 mi

3. Which number is between 2,351,298 and 2,361,928? **D**
   Ⓐ 2,362,928   Ⓑ 2,361,982   Ⓒ 2,351,289   Ⓓ 2,359,892

4. Subtract 2,789 from 5,121. **B**
   Ⓐ 1,668   Ⓑ 2,332   Ⓒ 3,668   Ⓓ not here

5. Find the product of 4 × 8 × 5. **D**
   Ⓐ 17   Ⓑ 28   Ⓒ 37   Ⓓ 160

6. Which numbers complete this pattern? 30, 45, 60, ▪, ▪ **C**
   Ⓐ 70, 80   Ⓑ 85, 100   Ⓒ 75, 90   Ⓓ 65, 70

7. Which product is the least? **D**
   Ⓐ 55 × 41   Ⓑ 18 × 27   Ⓒ 54 × 23   Ⓓ 87 × 2

8. Which product is greater than $100.00? **C**
   Ⓐ 5.50 × 13   Ⓑ $40.98 × 2   Ⓒ 3 × $34.21   Ⓓ 12 × $7.87

Test Prep Strategies
- Read Carefully
- Follow Directions
- Make Smart Choices
- Eliminate Choices
- Work Backward from an Answer

REVIEW AND PRACTICE

Practice

Name _____

Practice
Chapter 6
Cumulative Review

Cumulative Review
(Chapter 5 Lesson 2) Find each product.
1. 20 × 9 = __180__
2. 3,000 × 5 = __15,000__
3. 8 × 900 = __7,200__
4. 7 × 400 = __2,800__

(Chapter 2 Lesson 3) Write the word name for each number.
5. 6,300,000
   Six million, three hundred thousand
6. 34,056,107
   Thirty-four million, fifty-six thousand, one hundred seven

(Chapter 3 Lesson 14) Solve.
7. Loretta bought a flashlight for $3.50, a compass for $4.75, and a notepad for $0.95. How much change would she get if she gave the clerk $10.00? __$0.80__

(Chapter 5 Lesson 12) Solve.
8. Three tickets to the concert cost $6.50. How much would it cost to buy tickets for a class of 21 students and a class of 30 students? __$110.50__

(Chapter 6 Lesson 6) Estimate each product.
9. 138 × 38 __4,000__   10. 629 × 48 __30,000__   11. 316 × 92 __27,000__
12. 751 × 82 __64,000__   13. 377 × 56 __24,000__   14. 857 × 46 __45,000__

(Chapter 6 Lesson 7) Find each product.
15. 638 × 59 = 37,642
16. 4,023 × 94 = 378,162
17. 3,011 × 26 = 78,286
18. 4,500 × 70 = 315,000

Chapters 1–6 Cumulative Review

Students review and maintain skills and concepts taught in Chapters 1–6 and practice test-taking strategies. Special attention is given here to the Test Prep Strategy, Eliminate Choices: Estimate.

Introduce the Test Prep Strategy

Eliminate Choices: Estimate Read and discuss the Test Prep strategy note. After students work through the example, present the following problem:

What is the product of 42 and 395? **C**
Ⓐ 10,480   Ⓑ 1,720
Ⓒ 16,590   Ⓓ 2,370

Encourage students to find other problems on this page where Eliminate Choices: Estimate might be a helpful strategy.

Some students may prefer another strategy for some of the identified items. Have them tell which strategy they would use and explain why.

Review and Assess

Item Analysis	
Item	Lesson
1	1-10
2	1-7
3	2-6
4	3-7
5	5-11
6	3-16
7	6-2
8	6-9

Resources

Practice Masters
- Cumulative Review Chapters 1–6

Assessment Sourcebook
- Quarterly Test Chapters 1–6

Student Resources

Contents

Student Resources

Set 1
Find each sum or difference

1. $8 + 8$ 16	**2.** $6 + 7$ 13	**3.** $4 + 6$ 10	**4.** $2 + 7$ 9	**5.** $5 + 5$ 10
6. $12 - 3$ 9	**7.** $6 - 5$ 1	**8.** $9 - 4$ 5	**9.** $13 - 7$ 6	**10.** $10 - 2$ 8
11. $1 + 7$ 8	**12.** $6 + 5$ 11	**13.** $2 + 8$ 10	**14.** $3 + 4$ 7	**15.** $9 + 8$ 17
16. $9 - 6$ 3	**17.** $14 - 7$ 7	**18.** $11 - 8$ 3	**19.** $3 - 3$ 0	**20.** $15 - 9$ 6
21. $9 + 9$ 18	**22.** $6 + 8$ 14	**23.** $4 + 7$ 11	**24.** $5 + 9$ 14	**25.** $3 + 8$ 11
26. $17 - 8$ 9	**27.** $10 - 5$ 5	**28.** $8 - 2$ 6	**29.** $11 - 6$ 5	**30.** $13 - 5$ 8
31. $1 + 8$ 9	**32.** $3 + 7$ 10	**33.** $5 + 9$ 14	**34.** $9 + 7$ 16	**35.** $4 + 6$ 10
36. $16 - 7$ 9	**37.** $12 - 5$ 7	**38.** $8 - 3$ 5	**39.** $14 - 6$ 8	**40.** $6 - 4$ 2
41. $9 + 3$ 12	**42.** $6 + 7$ 13	**43.** $4 + 8$ 12	**44.** $3 + 2$ 5	**45.** $5 + 2$ 7
46. $14 - 5$ 9	**47.** $11 - 2$ 9	**48.** $7 - 4$ 3	**49.** $8 - 6$ 2	**50.** $10 - 3$ 7
51. $6 + 6$ 12	**52.** $8 + 7$ 15	**53.** $2 + 4$ 6	**54.** $5 + 8$ 13	**55.** $7 + 5$ 12
56. $11 - 7$ 4	**57.** $8 - 8$ 0	**58.** $13 - 9$ 4	**59.** $9 - 3$ 6	**60.** $7 - 5$ 2
61. $2 + 7$ 9	**62.** $5 + 7$ 12	**63.** $8 + 4$ 12	**64.** $9 + 8$ 17	**65.** $3 + 3$ 6
66. $10 - 6$ 4	**67.** $8 - 4$ 4	**68.** $4 - 3$ 1	**69.** $14 - 8$ 6	**70.** $12 - 6$ 6
71. $6 + 9$ 15	**72.** $7 + 3$ 10	**73.** $5 + 4$ 9	**74.** $9 + 4$ 13	**75.** $6 + 5$ 11
76. $13 - 6$ 7	**77.** $9 - 2$ 7	**78.** $6 - 3$ 3	**79.** $7 - 6$ 1	**80.** $15 - 8$ 7
81. $4 + 5$ 9	**82.** $6 + 8$ 14	**83.** $9 + 6$ 15	**84.** $7 + 7$ 14	**85.** $6 + 3$ 9
86. $16 - 9$ 7	**87.** $12 - 4$ 8	**88.** $9 - 7$ 2	**89.** $5 - 3$ 2	**90.** $15 - 7$ 8
91. $7 + 9$ 16	**92.** $3 + 8$ 11	**93.** $6 + 2$ 8	**94.** $8 + 5$ 13	**95.** $3 + 4$ 7
96. $12 - 9$ 3	**97.** $9 - 5$ 4	**98.** $8 - 1$ 7	**99.** $10 - 4$ 6	**100.** $14 - 9$ 5

Set 2

1. The park is 8 blocks from Emily's house. Emily walked 3 blocks to meet her friend. Then together they walked to the park. How many blocks did Emily walk with her friend? **5 blocks**

2. Alonso plans to draw some insects in his scrapbook. On one page he will draw 8 ants. On another page he will draw 4 grasshoppers. How many insects does he plan to draw? **12 insects**

Set 1 For use after page 11.
Use the Data File on page 7.

1. How many kangaroos jumped 40 feet? **6 kangaroos**

2. How many more kangaroos jumped 40 feet than 41 feet? **2 more**

Set 2 For use after page 15.
Use the line graph.

1. How many books did Ron read when he was 8? **10 books**

2. How old was Ron when he read 30 books? **11 years old**

3. How many more books did Ron read when he was 12 than when he was 8? **30 more books**

Books Read by Ron

Set 3 For use after page 19.
Use this stem-and-leaf plot.

Bus Ride (minutes)

1	4 9
2	1 8 7 5 1 5 3 0 1

1. What is the difference in time between the shortest and longest bus ride? **25 minutes**

2. How many bus rides are 21 minutes long? **3 bus**

Set 4 For use after page 27.
Copy and complete the bar graph of the trees.

Type of Tree	Elm	Oak	Fir
Number of Trees	10	25	30

1. How many more firs are there than elms? **20 more**

Title: **Trees**

Label: **Number of Trees**

Set 5 For use after page 31.
Use the data of judges' scores.

1. Find the range. **3**   2. Find the median. **8**

3. Find the mode. **7**

Scores for a Gymnastic Event

8	10	7	9	7	7	8	9	10

Set 6 For use after pages 23 and 39.

1. (Page 23) Jim has 34 pine cones. He gives 15 to Andrea. How many pine cones does Jim have now? **19 pine cones**

2. (Page 39) Jo finds 9 fossils. There are 3 more leaf fossils than insect fossils. How many are leaf fossils? **6 leaf fossils**

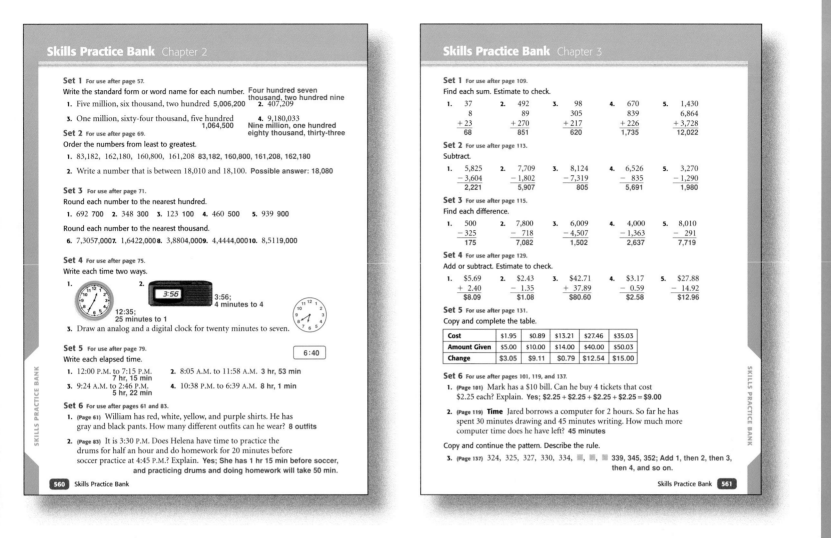

Skills Practice Bank Chapter 2

Set 1 For use after page 57.

Write the standard form or word name for each number.

1. Five million, six thousand, two hundred **5,006,200**
2. **407,209** Four hundred seven thousand, two hundred nine
3. One million, sixty-four thousand, five hundred **1,064,500**
4. **9,180,033** Nine million, one hundred eighty thousand, thirty-three

Set 2 For use after page 69.

Order the numbers from least to greatest.

1. 83,182, 162,180, 160,800, 161,208 **83,182, 160,800, 161,208, 162,180**
2. Write a number that is between 18,010 and 18,100. **Possible answer: 18,080**

Set 3 For use after page 71.

Round each number to the nearest hundred.

1. 692 **700** 2. 348 **300** 3. 123 **100** 4. 460 **500** 5. 939 **900**

Round each number to the nearest thousand.

6. 7,305 **7,000** 7. 1,642 **2,000** 8. 3,880 **4,000** 9. 4,444 **4,000** 10. 8,511 **9,000**

Set 4 For use after page 75.

Write each time two ways.

1. **12:35; 25 minutes to 1**
2. **3:56; 4 minutes to 4**
3. Draw an analog and a digital clock for twenty minutes to seven. **6:40**

Set 5 For use after page 79.

Write each elapsed time.

1. 12:00 P.M. to 7:15 P.M. **7 hr, 15 min**
2. 8:05 A.M. to 11:58 A.M. **3 hr, 53 min**
3. 9:24 A.M. to 2:46 P.M. **5 hr, 22 min**
4. 10:38 P.M. to 6:39 A.M. **8 hr, 1 min**

Set 6 For use after pages 61 and 83.

1. (Page 61) William has red, white, yellow, and purple shirts. He has gray and black pants. How many different outfits can he wear? **8 outfits**
2. (Page 83) It is 3:30 P.M. Does Helena have time to practice the drums for half an hour and do homework for 20 minutes before soccer practice at 4:45 P.M.? Explain. **Yes; She has 1 hr 15 min before soccer, and practicing drums and doing homework will take 50 min.**

Skills Practice Bank Chapter 3

Set 1 For use after page 109.

Find each sum. Estimate to check.

1. 37 + 8 + 23 = **68**
2. 492 + 89 + 270 = **851**
3. 98 + 305 + 217 = **620**
4. 670 + 839 + 226 = **1,735**
5. 1,430 + 6,864 + 3,728 = **12,022**

Set 2 For use after page 113.

Subtract.

1. 5,825 − 3,604 = **2,221**
2. 7,709 − 1,802 = **5,907**
3. 8,124 − 7,319 = **805**
4. 6,526 − 835 = **5,691**
5. 3,270 − 1,290 = **1,980**

Set 3 For use after page 115.

Find each difference.

1. 500 − 325 = **175**
2. 7,800 − 718 = **7,082**
3. 6,009 − 4,507 = **1,502**
4. 4,000 − 1,363 = **2,637**
5. 8,010 − 291 = **7,719**

Set 4 For use after page 129.

Add or subtract. Estimate to check.

1. $5.69 + 2.40 = **$8.09**
2. $2.43 − 1.35 = **$1.08**
3. $42.71 + 37.89 = **$80.60**
4. $3.17 − 0.59 = **$2.58**
5. $27.88 − 14.92 = **$12.96**

Set 5 For use after page 131.

Copy and complete the table.

Cost	$1.95	$0.89	$13.21	$27.46	$35.03
Amount Given	$5.00	$10.00	$14.00	$40.00	$50.03
Change	$3.05	$9.11	$0.79	$12.54	$15.00

Set 6 For use after pages 101, 119, and 137.

1. (Page 101) Mark has a $10 bill. Can he buy 4 tickets that cost $2.25 each? Explain. **Yes; $2.25 + $2.25 + $2.25 + $2.25 = $9.00**
2. (Page 119) **Time** Jared borrows a computer for 2 hours. So far he has spent 30 minutes drawing and 45 minutes writing. How much more computer time does he have left? **45 minutes**

Copy and continue the pattern. Describe the rule.

3. (Page 137) 324, 325, 327, 330, 334, ■, ■, ■ **339, 345, 352; Add 1, then 2, then 3, then 4, and so on.**

Set 1 For use after page 153.

Find each product.

1. 9 $\times 4$ 36	**2.** 5 $\times 3$ 15	**3.** 4 $\times 0$ 0	**4.** 3 $\times 7$ 21	**5.** 8 $\times 4$ 32
6. 3 $\times 3$ 9	**7.** 4 $\times 5$ 20	**8.** 2 $\times 4$ 8	**9.** 3 $\times 6$ 18	**10.** 8 $\times 3$ 24
11. 4 $\times 4$ 16	**12.** 9 $\times 3$ 27	**13.** 4 $\times 7$ 28	**14.** 3 $\times 4$ 12	**15.** 4 $\times 6$ 24

Set 2 For use after page 157.

Find each product.

1. 6×5 30 **2.** 7×7 49 **3.** 8×4 32 **4.** 6×6 36 **5.** 7×9 63

6. 8×6 48 **7.** 4×8 32 **8.** 7×3 21 **9.** 8×8 64 **10.** 6×3 18

11. 7 $\times 8$ 56	**12.** 9 $\times 7$ 63	**13.** 6 $\times 4$ 24	**14.** 8 $\times 9$ 72	**15.** 5 $\times 7$ 35

Set 3 For use after page 159.

Find each product.

1. 10×9 90 **2.** 11×8 88 **3.** 5×12 60 **4.** 11×0 0 **5.** 10×4 40

6. 2×12 24 **7.** 3×10 30 **8.** 6×11 66 **9.** 6×12 72 **10.** 10×8 80

11. 11 $\times 2$ 22	**12.** 3 $\times 12$ 36	**13.** 10 $\times 9$ 90	**14.** 7 $\times 11$ 77	**15.** 12 $\times 0$ 0

Set 4 For use after page 163.

1. Jessica earns $3 an hour delivering papers. Ethan earns $2 an hour walking a dog. How much can Jessica and Ethan earn if they both work 5 hours? $25

2. Ned has 4 bags of apples. Maggie has 5 bags. There are 10 apples to a bag. How many apples do Ned and Maggie have? 90 apples

Set 5 For use after page 171.

Find each quotient.

1. $2\overline{)14}$ 7 **2.** $5\overline{)40}$ 8 **3.** $9\overline{)36}$ 4 **4.** $2\overline{)12}$ 6 **5.** $9\overline{)81}$ 9

6. $5\overline{)20}$ 4 **7.** $2\overline{)2}$ 1 **8.** $9\overline{)45}$ 5 **9.** $5\overline{)30}$ 6 **10.** $9\overline{)54}$ 6

11. $16 \div 2$ 8 **12.** $18 \div 9$ 2 **13.** $35 \div 5$ 7 **14.** $4 \div 2$ 2 **15.** $10 \div 2$ 5

16. $25 \div 5$ 5 **17.** $9 \div 9$ 1 **18.** $6 \div 2$ 3 **19.** $8 \div 2$ 4 **20.** $5 \div 5$ 1

21. $3\overline{)9}$ 3 **22.** $2\overline{)2}$ 1 **23.** $9\overline{)72}$ 8 **24.** $5\overline{)15}$ 3 **25.** $9\overline{)63}$ 7

26. Money How many nickels are there in a quarter? 5 nickels

Set 6 For use after page 179.

Find each quotient.

1. $6\overline{)36}$ 6 **2.** $8\overline{)48}$ 6 **3.** $7\overline{)35}$ 5 **4.** $6\overline{)42}$ 7 **5.** $6\overline{)6}$ 1

6. $7\overline{)49}$ 7 **7.** $6\overline{)54}$ 9 **8.** $7\overline{)14}$ 2 **9.** $8\overline{)32}$ 4 **10.** $7\overline{)42}$ 6

11. $56 \div 8$ 7 **12.** $28 \div 7$ 4 **13.** $40 \div 5$ 8 **14.** $64 \div 8$ 8 **15.** $21 \div 7$ 3

16. $24 \div 8$ 3 **17.** $7 \div 7$ 1 **18.** $24 \div 6$ 4 **19.** $63 \div 7$ 9 **20.** $16 \div 8$ 2

21. $8\overline{)8}$ 1 **22.** $6\overline{)18}$ 3 **23.** $5\overline{)40}$ 8 **24.** $4\overline{)28}$ 7 **25.** $6\overline{)12}$ 2

26. $3\overline{)21}$ 7 **27.** $9\overline{)72}$ 8 **28.** $6\overline{)30}$ 5 **29.** $9\overline{)54}$ 6 **30.** $3\overline{)27}$ 9

Set 7 For use after page 189.

Use any strategy to solve each problem.

1. Peter and Juan were sharing a tape player with new batteries. The batteries ran out after 12 hours of use. If Peter used the player 2 more hours than Juan, how long did each use the player? Peter: 7 hours; Juan: 5 hours

2. Jean has 4 pairs of different colored shoes. What is the least number of shoes she can take out of a dark closet and be sure of having a matching pair? 5 shoes

Set 1 For use after page 203.

Find each product.

1. 9×50 450   2. 400×6 2,400   3. 3×70 210   4. 100×10 1,000   5. $8 \times 2,000$ 16,000

6. 300×9 2,700   7. $4 \times 8,000$ 32,000   8. 500×7 3,500   9. $9 \times 6,000$ 54,000   10. $7,000 \times 8$ 56,000

11. 7×90 630   12. 800×8 6,400   13. $5 \times 6,000$ 30,000   14. 30×8 240   15. 9×900 8,100

Set 2 For use after page 213.

Find each product. Estimate to check.

1.	42	2.	18	3.	23	4.	57	5.	84
	$\times\ 3$		$\times\ 5$		$\times\ 7$		$\times\ 6$		$\times\ 4$
	126		90		161		342		336

6.	96	7.	51	8.	37	9.	64	10.	79
	$\times\ 8$		$\times\ 4$		$\times\ 2$		$\times\ 8$		$\times\ 5$
	768		204		74		512		395

11.	48	12.	22	13.	35	14.	73	15.	17
	$\times\ 9$		$\times\ 7$		$\times\ 4$		$\times\ 6$		$\times\ 3$
	432		154		140		438		51

Set 3 For use after page 215.

Multiply.

1.	306	2.	235	3.	510	4.	627	5.	809
	$\times\ 4$		$\times\ 3$		$\times\ 8$		$\times\ 5$		$\times\ 9$
	1,224		705		4,080		3,135		7,281

6.	763	7.	221	8.	405	9.	617	10.	747
	$\times\ 7$		$\times\ 3$		$\times\ 6$		$\times\ 5$		$\times\ 8$
	5,341		663		2,430		3,085		5,976

11.	204	12.	469	13.	888	14.	711	15.	590
	$\times\ 7$		$\times\ 3$		$\times\ 4$		$\times\ 9$		$\times\ 3$
	1,428		938		3,552		6,399		1,770

Set 4 For use after page 217.

1. Doug bakes cupcakes. His pan holds 12 cupcakes. How many cupcakes can he make in 6 batches? **72 cupcakes**

2. A pizza recipe takes 20 minutes to prepare, 45 minutes for the dough to rise, and 15 minutes to bake. Melissa's guests will arrive in an hour. Can she make the pizza and have it ready for the guests when they arrive? Explain. **No; It will take 1 hr, 20 min to make the pizza.**

Set 5 For use after page 225.

Find each product.

1.	$3.64	2.	$8.25	3.	$6.06	4.	$2.43	5.	$9.95
	$\times\ 5$		$\times\ 4$		$\times\ 8$		$\times\ 7$		$\times\ 6$
	$18.20		$33.00		$48.48		$17.01		$59.70

6.	$5.99	7.	$1.78	8.	$6.17	9.	$0.87	10.	$5.08
	$\times\ 3$		$\times\ 2$		$\times\ 9$		$\times\ 6$		$\times\ 7$
	$17.97		$3.56		$55.53		$5.22		$35.56

11.	$4.50	12.	$3.29	13.	$7.04	14.	$2.22	15.	$4.12
	$\times\ 4$		$\times\ 9$		$\times\ 5$		$\times\ 6$		$\times\ 3$
	$18		$29.61		$35.20		$13.32		$12.36

16. $4 \times \$9.35$ $37.40   17. $9 \times \$6.17$ $55.53   18. $8 \times \$8.29$ $66.32   19. $3 \times \$4.18$ $12.54   20. $2 \times \$5.31$ $10.62

Set 6 For use after page 231.

Find each product.

1. $(3 \times 8) \times 5$ 120   2. $6 \times (4 \times 3)$ 72   3. $(9 \times 8) \times 2$ 144   4. $7 \times (5 \times 4)$ 140   5. $(7 \times 7) \times 7$ 343

6. $(9 \times 5) \times 6$ 270   7. $4 \times (4 \times 3)$ 48   8. $(1 \times 2) \times 8$ 16   9. $3 \times (12 \times 4)$ 144   10. $(4 \times 5) \times 6$ 120

11. $8 \times (9 \times 1)$ 72   12. $(3 \times 1) \times 7$ 21   13. $5 \times 5 \times 5$ 125   14. $4 \times 8 \times 6$ 192   15. $5 \times 3 \times 2$ 30

16. $2 \times (4 \times 4)$ 32   17. $8 \times 6 \times 5$ 240   18. $(3 \times 2) \times 9$ 54   19. $11 \times 3 \times 3$ 99   20. $7 \times (6 \times 4)$ 168

Set 7 For use after page 237.

1. Rivka needs 8 inches of ribbon for bows to decorate each pocket on a pair of overalls. Each pair of overalls has 3 pockets. How much ribbon does she need for 6 pairs of overalls? **48 inches**

2. If your pattern has 4 triangles, how many Power Polygons pieces will it have in all? **14 pieces**

Set 1 For use after page 255.

Find each product.

1. $\begin{array}{r} 40 \\ \times 52 \\ \hline 2,080 \end{array}$	2. $\begin{array}{r} 65 \\ \times 30 \\ \hline 1,950 \end{array}$	3. $\begin{array}{r} 74 \\ \times 10 \\ \hline 740 \end{array}$	4. $\begin{array}{r} 80 \\ \times 29 \\ \hline 2,320 \end{array}$	5. $\begin{array}{r} 20 \\ \times 18 \\ \hline 360 \end{array}$
6. $\begin{array}{r} 92 \\ \times 90 \\ \hline 8,280 \end{array}$	7. $\begin{array}{r} 60 \\ \times 21 \\ \hline 1,260 \end{array}$	8. $\begin{array}{r} 34 \\ \times 70 \\ \hline 2,380 \end{array}$	9. $\begin{array}{r} 80 \\ \times 50 \\ \hline 4,000 \end{array}$	10. $\begin{array}{r} 90 \\ \times 42 \\ \hline 3,780 \end{array}$

11. 78×30 2,340   12. 89×40 3,560   13. 30×75 2,250   14. 40×41 1,640   15. 63×80 5,040

Set 2 For use after page 263.

Find each product. Estimate to check.

1. $\begin{array}{r} 25 \\ \times 17 \\ \hline 425 \end{array}$	2. $\begin{array}{r} 68 \\ \times 34 \\ \hline 2,312 \end{array}$	3. $\begin{array}{r} 47 \\ \times 81 \\ \hline 3,807 \end{array}$	4. $\begin{array}{r} 93 \\ \times 55 \\ \hline 5,115 \end{array}$	5. $\begin{array}{r} 36 \\ \times 72 \\ \hline 2,592 \end{array}$
6. $\begin{array}{r} 84 \\ \times 67 \\ \hline 5,628 \end{array}$	7. $\begin{array}{r} 36 \\ \times 23 \\ \hline 828 \end{array}$	8. $\begin{array}{r} 71 \\ \times 15 \\ \hline 1,065 \end{array}$	9. $\begin{array}{r} 28 \\ \times 46 \\ \hline 1,288 \end{array}$	10. $\begin{array}{r} 55 \\ \times 32 \\ \hline 1,760 \end{array}$

11. 65×12 780   12. 81×43 3,483   13. 73×84 6,132   14. 42×54 2,268   15. 71×81 5,751

Set 3 For use after page 265.

Estimate each product.

1. $\begin{array}{r} 287 \\ \times 31 \\ \hline 9,000 \end{array}$	2. $\begin{array}{r} 113 \\ \times 56 \\ \hline 6,000 \end{array}$	3. $\begin{array}{r} 670 \\ \times 44 \\ \hline 28,000 \end{array}$	4. $\begin{array}{r} 249 \\ \times 15 \\ \hline 4,000 \end{array}$	5. $\begin{array}{r} 819 \\ \times 82 \\ \hline 64,000 \end{array}$
6. $\begin{array}{r} 961 \\ \times 73 \\ \hline 70,000 \end{array}$	7. $\begin{array}{r} 95 \\ \times 98 \\ \hline 10,000 \end{array}$	8. $\begin{array}{r} 206 \\ \times 39 \\ \hline 8,000 \end{array}$	9. $\begin{array}{r} 474 \\ \times 62 \\ \hline 30,000 \end{array}$	10. $\begin{array}{r} 736 \\ \times 45 \\ \hline 35,000 \end{array}$

11. 69×11 700   12. 78×39 3,200   13. 74×82 5,600   14. 37×51 2,000   15. 67×84 5,600

Set 4 For use after page 271.

1. The Ferris wheel holds 68 riders. There are 92 rides in a day. Can the Ferris wheel carry more than 6,500 people in a day? Explain. **No; $70 \times 90 = 6,300$, so the Ferris wheel can carry about 6,300 people in one day.**
2. Groups of 25 people can explore the Fun House at a time. If 56 groups tour the Fun House in an afternoon, how many people explored the Fun House? **1,400 people**

Set 5 For use after page 267.

Find each product.

1. $\begin{array}{r} 521 \\ \times 42 \\ \hline 21,882 \end{array}$	2. $\begin{array}{r} 172 \\ \times 26 \\ \hline 4,472 \end{array}$	3. $\begin{array}{r} 5,000 \\ \times 30 \\ \hline 150,000 \end{array}$	4. $\begin{array}{r} 3,862 \\ \times 49 \\ \hline 189,238 \end{array}$	5. $\begin{array}{r} 4,736 \\ \times 85 \\ \hline 402,560 \end{array}$
6. $\begin{array}{r} 458 \\ \times 16 \\ \hline 7,328 \end{array}$	7. $\begin{array}{r} 973 \\ \times 32 \\ \hline 31,136 \end{array}$	8. $\begin{array}{r} 3,311 \\ \times 53 \\ \hline 175,483 \end{array}$	9. $\begin{array}{r} 3,082 \\ \times 22 \\ \hline 67,804 \end{array}$	10. $\begin{array}{r} 5,699 \\ \times 13 \\ \hline 74,087 \end{array}$
11. $\begin{array}{r} 321 \\ \times 14 \\ \hline 4,494 \end{array}$	12. $\begin{array}{r} 518 \\ \times 43 \\ \hline 22,274 \end{array}$	13. $\begin{array}{r} 2,507 \\ \times 28 \\ \hline 70,196 \end{array}$	14. $\begin{array}{r} 7,000 \\ \times 60 \\ \hline 420,000 \end{array}$	15. $\begin{array}{r} 4,212 \\ \times 35 \\ \hline 147,420 \end{array}$
16. $\begin{array}{r} 822 \\ \times 15 \\ \hline 12,330 \end{array}$	17. $\begin{array}{r} 304 \\ \times 72 \\ \hline 21,888 \end{array}$	18. $\begin{array}{r} 4,000 \\ \times 90 \\ \hline 360,000 \end{array}$	19. $\begin{array}{r} 3,050 \\ \times 44 \\ \hline 134,200 \end{array}$	20. $\begin{array}{r} 8,161 \\ \times 29 \\ \hline 236,669 \end{array}$

Set 6 For use after page 275.

Multiply. Estimate to check.

1. $\begin{array}{r} \$3.15 \\ \times 18 \\ \hline \$56.70 \end{array}$	2. $\begin{array}{r} \$8.63 \\ \times 24 \\ \hline \$207.12 \end{array}$	3. $\begin{array}{r} \$10.49 \\ \times 31 \\ \hline \$325.19 \end{array}$	4. $\begin{array}{r} \$15.77 \\ \times 46 \\ \hline \$725.42 \end{array}$	5. $\begin{array}{r} \$28.04 \\ \times 32 \\ \hline \$897.28 \end{array}$
6. $\begin{array}{r} \$8.04 \\ \times 11 \\ \hline \$88.44 \end{array}$	7. $\begin{array}{r} \$2.45 \\ \times 16 \\ \hline \$39.20 \end{array}$	8. $\begin{array}{r} \$12.36 \\ \times 27 \\ \hline \$333.72 \end{array}$	9. $\begin{array}{r} \$17.81 \\ \times 33 \\ \hline \$587.73 \end{array}$	10. $\begin{array}{r} \$25.99 \\ \times 54 \\ \hline \$1,403.46 \end{array}$
11. $\begin{array}{r} \$6.32 \\ \times 12 \\ \hline \$75.84 \end{array}$	12. $\begin{array}{r} \$4.65 \\ \times 18 \\ \hline \$83.70 \end{array}$	13. $\begin{array}{r} \$53.21 \\ \times 74 \\ \hline \$3,937.54 \end{array}$	14. $\begin{array}{r} \$49.72 \\ \times 48 \\ \hline \$2,386.56 \end{array}$	15. $\begin{array}{r} \$19.45 \\ \times 38 \\ \hline \$739.10 \end{array}$
16. $\begin{array}{r} \$4.99 \\ \times 10 \\ \hline \$49.90 \end{array}$	17. $\begin{array}{r} \$7.35 \\ \times 25 \\ \hline \$183.75 \end{array}$	18. $\begin{array}{r} \$19.75 \\ \times 52 \\ \hline \$1,027 \end{array}$	19. $\begin{array}{r} \$34.05 \\ \times 22 \\ \hline \$749.10 \end{array}$	20. $\begin{array}{r} \$46.15 \\ \times 91 \\ \hline \$4,199.65 \end{array}$

Set 7 For use after page 281.

1. Bernie has 48 autographed baseball cards that he wants to frame. What are the different ways he can arrange the cards in rows so that there are the same number of cards in each row? **1. 6 rows of 8, 8 rows of 6, 4 rows of 12, 12 rows of 4, 16 rows of 3, 3 rows of 16, 2 rows of 24, 24 rows of 2, 1 row of 48, 48 rows of 1**

2. Alison is the middle musician in a marching band. There are the same number of musicians in each row. Alison has 4 musicians to the left of her, 4 to the right, 3 directly in front of her, and 3 directly behind her. How many musicians are there? **63 musicians**

Set 1 For use after page 305.

Divide. Check your answer.

1. $3\overline{)51}$ 17   2. $4\overline{)56}$ 14   3. $2\overline{)62}$ 31   4. $6\overline{)96}$ 16   5. $3\overline{)64}$ 21 R1

6. $5\overline{)79}$ 15 R4   7. $4\overline{)47}$ 11 R3   8. $8\overline{)96}$ 12   9. $9\overline{)97}$ 10 R7   10. $7\overline{)90}$ 12 R6

11. $7\overline{)91}$ 13   12. $6\overline{)83}$ 13 R5   13. $9\overline{)91}$ 10 R1   14. $2\overline{)32}$ 16   15. $8\overline{)99}$ 12 R3

16. $68 \div 5$ 13R3   17. $79 \div 7$ 11R2   18. $72 \div 4$ 18   19. $89 \div 8$ 11R1   20. $37 \div 2$ 18R1

Set 2 For use after page 311.

Divide. Check your answer.

1. $3\overline{)222}$ 74   2. $5\overline{)465}$ 93   3. $4\overline{)528}$ 132   4. $2\overline{)384}$ 192   5. $6\overline{)531}$ 88 R3

6. $7\overline{)684}$ 97 R5   7. $9\overline{)436}$ 48 R4   8. $8\overline{)944}$ 118   9. $5\overline{)697}$139 R2 10. $9\overline{)775}$ 86 R1

11. $4\overline{)345}$ 86 R2 12. $6\overline{)696}$ 116   13. $8\overline{)756}$ 94 R4 14. $2\overline{)837}$418 R1 15. $5\overline{)678}$135 R3

16. $384 \div 6$ 64   17. $257 \div 3$ 85 R2 18. $436 \div 9$ 48 R4   19. $152 \div 7$ 21 R5   20. $128 \div 4$ 32

Set 3 For use after page 315.

Divide. Check your answer.

1. $5\overline{)509}$ 101 R4 2. $2\overline{)181}$ 90 R1 3. $6\overline{)485}$ 80 R5 4. $4\overline{)282}$ 70 R2 5. $3\overline{)321}$ 107

6. $6\overline{)723}$ 120 R3 7. $8\overline{)865}$108 R1 8. $5\overline{)547}$109 R2 9. $9\overline{)998}$110 R8 10. $4\overline{)830}$ 207 R2

11. $3\overline{)609}$ 203   12. $7\overline{)842}$120 R2 13. $9\overline{)633}$ 70 R3 14. $8\overline{)878}$109 R6 15. $7\overline{)986}$ 140 R6

16. $602 \div 3$ 200 R2   17. $657 \div 6$ 109 R3   18. $484 \div 8$ 60 R4   19. $622 \div 3$ 207 R1   20. $263 \div 4$ 65 R3

Set 4 For use after page 317.

1. Andre invites 15 people to his party. He wants to buy a party hat for each person. If there are 6 party hats in a package, how many packages should Andre buy? **3 packages**

2. If 15 guests at Andre's party each drink one soda, how many six-packs of soda will they use? How many guests could drink more than one soda? **3 six-packs; 3 could drink 2 sodas.**

Set 5 For use after page 323.

Divide. Check your answer.

1. $3\overline{)\$4.74}$ \$1.58 2. $5\overline{)\$8.15}$ \$1.63 3. $2\overline{)\$9.74}$ \$4.87 4. $7\overline{)\$6.16}$ \$0.88 5. $6\overline{)\$9.12}$ \$1.52

6. $8\overline{)\$6.48}$ \$0.81 7. $4\overline{)\$4.16}$ \$1.04 8. $3\overline{)\$8.40}$ \$2.80 9. $7\overline{)\$0.63}$\$0.09 10. $8\overline{)\$8.40}$ \$1.05

11. $9\overline{)\$9.63}$\$1.07 12. $4\overline{)\$8.72}$\$2.18 13. $6\overline{)\$6.84}$\$1.14 14. $8\overline{)\$9.84}$\$1.23 15. $2\overline{)\$1.52}$\$0.76

16. $5\overline{)\$6.50}$\$1.30 17. $3\overline{)\$5.88}$\$1.96 18. $9\overline{)\$0.81}$\$0.09 19. $6\overline{)\$9.00}$\$1.50 20. $7\overline{)\$9.94}$\$1.42

21. $2\overline{)\$8.94}$\$4.47 22. $5\overline{)\$7.05}$\$1.41 23. $4\overline{)\$0.28}$\$0.07 24. $7\overline{)\$7.68}$\$1.28 25. $8\overline{)\$8.96}$\$1.12

Set 6 For use after page 331.

Copy and complete. Test each number to see if it is divisible by 3, 5, 6, or 9.
If it is, write the quotient.

		30	45	66	75	180
1.	By 3?	10	15	22	25	60
2.	By 5?	6	9		15	36
3.	By 6?	5		11		30
4.	By 9?		5			20

5. Without dividing, tell whether you can put 159 pennies in 3 equal piles. **Yes, 1 + 5 + 9 = 15; 15 is divisible by 3, so 159 is divisible by 3.**

6. Write an even number that is divisible by 9. **Possible answers: 18, 36, 54, 72, 90, …**

7. Write an odd number that is divisible by 5. **Possible answers: 5, 15, 25, 35, 45, …**

Set 7 For use after page 333.

1. Daniel used an 8-ounce package of chocolate chips for a trail mix. He used an unmeasured amount of nuts. He weighed the mix and found it weighed 20 ounces. What was the weight of the nuts he used? **12 ounces**

2. Anita mixed 32 ounces of orange juice with some seltzer. She filled seven 8-ounce glasses and had 4 ounces remaining. How much seltzer did she use? **28 ounces**

Set 1 For use after page 347.
Write the name of each polygon.

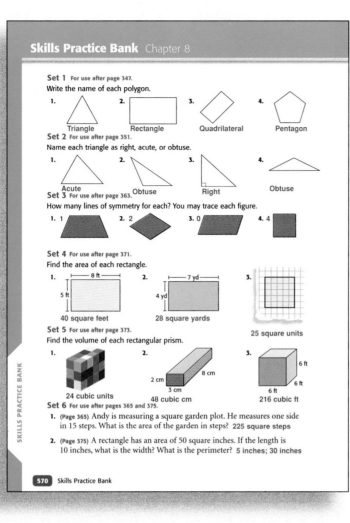

1. Triangle
2. Rectangle
3. Quadrilateral
4. Pentagon

Set 2 For use after page 351.
Name each triangle as right, acute, or obtuse.

1. Acute
2. Obtuse
3. Right
4. Obtuse

Set 3 For use after page 363.
How many lines of symmetry for each? You may trace each figure.

1. 1
2. 2
3. 0
4. 4

Set 4 For use after page 371.
Find the area of each rectangle.

1. 8 ft / 5 ft — 40 square feet
2. 7 yd / 4 yd — 28 square yards
3. 25 square units

Set 5 For use after page 373.
Find the volume of each rectangular prism.

1. 24 cubic units
2. 2 cm / 3 cm / 8 cm — 48 cubic cm
3. 6 ft / 6 ft / 6 ft — 216 cubic ft

Set 6 For use after pages 365 and 375.

1. (Page 365) Andy is measuring a square garden plot. He measures one side in 15 steps. What is the area of the garden in steps? **225 square steps**

2. (Page 375) A rectangle has an area of 50 square inches. If the length is 10 inches, what is the width? What is the perimeter? **5 inches; 30 inches**

Set 1 For use after page 389.
Write a fraction that compares the different balls to the whole set.

1. Basketballs $\frac{3}{11}$
2. Tennis balls $\frac{1}{11}$
3. Baseballs $\frac{4}{11}$
4. Soccer balls $\frac{2}{11}$
5. Round balls $\frac{10}{11}$

Set 2 For use after page 393.
Write each improper fraction as a whole or mixed number. Use fraction strips or draw pictures to help.

1. $\frac{5}{3}$ $1\frac{2}{3}$
2. $\frac{8}{4}$ 2
3. $\frac{9}{4}$ $2\frac{1}{4}$
4. $\frac{10}{2}$ 5
5. $\frac{7}{2}$ $3\frac{1}{2}$

Write each mixed number as an improper fraction.

6. $1\frac{1}{4}$ $\frac{5}{4}$
7. $2\frac{2}{3}$ $\frac{8}{3}$
8. $3\frac{3}{4}$ $\frac{15}{4}$
9. $1\frac{5}{6}$ $\frac{11}{6}$
10. $6\frac{1}{2}$ $\frac{13}{2}$

Set 3 For use after page 403.
Is each fraction in simplest form? If not, write it in simplest form.

1. $\frac{10}{20}$ $\frac{1}{2}$
2. $\frac{3}{7}$ Yes
3. $\frac{4}{6}$ $\frac{2}{3}$
4. $\frac{3}{9}$ $\frac{1}{3}$
5. $\frac{5}{8}$ Yes

6. $\frac{8}{10}$ $\frac{4}{5}$
7. $\frac{9}{16}$ Yes
8. $\frac{15}{25}$ $\frac{3}{5}$
9. $\frac{12}{18}$ $\frac{2}{3}$
10. $\frac{23}{24}$ Yes

Set 4 For use after page 409.
Find the number for each fraction of a set. You may use counters to help.

1. $\frac{1}{2}$ of 16 8
2. $\frac{2}{3}$ of 12 8
3. $\frac{1}{4}$ of 20 5
4. $\frac{3}{5}$ of 15 9

5. $\frac{1}{8}$ of 24 3
6. $\frac{3}{4}$ of 16 12
7. $\frac{2}{7}$ of 21 6
8. $\frac{5}{6}$ of 18 15

Set 5 For use after page 419.

1. Jackie walks 450 feet. If she walks 10 times as far, will she walk more or less than a mile? Explain. **Less; 4,500 ft < 5,280 ft.**

Set 6 For use after page 421.

1. One block has 15 recycling containers. There are three more paper containers than plastic containers. How many paper containers are there? How many plastic containers? **9 paper containers; 6 plastic containers**

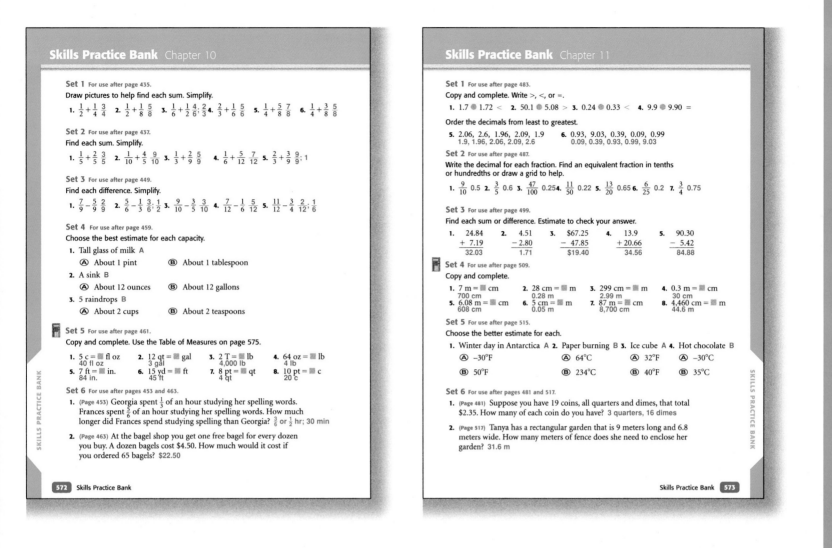

Set 1 For use after page 435.

Draw pictures to help find each sum. Simplify.

1. $\frac{1}{2} + \frac{1}{4}$ $\frac{3}{4}$
2. $\frac{1}{2} + \frac{1}{8}$ $\frac{5}{8}$
3. $\frac{1}{6} + \frac{1}{2}$ $\frac{4}{6}, \frac{2}{3}$
4. $\frac{2}{3} + \frac{1}{6}$ $\frac{5}{6}$
5. $\frac{1}{4} + \frac{5}{8}$ $\frac{7}{8}$
6. $\frac{1}{4} + \frac{3}{8}$ $\frac{5}{8}$

Set 2 For use after page 437.

Find each sum. Simplify.

1. $\frac{1}{5} + \frac{2}{5}$ $\frac{3}{5}$
2. $\frac{1}{10} + \frac{4}{5}$ $\frac{9}{10}$
3. $\frac{1}{3} + \frac{2}{9}$ $\frac{5}{9}$
4. $\frac{1}{6} + \frac{5}{12}$ $\frac{7}{12}$
5. $\frac{2}{3} + \frac{3}{9}$ $\frac{9}{9}; 1$

Set 3 For use after page 449.

Find each difference. Simplify.

1. $\frac{7}{9} - \frac{5}{9}$ $\frac{2}{9}$
2. $\frac{5}{6} - \frac{1}{3}$ $\frac{3}{6}, \frac{1}{2}$
3. $\frac{9}{10} - \frac{3}{5}$ $\frac{3}{10}$
4. $\frac{7}{12} - \frac{1}{6}$ $\frac{5}{12}$
5. $\frac{11}{12} - \frac{3}{4}$ $\frac{2}{12}; \frac{1}{6}$

Set 4 For use after page 459.

Choose the best estimate for each capacity.

1. Tall glass of milk A
   - Ⓐ About 1 pint
   - Ⓑ About 1 tablespoon
2. A sink B
   - Ⓐ About 12 ounces
   - Ⓑ About 12 gallons
3. 5 raindrops B
   - Ⓐ About 2 cups
   - Ⓑ About 2 teaspoons

Set 5 For use after page 461.

Copy and complete. Use the Table of Measures on page 575.

1. 5 c = ▦ fl oz 40 fl oz
2. 12 qt = ▦ gal 3 gal
3. 2 T = ▦ lb 4,000 lb
4. 64 oz = ▦ lb 4 lb
5. 7 ft = ▦ in. 84 in.
6. 15 yd = ▦ ft 45 ft
7. 8 pt = ▦ qt 4 qt
8. 10 pt = ▦ c 20 c

Set 6 For use after pages 453 and 463.

1. (Page 453) Georgia spent $\frac{1}{3}$ of an hour studying her spelling words. Frances spent $\frac{5}{6}$ of an hour studying her spelling words. How much longer did Frances spend studying spelling than Georgia? $\frac{3}{6}$ or $\frac{1}{2}$ hr; 30 min

2. (Page 463) At the bagel shop you get one free bagel for every dozen you buy. A dozen bagels cost $4.50. How much would it cost if you ordered 65 bagels? $22.50

Set 1 For use after page 483.

Copy and complete. Write >, <, or =.

1. 1.7 ● 1.72 <
2. 50.1 ● 5.08 >
3. 0.24 ● 0.33 <
4. 9.9 ● 9.90 =

Order the decimals from least to greatest.

5. 2.06, 2.6, 1.96, 2.09, 1.9 1.9, 1.96, 2.06, 2.09, 2.6
6. 0.93, 9.03, 0.39, 0.09, 0.99 0.09, 0.39, 0.93, 0.99, 9.03

Set 2 For use after page 487.

Write the decimal for each fraction. Find an equivalent fraction in tenths or hundredths or draw a grid to help.

1. $\frac{9}{10}$ 0.5
2. $\frac{3}{5}$ 0.6
3. $\frac{47}{100}$ 0.25
4. $\frac{11}{50}$ 0.22
5. $\frac{13}{20}$ 0.65
6. $\frac{6}{25}$ 0.2
7. $\frac{3}{4}$ 0.75

Set 3 For use after page 499.

Find each sum or difference. Estimate to check your answer.

1. 24.84
    + 7.19
    32.03

2. 4.51
    − 2.80
    1.71

3. $67.25
    − 47.85
    $19.40

4. 13.9
    + 20.66
    34.56

5. 90.30
    − 5.42
    84.88

Set 4 For use after page 509.

Copy and complete.

1. 7 m = ▦ cm 700 cm
2. 28 cm = ▦ m 0.28 m
3. 299 cm = ▦ m 2.99 m
4. 0.3 m = ▦ cm 30 cm
5. 6.08 m = ▦ cm 608 cm
6. 5 cm = ▦ m 0.05 m
7. 87 m = ▦ cm 8,700 cm
8. 4,460 cm = ▦ m 44.6 m

Set 5 For use after page 515.

Choose the better estimate for each.

1. Winter day in Antarctica A
2. Paper burning B
3. Ice cube A
4. Hot chocolate B
   - Ⓐ −30°F
   - Ⓐ 64°C
   - Ⓐ 32°F
   - Ⓐ −30°C
   - Ⓑ 50°F
   - Ⓑ 234°C
   - Ⓑ 40°F
   - Ⓑ 35°C

Set 6 For use after pages 481 and 517.

1. (Page 481) Suppose you have 19 coins, all quarters and dimes, that total $2.35. How many of each coin do you have? 3 quarters, 16 dimes

2. (Page 517) Tanya has a rectangular garden that is 9 meters long and 6.8 meters wide. How many meters of fence does she need to enclose her garden? 31.6 m

Set 1 For use after page 529.

Find each quotient.

1. $80 \div 40$ **2**   **2.** $100 \div 20$ **5**   **3.** $90 \div 30$ **3**   **4.** $120 \div 30$ **4**

5. $540 \div 90$ **6**   **6.** $48,000 \div 60$ **800**   **7.** $1,600 \div 80$ **20**   **8.** $360 \div 60$ **6**

Set 2 For use after page 533.

Divide and check.

1. $20\overline{)89}$ **4 R9**   **2.** $40\overline{)215}$ **5 R15**   **3.** $50\overline{)191}$ **3 R41**   **4.** $90\overline{)642}$ **7 R12**   **5.** $60\overline{)435}$ **7 R15**

6. $30\overline{)203}$ **6 R23**   **7.** $60\overline{)554}$ **9 R14**   **8.** $80\overline{)467}$ **5 R67**   **9.** $70\overline{)618}$ **8 R58**   **10.** $20\overline{)78}$ **3 R18**

Set 3 For use after page 535.

Divide and check.

1. $23\overline{)111}$ **4 R19**   **2.** $62\overline{)246}$ **3 R60**   **3.** $35\overline{)180}$ **5 R5**   **4.** $47\overline{)329}$ **7**   **5.** $81\overline{)560}$ **6 R74**

6. $18\overline{)151}$ **8 R7**   **7.** $59\overline{)437}$ **7 R24**   **8.** $74\overline{)147}$ **1 R73**   **9.** $98\overline{)613}$ **6 R25**   **10.** $60\overline{)195}$ **3R15**

Set 4 For use after page 545.

1. Emily can get 10 or 20 points when she tosses a bean bag at the first target. She can get 5, 15, or 25 points when she tosses a bean bag at the second target. Make a tree diagram to show the possible outcomes after two tosses.

Possible Outcomes

10 — 5   10, 5
10 — 15   10, 15
10 — 25   10, 25

20 — 5   20, 5
20 — 15   20, 15
20 — 25   20, 25

Set 5 For use after page 549.

1. Kim plans to toss a number cube numbered from 1 to 6. What is the probability of rolling:

a. an even number? $\frac{1}{2}$ **b.** a 5 or 6? $\frac{1}{3}$ **c.** a 7? **0**

Set 6 For use after page 551.

1. In Mr. Henri's class, there are 3 people wearing red T-shirts, 10 people wearing blue T-shirts, 5 people wearing yellow T-shirts, and 6 people wearing purple T-shirts. What is the probability that a person picked at random is:

a. wearing a yellow T-shirt? $\frac{5}{24}$

b. wearing a red T-shirt? $\frac{3}{24}$ or $\frac{1}{8}$

c. wearing a purple or blue T-shirt? $\frac{16}{24}$ or $\frac{2}{3}$

2. The shirt store has 3 T-shirt styles and 4 cap styles. How many T-shirt and cap combinations can you buy? **12 combinations**

Table of Measures

Customary Units of Measure

Length

1 foot (ft)	= 12 inches (in.)
1 yard (yd)	= 36 inches (in.)
	= 3 feet (ft)
1 mile (mi)	= 5,280 feet (ft)
	= 1,760 yards (yd)

Area

1 square foot (ft²)	= 144 square inches (in²)

Volume

1 cubic foot (ft³)	= 1,728 cubic inches (in³)

Capacity

1 tablespoon (tbsp)	= 3 teaspoons (tsp)
1 fluid ounce (fl oz)	= 2 tablespoons (tbsp)
1 cup (c)	= 8 fluid ounces (fl oz)
1 pint (pt)	= 2 cups (c)
1 quart (qt)	= 2 pints (pt)
1 gallon (gal)	= 4 quarts (qt)

Weight

1 pound (lb)	= 16 ounces (oz)
1 ton (T)	= 2,000 pounds (lb)

Fahrenheit Temperature

32°F	= freezing point of water
98.6°F	= normal body temperature
212°F	= boiling point of water

Time

1 minute (min)	= 60 seconds (sec)
1 hour (hr)	= 60 minutes (min)
1 day (d)	= 24 hours (hr)
1 week (wk)	= 7 days (d)
1 month (mo)	= about 4 weeks (wk)
1 year (yr)	= 365 days (d)
	= 52 weeks (wk)
	= 12 months (mo)
1 decade	= 10 years (yr)
1 century	= 100 years (yr)

Metric Units of Measure

Length

1 centimeter (cm)	= 10 millimeters (mm)
1 decimeter (dm)	= 100 millimeters (mm)
	= 10 centimeters (cm)
1 meter (m)	= 1,000 millimeters (mm)
	= 100 centimeters (cm)
	= 10 decimeters (dm)
1 kilometer (km)	= 1,000 meters (m)

Area

1 square meter (m²)	= 10,000 square centimeters (cm²)
	= 100 square decimeters (dm²)

Volume

1 cubic decimeter (dm³)	= 1,000 cubic centimeters (cm³)

Capacity

1 liter (L)	= 1,000 milliliters (mL)

Mass

1 gram (g)	= 1,000 milligrams (mg)
1 kilogram (kg)	= 1,000 grams (g)
1 metric ton (t)	= 1,000 kilograms (kg)

Celsius Temperature

0°C	= freezing point of water
37°C	= normal body temperature
100°C	= boiling point of water

A.M. (p. 74) Times from midnight to noon.

acute angle (p. 350) An angle that is less than a right angle.

acute triangle (p. 350) A triangle with all angles less than right angles.

addend (p. 108) A number added to find a sum. *Examples:* 2 + 7 = 9
      ↑ ↑
   Addend Addend

addition (p. 22) An operation that tells the total number when you put together two or more numbers.

analog clock (p. 74) A clock that displays time using hands.

angle (p. 350) Two rays with a common endpoint.

area (p. 370) The number of square units needed to cover a closed figure.

array (p. 148) Objects arranged in rows and columns.

average (p. 326) The number found when the sum of two or more numbers is divided by the number of addends. Also called the *mean*.

bar graph (p. 10) A graph that uses bars to show data.

benchmark (p. 390) A known measurement that is used to estimate other measurements.

capacity (p. 512) The amount a container can hold.

centimeter (cm) (p. 505) A unit for measuring length in the metric system. *See also* Table of Measures, page 575
1 centimeter

certain (p. 541) Definitely will happen.

chances (p. 540) The probability that a particular event will occur.

change (p. 129) The amount of money you receive back when you pay with more money than something costs.

circle (p. 347) A plane figure in which all the points are the same distance from a point called the center.

Center ——▶ · ◀— Circle

circle graph (p. 404) A graph in the form of a circle that shows how the whole is broken into parts.

cluster (p. 16) Data that group around one value of a line plot.

compare (p. 66) To decide which of two numbers is greater.

composite number (p. 185) A whole number greater than 1 with more than two different factors. *Example:* The composite number 6 has factors of 1, 2, 3, and 6.

cone (p. 345) A solid figure with one circular face and one vertex.

congruent figures (p. 353) Figures that have the same size and shape.

Congruent triangles

coordinate grid (p. 12) A graph used to locate points.

cube (p. 345) A solid figure whose 6 faces are all squares.

cubic centimeter (p. 373) A cube with 1 centimeter edges; Unit for measuring volume.

cubic inch (p. 373) A cube with 1 inch edges; Unit for measuring volume.

cubic unit (p. 372) A cube with 1 unit edges; Unit for measuring volume.

cup (c) (p. 458) A unit for measuring capacity in the customary system. *See also* Table of Measures, page 575

customary units of length, weight, capacity, and temperature *See* Table of Measures, page 575

cylinder (p. 345) A solid figure with two congruent circular faces.

data (p. 10) Information used to make calculations.

decimal (p. 476) A number that uses a decimal point to show tenths and hundredths. *Example:* 4.15

decimal point (p. 126) A symbol used to separate the ones place from the tenths place in decimals, or dollars from cents in money.
Example: 4.57
    ↑ Decimal point

decimeter (dm) (p. 505) A unit for measuring length in the metric system. *See also* Table of Measures, page 575

degree Celsius (°C) (p. 514) A unit for measuring temperature in the metric system. *See also* Table of Measures, page 575

degree Fahrenheit (°F) (p. 514) A unit for measuring temperature in the customary system. *See also* Table of Measures, page 575

denominator (p. 388) The bottom number of a fraction that tells the number of equal parts in the whole. *Example:* $\frac{7}{8}$ ← Denominator

diagonal (p. 363) A line segment other than a side that connects two vertices of a polygon.

Diagonal   Vertex
Vertex →

difference (p. 95) The number that is the result of subtracting one number from another.
Example: $6 - 4 = 2$ ← Difference

digits (p. 52) The symbols used to show numbers: 0, 1, 2, 3, 4, 5, 6, 7, 8, and 9.

digital clock (p. 74) A clock that displays time using numbers.

display (p. 404) The window on a calculator that shows the numbers as they are entered and the results of the calculations.

dividend (p. 170) The number to be divided in a division number sentence.
Example: $63 \div 9 = 7$
    ↑ Dividend

divisible (p. 330) Can be divided by another number without leaving a remainder.
Example: 18 is divisible by 6.

division (p. 166) An operation that tells how many groups there are or how many are in each group.

divisor (p. 170) The number by which a dividend is divided. *Example:* $63 \div 9 = 7$
    ↑ Divisor

edge (p. 344) A line segment where two faces of a solid figure meet.

←— Edge

elapsed time (p. 78) The difference between two times.

endpoint (p. 358) A point at the start of a ray or ar either end of a line segment.

equally likely (p. 541) Just as likely to happen as not to happen.

equation (p. 22) A number sentence that uses the equals sign (=) to show that two expressions have the same value. *See also* number sentence
Example: $9 + 2 = 11$

equilateral triangle (p. 349) A triangle with three equal sides.

equivalent fractions (p. 399) Fractions that name the same region, part of a set, or part of a segment. *Example:* $\frac{1}{2}$ and $\frac{2}{4}$

estimate (p. 70) To find a number that is close to an exact answer.

even number (p. 180) A whole number that has 0, 2, 4, 6, or 8 in the ones place; A whole number divisible by 2.

expanded form (p. 52) A way to write a number that shows the place value of each digit.
Example: $9{,}000 + 300 + 20 + 5$

experiment (p. 146) A test or trial.

face (p. 344) A flat surface of a solid figure.

←— Face

fact family (p. 169) A group of related facts using the same set of numbers.
Example: $4 + 3 = 7$
    $3 + 4 = 7$
    $7 - 3 = 4$
    $7 - 4 = 3$

factors (p. 148) Numbers that are multiplied together to obtain a product.
Examples: $7 \times 3 = 21$
  Factor ↑ ↑ Factor

fair game (p. 543) A game where each player has an equal chance of winning.

flip (p. 353) To turn a plane figure over.

fluid ounce (p. 459) A unit for measuring capacity in the customary system. *See also* Table of Measures, page 575

foot (ft) (p. 415) A unit for measuring length in the customary system. *See also* Table of Measures, page 575

fraction (p. 387) A way to compare equal parts to a whole. *Example:* $\frac{3}{10}$ is 3 equal parts out of 10 equal parts.

front-end estimation (p. 108) A way to estimate a sum by adding the first digit of each addend and adjusting the result based on the remaining digits.

gallon (gal) (p. 458) A unit for measuring capacity in the customary system. *See also* Table of Measures, page 575

gram (g) (p. 511) A unit for measuring mass in the metric system. *See also* Table of Measures, page 575

graph (p. 10) A picture that shows data in an organized way.

greater than (>) (p. 66) The relationship of one number being farther to the right on a number line than another number. *Examples:* 7 > 3

2 3 4 5 6 7 8

"Seven is greater than three."

grouping (associative) property (p. 230) When the grouping of addends or factors is changed, the sum or product stays the same. *Examples:* $(5 + 2) + 3 = 5 + (2 + 3)$
$(3 \times 2) \times 1 = 3 \times (2 \times 1)$

hexagon (p. 347) A polygon with six sides.

hundredth (p. 476) One out of 100 equal parts of a whole.

impossible (p. 541) Cannot happen.

improper fraction (p. 392) A fraction in which the numerator is greater than or equal to the denominator.

inch (in.) (p. 415) A unit for measuring length in the customary system. *See also* Table of Measures, page 575

1 inch

intersecting lines (p. 358) Lines that cross at a point.

isosceles triangle (p. 349) A triangle that has at least two equal sides.

key (p. 10) Part of a pictograph that tells what each symbol stands for. *See also* symbol

kilogram (kg) (p. 511) A unit for measuring mass in the metric system. *See also* Table of Measures, page 575

kilometer (km) (p. 506) A unit for measuring length in the metric system. *See also* Table of Measures, page 575

leaf (p. 18) The part of a stem-and-leaf plot that shows the ones digit of a number.

less than (<) (p. 66) The relationship of one number being farther to the left on a number line than another number. *Examples:* 3 < 7

2 3 4 5 6 7 8

"Three is less than seven."

likely (p. 541) Probably will happen.

line (p. 358) A straight path that is endless in both directions.

line graph (p. 14) A graph that connects points to show how data changes over time.

line of symmetry (p. 363) A line on which a figure can be folded so that both halves are congruent. Line of symmetry

line plot (p. 16) A graph that shows data along a number line.

line segment (p. 358) Part of a line that has two end points.

●━━━━━━━●

liter (L) (p. 512) A unit for measuring capacity in the metric system. *See also* Table of Measures, page 575

mass (p. 511) The amount of matter that something contains.

mean (p. 327) The number found when the sum of two or more numbers is divided by the number of addends. Also called the *average*.

median (p. 31) The middle number when data are arranged in order.

mental math (p. 120) Performing calculations without using pencil and paper or a calculator.

meter (m) (p. 505) A unit for measuring length in the metric system. *See also* Table of Measures, page 575

metric units of length, weight, mass, capacity, and temperature *See* Table of Measures, page 575

mile (mi) (p. 419) A unit for measuring length in the customary system. *See also* Table of Measures, page 575

milliliter (mL) (p. 512) A unit for measuring capacity in the metric system. *See also* Table of Measures, page 575

millimeter (mm) (p. 505) A unit for measuring length in the metric system. *See also* Table of Measures, page 575

mixed number (p. 392) A number that has a whole-number part and a fractional part. *Example:* $2\frac{3}{4}$

mode (p. 31) The number or numbers that occur most often in a set of data.

multiple (p. 150) The product of a given whole number and any other whole number.

multiplication (p. 148) An operation that tells the total number when you put together equal groups.

number line (p. 16) A line that shows numbers in order using a scale.

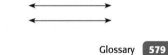

number sentence (p. 22) A way to show a relationship between numbers. *See also* equation
Examples: $2 + 5 = 7$
$6 \div 2 = 3$

numerator (p. 388) The top number of a fraction. It tells the number of equal parts compared to the number of equal parts in a whole. *Example:* $\frac{7}{8}$ ← Numerator

obtuse angle (p. 350) An angle that is greater than a right angle.

obtuse triangle (p. 350) A triangle with one angle greater than a right angle.

octagon (p. 347) A polygon with eight sides.

odd number (p. 180) A whole number that has 1, 3, 5, 7, or 9 in the ones place. A whole number not divisible by 2.

one property (p. 151) In multiplication, the product of a number and 1 is that number. In division, a number divided by 1 is that number. *Examples:* $5 \times 1 = 5$
$3 \div 1 = 3$

operation (p. 22) Addition, subtraction, multiplication, and division.

order (p. 68) To arrange numbers from least to greatest or from greatest to least.

ordered pair (p. 12) A pair of numbers used to locate a point on a coordinate grid. *Example:* (3, 5)

order (commutative) property (p. 151) Changing the order of addends or factors does not change the sum or product. *Examples:* $8 + 5 = 5 + 8$
$3 \times 6 = 6 \times 3$

ordinal number (p. 80) A number used to tell order. *Examples:* First, thirteenth, 1st, 4th

ounce (oz) (p. 457) A unit for measuring weight in the customary system. *See also* Table of Measures, page 575

outcome (p. 543) A possible result of an experiment.

P.M. (p. 74) Times from noon to midnight.

parallel lines (p. 358) Lines that do not intersect.

←————————→
←————————→

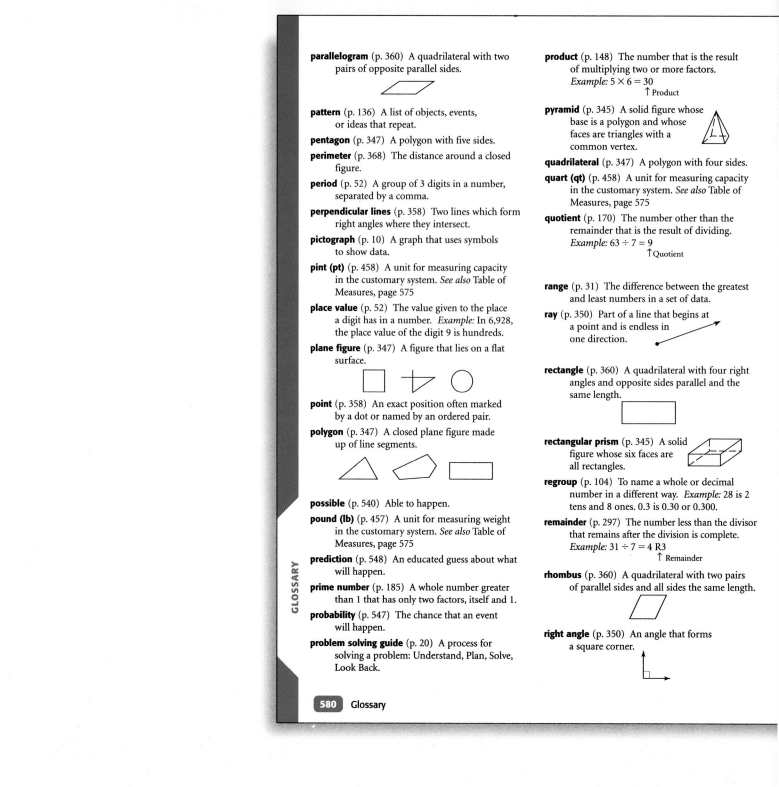

parallelogram (p. 360) A quadrilateral with two pairs of opposite parallel sides.

pattern (p. 136) A list of objects, events, or ideas that repeat.

pentagon (p. 347) A polygon with five sides.

perimeter (p. 368) The distance around a closed figure.

period (p. 52) A group of 3 digits in a number, separated by a comma.

perpendicular lines (p. 358) Two lines which form right angles where they intersect.

pictograph (p. 10) A graph that uses symbols to show data.

pint (pt) (p. 458) A unit for measuring capacity in the customary system. *See also* Table of Measures, page 575

place value (p. 52) The value given to the place a digit has in a number. *Example:* In 6,928, the place value of the digit 9 is hundreds.

plane figure (p. 347) A figure that lies on a flat surface.

point (p. 358) An exact position often marked by a dot or named by an ordered pair.

polygon (p. 347) A closed plane figure made up of line segments.

possible (p. 540) Able to happen.

pound (lb) (p. 457) A unit for measuring weight in the customary system. *See also* Table of Measures, page 575

prediction (p. 548) An educated guess about what will happen.

prime number (p. 185) A whole number greater than 1 that has only two factors, itself and 1.

probability (p. 547) The chance that an event will happen.

problem solving guide (p. 20) A process for solving a problem: Understand, Plan, Solve, Look Back.

product (p. 148) The number that is the result of multiplying two or more factors.
Example: 5 × 6 = 30
↑ Product

pyramid (p. 345) A solid figure whose base is a polygon and whose faces are triangles with a common vertex.

quadrilateral (p. 347) A polygon with four sides.

quart (qt) (p. 458) A unit for measuring capacity in the customary system. *See also* Table of Measures, page 575

quotient (p. 170) The number other than the remainder that is the result of dividing.
Example: 63 ÷ 7 = 9
↑ Quotient

range (p. 31) The difference between the greatest and least numbers in a set of data.

ray (p. 350) Part of a line that begins at a point and is endless in one direction.

rectangle (p. 360) A quadrilateral with four right angles and opposite sides parallel and the same length.

rectangular prism (p. 345) A solid figure whose six faces are all rectangles.

regroup (p. 104) To name a whole or decimal number in a different way. *Example:* 28 is 2 tens and 8 ones. 0.3 is 0.30 or 0.300.

remainder (p. 297) The number less than the divisor that remains after the division is complete.
Example: 31 ÷ 7 = 4 R3
↑ Remainder

rhombus (p. 360) A quadrilateral with two pairs of parallel sides and all sides the same length.

right angle (p. 350) An angle that forms a square corner.

Glossary

right triangle (p. 350) A triangle that has one right angle.

Roman numerals (p. 88) Numerals in a number system used by ancient Romans.
Examples: I = 1
IV = 4
V = 5
VI = 6

rounding (p. 70) Replacing one number with another number that tells about how many or how much.

sample (p. 526) A representative part of a large group.

scale (p. 10) Numbers that show the units used on a graph. Also, (p. 456) an instrument used to measure an object's weight.

scalene triangle (p. 349) A triangle with no equal sides.

schedule (p. 82) A list which shows the times events occur.

similar figures (p. 355) Figures that have the same shape and may or not have the same size.

Similar hexagons

simplest form (p. 402) A fraction in which the numerator and denominator have no common factors other than 1.

slide (p. 353) To move a plane figure in one direction.

solid figure (p. 344) A figure that has length, width, height, and volume.

Cube   Cylinder

sphere (p. 345) A solid figure that has the shape of a round ball.

square (p. 360) A quadrilateral that has four equal sides and four right angles.

square centimeter (p. 371) A square with 1 centimeter sides; Unit used for measuring area.

square inch (p. 371) A square with 1 inch sides; Unit used for measuring area.

square number (p. 155) The product of a number multiplied by itself. *Example:* $6 \times 6 = 36$
Square number ↑

square unit (p. 370) A square with 1 unit sides; Unit used for measuring area.

standard form (p. 52) A way to write a number that shows only its digits. *Example:* 9,325

stem (p. 18) The part of a stem-and-leaf plot that shows all but the ones digit of a number.

stem-and-leaf plot (p. 18) A graph that uses place value to organize numbers in data.

straight angle (p. 350) An angle that forms a straight line.

strategy (p. 4) A plan or method used to solve a problem. *Example:* Guess and Check

subtraction (p. 22) An operation that tells the difference between two numbers, or how many are left when some are taken away.

sum (p. 95) The number that is the result of adding two or more addends.
Example: $7 + 9 = 16$
↑ Sum

survey (p. 8) Question or questions answered by a group of people.

symbol (p. 10) A picture in a pictograph that stands for a given number of objects.

symmetry (p. 363) A figure has symmetry if it can be folded along a line so that both parts match exactly. *See also* line of symmetry

tablespoon (p. 459) A unit for measuring capacity in the customary system. *See also* Table of Measures, page 575

tally mark (p. 7) A mark used to record data.

$/ = 1$
$\cancel{||||} = 5$

Glossary **581**

581

teaspoon (p. 459) A unit for measuring capacity in the customary system. *See also* Table of Measures, page 575

tenth (p. 476) One out of 10 equal parts of a whole.

ton (p. 457) A unit for measuring weight in the customary system. *See also* Table of Measures, page 575

trapezoid (p. 360) A quadrilateral that has exactly one pair of parallel sides.

tree diagram (p. 544) A diagram showing all possible outcomes of an event.

triangle (p. 347) A polygon with three sides.

turn (p. 353) To rotate a plane figure.

unit (p. 77) A quantity used as a standard of measure.

units of time (p. 77) *See* Table of Measures, page 575

unlikely (p. 540) Probably will not happen.

variable (p. 32) A letter that stands for a number or a range of numbers.

vertex (plural, vertices) (p. 344) The point where two or more edges meet.

Vertex

volume (p. 372) The number of cubic units needed to fill a solid figure.

word name (p. 52) A way to show a number using words. *Example:* Nine thousand, three hundred twenty-five

yard (yd) (p. 415) A unit for measuring length in the customary system. *See also* Table of Measures, page 575

zero property (p. 151) In addition, the sum of a number and 0 is that number. In multiplication, the product of a number and 0 is 0. *Examples:* $7 + 0 = 7$
$$7 \times 0 = 0$$

Photographs

Credits

583

Scope and Sequence

Contents

Whole Number Concepts and Operations

Blue Text: Topic introduced for the first time.
Student Edition pages in italic.

Legend: ■ Teach and Apply □ Reinforce and Apply

Numeration

	K	1	2	3	4	5	MS 1	MS 2	MS 3
Meaning of numbers	■	■	□	□					
Reading and writing numbers	■	■	■	■	■	□	□		
Place value			■	■	■	□	□		
Ordinal numbers	■	■	□						
Comparing and ordering	■	■	■	■	■	□	□		
Rounding			■	■	■	□	□		
Powers and exponents						■	■	■	□
Square numbers and square roots				■	■	■	■	□	
Scientific notation							■	■	□

Number Theory

	K	1	2	3	4	5	MS 1	MS 2	MS 3
Even and odd numbers		■	■	■	□	□			
Prime and composite numbers						■	■	■	□
Prime factorization							■	■	□
Divisibility					■	■	■	□	
Factors and greatest common factors					■	■	□	□	
Multiples and least common multiples				■	■	■	□	□	

Addition

	K	1	2	3	4	5	MS 1	MS 2	MS 3
Meaning of addition	■	■	■	□					
Related to subtraction		■	■	□					
Basic facts and fact strategies	■	■	■	□	□	□			
Properties		■	■	■	□	□			
Three or more addends		■	■	■	■	□			
Adding 2-digit numbers		■	■	■	□	□			
Adding 3-digit numbers			■	■	□	□			
Adding with 4 or more digits				■	■	□	□		
Choosing a computation tool			■	■	■				
Addition expressions/sentences/equations	■	■	■	■	■	■	■	□	□
Estimation and mental math		■	■	■	■	■	□		
Problem solving	■	■	■	■	■	■	□		

Numeration

Reading and writing numbers, 48, 50, 52A–52B, 54A–54B, 56A–56B, *52–57*

Place value, 50, 52A–52B, 54A–54B, 56A–56B, *52–57,* 62–63, 292B

Comparing and ordering, 30B, 66A–66B, 68–68B, *66–69*

Rounding, 70A–70B, *70–71*

Square numbers, 154A–154B, *154–155*

Number Theory

Even and odd numbers, 180A–180B, *180–181*

Divisibility, 330A–330B, *330–331*

Factors, 152A–152B, *152–153,* 154A–154B, *154–155,* 184A–184B, *184–185*

Multiples, 150A–150B, *150–151,* 152A–152B, *152–153,* 154A–154B, *154–155,* 158A–158B, *158–159*

Addition

Basic fact strategies, 32–36, *182–185*

Properties, 94A–94B, *94–97*

Adding multi-digit numbers, 94A–94B, 96A–96B, *94–99,* 104A–104B, *104–109,* 116–117, 130B, 132–133

Three or more addends, 108A–108B, *108–109*

Choosing a computation tool, 122A–122B, *122–123*

Addition expressions/sentences/equations, 134A–134B, *134–135*

Estimation and mental math, 98A–98B, *98–99,* 120A–120B, *120–121,* 122B

Problem solving, 22A–22B, *22–23,* 100A–100B, *100–101,* 118A–118B, *118–119,* 136A–136B, *136–137*

Whole Number Concepts and Operations (cont'd)

Blue Text: Topic introduced for the first time.
Student Edition pages in italic.

Legend: ■ = Teach and Apply □ = Reinforce and Apply

Subtraction

	K	1	2	3	4	5	MS 1	MS 2	MS 3
Meaning of subtraction	■	■	■	□					
Related to addition		■	■	□					
Basic facts and fact strategies	■	■	■	□	□	□			
Properties			■	■	■	□			
Subtracting 2-digit numbers			■	■	■	□			
Subtracting 3-digit numbers			■	■	■	□			
Subtracting with 4 or more digits				■	■	□	□		
Choosing a computation tool				■	■	■			
Subtraction expressions/sentences/equations	■	■	■	■	■	■	■	□	□
Estimation and mental math			■	■	■	■	□		
Problem solving	■	■	■	■	■	■	□		

Multiplication

	K	1	2	3	4	5	MS 1	MS 2	MS 3
Meaning of multiplication			■	■	□				
Related to addition/division			■	■	□				
Basic facts and fact strategies				■	■	□			
Properties				■	■	■			
By a 1-digit number				■	■	■			
By multiples of 10 and 100				■	■	■			
By a multi-digit number				■	■	■	□		
Choosing a computation tool					■	■			
Multiplication expressions/sentences/equations				■	■	■	■	□	□
Estimation and mental math				■	■	■	■		
Problem solving			■	■	■	■	■		

Division

	K	1	2	3	4	5	MS 1	MS 2	MS 3
Meaning of division				■	■	□			
Related to subtraction/multiplication					■	□			
Basic facts and fact strategies					■	□			
Properties				■	■	■			
By a 1-digit divisor				■	■	■	□		
By multiples of 10 and 100				■	■	■	□		
By a multi-digit divisor					■	■	■		
Division expressions/sentences/equations				■	■	■	■	□	□
Estimation and mental math				■	■	■	■		
Problem solving				■	■	■	■		

■ *Teach and Apply*   □ *Reinforce and Apply*

Subtraction
Basic fact strategies, 32–36
Properties, 94A–94B, 94–97
Subtracting multi-digit numbers, 94A–94B, 96A–96B, 94–99, 110–117, 132–133
Choosing a tool, 122A–122B, 122–123
Subtraction expressions/sentences/ equations, 94–95, 102, 134A/B, 134–135
Estimation and mental math, 98A–98B, 98–99, 120A–120B, 120–121, 122B
Problem solving, 22–23, 100–101, 118–119, 136–137

Multiplication
Meaning of multiplication, 148–149
Related to addition/division, 148A–148B, 148–149, 168A–168B, 170A–170B, 168–171
Basic facts and fact strategies, 144, 146 150A–150B, 152A–152B, 150–157
Properties, 148A–148B, 150A–150B, 148–151, 206A–206B, 206–207, 230–231
By a 1-digit number, 202–203, 210–215
By multiples of 10 and 100, 158A–158B, 158–159, 200A–200B, 200–201, 254–255
By a multi-digit number, 210–211, 214–215, 244, 256–257, 260A–260B, 260–263
Choosing a computation tool, 218A–218B, 218–219, 266–267
Multiplication expressions/sentences/ equations, 148–149, 202–203, 250–251
Estimation and mental math, 204A–204B, 204–205, 214B, 218B, 224B, 228A–228B
Problem solving, 162–163, 216–217

Division
Meaning of division, 166A–166B, 166–167
Related to subtraction/multiplication, 166A–166B, 168A–168B, 166–169
Basic fact strategies, 144, 170–171, 176–179, 294A–294B
Properties, 172A–172B, 172–173, 330–331
By a 1-digit divisor, 288–290, 292–297, 300–315
By multiples of 10 and 100, 532A–532B, 532–533
By multi-digit divisor, 528–535, 556
 two-digit dividends, 302–305
 three-digit quotients, 306–309, 310–311
 zero in the quotient, 312A–312B, 312–315
Division expressions/sentences/equations, 292–293, 527–529
Estimation and mental math, 294A–294B, 294–295, 530A–530B, 528–531
Problem solving, 186–189, 316–317

Fraction Concepts and Operations

Blue Text: Topic introduced for the first time. Student Edition pages in italic.

Legend: ■ = Teach and Apply □ = Reinforce and Apply

Concepts	K	1	2	3	4	5	MS 1	MS 2	MS 3
Part of a whole/part of a set	■	■	■	■	■	□	□	□	
Mixed numbers, fractions greater than 1				■	■	□	□	□	
Equivalent fractions				■	■	■	□	□	□
Lowest terms/simplest form					■	■	□	□	□
Comparing and ordering				■	■	■	■	■	□
Common denominators					■	■	■	■	
Rounding/estimating	■	■	■	■	■	■	■	□	
Reciprocals						■	■	■	□
Related to decimals				■	■	■	■	■	□
Related to percents						■	■	■	□
Rational numbers									■

Operations	K	1	2	3	4	5	MS 1	MS 2	MS 3
Addition/subtraction, like denominators				■	■	□	□	□	□
Addition/subtraction, unlike denominators					■	■	■	□	□
Addition/subtraction, mixed numbers						■	■	□	□
Multiplication/division, by a whole number				■	■	■	□	□	□
Multiplication/division, fractions						■	■	□	□
Multiplication/division, mixed numbers						■	■	□	□
Estimation and mental math				■	■	■	■	□	
Problem solving				■	■	■	■	□	
Expressions/sentences/equations							■	■	■

Concepts

Part of a whole/part of a set, 386A–386B, *386–387,* 388A–388B, *388–389,* 408A–408B, *408–411,* 423, 426

Mixed numbers, fractions greater than 1, 392A–392B, *392–393*

Equivalent fractions, 398A–398B, 400A–400B, *398–401*

Lowest terms/simplest form, 402A–402B, *402–403,* 404–405

Comparing and ordering, 406A–406B, *406–407*

Common denominators, 434A–434B, 436A–436B, *434–437*

Rounding/estimating, 390A–390B, *390–391*

Related to decimals, 476B, *476–477,* 486A–486B, *486–487*

Operations

Addition, like denominators, 432A–432B, *432–433,* 436A–436B, *436–437*

Addition, unlike denominators, 434A–434B, *434–435,* 436A–436B, *436–437*

Subtraction, like denominators, 444A–444B, *444–445,* 446A–446B, *446–449,* 450–451

Subtraction, unlike denominators, 444A–444B, *444–445,* 446A–446B, *446–449*

Multiplication, by a whole number, 408A–408B, *408–409*

Estimation and Mental Math, 390A–390B, *390–391*

Problem solving, 394A–394B, *394–395,* 440A–440B, *440–441,* 452A–452B, *452–453*

Decimal Concepts and Operations

Concepts	K	1	2	3	4	5	MS 1	MS 2	MS 3
Meaning of decimals				■	■	■	□	□	
Related to fractions				■	■	■	□	□	□
Related to money/measurement				■	■	□			
Place value					■	■	□	□	
On a number line					■	■	□		
Comparing and ordering					■	■	■	□	□
Rounding					■	■	■	□	
Terminating and repeating							■	■	□
Nonrepeating/irrational numbers							■	■	□
Related to percent						■	■	■	□
Scientific notation							■	■	□

Operations	K	1	2	3	4	5	MS 1	MS 2	MS 3
Addition				■	■	■	□	□	□
Subtraction				■	■	■	□	□	□
Multiplication, by a whole number						■	□	□	□
Multiplication, by a power of ten						■	■	□	□
Multiplication, by a decimal						■	■	□	□
Division, by a whole number						■	■	□	□
Division, by a power of ten						■	□	□	□
Division, by a decimal							■	□	□
Estimation and mental math					■	■	■	□	
Problem solving				■	■	■	■	□	□
Expressions/sentences/equations							■	■	■

■ Teach and Apply   □ Reinforce and Apply

Concepts

Meaning of decimals, 476A–476B, *476–477,* 486A–486B, *486–487*

Related to fractions, 486A–486B, *486–487*

Related to measures, 508A–508B, *508–509*

Place value, 476A–476B, 478A–478B, *476–479*

On a number line, 484A–484B, *484–485*

Comparing and ordering, 482A–482B, *482–483*

Rounding, 484A–484B, *484–485*

Operations

Addition, 492A–492B, 494A–494B, 496A–496B, *492–499*

Subtraction, 492A–492B, 494A–494B, 496A–496B, *492–499*

Estimation and mental math, 492A–492B, *492–493*

Problem solving, 480A–480B, *480–481*

Number Sense, Estimation, and Mental Math

Blue Text: Topic introduced for the first time. Student Edition pages in italic.

Number Sense	K	1	2	3	4	5	MS 1	MS 2	MS 3
Meaning of whole numbers	■	■	■	■	□	□	□		
Fractions		■	■	■	■	□	□	□	□
Decimals				■	■	□	□	□	□
Percent and Ratios						■	■	■	□
Integers							■	■	□
Rational/real numbers									■
Number patterns	■	■	■	■	■	■	□	□	□
Number relationships	■	■	■	■	■	■	■	□	□
Relative magnitude of numbers	■	■	■	■	■	■	□	□	□

Estimation Strategies	K	1	2	3	4	5	MS 1	MS 2	MS 3
Deciding when to estimate				■	■	■	□	□	□
Underestimates and overestimates					■	■	□	□	□
Adjusting an estimate					■	■	□	□	□
Using front-end digits				■	■	■	□	□	□
Rounding whole numbers/decimals			■	■	■	■	□	□	□
Rounding fractions/mixed numbers				■	■	■	□	□	□
Substituting compatible numbers					■	■	□	□	□
Using a range						■	■	□	□
Use a reference point or benchmark						■	■	□	□
Clustering							■	□	□
Estimating quantities and measures	■	■	■	■					

■ *Teach and Apply*   □ *Reinforce and Apply*

Number Sense

Meaning of whole numbers, 52A–52B, 54A–54B, 56A–56B, *52–57*

Fractions, 386A–386B, *386–387,* 388A–388B, *388–389,* 408A–408B, *408–411*

Decimals, 476A–476B, *476–477,* 486A–486B, *486–487,* 488–489

Number patterns, 136A–136B, *136–137,* 202A–202B, *202–203, 250–251,* 292A–292B, *292–293*

Number relationships, 54A–54B, *54–55,* 478A–478B, *478–479*

Relative magnitude of numbers, 66A–66B, *66–67,* 68A–68B, *68–69,* 406A–406B, *406–407,* 482A–482B, *482–483*

Estimation Strategies

Deciding when to estimate, 92, 100A–100B, *100–101*

Underestimates and overestimates, 278A–278B, *278–279*

Adjusting an estimate, 530–531

Using front-end digits, 98A–98B, *98–99,* 108B, 204A–204B, *204–205,* 214B, *252–253, 264–265*

Rounding whole numbers, 70A–70B, *70–71,* 92, *98–99,* 204A–204B, *204–205, 252–253, 264–265, 294–295,* 530A–530B, *530–531*

Rounding decimals, 484A–484B, *484–485,* 492A–492B

Rounding fractions/mixed numbers, 390A–390B, *390–391*

Substituting compatible numbers, 204A–204B, *204–205, 252–253, 264–265, 294–295,* 530A–530B, *530–531*

A6

Number Sense, Estimation, and Mental Math (cont'd)

Mental Math Strategies	K	1	2	3	4	5	MS 1	MS 2	MS 3
Basic-fact strategies: add and subtract									
Count on/count back	■	■	■						
Use turnaround facts		■	■						
Add with doubles/doubles plus one		■	■						
Make ten	■	■	■						
Use doubles to subtract		■	■						
Think addition to subtract			■	▢	▢	▢			
Use families of facts			■	▢	▢	▢			
Basic-fact strategies: multiply and divide									
Skip count	■	■	■	▢	▢				
Multiply in any order			■	■	■				
Use doubling				■	■				
Use known facts				■	■				
Use patterns				■	■	▢			
Think multiplication to divide				■	▢	▢			
Mental-computation strategies									
Multiply/divide by 10, 100, 1,000				■	■	▢	▢	▢	▢
Use properties and patterns	■	■	■	■	▢		▢	▢	▢
Break apart numbers					■	▢	▢	▢	▢
Compatible numbers				■	■	▢	▢	▢	▢
Compensation						■	■	▢	▢
With fractions				■	■	■	■	▢	▢
With percents						■	■	▢	▢

■ *Teach and Apply*   ▢ *Reinforce and Apply*

Mental Math Strategies

Basic-fact strategies: add and subtract

Think addition to subtraction, 118–119

Use families of facts, 94, 95, 102, 134–135

Basic-fact strategies: multiply and divide

Skip count, 145, 148–149, 150A–150B, 150

Multiply in any order, 151, 156

Use doubling, 153, 155

Use known facts, 152, 153–154, 155, 157, 159, 166, 170, 178, 228, 229, 254

Use patterns, 150A–150B, 150–151, 158A–158B, 158–159

Think multiplication to divide, 166A–166B, 166–167, 176

Mental-computation strategies

Multiply/divide by 10, 100, 1000, 200A–200B, 200–201

Use properties and patterns
   addition/subtraction, 120A–120B, 120–121
   multiplication, 228A–228B, 228–229
   division, 528A–528B, 528–529

Break apart numbers, 228A–228B, 228–229

Compatible numbers, 204A–204B, 204–205, 252–253, 264–265, 294–295, 530A–530B, 530–531

With fractions, 408A–408B, 408–409

Mathematical Processes

Problem Solving	K	1	2	3	4	5	Middle School Course 1	2	3
Analyze Word Problems									
Choose an operation	■	■	■	■	■	■	□	□	□
Too much or too little information		■	■	■	■	■	□	□	□
Multiple-step problems			■	■	■	■	□	□	□
Choose an exact answer or an estimate				■	■	■	□	□	□
Estimating					■	■	□	□	□
Interpreting remainders				■	■	□			
Analyze Strategies									
Use objects/act it out	■	■	■	■	■	□			
Draw or use a picture/diagram	■	■	■	■	■	■	□	□	□
Guess and check	■	■	■	■	■	■	□	□	□
Look for a pattern	■	■	■	■	■	■	□	□	□
Make an organized list	■	■	■	■	■	■	□	□	□
Make a table		■	■	■	■	■	□	□	□
Use logical reasoning	■	■	■	■	■	■	□	□	□
Solve a simpler problem				■	■	■	□	□	□
Work backward				■	■	■	□	□	□
Choose/compare strategies	■	■	■	■	■	■	□	□	□
Decision Making									
Plan an event, make a choice, etc.	■	■	■	■	■	■	□	□	□

■ Teach and Apply   □ Reinforce and Apply

Blue Text: Topic introduced for the first time.
Student Edition pages in italic.

Problem Solving

Analyze Word Problems

Choose an operation, 22A–22B, *22–23,* 452A–452B, *452–453*

Too much or too little information, 186A–186B, *186–187*

Multiple–step problems, 98B, 118A–118B, *118–119,* 232A–232B, *232–233*

Choose an exact answer or an estimate, 70B, 100A–100B, *100–101*

Estimating, 92, 100–102, 204–205

Interpreting remainders, 316A–316B, *316–317*

Analyze Strategies

Use objects/act it out, 364A–364B, *364–365,* 480A–480B, *480–481*

Draw or use a picture/diagram, 188B, *188–189,* 280A–280B, *280–281,* 462A–462B, *462–463*

Guess and check, 36A–36B, *36–39,* 188B, *188–189*

Look for a pattern, 136A–136B, *136–137*

Make an organized list, 58A–58B, *58–61,* 480A–480B, *480–481*

Make a table, 234A–234B, *234–237,* 238, 328–329, 462A–462B, *462–463*

Use logical reasoning, 420A–420B, *420–421*

Solve a simpler problem, 550A–550B, *550–551*

Work backward, 332A–332B, *332–333*

Choose/compare strategies, 188A–188B, *188–189,* 462A–462B, *462–463,* 480A–480B, *480–481*

Decision Making

Plan an event, make a choice, etc., 82A–82B, *82–83,* 162A–162B, *162–163,* 216A–216B, *216–217,* 270A–270B, *270–271,* 374A–374B, *374–375,* 394A–394B, *394–395,* 440A–440B, *440–441,* 516A–516B, *516–517,* 536A–536B, *536–537*

Mathematical Processes (cont'd)

Blue Text: Topic introduced for the first time.
Student Edition pages in italic.

Legend: ■ = Teach and Apply ▨ = Reinforce and Apply

Problem Solving (cont'd)

	K	1	2	3	4	5	MS 1	MS 2	MS 3
Problem-Solving Guide/Checklist									
Understand									
Determine what you know			■	■	■	▨	▨	▨	▨
Use data from pictures, graphs,…			■	■	■	▨	▨	▨	▨
Tell what you need to find out					■	▨	▨	▨	▨
Plan									
Choose an operation/strategy			■	■	■	▨	▨	▨	▨
Choose a computation method			■	■	■		▨	▨	▨
Estimate the answer				■	■	■	▨	▨	▨
Solve									
Carry out the plan			■	■	■	▨	▨	▨	▨
Try another strategy if needed			■	■	■	▨	▨	▨	▨
Give the answer			■	■	■	▨	▨	▨	▨
Look Back									
Check your answer			■	■	■	▨	▨	▨	▨
Check reasonableness of answer				■	■	■	▨	▨	▨
Be sure the question is answered			■	■	■	▨	▨	▨	▨

Reasoning

	K	1	2	3	4	5	MS 1	MS 2	MS 3
Critical Thinking, Logical Reasoning									
Classifying/sorting	■	■	■	■	■	■	▨	▨	▨
Comparing/contrasting	■	■	■	▨	▨	▨	▨	▨	▨
Finding/extending/using patterns	■	■	■	■	■	■	▨	▨	▨
Making generalizations	■	■	■	■	■	■	▨	▨	▨
Drawing conclusions	■	■	■	■	■	■	▨	▨	▨
Making/testing conjectures			■	■	■	■	▨	▨	▨
Explaining/justifying answers					■	▨	▨	▨	▨
Visual and Creative Thinking									
Visual patterns	■	■	■	■	■	■	▨	▨	▨
Spatial reasoning	■	■	■	■	■	■	▨	▨	▨
Solve nonroutine problems				■	■	■	▨	▨	▨
Generate problems				■	■	■	▨	▨	▨
Develop alternative ways to solve problems						■	▨	▨	▨

■ Teach and Apply   ▨ Reinforce and Apply

Problem Solving (cont'd)

Sample pages given.

Problem-Solving Guide/Checklist

Understand

  Determine what you know, 20A–20B, *186–187*

  Use data from pictures, graphs, 36–39

  Tell what you need to find out, 20–21

Plan

  Choose an operation/strategy, 22–23, 188A–188B, *188–189,* 452–453, 462A–462B

  Choose a computation method, 22–23, 122A–122B, *122–123,* 218A–218B, *218–219, 266–267,* 452–453

  Estimate the answer, 100A–100B, *100–101*

Solve

  Carry out the plan, 20B, *20–21*

  Try another strategy if needed, 188A–188B, *188–189,* 462A–462B, *462–463, 480–481*

  Give the answer, 20–21

Look Back

  Check your answer, 20B, *20–21*

  Check reasonableness of answer, 20B, *20–21*

  Be sure the question is answered, 20–21

Reasoning

Critical Thinking, Logical Reasoning

Classifying/sorting, 344A–344B, *344–349*

Comparing/contrasting, 66–69, 406A–406B, *406–407, 482–483*

Finding/extending/using patterns, 136A–136B, *136–137*

Making generalizations, 32–33, 180–181

Drawing conclusions, 420A–420B, *420–421*

Making/testing conjectures, 548A–548B, *548–549*

Explaining/justifying answers, 82A–82B, *82–83,* 162A–162B, *162–163,* 216A–216B, *216–217,* 270A–270B, *270–271,* 374A–374B, *374–375, 394–395,* 440A–440B, *440–441,* 516A–516B, *516–517,* 536A–536B, *536–537*

Visual and Creative Thinking

Visual patterns, 364–365

Spatial reasoning, 344A–344B, *344–345,* 374A–374B, *374–375*

Solve nonroutine problems, 8, 43, 46, 50, 85, 88, 92, 139, 142, 146, 191, 198, 241, 244, 248, 283, 286, 290, 335, 338, 342, 377, 380, 384, 423, 426, 430, 467, 470, 474, 519, 522, 526, 553, 556

Generate problems, 41, 97, 115, 157, 212, 213, 237, 272, 314, 363, 448

Mathematical Processes (cont'd)

Blue Text: Topic introduced for the first time.
Student Edition pages in italic.

Connections	K	1	2	3	4	5	1	2	3
Curriculum Connections									
Social studies/history/geography	■	□	□	□	□	□	□	□	□
Health/physical education	■	□	□	□	□	□	□	□	□
Science	■	□	□	□	□	□	□	□	□
Music	■	□	□	□	□	□	□	□	□
Reading/language/literature	■	□	□	□	□	□	□	□	□
Art	■	□	□	□	□	□	□	□	□
Math Strand Connections									
Patterns	■	■	■	■	■	■	□	□	□
Estimation and mental math		■	■	■	■	■	□	□	□
Algebra readiness		■	■	■	■	■	■	□	□
Geometry	■	■	■	■	■	■	■	■	■
Using/collecting data	■	■	■	■	■	■	■	■	■
Real World Connections									
Students' daily life	■	□	□	□	□	□	□	□	□
Consumer	■	□	□	□	□	□	□	□	□
Career				■	□	□	□	□	□
Multicultural connections	■	□	□	□	□	□	□	□	□

Communication	K	1	2	3	4	5	1	2	3
Reading for math/reading assists	■	■	■	□	□	□			
Write about it/journal	■	■	■	□	□	□	□	□	□
Talk about it/share	■	■	■	□	□	□	□	□	□
Working in groups	■	■	■	□	□	□	□	□	□

■ Teach and Apply   □ Reinforce and Apply

Connections

Sample pages given.

Curriculum Connections

Social studies, 14A, 52A, 78A, 82A, 96A, 130A, 187, 230A, 267, 278A, 297, 311, 322A

History, 72, 75, 80A, 101, 153, 156, 190, 255, 354A, 479, 505, 520, 531

Geography, 107, 213, 267, 333, 349, 359, 424

Health/physical education, 75, 77, 79, 101, 153, 173, 189, 293, 304

Science, 10A, 15, 18A, 21, 70A, 77, 115, 122A, 124, 177, 219, 228A, 266A, 295, 350A, 362A, 391, 452, 460A, 463, 509, 551

Music, 348A, 530A, 531

Literature, 22A, 54A, 68A, 74A, 114A, 128A, 214A, 224A, 254A, 274A, 295, 307, 364A, 422

Art, 60, 95, 108A, 344A, 353, 360A, 369, 440A

Math Strand Connections

Patterns, 22A, 53, 54A, 75, 80A, 104A, 123, 126A, 135, 157, 181, 224A, 225, 344A

* Estimation and mental math, 10A, 12A, 14A, 15, 16A, 20A, 54A, 102, 108A, 109, 135, 200A, 203, 219, 240, 320A, 371, 400A

Algebra readiness, 53, 75, 115, 253, 275, 293, 307, 351, 369, 403, 433, 442, 529

Geometry, 13, 53, 95, 123, 231, 251, 293, 349, 357, 477, 509, 551

Using/collecting data, 11, 29, 69, 119, 189, 207, 225, 275, 351, 419, 469

Real World Connections

Students' daily life, 90–92, 141, 144–146, 162–163, 191, 196–197, 216–217, 335, 384–385, 423, 440–441, 474, 519

Consumer, 23, 38, 95, 108–109, 127–131, 186–187, 205, 224–225, 229, 296, 320–321

Career, 98A, 118A, 134A, 137, 204A, 251, 252A

Multicultural connections, 12B, 22B, 26B, 70B, 96B, 126B, 210B, 234B, 344B, 354B

Communication

Reading for math/reading assists, 12B, 20B, 36, 58, 82, 96B, 100B, 118, 130B, 214B, 345

Write about it/journal, 11, 15, 29, 55, 75, 77, 83, 99, 109, 113, 138, 203, 207, 217, 257, 265, 293, 387, 415, 511, 549

** Talk about it/share, 8, 10, 12, 14, 16, 66, 117, 148, 186, 221, 368, 402, 416, 444, 526

Working in groups, 20, 70, 130, 206, 234, 271, 346, 418, 441, 462, 548

* Mental math activities appear on all even (left–hand) interleaf pages.

** Appears on all even (left–hand) pages in core lessons.

Geometry

Key: ■ Teach and Apply □ Reinforce and Apply

Plane and Solid Shapes	K	1	2	3	4	5	MS 1	MS 2	MS 3
Identify plane figures	■	■	■	■	■	□	□	□	□
Identify solid figures	■	■	■	■	■	■	□	□	□
Relate plane figures to solid figures	■	■	■	■	■	□	□	□	□
Sides and corners/vertices			■	■	■	■	□	□	□
Symmetry		■	■	■	■	■	□	□	□
Lines, line segments, rays, planes, angles				■	■	■	□	□	□
Circles and parts of circles	■	■	■	■	□		□	□	□
Tessellations							■	■	■
Draw/construct/build	■	■	■	■	■	■	■	■	■
Visual thinking	■	■	■	■	■	■	■	■	■

Classification	K	1	2	3	4	5	MS 1	MS 2	MS 3
Similar figures					■	■	■	■	■
Congruent figures	■	■	■	■	■	■	■	■	■
Transformations (slides, flips, turns)			■	■	■	■	■	■	■
Dilations								■	■
Pairs of lines/line segments				■	■	■	□	□	□
Angles				■	■	■	□	□	□
Polygons			■	■	■	■	□	□	□
Triangles	■	■	■	■	■	□	□	□	□
Quadrilaterals	■	■	■	■	■	□	□	□	□
Polyhedrons/solid shapes		■	■	■	■	■	□	□	□

Formulas	K	1	2	3	4	5	MS 1	MS 2	MS 3
Perimeter and circumference				■	■	■	■	□	□
Area				■	■	■	■	□	□
Surface area						■	■	□	□
Volume				■	■	■	■	□	□
Pythagorean relationship								■	■
For trigonometric ratios								■	■

Plane and Solid Shapes

Identify plane figures, 346A–346B, 346–347

Identify solid figures, 342, 344A–344B, 344–345

Relate plane figures to solid figures, 346A–346B, 346–347

Sides and corners/vertices, 344–345, 346A–346B, 346–347

Symmetry, 362A–362B, 362–363

Lines, line segments, rays, planes, angles, 350A–350B, 350–351, 358A–358B, 358–359

Circles and parts of circles, 345, 381, 407, 411

Draw/construct/build, 374A–374B, 374–375

Visual thinking, 364A–364B, 364–365

Classification

Similar figures, 354A–354B, 354–355

Congruent figures, 352A–352B, 352–353

Slides, flips, turns, 352A–352B, 352–353

Pairs of lines/line segments, 358A–358B, 358–359

Angles, 350A–350B, 350–351

Polygons, 58B, 346A–346B, 346–347, 370B

Triangles, 346A–346B, 348A–348B, 348–349, 350A–350B, 350–351, 370A–370B

Quadrilaterals, 360A–360B, 360–361

Polyhedrons/solid shapes, 344A–344B, 344–345

Formulas

Perimeter, 368A–368B, 368–369, 374A–374B

Area, 370A–370B, 370–371, 374A–374B, 374–375

Volume, 372A–372B, 372–373

Patterns, Relationships, and Algebraic Thinking

Blue Text: Topic introduced for the first time.
Student Edition pages in italic.

Patterns

Patterns	K	1	2	3	4	5	MS 1	MS 2	MS 3
With objects/geometric figures	■	■	■	■	■	■	□		
With numbers	■	■	■	■	■	■	■	□	□
Skip counting	■	■	■	■					
Sequences									■
In tables, charts, and graphs				■	■	■	□	□	□
Used to make predictions	■	■	■	■	■	■	□	□	□
Logical reasoning	■	■	■	■	■	■	■	■	■

Relationships

Relationships	K	1	2	3	4	5	MS 1	MS 2	MS 3
Function tables			■	■	■	■	□	□	□
Ordered pairs				■	■	■	□	□	□
Linear							■	■	□
Nonlinear							■	■	
Graphing equations							■	■	■
Graphing inequalities							■	■	
Venn diagrams							■	■	□
Commutative and associative properties		■	■	■	■	■	□	□	□
Distributive property					■	■	□	□	□
Zero and identity properties		■	■	■	■	■	□	□	□

■ Teach and Apply   □ Reinforce and Apply

Patterns

With geometric figures, 136A–136B, *136–137, 364–365*

With numbers, 94A–94B, 136A–136B, *136–137,* 180A–180B, *180–181,* 202A–202B, *202–203,* 250A–250B, *250–251,* 292A–292B, *292–293*

In tables, charts, and graphs, 234–237, 462A–462B, *462–463*

Used to make predictions, 58B, *548–549*

Logical reasoning, 69, 72, 109, 327, 481

Relationships

Function tables, 32A–32B, *32–33*

Ordered pairs, 12A–12B, *12–13*

Commutative properies, 151

Associative properties, 108A–108B, *108–109, 230–231*

Distributive property, 206A–206B, *206–207,* 250A–250B, *250–251*

Zero and identity properties, 150A–150B, *150–151,* 172A–172B, *172–173*

Patterns, Relationships, and Algebraic Thinking (cont'd)

Blue Text: Topic introduced for the first time.
Student Edition pages in italic.

Legend: ■ = Teach and Apply ▩ = Reinforce and Apply

Algebraic Thinking	K	1	2	3	4	5	MS 1	MS 2	MS 3
Expressions, Equations, Inequalities									
Missing numbers and number sentences			■	■	■	■			
Variables						■	■	■	▩
Writing/evaluating expressions						■	■	■	▩
Writing/simplifying polynomials									■
Order of operations						■	■	▩	▩
Solving/writing for addition/subtraction							■	■	▩
Solving/writing for multiplication/division							■	■	▩
Solving/writing two-step equations							■	■	
Solving/writing inequalities							■	■	
Graphing equations							■	■	■
Graphing inequalities							■	■	
Systems of equations/inequalities									■
Related to formulas						■	■	▩	▩
Integers									
Writing and reading							■	▩	■
On a number line							■	▩	▩
Comparing and ordering							■	■	▩
Opposites							■	■	▩
Absolute value							■	▩	
Adding and subtracting							■	■	■
Multiplying and dividing							■	■	■
Graphing in four quadrants							■	■	■
Solving equations							■	■	
Rational and Real Numbers									
Computing with rational numbers									■
Repeating and nonrepeating decimals							■	▩	▩
Exponents and powers							■	▩	▩
Squares and square roots							■	■	▩
Irrational and real numbers							■	■	■

■ Teach and Apply   ▩ Reinforce and Apply

Algebraic Thinking

Expressions, Equations, Inequalities

Missing numbers and number sentences,
32A–32B, *32–33*, 134A–134B, *134–135*

A13

Measurement, Time, and Money

Blue Text: Topic introduced for the first time. Student Edition pages in italic.

Measurement	K	1	2	3	4	5	MS 1	MS 2	MS 3
Comparing lengths and sizes	■	■	■	■					
Nonstandard units	■	■	■	■	■				
Length, customary		■	■	■	■	□			
Length, metric		■	■	■	■	□			
Length, estimating	■	■	■	■	■	■			
Length, choosing appropriate units			■	■	■	□	□	□	□
Length, converting units				■	■	■	□	□	□
Capacity, customary		■	■	■	■				
Capacity, metric		■	■	■	■	□			
Capacity, estimating	■	■	■	■	■	■			
Capacity, choosing appropriate units			■	■	■	■	□	□	□
Capacity, converting units				■	■	■	□	□	□
Weight, customary		■	■	■	■				
Mass, metric		■	■	■	■				
Weight/mass, estimating	■	■	■	■	■	■			
Weight/mass, choosing appropriate units				■	■	■	□	□	□
Weight/mass, converting units				■	■	■	□	□	□
Temperature		■	■	■	■	□			
Angles						■	■		□
Precision									■
Significant digits									■
Indirect measurement								■	■

■ Teach and Apply   □ Reinforce and Apply

Measurement

Nonstandard units, 414A–414B, *414–415,* 504A–504B

Length, customary, 414A–414B, 416A–416B, 418A–418B, *416–419*

Length, metric, 504A–504B, 506A–506B, 508A–508B, *504–509*

Length, estimating, 414A–414B, 418A–418B, *414–419,* 504A–504B, 506A–506B, 508A–508B, *504–509*

Length, choosing appropriate units, 418A–418B, *418–419,* 504A–504B, 506A–506B, 508A–508B, *504–509*

Length, converting units, 418A–418B, *418–419,* 504A–504B, 506A–506B, 508A–508B, *504–509*

Capacity, customary, 458A–458B, *458–459*

Capacity, metric, 512A–512B, *512–513*

Capacity, estimating, 458A–458B, *458–459,* 512A–512B, *512–513*

Capacity, choosing appropriate units, 458A–458B, *458–459,* 512A–512B, *512–513*

Capacity, converting units, 460A–460B *460–461,* 512A–512B, *512–513*

Weight, customary, 456A–456B, *456–457*

Mass, metric, 510A–510B, *510–511*

Weight/mass, estimating, 456A–456B, *456–457,* 510A–510B, *510–511*

Weight/mass, choosing appropriate units, 456A–456B, *456–457,* 510A–510B, *510–511*

Weight/mass, converting units, 460A–460B, *460–461,* 510A–510B, *510–511*

Temperature, 514A–514B, *514–515,* 519

Measurement, Time, and Money (cont'd)

Blue Text: Topic introduced for the first time. Student Edition pages in italic.

Perimeter, Area, Volume	K	1	2	3	4	5	MS 1	MS 2	MS 3
Estimating			■	■	■	■	■	□	□
Perimeter and circumference			■	■	■	■	■	□	□
Area			■	■	■	■	■	■	■
Surface area						■	■	■	■
Volume				■	■	■	■	■	■
Perimeter/area/volume relationships			■	■	■	■	■	■	■
Irregular figures						■	■	■	□

Time	K	1	2	3	4	5	MS 1	MS 2	MS 3
Nearest hour/half-hour	■	■	■	■	□				
Minutes before/after the hour				■	□				
Estimating time			■	■	■	□			
Elapsed time			■	■	■	□		□		
A.M. and P.M.				■	□	□			
Calendar	■	■	■	■	□				
Time zones and time tables					■	□			

Money	K	1	2	3	4	5	MS 1	MS 2	MS 3
Identify coins and bills	■	■	■	□					
Count and show amounts	■	■	■	■	□				
Making change				■	■	□			
Comparing	■	■	■	■	□				
Adding/subtracting				■	■	□	□		
Multiplying/dividing				■	■	□			

■ *Teach and Apply*   □ *Reinforce and Apply*

Perimeter, Area, Volume
Estimating, 374A–374B, *374–375*
Perimeter, 368A–368B, *368–369*
Area, 370A–370B, *370–371,* 374A–374B, *374–375*
Volume, 372A–372B, *372–373*
Perimeter/area relationships, 374A–374B, *374–375*

Time
Nearest hour/half–hour, 74A–74B, *74–75*
Minutes before/after the hour, 74A–74B, *74–75*
Estimating time, 76A–76B, *76–77,* 82B
Elapsed time, 78A–78B, *78–79*
A.M. and P.M., 74A–74B, *74–75*
Calendar, 78A–78B, 80A–80B, *80–81*
Time tables, 82–83

Money
Count and show amounts, 126A–126, *126–127*
Making change, 128A–128B, *128–129,* 130A–130B, *130–131*
Comparing, 126–128
Adding/subtracting, 128A–128B, *128–129*
Multiplying/dividing, 224A–224B, *224–225,* 274A–274B, *274–275,* 320A–320B, 322A–322B, *320–323*

Data, Statistics, and Probability

Blue Text: Topic introduced for the first time. Student Edition pages in italic.

Graphing	K	1	2	3	4	5	MS 1	MS 2	MS 3
Reading pictographs	■	■	■	■	▨	▨	▨		
Making pictographs	■	■	■	■	▨	▨	▨		
Reading bar graphs		■	■	■	■	■	■	▨	▨
Making bar graphs			■	■	■	■	■	▨	▨
Reading histograms							■	■	
Making histograms							■	■	
Reading line graphs				■	■	■	■	■	▨
Making line graphs						■	■	■	▨
Reading line plots					■	■	■	▨	▨
Making line plots					■	■	■	▨	▨
Reading stem-and-leaf diagrams					■	■	■	■	▨
Making stem-and-leaf diagrams					■	■	■	▨	▨
Reading box-and-whisker plots							■	■	▨
Making box-and-whisker plots							■	■	▨
Reading scatterplots							■	■	▨
Making scatterplots							■	■	▨
Reading circle graphs						■	■	■	▨
Making circle graphs							■	▨	
Graphing ordered pairs				■	■	■	■	▨	▨
Graphing equations							■	■	■
Graphing inequalities							■	■	
Making predictions	■	■	■	■	■	■	■	■	■

■ *Teach and Apply*   ▨ *Reinforce and Apply*

Graphing

Reading pictographs, 6, 10A–10B, *10–11*
Making pictographs, *10–11*
Reading bar graphs, 10A–10B, *10–11*
Making bar graphs, 26A–26B, *26–27*
Reading line graphs, 14A–14B, *14–15*
Reading line plots, 16A–16B, *16–17*
Making line plots, 28A–28B, *28–29*
Reading stem–and–leaf diagrams, 18A–18B, *18–19*
Making stem–and–leaf diagrams, *18–19*
Graphing ordered pairs, 12A–12B, *12–13*
Making predictions, *16–17,* 526

Data, Statistics, and Probability (cont'd)

Blue Text: Topic introduced for the first time. Student Edition pages in italic.

Legend: ■ = Teach and Apply ▨ = Reinforce and Apply

Data and Statistics	K	1	2	3	4	5	MS 1	MS 2	MS 3
Collecting and organizing data	■	■	■	■	■	■	■	■	■
Reading/making charts and tables	■	■	■	■	■	■	▨	▨	▨
Tally charts	■	■	■	■	▨	▨	▨		
Survey/census							■	■	
Frequency distribution							■	■	■
Range, mode, median, mean					■	■	▨	▨	▨
Sampling						■	■	■	▨
Correlation/dispersed points							■	■	■
Using data in problem solving	■	■	■	■	■	■	■	■	■
Interpreting data					■	■	■	■	▨
Making predictions				■	■	■	■	■	■
Misleading statistics							■	■	

Probability	K	1	2	3	4	5	MS 1	MS 2	MS 3
Outcomes			■	■	■	■	▨	▨	▨
Tree diagrams					■	■	■	▨	▨
Writing probabilities		■	■	■	■	■	▨	▨	▨
Certain/possible/impossible events				■	■	■	■	▨	▨
Independent/dependent events								■	■
Compound events								■	■
Experimental/theoretical probability						■	■	▨	▨
Simulation					■	■	■	▨	▨
Fair and unfair games				■	■	■	■	▨	▨
Making predictions		■	■	■	■	■	■	■	▨
Fundamental counting principle								■	■
Permutations and combinations								■	■

■ *Teach and Apply*   ▨ *Reinforce and Apply*

Data and Statistics

Collecting and organizing data, 8, *26–31,* 40–41

Reading/making charts and tables, 36B, 234A–234B, *234–237,* 238, 462A–462B, *462–463*

Tally charts, 7, 28

Range, mode, median, mean, 30A–30B, 30–31, 326A–326B, 326–329

Using data in problem solving, 10–11, 14–21

Interpreting data, 26–31

Making predictions, 548A–548B, *548–549*

Probability

Outcomes, 540A–540B, *540–541,* 544A–544B, *544–545*

Tree diagrams, 544A–544B, 544–545

Writing probabilities, 546A–546B, *546–547*

Certain/possible/impossible events, 540–541, 552, 554

Simulation, 548A–548B, 548–551

Fair and unfair games, 542A–542B, *542–543*

Making predictions, 526, 548A–548B, *548–549*

Ratio, Proportion, and Percent

Legend: ■ = Teach and Apply · ▨ = Reinforce and Apply

Ratio and Proportion	K	1	2	3	4	5	MS 1	MS 2	MS 3
Read and write ratios						■	■	▨	▨
Equal (equivalent) ratios						■	■	▨	▨
Solve proportions						■	■	■	▨
Rate and unit price							■	■	▨
Related to maps and scale drawings						■	■	■	▨
Related to similar figures							■	■	▨
Sine, cosine, tangent ratios								■	■

Percent	K	1	2	3	4	5	MS 1	MS 2	MS 3
Related to ratios						■	■	▨	▨
Related to fractions/decimals						■	■	■	▨
Finding a percent of a number						■	■	■	▨
Finding what percent one number is of another							■	▨	
Finding a number when a percent is known							■	▨	
Interest, discount, commission							■	▨	
Related to circle graphs						■	■	■	▨
Estimation/mental math strategies						■	■	■	▨

(Grade = grades K–5; Middle School Course = 1, 2, 3)

■ *Teach and Apply*   ▨ *Reinforce and Apply*

Technology

Blue Text: Topic introduced for the first time. Student Edition pages in italic.

Calculators	K	1	2	3	4	5	MS 1	MS 2	MS 3
In problem solving		■	■	■	■	■	▨		
As a tool for computing		■	■	■	■	■	▨		
Counting and skip counting		■	■	■					
Reading a display			■	■	■	■			
Number/operation keys		■	■	■	■	■			
Scientific calculators							■	■	■
Fraction calculators					■	■	■		
Graphing calculators								■	■

Computers	K	1	2	3	4	5	MS 1	MS 2	MS 3
Spreadsheet tool					■	■	■	■	■
Graphing tool				■	■	■	■	■	■
Geometry tool		■	■	■	■	■	■	■	■
Internet access	■	■	■	■	■	■	■	■	■

■ Teach and Apply   ▨ Reinforce and Apply

Calculators

In problem solving, 488–489

As a tool for computing, 122–123, 218–219, 404–405, 410–411

Reading a display, 404–405

Number/operation keys, 404–405, 488–489

Fraction calculators, 404–405

Computers

Spreadsheet tools, 238–239, 328–329

Graphing tool, 40–41, 238–239, 410–411

Geometry tool, 368, 370

Internet access, 7–8, 43, 48, 49, 83, 85, 91, 139, 142, 144, 145, 163, 197, 217, 241, 246, 247, 271, 283, 288, 289, 335, 338, 340, 341, 342, 377, 383, 423, 428, 429, 467, 472, 473, 517, 519, 525, 553

A19

Inservice Workshops

Contents

Inservice Workshops

Getting the Most from Manipulatives as Math-Power Tools

Take a Moment

Using manipulatives helps students model and then solve mathematical problems. And manipulative work gives you a clear view of students' thought processes. Consider using color cubes for lessons dealing with surface area, volume, and patterns.

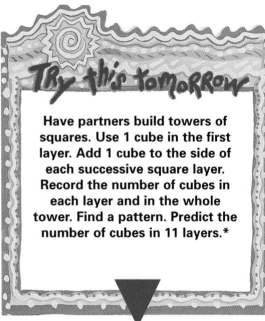

Try this tomorrow

Have partners build towers of squares. Use 1 cube in the first layer. Add 1 cube to the side of each successive square layer. Record the number of cubes in each layer and in the whole tower. Find a pattern. Predict the number of cubes in 11 layers.*

*Adapted from Cuisenaire's *the Super Source*™ series, ©1996.

Nine Ways to Use Manipulatives as Math Tools

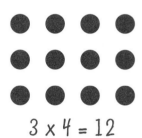

$\frac{1}{2}$ $\frac{1}{3}$ $\frac{1}{4}$ $\frac{1}{5}$ $\frac{1}{8}$

Numerical Models
for understanding numbers

$3 \times 4 = 12$

Numerical Models
for understanding operations

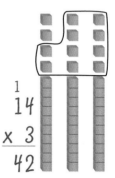

$$\begin{array}{r} 1 \\ 14 \\ \times\ 3 \\ \hline 42 \end{array}$$

Numerical Models
for understanding computation

Geometric Models
for flat and solid figures

Pattern Generators
for varied types of patterns

Measurement Tools
with or without standard units

Data Generators
for probability and statistics

Number Generators
for practice games

Clocks, Coins, Bills
for time and money

Sources for Manipulatives

Commercial Manipulatives Spend your money wisely by choosing manipulatives that build understanding, are used multiple times, and are not easy for you to make yourself.

Teacher-Made and Collected Manipulatives Spend your time wisely. Many materials don't take much time to create.

Student-Made and Collected Manipulatives Students enjoy making manipulatives. But don't let it take too much time.

Tips for Managing Manipulatives

Practical, Convenient Storage Pick a spot students can access. Use transparent or well-labeled containers.

Efficient Distribution and Retrieval Have one student in a group get materials for the group. Store items in equal packages so all materials get returned.

Management Tips During Activities Assign roles for group work, such as supply supervisor, recorder. Enforce behavior rules, but don't stop activities as punishment.

Deciding Which Manipulative to Use

Using One Manipulative over a Period of Time Stay with one manipulative for a concept long enough for students to understand the concept well using that representation.

Using Other Manipulatives for the Same Concept After students have learned the concept, use other models to deepen understanding.

Benefits of Using Manipulatives

Better Performance
- Higher test scores on skills, concepts, problem solving
- Longer retention of what is learned

Reaching All Learners
- Reaching students with varied learning styles
- Motivation through math that's fun

More Opportunities for Interaction
- More participation, cooperation, and group work
- Easier communication because students are talking about something that's concrete

Four Steps to Success

Focus Students' Attention
When you give them manipulatives, make sure the task is clear.

Guide Students' Thinking
Guide only when needed. Students will learn more by doing than by just watching.

Connect the Concrete to the Pictorial and the Abstract
Manipulatives help students do math (get answers). When you connect concrete models to pictorial and abstract work, they also help students learn math.

Assess Understanding
Have students explain what they did so you'll know if they understand.

Scott Foresman - Addison Wesley Math

Scott Foresman - Addison Wesley Math provides a wealth of resources to support work with manipulatives.

Student Book
- Hands-on work in Explore lessons
- Artwork that shows what to do
- Connections from concrete to pictorial to abstract

Teacher's Edition
- "Another Way to Learn," a non-book alternative to many of the lessons

Ancillaries
- Student Manipulative Kit
- Teacher's Overhead Manipulative Kit
- Teaching Tool Transparencies with materials for activities
- Calendar Time Kit

Building a Foundation for Number Sense

Take a Moment

What does "number sense" mean? Is it important? Does your class have it? How can it be taught? Some people say number sense is a way of thinking that unfolds as students explore the skills and concepts shown at the right. Stress these topics to build number sense—working with numbers, operations, basic facts, and computation in ways that make sense.

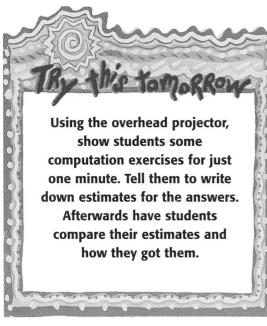

Try this tomorrow

Using the overhead projector, show students some computation exercises for just one minute. Tell them to write down estimates for the answers. Afterwards have students compare their estimates and how they got them.

Numbers

Number Meanings and Uses

- *Concrete and Pictorial Models:* Place value blocks, fraction strips
- *Number Uses:* Quantity (5 girls), measurement (5 feet), order (the fifth day)

Number Relationships

- *Breaking Apart Numbers:* 87 = 80 + 7.
- *Relative Size of Numbers:* 47 is 2 more than 45, is large compared to 4, and is small compared to 250.
- *Place-Value Relationships:* 247 can be made using 24 tens 7 ones. 1000 can be 10 hundreds or 100 tens.
- *Benchmark Numbers:* 97 is about 100.
- *Number Patterns:* Skip counting.

Estimation in Measurement

- *Estimates:* About 200 people; 10 to 20 feet long; about $\frac{1}{2}$ eaten.
- *Common-Object Benchmarks:* The end your thumb is about 1 inch.
- *Checking for Sensible Answers:* A person isn't 4 meters tall.

Operations

Operation Meanings

- *Knowing When to Add or Subtract:* For joining, separating, comparing
- *Knowing When to Multiply or Divide:* For joining or forming equal groups, for comparing using "times as many" or "fraction of"

Operation Relationships; Properties

- *Relationships Between Operations:* For multiplication and addition, for multiplication and division
- *Properties:* Add and multiply in any order. Adding zero. Distributivity: $3 \times 54 = (3 \times 50) + (3 \times 4)$.

Effects of Operations

- Start with 64. Compare 64 + 6, 64 − 6, 64 × 6, 64 ÷ 6.
- Start with 3 × 5. What is the effect of doubling the 3? the 5? both?
- Start with 2. Add 2 five times. Start again. Multiply by 2 five times.

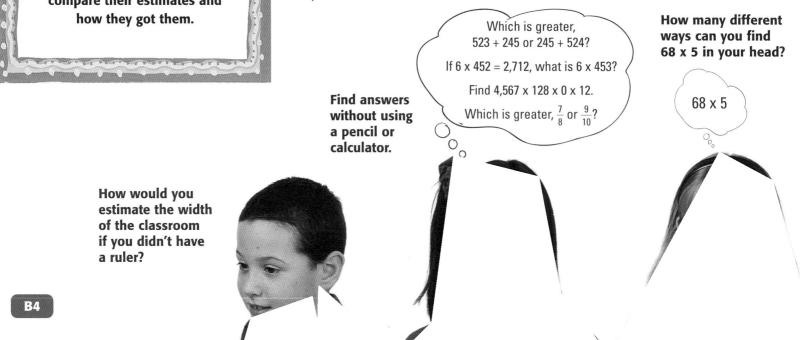

How would you estimate the width of the classroom if you didn't have a ruler?

Find answers without using a pencil or calculator.

Which is greater, 523 + 245 or 245 + 524?

If 6 x 452 = 2,712, what is 6 x 453?

Find 4,567 x 128 x 0 x 12.

Which is greater, $\frac{7}{8}$ or $\frac{9}{10}$?

How many different ways can you find 68 x 5 in your head?

68 x 5

*"Mathematics without number sense
is a sea of symbols without meaning."*
—Carne Barnett

Basic Facts and Computation

Basic Facts

Multiplication basic-fact strategies help students learn facts.

Multiplication Basic-Fact Strategies
Use the Order Property To find 7 x 4, use 4 x 7 = 28.
Skip Count To find 4 x 5, skip count by 5s: 5, 10, 15, 20.
Use Doubling For 2 x 6, use 6 + 6. For 4 x 7, use 2 x 7 plus 2 x 7 (a double double). For 8 x 6, use 4 x 6 plus 4 x 6.
Use Known Facts For 6 x 8, use 5 x 8 plus one more group of 8. For 7 x 6, use 5 x 6 plus 2 x 6.
Use Patterns For multiples of 9, the tens digit is 1 less than the multiplier and the sum of the digits is 9. For 8 x 9, the tens digits is 7 and 7 + 2 = 9, so 8 x 9 = 72.

Estimation and Mental Computation

Estimate before computing or when an exact answer isn't needed. Use estimation and mental-computation strategies.

Estimation Strategies in Computation
Front End 173 + 421 + 348 → 100 + 400 + 300 = 800.
Rounding 425 x 8 → 400 x 8 = 3,200. 284 − 39 = 280 − 40 = 240.
Compatible Numbers $\frac{1}{3}$ x 187 → $\frac{1}{3}$ x 180 = 60.
Clustering 627 + 658 + 589 + 613 → 4 x 600 = 2,400.
Benchmark 46 + 38 → 46 < 50 and 38 < 50. So 46 + 38 < 100.

Mental-Computation Strategies
Compensation 57 + 29 → 57 + 30 = 87. 87 − 1 = 86.
Breaking Apart Numbers 54 + 23 → 54 + 20 = 74. 74 + 3 = 77.
Special Numbers Look for numbers like 1, 10, 100 or 3, 30, 300. 400 x 20 = 8,000. 45 + 30 = 75. 3 + 79 + 7 = 3 + 7 + 79 = 10 + 79 = 89.

Paper-Pencil Computation; Choosing a Computation Tool

Connect concrete and symbolic work. When choosing a tool, try mental math first and don't use calculators instead of mental math or simple paper-pencil computation.

Number Sense Teaching Tips

Encourage Flexibility

People with good number sense use multiple strategies and can use different strategies for the same problem.

Basic Facts Mastery

Basic facts mastery is a key to good number sense. When appropriate, work for rapid recall of basic facts.

The Value of Estimation

Stress the value of estimates. Some students see them as wrong answers.

Put Strategies in Perspective

Point out that learning names of strategies for basic facts, mental math, and estimation is not important. Being able to use strategies is what's important.

Scott Foresman - Addison Wesley Math

Number sense is a foundation of the program.

Student Book

- Lessons that focus on many aspects of number sense including Exploring Place-Value Relationships, Exact or Estimate, Exploring Adding and Subtracting on a Thousand Chart, Estimating Sums (Differences, Products), Using Mental Math, Estimating Fractional Amounts, Overestimating and Underestimating

- Exercises identified as mental math, estimation, patterns

- Problem solving lessons where students Choose a Tool (mental math, paper-pencil, concrete materials, calculator)

- Number Sense exercises on the Stop and Practice pages

Teacher's Edition

- Support for number sense in notes and activities plus a special Mental Math activity in every lesson

Ancillaries

- Support for number sense in the program components including Performance Math CD-ROM for basic fact mastery and Calendar Time Kit with lots of pattern work

Keys to Success in Teaching Problem Solving

Take a Moment

Many teachers ask "What can I do to help my students do better in problem solving." There's no one simple answer. There may be a variety of reasons why students are struggling. One reason that can be overlooked is students may be having difficulty simply reading and understanding the problem. When that's the case, some of the skills and strategies used in reading instruction can be keys to success in teaching problem solving in math.

Try this tomorrow

Ask students to solve word problems that have nonsense words substituted for some of the nouns. Afterwards discuss whether context clues helped students attach meaning to the unfamiliar words. Let students make up similar problems.

Provide Tools for Learning the Problem-Solving Process

Problem-Solving Guide

Introduce a general problem-solving guide, and show how it's used with specific problems.

Understand
- What do you know?
- What do you need to find out?

Plan
- What will you do?
- What operation or strategy will you use?

Solve
- How will you use your plan?
- What is the answer?

Look Back
- Check your work.
- Is your answer reasonable?

Skills for Analyzing Word Problems

Include lessons that focus on skills for analyzing various types of word problems.

- Too Much or Too Little Information
- Multiple-Step Problems
- Choose an Operation
- Exact Answer or Estimate
- Overestimating and Underestimating
- Interpreting Remainders

Problem-Solving Strategies

Focus on specific strategies at times and let students choose strategies at other times.

- Use Objects/Act It Out
- Draw a Picture
- Look for a Pattern
- Guess and Check
- Use Logical Reasoning
- Make an Organized List
- Make a Table
- Solve a Simpler Problem
- Work Backward

Integrate Problem Solving into Daily Instruction

Teach Through Problem Solving Use real-world contexts. Introduce some new content by having students explore or do extended investigations, letting the math emerge during the problem-solving process.

Integrate Problem Solving Into Practice There's no substitute for solving lots of problems. Give routine, nonroutine, open-ended, and "write your own" problems. Do a problem of the day and multi-day projects.

Incorporate Decision Making Have lessons that focus on using problem-solving skills and strategies to make real-world decisions. Use a guide such as: Understand, Plan and Solve, Make a Decision, Present Your Decision.

Reading Skills and Strategies

Apply reading skills and strategies in math to help students access what's on the page as well as the ideas and relationships in the problem situations.

Reading Skills and Strategies	Are Keys to Understanding
Main Idea with Supporting Details	What's the main idea? What operation does it suggest?
Read Tables, Graphs, and Illustrations	How can you get data from tables, graphs, pictures?
Understand Organizational Devices	Can you gain meaning from captions, headings?
Understand Vocabulary	Do you understand the math words? Use context clues.
Word Meaning	Do you understand the other words in the problem?
Recognize Sequence	Sequence the events. Is this a multiple-step problem?
Make Predictions	Make an estimate of the answer.
Make Inferences	What can you conclude based on what you know?

Encourage Helpful Habits and Beliefs

Promote Good Problem-Solving Habits

- Perseverance
- Flexibility
- Confidence, risk taking
- Willingness to reflect on one's thinking

Foster Important Beliefs About Problem Solving

- There's more than one way to solve a problem.
- Some problems have more than one solution.

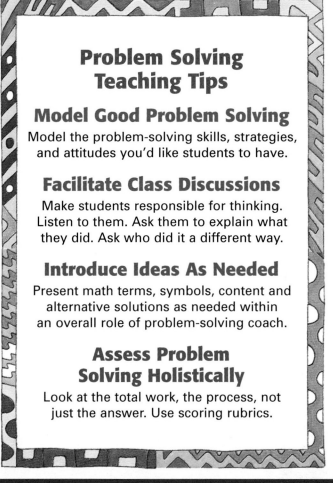

Problem Solving Teaching Tips

Model Good Problem Solving

Model the problem-solving skills, strategies, and attitudes you'd like students to have.

Facilitate Class Discussions

Make students responsible for thinking. Listen to them. Ask them to explain what they did. Ask who did it a different way.

Introduce Ideas As Needed

Present math terms, symbols, content and alternative solutions as needed within an overall role of problem-solving coach.

Assess Problem Solving Holistically

Look at the total work, the process, not just the answer. Use scoring rubrics.

Scott Foresman - Addison Wesley Math

Problem solving is a foundation of the program.

Problem-Solving Guide In lessons, on a transparency, and on a Reading Strategies for Math chart. Used on Guided Problem Solving pages in the Problem-Solving Masters.

Reading Assists In lesson notes for problem-solving lessons and in Options for Reaching All Learners. Reading Strategies for Math charts are large write-on-wipe-off charts with templates for connecting reading, writing, and oral language developement to math. Some charts focus on problems solving. Charts are also on blackline masters.

Problem-Solving Lessons There are 3 types: Analyze Word Problems, Analyze Strategies, Decision Making. In various lessons students compare strategies, choose a strategy, and choose a computation tool.

Integration of Problem Solving Engaging lesson contexts, Explore lessons with Problem Solving Connections named, Extended Investigations in the Teacher's Edition, a range of problems in lessons, a large Problem of the Day Flipchart, Team Projects, and Problem Solving Tips from mascots.

Technology in Math Class:
What Are Your Goals?

Take a Moment

What technology is available to you as you teach math? How do you use it? Whether you have a little or a lot and use it rarely or often, take a moment to think through your technology goals. Start by thinking about your students.

- Write down the year they will turn 21 and the year they'll be 65.

- Think about the math and the technology they will use as adults.

- Now set some goals. What math content will you emphasize and how would you like to use technology in your math class? Use the information at the right to help.

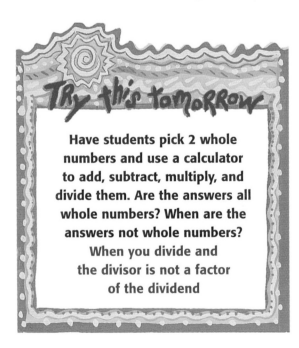

Try this tomorrow

Have students pick 2 whole numbers and use a calculator to add, subtract, multiply, and divide them. Are the answers all whole numbers? When are the answers not whole numbers?

When you divide and the divisor is not a factor of the dividend

Learning with Technology

4-Function Calculator *Fraction Calculator* *Scientific Calculator* *Graphing Calculator*   *Computer Software* *Interactive CD-ROM* *Internet Connections*

Learning with Calculators

Calculators as Problem-Solving Tools
Calculators save time when students solve problems involving data analysis, areas, number patterns, numerical conjectures, or any tedious computation. Calculators let students spend their time focusing on the problem-solving process.

Calculators as Concept-Development Tools While students should not use calculators to do basic facts, mental computation, or simple paper-pencil computation, calculators can help develop other number skills and concepts as shown in the Estimation Target Game below.

Graphing Calculators Graphing calculators can assist learning in statistics and algebra.

Estimation Target Game

One student enters a number and operation and says a target range: enter 8 ⨯ and say 2000–3000. Another student enters a number and presses =. If the answer is within the target range, it's a bull's-eye.

Learning with Computers

Tool Software and Practice Games
Computers help students explore and practice math concepts by providing:

- Graphing tools for bar graphs, line graphs, line plots, etc.
- Geometry tools for 2D, 3D work
- Number tools such as a place-value blocks tool and a fraction tool
- Probability tools for simulations
- Spreadsheet tools to explore patterns, relationships, pre-algebra
- Writing tools for journal work
- Practice games for motivation and instant feedback

Interactive, Multimedia CD-ROM For interactive teaching, math tools, sound, movies, and animation.

Internet Connections For worldwide gathering and sharing of data.

Learning with Video

You can bring real-world math into the classroom with:

- Videotape
- Video on CD-ROMs
- Videodisc, digital videodisc
- Other digital video sources

Learning About Technology

Learning About Calculators

Use key sequences like these to help students learn about their calculators.

- Automatic constant: 4 $+$ 3 $=$ $=$ $=$
- Order of operations: 4 $+$ 5 $\times$ 3
- Memory: 5 $M+$ 3 $+$ MR $=$
- Integer division: 26 $INT\div$ 3 $=$

Learning About Computers

Here are some basic computer skills students should learn.

- Starting up; using a floppy disk, CD-ROM, or network
- Finding, opening, and operating a document or program
- Changing, saving, and printing a document; shutdown

Learning About the Internet

Here are some Internet basics.

- Getting on the Internet: you need a computer, a modem to get information, and a browser to display information.
- Getting around the Internet: type a URL to find a "page" (like using an address to find a house); click on hyperlinks (underlined words) to go somewhere else (to "surf"); use a search engine or directory to find information sources.

Learning When to Use Technology

- Teach students that it's not appropriate to use technology as a substitute for thinking or doing basic facts, mental computation, and simple paper-pencil computation. To convince students, have a race between students doing these problems mentally and others using a calculator.

  3 x 5   200 + 500   2 x 800   30 + 10 + 20   100 + 78

- Teach students that it's appropriate to use technology when solving problems and exploring new ideas.
- Stress that technology makes estimation more important, not less, because it's easy to push a wrong button.

Technology for Teachers

To Plan Use an interactive CD-ROM lesson planner.

To Assess Use test and practice software.

To Present a Lesson Use an overhead display panel or large monitor to show computer screens during presentations.

To Help You Grow Gather and share ideas on the Internet.

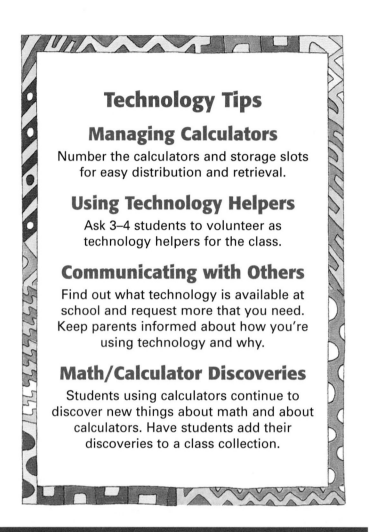

Technology Tips

Managing Calculators

Number the calculators and storage slots for easy distribution and retrieval.

Using Technology Helpers

Ask 3–4 students to volunteer as technology helpers for the class.

Communicating with Others

Find out what technology is available at school and request more that you need. Keep parents informed about how you're using technology and why.

Math/Calculator Discoveries

Students using calculators continue to discover new things about math and about calculators. Have students add their discoveries to a class collection.

Scott Foresman - Addison Wesley Math

The program offers many opportunities to use technology.

Student Book

- Calculators: There are opportunities for use in lessons (examples, exercises, Explore, Choose a Tool), in Your Choice, and in Technology pages (some that use fraction calculators).
- Computers: Tool software is used in Technology pages; there are on-page references to Mathsurf Internet site.

Teacher's Edition

- Technology options are keyed into chapters and lessons.

Ancillaries

- Calculator and computer activities in Technology Masters
- CD-ROMS: Interactive, multimedia CD-ROM with lessons and tools; Performance Math (basic facts), Math Workshop (skills), Logical Journey of the Zoombinis (reasoning)
- Software: DataWonder! for data analysis
- For teachers: Teacher's Resource Planner CD-ROM to preview ancillaries and plan lessons, TestWorks: Test and Practice Software, Mathsurf Internet site for teachers. Also a Mathsurf Internet site for parents.

Fostering a Community of Learners in the Math Classroom

Take a Moment

Think back to when your students entered your class. Did they have diverse learning styles, cultural backgrounds, socioeconomic backgrounds, levels of English proficiency, and perhaps physical, emotional, or mental challenges? Which of your students are the hardest to reach in math? In our information society, it is a priority for all students to succeed in math. The best way to achieve this is to build a community of learners in the classroom that support each other on the road to achieving math power.

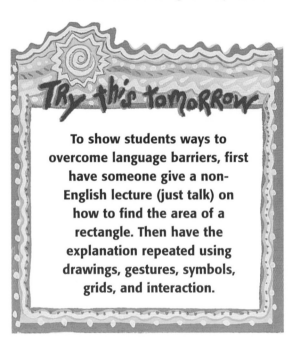

Try this tomorrow

To show students ways to overcome language barriers, first have someone give a non-English lecture (just talk) on how to find the area of a rectangle. Then have the explanation repeated using drawings, gestures, symbols, grids, and interaction.

ESL Students

"Show me what you mean."

Overcome Language Barriers When You Communicate

- Use real objects, manipulatives, and pictures, especially ones relating to the students' world.

- Use gestures and highlighting.

- Speak slowly in short, simple sentences and enunciate clearly.

- Provide ample repetition; check comprehension frequently.

- When you model, show what to do; don't just say what to do.

- Use tables and diagrams.

- Provide reading assists for math words and everyday words.

- Use "scaffolding;" rephrase what students say to help them be clear.

Vary How Students Communicate

- Have them demonstrate write, speak, role play, stand to agree (TPR: total physical response), draw, play math games, use computers, work with parents.

- Pair students with same-language or English-language speakers.

Inclusion Students

"Give me some more time."

Identify Student Needs

- Learning disabled (LD) students have normal intelligence but have problems with memory, perception, distractibility, and reasoning.

- Low achievers and the educable mentally handicapped (EMH) have problems with memory, attention span, learning rate, and reasoning.

- Students with attention deficit disorder, ADD, are easily distracted.

- Physical and emotional challenges vary: visual, auditory, speech, orthopedic, hyperactive, etc.

Modify Instruction

- Present lessons in a structured manner with regular checkpoints.

- Collaborate with specialized resource teachers about ways to customize instruction.

- Check activities for too many materials, memory skills, or steps.

- Don't deny students opportunities to learn important content; just modify how it's presented based on students' needs.

- Use graphic organizers, a file of math words, real-world links, group and pair work; have one student read to another when needed.

- Assign less; allow more time.

- Vary assessment methods; use students' writing, speaking, and hands-on work to gain insight into their understanding.

Diverse Learning Styles

"Let me try it my way."

Use Activities That Support Diverse Learning Styles

Learning Style	Learns Through
Verbal	Reading, writing, talking, listening.
Logical	Exploring, questioning, reasoning.
Visual	Drawing, building, designing, creating.
Kinesthetic	Movement, hands-on activities.
Musical	Rhythm, melody, tapping, rapping.
Social	Grouping, team participation, and sharing.
Individual	Thinking, reflecting, goal setting.

Gifted and Talented Students

"Give me a challenge."

- Provide challenging, interesting problems. Have gifted students work with others; then everyone benefits.

At-Risk Students

"Give me a chance."

- Provide extra encouragement and excitement in school, with emphasis on problem solving and critical thinking.

Gender Issues

"Treat me the same way."

- Some teachers pay more attention to boys, give them more praise, let them talk more, give them more help, and ask them higher-level questions. Be aware of how you interact with boys and girls during class discussions.

Cultural Diversity

"Respect my heritage."

- Clarify misconceptions, negative beliefs, and stereotypes. Provide relevant, interesting contexts. Encourage all students to share and celebrate their cultures.

A Community of Learners

An Accepting, Supportive Learning Environment

Create an atmosphere that honors students' unique ideas. Encourage peer coaching as a normal part of classroom culture.

Observing Students

Provide opportunities for interactions, and then observe to assess students' needs.

Promoting Self Confidence

Many students have been told they aren't good at math. Praise small positive steps that will lead to larger ones.

Teaching Strategies for All

Use a variety of teaching and assessment strategies that are age, gender, and culturally appropriate for all learners.

Scott Foresman - Addison Wesley Math

The program is designed to reach all learners.

Overcoming Language Barriers

Artwork and photographs that illustrate the math and show what to do. Vocabulary highlighted on the student page. Language development activities in the Teacher's Edition. Varied forms of assessment, not just written. Activities with manipulatives and technology. Explore lessons that model students doing the math. Reading Strategies for Math charts. Math-a-pedia picture dictionary. Multilingual Handbook including a multilingual glossary.

Accommodating Varied Abilities, Learning Styles, Backgrounds

Hands-on activities. Talk About It. Journal. Team Project. Work Together in Explore. Your Choice (learning styles). Tips from mascots. Multicultural and gender-sensitive contexts. Connections to the real world and to other disciplines. Alternative activities for different learning styles. Learning styles identified for activities in lesson notes. Inclusion tips and ideas for early finishers in lesson notes. Assignment guides. Daily blackline masters for practice, reteaching, enrichment, and problem solving.

A Teacher's Guide to Assessment: What, How, Why, and When

Take a Moment

Think about the students in your class. Write down the names of any students for whom you'd like more information about what they know and don't know about mathematics. Then write down two ways you might be able to get that information. Perhaps a different form of assessment would help.

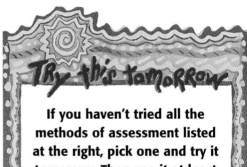

Try this tomorrow

If you haven't tried all the methods of assessment listed at the right, pick one and try it tomorrow. Then use it at least once more in the next week. The suggestions given in the Assessment Sourcebook can help you get started.

What to Assess

Assess Full Math Power

- Concepts
- Facts
- Skills and procedures
- Problem solving: routine problems, nonroutine problems, open-ended problems, decision making
- Mathematical reasoning and critical thinking

Assess Math Habits and Disposition

- Perseverance
- Flexibility
- Confidence, risk-taking
- Motivation
- Participation
- Cooperation
- Reflection on one's own work and learning

Assess content and approaches that are valuable in the real world; don't just assess what is easy to test.

How to Assess

Assess Various Types of Student Work

- Oral work: explanations, questions
- Written work: skills, drawings, graphs, explanations of student thinking, written reports
- Work with tools: manipulatives, calculators, computers
- Work with others: partners, small groups, and the whole class

Vary Assessment Methods

- Observation, interview
- Journal of student writing
- Performance tasks scored using assessment rubrics
- Free-response or multiple-choice tests
- Warm-ups, quick checks
- Self assessment, peer assessment
- Portfolio of selected student work

Use a variety of student work and assessment methods that reflect how students learn and how you teach.

> *"Timely, useful feedback turns ongoing assessments into learning opportunities for students."*
>
> —Diane Briars

Why and When to Assess

Assessment Purposes

- Monitor progress against criteria and give students feedback.
- Adjust instruction as needed.
- Do long-term planning.
- Send progress reports or grades home to parents.
- Compare an individual student or a group of students to other students in the district, state, or nation.

Assessment Times

- Ongoing assessment integrated with daily instruction
- End-of-section quizzes
- End-of-chapter tests
- End-of-quarter or semester tests
- Annual district, state, or national tests

Assess primarily to help students grow and to help you plan. Assess on an ongoing basis during instruction.

Assessment Tips

Ongoing Assessment

Carry a clipboard and checklist. Write on self-stick labels to transfer notes. Be a good listener; be nonjudgmental.

Using Assessment Rubrics

Score papers with a colleague at first.

Portfolios

Have students move papers from their work folder to an assessment portfolio at various times.

Test Prep

Share test prep strategies to help students do their best on multiple-choice tests.

Changing How You Assess

Don't change everything all at once. Show students criteria and sample work.

Scott Foresman - Addison Wesley Math

Here are some of the many built-in assessment options.

Student Book

- Check in lessons; Get Ready in section opener; Test Prep in lessons; Test Prep Strategies; Journal exercises
- Your Choice, assessment tasks for various learning styles
- Chapter Review/Test, Performance Assessment

Teacher's Edition

- Ongoing Assessment: Talk About It, Error Intervention
- Quick Check, Portfolio, Interview, Observation, Journal, Performance Assessment, Self-Assessment, Assessment Rubrics in lessons
- Standardized Test Correlation in front of each chapter

Ancillaries

- Assessment Sourcebook: Inventory Test, Quizzes, Chapter Tests (free-response, multiple-choice, mixed formats), Cumulative Tests, record forms, assessment tips, . . .
- TestWorks: Test and Practice Software with ready-made and customized tests, free response or multiple choice
- Interactive CD-ROM with a Journal feature

Additional Resources

Inservice Workshops from Scott Foresman - Addison Wesley

At Scott Foresman-Addison Wesley, we offer more than program materials. We also offer our commitment to service. This includes inservice workshops for professional staff development as well as support for implementation of program materials. As part of our ongoing partnership between teacher and publisher, we are at your service. Contact your sales representative to hear how our educational consultants can customize inservice programs to meet your needs.

Northeast   1-800-521-0011
Southeast   1-800-241-3532
Midwest   1-800-535-4391
West   1-800-548-4885
Southwest   1-800-527-2701
In Texas   1-800-441-1438

Web Site   http://www.sf.aw.com

Bibliography

Using Manipulatives

The *Learning With . . .* Teacher Guides. Available in English or Spanish. White Plains, NY: Cuisenaire Company of America.

Mathematics: With Manipulatives. Videotapes. White Plains, NY: Cuisenaire Company of America, 1988.

Ross, Rita, and Roy Kurtz. "Making Manipulatives Work: A Strategy for Success." Arithmetic Teacher, 40(5), 1993.

Start with Manipulatives Kit for Staff Development. Manipulatives and Resource Book. White Plains, NY: Cuisenaire Company of America, 1995.

Number Sense

McIntosh, A., B. Reys, and J. Hope. *Number Sense: Simple Effective Number Sense Experiences.* Palo Alto, CA: Dale Seymour Publications, 1996.

Mokros, Jan, Susan Jo Russell, and Karen Economopulos. *Beyond Arithmetic.* Palo Alto, CA: Dale Seymour Publications, 1993.

Patriarca, L, M. Scheffel, and S. Hedeman. Developing *Decimal Concepts: Building Bridges Between Whole Numbers and Decimals.* White Plains, NY: Dale Seymour Publications, 1995.

Schoen, H. L., and M. J. Zweng, eds. *Estimation and Mental Computation.* Reston, VA: NCTM, 1986.

Sowder, Judith. "Estimation and Number Sense." Grouws, Douglas A., ed. *Handbook of Research on Mathematics Teaching and Learning.* Reston, VA: NCTM, 1992.

Van de Walle, John A. *Elementary and Middle School Mathematics: Teaching Developmentally.,* 3rd ed. Reading, MA: Addison Wesley Longman, 1998.

Problem Solving

Burns, Marilyn. A *Collection of Math Lessons from Grades 3 through 6.* White Plains, NY: Cuisenaire Company of America, 1992.

Charles, Randall, and Frank Lester. *Teaching Problem Solving: What, Why, & How.* Palo Alto, CA: Dale Seymour Publications, 1982.

Charles, Randall, and Edward Silver, eds. *The Teaching and Assessing of Mathematical Problem Solving.* Hillsdale, NJ: Lawrence Erlbaum, 1989.

Polya, G. *Mathematical Discovery: On Understanding Learning, Teaching Problem Solving.* New York: John Wiley, 1962.

Silver, E. G., ed. *Teaching and Learning Mathematical Problem Solving.* Hillsdale, NJ: Lawrence Erlbaum, 1985.

Student Diversity

Baker, Gwendolyn C. *Planning and Organizing for Multicultural Instruction.* Palo Alto, CA: Dale Seymour Publications, 1983.

House, Peggy, ed. *Providing Opportunities for the Mathematically Gifted,* K–12. Reston, VA: NCTM, 1987.

Skolnick, J., C. Langbort, and L. Day. *How to Encourage Girls in Math and Science.* Palo Alto, CA: Dale Seymour Publications, 1982.

"Student at Risk." *Educational Leadership,* 50 (4), 1992.

Thornton, Carol A. *Teaching Mathematics to Children with Special Needs.* Palo Alto, CA: Dale Seymour Publications, 1983.

Assessment

Ann Arbor Public Schools. *Alternative Assessment: Evaluating Student Performance in Elementary Mathematics.* Palo Alto, CA: Dale Seymour Publications, 1993.

Barton, James. *Portfolio Assessment* Palo Alto, CA: Dale Seymour Publications, 1996.

Charles, Randall, Frank Lester, and Phares O'Daffer. *How to Evaluate Progress in Problem Solving.* Reston, VA: NCTM, 1987.

Freedman, Robin Lee Harris. *Open-Ended Questioning.* Palo Alto, CA: Dale Seymour Publications, 1993.

Hart, Diane. *Authentic Assessment.* Palo Alto, CA: Dale Seymour Publications, 1993.

Mathematics: Assessing Understanding. Videotapes and discussion guide. White Plains, NY: Cuisenaire Company of America.

Stenmark, Jean Kerr, ed. *Mathematics Assessment: Myths, Models, Good Questions, and Practical Suggestions.* Palo Alto, CA: Dale Seymour Publications, 1991.

NCTM Standards

Standards from the National Council of Teachers of Mathematics

Contents

NCTM Teaching Standards
Summary

The "Professional Standards for Teaching Mathematics" describe classrooms where teachers select worthwhile tasks, orchestrate classroom discourse, create a supportive environment, and analyze learning to make ongoing, instructional decisions.

Standards for Teaching Mathematics

1 Worthwhile Mathematical Tasks

2 The Teacher's Role in Discourse

3 Students' Role in Discourse

4 Tools for Enhancing Discourse

5 Learning Environment

6 Analysis of Teaching and Learning

Tasks

A powerful mathematics program must be built on a foundation of worthwhile tasks.

1 Worthwhile Mathematical Tasks

Consider the content. Choose tasks that promote:
- Mathematical understanding.
- Making connections.
- Skills within a context of problem solving and reasoning.
- Communication.
- Positive attitudes towards math.

Consider the students. Choose tasks with sensitivity to:
- What students know.
- What interests them.
- Social issues such as gender.

Consider the ways students learn. Choose tasks that:
- Accommodate diverse learning styles.

Discourse

Discourse is ways of representing, thinking, talking, agreeing, and disagreeing during class discussion.

2 The Teachers Role in Discourse

- Orchestrate classroom discourse.
- Provoke students' reasoning; say "Explain," "Why," "Who did it another way?" "Who agrees; who disagrees?" "How can we find out?"
- Do less talking, modeling, explaining; do more listening.
- Monitor and organize students' participation.

3 Students' Role in Discourse

- Actively participate; listen to others and respond.
- Ask questions, make conjectures.
- Make convincing arguments.

4 Tools for Enhancing Discourse

- Computers, calculators, and other technology
- Concrete materials used as models
- Pictures, diagrams, tables, and graphs
- Invented and conventional terms and symbols
- Metaphors, analogies, and stories
- Written hypotheses, explanations, and arguments
- Oral presentations and dramatizations

Major Shifts

The Teaching Standards call for major shifts towards mathematics teaching for the empowerment of all students.

Shift Towards	Shift Away From
Classrooms as mathematical communities	*Classrooms as simply a collection of individuals*
Logic and mathematical evidence as verification	*The teacher as the sole authority for right answers*
Mathematical reasoning	*Memorizing procedures*
Conjecturing, inventing, and problem solving	*Emphasis on mechanistic answer-finding*
Connecting mathematics ideas and applications	*Mathematics as isolated concepts and procedures*

Environment

The environment in the classroom should be one that fosters mathematical thinking.

5 Learning Environment

- Provide time for students to think and communicate.
- Encourage respect for everyone's ideas.
- Help students value reasoning and sense-making.
- Forge a classroom community through whole-class and group work.

Analysis

Monitor and analyze learning on an ongoing basis to assess and adjust your teaching.

6 Analysis of Teaching and Learning

- Use observation, interview, journal, written work.
- Examine effects of the task, the discourse, and the learning environment.
- Adjust activities while teaching.
- Make short- and long-range plans.
- Discuss students' learning with parents, administrators, students.

Standards for the Evaluation of the Teaching of Mathematics

1 **The Evaluation Cycle**

2 **Teachers as Participants in Evaluation**

3 **Sources of Information**

4 **Mathematical Concepts, Procedures, and Connections**

5 **Mathematics as Problem Solving, Reasoning, Communication**

6 **Promoting Mathematical Disposition**

7 **Assessing Students' Understanding of Mathematics**

8 **Learning Environments**

Standards for the Professional Development of Teachers of Mathematics

1 **Experiencing Good Mathematics Teaching**

2 **Knowing Mathematics and School Mathematics**

3 **Knowing Students as Learners of Mathematics**

4 **Knowing Mathematical Pedagogy**

5 **Developing as a Teacher of Mathematics**

6 **Teacher's Role in Professional Development**

Standards for the Support and Development of Mathematics Teachers and Teaching

1 **Responsibilities of Policy Makers in Government, Business, and Industry**

2 **Responsibilities of Schools and School Systems**

3 **Responsibilities of Colleges and Universities**

4 **Professional Organizations' Responsibilities**

NCTM Assessment Standards
Summary

Assess thinking and problem solving, not just skills.

Use ongoing assessment to enhance learning and teaching.

Help all students meet high expectations.

Mathematics Standard

Assessment Should Reflect the Mathematics That All Students Need to Know and Be Able to Do The world outside of schools places increasing importance on thinking and problem solving.

Assess with Realistic and Worthwhile Mathematical Activities Use activities that elicit important mathematics.

Give Appropriate Weight to Different Facets of Mathematics Create an assessment framework that views specific assessment activities within a balanced, integrated whole.

Learning Standard

Enhance Mathematics Learning By Integrating Assessment with Instruction Use informal, ongoing assessment daily to help students learn and to guide instruction.

Use Student Work, Teacher Judgment, and Student Reflections This will increase the fit between instructional goals and assessment.

Help Students Become Independent Self Assessors Show them sample tasks and criteria. Have them reflect on their own work and critique each other's work.

Equity Standard

Promote Equity with Assessment By Having High Expectations for Every Student Develop each student's mathematical power to the fullest.

Allow for Multiple Approaches Honor each student's unique qualities and experiences. Recognize students' background and experiences in judging work.

Provide Alternative Activities and Modes of Response Don't ignore differences in physical condition, gender, and ethnic, cultural, and social backgrounds in an effort to be fair.

Using the Standards for:

Monitoring Students' Progress

Judge students' progress towards mathematical power.

Communicate with students about their performance.

Use performance tasks, projects, and portfolios as assessment tools.

Help students learn to assess their own work to become independent learners of mathematics.

Using the Standards for:

Making Instructional Decisions

Integrate assessment with instruction by using observation, questioning, and listening to make moment-by-moment decisions.

Use multiple sources of evidence for short-term planning: observation, questioning, and written work.

As you use evidence of learning in long-range planning, consider the needs of diverse learners.

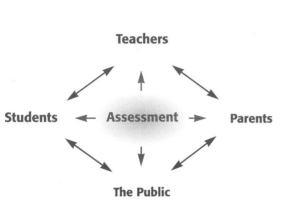

Teachers

Students ← Assessment → Parents

The Public

Curriculum
What is taught

Instruction
How it's taught

Assessment
What is tested

Keep students, parents, and the public informed.

Use multiple sources of evidence: observation, portfolios, tasks, etc.

Assess what's taught in the way that it's taught.

Openness Standard

Make Assessment an Open Process By Informing Students, Parents, and the Public Before formal assessment, tell students the expectations and the consequences of the assessment. Make examples of scored work available to parents and the public.

Teachers Should Actively Participate Teachers discuss goals, expectations, student work, and criteria.

The Assessment Process Is Open to Scrutiny and Modification It should be continually checked and revised.

Inference Standard

Promote Valid Inferences About Mathematics Learning By Using Multiple Sources of Evidence Use observations, interviews, open-ended tasks, portfolios, extended problem situations, plus multiple-choice and short-answer tests.

Look for Possible Bias Projects done at home may introduce bias. Do alternate activities for ESL students. Be sure scorers are trained experts.

Have Enough Evidence The type of evidence needed depends on the consequences of the inference.

Coherence Standard

Assessment Should Be a Coherent Process Aspects of the assessment work together like the instruments in an orchestra. A coherent system cannot be based on paper-and-pencil tests alone.

The Assessment Should Match Its Purposes Then the assessment has educational value.

Align Assessment with Curriculum and Instruction Students should see that their assessment experiences connect to both what they learn and how they learn.

Using the Standards for:

Evaluating Students' Achievement

Compare students' work with performance criteria, not with the work of other students.

Assess growth in mathematical power using worthwhile tasks.

For certification, use balanced sources of data; multiple-choice tests lack balance in types of tasks.

Use profiles of student achievement, not a single letter or number grade.

Using the Standards for:

Evaluating Programs

Use a variety of high-quality evidence such as tests created for the program and existing tests with a mix of simple formats and complex tasks.

Do detailed analysis of group data by content area and type of student; avoid using overall mean scores on norm-referenced tests.

Use the professional judgment of teachers to evaluate external exams and to decide how to use the results.

Chapter 1

Data, Graphs, and Facts Review

Standards	Pages
1 Problem Solving	
Skills and Strategies	20–21, 22–23, 36–39
Applications	11, 13, 15, 17
Explorations	26–27, 28–29, 30–31, 32–33
2 Communication	
Oral	[*Talk About It* appears in every core lesson.] 8, 10, 12, 14, *15,* 16, 18, 20, 22, 26, 28, 30, 32, 37
Written	[*Journal* appears in every explore lesson.] *11,* 15, *17, 19,* 21, 23, 24, 27, 29, 31, 33, 39, 42
Cooperative Learning	8, *10B, 12B, 16B, 30B,* 40–41
3 Reasoning	11, 13, 14–15, 16–17, 18
4 Connections	
Interdisciplinary	*8, 10A,* 10, 11, 12, *14A,* 15, *16A, 18A,* 19, *20A,* 21, *22A,* 22, 23, *26A, 28A,* 29, *30A,* 32, 43, 46
Technology	*12A, 32A, 36A,* 40–41
Cultural	*12B*
5 Estimation	36–38
6 Number Sense and Numeration	10–11, 14–15, 16–17, 18–19, 26–27, 28–29, 30–31
7 Whole Number Operations	22–23, 34–35
8 Whole Number Computation	22–23, 34–35
9 Geometry and Spatial Sense	13
11 Statistics and Probability	10–11, 14–15, 16–17, 18–19, 20–21, 26–27, 28–29, 30–31, 40–41
13 Patterns and Relationships	12–13, 32–33

Chapter 2

Place Value and Time

Standards	Pages
1 Problem Solving	
Skills and Strategies	58–61, 82–83
Applications	53, 57, 67, 69, 75, 79
Explorations	54–55, 70–71, 76–77, 80–81
2 Communication	
Oral	[*Talk About It* appears in every core lesson.] 50, 52, *53,* 54, 56, 59, 63, 66, 68, *69,* 70, 74, 76, 78, 80
Written	[*Journal* appears in every explore lesson.] 55, 58–59, 61, 63, 64, 71, 72, *75,* 77, 81, *83,* 84
Cooperative Learning	50, *52B, 56B,* 62–63, *66B*
3 Reasoning	53, 56–57, 67, 69, 71, 74–75, 78–79
4 Connections	
Mathematical	75, 79, 88
Interdisciplinary	*48, 50, 52A, 54A, 56A,* 60, 61, *66A, 68A,* 68, *70A,* 70, *74A,* 75, 77, *78A,* 79, *80A, 82A,* 85, 88
Technology	*48, 55, 58A, 76A,* 83, 85
Cultural	*52B, 70B, 82B*
5 Estimation	70–71, 76–77, 79
6 Number Sense and Numeration	48–49, 52–53, 54–55, 56–57, 65, 66–67, 68–69, *75, 79*
9 Geometry and Spatial Sense	53
10 Measurement	73, 74–75, 76–77, 78–79, 80–81, 82–83

Teacher's Edition pages in italic.

Chapter 3

Adding and Subtracting Numbers and Money

	Standards	Pages
1	**Problem Solving**	
	Skills and Strategies	100–101, 118–119, 136–137
	Applications	99, 107, 109, 112, 113, 115, 121, 123, 127, 129
	Explorations	94–95, 96–97, 130–131, 134–135
2	**Communication**	
	Oral	[*Talk About It* appears in every core lesson.] 92, 94, 96, 98, 100, 105, 108, 111, 114, *115,* 117, 118, 120, *121,* 122, 126, 128, 130, 134, 136
	Written	[*Journal* appears in every explore lesson.] 97, *99,* 101, 102, 107, *109,* 113, 124, 131, 135, 138
	Cooperative Learning	92, *98B, 104B,* 116–117, *118B*
3	**Reasoning**	99, 105, 106, 109, 111, 112, 115, 120, 121, 122, 123, 127, 129
4	**Connections**	
	Mathematical	123, 127, 129, 135, 138
	Interdisciplinary	*90, 92, 94A, 96A, 98A,* 101, *104A,* 104, 107, *108A,* 113, *114A, 118A, 122A,* 124, *126A, 128A, 130A, 134A,* 139, 142
	Technology	*90,* 91, *100A, 110A, 120A,* 135, *136A,* 139, 142
	Cultural	*96B,* 120, 122, 125, *126B,* 126
5	**Estimation**	92, 98–99, 100–101, 102
6	**Number Sense and Numeration**	98–99, *107, 109, 115, 121, 123, 127, 129,* 133
7	**Whole Number Operations**	94–95, 96–97, 98–99, 104–107, 108–109, 110–111, 114–115, 122–123
8	**Whole Number Computation**	94–95, 96–97, 98–99, 104–107, 108–109, 120–121, 134–135
9	**Geometry and Spatial Sense**	95, 107, 123
12	**Fractions and Decimals**	126–127, 128–129
13	**Patterns and Relationships**	94, 136–137

Chapter 4

Multiplication and Division Concepts and Facts

	Standards	Pages
1	**Problem Solving**	
	Skills and Strategies	162–163, 186–187, 188–189
	Applications	149, 153, 156, 157, 167, 171, 173, 177, 179, 193
	Explorations	150–151, 158–159, 168–169, 184–185
2	**Communication**	
	Oral	[*Talk About It* appears in every core lesson.] 146, 148, 150, 152, *153,* 155, 158, 166, 168, 170, 172, *173,* 176, 178, 180, 184, 186, 188
	Written	[*Journal* appears in every explore lesson.] 151, 157, 159, *163,* 164, 169, *171,* 173, 174, *179,* 181, 185, 190
	Cooperative Learning	146, *148B,* 193
3	**Reasoning**	149, 153, 155, 156, 163, 167, 169, 171, 172, 173, 176, 177, 178, 179
4	**Connections**	
	Mathematical	157, 171, 181
	Interdisciplinary	*146, 148A, 150A, 152A,* 153, 157, *158A, 166A, 168A, 172A,* 173, *176A,* 177, *180A, 184A, 186A,* 187, 191, 194
	Technology	*150B, 154A, 162A, 170A, 178A, 188A,* 191
	Cultural	*152B, 158B, 178B*
6	**Number Sense and Numeration**	*149, 153, 157, 167, 171, 173, 177, 179,* 180–181
7	**Whole Number Operations**	148–149, 166–167, 168–169
8	**Whole Number Computation**	150–151, 152–153, 154–157, 158–159, 168–169, 170–171, 172–173, 176–177, 178–179
13	**Patterns and Relationships**	150–151, 158–159, 180–181

Teacher's Edition pages in italic.

Chapter 5

Multiplying by 1-Digit Factors

Chapter 6

Multiplying by 2-Digit Factors

Teacher's Edition pages in italic.

Chapter 7

Dividing by 1-Digit Divisors

Standards	Pages
1 Problem Solving	
Skills and Strategies	316–317, 332–333
Applications	295, 304, 305, 307, 311, 314, 315, 323
Explorations	292–293, 296–297, 300–301, 320–321, 326–327, 330–331
2 Communication	
Oral	[*Talk About It* appears in every core lesson.] 290, 292, 294, 296, 300, 303, *305,* 306, *307,* 310, 313, *315,* 316, 320, 322, 325, 326, 330, 332
Written	[*Journal* appears in every explore lesson.] 293, *295,* 297, 298, 301, 305, 315, 318, 321, 327, 331, 334
Cooperative Learning	290, 324–325, *332B*
3 Reasoning	294, 295, 297, 298, 301, 303, 304, 305, 307, 311, 313, 314, 321, 323, 327, 331
4 Connections	
Interdisciplinary	*288, 290, 294A,* 295, *296A, 300A, 302A,* 304, 305, 307, *310A,* 311, *312A,* 313, 314, 315, *316A, 320A, 322A, 326A,* 327, *330A,* 333, 335, 338
Technology	*288, 292A,* 301, *306A,* 328–329, *332A,* 335, 338
Cultural	*306B, 322B*
5 Estimation	294–295
6 Number Sense and Numeration	*295, 305, 307,* 309, *311, 315, 323*
7 Whole Number Operations	292–293, 300–301, 326–327, 330–331
8 Whole Number Computation	292–293, 294–295, 296–297, 302–305, 306–307, 310–311, 312–315, 324–325, 330–331
9 Geometry and Spatial Sense	293
11 Statistics and Probability	326–327
12 Fractions and Decimals	320–321, 322–323
13 Patterns and Relationships	292–293

Chapter 8

Using Geometry

Standards	Pages
1 Problem Solving	
Skills and Strategies	364–365, 374–375
Applications	351, 359, 361
Explorations	344–345, 346–347, 348–349, 352–353, 354–355, 362–363, 368–369, 370–371, 372–373
2 Communication	
Oral	[*Talk About It* appears in every core lesson.] 342, 344, 346, 348, 350, *351,* 352, 354, 358, 360, 362, 364, 368, 370, 372
Written	[*Journal* appears in every explore lesson.] 345, 347, 349, 353, 355, 356, 363, 366, 369, 371, 373, *375,* 376, 387, 391
Cooperative Learning	342, *360B*
3 Reasoning	345, 347, 351, 353, 355, 358, 359, 361, 369, 373, 376
4 Connections	
Interdisciplinary	*340, 342, 344A, 346A, 348A,* 349, *350A, 352A,* 353, *354A, 358A, 360A, 362A, 364A,* 369, *370A, 372A,* 377
Technology	341, *368A, 374A,* 377
Cultural	*344B, 352B, 354B, 362B*
8 Whole Number Computation	351, 359, 361, 369
9 Geometry and Spatial Sense	344–345, 346–347, 348–349, 350–351, 352–353, 354–355, 358–359, 360–361, 362–363, 368–369, 370–371, 372–373, 379, 380
10 Measurement	368–369, 370–371, 372–373, 374–375
13 Patterns and Relationships	352–353, 354–355, 358–359, 362–363, 364–365

Teacher's Edition pages in italic.

Chapter 9

Fractions and Customary Linear Measurement

	Standards	Pages
1	**Problem Solving**	
	Skills and Strategies	394–395, 420–421
	Applications	389, 391, 401, 403, 407, 417
	Explorations	386–387, 392–393, 398–399, 408–409, 414–415, 418–419
2	**Communication**	
	Oral	[*Talk About It* appears in every core lesson.] 384, 386, 388, 390, *391*, 392, 398, 400, 402, 406, 408, 414, 416, 418, 420
	Written	[*Journal* appears in every explore lesson.] 387, 391, 393, *395,* 396, 399, *401,* 409, 412, 415, 419
	Cooperative Learning	384, *390B, 402B, 406B*
3	**Reasoning**	389, 390, 391, 393, 401, 402, 403, 407, 409, 417
4	**Connections**	
	Mathematical	393, 399, 417, 419
	Interdisciplinary	*382, 384, 386A, 388A, 390A,* 391, *392A,* 393, *398A, 400A,* 401, *402A,* 403, *408A,* 409, *414A,* 415, *416A, 418A,* 422, 423, 426
	Technology	383, *387, 394A,* 404–405, *406A,* 410–411, *420A,* 423
	Cultural	*388B, 398B, 408B, 414B*
5	**Estimation**	390–391, 419
6	**Number Sense and Numeration**	*389, 391, 401, 403,* 406–407
8	**Whole Number Computation**	389, 391, 403, 407
9	**Geometry and Spatial Sense**	387, 417, 426
10	**Measurement**	414–415, 416–417, 418–419
11	**Statistics and Probability**	382, 383, 407, 421
12	**Fractions and Decimals**	386–387, 388–389, 390–391, 392–393, 398–399, 400–401, 402–403, 406–407, 408–409
13	**Patterns and Relationships**	393

Chapter 10

Fraction Operations and Customary Measurement

	Standards	Pages
1	**Problem Solving**	
	Skills and Strategies	440–441, 452–453, 462–463
	Applications	437, 448, 449, 461
	Explorations	432–433, 434–435, 444–445, 456–457, 458–459, 464–465
2	**Communication**	
	Oral	[*Talk About It* appears in every core lesson.] 430, 432, 434, 436, 439, 444, 447, *449,* 452, 456, 458, 460, 462, 464
	Written	[*Journal* appears in every explore lesson.] 433, 435, *441,* 442, 445, *449,* 454, 457, 459, 465, 466, 468
	Cooperative Learning	430, *436B,* 438–439, *452B, 460B*
3	**Reasoning**	437, 447, 448, 451, 454, 460, 461, 466, 468
4	**Connections**	
	Mathematical	445, 466
	Interdisciplinary	*428, 430, 434A, 435, 436A, 440A,* 442, *446A,* 448, 449, *452A,* 453, *456A, 458A, 460A, 462A,* 467, 470
	Technology	429, *432A, 444A, 464A,* 465, 467
	Cultural	*432B, 436B, 456B,* 470
5	**Estimation**	451, 459, 461
6	**Number Sense and Numeration**	*437, 449,* 451, *461*
8	**Whole Number Computation**	461, 464–465
10	**Measurement**	437, 448, 456–457, 458–459, 460–461
11	**Statistics and Probability**	437
12	**Fractions and Decimals**	432–433, 434–435, 436–437, 444–445, 446–449
13	**Patterns and Relationships**	445, 462–463, 466

Teacher's Edition pages in italic.

Chapter 11
Decimal and Metric Measurement

	Standards	Pages
1	**Problem Solving**	
	Skills and Strategies	480–481, 516–517
	Applications	477, 483, 485, 493, 498–499, 507, 515
	Explorations	478–479, 486–487, 494–495, 504–505, 508–509, 510–511, 512–513
2	**Communication**	
	Oral	[*Talk About It* appears in every core lesson.] 474, 476, 478, 480, 482, 484, 486, 492, 494, 497, *499,* 501, 504, 506, 508, 510, 512, 514
	Written	[*Journal* appears in every explore lesson.] *477,* 479, 481, 487, 490, 495, 499, 502, 505, 509, 511, 513, *515, 517,* 518
	Cooperative Learning	474, *482B,* 487, 500–501, *506B*
3	**Reasoning**	477, 483, 484, 485, 487, 493, 495, 497, 498, 501, 507, 515, 521
4	**Connections**	
	Mathematical	479, 481
	Interdisciplinary	*472, 474, 476A, 482A, 484A, 486A,* 493, *494A, 496A,* 499, *504A,* 505, *506A,* 507, *508A,* 509, *510A, 512A, 514A,* 515, 519, 522
	Technology	473, *478A, 480A,* 488–489, *492A, 516A,* 519
	Cultural	*492B, 496B, 514B, 516B,* 522
5	**Estimation**	484–485, 492–493, 499
6	**Number Sense and Numeration**	476–477, 478–479, 482–483, *485,* 486–487, *493, 499, 507, 515*
8	**Whole Number Computation**	483, 493
9	**Geometry and Spatial Sense**	477, 505, 509
10	**Measurement**	472–473, 485, 499, 504–505, 506–507, 508–509, 510–511, 512–513, 514–515, 519, 521
11	**Statistics and Probability**	479, 485, 493
12	**Fractions and Decimals**	472–473, 476–477, 478–479, 484–485, 486–487, 488–489, 492–493, 494–495, 496–499, 500–501, 508–509, 510–511
13	**Patterns & Relationships**	488–489

Chapter 12
Dividing by 2-Digit Divisors and Probability

	Standards	Pages
1	**Problem Solving**	
	Skills and Strategies	536–537, 550–551
	Applications	531, 533, 535, 536–537, 545
	Explorations	528–529, 540–541, 542–543, 546–547, 548–549
2	**Communication**	
	Oral	[*Talk About It* appears in every core lesson.] 526, 528, 530, 532, 534, 540, 542, 544, 546, 548, 550
	Written	[*Journal* appears in every explore lesson.] 529, *531, 535,* 538, 541, 543, *545,* 547, 549, 552
	Cooperative Learning	526
3	**Reasoning**	531, 533, 535, 541, 543, 545, 555
4	**Connections**	
	Mathematical	533
	Interdisciplinary	*524, 526, 530A,* 531, *532A, 534A,* 535, *540A,* 541, *542,* 543, *544A, 546A, 548A,* 551, 553, 556
	Technology	*524,* 525, *526A, 536A, 550A,* 553
	Cultural	*536B, 548B*
5	**Estimation**	530–531, 532, 534, 535
6	**Number Sense and Numeration**	528–529, 542
7	**Whole Number Operation**	527–535
8	**Whole Number Computation**	528–529, 530–531, 532–533, 534–535
9	**Geometry and Spatial Sense**	529, 551
11	**Statistics and Probability**	524–525, 533, 540–541, 542–543, 544–545, 546–547, 548–549, 552, 555, 556
12	**Fractions and Decimals**	533, 535
13	**Patterns and Relationships**	528–529, 548–549

Teacher's Edition pages in italic.

To order copies of the NCTM Standards contact:

NCTM
1906 Association Drive
Reston, Virginia 20191-1593

Telephone (800) 235-7566
Fax (703) 476-2970
E-Mail orders@nctm.org

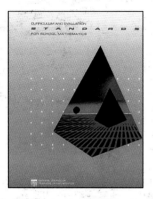

Curriculum and Evaluation Standards for School Mathematics

Professional Standards for Teaching Mathematics

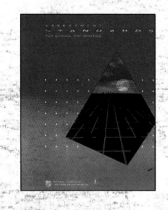

Assessment Standards for School Mathematics